ENGLISH EDITOR'S INTRODUCTION

PROFESSOR POPOV'S book on the theory of servomechanisms and control systems will be of interest to English readers in showing the meticulous detail into which Russian engineers and students are led when discussing these subjects.

A few standard and useful examples are taken and form the basis for discussion at all levels, from the most elementary to the most complete and advanced, so that a sense of continuity is preserved throughout the volume.

The translation preserves much of the Russian sentence structure and the editor did not find it possible to alter this without a more or less complete rewriting of the translator's manuscript. Nevertheless, it is hoped that a readable result has been obtained and that the spirit of the whole is faithful to that of the original.

A. D. B.

FOREWORD

THE WIDE study of the theory of automatic control in our institutions of higher education is a very recent development. Many engineers therefore have come to study it only when already engaged in practical work. The present book has the aim of assisting these broad circles of engineers and students to acquaint themselves in the most accessible form with the foundations of the theory of automatic control, in which the main role is played by the dynamics of control systems.

Following the aim of the most accessible development, the author has consciously tried to reduce to a minimum the use of operational calculus and the theory of functions of the complex variable and everywhere, where possible, to confine himself to the use of the symbolic operational method as a means of simplifying the notation and manipulation of differential equations.

The book presents those theoretical methods of analysis and synthesis of automatic control systems common to systems of various physical natures and designs. The concrete examples presented in the book, therefore, by no means pretend to reproduce the designs of contemporary automatic control systems. They will be only the simplest functional circuits serving to illustrate the principal ideas in the construction of automatic control systems and the application of the theoretical methods developed here. By analogy, the reader may then apply these ideas and methods to the concrete automatic control systems of interest to him.

Attempting to describe in detail the fundamental results of the theory of automatic control, the author has been forced to limit himself to brief remarks on a number of special questions. Statistical methods and questions of representation of automatic control systems have been completely neglected here. Each of these important fields is so specialised that it may constitute the subject of separate books.

The author expresses his appreciation to Comrades Ya. Z. Tsypkin, O. K. Sobolev and I. V. Korol'kov for valuable remarks when reviewing the manuscript.

CONTENTS

x

Contents

PART II. ORDINARY LINEAR AUTOMATIC REGULATION SYSTEMS

PART V. METHODS OF PLOTTING
THE REGULATION-PROCESS CURVE

PART I

GENERAL INFORMATION ABOUT AUTOMATIC CONTROL SYSTEMS

CHAPTER I

FORMS OF AUTOMATIC CONTROL SYSTEMS

1. The concept of closed automatic systems

There exist very many forms of automatic systems performing various functions in the control of the most varied physical processes in all branches of engineering. These systems consist of mechanical, electrical and other devices of widely different designs, assembled in an overall complex of mutually interacting circuits.

As examples of automatic systems we may list:

(a) automatic light switches including a photocell which reacts to the intensity of daylight and a special device for turning on the light, operating on a definite signal from this photocell;

(b) a machine for vending given objects (e.g. tickets, chocolates) when a given combination of coins is fed into it;

(c) automatic machines, automatic production lines and automatic factory departments;

(d) remote-control systems in which a defined combination of heavy or complicated operations in the controlled object are carried out upon depression of a button or an easy rotation of a handle on the control panel;

(e) automatic regulation of motor speed, maintaining constant angular velocity of the motor independently of the external load (analogously, temperature, pressure, voltage and frequency regulators, etc.);

(f) automatic pilots, maintaining a definite course and altitude of an aircraft without intervention by the pilot;

(g) servomechanisms in which an arbitrary variation in time of some quantity applied to the input is exactly copied at the output to a defined precision;

(h) a tracking system, in which the barrel of an anti-aircraft gun is automatically trained on a flying aircraft;

(i) a computer carrying out a defined mathematical operation (differentiation, integration, the solution of equations, etc.);

(j) measuring devices operating on the compensation principle;

(k) synchronous remote transmitters, etc.

All these and similar automatic systems may be divided into two main classes:

(1) automatic machines carrying out definite types of single or repeated operations; among these are, for example, lighting switches, ticket vendors, automatic machines, machine guns, velocity switching mechanisms, etc.;

(2) automatic systems which over a fairly long period of time vary some physical quantity in a necessary manner (or maintain it constant) (the coordinates of a moving object, velocity, voltage, frequency, temperature, pressure, acoustic level, etc.) in some controlled process. Among these are automatic controls, servo-mechanisms, automatic pilots, certain computing devices, certain measuring equipment, remote control systems, etc.

In the present book we shall consider only automatic systems of the second class. These are divided into open and closed loop automatic systems.

The general structural circuit of an open loop system is shown in two forms (*a* and *b*) in Fig. 1. This is the simplest control system: semi-automatic when the source of commands is the human being,

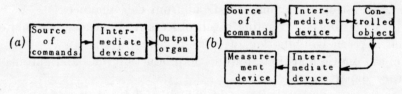

FIG. 1

and automatic if the source of commands is the variation of certain external conditions in which the given system operates (temperature or pressure of the surrounding medium, electric current, illumination, range of frequency, etc.).

The second structural circuit shown in Fig. 1 differs from the first in that besides control organs there are also measurement devices which permit the course of the process in the controlled object to be observed.

A characteristic of open loop systems is that the functioning of the system is not directly dependent on the result of its action.

A natural further improvement of automatic systems is the connection of the output (measuring instruments) back to the input (source of commands) so that the measuring instruments, measuring a certain quantity characterising a definite process in the control object should themselves be simultaneously a source of action on the system, where the magnitude of this action will depend on the magnitude by which the measured quantities in the controlled object deviate from their required values.

Closed loop automatic systems thus arise. It is easy to conceive that in the closed loop automatic system there is a complete interaction of operation of all circuits with each other. The courses of all processes in a closed loop system are radically different from processes in open loop systems. The closed loop system reacts completely differently to external perturbing forces. Various valuable properties of closed loop automatic systems make them irreplaceable in all cases where precise and high-speed automatic systems are required for control, measurement or for carrying out mathematical calculations. Dynamic calculations take on special importance in the design of any closed loop automatic system.

Closed loop automatic systems exist in engineering in the form of automatic regulators, servomechanisms, computers, compensation-type measuring systems, automatic pilots, stabilisation systems, remote control systems, etc.

All these forms of closed loop automatic systems may be reduced to the single general circuit represented in Fig. 2. If this represents

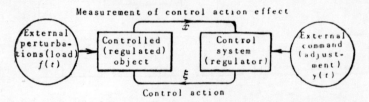

FIG. 2

a servomechanism the external driving force $y(t)$ may be arbitrary in time and it is required that the controlled object should repeat as exactly as possible this arbitrarily-given time variation in the form of a mechanical motion or displacement or in the form of variation of an arbitrary electrical or other physical quantity. At the same time it should be possible to eliminate as far as possible interference of all external perturbing forces $f(t)$ on the controlled object (and possibly on the control system itself).

If it represents an automatic regulation system the role of the control system (Fig. 2) is played by a regulator, the role of the external driving force $y(t)$ by the setting of the regulator or programme control. In this case it is always assumed that substantial external perturbing forces $f(t)$ act on the regulated object (for example, variation of load). The automatic regulation system should operate so that with actual external perturbing forces, regardless of their magnitude, the output should be as nearly as possible that to which the regulator is adjusted, or else this quantity should vary according to a definite programme given by the programme control.

All other forms of closed automatic systems (automatic controls, automatic pilots, computers, compensation-type instruments, stabilisation systems, remote-control systems, etc.) reduce to these two: either they are designed on the principle of a servomechanism or on the principle of the automatic regulation system. We observe that the difference between these, as is evident from the above, consists more in function than in the general principle of operation.

Therefore, the methods of dynamic calculation are essentially the same for automatic regulation systems and for servomechanisms (and for all closed-loop automatic systems in general).

2. Servomechanisms and control systems

Let us consider the operating principle of closed-loop automatic systems in greater detail, using examples.

Servomechanisms. The general structural circuit of a servomechanism is shown in Fig. 3.

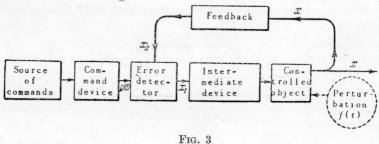

FIG. 3

It consists of a forward circuit (from the source to the controlled object) and feedback from the "output" of the system to its "input".

We also call servomechanisms such automatic systems in which the output quantity $x(t)$ reproduces the variations of the input quantity $y(t)$ where the automatic system reacts to the difference x_1 between the output and input quantities. We shall term the quantities x and y the regulated and desired quantities respectively.

The term "reproduces" employed here loosely denotes the equality of regulated and desired quantities at each moment of time, i.e. we are roughly concerned with the equality *

$$x(t) \approx y(t) . \tag{2.1}$$

Frequently the regulated quantity x differs from the desired quantity y in scale or in physical character. We then require

$$x(t) \approx k_0 y(t) , \tag{2.2}$$

* The sign of approximate equality is used in the formula since a real system cannot operate absolutely exactly; there is always a certain error (deviation).

where k_0 is a given constant coefficient. The same relates to the compensation-type measurement systems.

If we are considering a computer, operating on the servo principle, by the above term "reproduction" should be understood the satisfaction of a definite mathematical relationship, for example, for differentiating devices we require

$$x(t) \approx k_0 \frac{dy(t)}{dt}, \qquad (2.3)$$

and for integrating

$$x(t) \approx k_0 \int_0^t y(t)\, dt. \qquad (2.4)$$

Consequently, "reproduction" of an input quantity $y(t)$ at the output of the system $x(t)$ may occur in various forms.

A servomechanism has feedback from output to input (Fig. 3) which, in essence, serves for measurement of the result of the action of the system. At the input to the system subtraction occurs: $x_1 = y - x_2$. The device carrying out this subtraction will be termed the error detector (Fig. 3). The error magnitude x_1 acts on the intermediate circuit, and through it on the controlled object. The system operates so as constantly to reduce to zero the error x_1 and thus to satisfy the required relationship (2.1), (2.2), (2.3) or (2.4) with arbitrary form of variation of y with time.

Obviously the magnitude x_2 (Fig. 3) applied by the feedback should have the same physical character and the same scale as the driving quantity y. Therefore, the feedback loop should be able to transform the regulated quantity x, inversely to that which is carried out in the forward circuit of the system, namely, for (2.1), (2.2), (2.3) and (2.4) there should be

$$x_2 = x, \quad x_2 = \frac{x}{k_0}, \quad x_2 = \int_0^t x(t)\, dt, \quad x_2 = \frac{dx(t)}{dt}$$

respectively.

The source of commands for the input device (Fig. 3) may be either a special device or the variation of the external conditions in which the system operates.

For remote control of artillery and machine guns, in the circuit of Fig. 3 they are the controlled objects, and the input device is a handle on the control panel or sight, turned, for example, by a human hand according to an arbitrary function $y(t)$. The controlled object under the action of the intermediate circuits of the servomechanism must reproduce this motion in an appropriate manner (e.g. the circuit on p. 258 in reference 36).

For automatic stabilisation of antenna position (on an aircraft or vessel) the input device is a gyroscope measuring the angle of deviation of the aircraft or vessel from some given direction. This angle will be given by a function $y(t)$ (Fig. 3). For the controlled object (antenna) to retain a constant position in space, its servomechanism must carry out a motion $x(t)$ with respect to the body of the aircraft which exactly repeats the motion of the aircraft $y(t)$ measured by the gyroscope.

Contemporary electromechanical, electrical and electronic measurements of non-electrical quantities (distance, velocity, temperature, volume) are frequently based on the servomechanism principle.

An example is a device for measuring the airspeed of an aircraft, the block diagram of which is shown in Fig. 4. A Pitot tube, constituting the input device, establishes a pressure $p = y(t)$ dependent

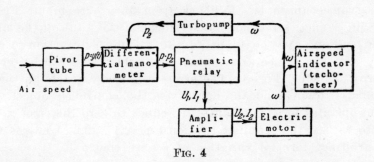

FIG. 4

on the airspeed of the aircraft. An electric motor at the output of the servomechanism gives an angular velocity $\omega = x(t)$ proportional to the pressure p. The forward circuit of the system carries out transformation of pressure into angular velocity of the electric motor, while the feedback (turbopump) effects the transformation of the angular velocity into pressure, which must be applied to the error detector (differential manometer). The scale of the tachometer, measuring the angular velocity of the electric motor, is calibrated in airspeed.

As an example of a computing system operating on the servomechanism principle we present the simplest structural scheme of an electromechanical integrator (Fig. 5). Here the angular velocity of the electric motor is proportional to an arbitrary voltage $V = y(t)$ and consequently the angle of rotation $\varphi = x(t)$ is proportional to the integral of the given function $y(t)$. The forward loop (amplifier and motor) integrates the input quantity. Therefore, the feedback (tachometer) should differentiate the output quantity of the system so that the input to the amplifier is a difference between similar quantities.

The simplest example of a servomechanical feedback amplifier is given in Fig. 6: *a* electromechanical; *b* hydraulic; *c* electronic; *d* magnetic). In all four diagrams the feedback is denoted by the letters *fb*.

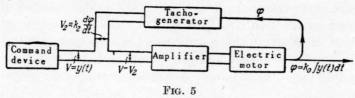

FIG. 5

In case *a* (Fig. 6) the error is the difference in angles $\varphi_{in} - \varphi_2$, i.e. the angle of rotation of the slide, rigidly coupled to the handle (input device), and the angle of rotation of the contact segments, rigidly coupled with the output shaft through the feedback gears. A volt-

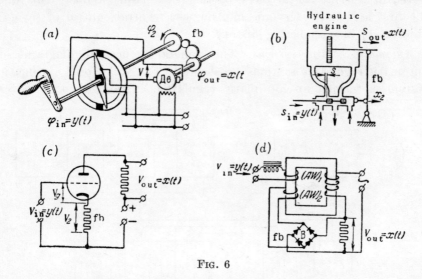

FIG. 6

age V is applied to the armature winding of the motor, the sign of which depends on the sign of the error ($\varphi_{in} - \varphi_2$). As a result the motor operates so as to reduce this error. The purpose of the equipment is to amplify power whilst preserving the angle of rotation in time (to a certain scale).

The same general operating principle and purpose occur in case *b* (Fig. 6), where the rate of motion of the hydraulic drive piston is here proportional to the opening of the slide valve *s*, which in turn is equal to the error ($y - x_2$).

Similarly, in case *c* (Fig. 6), the error voltage $V_g = V_{in} - V_2$ is applied to the grid of the amplifier.

In case *d* (Fig. 6) the error is the difference in ampere-turns, $(AN)_1 - (AN)_2$, between the control winding fed by the input voltage and the feedback winding fed by the output voltage after rectification.

This is an example where together with amplification there occurs transformation of direct current into alternating, as a result of which the inverse transformation using the bridge rectifier B must be present in the feedback loop.

In those cases where the control panel is at a substantial distance from the controlled object and the system includes means for overcoming this distance, a remote-controlled servomechanic system is obtained.

The first electromechanical servomechanism in the world was invented by Russian engineers. In the sixties of the last century V. F. Petrushevskii realised a synchronous coupling system. Of particular interest is the invention of A. P. Davydov, which was tested in 1867 at the artillery battery "Ne Tron' Menia". This was the first automatic servomechanism with central control of several objects [1] in engineering history.

Automatic control systems. The general structural diagrams of automatic regulation systems are shown in Fig. 7. A closed automatic system is termed an automatic regulation system when it serves

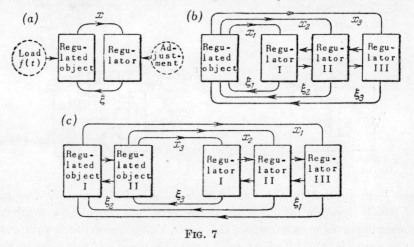

FIG. 7

to maintain a constant value (or a given form of variation) of a single quantity x or several quantities $x_1, x_2, x_3, \ldots$, characterising the course of the process over a long period for arbitrarily varying external perturbing forces, i.e. for variation of the load on the control object and other factors (feed, etc.). The quantities x, x_1, x_2, x_3, which are required be maintained constant (or varied in a given manner), are termed the regulated quantities.

An automatic control system consists of the regulated object and a control or several coupled regulated objects and controls (Fig. 7).

The regulated object is that aggregate in which the process subject to control occurs. The regulator is the automatic device detecting the undesired deviations of the regulated quantity x and acting on the regulated object in such manner as to eliminate this deviation. In Fig. 7 this regulating action is denoted by ξ, ξ_1, ξ_2, ξ_3.

With a single regulated quantity x, a single regulated object and a single regulator the automatic regulation system will be termed an isolated system (Fig. 7a). With several mutually coupled regulators with a single object (Fig. 7b) or several objects (Fig. 7c) the automatic regulation system is termed a coupled system. If several regulators are connected to a single object, but each of them operates independently of the others, we have several independent isolated automatic regulation systems.

To carry out its functions a regulator must first of all have at the input a detection element for determining the undesirable deviation of the regulated quantity; this may be the probe of a gauge for the corresponding physical quantity. Secondly, the regulator should have at the output a regulating organ, operating on the regulated object in a definite manner to eliminate undesirable deviations arising in the regulated quantity. Aside from the sensitive detection element (at the input) and the regulating organ (at the output) the regulator must have various intermediate devices. Therefore, the first of the structural schemes of Fig. 7 may be represented in a more developed form as shown in Fig. 8.

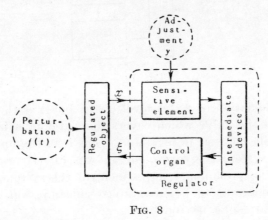

FIG. 8

The regulator should have, in addition, means for adjusting the system to the required constant (or variable, in a pre-assigned manner) value of the regulated quantity which it is the purpose of the regulator to maintain (Fig. 8).

If certain portions of the regulator are at a great distance from the regulated object, where the regulator has means for overcoming this distance, the automatic regulator system is termed a remotely-controlled system.

The first automatic regulator in the world in which the general principle of contemporary regulators was realised was invented by the great Russian mechanic Ivan Ivanovich Polzunov in 1765. This

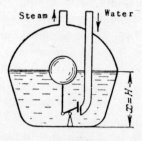

FIG. 9

was the water-level float regulator in the boiler of Polzunov's steam engine. The schematic and structural diagrams of this automatic regulation system are presented in Figs. 9 and 10.

Here the regulated object is the boiler, the regulated quantity the height of the water H, the external perturbation (load) is the consumption of steam from the boiler. The detector of the regulator,

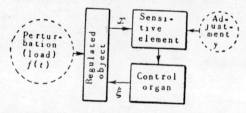

FIG. 10

detecting the deviation of water level in the boiler is the float. The control organ is the valve which covers the water inlet in the boiler at an undesirable increase in level and opens it in the opposite case. In Polzunov's system the control organ was directly coupled with the detector. The preliminary adjustment of the system to a given value of H which was to be maintained constant was realised by shifting the float along its rod.

At the present time the general operating principle of regulators, based on measurement of the deviation of the regulated quantity, is termed Polzunov's principle.

The inventor of the electric motor, the Russian scientist B. S. Yakobi, together with the Russian academician E. Kh. Lents, in 1841 constructed the world's first voltage regulator. V. N. Chikolev invented the differential regulator for arc lamps and was the first (in 1871) to employ electric drive in automatic regulators. K. E. Tsiol-kovskii was the inventor of the automatic pilot. Its diagram was published in 1898.

Let us consider the example of the system for automatic control of an aircraft's course (Fig. 11). The regulated object is the aircraft, the regulated quantity the course angle ψ, the external perturbing

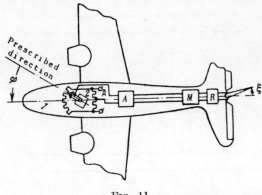

FIG. 11

forces, wind and inequality of the tractive forces of the motors, establishing a moment of rotation. The regulator is the automatic course pilot.

The sensitive element of the automatic course pilot, measuring the undesirable deviation of the aircraft from its course, may be a gyroscope, shifting a slide in an electrical bridge circuit. The re-sultant current appearing in the diagonal of the bridge is amplified and applied to an electric motor which turns the rudder (through a reduction box). The rudder is the regulating organ, establishing the rotary aerodynamic moment which returns the aircraft to the required course. The adjustment of the system to a determined course is carried out by a corresponding adjustment of the gyroscope or by shifting the zero position A of the bridge. This circuit, as we shall see below, requires substantial additions (as an unstable system is obtained here, see Section 33).

As an example of the simplest electric regulation system let us consider the automatic voltage regulation system for a d.c. generator, employing a vacuum tube (Fig. 12). In this case the regulated object is the d.c. generator, the regulated quantity the voltage V at the generator terminals, the external perturbing force is the power load into which the generator operates.

The detector of undesirable deviation of the regulated voltage V is the grid of the tube while the regulating organ is the anode circuit of the tube. With an undesirable change in voltage V (for example,

$V > V_1$) there appears a voltage V_g at the grid and a proportional change in current I_a in the anode circuit, and consequently in the current I_b through the field of the generator, which is connected in the anode circuit of the tube. This change of field current eliminates the undesirable deviation of the regulated voltage.

Adjustment of the system to a definite voltage V to be maintained constant is accomplished by setting the value of V_1 on the rheostat R_a.

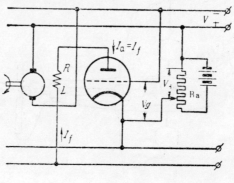

FIG. 12

The fundamental problem of automatic regulation consists in maintaining the necessary value of the regulated quantity (to a given precision) with varying load on the regulated object. Sometimes the problem may be posed of constructing an automatic regulation system such that when necessary it may automatically alter the regulated quantity according to a pre-assigned time programme. This is termed programme control.

There exists another form of programme control, when it is necessary to obtain a given form of variation of the regulated quantity not in time but in dependence on some other parameter. This is required, for example, in those cases where the problem of regulation is posed as the problem of automatic observation of the optimal operating conditions of some power system with varying external conditions.* Programme control of the first type (in time) occurs, for example, where the automatic course pilot has not merely to guide the aircraft in a straight line but must cause it to complete a turn automatically. Thus, to complete a turn through the arc of a circle with constant velocity it is necessary that the course angle vary proportionally to time ($\psi = \omega t$).

An example of a programme control system of the second type (not in time) may be a system which is required to vary the angular

* This other form of programme regulation is a combination of Pulzunov's principle with the principle of regulating according to the perturbing force which will be discussed below.

velocity of a motor shaft in a definite optimum manner with respect to the power load.

To accomplish programme control of both types, obviously, it is possible to use the adjustment element (Fig. 8). In the ordinary automatic regulation system the adjustment element is used for preliminary adjustment of the system to a definite constant value of the regulated quantity. In the case of programme control it is necessary to act continuously on the adjustment element during the operation of the system to vary the regulated quantity according to the pre-assigned variation. For this purpose the adjustment element is fitted with a special programme device, automatically varying the adjustment of the system according to the desired variation.

For example, for automatic execution of a turn by an aircraft it is possible to design a programme device which would automatically shift, let us say, the zero point A of the bridge of the automatic pilot detector (Fig. 11) at a definite velocity and for a given distance, corresponding to the termination of the turn.

To carry out automatic variation of motor shaft velocity in a given manner according to the power variation it is necessary to design a programme device which, measuring the motor power would alter the adjustment of the velocity regulator in an appropriate manner.

It is easy to see that a programmed regulation system resembles a servomechanism where the programme device plays the role of the input element of the servomechanism, the adjustment element the role of the error detector, and the sensitive element the role of feedback (Fig. 3). The difference between a programmed regulation system and a servomechanism consists, in essence, only in that in the first case the regulated quantity should vary according to a pre-assigned programme while in the latter there is no definite programme and the regulated quantity should reproduce an arbitrary variation of the input device.

From the theoretical point of view the difference between a servomechanism and an automatic regulation system is that of the two external forces (Fig. 2) for the servomechanism the main one is the input force $y(t)$ which should as exactly as possible be reproduced by the object, while for the automatic regulation system the main one is the external perturbation force on the object $f(t)$, the effects of which on the variation of the regulated quantity should be eliminated as exactly as possible. Therefore in servomechanisms the calculations are mainly carried out with regard to the external input force, while in regulation systems, they are according to the external perturbation (load). Basically the methods of their dynamic calculations are the same.

Principle of regulating according to perturbing forces. Above we have discussed control systems based on the measurement of the deviation of a regulated quantity from its required value (Polzunov's principle).

However there exist in practice other important methods of regulation: (1) the principle of regulation according to the perturbing force; (2) application of parametric stabilisers.

By the principle of regulation according to the perturbing force is understood automatic regulation in which the regulated quantity is not measured but action against the undersirable influence of an external force is carried out by the introduction of various other design (circuit) measures paralysing the effect of this force.

For example, let the voltage of a d.c. generator with variable angular velocity be required to be maintained constant. The previously considered principle of a closed regulation system (Fig. 8) would correspond to the following solution of the problem: the deviation of the regulated quantity V is measured (in the right side of the circuit in Fig. 12) and in accordance with this the field current is automatically varied (by the tube in Fig. 12), which leads to elimination of deviations which may arise in the regulated voltage V.

But it is also possible to proceed differently. Calculate in advance how it is necessary to vary the resistance of the generator field circuit with the angular velocity for the voltage at the terminals of the generator to be constant. It will then be possible to place a rheostat in the field circuit, the slide of which will be automatically shifted with variation of angular velocity. Here we do not measure the deviation of the regulated voltage but we eliminate the effects of undesirable external forces by another means: the direct reaction of the system to the perturbing force itself.

Under the principle of regulation according to perturbing force it is also possible to include the introduction of various auxiliary compensation and stabilising windings and compounding in electrical machines) the principle of regulating constant velocity of heat engines according to load; the so-called automatic carburettors, etc.

There exist a number of cases where the application of this principle is very useful. However, as is evident from the above, this principle in its pure form is less universal than the principle of measurement of the regulated quantity. In fact, the system of regulating according to the perturbing force may be used only against a definite predetermined form of perturbing force. A system based on the principle of measuring the regulated quantity (Polzunov's principle) always automatically eliminates undesirable deviations of the regulated quantity independently of what external perturbing force was the cause of the tendency to deviation. In a number of cases it is useful to combine both of these regulation principles, where regulation according to the external perturbing force is brought into action to improve the quality of operation of the regulation system based on Polzunov's principle.

Consideration of regulation according to the perturbing force in the above sense is outside the scope of this book. Certain questions of theory connected with this may be found in the work of V. S. Kulebakin [34] and A. G. Ivakhnenko.

Parametric stabilisers. Parametric stabilisers are devices which are based on variation of the parameters of individual elements of the system with variation of the external forces applied to them. In particular, this may be connected with the use of non-linear properties of various materials in electric circuits. Among these are barretters, ferro-resonant stabilisers, etc. These also, are, not considered in the present volume.

3. Direct and indirect-acting systems

All automatic regulation systems are divided among direct-acting and indirect-acting systems.

Direct-acting systems. A direct-acting regulation system is a system in which the action of the sensitive element on the regulating organ is carried out without the introduction of an additional source of energy. Its structural scheme is shown in Fig. 10.

Besides Polzunov's regulator (Fig. 9) examples may be the following systems: centrifugal regulator of steam engine shaft angular

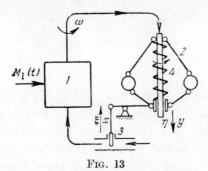

FIG. 13

velocity (Fig. 13); rheostatic voltage regulator at the terminals of a dynamo (Fig. 14); a thermostat regulating the water or oil temperature in a heat engine (Fig. 15).

In these three systems the regulating organ, 3 (slide valve, rheostat slider, valve), is moved directly by the sensitive element 2 (centrifugal mechanism, electromagnet, sylphon) without an additional source of energy, as in Polzunov's regulator.

Here an unwanted increase in the regulated quantity arising in any manner (angular velocity ω, voltage V, temperature θ) produces in the first example (Fig. 13) divergence of the bobs of the centrifugal mechanism, in the second (Fig. 14) increase in the tractive force of

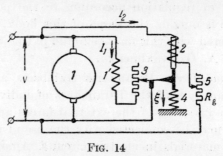

FIG. 14

the electromagnet, in the third (Fig. 15) increase in the vapour pressure of a highly volatile liquid inside the sylphon.

As a result of this the regulating organ, 3, receiving a displacement, produces on the object, 1 (steam engine, dynamo, water or oil system of the heat engine), a regulating action consisting in the

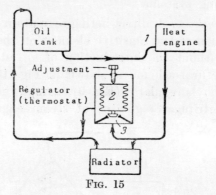

FIG. 15

first case in reduction of the free section of the steam feed to the machine, in the second case in increase of resistance of the field circuit 1′, i.e. reduction of the field current, in the third case in the connection of a cooling radiator in the water or oil system. Such a regulating effect on the object in all three cases causes reduction of the regulated quantity and, consequently, eliminates the undesirable increase assumed initially.

The external perturbing force on the system is a change in load (shaft load of the steam engine, power supplied by the dynamo; thermal regime of the engine).

Adjustment of the system to a definite value of the regulated quantity is carried out in the given examples by regulating the spring, 4 (Fig. 13), rheostat, 5 (Fig. 14) or screw (Fig. 15).

A direct-acting automatic regulation system may obviously only be realised when the sensitive element is itself a sufficiently powerful device for direct action on the regulating organ, as in the above examples. However, in many cases the sensitive element is relatively weak while the action on the regulating organ requires substantial power. In these cases an amplifier is introduced between the sensitive element and the regulating organ, as a result of which an indirect-acting system is obtained.

Indirect-acting systems. An indirect-acting automatic regulation system is a system in which the sensitive element acts on the regulating organ indirectly through a special amplifying and transforming circuit supplied by an auxiliary source of energy.

The simplest structural scheme of an indirect-acting system is shown in Fig. 16. Even for an isolated regulating system this structural

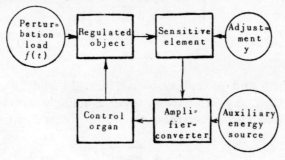

FIG. 16

scheme may become substantially more complicated since the amplifier-transducer shown in this circuit diagram in the form of a single block may consist of a number of circuits. It is intended for amplification of a weakly-acting sensitive element for transformation of one physical quantity into another and a number of other operations (introduction of derivatives, integrals, etc.).

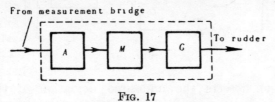

FIG. 17

For example, in the case of the automatic pilot (Fig. 11) this amplifier-transducer consists of three circuits: an electrical amplifier A, an electric motor M and a gear box G (Fig. 17). The task here consists not only of amplifying the energy but in transforming an electrical magnitude (voltage in the diagonal of the measuring bridge) into a mechanical one (angle of rotation of the rudder).

3

Other examples of indirect-acting systems may be: a system for regulating the velocity of a heat engine (Fig. 18), a voltage regulation, system (Fig. 19), a system for electric motor velocity control (Fig. 20). a servomechanism (Fig. 21), a radiocompass (Fig. 22).

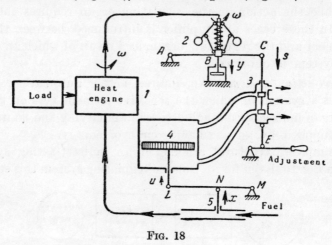

FIG. 18

For the first and second systems (Figs. 18 and 19), completely different in their physical nature, there is a single structural scheme (Fig. 23). Here the sensitive element, 2 (centrifugal mechanism,

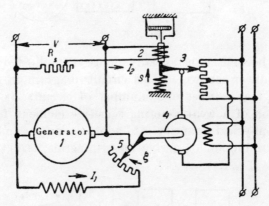

FIG. 19

electromagnet), detects the undesired deviation of the regulated quantity (velocity ω, voltage V) and shifts the control element, 3 (slide valve, rheostat slider) to the corresponding side. This connects the motor, 4 (hydraulic, electric), which moves the regulating organ, 5 (slide valve in the pipe feeding the heat engine, rheostat slide in the dynamo field circuit). The regulating organ now acts on the regulated object, 1 (heat engine, dynamo), so as to eliminate the undesired deviation of the regulated quantity.

The system for regulating the speed of the electric motor M (regulated object) shown in simplified form in Fig. 20 contains a tachometer T (sensitive element), which gives a voltage $V = V_1 - V_t$,

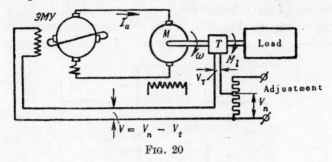

FIG. 20

proportional to the deviation of angular velocity (i.e. regulated quantity). Further, the system contains a rotary amplifier (dynamo with longitudinal-transverse field) which, amplifying the signal V

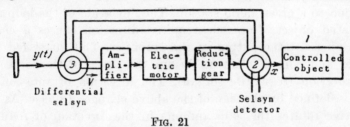

FIG. 21

fed to its field winding, gives a corresponding change of current in the armature circuit of the motor. The latter is the regulating action which eliminates the speed deviation tending to arise.

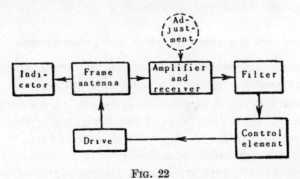

FIG. 22

In a servo-system (Fig. 21) the input angle of rotation y should be reproduced at the output in the form of the quantity x. The error detector, 3 (differential selsyn), gives a voltage V proportional to the error $y - x$. After amplification it is applied to the motor with gear box, rotating the controlled object, 1. The actual magnitude of the angle x at the controlled object is detected by a selsyn transmitter, 2, and transferred to selsyn, 3, where it is subtracted from the input angle y. As a result the motor operates on the error in the direction of its elimination.

The radiocompass (Fig. 22), in essence, also constitutes an indirect-acting closed loop automatic system. The problem here consists

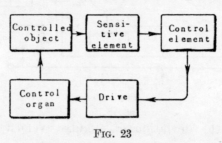

Fig. 23

in constantly training a loop antenna along a line indicating the direction to a given radio station. The deviation of the loop antenna (regulated object) from the required direction causes a change of signal phase at the output of the amplifier. This latter fed through a filter and control element, brings the drive of the loop antenna into rotation (regulating organ). The direction of rotation of the drive is defined by the sign of the above change of phase. As a result the drive rotates the loop antenna in the direction of reducing its deviation from the required direction.

We have discussed here the principle of indirect-acting systems by examples of the simplest isolated automatic regulation systems. In Chap. III additional circuits will be introduced into these systems, improving their quality of operation.

4. Continuous and discontinuous (relay and pulse) systems

All automatic regulation systems and servomechanisms may be divided into continuous and discontinuous systems.

Continuous systems. A continuous system is an automatic system in which continuous variations of mechanical, electrical and other quantities in all circuits of the system correspond to a continuous variation of the regulated quantity.

Examples of continuous systems are the systems considered above: velocity regulation (Figs. 13, 18, 20); voltage regulation (Figs. 14, 19); aircraft course regulator (Fig. 11); level regulator (Fig. 9); loop antenna position regulator (Fig. 22); and servomechanisms (Figs. 4, 5, 21).

Discontinuous systems. A discontinuous system is an automatic system in which in at least one circuit the continuous variation of mechanical, electrical or other quantities is violated. Discontinuous systems may be divided into two basic groups: relay systems and pulse systems.

Relay systems. A relay system is an automatic system having among its fundamental circuits at least one relay circuit. By relay circuit is understood a circuit of the system in which to a continuous variation of the input quantity there corresponds a discontinuous variation of the output quantity, appearing only at completely defined values of the input quantity.

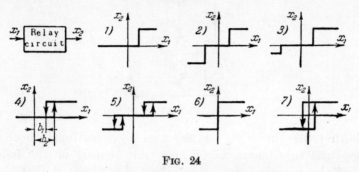

FIG. 24

In Fig. 24 are shown certain possible forms of dependence between the output and input quantities for relay circuits. These dependencies will be termed the characteristics of the relay circuits. Characteristics of the forms, 4, 5, 7 (Fig. 24) have, so to speak, a hysteresis loop.

For example, a simple electromagnetic relay has the well-known characteristic of form 4 (Fig. 24), if x_1 is the current in the control circuit of the relay, b_2 and b_1 are the operating and release currents, x_2 is the voltage in the control circuit. This is the essential difference between the present device and the otherwise similar ordinary electromagnet (2 in Fig. 14) with continuous characteristic.

In formulating the concept of the relay system the relay circuit was mentioned in particular as one of the fundamental units of the system. Generally speaking, in an automatic system there may be present various relays of an auxiliary character, the discontinuous variation of whose output quantities has no essential influence on the character of the process of varying the regulated quantity. Such systems may be considered continuous. We therefore define particularly only two types of relay systems, in which the relay circuit acts in an essential manner on the character of the processes of regulating and following:

1) when the regulating organ itself operates in a relay manner;

2) when the relay circuit is the control element of a motor moving the regulated organ or controlled object (system with constant velocity).

Examples of relay systems of the first type are: systems for regulating electric motor velocity and the course of marine torpedoes [38]. They are shown in Figs. 25 and 26.

FIG. 25

In both cases the sensitive element, 2 (centrifugal mechanism, gyroscope), is continuous, i.e. it acts continuously on the following circuit of the system (continuous shift of contact, 3 (Fig. 25), or gate valve (Fig. 26)). But this continuous action of the sensitive

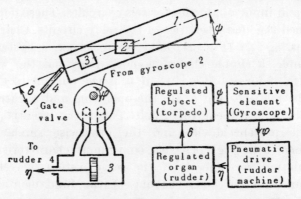

FIG. 26

element causes discontinuous action of the regulating organ (relay character). The latter is expressed in the instantaneous connection and disconnection of the series resistance R_s (Fig. 25) or in the instantaneous shifting of the rudder from one extreme position to the other (Fig. 26), as the piston of the pneumatic feed in this case practically instantaneously shifts from one extreme position to the other with the admission of compressed air on one or other side of the cylinder. In the electric motor example the relay element has characteristic, 1 (Fig. 24), while in the marine torpedo example characteristic, 6 or 7 (Fig. 24).

Relay systems of the first type are sometimes termed two-or three-position systems in dependence on the number of possible positions of the regulating organ. Two-position systems are frequently termed "yes-no", "on-off" or "bang-bang" systems.

Examples of relay systems of the second type may be electromechanical temperature regulation systems with constant velocity motors (Fig. 27) and servomechanisms (Fig. 6a).

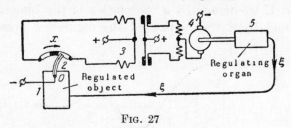

FIG. 27

In the first example (Fig. 27) with change in regulated quantity (temperature of the cooled portion of the heat engine, 1) a bimetallic plate, 2, bends. As a result current is turned on in one of the control windings of relay, 3. With continuous motion of the bimetallic plate, 2, the movable contacts of relay, 3, jump instantaneously to one or the other extreme position in accordance with a characteristic of form 6 or 7 (Fig. 24). First one, then the other, field winding of the constant velocity electric motor, 4, are connected (Fig. 27). As a result the regulating organ, 5, (radiator damper) moves to one or the other side to liquidate undesired temperature deviations in the regulated object, 1.

The automatic aircraft-course regulation system can operate completely analogously (Fig. 11) if plates and a relay are introduced in place of the bridge. The angle of deviation from course of the aircraft, 1, is measured by the gyroscope, 2, the continuous action of which leads to instantaneous connection through the relay of first one and then the other field winding of the electric motor and a corresponding motion of the rudder through the reduction gear.

A feature of these two systems, in contradistinction to the corresponding continuous systems considered previously, is the violation of continuity of motion in the control element by the drive and the absence from the drive of equipment for continuous measurement of the rate of turning.

A contact servomechanism (Fig. 6a) has the same property in contra distinction to a continuous servomechanism (Fig. 5). In this case (Fig. 6a) connection of the drive is defined only by the sign of the error $\varphi_{in} - \varphi_2$, but not by its magnitude as in the continuous system. The control element characteristic has a form 6 (Fig. 24) or 2 (taking into account the insensitive zones about the neutral positions), where the error quantity is plotted along the axis of abscissae.

We note that the relay system of Fig. 25 is a direct-acting system while the others (Fig. 26, 27, 6a) are indirect.

The basic advantage of a relay system is the simplicity of design and the ease of obtaining a high gain factor.

Discontinuity of operation may be here represented in the following manner. If we denote by x the motion of the bimetallic plate, 2 (Fig. 27), and by ξ the motion of the regulating organ (damper),

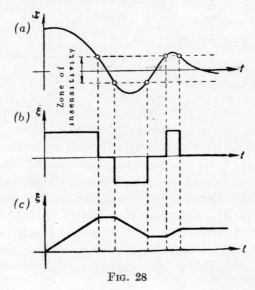

FIG. 28

with variation of the magnitude x, for example, in the form of Fig. 28a, the motion of the regulating organ in the first rough approximation will have the form of Fig. 28c (if we assume that when the motor is connected the regulating organ moves with constant velocity ξ, while in the insensitive zone, where the motor is disconnected, it remains in place). In practice this pattern of motion of the regulating organ will be distorted through inertia of the field windings and the moving portions of the system.

For relay systems an essential circumstance is that the moments of connection and disconnection of various circuits of the system by the relay element are defined by the system itself, by the change in its dynamic state in the course of time (in distinction to forced connection and disconnection externally in the pulse systems considered below).

Pulse systems. A pulse system of automatic regulation is one in which there is a pulse circuit transforming continuous input signals to a series of short pulses with defined repetition period. The pulse repetition period is given externally from an independent special device. In works on this subject such systems are frequently termed discontinuous regulation systems.

We note three types of pulse circuits, differing in pulse form (rectangular pulses are assumed):

(a) the durations of all pulses are the same and their magnitudes vary in dependence on the value of the input quantity s at the corresponding moment of time (Fig. 29a);

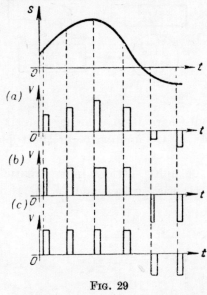

FIG. 29

(b) the pulse durations depend on the values of the input quantity s while the magnitude of the pulse is constant (Fig. 29b);

(c) The duration and magnitude of pulses is constant but their signs vary with change of sign of input quantity (Fig. 29c).

Pulse systems are frequently applied in practice for temperature regulation. In addition, pulse automatic control systems find wide application in radio distance finders and other instruments.

An advantage of pulse systems is the simplicity of achieving multichannel circuits and the absence of prolonged loading of the sensitive element. In particular, this permits being satisfied by a small output power of the sensitive element of the system and finer and more exact means of measuring the deviation of the regulated quantity may be used.

An example of a pulse regulation system occurs in temperature regulation, the block diagram of which is shown in Fig. 30.

Here, with variation of the regulated quantity (temperature of the regulated object) the resistance, 2 (resistance thermometer), varies. As a result the balance of bridge, 3, is upset and in its diagonal, in which a galvanometer is connected, a current arises. Thus, continuous variation of the regulated temperature causes continuous motion s of the galvanometer pointer, 4. The latter is the input

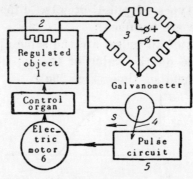

FIG. 30

quantity for the pulse circuit, 5, which at equal intervals of time connects the supply of the motor, 6, in short pulses, moving the regulating organ.

Three examples of pulse devices in schematic form are shown separately in Fig. 31; they correspond to the three types of pulse shown in Fig. 29.

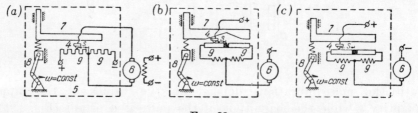

FIG. 31

The idea of these pulse circuits is as follows: The current in the bridge diagonal, 3 (Fig. 30), depending on the deviation of the regulated temperature, passes through the galvanometer. The pointer, 4 (Fig. 30 and 31) of the galvanometer moves, as a result, by the magnitude s, dependent on the given deviation of the regulated quantity. Above the pointer is a "chopper bar" not connected with it, 7 (Fig. 31). By the aid of a special drive, 8, independent of the given system, the chopper bar oscillates at a pre-determined frequency ω. During a long period the pointer, 4, of the galvanometer moves freely without any load. It is pressed to the resistance, 9 (Figs. 31b and c) for short periods by the chopper bar when the latter is at the lowest point of its oscillation.

The dependence of the pulse magnitude on the deviation of the regulated quantity in the first case (Fig. 31a and 29a) is achieved by the voltage V applied to the armature of the motor being proportional to the displacement of the pointer, 4, i.e.

$$V = ks, \ \tau = \text{const},$$

where τ is the pulse duration.

The dependence of the pulse duration on the deviation of the regulated quantity in the second case (Fig. 31*b* and 29*b*) is brought about by a system of bevels on the lower surface of the chopper as a result of which we obtain

$$\tau = ks, \ V = \text{const}.$$

Finally, in the third case (Fig. 31*c* and 29*c*) we have the simplest device

$$\tau = \text{const}, \ V = \pm C$$

in dependence on the sign of *s*.

Obviously, transformation of the continuous action into pulses of these types may be accomplished by many other electromechanical and electronic devices which, consequently, also may serve as examples of pulse circuits in automatic regulation systems.

If the pulse circuit is designed as the type shown in Fig. 31*a*, the form of motion of the regulating organ may be represented approximately by the graph of Fig. 32 with the assumption that during

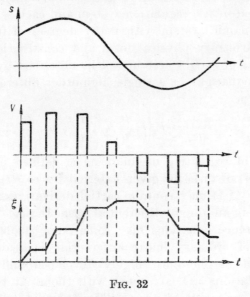

Fɪɢ. 32

the short pulses the regulating organ moves and in the interval between them (open circuit) it is motionless. The slopes of the segments of motion are determined by the velocity of the electric motor and the reduction drive ratio. Actually, this curve will be somewhat distorted by the motor field winding inductance and the moving portions connected with the motor shaft.

TRANSIENTS IN AUTOMATIC REGULATION SYSTEMS

5. Linear and non-linear systems

Let us employ the general circuit of a closed loop automatic system shown in Fig. 2. Let x denote the regulated quantity or its deviation (error), $y(t)$ the external driving force (variation of adjustment), $f(t)$ the external perturbing force (load variation).

As has been shown by examples, each closed loop automatic system (both servomechanisms and regulation systems) consists of a number of different circuits (mechanical, electrical and others). There are always external perturbations $f(t)$ and driving forces $y(t)$ of arbitrary form, as a result of which the system operates continuously in transient dynamic regimes. Consequently, we should consider each automatic regulation system and each servomechanism as a closed dynamic system with many degrees of freedom, which may take an arbitrary physical form and construction.

The dynamics of such a system will be described by some system of differential equations or a single high-order differential equation of arbitrary type

$$F_1\left(x, \frac{dx}{dt}, ..., \frac{d^n x}{dt^n}\right) = F_2\left(f, \frac{df}{dt}, ..., \frac{d^m f}{dt^m}; \; y, \frac{dy}{dt}, ..., \frac{d^\nu y}{dt^\nu}\right) \qquad (5.1)$$

The process of regulation or following is defined by the general solution $x = x(t)$ of (5.1) for given external forces $f(t)$ and $y(t)$. For certain systems (5.1) may contain partial derivatives. Sometimes it may be written in an integro-differential form. In place of differential equations difference equations may sometimes be obtained.

The theory of ordinary linear differential equations with constant coefficients, is the most highly developed and the simplest practical calculations are connected with them. At the same time they cover the majority of practically important problems in the theory of automatic regulation. It is, therefore, very important to classify all automatic regulation systems (and also servomechanisms) from this point of view. We shall divide them into three classes:

(1) ordinary linear systems,
(2) singular linear systems,
(3) non-linear systems.

Ordinary linear systems. Ordinary linear systems are those whose dynamic processes are exclusively described by ordinary linear differential equations with constant coefficients. This requires all circuits of the system to be linear with lumped constants. The parameters of the system are those physical quantities or their combinations entering into the coefficients of the differential (and other) equations describing the dynamics of the given system or any of its circuits. Such quantities are mass, moment of inertia, inductance, resistance, capacitance, gain factor, modulus of elasticity, "time constant", etc., etc.

It is important to bear in mind that the linearity of circuits is understood here in a limited sense, namely, by linear circuit is understood every circuit, the static characteristic* of which is represented by a straight line in the operating range of the given circuit in a given dynamic process. For example, the dependence between the angular velocity ω of the shaft of an electric motor and the d.c. voltage V, applied to the armature circuit, may be curved (Fig. 33). However,

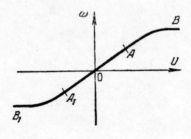

FIG. 33

this electric motor, as a member of a system, will be linear if in the dynamic process investigated in the given system only that part of the characteristic A_1OA is used which may be represented by a straight line to a sufficient precision for calculations. This substitution of a real characteristic by a linear one is termed linearisation (the general method of linearisation will be presented in Section 18).

The overwhelming majority of continuous automatic regulation systems and servo-systems belong to the class of ordinary linear systems as their real characteristics, always more or less non-linear, may frequently be linearised over definite limits.

The equation of motion for ordinary automatic regulation systems (and servomechanisms) has the general form

---

* The static characteristic of a circuit is the dependence between the output and input quantities in various stable states of the given circuit. Ordinarily it is represented graphically.

$$a_0 \frac{d^n x}{dt^n} + a_1 \frac{d^{n-1} x}{dt^{n-1}} + \dots + a_{n-1} \frac{dx}{dt} + a_n x =$$

$$b_0 \frac{d^m f}{dt^m} + b_1 \frac{d^{m-1} f}{dt^{m-1}} + \dots + b_{m-1} \frac{df}{dt} + b_m f + c_0 \frac{d^\nu y}{dt^\nu} + c_1 \frac{d^{\nu-1} y}{dt^{\nu-1}} +$$

$$+ \dots + c_{\nu-1} \frac{dy}{dt} + c_\nu y , \qquad (5.2)$$

where n, m and ν are arbitrary whole positive numbers (ordinarily) $m \leqslant n$ and $\nu \leqslant n$, where the "less than" sign occurs more frequently); $a_0, a_1, \dots, a_n, b_0, b_1, \dots, b_m, c_0, c_1, \dots, c_\nu$ are constant coefficients defined by the parameters of the given system. We note that in general there need not be only a single perturbing force $f(t)$, as here, but several.

For conciseness of notation we shall everywhere below employ the symbolic operational form of notation for differential equations, introducing the notation

$$\left. \begin{array}{l} \dfrac{dx}{dt} \equiv px , \ \dfrac{d^2 x}{dt^2} \equiv p^2 x , \ \dots, \dfrac{d^n x}{dt^n} \equiv p^n x , \\[2mm] \displaystyle\int x\, dt \equiv \dfrac{x}{p} , \quad \displaystyle\int \left(\int x\, dt \right) dt \equiv \dfrac{x}{p^2} . \end{array} \right\} \qquad (5.3)$$

For example, the equation

$$a_0 \frac{d^2 x}{dt^2} + a_1 \frac{dx}{dt} + a_2 x = 0 \qquad (5.4)$$

will be written in the form

$$(a_0 p^2 + a_1 p + a_2) x = 0 . \qquad (5.5)$$

We shall not assign any further significance to the symbolic operational notation (5.5) in comparison with the ordinary form of notation (5.4), other than being a more concise method of denoting derivatives with regard to time (a different significance is assigned to the symbols in operational calculus, Section 74).

The differential equation of motion (5.2) of an ordinary linear system in operational notation, therefore, takes on the form

$$(a_0 p^n + a_1 p^{n-1} + \dots + a_{n-1} p + a_n) x =$$
$$(b_0 p^m + b_1 p^{m-1} + \dots + b_{m-1} p + b_m) f(t) + \qquad (5.6)$$
$$+ (c_0 p^\nu + c_1 p^{\nu-1} + \dots + c_{\nu-1} p + c_\nu) y(t) ,$$

or, still more concisely,

$$L(p)x = S(p)f(t) + N(p)y(t) , \qquad (5.7)$$

where $L(p)$, $S(p)$ and $N(p)$ are the abbreviated notations for the operational polynomials in (5.6) before the variables x, $f(t)$ and $y(t)$.

Singular linear systems. Singular linear systems are automatic systems in which the dynamic processes are described by linear equations, but not all equations are ordinary differential equations with constant coefficients. The following forms of automatic systems are included in the class of singular linear systems:

1. *Linear systems with variable parameters.* These are automatic systems in which all circuits are described only by ordinary linear differential equations, where some of the coefficients in these equations vary with time. Among these are certain continuous automatic systems where a portion of the parameters entering into the coefficients of the equations must be considered variable with time.

Systems with variable parameters will not be considered in detail in this book. We shall show only that the theorems of Liapunov's direct method (Section 57) apply to the study of stability of such systems, and shall give a numerical-graphical method for plotting the regulation process in such systems (Section 72). There are analytic methods for certain systems with periodically varying parameters. When the parameters of the system vary relatively slowly, the entire process is divided into time intervals, within each of which the parameters are considered constant, but different in different intervals, and the process within each interval is considered as a process in an ordinary linear system.

2. *Linear systems with distributed parameters.* These are automatic systems where it is not possible to consider all parameters to be lumped. These occur, for example, in all cases where long pipes are present in a continuous automatic system, in which it is necessary to consider the wave processes, or a long line in which it is necessary to consider the effect of distributed capacitance or inductance along its length.

In these cases, together with ordinary differential equations (describing the dynamic processes in the remaining circuits of the system), there appear partial differential equations for the circuit with distributed parameters (Section 46).

In investigating systems of this form the overall characteristic equation is found to be transcendental in contradistinction to ordinary linear systems.

3. *Linear systems with delay.* In these one or several circuits have a time delay in transmitting the signal applied to the input of the circuit. In a circuit with delay the process of variation of the output quantity begins only after a certain time interval τ following the start of variation of the input quantity (Section 45).

Methods of investigating linear systems with delay coincide with the methods of studying one of the classes of systems with distributed parameters.

4. *Linear pulse systems.* These are automatic systems which consist only of linear circuits and include linear pulse circuits, i.e. circuits in which any of the pulse characteristics (magnitude or duration) varies proportionally to the input quantity. Examples of linear pulse circuits are given in diagrams *a* and *b* of Fig. 31, corresponding to the graphs of Fig. 29*a* and 29*b* (the diagram in Fig. 31*c* and the graph of Fig. 29*c* represent a non-linear pulse circuit, which will be discussed below).

5. *Non-linear systems.* Non-linear systems are automatic systems including, together with linear circuits, at least one non-linear circuit, i.e. a circuit with non-linear static [characteristic or non-linearity of another type in the equation describing its dynamics. Above it was stated that the real characteristics of circuits are always more or less non-linear. Therefore, a non-linear circuit will be one for which the characteristics, for some reason, cannot be subjected to linearisation, i.e. they are, so to speak, essentially non-linear.

For example, if an electric motor with the characteristic represented in Fig. 33 is employed, where not only the rectilinear segment A_1OA takes part in the dynamic process investigated, as before, but the entire curved characteristic B_1OB, then this electric motor will now represent a non-linear element. The system as a whole will be non-linear even if all remaining elements are linear.

Non-linear elements may have widely differing forms. We shall list the more important of them.

(a) *A non-linear relay-type circuit* is one in which to a continuous variation of the input quantity x_1 there corresponds a discontinuous variation of the output quantity x_2 appearing only at defined values of the input quantity. Various forms of non-linear characteristics of relay type have been shown in Fig. 24. Some of them have hysteresis loops. Among the non-linear systems with this type of circuit are all relay automatic regulation systems (Section 4).

(b) *A non-linear circuit* with piecewise linear characteristic is a circuit the characteristic of which $x_2(x_1)$ is continuous, but has the form of a broken line consisting of rectilinear segments (not having continuous derivatives). Various forms of piecewise-linear characteristics are shown in Fig. 34. This type of non-linear circuit will also include those which are described by linear differential equations of various forms in various parts of the operation.

The first two characteristics (Figs. 34*a* and *b*) may be termed limited linear characteristics while the first, a saturation characteristic (in dependence on whichever of these terms better corresponds to the physical significance of the process in the given circuit). A characteristic of form *a* (Fig. 34) is obtained, for example, for each mechanical regulating organ having stops in the limiting position (rudder, slide valve) or limited cross-sectional dimension (gate valve). This form of characteristic may be used, as simplified, for an electric motor in place of Fig. 33. The same relates to hydraulic and other motors, used in automatic systems.

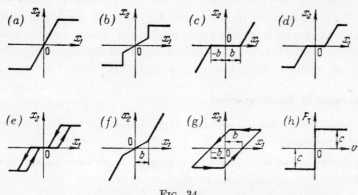

FIG. 34

The third graph of Fig. 34*c* represents a characteristic with an insensitive zone or with a dead zone of width 2*b*.

The characteristic of Fig. 34*d* combines a dead zone and saturation (limitation of the linear part), while a hysteresis loop is added in Fig. 34*e*.

The characteristic of Fig. 34*f* corresponds to a circuit for which the transfer factor (or gain factor) increases with increase in input magnitude x_1 above a certain value $x_1 = b$. Sometimes this is necessary for strengthening the effect of the control system.

The characteristic of Fig. 34*g* is obtained in the presence of back-lash (free play) in the mechanical transmission of width 2*b*. This characteristic has a hysteresis loop. The characteristic for dry friction (Fig. 34*h*) also reduces in certain cases to the form 34*g*, but not always (see Part IV).

(c) *A non-linear circuit with curved characteristic* may be directly considered. Its characteristic may be approximated by a second curve more convenient for analytic investigation. This characteristic in individual cases may also be approximately substituted by a piecewise-linear or relay characteristic. Finally, it may frequently be substituted by a linear characteristic in a limited operating region, i.e. linearised. Curved characteristics may also have hysteresis loops.

This category also includes non-linear circuits the dynamics of which are described by non-linear equations containing the products of variables or their derivatives and various more complicated combinations. These equations may also frequently be linearised.

(d) *A non-linear circuit with delay* is one in which together with non-linearity of any of the above forms there is also time delay τ in the transmission of the signal arriving at the input of the circuit.

(e) *A non-linear pulse circuit* is one in which the pulse characteristics (magnitude and duration) do not vary in direct proportion to the input quantity but according to one of the above forms of non-linearity. For example, the circuit of Fig. 31c and the graph of Fig. 29c represent a possible relay type non-linear pulse circuit since the magnitude and duration of pulses is constant but only the sign varies, as in the relay characteristic of type 6 in Fig. 24.

6. Processes in linear systems

We shall first define certain basic concepts to be employed in further discussion.

Regulation process, transient response and steady-state response. The differential equation of motion of an ordinary linear automatic regulation system has from (5.7) the form

$$L(p)x = S(p)f(t) + N(p)y(t), \qquad (6.1)$$

where the coefficients of the operational polynomials are defined by the parameters of the system.

Let us introduce the notation

$$f(t) = f^0(t) + \Delta f(t), \qquad y(t) = y^0(t) + \Delta y(t), \qquad (6.2)$$

where $f(t)$ is a perturbation the influence of which should be suppressed as completely as possible in the system, $f^0(t)$ is the fundamental portion of the perturbation, according to which calculation of the given system is carried out, $\Delta f(t)$ is an additional perturbation which in one or another form always exists in reality, $y^0(t)$ is the input command on the regulator (servomechanism) which should be reproduced by the given system, $\Delta y(t)$ is noise applied to the system together with the input action.

The solution of the linear differential equation (with constant coefficients) will be

$$x = x_t(t) + x^0(t) + x_\Delta(t), \qquad (6.3)$$

where $x_t(t)$ is the general solution of the homogeneous equation $L(p)x = 0$, having the form

$$x_t = C_1 e^{z_1 t} + C_2 e^{z_2 t} + \ldots + C_n e^{z_n t}, \qquad (6.4)$$

where $C_1, C_2, \ldots, C_n$ are arbitrary constants defined from the given initial conditions of the process; $z_1, z_2, \ldots, z_n$ are the roots of the characteristic equation $L(z) = 0$, which from (5.2) has in expanded form

$$a_0 z^n + a_1 z^{n-1} + \ldots + a_{n-1} z + a_n = 0;$$

$x^0(t)$ is the particular solution corresponding to the basic term

$$S(p) f^0(t) + N(p) y^0(t)$$

in the right-hand side of the equation; $x_\Delta(t)$ is the additional part of the solution, corresponding to the additional term

$$S(p) \Delta f(t) + N(p) \Delta y(t).$$

Expression (6.4) is written for the case where the characteristic equation does not have multiple or zero roots.

A complete solution of (6.3) describes the regulation process in the linear system (the general case of perturbed motion of the system).

The first portion of this solution $x_t(t)$ in the form of (6.4) represents a transient response (the characteristic motion of the system superimposed on the forced motion defined by the remaining terms of the solution).

The particular fundamental solution $x^0(t)$ represents the steady-state response or the steady (equilibrium) state of the system.

The simplest cases of external driving forces are

1) $f^0 = \text{const},\qquad y^0 = \text{const};$

2) $f^0 = \text{const},\qquad y^0 = \omega t;$

3) $f^0 = \text{const},\qquad y^0 = \omega t + \dfrac{\varepsilon t^2}{2};$

4) $f^0 = \text{const},\qquad y^0 = a \sin \omega t;$

5) $f^0 = a \sin \omega t,\qquad y^0 = \text{const},$

where the symbol 'const' also includes zero.

The corresponding particular solutions will be

1) $x^0 = \text{const},$

2) $x^0 = b + \omega_1 t,$

3) $x^0 = b + \omega_1 t + \dfrac{\varepsilon_1 t^2}{2},$

4) $x^0 = b + A_y \sin(\omega t + \beta_y),$

5) $x^0 = b + A_f \sin(\omega t + \beta_f).$

These forms of steady-state response are termed respectively: (1) equilibrium state, (2) following with constant velocity, (3) following with constant acceleration, (4) following a sinusoidal input force, (5) forced oscillations with sinusoidal perturbation. In addition, it is also possible, of course, to have many other more complicated forms of steady-state response corresponding to more complicated input forces $f^0(t)$ and $y^0(t)$.

In Figs. 35, 36, 37 and 38 are presented the simplest examples of regulation (and following) processes, which are composed of steady-state and transient components. Thus, Fig. 35 illustrates the transition of a system in the regulation process from one equi-

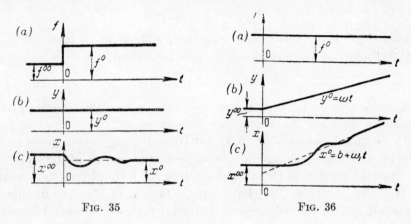

FIG. 35   FIG. 36

librium state to another with a discontinuous change of load from some previous value f^{00} to a new one f^0. In Fig. 36 is shown the transition of the system from the equilibrium state to a state of following with constant velocity and in Fig. 37 to a state of following a sinu-

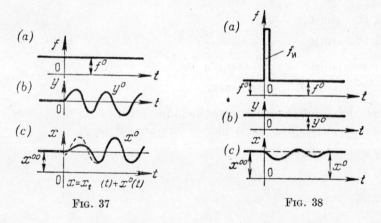

FIG. 37   FIG. 38

soidal input force. In Fig. 38 is shown a process with pulsed external perturbation. In all cases the broken line shows the graph of the steady state response for the quantity x and the difference between the ordinates of the full-line curve and the broken-line curve represents the transient response.

Defining in this way the regulation process consisting of steady-state and transient components, it is necessary to remember that in the real system there will always be an additional distortion of the process introduced by the additional input forces and noise

$\Delta f(t)$ and $\Delta y(t)$. These distortions are expressed in (6.3) in the form of an additional term $x_\Delta(t)$. An example may be the process shown in Fig. 39.

It is necessary to consider the following important circumstance. The particular solution $x^0(t)$ consists of individual terms corresponding to the individual terms terms in the right-hand side of the differential equation $S(p)f^0(t)$ and $N(p)y^0(t)$. If several perturbing forces

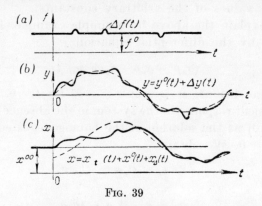

FIG. 39

act, there will correspondingly be several terms in the solution. Then each term of the particular solution $x^0(t)$ may be defined separately for each perturbation or driving force, independently of the other, and then they may be added. This is the so-called superposition principle. Consequently, if there exists a differential equation

$$L(p)x = S_1(p)f_1^0(t) + S_2(p)f_2^0(t) + N(p)y^0(t) ,$$

the particular solution defining the steady-state response of the system will be

$$x^0(t) = x_1^0(t) + x_2^0(t) + x_3^0(t) ,$$

where each term may be defined individually as the particular solution of one of the equations

$$L(p)x = S_1(p)f_1^0(t) ,$$
$$L(p)x = S_2(p)f_2^0(t) ,$$
$$L(p)x = N(p)y^0(t) .$$

The situation will be somewhat different with regard to the transient response. In the solution for the transient response

$$x_t = C_1 e^{z_1 t} + C_2 e^{z_2 t} + \dots + C_n e^{z_n t}$$

(which is superimposed on the steady-state response forming the total regulation process) the arbitrary constants $C_1, C_2, \dots, C_n$ must be calculated from the initial conditions necessarily utilising the complete expression of the solution (6.3). Otherwise the initial conditions $x_0, \dot{x}_0, \ddot{x}_0, \ldots, x_0^{(n-1)}$ should be transformed to $x_{0t} = x_0 - x_0^0$, $\dot{x}_{0t} = \dot{x}_0 - \dot{x}_0^0$, where $x_0^0, \dot{x}_0^0, \ldots$ are the values of $x^0, \dot{x}^0, \ldots$ of the particular solution for $t = 0$. Consequently, the form of the transient response may substantially depend on the form of the driving force. In other words (in the terminology of mechanics), the form of the characteristic motion of the system which is superimposed on the forced motion may depend substantially on the form of the latter (through the values of the arbitrary constants).

We shall explain the above by a simple example. Let the system be described by the differential equation

$$(a_0 p^2 + a_1 p + a_2)x = f(t) \tag{6.5}$$

with initial conditions: $x = x_0$ and $\dot{x} = \dot{x}_0$ for $t = 0$. We shall first find the transient response in the system in the absence of the external force $\big(f(t) = 0\big)$ as the solution of the homogeneous equation $(a_0 p^2 + a_1 p + a_2)x = 0$. We obtain

$$x = x_t = C_1 e^{z_1 t} + C_2 e^{z_2 t}, \tag{6.6}$$

where

$$z_{1,2} = \frac{-a_1 \pm \sqrt{a_1^2 - 4a_2 a_0}}{2a_0}.$$

We shall assume that the roots are real. Determining the arbitrary constants from the initial conditions, we obtain

$$C_1 = \frac{x_0 z_2 - x_0}{z_2 - z_1}, \qquad C_2 = \frac{x_0 z_1 - x_0}{z_1 - z_2}. \tag{6.7}$$

The solution of (6.6) is represented, let us assume, by the graph of Fig. 40a.

We shall now find the transient response in the same system for the same initial conditions, but in the presence of a perturbation $f(t) = a \sin(\omega t + \delta)$. The particular solution of (6.5), defining the steady-state response, will be

$$x^0 = A \sin(\omega t + \beta), \tag{6.8}$$

where

$$A = \frac{a}{\sqrt{(a_2 - a_0 \omega^2)^2 + a_1^2 \omega^2}}, \qquad \beta = \delta - \tan^{-1} \frac{a_1 \omega}{a_2 - a_0 \omega^2}.$$

This is shown by the broken line in Fig. 40b.

The transient response as the general solution of the homogeneous equation will be

$$x_t = C_1 e^{z_1 t} + C_2 e^{z_2 t}, \tag{6.9}$$

where the arbitrary constants are defined from the initial conditions on the basis of the complete solution

$$x = x_t(t) + x^0(t) = C_1 e^{z_1 t} + C_2 e^{z_2 t} + A \sin(\omega t + \beta). \tag{6.10}$$

Their calculation gives

$$C_1 = \frac{(x_0 - A\sin\beta)z_2 - (\dot{x}_0 - A\omega\cos\beta)}{z_2 - z_1},$$
$$C_2 = \frac{(x_0 - A\sin\beta)z_1 - (\dot{x}_0 - A\omega\cos\beta)}{z_1 - z_2}. \qquad (6.11)$$

The complete solution (6.10) is represented by the solid curve in Fig. 40b. The transient component (transient response) of this solution x_t is represented by hatching in Fig. 40b. It is shown separately in Fig. 40c.

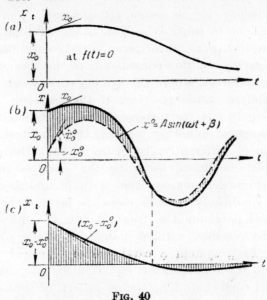

FIG. 40

From this it is evident that in the presence of an external force the transient responses, without regard to uniqueness of the general expressions (6.9) and (6.6) will differ, due to the essential differences in values of the arbitrary constants (6.11) and (6.7).

From this there follows a second conclusion. The formula for the arbitrary constants (6.11) may be obtained from (6.7) if in the latter we substitute the quantity x_0 by $x_0 - A\sin\beta$ and the quantity $\dot{x}_0$ by $\dot{x}_0 - A\omega\cos\beta$. But from (6.8) the quantities $A\sin\beta$ and $A\omega\cos\beta$ are the values of x^0 and $\dot{x}^0$ at $t = 0$. Consequently, the transient response in the presence of $f(t)$ in the given system can be calculated from the homogeneous differential equation, but it is first necessary to transform the initial conditions to the form

$$x_{0t} = x_0 - x_0^0, \qquad \dot{x}_{0t} = \dot{x}_0 - \dot{x}_0^0 \qquad \text{at} \qquad t = 0,$$

where x_0^0 and $\dot{x}_0^0$ are the values of x^0 and $\dot{x}^0$ of the steady state components of the solution at $t = 0$. This is clearly shown in Fig. 40.

It should be noted that in automatic regulation systems (and in servomechanisms) such a transformation of the initial conditions, necessary for determination of the transient response from the homogeneous differential equation, is more complicated. This is connected not only with the high order of the equations but also with the presence in the system equation (6.1) of an operational polynomial before the external forces $f(t)$ and $y(t)$. But even there it may be carried out.

Thus, in investigating the transient response of automatic regulation systems it is always necessary to define the corresponding external conditions, i.e. to assign $f(t)$ and $y(t)$.

If the transient response is sought as the solution of the homogeneous equation $L(p)x = 0$ for given initial conditions of the system, the result of such a solution corresponds to the absence of perturbations and input forces, where the system carries out a free motion from some shifted initial position. If the transient is a variation of external conditions (perturbing forces, variation of load, readjustment, change of following regime), then the transient response must be studied differently, by defining the arbitrary constants of the complete solution, including the steady-state component, or from the homogeneous equation with preliminary recalculation of the initial conditions. In both cases the form of the force $f(t)$ and the operational polynomial in front of it have critical significance.

It would be possible, without assigning specific $f(t)$ and $y(t)$, to assemble for each system a catalogue of transient responses determined from the homogeneous equation for all possible combinations of initial conditions. This would reflect, of course, all forms of transient response which could occur in the given system for various perturbing forces. But, firstly, for a high-order system the number of different combinations of initial conditions will be very great and, secondly, many of these combinations are excluded from the point of view of real operating conditions of the system. Therefore, it is more useful to assign certain typical external perturbations $f(t)$ and $y(t)$ which are either the most probable, the most difficult, or the most dangerous for the given system. The transient responses should be determined for them.

In the theory of automatic regulation either an instantaneous jump in the magnitude f (or the quantity y) from one constant value f^{00} to another f^0 (Fig. 35) or an instantaneous impulse f (Fig. 38) are most frequently taken as the typical external force, although it is equally important to study the transient responses in the transition from one following regime to another (Figs. 36 and 37).

The typical step or impulse input forces are usually taken of unit magnitude (Fig. 41) since the solution obtained may then be multiplied by the actual magnitude of the jump or impulse to obtain the solution for a force not equal to unity. It is well known that it is possible to find the responses for any other forces (Section 74) from the reaction of the system to the unit pulse.

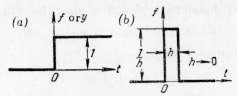

FIG. 41

The unit step for perturbation f and input force y (Fig. 41a) is conventionally written in the form

$$f = 1(t) \quad \text{and} \quad y = 1(t), \qquad (6.12)$$

which in a more complete notation signifies

$$\left. \begin{array}{llll} 1(t) = 0 & \text{with} & t < 0 & \text{and} & t = -0, \\ 1(t) = 1 & \text{with} & t > 0 & \text{and} & t = +0, \end{array} \right\} \qquad (6.13)$$

where the instant $t = 0$ is divided into two, -0 and $+0$, corresponding to approach to it from negative and positive values of t.

The unit impulse is written in the form

$$f = 1'(t), \qquad (6.14)$$

where

$$1'(t) = \lim_{h \to 0} f(t, h), \qquad (6.15)$$

if $f(t, h)$ denotes the delta function represented in Fig. 41b, i.e.

$$\left. \begin{array}{llll} f(t, h) = 0 & \text{with} & t < 0 & \text{and} & t > h, \\ f(t, h) = \dfrac{1}{h} & \text{with} & 0 \leqslant t \leqslant h. \end{array} \right\} \qquad (6.16)$$

This function has the property that its area is equal to unity for arbitrary h, including $h \to 0$. Therefore, in passage to the limit in (6.15) there is obtained an instantaneous impulse (zero duration with infinite value f), but the magnitude of the impulse (area) is equal to unity.

From this there follows in particular that

$$\int_0^{+\infty} 1'(t)\,dt = \lim_{h \to 0} \int_0^{+\infty} f(t, h)\,dt = \lim_{h \to 0} \int_0^h \frac{1}{h}\,dt = 1, \qquad (6.17)$$

where it is obvious that

$$\int_{-\infty}^{-0} 1'(t)\,dt = 0.$$

The integral of the unit impulse $1'(t)$ is consequently a unit step $1(t)$ and signifies that the unit impulse which we denote by $1'(t)$ is the time derivative of the unit step $1(t)$.

An external force having the form of an instantaneous non-unit step of arbitrary magnitude f^0 and y^0 may be written in the form

$$f = f^0 \cdot 1(t) \quad \text{and} \quad y = y^0 \cdot 1(t) \tag{6.18}$$

and the instantaneous impulse

$$f = f_t \cdot 1'(t) \tag{6.19}$$

or, with regard to Fig. 38a

$$f = f^0 + f_t \cdot 1'(t) \ .$$

A step of the form of Fig. 35a may be written analogously in the form

$$f = f^{00} + (f^0 - f^{00}) \cdot 1(t) \ . \tag{6.20}$$

The application of driving forces of type Fig. 36b and Fig. 37b is written in the forms

$$y = y^{00} + \omega t \cdot 1(t) \text{ and } y = a \sin \omega t \cdot 1(t) \ . \tag{6.21}$$

respectively.

Thus, using functions of the form of the unit step it is possible to describe the instantaneous application of arbitrary forces to the systems.

Initial conditions. If the differential equation of the system is given in the form (6.1), the initial conditions, as is well known, should be given in the form

$$x = x_0, \ \dot{x} = \dot{x}_0, \ \ddot{x} = \ddot{x}_0, \ \dots, \ x^{(n-2)} = x_0^{(n-2)}, \ x^{(n-1)} = x_0^{(n-1)}$$
$$\text{at } t = 0 \ , \tag{6.22}$$

where n is the order of (6.1), i.e. the degree of the operational polynomial $L(p)$; the indices $(n-1)$, $(n-2)$, ... here denote the time derivatives of corresponding order, while the index 0 denotes their values at $t = 0$. The physical significance of these initial conditions is clarified by dividing the general equation of the system (6.1) into a series of equations of the individual circuits of the given system, which may be done for each concrete system (e.g. Example 1 at the end of this paragraph).

These initial conditions define the state of the system at $t = 0$, at which the examination of the process begins.

In those cases where at $t = 0$ an input in the form of a step or impulse occurs, and in those cases where at $t = 0$ there occurs an instantaneous application of a force of any arbitrary form (e.g. (6.18)–(6.21)), it is necessary to distinguish the instants $t = -0$ and $t = +0$.

This division of the time $t = 0$ has a definite physical significance. In essence, in nature there cannot actually be "pure" instantaneous steps, pulses and applications of forces, but only relatively fast variations taking place during such short time intervals as may be neglected in comparison with the duration of the process studied in the system. Therefore, actual steps, impulses and applications of arbitrary forces, for example, in passage from one following regime to another, will occur over some small time interval from $t = -\varepsilon$ to $t = +\varepsilon$ (where ε is some positive quantity). Neglecting the magnitude of this interval ($\varepsilon \to 0$), we obtain the moments of time $t = -0$ and $t = +0$ for the start and finish respectively of the step (or impulse or application of arbitrary force). They actually correspond to two different states of the system, which are very close to each other in time, but may differ from each other by relatively large differences in the magnitudes of the coordinates, velocities and other variable quantities. Thus, for example, it is familiar from mechanics that application of an "instantaneous" impulse (shock) to a mass causes "instantaneous" change in its velocity by a definite finite quantity. The term "instantaneous" is understood in the sense of "during the time: $-\varepsilon < t < +\varepsilon$" or, according to the above convention, from $t = -0$ to $t = +0$ (as $\varepsilon \to 0$).

From this it follows that in all cases where for $t = 0$ there occurs a step, impulse or instantaneous application of arbitrary force, it is necessary clearly to distinguish what is actually meant by the initial conditions of the process: the state of the system at the instant $t = -0$ (directly before the step) or the instant $t = +0$ (immediately after the step). Both of these have their significance. In the former, the step itself is included in the process considered by us, while in the latter the process in the system after the step has already occurred is considered.

The initial conditions written for $t = -0$ correspond to the state of the system before the step. For example, for the processes shown in Figs. 35, 36, 37, 38 and 39, we have

$$x = x^{00}, \dot{x} = \ddot{x} = \ldots = x^{(n-1)} = 0 \quad \text{at} \quad t = -0 .$$

The initial conditions written for $t = +0$:

$$x = x_0, \dot{x} = \dot{x}_0, \ddot{x} = \ddot{x}_0, \ldots, x^{(n-1)} = x_0^{(n-1)} \quad \text{at} \quad t = +0 ,$$

express the instantaneous change of the corresponding quantities, occuring during the step. Therefore, in Figs. 35–39, where $\dot{x} = 0$ at $t = -0$, in general, we may obtain $\dot{x}_0 \neq 0$ at $t = +0$, i.e. there may occur a break in the curve at the point $t = 0$.

From the above there follows the necessity of having formulae for transforming the given initial conditions for $t = -0$, expressing the state of the system before the jump, to the initial conditions for $t = +0$, defining the initial data of the required course of the process immediately after the step.

The derivation of these formulae is easily carried out using operational calculus which gives: 1) the application of the step itself and the state of the process under consideration employing the initial conditions for $t = -0$; 2) consideration of the process after the jump with initial conditions for $t = +0$. By comparison of these two forms the initial conditions for $t = +0$ are defined through the conditions for $t = -0$. This will be proved in Section 74 (p. 737). Here we give only the final formulae for calculating the initial conditions. The value of x and its derivatives for $t = -0$ (before the jump) will be given the index -0, while for $t = +0$ (after the jump), the index $+0$.

When a unit step of the variable f acts (Fig. 41a) we have the following formulae for transforming the initial conditions:

$$
\left.
\begin{aligned}
& x_{+0} = x_{-0}, \ \dot{x}_{+0} = \dot{x}_{-0}, \ \dots, \ x_{+0}^{(n-m-1)} = x_{-0}^{(n-m-1)}, \\[2mm]
& x_{+0}^{(n-m)} - x_{-0}^{(n-m)} = \frac{b_0}{a_0} \cdot 1, \\[2mm]
& x_{+0}^{(n-m+1)} - x_{-0}^{(n-m+1)} = \frac{b_1}{a_0} \cdot 1 - \frac{a_1}{a_0}(x_{+0}^{(n-m)} - x_{-0}^{(n-m)}), \\[2mm]
& x_{+0}^{(n-m+2)} - x_{-0}^{(n-m+2)} = \frac{b_2}{a_0} \cdot 1 - \frac{a_2}{a_0}(x_{+0}^{(n-m)} - x_{-0}^{(n-m)}) - \\[2mm]
& \qquad\qquad\qquad\qquad - \frac{a_1}{a_0}(x_{+0}^{(n-m+1)} - x_{-0}^{(n-m+1)}), \\[2mm]
& \cdots\cdots\cdots\cdots\cdots\cdots\cdots\cdots\cdots\cdots\cdots\cdots\cdots \\[2mm]
& x_{+0}^{(n-1)} - x_{-0}^{(n-1)} = \frac{b_{m-1}}{a_0} \cdot 1 - \frac{a_{m-1}}{a_0}(x_{+0}^{(n-m)} - x_{-0}^{(n-m)}) - \dots - \\[2mm]
& \qquad\qquad\qquad\qquad - \frac{a_1}{a_0}(x_{+0}^{(n-2)} - x_{-0}^{(n-2)}),
\end{aligned}
\right\} \quad (6.23)
$$

where m and n are the degrees of the operational polynomials in the differential equation of the given system (5.6), $m \leqslant n$; $a_0, a_1, \dots, b_0, b_1, \dots$ are the coefficients of these equations defined by the parameters of the system.

In these formulae the operator 1 has the dimensions of the quantity f. If the force is applied in the form of a step, not equal to unity, in place of 1 the magnitude of the step should be substituted.

With a force in the form of a unit step of the variable y we obtain from (6.23) formulae for transformation of the initial conditions by substitution of the quantity m by ν and the quantities $b_0, b_1, \dots$ by $c_0, c_1, \dots$ from the differential equation (5.6) of the system.

From formulae (6.23) it is evident that for equality of the degrees of the operational polynomials in the right and left sides of the differential equations of this system ($m = n$ or $\nu = n$) the step at the point $t = 0$ will occur not only for the derivatives in x but also for x itself, namely, $x_{+0} - x_{-0} = b_0/a_0 \cdot 1$.

Formulae (6.23) also show that if $m = 0$, i.e. if the operational polynomial for $f(t)$ is absent and the equation of the system has the form

$$L(p)x = b_0 f(t) , \qquad (6.24)$$

for a step of the variable f, the initial conditions for $t = +0$ are equal to the initial conditions for $t = -0$. The same occurs for a step of the variable y in the equation

$$L(p)x = c_0 y(t) . \qquad (6.25)$$

If in the equation of the system for $f(t)$ there is an operational polynomial $b_0 p + b_1$, with a step in the variable f, the initial conditions for $t = +0$ and $t = -0$ will differ only in the values of the $(n-1)$st derivative. The higher the degree of the operational polynomial $S(p)$ for $f(t)$, the more derivatives in the initial conditions will change discontinuously at the step f. In this case, when the degree of $S(p)$ in (5.7) is one less that the degree of $L(p)$, for a step in f, there will necessarily be a discontinuity in the first derivative, i.e. a break in the curve of the process $x(t)$.

Formulae (6.23) may be transformed also with regard to a force in the form of a unit impulse in f. Having in view that the impulse is the derivative of the step with regard to time, for the unit impulse $f(t) = 1'(t)$ in (5.7) the expression $S(p)1'(t)$ may be substituted by $S(p)p1(t)$. This signifies that in formulae (6.23) it is necessary to replace m by $m+1$ and put $b_{m+1} = 0$. As a result we obtain the following formulae for calculating the initial conditions under a unit impulse of the variable f, when in (5.6) $m < n$:

$$
\left.
\begin{aligned}
&x_{+0} = x_{-0}, \ \dot{x}_{+0} = \dot{x}_{-0}, \ ..., \ x_{+0}^{(n-m-2)} = x_{-0}^{(n-m-2)} , \\[2mm]
&x_{+0}^{(n-m-1)} - x_{-0}^{(n-m-1)} = \frac{b_0}{a_0} \cdot 1 , \\[2mm]
&x_{+0}^{(n-m)} - x_{-0}^{(n-m)} = \frac{b_1}{a_0} \cdot 1 - \frac{a_1}{a_0} (x_{+0}^{(n-m-1)} - x_{-0}^{(n-m-1)}) , \\[2mm]
&x_{+0}^{(n-m+1)} - x_{-0}^{(n-m+1)} = \frac{b_2}{a_0} \cdot 1 - \frac{a_2}{a_0} (x_{+0}^{(n-m-1)} - x_{-0}^{(n-m-1)}) - \\[2mm]
&\qquad\qquad\qquad\qquad - \frac{a_1}{a_0} (x_{+0}^{(n-m)} - x_{-0}^{(n-m)}) , \\[2mm]
&\ \cdots\cdots\cdots\cdots\cdots\cdots\cdots\cdots\cdots\cdots\cdots\cdots\cdots \\[2mm]
&x_{+0}^{(n-1)} - x_{-0}^{(n-1)} = \frac{b_m}{a_0} \cdot 1 - \frac{a_m}{a_0} (x_{+0}^{(n-m-1)} - x_{-0}^{(n-m-1)}) - ... - \\[2mm]
&\qquad\qquad\qquad\qquad - \frac{a_1}{a_0} (x_{+0}^{(n-2)} - x_{-0}^{(n-2)}) ,
\end{aligned}
\right\} \quad (6.26)
$$

where 1 has the dimensions of the impulse in f, i.e. the dimensions of f multiplied by time. If the force is applied in the form of a non-unit impulse, it is necessary to substitute in place of 1 in these formulae the given magnitude of the impulse f_i.

As is evident from (6.26), with the input in the form of an impulse, in contradistinction to a step, equality of the initial conditions for $t = +0$ and $t = -0$ will not occur, even in the case (6.24), since there will be a discontinuity in the value of the $(n-1)$st derivative. The discontinuity of the first derivative $\dot{x}$ (i.e. a break in the curve) will already occur for $m = n-2$, and a discontinuity in the magnitude of x itself for $m = n-1$.

On the form of the equation for the transient process. Let the differential equation of the system have the form

$$L(p)x = S(p)f(t) \tag{6.27}$$

and let it be required to find the transient response with input in the form of a step $f(t) = f^{00} + 1(t)$, if before this the system was in equilibrium with $x = \text{const} = x^{00}$. The differential equation of the system (6.27) will be

$$L(p)x = S(p)[f^{00} + 1(t)] \tag{6.28}$$

with initial conditions

$$x = x^{00}, \ \dot{x} = \ddot{x} = \ldots = x^{(n-1)} = 0 \quad \text{at} \quad t = -0 . \tag{6.29}$$

If these initial conditions are reduced by means of formulae (6.23) to the instant $t = +0$, the step itself is eliminated from consideration and in place of (6.28) the differential equation of the system takes the form

$$L(p)x = b_m \cdot (f^{00} + 1) , \tag{6.30}$$

where b_m is the free term of the polynomial $S(t)$, while 1 has the dimensions of f.

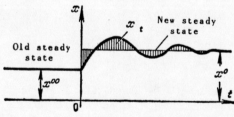

FIG. 42

In this case, the system passes from one steady state ("old", Fig. 42) to another, a "new" one. The values of x for them as particular solutions are defined by

$$x^{00} = \frac{b_m}{a_n}f^{00}, \ x^0 = \frac{b_m}{a_n}(f^{00} + 1) = x^{00} + \frac{b_m}{a_n} \cdot 1 , \tag{6.31}$$

respectively, where a_n is the constant term of the polynomial $L(p)$. The solution of (6.30) will be

$$x = x_t(t) + x^0 = C_1 e^{z_1 t} + C_2 e^{z_2 t} + \ldots + C_n e^{z_n t} + x^{00} + \frac{b_m}{a_n} \cdot 1 \,, \quad (6.32)$$

where the arbitrary constants $C_1, C_2, \ldots, C_n$ are defined from the initial conditions for $t = +0$, obtained from (6.29) by means of formulae (6.23). The solution of (6.28) with initial conditions for $t = -0$ may be found by the operational method without preliminary transformation of the initial conditions (Section 74). The result in both cases will be, of course, the same.

The transient response is represented by vertical hatching in Fig. 42. Its ordinates, as always, are subtracted from the new steady state of the system. It may be found as the solution to the homogeneous equation $L(p)x_t = 0$, i.e.

$$x_t = C_1 e^{z_1 t} + C_2 e^{z_2 t} + \ldots + C_n e^{z_n t} \,,$$

if in the initial conditions transformed by formulae (6.23) we take

$$x_{0t} = x^{00} - x^0 = -\frac{b_m}{a_n} \cdot 1 \,. \quad (6.33)$$

Sometimes the variable x is read from the old steady-state, and the solution takes the form (6.32) without the quantity x^{00}, while the initial conditions will contain $x_0 = 0$.

This relates also to the equation

$$L(p)x = N(p)y(t)$$

with the input force in the form of a unit step $y(t) = y^{00} + 1(t)$, with the difference only that from (5.6) it is necessary to substitute c_v in place of b_m in expressions (6.30)–(6.33).

Similarly, for a force in the form of a unit impulse, in place of the equation

$$L(p)x = S(p)1'(t) \quad (6.34)$$

with initial conditions at $t = -0$ it is possible to solve the homogeneous differential equation $L(p)x_t = 0$, but with other initial conditions for $t = +0$, calculated from (6.26)*.

Let us consider the example of determining the transient response of an automatic regulation system by solution of the homogeneous equation, and also of examples of transformation of the initial conditions.

---

* It should be noted that a similar transformation of the initial conditions to determine the transient response from the homogeneous equation is possible for various other types of external forces on the system.

Example 1. Let us find the transient response in the absence of perturbations in an automatic frequency control system, the schematic diagram of which is represented in Fig. 43.

The regulated object is a vacuum tube oscillator consisting of the triode T and the tuned circuit LC. The regulated quantity is the frequency of oscillation ω.

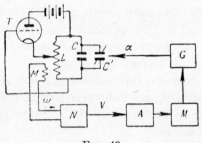

FIG. 43

The sensitive element of the regulator is a coil M with phase discriminator N. The voltage induced in the coil M is applied to the phase discriminator N. At the output of the latter a d.c. voltage V is obtained which is proportional to the deviation $\Delta\omega$ of the oscillation frequency ω.

The voltage V is then amplified in the d.c. amplifier A and is applied to the electric motor M which rotates the variable capacitor C' through a reduction gear with damper C. The capacitor is the regulating organ acting on the object for the purpose of eliminating the undersired deviation in frequency tending to arise in it.

Let the deviation of the regulated quantity (frequency), in the absence of perturbations, be expressed as a function of the angle of rotation of the capacitor by the equation (the equation of the regulated object)

$$T_1\Delta\dot{\omega} + \Delta\omega = -k_1\alpha , \qquad (6.35)$$

where T_1 and k_1 are given constants, α is the angle of rotation of the capacitor axis, $\Delta\omega$ is the deviation of the regulated quantity ω.

The equation of the sensitive element will be

$$V = k_2\Delta\omega . \qquad (6.36)$$

The equation of the amplifier, motor and transmission to the capacitor C' will be

$$J\ddot{\alpha} = c_1V - c_2\dot{\alpha} , \qquad (6.37)$$

where J is the moment of inertia of the entire rotating mass reduced to the axis of the capacitor and c_1V and $c_2\dot{\alpha}$ are the torque and damping moment reduced to the same axis.

Eliminating from these three equations α and V, we obtain a single equation for the closed system in the form

$$\Delta\ddot{\omega} + a_1\Delta\ddot{\omega} + a_2\Delta\dot{\omega} + a_3\Delta\omega = 0 , \qquad (6.38)$$

where

$$a_1 = \frac{J + c_2 T_1}{J T_1} , \qquad a_2 = \frac{c_2}{J T_1} , \qquad a_3 = \frac{c_1 k_1 k_2}{J T_1} .$$

The characteristic equation will be

$$z^3 + a_1 z^2 + a_2 z + a_3 = 0 . \qquad (6.39)$$

Let us first find the real roots (there is at least one such root in an equation of third degree). For this we construct the graph of the function

$$f(z) = z^3 + a_1 z^2 + a_2 z + a_3$$

in the interval $-M < z < -m$, where M and m are the minimum and maximum of the numbers*

$$\frac{J + c_2 T_1}{J T_1} , \qquad \frac{c_2}{J + c_2 T_1} , \qquad \frac{c_1 k_1 k_2}{c_2} .$$

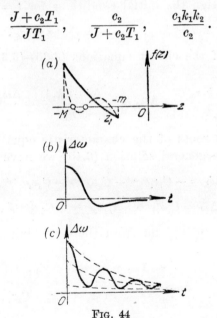

FIG. 44

The point of intersection (Fig. 44a) gives an approximate value of the root which may be made more exact by interpolation. If all three roots of (6.39) are real, the curve $f(z)$ will have three points of intersection (broken line in Fig. 44a) and thus all three roots will be found.

If there is a single point of intersection (z_1), the remaining two roots are complex. To determine them we have the quadratic equation

$$z^2 + 2b_1 z + b_2 z = 0 ,$$

* See Section 39.

obtained by dividing the polynomial (6.39) by $(z - z_1)$. The complex roots of the cubic equation (6.39), consequently, will be

$$z_{2,3} = -b_1 \pm i \sqrt{b_2 - b_1^2}.$$

As a result we obtain the equation of the curve of the transient response as a solution of (6.38) in the form

$$\Delta \omega = C_1 e^{-z_1 t} + C_2 e^{-z_2 t} + C_3 e^{-z_3 t}, \qquad (6.40)$$

when all roots are real and distinct, and

$$\Delta \omega = C_1 e^{-z_1 t} + A e^{-b_1 t} \sin\left(\sqrt{b_2 - b_1^2}\, t + \beta\right), \qquad (6.41)$$

when two roots are complex. Here C_1, C_2, C_3, A, β are arbitrary constants defined by the initial conditions and by the parameters of the system in the following manner.

Let us next assign the initial conditions for $t = 0$. For example:

$$\Delta \omega = \Delta \omega_0, \quad \alpha = \alpha_0, \quad \dot{\alpha} = \alpha_0.$$

On the basis of the circuit equations (6.35)–(6.37) we obtain for $t = 0$

$$\Delta \dot{\omega}_0 = -\frac{\Delta \omega_0 + k_1 \alpha_0}{T_1}, \quad \Delta \ddot{\omega}_0 = -\frac{\Delta \dot{\omega}_0 + k_1 \dot{\alpha}_0}{T_1} = \frac{\Delta \omega_0 + k_1 (\alpha_0 - T_1 \dot{\alpha}_0)}{T_1^2}.$$

When all three roots of the characteristic equation are real and distinct, from the general solution (6.40) we have

$$\Delta \dot{\omega} = -C_1 z_1 e^{-z_1 t} - C_2 z_2 e^{-z_2 t} - C_3 z_3 e^{-z_3 t},$$

$$\Delta \ddot{\omega} = C_1 z_1^2 e^{-z_1 t} + C_2 z_2^2 e^{-z_2 t} + C_3 z_3^2 e^{-z_3 t}.$$

Substituting in (6.40) and from there the initial conditions, we obtain

$$\Delta \omega_0 = C_1 + C_2 + C_3,$$

$$\frac{\Delta \omega_0 + k_1 \alpha_0}{T_1} = C_1 z_1 + C_2 z_2 + C_3 z_3,$$

$$\frac{\Delta \omega_0 + k_1 (\alpha_0 - T_1 \dot{\alpha}_0)}{T_1^2} = C_1 z_1^2 + C_2 z_2^2 + C_3 z_3^2.$$

From this we find the arbitrary constants

$$C_1 = \frac{(T_1 z_2 - 1)(T_1 z_3 - 1)\Delta \omega_0 - (T_1 z_2 + T_1 z_3 - 1) k_1 \alpha_0 - T_1 k_1 \dot{\alpha}_0}{T_1^2 (z_2 - z_1)(z_3 - z_1)},$$

$$C_2 = \frac{(T_1 z_3 - 1)(T_1 z_1 - 1)\Delta \omega_0 - (T_1 z_3 + T_1 z_1 - 1) k_1 \alpha_0 - T_1 k_1 \dot{\alpha}_0}{T_1^2 (z_3 - z_2)(z_1 - z_2)},$$

$$C_3 = \frac{(T_1 z_1 - 1)(T_1 z_2 - 1)\Delta \omega_0 - (T_1 z_1 + T_1 z_2 - 1) k_1 \alpha_0 - T_1 k_1 \dot{\alpha}_0}{T_1^2 (z_1 - z_3)(z_2 - z_3)}.$$

Calculating in this way the arbitrary constants for the case (6.40), and analogously for (6.41), we obtain the corresponding curves of the transient process (Fig. 44b and 44c) in the given automatic regulation system.

A solution of this example by the operational method is given on p. 742.

Example 2. Given the differential equation of an automatic regulation system

$$(a_0 p^4 + a_1 p^3 + a_2 p^2 + a_3 p + a_4) x = -(b_0 p^2 + b_1 p + b_2) f(t) . \quad (6.42)$$

It is required to find the initial conditions at $t = +0$ and the transient response (Fig. 45a) from the homogeneous differential equation

$$(a_0 p^4 + a_1 p^3 + a_2 p^2 + a_3 p + a_4) x_t = 0 , \quad (6.43)$$

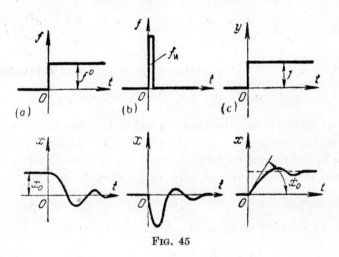

Fig. 45

if it is given that at $t = 0$ the load f on the object changes discontinuously from zero to a given value f^0, and that before the step the system was in the steady state

$$(x = \dot{x} = \ddot{x} = \dddot{x} = 0 \quad \text{at} \quad f = \dot{f} = 0 \quad \text{with} \quad t \leqslant -0) .$$

From (6.23) and (6.33), noting that in the right-hand side of (6.42), in contradistinction to the general formula (5.6), there is a minus sign before all coefficients, with $n = 4$ and $m = 2$, we obtain the required initial conditions for $t = +0$:

$$x_0 = \frac{b_2}{a_4} f^0 , \quad \dot{x}_0 = 0 , \quad \ddot{x}_0 = -\frac{b_0}{a_0} f^0 ,$$

$$\dddot{x}_0 = -\frac{b_1}{a_0} f^0 - \frac{a_1}{a_0} \ddot{x}_0 = \left(-\frac{b_1}{a_0} + \frac{a_1 b_0}{a_0^2}\right) f^0 .$$

These initial conditions permit solving the homogeneous equation (6.43), in place of the equation

$$a_0 p^4 + a_1 p^3 + a_2 p^2 + a_3 p + a_4) x = - (b_0 p^2 + b_1 p + b_2) f^0 \cdot 1(t) ,$$

having zero initial values before the step.

Analogously, in the case of an instantaneous impulse f_i' (Fig. 45b), to be able to solve in place of the equation

$$(a_0 p^4 + a_1 p^3 + a_2 p^2 + a_3 p + a_4) x = - (b_0 p^2 + b_1 p + b_2) f_i 1'(t) ,$$

the homogeneous equation (6.43), we find from (6.26) the following initial conditions for $t = +0$:

$$x_0 = 0 , \quad \dot{x}_0 = - \frac{b_0}{a_0} f_i , \quad \ddot{x}_0 = - \frac{b_1}{a_0} f_i - \frac{a_1}{a_0} \dot{x}_0 = \left(- \frac{b_1}{a_0} + \frac{a_1 b_0}{a_0^2} \right) f_i ,$$

$$\dddot{x}_0 = - \frac{b_2}{a_0} f_i - \frac{a_2}{a_0} \dot{x}_0 - \frac{a_1}{a_0} \ddot{x}_0 = \left(- \frac{b_2}{a_0} + \frac{a_2 b_0}{a_0^2} + \frac{a_1 b_1}{a_0^2} - \frac{a_1^2 b_0}{a_0^3} \right) f_i' .$$

Example 3. Given the differential equation of a servomechanism

$$(a_0 p^3 + a_1 p^2 + a_2 p + a_3) x = (c_0 p^2 + c_1 p + c_2) y , \qquad (6.44)$$

where the external applied force y takes the form of a unit step, before which the system was in equilibrium with $x = \dot{x} = \ddot{x} = 0$, $y = \dot{y} = 0$. It is required to find again the initial conditions so that to obtain the transient response (Fig. 45c), in place of equation

$$(a_0 p^3 + a_1 p^2 + a_2 p + a_3) x = (c_0 p^2 + c_1 p + c_2) \cdot 1(t) ,$$

it would be possible to solve the following equation (after the step):

$$(a_0 p^3 + a_1 p^2 + a_2 p + a_3) x = c_2 ,$$

where x is read from the old steady state. For this we calculate from (6.23) the initial conditions for $t = +0$:

$$x_0 = 0 , \quad \dot{x}_0 = \frac{c_0}{a_0} , \quad \ddot{x}_0 = \frac{c_1}{a_0} - \frac{a_1}{a_0} \dot{x}_0 = \frac{c_1}{a_0} - \frac{a_1 c_0}{a_0^2}$$

(in this example, in accordance with (6.44), the symbols b in formulae (6.23) are replaced by c).

7. Stability and errors of linear systems

The complete solution (6.3) of the differential equation of motion of the linear automatic regulation system (6.1) includes, firstly, the useful portion, i.e. the reproduction of the input force, and, secondly, an entire complex of additional terms constituting the error of the given system. Let us now consider this question.

Stability of a linear system. First of all it is necessary to note that the general solution of the homogeneous equation (6.4) may be divergent, i.e. $x_t \to \infty$ as $t \to \infty$. Then the system will not be useful since it will diverge from the steady state defined by the particular solution $x^0(t)$. In this case the system is termed unstable; in general it will not reproduce the input signal. Therefore, it is first necessary to consider this undesirable property of the transient response.

The transient response (6.4) has the form

$$x_t = C_1 e^{z_1 t} + C_2 e^{z_2 t} + \ldots + C_n e^{z_n t}, \qquad (7.1)$$

where $C_1, C_2, \ldots, C_n$ are arbitrary constants defined by the initial conditions; $z_1, z_2, \ldots, z_n$ are the roots of the characteristic equation of the given system

$$a_0 z^n + a_1 z^{n-1} + \ldots + a_{n-1} z + a_n = 0 \qquad (7.2)$$

(the form (7.1) is valid when all roots are distinct).

The roots $z_1, z_2, \ldots, z_n$ may be both real and complex conjugate. We assume for concreteness that the first two roots are complex, the third and nth real and all remaining roots may be either complex or real in arbitrary order. In accordance with this we write

$$z_{1,2} = \alpha_1 \pm i\omega_1, \ z_3 = \alpha_3, \ \ldots, \ z_n = \alpha_n.$$

Then the solution of (7.1) is

$$x = A e^{\alpha_1 t} \sin(\omega_1 t + \beta) + C_3 e^{\alpha_3 t} + \ldots + C_n e^{\alpha_n t},$$

where A and β are real arbitrary constants replacing C_1 and C_2, which, with complex roots, will also be complex.

If $\alpha_1 < 0$, the first term of the solution $A e^{\alpha_1 t} \sin(\omega_1 + \beta)$ will tend to zero as $t \to \infty$, i.e. it will be attenuated (Fig. 46a). If $\alpha_1 > 0$, however, this term will be divergent (Fig. 46b).

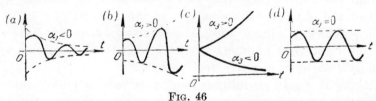

FIG. 46

The second term of the solution, i.e. $C_3 e^{\alpha_3 t}$, will be attenuated for $\alpha_3 < 0$ but divergent for $\alpha_3 > 0$ (Fig. 46c).

The same conclusion relates to all remaining roots of the characteristic equation.

Thus, the transient response (7.1) will be attenuated only when all real parts* of the roots of the characteristic equation (7.2)

* By the term "real part of a root" we mean also real roots, which are considered as particular cases of complex roots when the imaginary part vanishes.

are negative, independently of the values of the arbitrary constants, i.e. independently of which initial conditions and external forces on the system occur in the given transient. If at least one of the roots has a positive real part, the corresponding term of the solution (7.1) will be divergent. In this case the entire process, regardless of attenuation of the remaining terms of the solution, will obviously be divergent. This conclusion remains valid in the presence of multiple roots in the characteristic equation. For example, for a root $z = \alpha$ having a multiplicity k, the solution is obtained in the form $(C_1 + C_2 t + \ldots + C_k t^{k-1})e^{\alpha t}$, and if $\alpha < 0$, the quantity $e^{\alpha t}$ will tend to zero more rapidly as $t \to \infty$ than the factor in parentheses tends to infinity; thus, the general expression will tend to zero when $t \to \infty$.

We have not discussed zero, infinite and purely imaginary roots. They represent special cases. We remark that to a pair of imaginary roots $z = \pm i\omega$ there corresponds a term of the solution $A\sin(\omega t + \beta)$, which represents a harmonic oscillation with constant amplitude (Fig. 46d). These cases will not be specially considered below but it will be assumed that a zero root represents the boundary between positive and negative real roots, a purely imaginary root the boundary between complex roots with positive and negative real parts, and an infinite root the limiting case for $\omega = \alpha$. It thus follows that in a linear system, excluding the limiting case, the transient response may either attenuate to zero for arbitrary initial conditions and external forces or diverge to infinity*. Therefore, defining the concept of stability for linear systems is very simple.

A linear system in which a transient attenuates, i.e. $x_t(t) \to 0$ as $t \to \infty$, is termed stable. If the linear system has a divergent transient response, it is termed unstable.

From the above, there follows the following requirement on the roots of the characteristic equation of the system.

For stability of a linear automatic regulation system it is necessary and sufficient that all roots of the characteristic equation of the given system have negative real parts†.

If there is a zero or infinite root, or a pair of purely imaginary roots, while all remaining roots have negative real parts, the system is at the limit of stability. In the presence of a zero root (and all

---

* As a result of addition of several attenuating exponents and several attenuating sinusoids in the curve of the process $x_t(t)$, the attenuation of the process as a whole may not occur immediately from the time $t = 0$ but after some finite interval of time. This also relates to the divergent process.

† As was mentioned in Section 5, all real systems are more or less non-linear systems, but are linearized to assist calculation. The validity of the above condition regarding the roots of the characteristic equation for a linearised system was proved by A. M. Liapunov, as will be considered in Section 18.

remaining roots with negative real parts) the system is termed neutral, since with this there is observed an "indifference" of the system to the value of the regulated quantity (the external force may change it in arbitrary manner).

Let us introduce a geometric interpretation of the above requirement on the roots of the characteristic equation.

In the complex plane $(\alpha, i\omega)$ each root corresponds to a definite point. We shall mark them by crosses (Fig. 47). This plane is termed the root plane.

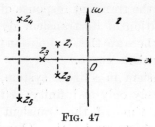

FIG. 47

From the above, it is obvious that for stability of a linear automatic regulation system, it is necessary and sufficient that all roots of the characteristic equation of the given system lie in the root plane to the left of the imaginary axis.

The imaginary axis in the root plane corresponds to the limit of stability; on it are located all purely imaginary roots of the characteristic equation as well as the zero root ($\omega = 0$) and the root at infinity ($\omega = \infty$).

A similar concept of stability is introduced for the class of singular linear systems. However, the characteristic equation obtained here is different (see Part III).

Quality of the transient response and the transient dynamic error. The concept of stability and instability of linear systems relates only to the presence or absence of attenuation of a transient in the system. Obviously, stability of an automatic system is the first (but by no means sufficient) requirement.

It is necessary to design an automatic system and select the parameters (masses, resistances, capacitances, etc.) entering into the coefficients of the equation so that the system will be first of all stable. But not every stable system (i.e. a system with attenuated transient response) will be good. Attenuation may occur rapidly or slowly, with large or small deviations $x_t(t)$; the transient response may be oscillatory or monotonic, etc. All these factors are various aspects of the so-called quality of the transient response and require special investigation.

In the full solution (6.3) of the differential equation of motion of a linear system (6.1), the useful part, defining the reproduction

of the input action, enters into the particular solution $x^0(t)$. Therefore, the entire transient component $x_t(t)$ is an error of the system.
In distinction to other errors of a stationary and dynamic character,
it is termed the transient dynamic error:

$$\Delta_{td} = x_t(t) . \tag{7.3}$$

It is represented, for example, in the form of hatching in Fig. 42
and Fig. 40 and in the form of the difference between the full curve
and the broken-line curve in Figs. 36c and 38c. Consequently, the
study of the quality of the transient response of an automatic system
involves the determination of its transient dynamic error Δ_{td}. The
most important factors here are the attenuation time, maximum deviation and shape of transient curve.

Theoretically, a transient in a linear system, as mentioned above,
may attenuate completely only at infinity: $x(t) \to 0$ as $t \to \infty$. Practically, the attenuation time of the transient is considered finite.
As the magnitude of the attenuation time (duration) of the transient,
that time interval t_1 is taken after which the deviation of the regulated
quantity $x(t)$ in the process becomes and remains in absolute value
less than some preassigned positive quantity ε (Fig. 48). In each
concrete problem the quantity ε is assigned so that it may be considered negligibly small in calculating the given system.

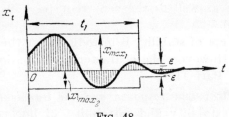

FIG. 48

The maximum deviations in the transient process $x_t(t)$ in both
directions (x_{max1} and x_{max2}, Fig. 48) constitute the maximum values
of the transient dynamic error. Ordinarily, their relative values
are of interest:

$$\Delta_{td\,max}\% = \frac{x_{max}}{x_n^0} 100\% , \tag{7.4}$$

where x_n^0 is some nominal value of the regulated quantity. The
maximum deviation in the transient response in a direction opposde
to the initial deviation, i.e. the magnitude x_{max2} in Fig. 48, is termed
the overshoot.

One of the problems in the rational design of an automatic regulation system and of its parameters is ensuring that the attenuation

time of a transient and the maximum value of the transient dynamic error do not exceed pre-assigned limits.

In addition, it is important to ensure satisfaction of additional requirements on the form of the transient curve (monotonicity of the process, defined character of transient oscillations with the absence of undesired frequencies, etc.).

The concept of stationary errors. The above-considered concepts of system stability and quality of transient response relate to the first component $x_t(t)$ of the complete solution (6.3). We now turn to the second component $x^0(t)$, which represents the particular solution of the differential equation of motion of the system

$$L(p)x = S(p)f^0(t) + N(p)y^0(t) . \qquad (7.5)$$

As discussed above, the particular solution $x^0(t)$ contains the useful part $x_n^0(t)$, constituting the reproduction of the input signal $y^0(t)$. The difference

$$\Delta_{sd} = x^0(t) - x_n^0(t) \qquad (7.6)$$

is termed the steady-state dynamic error of the system. The quantity $x_n^0(t)$ may be termed the nominal value.

In the usual automatic regulation problem x_n^0 is that value of the regulated quantity which must be maintained constant in the given system. The regulator is adjusted to it initially (i.e. the appropriate $y^0 = $ const is set) in some nominal stationary regime of the given system corresponding to constant nominal value f_n^0 of the load or other external forces on the regulated object. Actually, the system will operate at loads (or other forces) $f(t)$ differing more or less on either side from the adopted nominal value f_n^0. The automatic regulation system is intended to overcome the effects of these large deviations of the load on the variation of the regulated quantity. In this case, if the expanded expression for $N(p)$ (5.2) is taken into account, the differential equation (7.5) takes the form

$$L(p)x = S(p)f^0(t) + c_v y^0 \qquad (y^0 = \text{const}) . \qquad (7.7)$$

By finding the particular solution $x^0(t)$ of this equation for various forms of variation of $f^0(t)$, it is possible to determine from (7.6) the stationary dynamic errors

$$\Delta_{sd} = x^0(t) - x_n^0 . \qquad (7.8)$$

Most frequently, we are concerned with cases where $f^0(t)$ has a discontinuous pulse or oscillatory character. In the latter case, the stationary error Δ_{sd} represents a forced oscillation.

In particular, if f^0 is a constant quantity (different from the nominal f_n^0), the particular solution will be $x^0 = $ const and the stationary error (7.8) becomes constant. In this case it is termed the static error:

$$\Delta_{st} = x^0 - x_n^0 = \text{const} \quad \text{or} \quad \Delta_{st}\% = \frac{x^0 - x_n^0}{x_n^0} \cdot 100\%; \quad (7.9)$$

which is also sometimes termed the residual error of the regulated quantity.

For programmed regulation systems and servo-systems it is necessary to use the general formula for the stationary dynamic error (7.6). With programmed regulation the expression $x_n^0(t)$ in this formula denotes the required form of variation of the regulated quantity. For servo-systems, for the same scale and the same physical character of input and output quantities of the system, the quantity $x_n^0(t)$ in (7.6) will be

$$x_n^0(t) = y^0(t), \quad (7.10)$$

and in the contrary case

$$x_n^0(t) = k_0 y^0(t). \quad (7.11)$$

This also relates to measuring devices operating on the compensation principle.

If the stationary dynamic error of a computer is investigated, we have for its differential equation in (7.6)

$$x_n^0(t) = \frac{dy^0(t)}{dt}; \quad (7.12)$$

for an integrating device:

$$x_n^0(t) = \int_0^t y^0(t)\, dt; \quad (7.13)$$

$x_n^0(t)$ is written analogously for devices carrying out other mathematical operations.

For servo-systems and computers the typical input functions are the following: (1) constant value of y^0; (2) a change with constant velocity $y_0 = \omega t$ or, with constant acceleration, $y^0 = \varepsilon t^2/2$; (3) an oscillation $y^0 = a \sin \omega t$, or more complicated functions. All these typical forces may be connected with simultaneous variation of load $f^0(t)$ at the output of the system. But most frequently such perturbations are either neglected or considered constant in magnitude (for example, a constant load f^0 at the output of the system). Then, if the significance of the expression $S(p)$ in (5.2) is taken into account, the differential equation of the system, in place of (7.5) is written in the form

$$L(p)x = b_m f^0 + N(p)y^0(t) \quad (f^0 = \text{const}). \quad (7.14)$$

For constant value of y^0 the stationary dynamic error in this case becomes the static error.

In the present section, the determination of the static error as well as the stationary dynamic errors in following regimes with constant velocity and constant acceleration will be investigated. The determination of the stationary dynamic errors of forced oscillations in regulating systems and stationary dynamic errors of following with oscillatory input will be given in Section 8.

Static error, residual deviation. In the case of constant values of the external forces f^0 (constant load) and y^0 (constant adjustment) the differential equation both for a regulating system (7.7) and for a servomechanism (7.14) takes the form

$$x^0 = \varphi_1 + \omega_1 t \, .$$

Therefore, for a regulating system, we obtain from (5.2) the particular solution

$$x^0 = \frac{b_m}{a_n} f^0 + \frac{c_\nu}{a_n} y^0 \, , \qquad x_n^0 = \frac{b_m}{a_n} f_n^0 + \frac{c_\nu}{a_n} y^0 \, , \qquad (7.15)$$

and calculate from (7.9) the static error, or residual deviation of the regulated quantity

$$\Delta_{st} = \frac{b_m}{a_n} (f^0 - f_n^0) \quad \text{or} \quad \Delta_{st}\% = \frac{b_m}{a_n} \frac{f^0 - f_n^0}{x_n^0} \cdot 100\% \, . \qquad (7.16)$$

For servomechanisms, with the problem stated in the form (7.11) we require $x_n^0 = k_0 y^0$. Therefore, from (7.9) the static error is as follows:

$$\Delta_{st} = \frac{b_m}{a_n} f^0 + \left(\frac{c_\nu}{a_n} - k_0 \right) y^0 \, . \qquad (7.17)$$

However, a servomechanism always satisfies

$$c_\nu = k_0 a_n \, , \qquad (7.18)$$

which will be termed the fundamental relationship. In particular, for $k_0 = 1$, i.e. with statement of the problem in the form (7.10), which is frequently encountered in practice, the fundamental relationship (7.18) for a servo-system takes the form

$$c_\nu = a_n \, . \qquad (7.19)$$

Therefore, in place of (7.17), the static error of the servomechanism will be

$$\Delta_{st} = \frac{b_m}{a_n} f^0 \, . \qquad (7.20)$$

The stationary dynamic error in following with constant velocity. Given the input force

$$y^0 = \varphi_0 + \omega t \, . \qquad (7.21)$$

The servomechanism must satisfy (7.11), and we require

$$x_n^0 = k_0 y^0 = k_0 \varphi_0 + k_0 \omega t . \qquad (7.22)$$

Given, further, that the load f_0^0 at the output of the system is constant. Substituting (7.22) and $f = \text{const}$ in the right-hand side of the differential equation (5.2) let us seek a particular solution in the form

$$x^0 = \varphi_1 + \omega_1 t .$$

Equation (5.2) now takes the form

$$a_{n-1} \omega_1 + a_n(\varphi_1 + \omega_1 t) = b_m f^0 + c_{\nu-1} \omega + c_\nu (\varphi_0 + \omega t) ,$$

from which the quantities φ_1 and ω_1 are found by equating coefficients of t in both parts of the given 'expression. As a result we obtain the required particular solution

$$x^0 = \frac{b_m}{a_n} f^0 + \frac{c_\nu}{a_n} \varphi_0 + \left(\frac{c_{\nu-1}}{a_n} - \frac{a_{n-1} c_\nu}{a_n^2} \right) \omega + \frac{c_\nu}{a_n} \omega t .$$

From this, (7.6), (7.22) and the fundamental relationship (7.18), we find the stationary dynamic error

$$\Delta_{sd} = x^0 - x_n^0 = \frac{b_m}{a_n} f^0 + \frac{c_{\nu-1} - k_0 a_{n-1}}{a_n} \omega . \qquad (7.23)$$

Consequently, in following with constant velocity, there is a constant error proportional to the velocity. It is not difficult to verify that without the fundamental relationship (7.18) there would be an error which increased with time. To eliminate the error proportional to the velocity of following ω (for $\omega = \text{const}$) it is necessary to design the servomechanism so that, aside from the fundamental relationship (7.18), there would be satisfied a further relationship

$$c_{\nu-1} = k_0 a_{n-1} . \qquad (7.24)$$

Stationary dynamic error in following with constant acceleration. Given

$$y^0 = \varphi_0 + \omega t + \frac{\varepsilon t^2}{2} \qquad (7.25)$$

and required

$$x_n^0 = k_0 y^0 = k_0 \varphi_0 + k_0 \omega t + k_0 \frac{\varepsilon t^2}{2} .$$

With

$$f = f^0 = \text{const} .$$

Substituting the given function y^0 in the differential equation of the system (5.2) and seeking a particular solution in the form

$$x^0 = \varphi_1 + \omega_1 t + \frac{1}{2} \varepsilon_1 t^2 ,$$

analogously to the above we obtain in the result

$$x^0 = \left[\frac{b_m}{a_n} f^0 + \frac{c_\nu}{a_n} \varphi_0 + \left(\frac{c_{\nu-1}}{a_n} - \frac{a_{n-1}c_\nu}{a_n^2} \right) \omega + \right.$$

$$\left. + \left(\frac{c_{\nu-2}}{a_n} - \frac{a_{n-2}c_\nu}{a_n^2} - \frac{a_{n-1}c_{\nu-1}}{a_n^2} + \frac{a_{n-1}^2 c_\nu}{a_n^3} \right) \varepsilon \right] +$$

$$+ \left[\frac{c_\nu}{a_n} \omega + \left(\frac{c_{\nu-1}}{a_n} - \frac{a_{n-1}c_\nu}{a_n^2} \right) \varepsilon \right] t + \frac{1}{2} \frac{c_\nu}{a_n} \varepsilon t^2 .$$

If the servomechanism satisfies the fundamental relationship (7.18), the stationary dynamic error from this will be

$$\Delta_{sd} = x^0 - x_n^{0'} = \left[\frac{b_m}{a_n} f^0 + \frac{c_{\nu-1} - k_0 a_{n-1}}{a_n} \omega + \right.$$

$$\left. + \left(\frac{c_{\nu-2} - k_0 a_{n-2}}{a_n} - \frac{a_{n-1}}{a_n} \frac{c_{\nu-1} - k_0 a_{n-1}}{a_n} \right) \varepsilon \right] + \left(\frac{c_{\nu-1} - k_0 a_{n-1}}{a_n} \varepsilon \right) \cdot t, \quad (7.26)$$

i.e., it will increase with time. If, in addition to (7.18), the supplementary relationship (7.24) is satisfied, the stationary dynamic error in the process of following with constant acceleration will be constant and proportional to the magnitude of acceleration

$$\Delta_{sd} = \frac{b_m}{a_n} f^0 + \frac{c_{\nu-2} - k_0 a_{n-2}}{a_n} \varepsilon . \quad (7.27)$$

Additional dynamic errors. In addition to the errors considered above, defined by the terms $x_i(t)$ and $x^0(t)$ in the complete solution of (6.3), there are additional distortions of the regulation process due to the fact that in a real system perturbations $f(t)$ and input forces $y(t)$ do not ideally follow the assumed forms of variation $f^0(t)$ and $y^0(t)$, but contain additional perturbations $\Delta f(t)$ and noise $\Delta y(t)$, i.e.

$$f(t) = f^0(t) + \Delta f(t) , \qquad y(t) = y^0(t) + \Delta y(t) .$$

As a result of this, an additional dynamic error is obtained defined by the differential equation

$$L(p) \Delta_{ad} = S(p) \Delta f(t) + N(p) \Delta y(t) . \quad (7.28)$$

$\Delta f(t)$ and $\Delta y(t)$ are frequently random functions arising from external fluctuations: they cannot be given as defined functions of time but may be characterised in one of the following ways:

(1) the functions $\Delta f(t)$ and $\Delta y(t)$ take on arbitrary values, whose moduli do not exceed definite assigned positive quantities φ and η, i.e.

$$|\Delta f(t)| \leqslant \varphi \qquad \text{and} \qquad |\Delta y(t)| \leqslant \eta; \quad (7.29)$$

(2) the functions $\Delta f(t)$ and $\Delta y(t)$ are defined by their probability distributions.

In the former case, it is possible to carry out a rough evaluation and define a positive quantity ε which the additional dynamic error of the system does not exceed in absolute value:

$$|\Delta_{ad}| < \varepsilon . \tag{7.30}$$

In the latter case it is possible to carry out a more detailed statistical calculation.

Both of these methods may sometimes be required for estimation not only of the additional dynamic error but for the sum of all forms of system errors.

Total system error. The total error of an automatic system is thus composed of three parts:

$$\Delta = \Delta_{td} + \Delta_{sd} + \Delta_{ad} \tag{7.31}$$

where Δ_{td} is the transient dynamic error, Δ_{sd} is the stationary dynamic error (which, in particular, may be a static error Δ_{st}) and Δ_{ad} is the additional dynamic error.

We remark that if, after a certain period of time, the total error Δ of a given system should become, and then remain, smaller than some prescribed small quantity for defined bounds on the initial conditions and the perturbing forces, this is sometimes termed "technical stability". In the present discussion, however, this term will not be employed.

All concepts considered in the present section may be extended to singular linear systems, since the principle of superposition of individual solutions remains in force, and only the form of the equations of the dynamic system is changed.

8. Forced oscillations and frequency characteristics of linear systems

The steady-state process of forced oscillations in a linear system is defined by the particular solution of the equation of motion of the system (5.6) or (5.7) corresponding to a periodic right-hand side, namely, to an oscillatory perturbation f on the regulated object or an oscillatory input signal y to the regulator or the controlled system. Let the oscillatory force on the system be sinusoidal:

$$f = a\sin\omega t \quad \text{or} \quad y = a\sin\omega t , \tag{8.1}$$

where the amplitude a of this oscillation is taken equal to unity, or, more exactly, as the unit of measurement of all other amplitudes which appear in the system as a result of this oscillatory force.

In the first case, the forced oscillations of the regulated quantity from (5.7) are defined by the particular solution of the differential equation

$$L(p)x = S(p)f(t) , \tag{8.2}$$

and in the second case

$$L(p)x = N(p)y(t) . \tag{8.3}$$

The particular solution (form of forced oscillations) is sought in the form $x = Aa\sin(\omega t + \beta)$, where Aa is the amplitude of the forced oscillation*, β the phase. To distinguish between the perturbing (f) and input (y) forces, the particular solutions of (8.2) and (8.3) are respectively

$$x = A_f a\sin(\omega t + \beta_f) \quad \text{and} \quad x = A_y a\sin(\omega t + \beta_y) . \tag{8.4}$$

The usual method of finding a particular solution is to substitute the given function (8.1) and the required solution (8.4) in (8.2) or (8.3), after which the unknown constants A_f and β_f (or A_y and β_y) are determined by equating the coefficients of $\sin\omega t$ and $\cos\omega t$ in the left- and right-hand sides of the equation. However, for a high-order system this method is cumbersome. We shall describe a second method widely used in the theory of automatic regulation.

Transfer function of the system. The operational differential equations (8.2) and (8.3) may be conventionally re-written in the form

$$\frac{x}{f} = \frac{S(p)}{L(p)} \quad \text{and} \quad \frac{x}{y} = \frac{N(p)}{L(p)} . \tag{8.5}$$

This new operational notation will not represent anything new in comparison with (8.2) and (8.3) or with the ordinary form of the differential equation (5.2). From (8.5) it is easy to pass to (8.2), (8.3) and (5.2) or vice versa.

In (8.5) we have, as it were, the ratio of the result x ("output quantity") to the force f or y (to the "input quantity"), written in symbolic operational form. This ratio is termed the transfer function of the system. We denote it by

$$W_f(p) = \frac{S(p)}{L(p)} \quad \text{and} \quad W_y(p) = \frac{N(p)}{L(p)} \tag{8.6}$$

respectively.

Complex transfer factor (complex gain factor). Let us now write the harmonic oscillations (8.1) and (8.4) in complex form, recalling the relationship

$$e^{i\omega t} = \cos\omega t + i\sin\omega t \quad (i \equiv \sqrt{-1}) . \tag{8.7}$$

Geometrically (Fig. 49), this is a unit vector in the complex plane, rotating counter-clockwise with angular velocity ω. Its projection on the imaginary axis represents the harmonic oscillation (8.1), and its projection on the real axis gives at the same time the other possible harmonic oscillation in the form $\cos\omega t$. In analytic notation we have

$$\sin\omega t = \text{Im}\, e^{i\omega t} , \quad \cos\omega t = \text{Re}\, e^{i\omega t} .$$

* A denotes the ratio of amplitudes.

Considering the above, we shall write the harmonic oscillation (8.1) in complex form, as is frequently done, omitting the symbol Im:

$$f = ae^{i\omega t} \quad \text{and} \quad y = ae^{i\omega t}, \tag{8.8}$$

and the particular solution (8.4), i.e. the forced oscillation of the regulated quantity in the same complex form:

$$x = A_f a e^{i(\omega t + \beta_f)} \quad \text{and} \quad x = A_y a e^{i(\omega t + \beta_y)}.$$

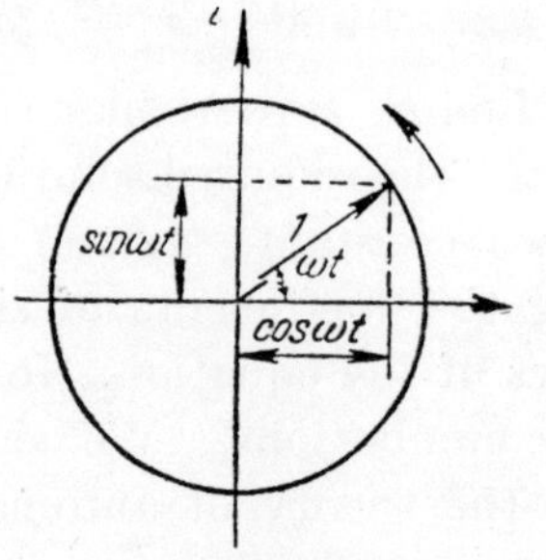

FIG. 49

If we take the ratios of these "output" quantities to the "input" (8.8), we obtain

$$\frac{x}{f} = A_f e^{i\beta_f} \quad \text{and} \quad \frac{x}{y} = A_y e^{i\beta_y}.$$

respectively.

This ratio of steady-state forced harmonic oscillations of the linear system to the external harmonic force on the system written in complex form is termed the complex transfer factor of the system or, which is the same, the complex gain factor of the system. We denote it by

$$K_f = A_f e^{i\beta_f} \quad \text{and} \quad K_y = A_y e^{i\beta_y}. \tag{8.9}$$

This is a complex number, the modulus A of which represents the amplitude of the output quantity (more exactly, the ratio of amplitudes of output and input oscillations), while the argument β is the phase (more exactly, the difference of phase of output and input oscillations). Thus, the complex transfer factor K gives directly a complete characteristic of the forced oscillations in the given linear system.

We shall prove that the complex transfer factor of the system may be calculated by substituting $i\omega$ in place of p in the expression for the transfer function of the system (8.6), i.e. we shall prove that

$$\left. \begin{aligned} K_f &= W_f(i\omega) = \frac{S(i\omega)}{L(i\omega)}, \\ K_y &= W_y(i\omega) = \frac{N(i\omega)}{L(i\omega)}. \end{aligned} \right\} \tag{8.10}$$

In fact, let there be given, for example the differential equation of the system in the form

$$a_0\frac{d^3x}{dt^3} + a_1\frac{d^2x}{dt^2} + a_2\frac{dx}{dt} + a_3x = b_0\frac{d^2f}{dt^2} + b_1\frac{df}{dt} + b_2f(t) . \qquad (8.11)$$

We shall rewrite this in symbolic operational form

$$(a_0p^3 + a_1p^2 + a_2p + a_3)x = (b_0p^2 + b_1p + b_2)f(t) .$$

Consequently, the transfer function of the system will be

$$W_f(p) = \frac{b_0p^2 + b_1p + b_2}{a_0p^3 + a_1p^2 + a_2p + a_3} . \qquad (8.12)$$

The external force is

$$f = ae^{i\omega t} ,$$

while the particular solution (forced oscillation) is sought in the form

$$x = A_f a e^{i(\omega t + \beta_f)} = K_f a e^{i\omega t} .$$

We employ the usual method of finding the particular solution, i.e. we substitute f and x in (8.11). We obtain

$$a_0 K_f(i\omega)^3 a e^{i\omega t} + a_1 K_f(i\omega)^2 a e^{i\omega t} + a_2 K_f i\omega a e^{i\omega t} + a_3 K_f a e^{i\omega t} =$$
$$b_0(i\omega)^2 a e^{i\omega t} + b_1 i\omega a e^{i\omega t} + b_2 a e^{i\omega t} .$$

whence

$$K_f = \frac{b_0(i\omega)^2 + b_1 i\omega + b_2}{a_0(i\omega)^3 + a_1(i\omega)^2 + a_2 i\omega + a_3} .$$

From comparison of the result obtained with (8.12) the validity of (8.10) follows (although this has been demonstrated for an equation of third order, the same result can clearly be obtained for an equation of arbitrary order).

We thus arrive at the following simple method of calculating the steady-state forced harmonic oscillations in a linear system of arbitrary order. If the differential equation of the system (5.2) is given, it is necessary to write it in operational form (5.6) or (5.7) and then as a transfer function (8.6). In the latter p must everywhere be replaced by $i\omega$.

As a result a certain complex number (8.10) is obtained, the modulus of which gives A, the ratio of amplitudes of oscillations in the system, and the argument gives the phase (the true amplitude will be equal to Aa).

If we denote the modulus and argument of the complex number in the denominator $L(i\omega)$ of (8.10) by A_L, β_L, and the modulus and argument of the numerator $S(i\omega)$ by A_S, β_S, the required amplitude and phase will be, by the rule of division of complex numbers,

$$A_f = \frac{A_S}{A_L}, \qquad \beta_f = \beta_S - \beta_L , \qquad (8.13)$$

and, correspondingly, for the second of the expressions (8.10)

$$A_y = \frac{A_N}{A_L}, \qquad \beta_y = \beta_N - \beta_L. \tag{8.14}$$

The amplitude-phase frequency characteristics of the system. It is well known that the amplitude and phase of forced oscillations in a given linear system depend on the frequency ω of the external force or, which is the same thing, on the frequency of forced oscillations. Therefore, in the complex transfer factor $K = W(i\omega)$ the modulus and argument are functions of frequency ω, i.e.

$$K = W(i\omega) = A(\omega)e^{i\beta(\omega)} \tag{8.15}$$

(we omit here for conciseness the indices f and y, which should be used in specific calculations).

In the complex plane W (Fig. 50) this will be a vector of length A with angle of inclination β to the abscissae. In Fig. 50 the angle β is shown negative (clockwise), as forced oscillations in real systems are usually delayed in phase (i.e. the phase is usually negative).

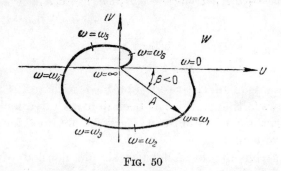

FIG. 50

Since to differing frequencies ω there correspond differing amplitudes A and phases β, with variation of frequency ω the tip of the vector (Fig. 50) describes a certain curve, each point of which corresponds to a definite frequency ω and indicates the value of the amplitude A and the phase β obtained at that frequency. Consequently, the curve $W(i\omega)$ gives a complete characterisation of the properties of the steady-state forced harmonic oscillations in the given linear system for arbitrary frequency. This curve is termed the amplitude-phase frequency characteristic (the word "frequency" is usually omitted for conciseness.

We have constructed the amplitude-phase characteristic $W(i\omega)$ of the system in polar coordinates A and β. But frequently it is more convenient to calculate its rectangular coordinates U, iV. In this case, obtaining from the differential equation of system the expression for the complex transfer factor (8.10), we separate it into real and imaginary parts, i.e. we represent it in the form

$$K = W(i\omega) = U(\omega) + iV(\omega) . \tag{8.16}$$

If in expression (8.10) we denote by U_L, iV_L the real and imaginary parts of the denominator $L(i\omega)$, and by U_S, iV_S the numerator $S(i\omega)$, we obtain

$$K_f = W_f(i\omega) = \frac{U_S + iV_S}{U_L + iV_L} = \frac{U_S U_L + V_S V_L + i(V_S U_L - U_S V_L)}{U_L^2 + V_L^2} .$$

From this we obtain for the amplitude-phase characteristic $W(i\omega)$ the real and imaginary parts

$$U_f(\omega) = \frac{U_S U_L + V_S V_L}{U_L^2 + V_L^2} , \qquad V_f(\omega) = \frac{V_S U_L - U_S V_L}{U_L^2 + V_L^2} , \tag{8.17}$$

and analogously for the amplitude-phase characteristic $W_y(i\omega)$, with substitution of the index S by N.

Thus, in example (8.12):

$$W_f(i\omega) = \frac{-b_0 \omega^2 + b_1 i\omega + b_2}{-a_0 i\omega^3 - a_1 \omega^2 + a_2 i\omega + a_3} ,$$

from which:

$$U_S = b_2 - b_0 \omega^2 , \qquad V_S = b_1 \omega , \qquad U_L = a_3 - a_1 \omega^2 , \qquad V_L = \omega(a_2 - a_0 \omega^2) .$$

If we wish to construct the amplitude-phase characteristic in the rectangular coordinates (U, iV), it is necessary to substitute U_S, V_S, U_L, V_L from (8.17) and, assigning various values of ω, to plot the curve point by point (Fig. 50). If the amplitude-phase characteristic should be plotted in polar coordinates (A, β), it is necessary to find first the moduli and arguments of the numerator and denominator

$$\left.\begin{aligned}
A_S &= \sqrt{U_S^2 + V_S^2} , & \beta_S &= \tan^{-1} \frac{V_S}{U_S} , \\
A_L &= \sqrt{U_L^2 + V_L^2} , & \beta_L &= \tan^{-1} \frac{V_L}{U_L} ,
\end{aligned}\right\} \tag{8.18}$$

and then, employing (8.13) and substituting various values of ω, to plot the curve (Fig. 50) point by point. The result will, of course, be the same in both cases.

The amplitude-phase characteristics of the system may also be obtained experimentally. Applying to the system harmonic oscillations (8.1) of defined frequency ω and with unit amplitude, we record, oscillographically, the steady state oscillation of the regulated quantity x. From the oscillograms we find the amplitude A and the phase β for the given frequency ω. This gives one point of graph.

Carrying out similar measurements at other frequencies, we obtain several points which are then joined by a smooth curve (Fig. 50).

In determining the amplitude-phase characteristic the amplitude of the input quantity has been taken as unity. If this amplitude has some other magnitude a the amplitude of output oscillations will be Aa, where the quantity A is taken from the amplitude-phase characteristic (Fig. 50).

Other frequency characteristics. Above were obtained the relationships

$$A(\omega), \quad \beta(\omega), \quad U(\omega), \quad V(\omega)$$

which in concrete calculations will have indices f or y depending on whether the forced oscillations of the system arise from perturbations f in the regulated object or from the input force y on the regulator. These relationships may also be separately represented. (Fig. 51). The first is termed the amplitude-frequency characteristic

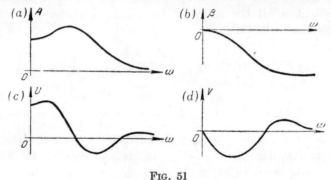

Fig. 51

or resonance curve, the second the phase-frequency characteristic, the third the real frequency characteristic and the fourth the imaginary frequency characteristic. They are also used in the theory of regulation.

These frequency characteristics (Fig. 51) express individual properties of the steady-state forced harmonic oscillations of the system while the amplitude-phase characteristic (Fig. 50) joins them all in a single graph.

In a number of calculations the logarithmic frequency characteristic, which represents the same graphs of dependencies $A(\omega)$ and $\beta(\omega)$ as before, but in a logarithmic scale, is employed. This gives a certain computational convenience (Section 20). Here the quantity $\log \omega$ is always taken as the abscissa. Along the axis of ordinates in the phase-frequency characteristic the phase β is plotted in degrees or in radians, while along the axis of ordinates of the amplitude-frequency characteristic the quantity $20 \log A$ is plotted, the unit of which is termed the "decibel" (dB).

Stationary error of a system with sinusoidal force. For a perturbation $f = a \sin \omega t$ the stationary dynamic error of the system will be

$$\Delta_{sd} = A_f a \sin (\omega t + \beta_f) ,$$

where A_f and β_f are defined from the corresponding amplitude-phase characteristic of the given closed loop regulation system.

For an input force $y = a \sin \omega t$ to be reproduced by the system in the form $x_n = k_0 a \sin \omega t$ (frequently $k_0 = 1$), the stationary dynamic error will be

$$\Delta_{sd} = A_y a \sin (\omega t + \beta_y) - k_0 a \sin \omega t ,$$

where for convenience of calculation this is characterised by both error in amplitude and the error in phase

$$\Delta_A = \frac{A_y - k_0}{k_0} 100\% \quad \text{and} \quad \Delta_\beta = \beta_y ,$$

where A_y and β_y are defined from the amplitude-phase characteristic of the given closed system.

Forced oscillations of a system with arbitrary external periodic force. An arbitrary (single-valued and piecewise continuous) periodic function $f(t)$ may be expanded in the Fourier series

$$f(t) = a_0 + \sum_{k=1}^{\infty} a_k \cos k \omega_0 t + \sum_{k=1}^{\infty} b_k \sin k \omega_0 t , \qquad (8.19)$$

where ω_0 is the frequency of the fundamental harmonic and a_0, a_k, b_k are Fourier coefficients

$$\left. a_0 = \frac{\omega_0}{2\pi} \int_0^{\frac{2\pi}{\omega_0}} f(t)\,dt , \qquad a_k = \frac{\omega_0}{\pi} \int_0^{\frac{2\pi}{\omega_0}} f(t) \cos k \omega_0 t\,dt , \right.$$

$$\left. b_k = \frac{\omega_0}{\pi} \int_0^{\frac{2\pi}{\omega_0}} f(t) \sin k \omega_0 t\,dt . \right\} \qquad (8.20)$$

Using (8.7), we pass to the complex notation for harmonic oscillations (8.8) and thus in place of (8.19) and (8.20), obtain the complex form of the Fourier series

$$f(t) = \sum_{k=-\infty}^{+\infty} E_k e^{ik\omega_0 t} , \qquad (8.21)$$

where

$$E_k = \frac{\omega_0}{2\pi} \int_0^{\frac{2\pi}{\omega_0}} f(t) e^{-ik\omega_0 t} dt . \qquad (8.22)$$

Let this expansion be given so that E_k and ω_0 are known for an external periodic force f and a given amplitude-phase characteristic of the system $W_f(i\omega)$ (Fig. 50). Then, if the system is stable, the steady-state forced oscillations "at the output" of the system for the input component $E_k e^{ik\omega_0 t}$ will be $W_f(ik\omega_0)E_k e^{ik\omega_0 t}$. Consequently, in the total steady-state forced oscillations at the output of the system there will be

$$x = \sum_{k=-\infty}^{+\infty} E_k W_f(ik\omega_0) e^{ik\omega_0 t}; \qquad (8.23)$$

the amplitude A_k and phase β_k of each component is found, as shown in Fig. 50, at corresponding points $\omega = k\omega_0$, where the value of the amplitude A, taken from the graph, should be multiplied each time by the corresponding value of the coefficient E_k. Since in Fig. 50 as $\omega \to \infty$ (i.e. $k \to \infty$) we have $A \to 0$, it is frequently possible in practice to take a small number of terms in (8.21) and (8.23). To negative values of ω there correspond the same amplitudes A, as for positive ω, but with opposite sign of phase β.

9. Non-linear systems

Let the motion of a closed loop automatic system be described by a non-linear differential equation of general form (5.1). It is well known that individual solutions of non-linear equations do not have the superposition property. Therefore, it is not possible here to add the particular solutions of the inhomogeneous equation to each other and they cannot be added to the solution of the homogeneous equation as was done for the linear systems. Thus, for each form of the right-hand side it is necessary to solve a new (5.1).

Regulation process for $f = const$ and $y = const$. Let us consider the simplest case when the external conditions (perturbations and input force) are characterised by constant values $f = f^0$ (constant load) and $y = y^0$ (constant adjustment). Then all derivatives of f and y with regard to time will vanish and the differential equation of motion (5.1) takes the form

$$F_1\left(x, \frac{dx}{dt}, \dots, \frac{d^n x}{dt^n}\right) = F_2(f^0, 0, \dots, 0; \; y^0, 0, \dots, 0) . \qquad (9.1)$$

The solution $x(t)$ of this equation defines the regulation process $f_0 = const$ and $y = const$. It may also be divided into steady state $x(t)$ and transient $x_t(t)$ components. The steady state response $x^0(t)$ is defined as the solution of differential equation (9.1) for such specially selected initial conditions which give the solution defined stationary properties. Such a solution, in contrast to the solution of the same equation for arbitrary initial conditions, is termed the particular solution of the non-linear equation. After this the transient response $x_t(t)$ is defined as the difference

$$x_t = (t) = x(t) - x^0(t) \, . \qquad (9.2)$$

The steady-state response is thus defined (in the above sense) as a particular solution of the non-linear differential equation of motion of the system. The steady-state response in non-linear systems has a number of specific properties in comparison with linear systems. In the linear system under the condition $f = \text{const}$ and $y = \text{const}$ the steady-state response is defined by a constant value x^0 by (7.15), where to each pair of values f^0, y^0 there corresponds a completely defined unique value of the regulated quantity x^0. In contradistinction to this in the non-linear system there may occur multi-valued steady-states.

Firstly, to each pair of constant values f^0, y^0 there may correspond not only one but two or several or even a whole region of constant values f^0 of the regulated quantity. In other words, the non-linear system may have not one but a whole region of possible equilibrium states. Secondly, for constant values f^0 and y^0 it is possible, in addition, to have a periodic solution $x^0(t)$ of the non-linear differential equation (9.1), i.e. for constant external conditions $f = \text{const}$ and $y = \text{const}$ the non-linear system may have an oscillatory steady-state $x^0(t)$ with constant frequency and constant amplitude, where it is possible to have a constant component in this process, i.e.

$$x^0(t) = x_c^0 + x_k^0(t) \, , \qquad (9.3)$$

where x_c^0 is the constant and $x_k^0(t)$ the oscillatory periodic solution.

Of course, these properties will not occur in every non-linear system, but they are possible only in non-linear systems. Since these properties are encountered in practice in real automatic regulation systems, it is not possible in practical calculations to remain within the limits of the linear theory of regulation since the latter is not capable of determining these important properties.

Both cases noted, $x^0 = \text{const}$ and $x^0 = x^0(t)$, will be considered in detail separately for $f = \text{const}$ and $y = \text{const}$.

Steady state with constant value of regulated quantity (equilibrium state). To determine the possible steady-state values of the regulated quantity x^0 for given f^0 and y^0 we shall write (9.1) in the form

$$F_1(x^0, 0, ..., 0) = F_2(f^0, 0, ..., 0; \ y^0, 0, ..., 0) \, . \qquad (9.4)$$

This is an algebraic equation. It is well known that to the extent that it is not linear it may have not one but a large number of solutions for x^0. But we are not interested in all solutions, only in real ones. If (9.4) has several real solutions then, consequently, in general, several equilibrium states are possible in the given system. Which of them will really exist depends on their stability and on the width of the band of values x^0 which may actually occur in the given system.

Most frequently for concrete objects and regulation systems relationship (9.4) is not given analytically but in the form of graphs of various static load and other characteristics which do not alter the matter essentially.

The magnitude of the static error of a non-linear system is defined by the difference

$$\Delta_{st} = x^0 - x_n^0 \tag{9.5}$$

where x_n^0 is the nominal value of the regulated quantity which is to be realised in the given system.

If in the non-linear system the characteristic of any non-linear branch circuit has a zone of insensitivity $\pm b$ (Fig. 34, *c, d, e, g* and curves 2 and 5 in Fig. 24), this circuit does not transfer the signal applied to it as long as it does not exceed the value b in absolute magnitude. Consequently, in such non-linear systems there exists a certain zone of possible steady-state values of the regulated quantity x^0. The regulator will be in equilibrium when the regulated quantity takes on any value inside this zone. The presence of dry friction has an analogous effect. This situation introduces an additional static error. In this case we have

$$\Delta_{st} = x^0 - x_n^0 + \Delta x^0 , \tag{9.6}$$

where x^0 is the steady-state value of regulated quantity calculated for the mean position of the system within the zone of equilibrium states, while Δx^0 is an arbitrary deviation from this value (positive or negative) in the limits of this zone.

Periodic solution, self-oscillation, transients. If the steady-state response is defined by a certain constant value of the regulated quantity x^0 for constant f^0 and y^0, then, substituting in (9.1) $x = x^0 + x_t(t)$ and subtracting from it termwise (9.4), we obtain a homogeneous non-linear equation

$$F_1 \left(x_t + x^0 , \frac{dx_t}{dt} , ... , \frac{d^n x_t}{dt^n} \right) - F_1(x^0, 0, ..., 0) = 0 , \tag{9.7}$$

defining the transient $x_t(t)$, where the quantity x^0 is considered already known from (9.4). For this and the initial conditions we should from (9.2) assume $x_{0t} = x_0 - x_0^0$.

If a steady-state oscillatory process (9.3) is possible in the system for constant f^0 and y^0, it is defined from (9.1) by the differential equation

$$F_1\left(x_k^0 + x_c^0, \ \frac{dx_k^0}{dt}, \ ..., \ \frac{d^n x_k^0}{dt^n}\right) = F_2(f^0, 0, ..., 0; \ y^0, 0, ..., 0), \quad (9.8)$$

where the constant component x_c^0 by analogy with (9.4) may be defined by the equation

$$F_1(x_c^0, 0, ..., 0) = F_2(f^0, 0, ..., 0; \ y^0, 0, ..., 0). \quad (9.9)$$

Subtracting this from (9.8), we obtain the homogeneous differential equation for determining the periodic solution in the form

$$F_1\left(x_k^0 + x_c^0, \ \frac{dx_k^0}{dt}, \ ..., \ \frac{d^n x_k^0}{dt^n}\right) - F_1(x_c^0, 0, ..., 0) = 0, \quad (9.10)$$

where x_c^0 is defined from (9.9).

From a comparison of (9.10) and (9.7) it is evident that the steady-state periodic response in the non-linear system for constant f^0 and y^0 may be defined as the particular solution of the equation of the transient response (9.7). It is therefore expedient to proceed as follows: on the basis of (9.4) find the equilibrium state and obtain the equation of the transient response, (9.7), and then determine the possibility of a periodic solution $x_k^0(t)$ of this equation.

If a periodic steady state process $x_c^0 + x_k^0(t)$ is found, the transient of its establishment will be $x_t(t) = x(t) - x_c^0 - x_k^0(t)$, where $x(t)$ is a solution of (9.1) for arbitrary initial conditions.

In all cases the transient includes the transient dynamic error of the system

$$\Delta_{td} = x_t(t), \quad (9.11)$$

while the steady-state periodic process contains the stationary dynamic error of the system

$$\Delta_{sd} = x_c^0 + x_k^0(t) - x_n^0. \quad (9.12)$$

In linear systems the steady-state periodic response was possible only in the presence of an external periodic force $f(t)$ or $y(t)$; the stationary periodic dynamic error was related to this and undamped self-oscillations with constant amplitude were possible only as the limit of stability of the system, Section 7.

In non-linear systems a stable periodic process is possible—a stable oscillation of the system with defined amplitude in the absence of external periodic forces ($f = $ const and $y = $ const). Such oscillations are termed self-oscillations. In a number of non-linear systems, most frequently of relay type, the self-oscillatory regime is the fundamental steady-state operating condition of the system. Such systems are termed self-oscillatory systems. The frequency and amplitude of self-oscillation are determined by the parameters of the system. They may also depend on the magnitudes of f^0 and y^0.

The possibility of self-oscillations is one of the important properties of processes in non-linear systems (in distinction from linear), which are widely utilised in engineering. Transients in non-linear systems may differ very strongly from those in linear. It is important that here the general character of the process (its convergence and divergence, monotonicity and oscillatory character) may depend to a strong degree on the initial conditions, where the frequency

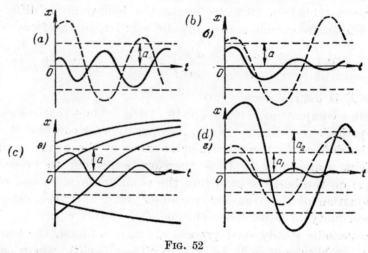

Fig. 52

of attenuated or increasing oscillations varies with amplitude. Consequently, a case may occur where for small initial deviations the transient process diverges, while for large, converges (Fig. 52*a*), or vice versa (Fig. 52*b*), remaining always oscillatory. Cases may be encountered where for some initial conditions the process is oscillatory, while for others monotonic (Fig. 52*c*). The pattern shown in Fig. 52*d* is also possible; here for small initial deviations the process converges, for "medium" diverges and for large again converges. More complicated cases may occur of substantial variation of the character of the transient response with change in magnitude of deviation.

In addition, there may exist so-called almost-periodic processes, which are undamped but do not have a defined period.

Processes with variable external forces. We have considered above processes for constant values of f^0 and y^0. Even these are quite varied in non-linear systems. It is natural to expect that the possible types of processes will be even more varied in the presence of variable external forces $f(t)$ and $y(t)$, for example, forced oscillations of the system with perturbations $f^0(t) = a \sin \omega t$, following with constant velocity or with constant acceleration for input forces $y^0(t) = \omega t$ for $y^0(t) = \varepsilon t^2/2$ respectively, following a sinusoidal input force $y^0(t) = a \sin \omega t$.

In these cases the general process of regulation $x(t)$ is defined by the solution of a non-linear equation of type (5.1) with corresponding substitution of the given $f = f^0(t)$ and $y = y^0(t)$. The steady-state response $f^0(t)$ is defined as the solution of the same equation for those specially selected initial conditions which lead to a solution having a definite stationary property (particular solution of the non-linear equation). The transient response is defined as the difference $x_t(t) = x(t) - x^0(t)$. Here, as before, there will exist transient $\Delta_{td} = x_t(t)$ and stationary $\Delta_{sd} = x^0(t) - x_n^0(t)$ dynamic errors of the system. However in their definition more detailed account must be taken of the possible characteristics of the processes.

For a given variable force $f^0(t)$ or $y^0(t)$, as in the case of constant forces, a non-unique steady-state process is possible, i.e. for a given input perturbation function the non-linear differential equation may have several steady-state solutions $x^0(t)$ (for example, several periodic solutions and almost-periodic solutions). Self-oscillations of the system may also be superimposed on the process of following with constant velocity. For change in initial conditions as well as in change of amplitude of the external force on the system it may pass discontinuously from one oscillation frequency to another and in an even more substantial form change the general character of the response.

All the above circumstances should be considered in investigating non-linear systems. But this does not mean that all non-linear systems must have all these properties. A number of non-linear systems of automatic regulation have for defined conditions properties close to linear, differing from them only quantitatively.

Finally, it is necessary to remark that in non-linear systems, as in linear, there occurs an additional dynamic error of a random character Δ_{ad} as a result of additional perturbations $\Delta f(t)$ and noise $\Delta y(t)$.

Stability of non-linear systems. In connection with the above characteristics of non-linear systems the concept of stability cannot here be defined as simply as was done for linear systems (Section 7). In purely linear systems a transient either attenuates to zero or diverges to infinity for arbitrary initial conditions (excluding the boundary of stability itself); therefore, the question of stability was solved by considering only the signs of the real parts of the roots of the characteristic equation, i.e. by a relationship among the parameters of the system, independently of the initial conditions and the external forces.

In non-linear systems the existence of attenuation or divergence
of the process depends, firstly, on the initial conditions as well as
on the parameters of the system. Secondly, the process may not
attenuate to zero or not diverge to infinity, but may be accompanied
by a complex variation of the general character of the process.
Thirdly, non-uniqueness of the steady-state may occur both in the
absence of external forces and in their presence.

It is necessary to distinguish asymptotic and non-asymptotic
stability*. In further discussion we shall employ the following
concepts.

Asymptotic stability is a case where for initial conditions lying
in a certain region $(x_{0t} < \eta_0, \dot{x}_{0t} < \eta_1, \ddot{x}_{0t} < \eta_2, ..., x_{0t}^{(n-1)} < \eta_{n-1})$
a transient attenuates to zero: $x_t(t) \to 0$ as $t \to \infty$.

If under initial conditions lying in a certain region the transient
does not attenuate to zero but the deviation remains for all time
sufficiently small $x_t(t) < \varepsilon$ for $t_0 \leqslant t \leqslant \infty$ non-asymptotic stability
in an infinite time interval occurs.

Finally, if for initial conditions lying in a certain region, it is
established that the transient has the property $x_t(t) < \varepsilon$ for $t_0 \leqslant t \leqslant t_1$,
this is a non-asymptotic stability in a finite time interval.

Let us consider certain illustrations.

If the response of the system has the form shown in Fig. 52a
the equilibrium state $(x^0 = 0)$ may be considered unstable, or non-
asymptotically stable if the quantity a is sufficiently small. In
this case, when both oscillations shown in Fig. 52a asymptotically
tend to the same amplitude and to the same frequency, the system
will have two steady states: (1) a constant value of the regulated
quantity $(x^0 = 0)$; (2) self-oscillatory with amplitude a. The former
is unstable (the transient response about it diverges), while the
latter is stable (the transient response converges from both sides
to a self-oscillation with amplitude a).

In Figs. 52b and c we have cases where the equilibrium state
$(x^0 = 0)$ of the system is stable "in small", i.e. for initial conditions not taking the deviation in the transient beyond the magnitude a, and unstable "in large", i.e. with initial conditions taking
the deviation and the transient beyond the limits of the magnitude a. Here the limit may be a periodic self-oscillation of the system
with amplitude a. However, here it is unstable, since the transient
response about it diverges on both sides (in distinction to the stable
self-oscillations in Fig. 52a).

In Fig. 52d three possible steady-state cases are shown: (1) an
equilibrium state $(x^0 = 0)$; (2) oscillation with constant amplitude a_1;

* Liapunov's definition of stability will be given in Section 10.

(3) oscillation with constant amplitude a_2. Then the oscillations with amplitude a_1 are unstable. As a result the system will be stable "in small" with regard to the equilibrium state $x^0 = 0$, while "in large" the system has a stable self-oscillation with amplitude a_2.

To the extent that non-linear theory considers large deviations of the variables and that real systems are always non-linear it is particularly important here to emphasise the following circumstance. In theory, certain non-linear equations and the properties of their solutions are studied for defined non-linearities. But these equations themselves are always composed with certain assumptions idealising the actual system. Therefore, the results obtained from non-linear theory will be valid not for arbitrarily great deviations but for definite bounds within which the equations of the systems are valid and only to the extent that the real character of non-linearity is fully reflected in them. To this is frequently added a necessary incompleteness of solution due to the difficulty of solving non-linear problems.

Linearised systems. As already noted, all real automatic systems are more or less non-linear as it is difficult to imagine a system in which the characteristics of all circuits in all states of operation of the system will be ideally linear. But the calculation of a linear system is always substantially simpler than non-linear. Therefore, in all cases where it is practically possible, we try to substitute for a non-linear differential equation of a real system (5.1) an approximately linear one (5.6)*.

Such linearisation of the non-linear equations of the system assumes that in the given concrete process to be calculated all variables in all circuits of the system vary in such manner that the operating portions of the characteristics of each circuit may be substituted by an approximately straight line. Of course, this is not always possible.

For the majority of real automatic systems it is found that calculations of the steady-state must be carried out in non-linear form, as described in this section, taking fully into account the real non-linear characteristics (at least for the regulated object)†.

The calculations of transient responses and dynamic errors may frequently, but not always, be carried out on the linearised differential equations of the system since they usually include small sections of the characteristics. However, certain automatic systems (for example of relay type or with dry friction, saturation, hysteresis, etc.) should be considered as non-linear even in the transient.

---

* A detailed discussion of this operation will be given in Chapters V and VI.
† See examples in Chapter VI.

Example. Let us examine the transient response and self-oscillations in the relay system for automatic temperature regulation, shown in Fig. 27. For this, we first construct the equations of the regulated object and the regulator.

Let the regulated object be some chamber of mass m and specific heat c, the surface area of the chamber S and the coefficient of heat emissivity α. The equation of thermal balance at an arbitrary moment of time with heating power q will be

$$mc\,d\theta + S\alpha\theta\,dt = q\,dt ,\qquad(9.13)$$

where θ is the deviation of the chamber temperature from some nominal value. The heating power q depends, firstly, on the position of the regulating organ ξ (for example, the damper) and, secondly, on various external thermal forces on the chamber $f(t)$ independent of the system considered, i.e.

$$q = -k\xi + f(t) . \qquad(9.14)$$

Substituting this in (9.13) and dividing through by $S\alpha\,dt$, we obtain the equation of the regulated object in the form

$$T_1\frac{d\theta}{dt} + \theta = -k_1\xi + f_1(t) , \qquad(9.15)$$

where we put

$$T_1 = \frac{mc}{S\alpha}, \qquad k_1 = \frac{k}{S\alpha}, \qquad f_1(t) = \frac{f(t)}{S\alpha} . \qquad(9.16)$$

With movement of the tip of the bimetallic plate [2] (sensitive element of the regulator, Fig. 27) the control circuit of one of the relays [3] is closed, applying d.c. voltage to one of the field windings of the electric motor [4]. Taking into account some delay in this switching process we obtain here a relay characteristic of form 7 (Fig. 24). Further, considering roughly that the motion of the end of the bimetallic plate [2] is proportional to the deviation of the object temperature θ, while the velocity ξ of motion of the damper [5] (regulating organ) is proportional to the voltage on the field windings of the electric motor [4], we may in this case consider the output quantity in the given relay characteristic proportional to ξ while the input to θ (Fig. 53a). The origin of coordinates of the characteristic $\theta = 0$ corresponds to some nominal temperature of the object for which the bimetallic plate is in the neutral position.

This relay characteristic determines in the first rough approximation the operation of the given regulator. In particular, for arbitrary oscillations of object temperature (Fig. 53b) the regulator will switch the rate of motion of the damper ξ for deviation of temperature $\theta = -b$ when the temperature is reduced, and for $\theta = +b$ when it is increased (Fig. 53c and b), where the quantity b is given by the characteristic (Fig. 53a). Consequently, the equation of the regulator is written:

$$\begin{aligned} \xi &= +c \quad \text{with} \quad \theta > +b \\ \xi &= -c \quad \text{with} \quad \theta < +b \end{aligned}\Bigg\} , \quad \text{when} \quad \dot\theta > 0 , \qquad (9.17)$$

$$\begin{aligned} \xi &= +c \quad \text{with} \quad \theta > -b \\ \xi &= -c \quad \text{with} \quad \theta < -b \end{aligned}\Bigg\} , \quad \text{when} \quad \dot\theta < 0 . \qquad (9.18)$$

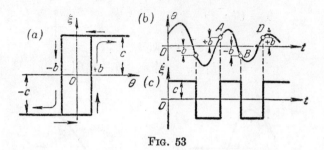

FIG. 53

If we consider the transient and the self-oscillations of the system for constant value of external force ($f_1 = 0$), the equation of the regulated object (9.15) becomes

$$T_1 \frac{d\theta}{dt} + \theta = -k_1 \xi . \qquad (9.19)$$

Consider two arbitrary sections of the transient process in the given system (sections AB and BD in Fig. 53b).

In section AB the equation of the regulator in accordance with Fig. 53c will be $\xi = +c$. Differentiating (9.19) with respect to t and substituting $\dot\xi = c$, we obtain the following equations of the regulation system in the section AB:

$$T_1 \frac{d\dot\theta}{dt} + \dot\theta = -k_1 c , \qquad (9.20)$$

Similarly, for section BD

$$T_1 \frac{d\dot\theta}{dt} + \dot\theta = +k_1 c . \qquad (9.21)$$

The solution of (9.20) will be

$$\dot\theta = C_1 e^{-\frac{t}{T_1}} - k_1 c , \qquad (9.22)$$

from which we obtain

$$\theta = -T_1 C_1 e^{-\frac{t}{T_1}} - k_1 c t + C_2 . \qquad (9.23)$$

We shall agree for the sake of simplicity to read time t from the origin of section AB (Fig. 54a). Then the initial conditions will be

$$\theta = +b , \quad \dot\theta = \dot\theta_A \quad \text{at} \quad t = 0 ,$$

where $\dot\theta_A$ is as yet unknown. Employing the initial conditions, we find the arbitrary constants for (9.23)

$$C_1 = \dot\theta_A + k_1 c \,, \qquad C_2 = b + T_1 C_1 \,. \tag{9.24}$$

Similarly, for the section BD from (9.21), also reading the time t from the start of this segment (Fig. 54b), we obtain the solution

$$\left.\begin{aligned}
\dot\theta &= C_1' e^{-\frac{t}{T_1}} + k_1 c \,, \\
\theta &= -T_1 C_1' e^{-\frac{t}{T_1}} + k_1 ct + C_2 \,, \\
C_1' &= \dot\theta_B - k_1 c \,, \qquad C_2' = -b + T_1 C_1' \,.
\end{aligned}\right\} \tag{9.25}$$

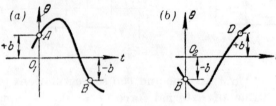

Fig. 54

All remaining sections of the curves of the transient response obviously will be defined by the same solutions as (9.22)–(9.25), but only with other numerical values of the quantities C_1, C_2, $\dot\theta_A$, C_1', C_2', $\dot\theta_B$. We note that the quantities $\dot\theta_A$ and $\dot\theta_B$, necessary to determine the arbitrary constants, are found as values of $\dot\theta$ at the ends of the preceding sections. Therefore, if the value of $\dot\theta$ be given at the initial point of the first section of the process, the entire above-described solution for the transient response of the system will be defined. Such a method of solving the problem is termed the method of matching solutions.

We shall now determine whether self-oscillation is possible in the given system, i.e. a stable periodic solution. For this it is necessary, obviously, that at the end D of the first period of oscillation (Fig. 53b) there be obtained exactly such values of θ and $\dot\theta$ as existed at its start A. It is easy to see from symmetry that then both half-periods (AB and BD) should be the same (Fig. 53a). Therefore, to determine self-oscillation it is sufficient to consider only a single segment AB and require that

$$\dot\theta_B = -\dot\theta_A \,. \tag{9.26}$$

Denoting the period of the self-oscillations sought by $2T$ and the duration of the segment AB, consequently, by T, from (9.22) we find

$$\dot\theta_B = C_1 e^{-\frac{T}{T_1}} - k_1 c \,.$$

Substituting in this (9.26) and remarking that from (9.24) $\dot{\theta}_A = C_1 - k_1 c$, we obtain the expression

$$C_1(1 + e^{-\frac{T}{T_1}}) = 2k_1 c , \qquad (9.27)$$

in which there are two unknowns, C_1 and T. The quantity T (duration of the segment AB) may be expressed from (9.23), since it is known that at the end of the segment $\theta = -b$. From (9.23) and (9.24) we find

$$T_1 C_1(1 - e^{-\frac{T}{T_1}}) = k_1 c T - 2b .$$

Substituting in this the value of C_1 from (9.27), we obtain the equation for determining the half-period of self-oscillation

$$\frac{1 - e^{-\frac{T}{T_1}}}{1 + e^{-\frac{T}{T_1}}} = \frac{T}{2T_1} - \frac{b}{k_1 c T_1}$$

or

$$\tanh \frac{T}{2T_1} = \frac{T}{2T_1} - \frac{b}{k_1 c T_1} . \qquad (9.28)$$

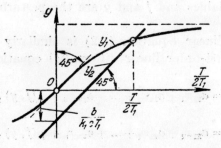

FIG. 55

This transcendental equation for T is easily solved graphically (Fig. 55) by the intersection of the two curves

$$y_1 = \tanh \frac{T}{2T_1}$$

and

$$y_2 = \frac{T}{2T_1} - \frac{b}{k_1 c T_1} .$$

The fact that we have found a real positive value for T indicates the presence of a periodic solution in the given system. To prove that this corresponds to self-oscillation it is necessary to investigate its stability, i.e. to prove that the system responds to the transient as shown in Fig. 52a but not as in Fig. 52b. This will be proved below in Section 10.

The amplitude of the non-linear self-oscillation is defined as θ_{max} on the section AB (Fig. 54a) by testing the function (9.23) for a maximum in the usual manner.

7

10. Representation of responses using phase trajectories

It is well known that the nth-order differential equation (5.1) may be transformed to a system of n first-order differential equations of the form

$$\left.\begin{aligned}
\frac{dx_1}{dt} &= \Phi_1(x_1, x_2, \ldots, x_n, f, y)\,, \\[4pt]
\frac{dx_2}{dt} &= \Phi_2(x_1, x_2, \ldots, x_n, f, y)\,, \\
&\quad \ldots\ldots\ldots\ldots\ldots \\
\frac{dx_n}{dt} &= \Phi_n(x_1, x_2, \ldots, x_n, f, y)
\end{aligned}\right\} \tag{10.1}$$

with initial conditions

$$x_1 = x_{10},\ x_2 = x_{20},\ \ldots,\ x_n = x_{n0} \quad \text{at} \quad t = 0\,,$$

where $x_1, x_2, \ldots, x_n$ are variables constituting required functions of time, and x_1 may denote the regulated quantity, while $x_2, \ldots, x_n$ are auxiliary variables and f and y are the perturbation and input forces.

An nth-order linear equation (5.2) is similarly transformed to a system of n first-order linear differential equations of the form

$$\left.\begin{aligned}
\frac{dx_1}{dt} &= a_{11}x_1 + a_{12}x_2 + \ldots + a_{1n}x_n + \varphi_1(f, y)\,, \\[4pt]
\frac{dx_2}{dt} &= a_{21}x_1 + a_{22}x_2 + \ldots + a_{2n}x_n + \varphi_2(f, y)\,, \\
&\quad \ldots\ldots\ldots\ldots\ldots\ldots\ldots\ldots \\
\frac{dx_n}{dt} &= a_{n1}x_1 + a_{n2}x_2 + \ldots + a_{nn}x_n + \varphi_n(f, y)\,.
\end{aligned}\right\} \tag{10.2}$$

It is possible to return to the previous equations (5.1) and (5.2) by elimination of the variables $x_2, \ldots, x_n$ from (10.1) or (10.2) respectively.

To obtain the equation of the transient in a linear automatic regulation system $x_{it}(t) = x_i(t) - x_i^0(t)$ $(i = 1, 2, \ldots, n)$ for given $f = f^0(t)$ and $y = y^0(t)$, we write the equations of the steady-state

$$\frac{dx_1^0}{dt} = a_{11}x_1^0 + a_{12}x_2^0 + \ldots + a_{1n}x_n^0 + \varphi_1(f, y)\,,$$

$$\frac{dx_2^0}{dt} = a_{21}x_1^0 + a_{22}x_2^0 + \ldots + a_{2n}x_n^0 + \varphi_2(f, y)\,,$$

$$\ldots\ldots\ldots\ldots\ldots\ldots\ldots\ldots\ldots$$

$$\frac{dx_n^0}{dt} = a_{n1}x_1^0 + a_{n2}x_2^0 + \ldots + a_{nn}x_n^0 + \varphi_n(f, y)$$

and subtract them from (10.2). As a result we obtain homogeneous differential equations of the transient in the form

$$\frac{dx_{1t}}{dt} = a_{11}x_{1t} + a_{12}x_{2t} + \dots + a_{1n}x_{nt},$$

$$\frac{dx_{2t}}{dt} = a_{21}x_{1t} + a_{22}x_{2t} + \dots + a_{2n}x_{nt},$$

$$\dots \dots \dots \dots \dots \dots \dots \dots \dots$$

$$\frac{dx_{nt}}{dt} = a_{n1}x_{1t} + a_{n2}x_{2t} + \dots + a_{nn}x_{nt}.$$

$$(10.3)$$

We proceed similarly when obtaining homogeneous equations of the transient response of the non-linear system, which gives

$$\frac{dx_{1t}}{dt} = X_1(x_{1t}, x_{2t}, \dots, x_{nt}),$$

$$\frac{dx_{2t}}{dt} = X_2(x_{1t}, x_{2t}, \dots, x_{nt}),$$

$$\dots \dots \dots \dots \dots \dots \dots$$

$$\frac{dx_{nt}}{dt} = X_n(x_{1t}, x_{2t}, \dots, x_{nt}),$$

$$(10.4)$$

where

$$X_i(x_{1t}, x_{2t}, \dots, x_{nt}) = \Phi_i(x_{1t} + x_1^0, x_{2t} + x_2^0 \dots$$
$$\dots, x_{nt} + x_n^0, f^0, y^0) - \Phi_i(x_1^0, x_2^0, \dots, x_n^0, f^0, y^0) \quad (i = 1, 2, \dots, n).$$

In all cases the initial conditions should simultaneously be transformed as well

$$x_{10t} = x_{10} - x_{10}^0, \; x_{20t} = x_{20} - x_{20}^0, \; \dots, \; x_{n0t} = x_{n0} - x_{n0}^0.$$

Phase space. For example, in (10.3) or (10.4) let $n = 3$ (a third-order system). The variables x_{1t}, x_{2t}, x_{3t} here may have arbitrary

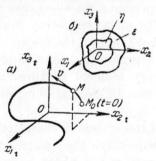

Fɪɢ. 56

physical significance. But it is possible to conceive them conventionally as rectangular coordinates of some point M (Fig. 56a).

In a real regulation process at each moment of time the quantities x_{1t}, x_{2t}, x_{3t} have completely defined values. These correspond to

a fully defined position of the point M in space (Fig. 56a). In the
course of time in a real process the quantities x_{1t}, x_{2t}, x_{3t} vary in
a definite manner. This corresponds to a defined motion of the
point M in the space over a defined trajectory. Consequently, the
trajectory of the point M may serve as a convenient geometric
illustration of the dynamic behaviour of the system in the transient
process.

The point M is termed the generating point, its trajectory is
termed the phase trajectory and the space (x_{1t}, x_{2t}, x_{3t}) is termed
the phase space.

Since the derivatives with regard to time of the coordinates of
the point represent the projections of its velocity on the coordinate
axes, the differential equations of a system in the forms (10.3) and
(10.4) represent the expressions for projections of the velocity v
of the generating point M (Fig. 56a) on the coordinate axis. Consequently, from the values of the right-hand sides of (10.3) or (10.4)
it is possible at each time to determine the direction of motion of
the generating point M and together with this the behaviour of
the corresponding real system in the transient process.

The initial conditions of the process $(x_{10t}, x_{20t}, x_{30t})$ define the
coordinates of the initial point of the phase trajectory M_0 (Fig. 56a).

If there are only two variables X_{1t} and X_{2t} (a second order system),
in (10.3) or (10.4), the generating point will not move in a volume
but in a phase plane.

If there is an arbitrary number of variables $n > 3$ (an nth-order
system the phase space will not be three-dimensional but n-dimen-
sional.

Thus, the phase space and phase trajectory represent only a geometric image of the dynamic processes occuring in the system.
In this geometric representation the coordinates take part, while
time is eliminated. The phase trajectory itself is only a qualitative
representation of the behaviour of the system. To determine a quantitative position of the generating point (and thus the state of the
system) at an arbitrary moment of time, it is necessary to find
the solution of the given differential equations (10.3) or (10.4) with
regard to time.

The steady-state of the system is characterised by values $x_{1t} = x_{2t}$
$= \ldots = x_{nt} = 0$. Consequently, the image of the steady-state is
the origin of coordinates of the phase space.

From this it follows that the phase trajectory of a stable linear
system will asymptotically approach the origin of coordinates with
unlimited increase in time. The phase trajectory of an unstable
linear system will diverge without limit from the origin of coordinates.

For a non-linear system, as a result of a number of the properties noted in Section 9, the phase trajectories may take on the most varied patterns. If there exists asymptotic stability for a definite circle of initial conditions, all phase trajectories which begin within the defined region η surrounding the origin of coordinates of the phase space (Fig. 56b) will asymptotically approach the origin of coordinates. If the stability is non-asymptotic, the phase trajectories beginning within a defined region η about the origin of coordinates of the phase space may have arbitrary patterns but will not emerge beyond the limits of some defined region ε, surrounding the origin of coordinates (Fig. 56b).

Formulation of Liapunov's concept of stability. An unperturbed motion (in our terminology a steady-state process) is termed stable if for a given arbitrarily small region ε (Fig. 56b) it is possible to find such a region η that for initial conditions located within these regions the perturbed motion (here, the transient response) will be such that the generating point does not emerge from the region ε for arbitrarily large value of time t.

In analytic notation the formulation of Liapunov's stability concept will be as follows. The unperturbed or steady-state motion will be stable, if for a given positive arbitrarily small number ε it is possible to find such a positive number η (dependent on the given ε), that with initial conditions

$$|x_{iot}| < \eta \quad (i = 1, 2, ..., n) \tag{10.5}$$

the solutions of the differential equations of perturbed motion (transient process) (10.4) will satisfy the inequalities

$$|x_{it}(t)| < \varepsilon \quad (i = 1, 2, ..., n)$$

for arbitrarily large t.

For this analytic statement let us consider a geometric image in the phase space. It is obvious that limiting the initial conditions in each coordinate by inequalities (10.5), we obtain a cube with side 2η, within which should lie the initial point of the phase trajectory $M_0(x_{10t}, x_{20t}, ..., x_{n0t})$. It is easy to imagine such a cube in a three-dimensional space ($n = 3$); this term "cube" is extended to n-dimensional space; in the phase plane ($n = 2$) it becomes a square. Similarly, the other inequalities denote geometrically that the phase trajectories should not emerge from the cube with side 2ε. Consequently, for the analytic notation of Liapunov's stability concept the regions η and ε in Fig. 56b have the forms of cubes.

Liapunov's formulation includes the requirement of an arbitrary smallness of these regions. However, in practice this definition and

Liapunov's theorems, which we shall encounter in Section 57, are applicable even when these regions have defined finite dimensions.

We note that in Liapunov's theory the deviations of all variables x_{it} in the transient regime are termed "perturbations" while their initial values x_{iot} are "initial perturbations". In the present book, however, these terms will not be used to avoid confusing them with the perturbations acting on the system $f(t)$.

Phase trajectories for ordinary linear systems. To obtain a clear general concept of the description of the behaviour of an automatic regulation system using phase trajectories, let us plot them first for ordinary second-order linear systems, the general properties of which are widely known. This background will also permit a more extensive description of the properties of behaviour of non-linear automatic regulation systems.

Let there be given some system, the transient response of which is described by a second-order equation

$$\ddot{x} + a_1 \dot{x} + a_2 x = 0 , \qquad (10.6)$$

where x is the deviation of the regulated quantity in the transient and a_1 and a_2 constant coefficients expressed through the parameters of the system (mass, inductance, resistance, gain factors, transfer factors, etc.).

Let us introduce the notation for the rate of change of deviation of the regulated quantity $y = \dot{x}$. Then the equation of the system (10.6) is represented in the form

$$\left. \begin{aligned} \frac{dy}{dt} &= -a_1 y - a_2 x , \\ \frac{dx}{dt} &= y \end{aligned} \right\} \qquad (10.7)$$

(this operation is equivalent to transformation of (5.2) to the form (10.2)).

Let us eliminate the time t from (10.7), dividing the first of them by the second. We obtain

$$\frac{dy}{dx} = -a_1 - a_2 \frac{x}{y} . \qquad (10.8)$$

The solution $y = \varphi(x)$ of this differential equation with a single arbitrary constant defines a certain family of so-called integral curves in the phase plane (x, y), each of which corresponds to a single defined value of the arbitrary constant.

The solutions $x = x(t)$ and $y = y(t)$ of the differential equations (10.7) defining the transient response of the given automatic regulation system may be considered as the parametric equations of the same integral curves in the phase plane (x, y) with parameter t.

The initial conditions of the transient in the system: $x = x_0$, $y = y_0 = \dot{x}_0$ at $t = 0$ are defined by the initial position of the generating point $M_0(x_0, y_0)$ in the phase plane.

That integral curve which passes through this point M_0 will be the phase trajectory representing the course of the transient process in the automatic regulation system for the given initial conditions.

The entire set of integral curves represents all possible phase trajectories, including all possible forms of the transient response in the given automatic regulation system for arbitrary initial conditions.

Let us consider the various cases individually. To (10.6) correspond the roots of the characteristic equation

$$z_{1,2} = -\frac{a_1}{2} \pm \sqrt{\frac{a_1^2}{4} - a_2},$$

where six cases are possible:

(1) the roots are purely imaginary, with $a_1 = 0$, $a_2 > 0$ (limiting stability of the linear system);

(2) the roots are complex and have negative real parts with $a_1^2 < 4a_2$, $a_1 > 0$, $a_2 > 0$ (stable linear system);

(3) the roots are complex and have positive real parts with $a_1^2 < 4a_2$, $a_1 < 0$, $a_2 > 0$ (unstable linear system);

(4) the roots are real and negative with $a_1^2 > 4a_2$, $a_1 > 0$, $a_2 > 0$ (stable linear system);

(5) the roots are real and positive with $a_1^2 > 4a_2$, $a_1 < 0$, $a_2 > 0$ (unstable linear system);

(6) the roots are real and have opposing signs for $a_2 < 0$ (unstable linear system), in particular one of the roots will vanish at $a_2 = 0$ (limiting stability of linear system).

Case 1. In the first case, as is well known, undamped oscillations are obtained.

$$\left.\begin{array}{l} x = A\sin(\omega t + \beta), \\ y = \dot{x} = \omega A\cos(\omega t + \beta), \end{array}\right\} \quad \omega = \sqrt{a_2} \qquad (10.9)$$

with constant amplitude A and initial phase β, dependent on the initial conditions. Equation (10.9) represents the parametric equation of an ellipse with semi-axes A and ωA (Fig. 57a), where from the initial conditions ($x = x_0, y = y_0 = \dot{x}_0$ at $t = 0$) we have

$$A = \sqrt{x_0^2 + \frac{y_0^2}{\omega^2}}, \qquad \beta = \tan^{-1}\frac{\omega x_0}{y_0} \qquad (y_0 = \dot{x}_0).$$

To different values of the constant A there uniquely correspond different ellipses in the phase plane (x, y), as shown in Fig. 57a;

to differing values of β correspond various initial positions of the generating point $M_0(x_0, y_0)$ on a given ellipse. Then, with increase in time t, the generating point M will move continuously over a given ellipse, which corresponds to an oscillatory process in time (Fig. 57b). In this it passes over the entire ellipse, returning to the previous position M_0 during a single period $T = 2\pi/\omega$.

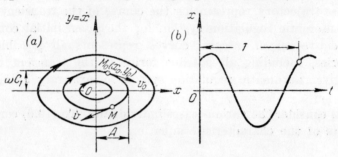

FIG. 57

Let us find the equations of the phase trajectories by elimination of the time t. In the given case where $a_1 = 0$ and $a_2 > 0$, from (10.8), substituting $a_2 = \omega^2$, we have

$$\frac{dy}{dx} = -\omega^2 \frac{x}{y}$$

or

$$2y\,dy = -\omega^2 2x\,dx\,,$$

which gives

$$y^2 = -\omega^2(x^2 - A^2)\,,$$

where A^2 is an arbitrary constant. This may be rewritten in the form

$$\frac{x^2}{A^2} + \frac{y^2}{(\omega A)^2} = 1\,, \tag{10.10}$$

which represents the family of ellipses shown in Fig. 57a.

The entire set of these ellipses (with $0 \leqslant A \leqslant \infty$) corresponds to all possible phase trajectories in the given system. Which of them will occur in reality is defined by the initial conditions, i.e. the initial position of the generating point $M_0(x_0, y_0)$. In particular, for initial conditions $x_0 = 0$, $y_0 = 0$ the generating point coincides with the origin of coordinates 0 of the phase plane (Fig. 57a) and it remains there for all time. This corresponds to a stable state of the system.

Let us determine the velocity v of motion of the generating point M over the phase trajectory. Obviously, its projection on the coordinate axes will be

$$v_x = \frac{dx}{dt}\,, \qquad v_y = \frac{dy}{dt}\,, \tag{10.11}$$

and the modulus

$$v = \sqrt{\left(\frac{dx}{dt}\right)^2 + \left(\frac{dy}{dt}\right)^2}. \qquad (10.12)$$

In this case, when $a_1 = 0$, $a_2 = \omega^2$, from (10.7) and (10.9) we have

$$
\begin{aligned}
v_x &= y = \omega A \cos(\omega t + \beta), \\
v_y &= -\omega^2 x = -\omega^2 A \sin(\omega t + \beta), \\
v &= \sqrt{y^2 + \omega^4 x^2} = \sqrt{\dot{x}^2 + \omega^4 x^2}.
\end{aligned}
\qquad (10.13)
$$

Thus, to a periodic oscillation of the system (Fig. 57*b*) there corresponds a motion of the generating point over a closed curve (Fig. 57*a*) with periodically varying velocity.

Case 2. In this case (complex roots with negative real parts), as is well known, there occur damped oscillations

$$
\left.
\begin{aligned}
x &= A e^{-\alpha t} \sin(\omega t + \beta), \\
y &= \dot{x} = \gamma A e^{-\alpha t} \cos(\omega t + \beta + \delta),
\end{aligned}
\right\}
\qquad (10.14)
$$

where

$$
\left.
\begin{aligned}
\alpha &= \frac{a_1}{2}, \qquad \omega = \sqrt{a_2 - \left(\frac{a_1}{2}\right)^2}, \\
\gamma &= \sqrt{a_2}, \qquad \delta = \tan^{-1}\frac{\alpha}{\omega},
\end{aligned}
\right\}
\qquad (10.15)
$$

and the arbitrary constants A and β are determined from the initial conditions: $x = x_0$, $y = y_0 = \dot{x}_0$ at $t = 0$.

The values of x and $y = \dot{x}$ do not return after a period of oscillation to the previous values, but become smaller. This gives a curve (Fig. 58*b*) in the phase plane (x, y) which does not return to the previous point M_0 in a single revolution, but comes closer to the origin of coordinates. Equations (10.14) are thus the parametric equations of a family of spirals, asymptotically approaching the origin of coordinates (Fig. 58*c*), where to each value of the constant A there uniquely corresponds a defined spiral, while the constant β corresponds to the initial position of the generating point $M_0(x_0, y_0)$ on the given spiral. Assignment of initial conditions (x_0, y_0) defines, consequently, the initial point M_0, after which the generating point M with increase in time t moves continuously over a given spiral as shown by the arrows in Fig. 58*c*, asymptotically approaching the origin of coordinates 0.

Thus, to damped oscillations of the system (Fig. 58*a*) there correspond phase trajectories in the form of spirals, over which the generating point approaches the origin of coordinates (Fig. 58*c*).

The velocity v of motion of the generating point M over the phase trajectory is defined by the same general formulae (10.11) and

(10.12) where in the present case from (10.7) and (10.14) we have

$$v_x = \frac{dx}{dt} = y, \qquad v_y = \frac{dy}{dt} = -2\alpha y - \gamma^2 x . \qquad (10.16)$$

Case 3. This case (complex roots with positive real parts) corresponds to divergent oscillations (Fig. 59a). Proceeding as above, we obtain the set of all possible phase trajectories also in the form

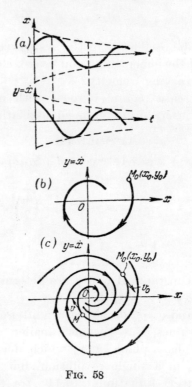

Fig. 58

of a family of spirals, as in Fig. 58c, but the generating point will not move over them in the direction of the origin of coordinates but away from it (Fig. 59b).

Thus, to divergent oscillations of the system (Fig. 59a) there correspond phase trajectories in the form of spirals over which the generating point diverges from the origin of coordinates.

Case 4. This case (real negative roots) corresponds to an aperiodic process

$$x = C_1 e^{-a_1 t} + C_2 e^{-a_2 t} ,$$
$$y = \dot{x} = -\alpha_1 C_1 e^{-a_1 t} - \alpha_2 C_2 e^{-a_2 t} , \qquad \left. \right\} \qquad (10.17)$$

where

$$\alpha_{1,2} = \frac{a_1}{2} \pm \sqrt{\frac{a_1^2}{4} - a_2} .$$

In Fig. 60a are shown two possible types (curves 1 and 2) of the course of this process. It is easy to see that in the phase plane (x, y) this is represented by curves 1 and 2 respectively (Fig. 60b), since in the first variant for all time $x > 0$ and $y < 0$, while in the second

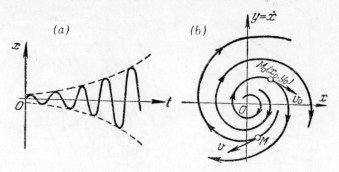

FIG. 59

variant the signs of x and y each change once. The boundaries of regions 1 and 2 are the lines $y = -\alpha_1 x$ and $y = -\alpha_2 x$ obtained from (10.17) with $\alpha_2 = 0$ and $\alpha_1 = 0$ respectively (vanishing of one of the roots).

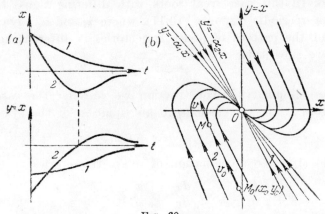

FIG. 60

In contrast to the above, here all phase trajectories merge directly in the origin of coordinates 0 of the phase plane. However, the generating point M does not arrive at the origin of coordinates in a finite time, as from (10.11) and (10.7) its velocity

$$v_x = y, \qquad v_y = -a_1 y - a_2 x, \qquad (10.18)$$

and the coordinates x and y themselves (10.17) decrease, asymptotically approaching zero.

Thus, to attenuated aperiodic responses in the system there correspond phase trajectories merging at the origin of coordinates.

Case 5. This case (real positive roots) also corresponds to an aperiodic response defined by the same equations (10.17) but with $\alpha_1 < 0$ and $\alpha_2 < 0$. Similarly we obtain the curves of the response and phase trajectories represented in Fig. 61.

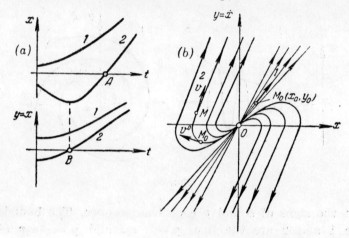

FIG. 61

Case 6. In this case (real roots with differing signs) there also occurs an aperiodic response (10.17), where α_1 and α_2 have opposing signs, but the pattern of phase trajectories is different here. Since $a_2 < 0$, we substitute

$$\alpha^2 = -a_2 \, ,$$

where for simplicity of construction we consider the case $a_1 = 0$, which from (10.6) corresponds to an equation of the system

$$\ddot{x} - \alpha^2 x = 0$$

and from (10.8) to an equation of phase trajectories

$$\frac{dy}{dx} = \alpha^2 \frac{x}{y} \, .$$

Integration of the latter analogously to Case 1 gives

$$\frac{x^2}{C} - \frac{y^2}{(\alpha C)^2} = 1 \, , \tag{10.19}$$

i.e. the family of hyperbolae represented in Fig. 62a. The velocity of the generating point (10.18) in this case will be

$$v_x = y \, , \qquad v_y = \alpha^2 x \, . \tag{10.20}$$

The directions of motion of the generating point M over the phase trajectories, shown in Fig. 62a, are easily defined in each quadrant of the plane from the signs of v_x and v_y, since from (10.20), the projections of the velocities v_x have the same signs as the coordinate y while the projections of v_y the same signs as the coordinate x. The phase trajectory with initial position $M_0(x_0, y_0)$, shown in Fig. 62a, corresponds to an aperiodic response of the system, represented in Fig. 62b.

Analogous patterns of phase trajectories are obtained in the given case for $a_1 \neq 0$.

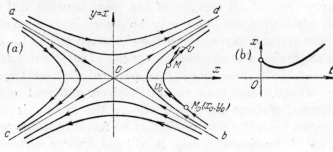

Fig. 62

Thus, to divergent aperiodic responses in a system there correspond phase trajectories of the type of Fig. 61b or the type of Fig. 62a, where the generating point moving over them eventually diverges from the origin of coordinates.

Singular points and singular lines. At points which correspond to stable states, we obtain from (10.8) the indeterminate expression

$$\frac{dy}{dx} = -a_1 - a_2 \frac{0}{0},$$

i.e. indeterminate direction of the tangents to the integral curves (phase trajectories). Such points are termed singular points, classified as follows:

(a) singular points of the type of point O in Fig. 57a are termed centres;

(b) singular points of type Fig. 58c are termed stable foci;

(c) singular points of the type of Fig. 59b are termed unstable foci;

(d) singular points of the type of Fig. 60b are termed stable nodes;

(e) singular points of the type Fig. 61b are termed unstable nodes;

(f) singular points of the type of Fig. 62a are termed saddles (saddles are always unstable).

Aside from the concept of singular points there exists the concept of singular lines. This is important for non-linear systems.

As has already been mentioned, real automatic regulation systems may be considered linear most frequently under the assumption of smallness of deviation of the variables from their values in a definite stable state. In such cases the patterns of phase trajectories for linear systems constructed above with regard to real automatic regulation systems have force only within a defined bounded region about the singular point O (Figs. 57–62), corresponding to the stable states of operation of the automatic regulation system. The dimensions of this region are determined by the largest value of deviation x of the regulated quantity from its steady-state value for which the characteristics of all circuits of the given system still remain sufficiently close to linear. This may be determined in practice for each concrete system, having given the characteristics of its circuits.

Beyond the limits of this region, as a result of substantial deviation of the characteristics from linear, the pattern of phase trajectories may vary strongly and take on qualitatively different character.

In particular, if from the linear theory the system is unstable and the process begins to diverge, it may be found that due to actual non-linearity of the characteristics it will not diverge without limit. The amplitude of divergent oscillations may increase only to a defined value and then remain constant, i.e. an unstable linear automatic system changes to a stable non-linear self-oscillatory system (the system "generates" stable oscillations of a definite form).

The pattern of phase trajectories for such a system is represented in Fig. 63a. Here, close to the origin of coordinates, spirals are obtained as in the unstable linear system (Fig. 59b), but remote from it diverge not to infinity but approach asymptotically to some closed contour of bounded dimensions, as shown in Fig. 63a. To it also approach all spirals located outside the contour. This corresponds to the pattern of processes in time represented in Fig. 52a. Such a closed contour representing the most important case of singular lines in the phase plane in regulation theory, is termed a stable limiting cycle.

A stable limiting cycle corresponds to a self-oscillatory system. The dimensions of the limiting cycle A and B (Fig. 63a) represent the amplitude of oscillation of the quantity x and the velocity of its variation $y = \dot{x}$. To determine the period of oscillation it is necessary to solve the equation with respect to time.

To the case of a system stable "in small" and unstable "in large" (Fig. 52b) there corresponds the pattern of phase trajectories shown in Fig. 63b. The limit of initial conditions at which the system is stable most frequently has the form of an unstable limiting cycle in the phase plane (Fig. 63b), from which on both sides the spiral phase trajectories diverge. This, the second important type of singular line, defines a system stable "in small" and unstable "in large".

We note that in this case it is also possible to have a still more remote stable limiting cycle (Fig. 63c), corresponding to self-oscillations of large amplitude. This corresponds to the time processes shown in Fig. 62*d*. These fundamental qualitative changes in the pattern of phase trajectories for sufficiently large deviations may be observed for aperiodic processes (Figs. 61*b* and 62*a*), including

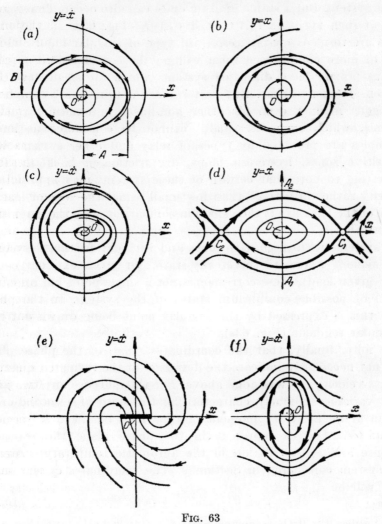

FIG. 63

their transformation into oscillatory and vice versa. For example, to the pattern of processes in time shown in Fig. 52*c* there corresponds the pattern of phase trajectories, Fig. 63*f*.

Similarly, for systems existing, in accordance with linear theory, at the limit of stability (with purely imaginary roots), the pattern of phase trajectories shown in Fig. 57*a* may occur only close to the steady-state regime *O*. For large deviations, if the linearity of the characteristics of the system circuits is disturbed, the pattern of phase trajectories will differ. One of the possible forms of variation of large deviation phase trajectories in this case is shown in Fig. 63d. Here, in addition to the singular point O of the type of a centre, there appear two saddles C_1 and C_2, which leads, in fact, to instability of the system. But a stable limiting cycle can also occur. The singular lines of such types as $C_1A_1C_2$ and $C_2A_2C_1$ (Fig. 63d) in the phase plane are termed separatrices (third type of singular line). Singular lines of more complicated form will not be considered*.

Thus far we have discussed systems which for small deviations are considered as linear. But patterns are obtained in a completely analogous manner even for other non-linear automatic regulation systems, which even "in small" cannot be considered as linear. Examples are provided by types of relay and other systems with insensitive zones, hysteresis loops, dry friction or backlash. It is interesting to note that certain of these systems may approximate linearity rather in "large" than in "small" since the zone of insensitivity or the backlash is then small in comparison with the magnitude of deviation x.

In systems with insensitive zones and with dry friction there exist dead regions where, to the steady-state, for given external conditions (given load), there corresponds not a single point but an entire region of possible equilibrium states of the system. In the phase plane this is expressed by the singular point being drawn out into a singular segment (Fig. 63e).

We note, finally, that the coordinates (x, y) of the phase plane need not necessarily indicate the deviation of the regulated quantity and its velocity, as was done above. For this purpose any two arbitrary variables uniquely characterising the state of a second-order system at an arbitrary moment of time may be taken.

Example. Let us represent in the phase plane the transient response and self-oscillation in the automatic temperature regulation system considered in Section 9. The coordinates of the phase plane will be

$$x = \theta \quad \text{and} \quad y = \dot{\theta}. \tag{10.21}$$

To values $\dot{\theta} > 0$ there corresponds the upper half-plane (Fig. 64), and to $\dot{\theta} < 0$, the lower. If $\dot{\theta} > 0$, from (9.17) and Fig. 53a, the regulator is switched at $\theta = +b$ (line EF in Fig. 64), if $\dot{\theta} < 0$, then at $\theta = -b$ (line GH). To the right of the switching line $EFGH$ the system equation (9.20) is valid, to the left (9.21).

Equation (9.20) in the notation of (10.21) takes the form

$$y = \frac{dx}{dt}, \quad T_1\frac{dy}{dt} + y = -k_1c,$$

* See A. A. Andronov and S. E. Khaikin [7].

from which we obtain the differential equation of the phase trajectories

$$\frac{dy}{dx} = -\frac{1}{T_1} - \frac{k_1 c}{T_1 y}. \tag{10.22}$$

Integration gives

$$x = k_1 c T_1 \ln |y + k_1 c| - T_1 y + C_1, \tag{10.23}$$

where C_1 is an arbitrary constant. To each concrete value C there
corresponds a definite curve in the phase plane. The family of curves

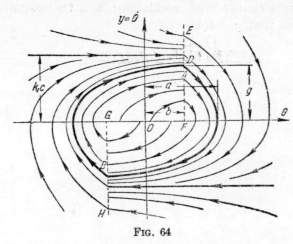

Fig. 64

corresponding to various values of C_1 is shown in Fig. 64 to the
right of the line $EFGH$. These curves have asymptote $y = -k_1 c$.
The direction of motion of the generating point over them, indicated
by arrows, is determined from the condition $y = dx/dt$, i.e. x increases
for $y > 0$ and decreases for $y < 0$.

Equation (9.21) in the notation of (10.21) will be

$$\frac{dy}{d\dot{x}} = -\frac{1}{T_1} + \frac{k_1 c}{T_1 y}, \tag{10.24}$$

which has the solution

$$x = -k_1 c T_1 \ln |y - k_1 c| - T_1 y + C_2, \tag{10.25}$$

in accordance with which the family of phase trajectories to the left
of the line $EFGH$ is plotted (Fig. 64).

As a result it is found that all phase trajectories diverge from the
origin of coordinates and converge from infinity, i.e. a case similar
to Fig. 63a occurs which signifies that there should be some stable
limiting cycle. It is denoted by the thick line in Fig. 64.

There will thus be observed in the given automatic regulation
system a stable oscillation to which the transient converges from

both sides, i.e. for arbitrary initial conditions. Self oscillation is the only possible form of steady-state here, strict maintenance of constant temperature ($\theta = 0$) is impossible. The amplitude of temperature oscillations in the given regulation system is represented in Fig. 64 by the segment a. The period of oscillation is found only by solving the equations with regard to time (Section 9). The halves AB and BD (Fig. 64) of the limiting cycle correspond to half-periods of oscillation AB and BD (Fig. 53b).

The segment g (Fig. 64) represents the magnitude of the rate of temperature-change with oscillation; it is the magnitude (9.26). It is obvious that $g < k_1 c$.

CHAPTER III

METHODS OF IMPROVING THE REGULATION PROCESS

11. Static, astatic and oscillatory systems. Reduction of static and stationary dynamic errors

A discussion of various forms of errors in automatic regulation systems has been given previously; in this chapter we shall consider methods of reducing these errors.

Static systems. An automatic regulation system (stable with regard to the steady-state with constant value of the regulated quantity) is termed static when in principle it does not permit maintaining a single value of the regulated quantity in all steady-

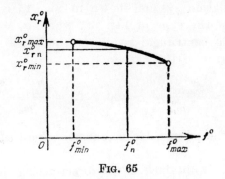

FIG. 65

states, corresponding to various constant values of external perturbation f^0 on the regulated object (with constant adjustment y^0 of the regulator). In other words, a static system is a system which according to its operating principle has a definite static error.

Static systems are thus characterised by the fact that the right-hand side of steady-state equality (7.15) or (9.4) for such systems contains the quantity f^0, as a result of which a definite relation between the steady-state value of the regulated quantity X_r^0 and the load f^0 is obtained (for example, in the form of the curve in Fig. 65).

An example of a static system is the system for regulating engine velocity by direct action of a centrifugal regulator shown in Fig. 13.

In this case, the greater the steady state moment of the load M_l^0 on the engine shaft 1, the greater will be the required supply of energy, i.e. the slide valve 3 must open more.

Consequently,

$$\xi^0 = f_1(M_l^0) . \qquad (11.1)$$

But then the coordinate η of the position of the coupling of the centrifugal mechanism 2 must change since it is rigidly related to the coordinate ξ (with the arm), namely:

$$\eta^0 = k\xi^0 . \qquad (11.2)$$

This in turn may occur only when the weights 2 are lower, i.e. the angular velocity ω^0 becomes smaller, since

$$\eta^0 = f_2(\omega^0) . \qquad (11.3)$$

From (11.1), (11.2) and (11.3) we obtain:

$$\omega^0 = f_3(M_l^0) . \qquad (11.4)$$

This means that the regulated quantity ω cannot in principle have a single value for all steady-state regimes of operation of this system; it will decrease with increase of the load moment M_l^0.

Thus, the regulation system shown in Fig. 13 is static and has a characteristic of the type of Fig. 65, where $x_r = \omega$, $f = M_l$. The parameters of the centrifugal regulator should be here chosen so that the static error of the system

$$\Delta_1 = \frac{\omega_{max}^0 - \omega_n^0}{\omega_n^0} \quad \text{and} \quad \Delta_2 = \frac{\omega_{min}^0 - \omega_n^0}{\omega_n^0}$$

does not exceed the permissible magnitude where ω_n^0 is the required nominal value.

The same result is obtained in the direct-acting rheostatic voltage regulator (Fig. 14) and Polzunov's regulator (Fig. 9). In both these cases to steady-state values of the load I_l^0 (load current, steam consumption) there correspond differing steady-state currents I_1^0 (field current, water feed), i.e. there exists a definite relationship

$$I_1^0 = f_1(I_l^0) . \qquad (11.5)$$

This is provided by varying the steady-state positions ξ^0 of the regulating organ (rheostat contact, valve), i.e.

$$I_1^0 = f_2(\xi^0) . \qquad (11.6)$$

However in order that the regulating organ occupy differing steady-state positions, in Polzunov's regulator (Fig. 9) differing positions of the float are required, and so differing steady-state values of the regulated quantity H^0. In the voltage regulator (Fig. 14) various steady-state values of tractive force of the electromagnet F_2^0 are required for this purpose, since in the equilibrium state

$$F_2^0 = F_s^0 + F_w \,, \tag{11.7}$$

where F_2, F_s, F_w are respectively the forces of the electromagnet, spring and weight. The first depends on the voltage V and the position of the armature ξ, while the second is proportional to the spring extension $(F_s = c\xi)$. Therefore (11.7) may be written in the form

$$F_2(V^0, \xi^0) = c\xi^0 + F_w \quad (F_w = \text{const}) \,, \tag{11.8}$$

from which by virtue of (11.5) and (11.6) we again obtain:

$$V^0 = f_3(I_l) \,, \tag{11.9}$$

which defines this system as static with a characteristic of the type of Fig. 65, where $x_r = V$, $f = I_1$.

The system for regulating electric motor velocity with a rotary amplifier (Fig. 20) is also static since for large steady-state load on the motor shaft a large torque is required which requires a larger current in the armature circuit, i.e.

$$I_a^0 = f_1(M_l^0) \,.$$

But this may be provided only by a greater magnitude V^0 in the excitation circuit of the rotary amplifier, i.e.

$$I_a^0 = f_2(V^0) \,.$$

Then we obtain a smaller value of V_t^0 since $V_t^0 = V_l - V^0$. Considering the voltage of the tachometer, $V_t^0 = k\omega^0$, we find on the basis of the preceding relationship

$$\omega^0 = f_3(M_l^0) \,, \tag{11.10}$$

which is the criterion of a static system.

Astatic systems. Automatic regulation systems (servo-systems) are termed astatic when in operating principle they permit maintaining single values of the regulated quantity at all steady-states of the system, corresponding to different constant values of external perturbation (load) f^0 on the regulated object (with constant adjustment y^0 of the regulator). In other words, in an astatic system there is no static error connected with the magnitude of the load f^0; however there may of course occur additional static error caused by non-linearity in the form of zones of instability or dry friction.

Consequently, an astatic system should not have a dependence of the type of (11.10) or (11.9) between the regulated quantity and in the steady-state.

For this the right-hand side of the steady-state equation (7.15) or (9.4) should not contain the quantity f^0. In particular, the equations of the linear system (5.2) should not contain in the right-hand side a for $f(t)$, i.e. we require $b_m = 0$.

There exist various methods of making a system astatic. We shall demonstrate here in simplified form four possible means using the examples of the rheostatic voltage regulator and centrifugal velocity regulator, two further methods will be given below, in Section 12 and Section 14, and similar methods can be adopted in other systems.

1. The method of matching of characteristics of the tractive force of the electromagnet 2 and the resisting force of the spring 4

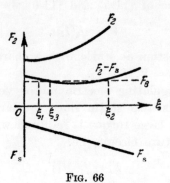

Fig. 66

(Fig. 14). It is possible to select a curve of tractive force of the electromagnet F_2 as a function of the armature position ξ for constant voltage V^0, on the one hand, and the stiffness of the spring, on the other, such that in the required region the difference of the forces will be approximately constant and equal to the weight (Fig. 66). For this we require, firstly, equality of forces in some single position, for example

$$F_2(\xi_3, V^0) = F_s(\xi_3) + F_w ,$$

and, secondly, equality of the slopes of the characteristics $F_s(\xi)$ and $F_2(\xi)$ for $V = \mathrm{const} = V^0$, i.e.

$$-\left(\frac{\partial F_2}{\partial \xi}\right)_{V=V^0} = \frac{dF_s}{d\xi} = c \quad \text{with} \quad \xi_1 \leqslant \xi \leqslant \xi_2 . \quad (11.11)$$

In this case in place of dependency (11.9) we obtain:

$$V^0 = \mathrm{const} \quad \text{with} \quad \xi_1 \leqslant \xi^0 \leqslant \xi_2 ,$$

i.e. the regulated voltage V^0 will be constant for various positions of the contact ξ^0, corresponding to various loads I_1^0.

2. The method of removing the spring 4 (Fig. 14), and establishing static conditions in which the tractive force F_2 is practically inde-

pendent of the deflection ξ. In this case, without the spring equation (11.7) takes the form

$$F(V^0) = F_w = \text{const} \quad \text{and} \quad V^0 = \text{const} . \qquad (11.12)$$

3. The method of connecting one of the ends of the spring 4 through a damper (Fig. 67). This is termed an isodromic system (comp. Fig. 14). In this case, again, in the steady-state regime we obtain equality (11.12). However the transient responses of these two systems differ very substantially.

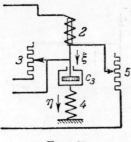

FIG. 67

4. The method of connecting an integrator for which instead of the deflection the velocity depends on the magnitude of the input force* (Figs. 18 and 19), i.e. when in the transient

$$\frac{d\xi}{dt} = F(s) \quad \text{or} \quad \frac{d\xi}{dt} = c_4 s , \qquad (11.13)$$

where ξ is the deflection of the regulating organ and s is the deflection of the control element while $F(s)$ has the usual form, represented in Fig. 33. Then the steady-state, connected in the given case with absence of motion of the drive ($\xi = \text{const} = \xi^0$), may occur only for $s = 0$, as follows from expression (11.13) and Fig. 33. But to the value $s = 0$ there corresponds a completely defined state of the sensitive element 2 (Figs. 18 and 19), which implies a completely defined value of the regulating quantity, the same for all steady-state positions of the regulating organ and external load.

All four types of astatic systems described above are equivalent with respect to the absence of static error. They are characterised by the graph of Fig. 68 in place of the previous graph of Fig. 65. However these systems differ in their dynamic properties. We shall demonstrate this difference for the present in a first coarse approximation.

For this we construct the equations of the transient first for the slider of the rheostat 3, considering that the resisting force against

---

* Then the deflection will be the integral of the input force.

its motion is proportional to the velocity while the force of the spring is proportional to the deflection.

For a static system (Fig. 14) we obtain:

$$m\ddot{\xi} + c_2\dot{\xi} + c_1\xi = k\Delta V , \qquad (11.14)$$

where m is the mass of the moving part, $c_2\dot{\xi}$ is the force resisting the motion, $c_1\xi$ is the change of spring force, $k\Delta V$ is the change in electromagnet force (subtracting the initial extension of the spring and the weight of the moving parts).

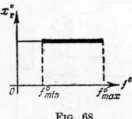

FIG. 68

For an astatic system, designed according to either of the first two methods (matching of characteristics, removal of spring), we will have:

$$m\ddot{\xi} + c_2\dot{\xi} = k\Delta V . \qquad (11.15)$$

For an astatic system designed according to the circuit of Fig. 67, we obtain two equations

$$\left.\begin{array}{r} m\ddot{\xi} + c_2\dot{\xi} + c_3(\dot{\xi} - \dot{\eta}) = k\Delta V , \\ c_3(\dot{\xi} - \dot{\eta}) = c_1\eta \end{array}\right\} \qquad (11.16)$$

(here the damper force is proportional to the difference of velocities of its piston and body and is equal to the spring force). Eliminating η, we come to the equation

$$c_3 m\dddot{\xi} + (c_1 m + c_2 c_3)\ddot{\xi} + c_1(c_2 + c_3)\dot{\xi} = c_3 k\Delta\dot{V} + c_1 k\Delta V \qquad (11.17)$$

Finally, for an astatic system designed according to the circuit of Fig. 19, equation (11.14) must be applied to the deflection s and equation (11.13) added, specifically:

$$\left.\begin{array}{r} m\ddot{s} + c_2\dot{s} + c_1 s = k\Delta V , \\ \xi = c_4 s . \end{array}\right\} \qquad (11.18)$$

whence

$$m\ddot{\xi} + c_2\dot{\xi} + c_1\xi = c_4 k\Delta V . \qquad (11.19)$$

Let us assume further that in the first linear approximation the regulated object (dynamo) is described by the equation

$$\Delta V = -k_1\xi - f(t) , \qquad (11.20)$$

where ΔV is the deviation of voltage from the required constant value, $-k_1 \xi$ is the reduction of voltage with introduction of the regulating rheostat 5 (Fig. 19) and $-f(t)$ is the reduction of voltage with increase in load in the system and angular velocity of the dynamo armature.

Then, assuming that the mass of the rheostat slider is negligible $(m \approx 0)$, we obtain the equation of the transient response for a static regulation system (Fig. 14) from (11.14) and (11.20) (after elimination of ξ) in the form

$$c_2 \dot{\Delta V} + (c_1 + kk_1)\Delta V = -c_2 k_1 \dot{f} - c_1 f . \tag{11.21}$$

The static error of the system is:

$$\Delta V_{st} = -\frac{c_1}{c_1 + kk_1} f^0 .$$

The equation of the transient process for the first two cases of the astatic system from (11.15) and (11.20) will take on the form

$$c_2 \dot{\Delta V} + kk_1 \Delta V = -c_2 \dot{f} , \tag{11.22}$$

while for the astatic system with isodrome (Fig. 67) from (11.17) and (11.20) we have:

$$c_2 c_3 \ddot{\Delta V} + (c_2 c_1 + c_3 c_1 + c_3 kk_1)\dot{\Delta V} + c_1 kk_1 \Delta V =$$
$$-c_2 c_3 \ddot{f} - c_1(c + c_3)\dot{f} . \tag{11.23}$$

For an astatic system of the time shown in Fig. 19, from (11.19) and (11.20) we find:

$$c_2 \ddot{\Delta V} + c_1 \dot{\Delta V} + c_4 kk_1 \Delta V = -c_2 \ddot{f} - c_1 \dot{f} . \tag{11.24}$$

From equations (11.22), (11.23) and (11.24) we see that actually in all these astatic systems the static error is equal to zero, since the load f itself does not enter into the right side of the equations, but only its time derivatives.

A solution of equations (11.21) and (11.22) without the right-hand side, i.e. the curve of the transient response with constant load $(f = 0)$, has the form

$$\Delta V = C_1 e^{-\frac{t}{T}} ,$$

where C_1 is the integration constant and the magnitudes of T for the cases (11.21) and (11.22) are determined respectively from the formulae

$$\left.\begin{array}{l} T = \dfrac{c_2}{c_1 + kk_1} \equiv T_{st} , \\[3mm] T = \dfrac{c_2}{kk_1} \equiv T_{ast} . \end{array}\right\} \tag{11.25}$$

Since the quantity T in the second case is larger, the transient (Fig. 69a) will attenuate more slowly. From formulae (11.25) it is evident that the cause of this is the absence of the spring ($c_1 = 0$) or matching of the characteristics. The quantity T, indicating to a certain degree the duration of the transient, is termed the time constant.

From this there follows the conclusion: an astatic system designed according to one of the first two methods, although distinguished

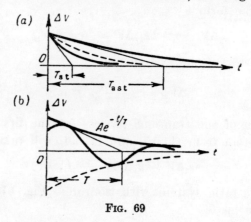

Fig. 69

from a static system (Fig. 14) by the absence of static error, has a poorer attenuation of the transient, which may become unacceptably slow.

In the case of (11.23) the solution takes the form

$$\Delta V = C_1 e^{-\frac{t}{T_1}} + C_2 e^{-\frac{t}{T_2}}, \tag{11.26}$$

where C_1 and C_2 are constants of integration,

$$T_{1,2} = \frac{2c_2 c_3}{c_1 c_2 + c_1 c_3 + c_3 k k_1 \pm \sqrt{(c_1 c_2 + c_1 c_3 + c_3 k k_1)^2 - 4 c_1 c_2 c_3 k k_1}}.$$

In degree of damping this solution takes an intermediate position among the solutions (11.25) (see broken-lines in Fig. 69a). Therefore in the astatic system shown in Fig. 67 the absence of static error is combined with a better degree of damping of the transient than in the preceding cases. Such an astatic system, with an isodromic device, is frequently termed an isodromic regulation system or a system with transient statism, as at the start of the transient for high velocities of the slider 3 the damper c_3 (Fig. 67) does not operate and moves almost as a rigid body. Therefore initially the system operates almost as a static one (Fig. 14), with good damping. Then at the end of the transient, when the slider moves slowly, the body of the damper shifts more substantially with regard to its piston, which eliminates the static error occuring in the system of Fig. 14 (in the graph of Fig. 69a only the transient responses are compared in the three systems without regard to the static error of the first system).

Finally, for the astatic system represented in Fig. 19 and similarly in Fig. 18), the curve of the transient response as a solution of equation (11.24) will have the form (Fig. 69b)

$$\Delta V = A e^{-\frac{t}{T}} \sin(\omega t + \beta) , \qquad (11.27)$$

if the roots of the characteristic equation are complex. Here A and β are arbitrary constants,

$$T = \frac{2c_2}{c_1}, \quad \omega = \sqrt{\frac{c_4 k k_1}{c_2} - \left(\frac{c_1}{2c_2}\right)^2} . \qquad (11.28)$$

In such a system the damping of the transient usually occurs more poorly than in a static one (Fig. 14), which is evident from comparison of the magnitudes of time constants T in the first of formulae (11.25) and in (11.28). Naturally, such an indirect-acting astatic system (Fig. 19), from energy considerations (Section 3), cannot replace the better direct-acting astatic system (Fig. 67), as was done with the system of Fig. 14. Improvement of the quality of an indirect-acting system requires the introduction of special auxiliary devices which will be considered separately in Section 12 and Section 15.

We remark that the oscillation of the regulated quantity in the transient as shown in Fig. 69b for the latter system is possible, generally speaking, also in the systems previously considered, if the dynamic properties of the regulated object itself are taken into consideration in greater detail (sect. 24). However in the system shown in Fig. 19 it is usually more clearly expressed than in those considered previously.

In these examples the equations of the astatic regulators (11.15), (11.17), (11.19) differ from the static (11.14) in the absence of a term with the coordinates of the regulated organ. In addition, comparing these equations, it is evident that equation (11.17) of the astatic regulator with isodromic device (Fig. 67) differs from the others (astatic), by the presence of an additional term in the right side with the time derivative of the regulated quantity, which is the cause of improvement of the transient response of the given system. The design realisations of these conclusions, leading to astaticity of the system, may be very varied.

Self-oscillatory systems. An automatic regulation system (and servomechanism) is termed self-oscillatory if under stationary external conditions defined by the values $f^0 = \text{const}$ and $y^0 = \text{const}$, it has a stable oscillatory process, which is the steady-state operating regime of the given system.

An example of such a system may be the temperature regulation system, shown in Fig. 27, where self-oscillations were found in the examples of Section 9 and Section 10. Another form of self-oscillatory system is the vibrator voltage regulator (Section 56).

If self-oscillations are admissible in the system, its parameters are selected so that the amplitude and frequency of oscillation will have practical values for the given system. If oscillations are not permissible, it is necessary either to change the parameters of the system to pass out of the region of oscillation or, when this is not possible, to change the structure of the system or introduce special external periodic forces (Section 13).

Self-oscillations represent a periodic stationary error of the system in addition to the static error, which may occur here as before.

Reduction of the stationary dynamic errors of the system. To reduce the stationary dynamic error in the process of following with constant velocity (for constant load $f^0 = $ const), from (7.23) we require, if the system is static, reduction of the coefficient b_n and increase of a_n but, in addition, it is always necessary to minimise the difference $c_{\nu-1} - k_0 a_{n-1}$ where k_0 is a given scale coefficient relating the output and input quantities of the given servo-system. Here it is assumed that the basic relationship $c_\nu = k_0 a_n$ (7.18) is satisfied exactly. If the system is so designed that in the equation of motion of the system (7.14) we have $b_m = 0$ (astatic system) and, in addition, also $c_{\nu-1} = k_0 a_{n-1}$, then the stationary dynamic error is eliminated in the constant velocity regime.

When the given system is oscillatory there remains a periodic stationary error as a result of superposition of oscillation on the steady-state constant-velocity motion.

If more stringent requirements are placed on the automatic system— to ensure the minimum stationary dynamic error in the process of following with constant acceleration then, from (7.27), to the previous conditions is added a new one: it is necessary in the equation of motion of the system (7.14) to make the difference $c_{\nu-2} - k_0 a_{n-2}$ as small as possible. For complete elimination of the stationary error we require, consequently, $b_m = 0$, $c_{\nu-1} = k_0 a_{n-1}$, $c_{\nu-2} = k_0 a_{n-2}$ (in addition to the fundamental relationship $c_\nu = k_0 a_n$).

The technical realisation of all these recommendations will be clear from the following, when in assembling the equations these coefficients will be expressed through the system parameters.

We note, finally, the requirements on an automatic system permitting reduction of the stationary dynamic error with sinusoidal input to the system.

Let it be required that an automatic regulator maintain constant the value of the regulated quantity (for example, a ship's course) with oscillatory perturbations $f(t)$ on the object (for example, due to a regular wave). Then by constructing the amplitude-phase characteristic $W_f(i\omega)$ for the given closed regulation system (ship-regulator) it is possible to find what amplitude Aa will be attained by the ship's course for the given wave amplitude a and frequency ω. The circuit and parameters of the system are chosen so that the amplitude-phase characteristic of the system (Fig. 50 or 51a) in a defined frequency band ω of possible wave frequencies would give an amplitude Aa not exceeding a permissible magnitude.

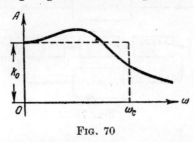

FIG. 70

If there is an automatic servomechanism which should reproduce a given sinusoidal oscillation $y(t) = a\sin\omega t$, then, by constructing the amplitude-phase characteristic $W_y(i\omega)$ it is possible to determine the stationary dynamic error of reproduction of this input in amplitude and in phase at a given frequency ω. In this case it is required that in a given band of possible frequencies of the external input force, ω, the amplitude-phase characteristic (Fig. 50) would have the magnitude A, as close as possible to unity or to an arbitrary desired value k_0, while the quantity β as close as possible to zero or to some required phase value.

These requirements are sometimes conveniently analysed from other frequency characteristics (Fig. 51). For example, closeness of the amplitude A to the required scale coefficient k_0 in the interval of frequencies $0 \leqslant \omega \leqslant \omega_c$ is easily studied by construction of the amplitude frequency characteristic (Fig. 70). The band of frequencies $0 \leqslant \omega \leqslant \omega_c$ in which the value A is not permitted below some given value is termed the passband of the given system; ω_c is the cut-off frequency.

It is also possible to estimate the stationary dynamic errors of the system for arbitrary periodic perturbations and input forces from the amplitude-phase characteristics in accordance with the discussion at the end of Section 8. Finally, it is usually important to investigate the system for dynamic errors of a random character, which will not be considered here.

12. Auxiliary feedback in linear systems

Feedback is one of the most powerful means of decreasing dynamic errors of all types and to a lesser extent this also applies to static errors.

Feedback is the term for a branch of the system which connects some subsequent circuit with a preceding one, forming a closed circuit (Fig. 71a or Fig. 71b).

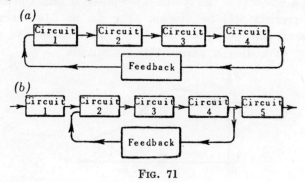

FIG. 71

Automatic regulation systems and mechanisms, as we already know, always have a closed loop (Figs. 10, 21, 23). From this point of view they already always contain feedback. But, in addition, in automatic regulations systems and servomechanisms auxiliary feedback is employed which establishes in the system additional closed loops (Fig. 72). Frequently they are simply termed feedback, eliminating the word "auxiliary", as self-understood, since one closed circuit is always present in the system.

Positive and negative feedback. In general, feedback may be positive or negative. Feedback is termed positive when the variables x_{fb} and x (Fig. 72) enter with the same sign into the equation of that loop of the system at the input of which it is applied. If the signs of the variables x_{fb} and x are opposed, the feedback is termed negative (this occurs also in Fig. 3, where $x_1 = y - x_2$). Negative feedbacks of various forms have obtained wide application in automatic regulation systems and servomechanisms.

Positive feedback is usually applied to increase the gain factor of one or another circuit of the basic network. Negative feedback usually has as its purpose "stabilisation" of the system, i.e. transforming an unstable system into a stable one or increasing the rate of attenuation of the transient process in a stable system. We shall explain this by simple examples.

Let circuit 1 (Fig. 73), taken individually, be described by the equation

$$T_1\dot{x}_2 + x_2 = k_1 x_1 , \qquad (12.1)$$

where k_1 is the gain factor of the circuit. We shall apply feedback 2 to it with the equation

$$x_{fb} = k_{fb}x_2 .$$ (12.2)

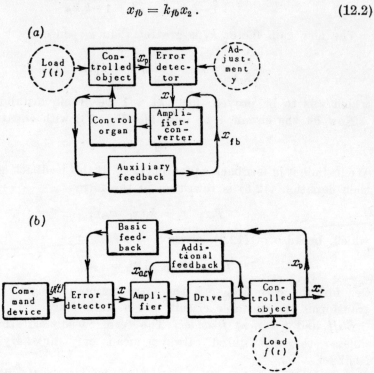

FIG. 72

Then in the case of positive feedback equation (12.1) should be rewritten in accordance with the circuit (Fig. 73) in the form

$$T_1\dot{x}_2 + x_2 = k_1(x_1 + x_{fb}) ,$$ (12.3)

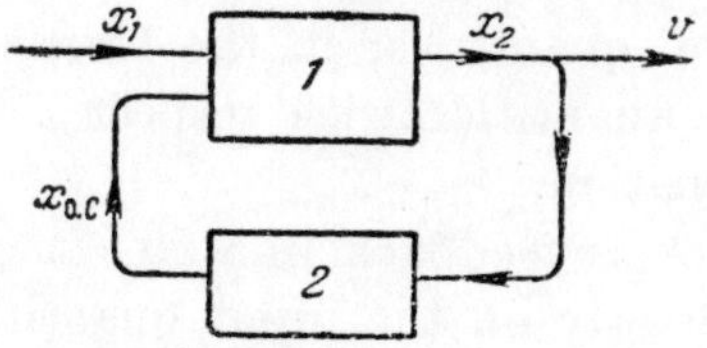

FIG. 73

From which, with regard to (12.2), we obtain:

$$T_1\dot{x}_2 + (1 - k_1k_{fb})x_2 = k_1x_1$$

or

$$T_2\dot{x}_2 + x_2 = k_2x_1 ,$$ (12.4)

where

$$T_2 = \frac{T_1}{1-k_1 k_{fb}}, \qquad k_2 = \frac{k_1}{1-k_1 k_{fb}}. \qquad (12.5)$$

The new gain factor k_2 is greater than k_1, since

$$\frac{k_1}{1-k_1 k_{fb}} > k_1 \quad (\text{with } 0 < k_1 k_{fb} < 1),$$

which was to be proved (for $k_1 k_{fb} > 1$ we obtain instability).

Now let the circuit 1 be unstable (Fig. 73) with equation

$$T_1 \dot{x}_2 - x_2 = k_1 x_1. \qquad (12.6)$$

We include it in feedback equation (12.2). If this feedback is negative, then equation (12.6) is rewritten in the form

$$T_1 \dot{x}_2 - x_2 = k_1 (x_1 - x_{fb}), \qquad (12.7)$$

which, because of (12.2), gives:

$$T_1 \dot{x}_2 + (k_1 k_{fb} - 1) x_2 = k_1 x_1, \qquad (12.8)$$

i.e. for the case $k_1 k_{fb} > 1$ the introduction of negative feedback transforms the unstable circuit into a stable one.

Stiff and transient feedback. The term "feedback" shall below, unless otherwise stated, always mean only auxiliary negative feedback.

Stiff feedback is feedback which is characterised in the steady-state by the following equation (direct dependence):

$$x_{fb}^0 = x_{fb} x_i^0 \qquad (12.9)$$

or more generally

$$x_{fb}^0 = f(x_i^0), \qquad (12.10)$$

where x_i and x_{fb} denote the input and output quantities of the circuit, playing the role of feedback. The index "0" above, as always, denotes steady-state quantities; in the transient process a further derivative of these quantities with respect to time may be added to the feedback equation.

Transient feedback is feedback in which the output quantity x_{fb} does not depend directly on the input quantity x_i but is expressed through its derivative with respect to time (velocity). Therefore transient feedback may involve the same value of the output quantity x_{fb}^0 for various steady-state values of the input quantity x_i^0, transient feedback is often termed velocity feedback.

Examples of automatic regulation systems with stiff feedback are: the velocity regulation system (Fig. 74) and voltage regulation system (Fig. 75). The structural diagram of these systems is shown in Fig. 72*a* (compare the circuits of Figs. 74 and 75 with the circuits of Figs. 18 and 19).

In the first example (Fig. 74) stiff feedback is realised by the rigid mechanical transmission 6 from the output of the hydraulic

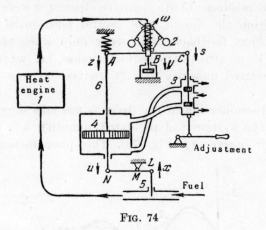

Fig. 74

drive to the input of the control element i.e., the slide valve 3, through the arm *ABC*. Here the feedback causes displacement of the gate valve, opposite to its displacement by the sensitive element 2.

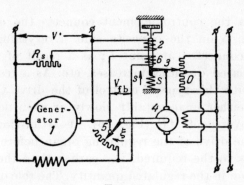

Fig. 75

In the second example (Fig. 75) the role of stiff feedback is carried out by the auxiliary winding 6 of the electromagnet, excited by the voltage V_{fb}, obtained from the regulating rheostat 5. In this case a change of the total tractive force of the electromagnet takes place due to the change in current in the feedback circuit while the latter depends "directly" on the magnitude of displacement ξ of the slider of rheostat 5. Winding 6 is connected to oppose the winding of the sensitive element 2.

In both examples the effect of stiff feedback may be roughly considered as an anticipatory disconnection of the drive of the

9

regulating organ with succeeding reduction of the approach velocity of the system to steady-state.

In essence, in the absence of feedback the control element 3 (Figs. 18 and 19) disconnects the drive only when the sensitive element 2 places it in the neutral position. If the sensitive element 2 were ideal, then, as is evident from the circuit, the neutral position of the control element 3 (without feedback) will occur only when the regulated quantity (ω or V) returns to the required value, i.e. when the deviation of the regulated quantity—ω, ΔV reduces to zero (point A in Fig. 76).

But such a disconnection of the drive is too late since because of the inertia of the system the regulated quantity will continue to decrease further (curve AB Fig. 76). This phenomenon is termed

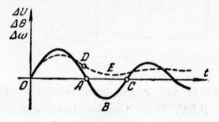

FIG. 76

overshoot. Then the control element connects the drive 4 of the regulating organ 5 on the opposite side. Everything is repeated: the drive is disconnected at point C; as a result of the system of inertia the regulated quantity increases, etc. As a result in a regulation system with this type of control of the drive the oscillations are attenuated either unacceptably slowly or even not at all.

To prevent overshoot AB (Fig. 76), it is obviously necessary to disconnect the drive of the regulating organ before the regulated quantity returns to the required, i.e. earlier than the point A and "brake" reduction in the regulated quantity. The role of such a "cut-off" and "brake" is played by negative feedback. In particular, when an increase $\Delta\omega$ of the regulated quantity ω appears in the circuit of Fig. 74, the weights of the sensitive element 2 shift the position of the gate valve 3 from the neutral position upwards. Meanwhile the piston of the drive 4 moves upwards and shifts the regulating organ 5 downwards, reducing the supply of energy to the regulated object or engine. Simultaneously with this the feedback 6 shifts the point A of the arm AB upwards, covering the gate valve 3. As a result the drive disconnection occurs not at point A as before, but at some point D (Fig. 76), after which the drive switches to motion in the reverse direction, playing the role of a brake. As a result of this the curve of variation of the regulated quantity takes the form DE. Consequently, in this case the introduction of stiff feedback as a drive cut-off gives a more rapid attenuation of the transient and eliminates undesired oscillations of the regulated quantity. The same occurs in the other example (Fig. 75).

However stiff feedback, together with this basic property of forming a stable system and reducing the dynamic errors, has one defect, namely that it introduces a static error into the system.

Thus, in the present example the velocity regulation in the absence of feedback (Fig. 18) gave an astatic system (Section 11). We shall show that with introduction of the stiff feedback (Fig. 74) a static system is obtained. In fact, the steady-state of the system is possible only at a neutral position of the gate valve since otherwise the regulation organ 5 will move. This corresponds to a definite position of the point C on the arm ABC. But for various steady-states involving constant values of the load torque on the shaft we should have differing positions of the regulating organ 5 meaning, in view of the rigid coupling, various positions of the point A of the arm ABC. This requires that the point B should be located correspondingly in differing positions for constant position C. Consequently various positions of the weights 2 are obtained, and thus various steady-state values of the regulated quantity ω, the angular velocity of the engine.

Thus in the present case the introduction of direct feedback transforms the astatic characteristic of the system (Fig. 68) to static (Fig. 65).

The second example (Fig. 75) behaves analogously. If in the first linear approximation it is assumed that variation of tractive force of electromagnet as a result of feedback 6 will be proportional to the displacement of the rheostat 5, i.e.

$$\Delta F_{fb} \approx -k_{fb}\xi , \qquad (12.11)$$

then in place of the equations of the transient process of the system (11.19) and (11.20) here in the presence of direct feedback in accordance with Fig. 75 and (12.11) we obtain, neglecting the mass m:

$$\left. \begin{array}{l} c_2\ddot{\xi} + c_1\dot{\xi} = c_4(k\Delta V - k_{fb}\xi) , \\ \Delta V = -k_1\xi - k_2 f , \end{array} \right\} \qquad (12.12)$$

or, eliminating ξ.

$$c_2\ddot{\Delta V} + c_1\dot{\Delta V} + c_4(k_{fb} + kk_1)\Delta V = -c_2 k_2 \ddot{f} - c_1 k_2 \dot{f} - c_4 k_{fb} k_2 f . \qquad (12.13)$$

From (12.12) it is evident that the term $k_{fb}\xi$, introduced by the feedback, if it is shifted to the left, is just such a term which previously distinguished a static regulator (11.14) from an astatic one

(11.15), (11.17) and (11.19). The static error of the system here will be:

$$\Delta V_{st} = -\frac{k_{fb}k_2}{k_{fb}+kk_1};$$

in the absence of feedback ($k_{fb} = 0$) it will be zero.

The attempt to employ the valuable dynamic properties of a system with feedback without introducing static error leads to the application of transient feedback. Examples of systems of automatic regula-

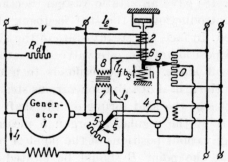

FIG. 77

tion with transient feedback may be voltage regulation systems (Fig. 77) and velocity regulation systems (Fig. 78). The block diagrams remain as before (Fig. 72a).

In the first example (Fig. 77) a direct dependence (12.11) is absent from the feedback, which is attained by introduction of a trans-

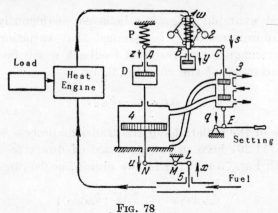

FIG. 78

former 7–8 into its circuit. In this case in the feedback secondary circuit 8, containing the winding 6, there will be induced currents only in the dynamic state, when a change of current in the primary circuit 7 occurs. Then in the first approximation it is possible to write:

$$\Delta I_{fb} = -k_3\frac{dI_3}{dt} = -k_4\dot{\xi},$$

or, passing to the change of tractive force of the electromagnet,

$$\Delta F_{fb} \approx -k_{fb}\dot{\xi},\tag{12.14}$$

which replaces the previous relationship (12.11).

In place of (12.12) we obtain:

$$c_2\ddot{\xi}+c_1\dot{\xi}=c_4(k\Delta V-k_{fb}\dot{\xi}),\quad \Delta V=-k_1\xi-k_2f,\tag{12.15}$$

or

$$c_2\Delta\ddot{V}+(c_1+c_4k_{fb})\Delta\dot{V}+c_4kk_1\Delta V=$$
$$-c_2k_2\ddot{f}-(c_1+c_4k_{fb})k_2\dot{f}.\tag{12.16}$$

In the present case the system remains astatic as it was without feedback ((11.19) and (11.24)), but only because the feedback increases the coefficient c_1 for the first derivative by the magnitude c_4k_{fb}. This, as is evident from (11.18), reduces the time constant T to the value

$$T=\frac{2c_2}{c_1+c_4k_{fb}},\tag{12.17}$$

and reduction of T signifies more rapid attenuation of the transient (Figs. 79 and 69b).

In the second example (Fig. 78) a transient isodromic feedback is shown, consisting of the damper D and the spring S. The equation

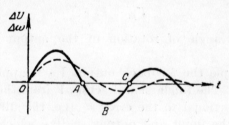

Fig. 79

of motion of the damper piston (and the point A at the output of the feedback) will be:

$$m\ddot{z}=\Delta F_s-F_d,$$

where

$$\Delta F_s=c_1z,\quad F_d=c_2(\dot{z}-\dot{u}),$$

and z and u are the displacements of the piston and cylinder, $(\dot{z}-\dot{u})$ their relative velocity. From this, neglecting the mass m, we obtain:

$$c_2\dot{z}+c_1z=c_2\dot{u}.\tag{12.18}$$

Dividing this by c_1 and noting that the displacement u of the feedback cylinder D is proportional to the displacement x of the regulating organ 5, (12.18) may be written in the form

$$T_{fb}\dot{z}+z=k_{fb}\dot{x}.\tag{12.19}$$

This formula, just as (12.14), states that the output quantity is not directly dependent on the input quantity of the feedback circuit, but on its rate of change. This also provides more rapid attenuation of the transient than without feedback (Fig. 79), preserving the absence of static error in the system. The feedback described by an equation of type (12.19), in distinction to (12.14), and termed transient isodromic feedback, provides better and more rapid attenuation of the transient process.

Finally, consider the circuit of a servo mechanism with auxiliary transient feedback (Fig. 80). In this the feedback is supplied by the

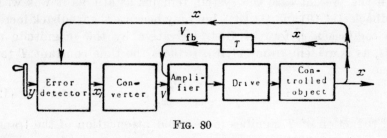

FIG. 80

tachometer Tm, which produces a voltage proportional to the angular velocity of the output shaft of the system, i.e.

$$V_{fb} = k_{fb}\dot{x}, \qquad (12.20)$$

where x is the angle of rotation of the output shaft (regulated quantity).

In this example the feedback output V_{fb} is applied to the input of the amplifier. The fundamental action V from the control element (Fig. 80), proportional to the error x_1 (i.e. the difference in angles of rotation of the input and output shafts), which is processed by the error detector, designed, for example, in the form of a mechanical differential, is also applied to this point. The effect of the feedback V_{fb} is subtracted from the effect of the control element V.

We remark that the introduction of various forms of feedback does not have the same effect in all systems. Therefore in each concrete case it is necessary to analyse it with the aid of stability and quality criteria taking into account the calculated static and dynamic errors.

13. Auxiliary feedback in non-linear systems

Practical methods of linearisation.

In non-linear systems feedback carries out the same functions as in linear (Section 12), but here there appear new properties: (1) suppression of oscillations and (2) linearisation of the system which, to avoid repetition, we shall just touch on in the present paragraph. Here we shall also discuss practical methods of linearisation for non-linear vibrating systems.

Suppression of oscillation. As an example let us take a temperature regulation system (Fig. 27) and introduce auxiliary stiff feedback into it in the form of a mechanical transmission from the drive shaft of the regulating organ to the contact panel 7 (Fig. 81). As

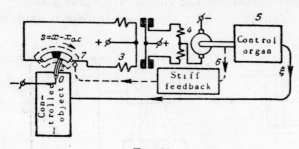

FIG. 81

a result we obtain an angle of rotation x_{fb} of the panel proportional to the displacement of the regulating organ ($x_{fb} = k_{fb}\xi$). We shall construct this transmission so that the rotation of the panel 7 under the action of feedback would occur on the same side as the deviation of the sensitive element of the regulator—the bimetallic plate 2. Then the relative displacement s of the bimetallic plate 2 and the contact plate 7 will be equal to the difference of effects of the sensitive element and the feedback, i.e. we obtain negative feedback.

In the example in Section 10 we have seen that without feedback in this system with a relay characteristic of the form of Fig. 53a the only possible steady-state process in the system was oscillatory and a constant value of the regulated quantity could not be established. Feedback 6, acting in the presence of these oscillations approximately as described in Section 12 (Fig. 76), will either substantially reduce the amplitude of oscillations or completely eliminate oscillation and make the system stable with regard to the steady-state process with constant value of the regulated quantity. In the latter case a neutral position of the relay on an insensitive zone is necessary.

As will be explained later (Part IV), the presence of a sufficiently wide insensitive zone of the relay may eliminate oscillation by itself without the introduction of feedback. But then there will also appear a static regulation error due to the insensitive zone. This measure is less effective. To suppress oscillation it is also possible to introduce the derivative into the regulation formula (Section 15).

Linearisation with the use of feedback. We shall now explain how feedback in a non-linear system may linearise it.

Consider, for example, a system for regulating the course of a marine torpedo (Fig. 26). Here, with continuous deviation of the torpedo from the course ψ, the gyroscope 2 shifts the gate valve (angle of rotation φ), opening the compressed-air feed in the cylinder 3 of the rudder drive. As a result of this the piston and the rudder together with it shifts from one extreme position to the other. Therefore the characteristic of the rudder drive has a clearly non-linear form (Fig. 82a). The loop in the characteristic is explained by the

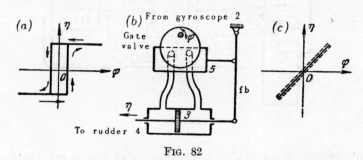

FIG. 82

fact that before opening the air inlet in one of the channels passing to the cylinder, the gate valve, as is evident from Fig. 26, turns by some angle, termed the angle of overlap.

Now let us introduce stiff feedback as shown in Fig. 82b; in particular, we shall place the inlets of the air channels leading to the cylinder on a movable block 5, joining the latter by a linkage mechanism with the piston of the rudder drive 3. Then with reversal of the gate valve (by the gyroscope), for example clockwise, the air inlet in the right chamber of cylinder 3 is opened and the piston moves to the left. Simultaneously with this the feedback arm (fb) will move the block 5 to the left, keeping it always under the gate valve and by this blocking further air admission to the cylinder. As a result, to each steady-state position of the gate valve φ there will correspond a definite position of the coupling rod of the rudder drive η, where the quantity η will be proportional to the angle φ in view of the stiffness of the feedback.

Thus, the characteristic of the rudder drive has, with feedback, become linear (Fig. 82c). However as a result of the presence of the angle of overlap of the gate valve, the piston with the feedback may for some given φ not settle in an exactly defined position η but in some zone about it. The characteristic of the rudder drive will therefore be somewhat diffuse, which is shown by the broken line in Fig. 82c.

In the present case the rudder drive becomes a closed loop servomechanism included in turn as a circuit of the closed loop torpedo-course regulation system. This servomechanism is non-linear from the point of view of its internal processes but has an approximately linear character as a whole. Therefore in studying the entire present regulation system it is possible to consider the rudder drive with feedback as a single linear circuit without regard to its internal processes.

The particular role of feedback in non-linear systems consists in the following two important additional properties.

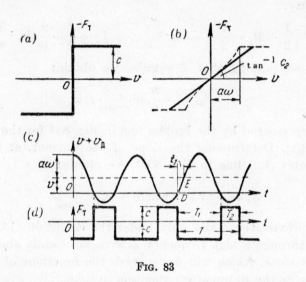

Fig. 83

Linearisation employing vibration. Here we shall discuss a further practical method of linearising non-linear circuits of automatic systems—the generation of supplementary vibration at relatively high frequencies using an external periodic force.

As the first example consider non-linearity in the form of dry friction when the friction force F_f is approximately constant in magnitude and changes its sign with change of sign of the velocity v of the relative motion of the rubbing parts (Fig. 83a). It is well known that if the foundation of a mechanism in which dry friction occurs is caused to vibrate by an external force at sufficiently high frequency (several times the natural frequency of the mechanism), the mechanism will operate as if the non-linear dry friction has been replaced by approximately linear friction, proportional to the velocity. This is explained by the fact that with application of the vibration $X = a \sin \omega t$, a vibration velocity $V_a = a\omega \cos \omega t$, is superimposed on the velocity V of relative motion of the rubbing part (Fig. 83c); and if

$$a\omega > v,$$ (13.1)

the dry friction force will change sign (Fig. 83*d*); the mean friction force in a single period will be:

$$F_{av} = \frac{-cT_1 + cT_2}{T}.$$

From the segment of the curve *DE* we have $v = a\omega \sin \omega t_1$ or

$$t_1 = \frac{1}{\omega} \sin^{-1} \frac{v}{a\omega}.$$

Consequently,

$$T_1 = \frac{T}{2} + 2t_1 = \frac{T}{2} + \frac{2}{\omega} \sin^{-1} \frac{v}{a\omega}, \qquad T_2 = \frac{T}{2} - \frac{2}{\omega} \sin^{-1} \frac{v}{a\omega}.$$

Therefore, considering that $T = 2\pi/\omega$, we obtain:

$$F_{av} = -\frac{2c}{\pi} \sin^{-1} \frac{v}{a\omega},$$

which is represented by the broken line in Fig. 83*b* for the condition $v < a\omega$ (13.1). Determining the slope of the tangent, at the origin of coordinates (full line in Fig. 83*b*), we obtain:

$$F_1 \approx -c_2 v, \qquad \text{where} \qquad c_2 = \frac{2c}{\pi a\omega}. \tag{13.2}$$

This is approximately valid only under the condition (13.1), which is realised through a high frequency ω with sufficiently small oscillation amplitude *a*, which will not disturb the functions of the given mechanism in the automatic regulation system.

A second example is an electromagnetic relay operating as a vibrator. Let its characteristic without vibration have the form of Fig. 84*a*, where *I* is the current in the control circuit, *V* is the voltage in the control circuit, I_0 is the current at which the relay switches. On the constant input current *I* we superimpose from outside an additional oscillation of such amplitude and frequency that the relay armature vibrates continuously, closing and opening the control circuit (output voltage *V*).

Then, if the input current *I* (constant component) is equal to zero (Fig. 84*b*), the relay will vibrate about a mean position and therefore the mean value of the output voltage *V* will be zero. If the input current *I* has some non-zero constant value, for example positive, the vibration then will occur about this positive value (Fig. 84*c*) and therefore the relay will be connected to the positive side for a greater portion T_2 of the oscillation period *T* and for a smaller portion T_1 of the period *T* to the negative side.

As a result we obtain at the output

$$V_{av} = \frac{T_2 - T_1}{T} c, \tag{13.3}$$

where

$$T_2 = \frac{T}{2} + \frac{2}{\omega}\sin^{-1}\frac{I}{A}, \qquad T_1 = \frac{T}{2} - \frac{2}{\omega}\sin^{-1}\frac{I}{A}.$$

From this, considering that $T = 2\pi/\omega$, we find:

$$V_{av} = \frac{2c}{\pi}\sin^{-1}\frac{I}{A}. \tag{13.4}$$

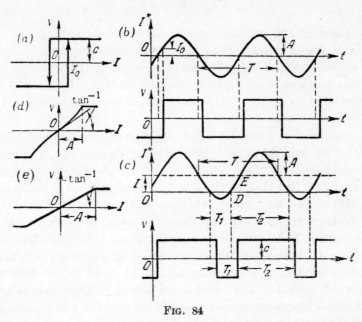

Fɪɢ. 84

Thus, to each value of the constant component of the input current I will correspond a definite mean value of the output voltage V, which is represented by a continuous characteristic (Fig. 84d) replacing the previous relay characteristic (Fig. 84a). This effect is maintained when I varies at a substantially slower rate than the superimposed sinusoidal current. In order for the whole automatic system of which the given relay is a part to operate on the mean value of the voltage and not to reproduce the external vibration, it is necessary that the frequency of the latter should be several times the natural frequency of the system. All this is valid, as is evident from Fig. 84c, with

$$I < A. \tag{13.5}$$

The characteristic obtained (Fig. 84d) may be considered linear in its initial portion with

$$V \approx kI, \qquad k = \frac{2c}{\pi A}. \tag{13.6}$$

If the sinusoidal curve of current variation in Fig. 84c be replaced by a triangular or a sawtooth curve the segment DE will be rectilinear with some definite slope angle. Therefore we obtain

$$T_1 = \frac{T}{2} + 2I \cot \alpha , \qquad T_2 = \frac{T}{2} - 2I \cot \alpha ,$$

where $\cot \alpha$ is measured in seconds per ampere or milliampere. Consequently, expression (13.3) takes the form

$$V_{av} = kI , \qquad k = \frac{4 \cot \alpha}{T} ,$$

i.e. in place of the curvilinear characteristic (Fig. 84*d*) we obtain an exactly linear characteristic (Fig. 84*e*), which replaces the original relay characteristic (Fig. 81*a*) under condition (13.5).

Similar methods are frequently employed where for ease of design it is desirable to apply a relay and at the same time retain system linearity.

We remark that a similar effect is obtained in a chopper-bar pulse regulation system of type *b* (Fig. 31). If the pointer 4 slides over the contact plate 9, there would be a relay characteristic of form 2 or 6 (Fig. 24). But due to the oscillation of the bar 7 the pointer 4 (Fig. 31*b*) closes the circuit at time intervals proportional to the input pointer displacement *s*. Then the average voltage oscillation over a period (4.1) will be proportional to the input quantity *s*.

Finally, we note that the introduction of auxiliary vibration in the mechanism causes the elimination of dead zones due to the presence of backlash and insensitive zones, always assuming that the vibration frequency is sufficiently high and the amplitude exceeds half of the backlash or insensitive zone.

All the above, aside from the direct technical advantages connected with a simple means of realising continuous regulation, is very important in permitting an approximate theoretical analysis of essentially non-linear, and linear pulse, systems by the methods of ordinary linear theory, which are substantially simpler and better developed than the theory of non-linear systems.

In Chap. XVII, there will be a more detailed discussion of the conditions for vibrational linearisation of non-linearities.

14. Regulation function

Introduction of the integral into the regulation function.

The differential equation of an automatic regulation system (Fig. 85) may be divided into two parts: (1) the equation of the regulated object, for example in a linear system:

$$Q_1(p)x = -R_1(p)\xi - S_1(p)f(t) , \tag{14.1}$$

and (2) the equation of the regulator

$$Q_2(p)\xi = R_2(p)x , \tag{14.2}$$

where x is the deviation of the regulated quantity (error), ξ is the regulating force, $f(t)$ is the perturbation (load) on the object, $Q_1(p)$, $R_1(p)$, $S_1(p)$, $Q_2(p)$, $R_2(p)$ are the corresponding operational polynomials.

For example, we had the equations of the regulated object (11.20) and the regulator (11.14) and, eliminating the variable ξ, we obtained a single equation for the system (11.21), i.e. that which was written in the general form (5.2) or (5.7).

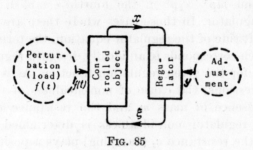

FIG. 85

If the operational polynomial $Q_2(p)$ in the hand side of the regulator equation has a constant term i.e. the equation contains the quantity ξ and not only its derivatives, it may be stated that the right-hand side of the regulator equation $R_2(p)x$ indicates on what the regulating force ξ on the object depends—if on the deviation alone of the regulated quantity x, when in place of $R_2(p)$ there is a constant coefficient, or if also on the derivatives of this deviation, describing the velocity and acceleration of the deviation of the regulated quantity, etc.

Therefore if the operational term $Q_2(p)$ in the left-hand side of the equation contains a constant term, the right-hand side $R_2(p)X$ of the regulator equation is termed the regulation function. If $Q_2(p)$ does not have a constant term, the regulation function must be considered, obviously to be $R_2(p)x/p$. If $Q_2(p)$ does not contain p in the first power, the regulation function will be $R_2(p)/p^2$.

Thus, for example, in Section 11, where the role of x was played by the deviation of the regulated voltage ΔV, the equations of four different regulators: (11.14), (11.15), (11.17), (11.19) where given and the operational polynomials $Q_2(p)$ and $R_2(p)$ had the following forms respectively:

$$1) \quad Q_2(p) = mp^2 + c_2 p + c_1\,, \qquad R_2(p) = k;$$
$$2) \quad Q_2(p) = mp^2 + c_2 p\,, \qquad R_2(p) = k;$$
$$3) \quad Q_2(p) = c_3 mp^3 + (c_1 m + c_2 c_3)p^2 + c_1(c_2 + c_3)p\,,$$
$$R_2(p) = c_3 kp + c_1 k;$$
$$4) \quad Q_2(p) = mp^3 + c_2 p^2 + c_1 p\,, \qquad R_2(p) = c_4 k\,.$$

Consequently, in the first case the regulation function with respect to the deviation of the regulated quantity was $K\Delta V$, in the second case $k\Delta V/p$ in the third case $C_3 K\Delta V + Ck\Delta V/p$ with respect to deviation and integral and in the fourth case $C_4 K\Delta V/p$.

This is the role of the right-hand side of the regulator equation $R_2(p)x$ and the last term of the expression $Q_2(p)$. The remaining terms of the left-hand side of the regulator equation $Q_2(p)$, i.e. $mp^2 + c_2 p$ in the first case, mp^2 in the second, $c_3 mp^3 + (c_1 m + c_2 c_3)p^2$ in the third and $mp^3 + c_2 p^2$ in the fourth establish the dynamic errors of the regulator. In those cases where there are no additional terms in the left side of the regulator equation, the term ideal regulator is used, which corresponds to an ideally designed regulator without dynamic errors for the given regulation function. As is evident from the above expressions, the cause of non-idealness of the first regulator is the presence of mass m and the resistance coefficient c_2. In the second regulator non-idealness is determined only by the mass m, while the resistance c_2 (damping) plays a positive role since here it enters into the last term of the expression $Q_2(p)$.

From the above examples of the four regulator equations it is evident that the first of them has a regulation function which only takes into account the deviation of the regulated quantity, while in the remaining three the regulation function contains the integral of the deviation of the regulated quantity. From Section 11 it follows that the first of these regulators is static, the remaining three astatic.

From this it is possible to draw the conclusion that the introduction of the integral into the regulation function gives an astatic system, i.e. eliminates static errors from automatic regulation systems. Here it is necessary only to remark that the question of astaticity of the system is not decided finally by the equation of the regulator alone but by the equation of the entire system (the absence of a constant term in the operational polynomial for perturbation f in the right-hand side of the equation of the overall system), which for the examples considered was expressed in the forms (11.22)–(11.24). Therefore the above formulated rule may have exceptions if the equation of the regulated object has singularities.

Aside from the four methods of introducing the integral into the regulation function, presented in the paragraphs on astatic systems in Section 11, and the fifth method in Section 12, there exists a further method of direct inclusion of an integrating device in parallel with the action of the sensitive element of the regulator, as shown in Fig. 86. Here the sensitive element applies to the regulator circuit the quantity kx proportional to the measured deviation of the regulated quantity x; simultaneously with this quantity kx passes through the integrating device and is applied further in the form $k_1 \int x\, dt$. As a result the quantity applied to the succeeding circuit of the regulator is

$$kx + k_1 \int x\, dt \quad \text{or} \quad \frac{(kp + k_1)x}{p},$$

which introduces the integral into the regulation function. The principles of operation of integrating devices are quite varied (mechanical, hydraulic, electric motor, electrical circuits, electronic, electromechanical, etc.) and are considered in the specialised literature.

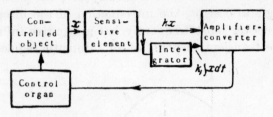

FIG. 86

For example, let the equation of the regulator of a static voltage regulation system have the form (11.14), namely

$$m\ddot{\xi} + c_2\dot{\xi} + c_1\xi = k\,\Delta V.$$

Let us introduce an integrating device into this system. Then in place of the above equation we obtain

$$m\ddot{\xi} + c_2\dot{\xi} + c_1\xi = k\,\Delta V + k_1 \int \Delta V\, dt,$$

or, after differentiation with respect to t:

$$m\dddot{\xi} + c_2\ddot{\xi} + c_1\dot{\xi} = k\,\Delta\dot{V} + k_1\Delta V; \qquad (14.3)$$

this has the same form as the regulator equation (11.17) of an astatic system, the term in the variable ξ being absent.

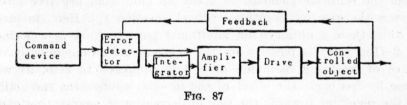

FIG. 87

The structural diagram of a servomechanism with error integral is shown in Fig. 87. The integral is introduced into servomechanisms for the purpose of eliminating stationary errors in the process of following with constant velocity or with constant acceleration. In the latter case a double introduction of integrals is required *.

* A concrete example is given in Section 38.

For a double introduction of integrals

$$kx + k_1 \int x\,dt + k_2 \int \left(\int x\,dt \right) dt \quad \text{or} \quad \frac{(kp^2 + k_1 p + k_2)x}{p^2}$$

the system is termed double-astatic, as this usually leads to absence in the overall system equation (5.2) not only of the constant term $b_m f$ but also of the term in the first derivative of the load $b_{m-1} \dot{f}$, as a result of which static error will be absent from the system not only with constant but with uniformly varying loads.

We shall now show that simultaneously with the positive property of eliminating static error, the introduction of the integral into the regulation function most frequently has a negative influence on the quality of the transient response of an automatic regulation system.

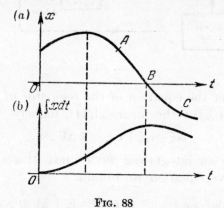

Fig. 88

For example, let the deviation of the regulated quantity x vary as shown in Fig. 88a. Then $\int x\,dt$ will have approximately the form of Fig. 88b. To prevent overshoot BC and consequently accelerate attenuation of the transient process it would already be necessary on the segment AB, simultaneously with the positive force kx from the sensitive element, to apply an additional negative force, as was the case for negative feedback (Section 12). Here, in place of this, there is obtained an additional positive force $k_1 \int x\,dt$ since $\int x\,dt$ (Fig. 88b) is positive on the segment AB. Consequently, in place of retarding reduction of x with approach to zero, as was done by feedback, the effect of the integral strengthens the action of the regulator towards the side of decreasing x, aggravating overshoot.

In addition, even on the segment BC, where a reverse action of the regulator is already required to return the deviation x to zero, the integral $\int x\,dt$ remains positive as before; consequently, it again prevents the regulator from acting towards the side of further reduction of the regulated quantity, since the effect from the deviation kx does not overcome this deleterious effect of the integral.

Thus we see that introduction of the integral into the regulation function strongly influences increase of oscillation of the regulated quantity in the transient regime, worsening by this attenuation of the transient and may even cause free oscillations, i.e. make the system unstable.

That is how matters stand when the deviation of the regulated quantity x and its integral enter into the regulation function. Obviously, the transient response may be worsened still more when the integral enters into the regulation function without the deviation x. But this is precisely what occurs, in accordance with the remarks at the beginning of the present section, in the following four methods of establishing astaticity of the system (Section 11 and Section 12): matching of characteristics, removal of the spring, introduction of an integrating drive, introduction of transient feedback of the type (12.14) in the presence of an integrating drive. Consequently, in all these four methods of eliminating static errors in an automatic regulation system, it is particularly necessary to analyse carefully the quality of the transient responses and, when necessary, to adopt additional methods for its improvement.

In this respect the third method of establishing astaticity of the system is advantageously distinguished from the others—the introduction of an isodromic device (Section 11) and the method of introducing isodromic feedback of the type (12.19). These methods, simultaneously with introduction of the integral, retain in the regulation function the deviation of the regulated quantity, by which is explained the improved quality of the transient response when using these methods.

These conclusions also relate to methods of introducing integrals into servomechanisms.

The considerations in the present section have been simplified. The question of the effects of introducing the integral into the regulation function require in each system a more detailed analysis by the methods described in succeeding parts of this volume.

15. Introduction of derivatives into the regulation function

The introduction of derivatives into the regulation function is an important means for improving the rate of attenuation of transients, where the introduction of derivatives has no direct influence on the static error of the system* (in contrast, for example, to stiff

---

* However, improving the transient response, introduction of derivatives into the regulation function establishes conditions favouring reduction of the static error by other means.

10

feedback, which very effectively improves the transient response but gives rise to static error).

It is possible to introduce derivatives into the regulation function by introducing several sensitive elements (Fig. 89a), the first of which measures the deviation of the regulated quantity, the second the

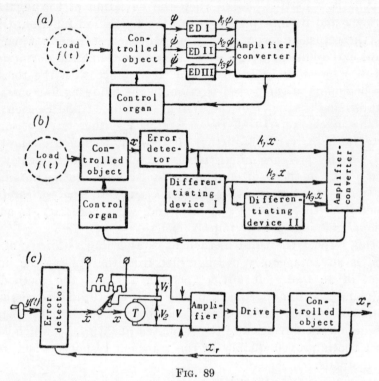

Fig. 89

velocity of deviation, the third the acceleration of deviation. The outputs of all the sensitive elements are added at the input to an amplifier-transducer.

An example of such a system is an automatic pilot in an aircraft which has as the sensitive element *I* (Fig. 89a) a free gyroscope, measuring the angle of the aircraft from its course ψ, as sensitive elements *II* and *III*, a rate gyroscope, measuring the angular velocity $\dot{\psi}$ and the angular acceleration $\ddot{\psi}$ of the deviation of the aircraft from course. Consequently the sum of three forces is applied to the amplifier:

$$k_1\psi + k_2\dot{\psi} + k_3\ddot{\psi} \quad \text{or} \quad (k_1 + k_2 p + k_3 p^2)\psi . \qquad (15.1)$$

However it is not always possible to realise so simply devices measuring directly the derivatives of the regulated quantity. Therefore other methods of introducing derivatives into the regulation function are adopted, shown schematically in Fig. 89b. Here there is a single sensitive element, measuring only the deviation of the regulated quantity. Its derivatives are obtained by the application of differentiating devices *I* and *II*. Differentiating devices may be as varied as integrating ones i.e. mechanical, electrical, electro-mechanical, electronic, thermal, etc.

An example of a servomechanism with first derivative is shown in Fig. 89*c*. Here from the rheostat *R*, the slider of which is rigidly connected with the shaft *x*, is detected the voltage V_1, proportional to the error quantity *x*. The tachometer *T*, connected with the

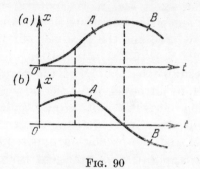

FIG. 90

same shaft, produces a voltage V_2 proportional to the angular velocity, i.e. the first derivative $\dot{x}$ of the error angle. The sum of these two voltages is applied to the amplifier

$$V = V_1 + V_2 = k_1 x + k_2 \dot{x} = (k_1 + k_2 p)x . \qquad (15.2)$$

The significance of introducing derivatives into the regulation function may be roughly explained in the following manner.

Let the deviation of the regulated quantity *x* vary as shown in the graph Fig. 90*a*. The graph *b* shows how the derivative $\dot{x}$ will vary at the same time.

If, as a result of the non-ideal sensitivity and some inertia, the regulator reacts only to the deviation *x* it begins to act effectively only when the deviation *x* attains a certain magnitude. If the regulator reacts not only to the deviation *x* but to the derivative $\dot{x}$ (which may immediately attain some finite value, as soon as a deviation arises), it comes into operation substantially more quickly.

Reacting to the derivative $\dot{x}$, the regulator appears to sense not only the deviation of the regulated quantity which has already appeared, but also the tendency of its further variation. Therefore derivative regulation is sometimes termed lead or anticipation regulation.

The following appears important. The effect on the object by a regulator reacting only to the deviation *x* will be the same at point *A* (Fig. 90*a*), where the deviation is increasing, and at point *B*, where it is decreasing. At the same time it would be useful for the regulator to act more strongly in the first case to prevent undesirable increase of the deviation of the regulated quantity more effectively, while more weakly in the second case to prevent overshoot, i.e. the possible passage of the curve x through zero to the opposite side.

Both these aims are achieved by introduction of the derivative $\dot{x}$, since when the regulator reacts to x and $\dot{x}$, as is evident from Fig. 90b, its action is increased at the point A (since here the effects due to x and $\dot{x}$ have the same signs) and is weakened at the point B (since here the effects of x and $\dot{x}$ have opposite signs). As a result the maximum deviation x is reduced and the approach of x to zero is retarded; as a whole this leads to a faster attenuation of transients and to elimination of undesirable oscillation of the regulated quantity, if this was present before introduction of the derivative. At the same time, by introducing derivatives it is also possible to eliminate divergent oscillations from the system, i.e. an unstable system may be made stable and self-oscillation opposed.

We note that the application of transient isodromic feedback of the type (12.19) in place of simple transient feedback of the type (12.14) and application of an isodromic device in place of a simple damper (Section 11), which give improvement of the rate of attenuation of transients, are directly connected with introduction of the derivative. This is evident from comparison of the corresponding equations of the regulators (11.17) and (11.15). But there, in view of the astaticity of the system (the presence of the integral), this introduction of the derivative was expressed by addition of the deviation of the regulated quantity to the integral of the deviation in the regulation function.

In addition it is possible to introduce into the regulation function the derivative when introducing the integral, i.e.

$$\frac{(k_1 p^2 + k_2 p + k_3)x}{p} \quad \text{or} \quad k_1\dot{x} + k_2 x + k_3 \int x\,dt \ . \qquad (15.3)$$

Then introduction of the integral eliminates the static error while the additional introduction of the derivative accelerates attenuation of transients.

The recommendations presented here are not universal and require careful analysis in each specific system through investigation of the stability and quality of the transient response. There may be individual cases where introduction of the derivative does not give the expected effect.

CHAPTER IV

SOME PROBLEMS IN THE THEORY OF AUTOMATIC REGULATION

16. The theory of automatic regulation

We have already remarked that automatic systems may have varying physical bases and may relate to any branch of engineering.

A given automatic system will frequently contain mechanical, electrical and electronic circuits. Heat engines are fitted with electro-mechanical and electronic regulators; electronic devices are fitted with electromechanical automatic devices; remote-control systems for moving mechanical objects include a complex of mechanical, electronic, electrical devices, etc.

Therefore each circuit of an automatic system must be studied in detail and calculated individually by the appropriate specialist (combustion engineer, mechanical engineer, electrical engineer, electronic engineer, aerodynamicist, etc.). But this is not enough. From the preceding chapters it is obvious that the practical applicability of each automatic regulation system and each servomechanism may be finally settled only by investigation of the static errors, stability, transient response, etc. for the entire system. Otherwise there will be no guarantee that the system produces the right effect, no matter how carefully its individual elements have been calculated and produced.

The most important circumstance here is that the regulated or controlled object itself must enter as a component of the closed regulation system or servomechanism. Therefore the quality of a given regulator or servomechanism cannot be finally decided without simultaneous investigation of the statics and dynamics of the regulator with its object (taking into detailed account the static and, in particular, the dynamic properties of the latter). No conclusion can be made about the goodness or badness of a regulator or control system if the static and dynamic properties of the regulated object are not given.

It would however be unreasonable to find that a system is poor only in the final calculations. Therefore, before calculating in detail each individual circuit of the system, it is necessary to design the overall system and to select the fundamental parameters of each of its circuits, starting from an investigation of the statics and dynamics of the system as whole (including the regulated object).

The static and dynamic errors of a system do not consist simply of the sum of static and dynamic properties of the individual circuits, but are defined by the overall system of their equations and characteristics. Stability or instability of individual circuits of the system does not say anything about the stability and quality of the system as a whole. For example, a closed system consisting only of stable circuits may be unstable as a whole. On the other hand, a closed system containing individual unstable circuits may be as a whole stable (this determines, in particular, the possibility of automatic regulation and control of unstable objects).

It is important, further, that questions of static error, stability, transient response, etc. cannot be considered in isolation. In fact, the contradiction between the static behaviour and the transient response in an automatic regulation system has already been clearly seen in Section 14. In trying to eliminate the static error there, we unavoidably encountered a lengthening of the transient disturbance and even the possibility of system instability; this contradiction will be considered more fully below.

It is therefore not possible to select the parameters of an automatic regulation system only from the static characteristics and steady-state properties of the system, without carrying out at the same time an investigation of stability and transient response, and vice versa.

Only the joint investigation of the statics and dynamics of the system as a whole can decide what structure is best chosen for the system; if additional feedback should be introduced into the system and in particular what kind; if it is expedient to achieve an astatic system or if it would be better to make it static; if it is necessary to introduce derivatives into the regulation function; what influence its non-linearities have on the operating quality of the system; and, finally, which are the best numerical values of the fundamental system parameters to choose (transfer factors, gain factors, time constants, resistances, masses, inductances, etc.).

Since the objects and circuits entering into complete automatic systems relate to different branches of engineering, the study of the general methods of the statics and dynamics of automatic systems cannot be the subject of mechanics or thermodynamics or electrical engineering or radio engineering, etc. separately. At the same time it is well known that many essential questions of statics and, in particular, the dynamics of automatic systems in all branches of engineering are solved by the same mathematical and experimental methods.

A specialised science has therefore arisen—the theory of automatic regulation—studying the principles common to all closed automatic systems for determining the structures, methods of investigating the overall static and dynamic properties, methods of selecting the fundamental parameters of the individual circuits on the basis of the quality requirements placed on the overall system.

One important aspect of the theory of regulation is its characteristic form of analysis and evaluation of the solutions of various algebraic, differential, difference and other equations, sometimes with recourse to statistical methods as well as corresponding experimental investigations on models and their special mathematical processing. In view of the high order of the equations, the difficulty of their construction for a real system and the particular requirements for the systems, frequent recourse is had to special approximate evaluations and indirect theoretical and experimental procedures, which avoid the difficulties of a direct solution, but still provide sometimes even the setting up of the equations, a convenient technical method of calculation in the synthesis of automatic systems.

Aside from direct application to the investigation and design of automatic systems, the methods of the theory of automatic regulation may be used in other fields of science and engineering where the investigation of stability and the determination of the static and dynamic errors are required for an arbitrary system, described by high-order differential equations. On the other hand, the theory of automatic regulation itself is substantially enriched through the adoption of the methods of investigation of the dynamics of these other systems and the methods of the general theory of oscillation.

The theory of automatic regulation has flourished in the last decade because of its connection with the practical requirements of contemporary engineering, and with the complete automation of many processes in all branches of engineering. This is its great practical significance. The theory of automatic regulation, by giving an understanding of the general principles of construction and the general dynamic properties of automatic systems, as well as means of their improvement, now becomes a necessary discipline for all engineers.

The present theory of automatic regulation includes a broad range of questions and is divided into the following specialised fields.

1. The study and development of general principles of designing automatic regulation systems.

2. Static calculation and selection of the structures and parameters of the system, starting from the admissible static error.

3. Investigation of the stability and choice of structures and parameters of the system, starting from the requirements of stability of the system.

4. Investigation of the transient response and the selection of structures and parameters of the system, starting from requirements placed on the transient response in the given system.

5. Investigation of the process of regulation in the presence of an arbitrary perturbation, the influence of which should be damped out of the system. The perturbation may be given as a function of time or by its probability characteristics or it may be known only by limiting values between which the perturbation varies arbitrarily.

6. Investigation of the process of following an arbitrarily varying input signal which should be reproduced by the system to a certain precision. Simultaneously with investigation of the quality of reproduction of a useful signal it may be required to take into account the effects of random noise applied to the system together with the useful signal.

7. The study and development of the general principles of dynamic simulation of automatic regulation systems and servomechanisms, the construction of models and the carrying out of experiments; the experimental measurement of frequency and time characteristics of the system and its individual circuits.

The present book will give only the foundations of the dynamics of automatic-regulation systems mainly with respect to isolated automatic regulation systems and servomechanisms. We shall not consider here the dynamics of coupled systems with several objects and regulators which constitute an important and difficult field of investigation. The simulation of automatic systems, which has at the present time a very great importance, is not considered. Special methods of calculating the errors in automatic systems in the presence of arbitrarily varying perturbing factors and methods of investigating random forces of a statistical nature are not considered. This last question is discussed in a specialised monograph of V. V. Solodovnikov (Reference 12).

As will be evident later, in the theory of automatic regulation there exist many different methods having a common aim; the best choice of structure and parameters of closed automatic systems. For the present it is not possible to give preference to any of these methods over the others in all practical cases. Each of them is good for specific conditions. This is explained, on the one hand, by the great differences in design and technical problems solved by automatic systems, which require differing interpretations of the terms "highest quality of the regulation process", "best parameters of the system", etc. On the other hand, the attempt to develop more and more new methods of investigating the dynamics of automatic systems is explained by the fact that none of them completely satisfy the needs of practice.

17. On the history of the theory of automatic regulation

The founder of the theory of automatic regulation is the celebrated Saint Petersburg professor and engineer Ivan Alekseevich Vyshnegradskii (1831–1895). Before the publication of his first work in this field in 1876 the theory of automatic regulation in fact did not exist, despite the fact that the design of regulators had already developed from the time when the first automatic regulator was invented by I. I. Polzunov in 1765.

The period before 1876 was characterised by intuitive invention and the development of individual, mainly static calculations. In the middle of the nineteenth century, in connection with the increase in speed of steam engines and the appearance of steam turbines, the problem arose of improving the quality of centrifugal governors. Here engineering came into practical contact with the contradiction between the static and dynamic behaviour of an automatic-regulation system, namely: attempts to increase the static precision led to slower attenuation of transient oscillations and even to instability. But this problem cannot be solved by static methods of calculation and intuitive design. Individual dynamic investigations carried out by various authors did not solve this problem.

The first work in which the problem of the dynamics of simple regulators was correctly solved is due to I. A. Vyshnegradskii. The moment of publication of his work "On the general theory of regulators" (Reference 2) in 1876 is the birthday of the theory of automatic regulation. This work contains a brief description of the results obtained by the author. A detailed discussion was given in his work "On direct-acting regulators" (1877) and in the appendix to this work (Reference 2). There is information that a part of these results was already reported by I. A. Vyshnegradskii in 1872.

By correctly solving this important problem in the design of regulators Vyshnegradskii was a founder of contemporary automatic-regulation theory and his work retains its importance up to the present time. He gave engineers specific indications which showed how the different design parameters of a system influence the quality of regulation.

Vyshnegradskii, by his specific study, showed that a high-quality regulator may be developed only on the basis of simultaneous calculation of this regulator with the regulated object. He also demonstrated that it is in no case possible to employ only the static calculations but it is necessary simultaneously to carry out dynamic calculations taking into account the static and dynamic properties of the object and regulator. Conversely, it is not possible to limit the calculation to the transient behaviour without determining at the same time the static error of the given regulation system.

In his investigation he applied linearisation to the equations of motion of a regulation system, now a basic technique in the theory of regulation.

Vyshnegradskii derived the stability condition of a dynamic system described by a third-order linear differential equation. He first introduced representation of the stability region in the plane of the fundamental system parameters.

Vyshnegradskii constructed a diagram where the stability region was divided into three parts, one of which corresponded to an oscillatory transient process and the two others to different types of aperiodic processes. In this he originated the investigation of the quality of the transient response. He showed in particular that the presence of complex roots in the characteristic equation in itself does not signify an oscillatory transient process. Vyshnegradskii's diagram is even now directly used in technical calculations.

A. M. Liapunov and the significance of his work on stability. Since an essential role is played in the theory of automatic regulation by the theory of the stability of equilibrium and motion of a dynamic system, it is necessary here to describe the role of the founder of the rigorous theory of stability of motion—the great Russian mathematician, Academician Aleksandr Mikhailovich Liapunov (1857–1918).

The term "stability" was used earlier, but Liapunov first gave a mathematically exact definition of the concept of stability. In his doctoral dissertation "The general problem of stability of motion", 1892 (reprinted in 1935 and 1950), he proved theorems on the laws of stability studied in the first approximation, i.e. according to linearised equations. These theorems of Liapunov have served as the mathematical foundation for the entire linear theory of automatic regulation from Vyshnegradskii to the present.

In addition, by very refined mathematical methods, in the same work Liapunov also investigated a number of particular cases, obtained in the presence of zero and purely imaginary roots. He gave a number of superb mathematical results. An important role is played at present by Liapunov's method for the investigation of equations with periodic coefficients, in particular in the study of stability of non-linear periodic processes.

Finally the direct method of Liapunov, termed also "the second method", is of particular importance; it contains his celebrated general theorems on stability and instability of motion and equilibrium of arbitrary dynamic systems, which are used most frequently in the investigation of non-linear systems and systems with variable parameters.

The theory of regulation in Russia before 1917. The outstanding work of the Russian mathematician, Academician Pafnutie L'vovich Chebyshev (1821–1894) has an important significance, in particular his work "On the centrifugal governor". For the contemporary theory of automatic regulation the works of P. L. Chebyshev devoted to the problem of the smallest deviation from zero of a polynomial are also very interesting.

A substantial contribution in the initial stages of development of the theory of regulation was the work of the Slovak scientist A. Stodola on the regulation of steam turbines (1893), which continued and developed the ideas of I. A. Vyshnegradskii.

Important investigations were carried out in the works of A. V. Grechaninov in 1896 and 1899, Ia. I. Grdin in 1898, 1899 and 1900 and A. I. Sidorov in 1900.

The work of Nikolai Egorovich Zhukovskii "The theory of regulation of machines", published in 1909 had great significance and was a presentation of lectures on the theory of regulation delivered at a higher technical institute. It is a presentation of the theory of automatic regulation of the time and contains results on the non-linear problem of the effect of dry friction on the process of direct regulation and on the theory of pulse regulation by cutting off steam with application of linear finite-difference equations. Zhukovskii demonstrated that under certain conditions pulse regulations may be considered as continuous while the finite differences equations pass into ordinary differential equations.

Initially the theory of regulation was applied to steam engines and turbines. From the beginning of the twentieth century it began to be applied to the regulation of electric motor speed, electric generator voltage, temperature, pressure, etc. and later, to automatic control instruments of marine torpedoes, artillery and automatic pilots, i.e. to automatic regulation of course, height, banking, etc. of aircraft.

Theory of regulation in the U.S.S.R. after 1917. The theory of automatic regulation began to develop intensively in the years of the pre-war five-year plans in connection with automation of productive processes, large electric power installations, etc.

As a result of the practical work of various organisations in individual branches of engineering it became clear that the principles of design and the methods of investigating various automatic systems intended for the control of processes differing in their physical nature have a common theoretical basis. In addition, it became clear that in the majority of cases it was necessary to electrify the control systems of all processes, including mechanical processes. It was necessary to generalise the individual experience of various organisations, to coordinate all work on automation in the U.S.S.R. in a single center, to turn attention to the necessity of theoretical treatments for the perfecting of the general scientific foundation for the design of automatic systems.

In this connection a unified commission for remote control and automation was established in 1934 at the Academy of Sciences of the U.S.S.R., having 18 sections in the individual fields of the national economy. This commission began to publish the bi-monthly journal "Automatika i Telemekhanika" ("Automation and remote control") in 1936.

The Academy of Sciences of the U.S.S.R., taking part in the general preparation for assembly of the third five-year plan, at its session of March 1936 included among the eight key problems the development of means of automation and remote control and also the founding a single scientific basis for this work. One of the scientific bases for these developments was the theory of automatic regulation.

The most prominant representatives of this science at that time were Ivan Nikolaevich Voznesenskii, Corresponding member of the Academy of Sciences of the U.S.S.R and Academician Viktor Sergeevich Kulebakin. Important works on the theory of regulation in the early period were also those of K. E. Rerikh in 1924, E. L. Nikolai in 1928, Ia. I. Grdin in 1931, G. N. Nikol'skii in 1934, P. S. Zhdanov and A. L. Lebedev in 1934, and others.

From 1934 such a large number of works on automatic regulation have appeared that their listing would take up very much space. Therefore, referring the reader to the detailed bibliography published in the journal "Automatika i Telemekhanika" No. 5, 1948 and No. 6, 1949, we shall mention here only the most important contributions to the development of the theory of automatic regulation.

V. S. Kulebakin founded his school in the field of electrical automation and regulation whilst I. N. Voznesenskii founded a school in the field of the regulation of heat and hydraulic machines.

In 1940 the first All-Union Conference on the theory of automatic regulation was held, summed up the results and marked out the further course of development of this important young science.

In 1942 as a result of investigation of coupled regulation systems I. N. Voznesenskii gave conditions for the so-called autonomous regulation. In 1941 in one of his reports he mentioned the idea of the approximate definition of the duration of the regulation process, i.e. the time in which the deviation of the regulated quantity becomes equal to a given small fraction of the initial deviation and further remains smaller than it.

In 1943 G. N. Nikol'ski proposed a method for choosing the parameters of a regulation system. Independently of this in 1945 Ia. Z. Tsypkin and P. V. Bromberg developed the definition of the so-called degree of stability, which is also characterised by the smallest absolute value of the real parts of the roots of the characteristic equation and constitutes an approximate measure of the state of attenuation of the transient process.

In 1946 A. A. Krasovskii and A. A. Fel'dbaum developed the application of integral estimates of the quality of transient processes to automatic regulation systems.

An approximate criterion of the quality of the transient response according to the roots of the characteristic equation was also given by V. K. Popov in 1947 and further developed by T. N. Sokolov in 1950. These questions were also considered in the work of V. A. Bodner.

The effects of the relative positions of the poles and zeros of the transfer function of a closed automatic system on its quality were investigated in the work of S. P. Strelkov in 1948.

The approximate methods of investigating the behavior of dynamic systems for arbitrarily variable (bounded in magnitude) external perturbations developed in the theory of oscillations (B. V. Bulgakov) and in the theory of stability (N. D. Moiseev) also were reflected in the theory of regulation. An approximate estimate of the maximum deviation of the regulated quantity during the transient process for perturbations bounded in absolute value was considered in the work of G. M. Ulanov (1948).

A fairly simple method was given in the work of D. A. Bashkirov (1949) for plotting curves of transient processes in automatic regulation systems as well as in the regulation process in the presence of an arbitrary perturbing function.

The work of A. N. Kolmogrov on the theory of stationary random processes and V. S. Pugachev on the theory of random functions is very important for contemporary automatic-regulation theory, permitting investigation of the effects of random external forces on the dynamic system, if their probability characteristics are given.

Finally, a somewhat special branch of the theory of regulation is the study of systems based on the principle of regulation with respect to the perturbation. It was developed in the works of V. S. Kulebakin and N. N. Luzin, beginning in 1940. A representative of this direction was also G. V. Shchipanov. Aleksander Vasil'evich

Mikhailov proposed in 1936 and published in 1938, in the work "The method of harmonic analysis in the theory of regulation" (Reference 8), results which signalised the start of the development and application of new methods in the theory of automatic regulation.

This work established basically three new techniques. Firstly, Mikhailov proposed an original and fairly simple new stability criterion, now known as Mikhailov's criterion. Secondly, he described and proved mathematically the possibility of employing a frequency criterion of stability for the investigation of automatic regulation systems; in this he substantially generalised the frequency criterion which was proposed. Nyquist in 1932 for the investigation of electronic feedback amplifiers. Frequency methods were not generally used in calculating regulation systems before Mikhailov. Thirdly, Mikhailov founded structural analysis on the basis of the classification of the circuits of automatic regulation systems according to their dynamic properties. At the present time all three ideas have obtained exceedingly wide application and development in the works of many Soviet scientists and engineers. Mikhailov's stability criterion has been found more convenient in many cases than the well-known Hurwitz criterion.

A large role in the development of frequency methods in the theory of regulation was played by the works of V. V. Solodovnikov. In a number of articles, beginning in 1939, he proposed and developed frequency methods of investigating the character of the transient response in regulation and following. These works concerned approximate estimates of the quality of a system from the form of the frequency characteristics of a closed system and from the form of the real frequency characteristic of a closed system, applying logarithmic frequency characteristics to the analysis of stability and quality and for the choice of the system parameters.

The method of constructing the transient response curve using frequency characteristics is due to V. V. Solodovnikov (Reference 11).

The application of frequency methods to servomechanisms was also considered in the works of K. S. Bobov.

The use of frequency methods for the solution of problems on the influence of random external forces on a closed automatic system, presented in the monograph of V. V. Solodovnikov (Reference 12), is important at the present time. It is also necessary to note the works of B. N. Petrov and B. V. Bulgakov on the structural analysis of automatic systems.

A. A. Sokolov, who died in 1941 in the battle of Leningrad, established in 1940 a criterion for the stability of automatic regulation systems with distributed parameters and described a general method for plotting the stability regions for linear systems with distributed and lumped parameters. In the absence of distributed parameters Sokolov's criterion degenerates into Mikhailov's criterion, mentioned above. A detailed working out of the application of Mikhailov's criterion to systems with delay was carried out by N. N. Miasnikov in 1949.

In 1948 Iu. I. Neimark developed in greater detail the method described by A. A. Sokolov for plotting the stability regions of linear systems. In essence this is a plot of the stability regions according to Mikhailov's criterion (see Section 34). It is interesting to note that a similar idea was developed earlier by V. S. Vedrov.

In 1941 N. G. Chebotarev gave an algebraic investigation of the stability of systems with delay and systems with distributed parameters. Similar ideas were substantially developed by L. S. Pontriagin in 1942, giving several important theorems in this field. An algebraic method of investigating such systems was also proposed later by Iu. V. Vorob'ev.

In 1941 V. V. Solodovnikov described the application of the frequency stability criterion to systems with distributed parameters. In 1946 Ia. Z. Tsypkin developed in detail the frequency method of investigating systems with delay and systems with distributed parameters.

A somewhat specialised division of the linear theory of automatic regulation is the investigation of pulse (discontinuous) regulation systems. Aside from the above-mentioned early works of N. E. Zhukovskii in this field we should note the work of Iu. G. Kornilov (1941), in which linear difference equations of the system are assembled and the stability conditions studied.

In 1949 Ia. Z. Tsypkin, employing the discrete Laplace transform and frequency characteristics, found procedures for investigating pulse regulation systems analogous to the methods of investigating linear continuous regulation systems.

Non-linear problems. Aleksandr Aleksandrovich Andronov was a leading scientist in the field of solving non-linear problems of the theory of regulation. He founded a scientific school in this field.

A. A. Andronov proposed and his pupils developed a method of point transformation. Individual problems were solved by this method in the works of A. A. Andronov, N. N. Bautin, and A. G. Maier (1944–1947). The method is based on the geometric interpretation of the behaviour of a dynamic system in the form of the motion of a generating point in phase space and on the analysis of the entire set of phase trajectories with introduction of a certain time parameter. Important works in this field are due also to V. V. Petrov and N. A. Fufaev.

In applications of A. M. Liapunov's theorem to the investigation of non-linear regulation systems an important role was played by the works of A. I. Lur'e. In a work by A. I. Lur'e and V. N. Postnikov (1944) Liapunov's method was applied to the solution of a special non-linear problem. The results of A. I. Lur'e obtained in this field in recent years have been collected in his monograph (Reference 20). An exact analytic definition of self-oscillations in relay systems is also given there.

Another important category of methods are the approximate methods issuing mainly from the works of N. M. Krylov and N. N. Bogoliubov in 1934 and 1937 (References 5 and 6). These methods are the most effective at the present time in practical calculation of non-linear automatic regulation systems. A similar method was developed in the works of B. V. Bulgakov, beginning in 1942. His method was followed by A. M. Letov (1948). A frequency variant of one of the Krylov-Bogoliubov methods was developed by L. S. Gol'dfarb. In the present book another variant is given of the use of the Krylov-Bogoliubov methods in combination with the method of plotting the stability regions according to Mikhailov's criterion. The development of approximate methods was also considered in works by many other scientists (V. A. Kotel'nikov, V. A. Bodner, G. S. Pospelov, N. V. Butenin and many others). A more exact frequency method for the the simplest form of non-linear system—a relay system—was developed recently by Ia. Z. Tsypkin.

In the above mentioned work of D. A. Bashkirov a graphical method was developed for plotting the transient curve also for non-linear automatic regulation systems, for systems with delay and for systems with variable parameters (i.e. for equations with variable coefficients).

This short historical survey does not pretend to completeness with respect to discussing the work of domestic scientists and does not reflect the work of foreign authors.

PART II
ORDINARY LINEAR AUTOMATIC REGULATION
SYSTEMS

CHAPTER V

LINEARISATION AND TRANSFORMATION OF THE DIFFERENTIAL EQUATIONS OF AN AUTOMATIC REGULATION SYSTEM

18. Linearisation of the equations. Liapunov's theorem on the stability of linearised systems

In setting up the differential equations of motion of any automatic system, the system is divided into individual parts as described above, and the equations of each part are written individually. The equations of all the parts form a system of equations which may be transformed to a single equation (5.1) or (5.6) by elimination of the intermediate variables.

The equation of a part should be set up so that it expresses the relation (in the dynamic process) between those quantities which are indicated at the output and input of the part of the system under investigation, i.e. between those quantities which represent the effect of the given part on the succeeding part in the system and those which represent effect of the preceding part on the given one. The dynamic equation of an individual part is written according to the rules of the corresponding branch of engineering science (a part may be a heat engine, electric motor, mechanical transmission, electric network, electronic circuit, etc.).

The part may sometimes have more than one input quantity (for example, in the presence of auxiliary feedback). Aside from the input and output quantities of the part, which express the internal connection between parts of a given system, external forces may be present.

Let, for example, the element (Fig. 91a) of some automatic system have input quantities x_1, x_2, output x_3 and external force $f(t)$, while the dynamic equation of the element has an arbitrary non-linear form*

$$F(x_1, x_2, \dot{x}_2, x_3, \dot{x}_3, \ddot{x}_3, \dddot{x}_3) = \varphi(f, \dot{f}) \tag{18.1}$$

* If the equation has time-variable coefficients the function F also includes t in explicit form. Linearisation is carried out in the same way.

149

(for the example a definite order of the derivatives of x_2, x_3, f entering into the equation is taken; in general there may be here any other arbitrary arrangement).

Let us assume that the steady-state of the system occurs for certain constant values* $x_1 = x_1^0$, $x_2 = x_2^0$, $x_3 = x_3^0$ and $f = f^0$.

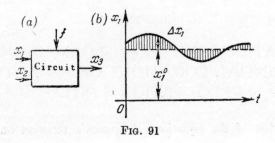

FIG. 91

Then from (18.1) the steady-state equation for the given element will be:

$$F(x_1, x_2\, 0, x_3\, 0, 0, 0) = \varphi(f^0, 0) . \tag{18.2}$$

The assumption that in the dynamic process under investigation the variables (in this case x_1, x_2, x_3) vary in such a way that their deviations (from the steady-state values x_1^0, x_2^0, x_3^0) remain for all time sufficiently small (Fig. 91b) lies at the root linearisation of the non-linear equations.

Let us denote these deviations by Δx_1, Δx_2, Δx_3. Then in the dynamic process we have:

$$\left.\begin{array}{l} x_1(t) = x_1^0 + \Delta x_1(t) , \qquad x_2(t) = x_2^0 + \Delta x_2(t) , \qquad\quad \dot{x}_2 = \dot{\Delta x}_2 , \\[4pt] x_3(t) = x_3^0 + \Delta x_3(t) , \qquad \dot{x}_3 = \dot{\Delta x}_3, \quad \ddot{x}_3 = \ddot{\Delta x}_3, \quad \dddot{x}_3 = \dddot{\Delta x}_3 . \end{array}\right\} \tag{18.3}$$

Sufficiently small dynamic deviations of the variable from certain steady-state values are usually satisfied in automatic control systems and servomechanisms. This is required by the very concept of operation of a closed automatic system.

The external force f is independent of the operation of the automatic system, its variation may be arbitrary and therefore the right-hand side of equation (18.1) is usually not subject to linearisation (in individual cases even this may be linearised).

First method of linearisation. Let us expand the function F, on the left-hand side of equation (18.1), in a power series in small deviations, considering all derivatives also as independent variables. Then equation (18.1) takes the form

---

* The same method of linearisation is also used for variable values $x_1^0(t)$, $x_2^0(t)$, $x_3^0(t)$, $f^0(t)$.

$$F(x_1^0, x_2^0, 0, x_3^0, 0, 0, 0) + \left(\frac{\partial F}{\partial x_1}\right)^0 \Delta x_1 + \left(\frac{\partial F}{\partial x_2}\right)^0 \Delta x_2 + \left(\frac{\partial F}{\partial \dot{x}_2}\right)^0 \Delta \dot{x}_2$$

$$+ \left(\frac{\partial F}{\partial x_3}\right)^0 \Delta x_3 + \left(\frac{\partial F}{\partial \dot{x}_3}\right)^0 \Delta \dot{x}_3 + \left(\frac{\partial F}{\partial \ddot{x}_3}\right)^0 \Delta \ddot{x}_3 + \left(\frac{\partial F}{\partial \dddot{x}_3}\right)^0 \Delta \dddot{x}_3$$

$$+ \text{(higher order infinitesimals)} = \varphi(f, \dot{f}), \qquad (18.4)$$

where $\left(\dfrac{\partial F}{\partial x_1}\right)^0$ for conciseness denotes the quantity $\dfrac{\partial F}{\partial x_1}$ taken for $x_1 = x_1^0, \; x_2 = x_2^0, \; \dot{x}_2 = 0, \; x_3^0, \ldots, \ddot{x}_3 = 0$ (i.e. it is necessary to take the partial derivative of the function F with respect to x_1 in general form, after which it is necessary to substitute their constant values $x_1^0, x_2^0, 0, x_3^0, \ldots, 0$ in place of all variables).

Consequently, all partial derivatives in equation (18.4) represent certain constant coefficients. They will be time variables, if the function F contains t in explicit form or if the steady-state process in the system is defined by the variable values $x_1^0(t), x_2^0(t), x_3^0(t)$.

Terms of higher order infinitesimals, indicated in equation (18.4), consist of the products and powers of the small deviations $\Delta x_1, \ldots$ with coefficients in the form of mixed partial derivatives and partial derivatives of second and higher order of the function F with respect to all variables.

Subtracting from equation (18.4) termwise the steady state (18.2) and dropping terms of higher-order infinitesimals, we obtain the required linearised equation of motion of the given element in the form

$$\left(\frac{\partial F}{\partial x_1}\right)^0 \Delta x_1 + \left(\frac{\partial F}{\partial x_2}\right)^0 \Delta x_2 + \left(\frac{\partial F}{\partial \dot{x}_2}\right)^0 \Delta \dot{x}_2 + \left(\frac{\partial F}{\partial x_3}\right)^0 \Delta x_3 +$$

$$+ \left(\frac{\partial F}{\partial \dot{x}_3}\right)^0 \Delta \dot{x}_3 + \left(\frac{\partial F}{\partial \ddot{x}_3}\right)^0 \Delta \ddot{x}_3 + \left(\frac{\partial F}{\partial \dddot{x}_3}\right)^0 \Delta \dddot{x}_3$$

$$= \varphi(f, \dot{f}) - \varphi(f^0, 0). \qquad (18.5)$$

This differential equation, just as the previous one (18.1), describes the same dynamic process in the same element of the automatic system. The difference between these two equations consists in the following:

(1) this equation is more approximate, since in its derivation higher-order infinitesimals were dropped;

(2) the unknown functions of time in this equation are not the previous total quantities x_1, x_2, x_3 but their deviations $\Delta x_1, \Delta x_2, \Delta x_3$ from certain steady-state values x_1^0, x_2^0, x_3^0;

(3) the equation obtained is linear with respect to the deviations $\Delta x_1, \Delta x_2, \Delta \dot{x}_2, \Delta x_3, \ldots, \Delta \dddot{x}_3$ with constant coefficients $\left(\dfrac{\partial F}{\partial x_1}\right)^0, \left(\dfrac{\partial F}{\partial x_2}\right)^0, \ldots,$ or with variable coefficients if F contains t explicitly or if the steady-state process is defined by variable quantities $x_1^0(t), x_2^0(t), x_3^0(t)$.

Thus, the aim of obtaining a linear differential equation in place of the non-linear one has been achieved. Equation (18.5) is termed the differential equation of the element in deviations. Carrying out the same procedure for all elements of the system, we obtain as a result the linearised equations of the regulation process in deviations (or, as they are sometimes termed, "variational" equations).

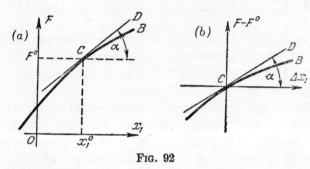

FIG. 92

In what follows it will be possible to carry out linearisation of non-linear equations directly by analogy with formula (18.5), without the preliminary calculations.

Let us present a geometric interpretation of this method of linearisation. We shall represent the dependence of F on x_1 graphically with constant values of all remaining variables: $x_2 = x_2^0$, $\dot{x}_2 = 0$, $x_3 = x_3^0$, $\dot{x}_3 = \ddot{x}_3 = \dddot{x}_3 = 0$. Let this dependence have the form of the curve shown in Fig. 92a. We mark the value x_1^0 and plot the tangent. Then

$$\left(\frac{\partial F}{\partial x_1}\right)^0 = \tan\alpha\,, \tag{18.6}$$

where α is the slope at the point $C(x_1^0, F^0)$, if we put

$$F^0 = F(x_1^0, x_2^0, 0, x_3^0, 0, 0, 0)\,. \tag{18.7}$$

The substitution $x_1 = x_1^0 + \Delta x_1$ and the cancelling of the term (18.7), previously carried out analytically, are here equivalent to the transfer of the origin of coordinates to the point C (Fig. 92a), as a result of which the graph of Fig. 92b is obtained.

The first term of the linear equation (18.5), in accordance with (18.6), indicates that the linearised equation may be interpreted geometrically as the replacement of the initial curve CB by its tangent at the point CD. From the graph of Fig. 92b it is obvious that, firstly, this substitution is the more exact, the smaller the magnitude of deviation Δx_1 with which we are concerned in the given dynamic process (the basic assumption for linearisation), and, secondly, the limits of the deviation Δx_1 for which linearisation is permissible are the wider, the closer the curve CB to the straight line CD. This last condition is determined in practice in each problem by the boundaries within which the deviation may be considered "sufficiently small".

In a number of problems the difference from linearity shown in Fig. 92*b* is so negligible that even in relatively wide ranges of deviation Δx_1 the system may be considered linear. With a strongly curved dependence linearisation will be valid only in a correspondingly narrower range of deviation Δx_1. Linearisation may be completely inadmissible with discontinuous functions (relay characteristics, dry friction). Such a form of dependence is termed essentially non-linear.

It is important to note the following: if for the above reasons only a single element of the system or even only a part of a function F in the left-hand side of the equation of a given element cannot be subjected to linearisation, then linearisation of all remaining non-linear dependencies should be carried out, leaving only the essentially non-linear ones.

Second method of linearisation. From the above geometric illustration there follows a second method of linearising the equations of an automatic control system which is very frequently applied in practice. This method consists in replacing, at the start, all curved dependencies employed in composing the equations of the element by rectilinear ones, i.e. by the tangents at the appropriate points of the curve. Then the equations of the element will be immediately found to be in linear form (see for example, Section 26).

Standard form of linearised equations of the circuits of an automatic system. At the present time in the theory of automatic regulation it is usual to write the dynamic equations of the elements so that the output quantity and its derivative are on the left-hand side of the equation while the input quantity and all remaining terms are on the right-hand side. In addition, it is customary that the output quantity itself enter into the equation with unity coefficient. To reduce the linearised equation (18.5) to such a form, we introduce the notation:

$$k_1 = \left| \left(\frac{\partial F}{\partial x_1}\right)^0 : \left(\frac{\partial F}{\partial x_3}\right)^0 \right|, \quad k_2 = \left| \left(\frac{\partial F}{\partial x_2}\right)^0 : \left(\frac{\partial F}{\partial x_3}\right)^0 \right|,$$

$$k_2' = \left| \left(\frac{\partial F}{\partial \dot{x}_2}\right)^0 : \left(\frac{\partial F}{\partial x_3}\right)^0 \right|,$$

$$T_1 = \left| \left(\frac{\partial F}{\partial \dot{x}_3}\right)^0 : \left(\frac{\partial F}{\partial x_3}\right)^0 \right|, \quad T_2^2 = \left| \left(\frac{\partial F}{\partial \ddot{x}_3}\right)^0 : \left(\frac{\partial F}{\partial x_3}\right)^0 \right|,$$

$$T_3^3 = \left| \left(\frac{\partial F}{\partial \dddot{x}_3}\right)^0 : \left(\frac{\partial F}{\partial x_3}\right)^0 \right|,$$

$$f_1(t) = \frac{\varphi(f, \dot{f}) - \varphi(f^0, 0)}{\left(\frac{\partial F}{\partial x_3}\right)^0}.$$

$$(18.8)$$

Then equation (18.5) takes the form (in symbolic operational notation):

$$(T_3^3 p^3 + T_2^2 p^2 + T_1 p + 1)x_3 = k_1 \Delta x_1 + (k_2 + k_2' p)\Delta x_2 + f_1(t), \quad (18.9)$$

where positive signs are conventionally employed throughout but at any place there may be a negative sign since k_1, k_2, k_2', T_1, T_2^2, T_3^3 denote the absolute values of expressions (18.8).

If the non-linear function F does not contain the quantity x_3 but contains only its derivatives, i.e. if

$$\left(\frac{\partial F}{\partial x_3}\right)^0 = 0,$$

then in formulae (18.8) the entire division will be carried out not by $\left(\frac{\partial F}{\partial x_3}\right)^0$, but by $\left(\frac{\partial F}{\partial \dot{x}_3}\right)^0$ and we obtain the equation

$$(T_2^2 p^2 + T_1 p + 1)p\Delta x_3 = k_1 \Delta x_1 + (k_2 + k_2' p)\Delta x_2 + f_1(t), \quad (18.10)$$

where

$$T_1 = \left|\left(\frac{\partial F}{\partial \ddot{x}_3}\right)^0 : \left(\frac{\partial F}{\partial \dot{x}_3}\right)^0\right|, \qquad T_2^2 = \left|\left(\frac{\partial F}{\partial \dddot{x}_3}\right)^0 : \left(\frac{\partial F}{\partial \dot{x}_3}\right)^0\right|, \ldots$$

The standard form of notation (18.9) and (18.10) of the constituent equations of automatic systems may be applied both to the dimensional deviations of the real input and output quantities of the element as well as to arbitrary dimensionless relative deviations, sometimes introduced especially to simplify the form of the equations and for convenience of their investigation (see examples in further chapters).

In such a standard form (18.9) or (18.10) the coefficients k_1, k_2, k_2' are termed the transfer factors or gain factors of the given element and T_1, T_2, T_3 its time constants. In the notation adopted (18.8) these are positive numbers before which may be either plus or minus signs in the element equation (18.9) itself (in individual cases it is convenient to consider that the transfer factors and time constants themselves may take on negative values).

The significance of this terminology is that if only a constant value Δx_1^0 is applied to the input of the element and the steady-state value of the output quantity Δx_3^0 is found, then from (18.9) we obtain:

$$\Delta x_3^0 = k_1 \Delta x_1^0,$$

i.e. the factor k_1 indicates by what factor the steady-state value of the input quantity changes in passage through the given element to its output. This also explains the significance of the term "transfer factor" or "gain factor", both terms mean exactly the same in each particular case but ordinarily that one is used which better suits the technical problem solved by the given element.

Consequently, "the transfer factor", or the "gain factor", defines the slope of the linear static characteristic of the element (Fig. 93a). We note that non-linear characteristic of an element (for example, Fig. 33) is frequency termed a characteristic with variable gain factor with respect to the input quantity. From (18.8) it is obvious that

$$\text{dimensions of } k_1 = \frac{\text{dimensions of the output quantity } \Delta x_3}{\text{dimensions of the input quantity } \Delta x_1}.$$

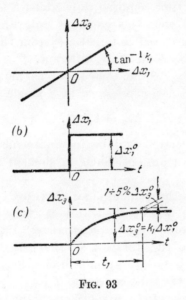

FIG. 93

The quantities T_1, T_2, T_3, termed "time constants" have, as is evident from (18.8), the dimensions of time (seconds). Physically their significance may be explained by a simple example. Let there be applied to the input of the element a step of constant value Δx_1^0 (Fig. 93b). It is required to find the curve of the transient in the element if the circuit has only a single time constant T_1, while the others $T_2 = T_3 = 0$. From (18.9) the equation of the transient process in this case will be

$$(T_1 p + 1)\Delta x_3 = k_1 \Delta x_1^0 \cdot 1(t).$$

Directly after the step we obtain the equation $(t \geqslant +0)$:

$$(T_1 p + 1)\Delta x_3 = k_1 \Delta x_1^0 \qquad (18.11)$$

with the initial condition $\Delta x_3 = 0$ at $t = +0$. Its solution will be:

$$\Delta x_3 = k_1 \Delta x_1^0 (1 - e^{-\frac{1}{T_1}}), \qquad (18.12)$$

i.e. the curve of the transient has an exponential form (Fig. 93c).
If we consider the transient to terminate when the difference

$$\Delta x_3^0 - \Delta x_3(t) = 5\% \, \Delta x_3^0 , \qquad (18.13)$$

then from (18.12) it is easy to calculate the duration of the transient

$$t_1 = T_1 \ln 20 \approx 3T_1 \qquad (18.14)$$

(if a precision of 5 per cent is insufficient and it is desired to have
1 per cent, the duration will be $t_1 = 4 \cdot 6 \; T_1$).

The element time constant T_1 thus defines "the inertia" of the
given element i.e. the time required to establish the output quantity.
It should be recalled that this concerns only an isolated element.
In the assembly of a closed automatic system the transient in the
given element may be completely different.

If we have $T_1 = T_2 = T_3 0$, i.e. the equation of motion of the element
(18.9) has the form (in the presence of a single input quantity)

$$\Delta x_3 = k_1 \Delta x_1 , \qquad (18.15)$$

any arbitrary input action will be instantaneously transmitted to
the output without a transient. Such an element is termed an ideal
element.

If in the equation of the element (18.9) there are two time constants:
T_1 and T_2 or three: T_1, T_2, T_3, the transient in the individual element
will be somewhat more complicated than (18.12); it may even be
oscillatory. But again the duration of the period of establishment
of the output quantity Δx_3^0 (duration of oscillation) will be dependent
on the magnitudes of the time constants T_1, T_2, T_3, i.e. they charac-
terise the non-idealness of the given element in transmission of the
input action.

The dynamic properties of different types of elements will be
discussed in greater detail in the following section.

Liapunov's theorem on the stability of linearised systems. Thus,
the linear equations of real automatic systems are always obtained
as a result of some linearisation, i.e. as a result of dropping terms
containing second and higher powers of the deviations of the variable
and their derivatives. We may pose the question: to what degree do
considerations of the stability of such a linearised equation correspond
to the stability of a real system? Do not the neglected terms influence
the stability of the system?

A. M. Liapunov (Reference 3) gave many theorems and methods
for investigating stability and the general behaviour of dynamic
systems in various cases which are difficult to analyse by normal
methods. The best known are his methods for studying non-linear
systems (see Section 57). Here we shall be interested only in the

following theorems of Liapunov on the stability of linearised systems (or, in Liapunov's expression, on the validity of investigating stability in the first approximation), which we present without proof.

1. If all the roots of the characteristic equation of a linearised system have negative real parts, both the actual and the linearised systems will be stable, no addition in the form of terms of second and higher powers of the variables and their derivatives can "spoil" the stability of the system.

2. If the characteristic equation of a linearised system has at least one root with positive real part both the actual and the linearised systems will be unstable i.e. no addition in the form of terms of second and higher powers of the variables and their derivatives can give stability to the system.

3. In the presence of zero and at least one purely imaginary root the behaviour of the real system cannot always be determined even qualitatively by its linearised equations. In a number of cases additions in the shape of terms of second and higher powers of the variables and their derivatives may fundamentally change the character of the dynamic response of the system.

Therefore in general we cannot judge from the linearised equations what takes place at the limit of stability of the system (i.e. with zero or purely imaginary roots). But we shall be interested in the study and design of just such automatic systems which should be stable and sufficiently far from the boundary of stability.

With this in mind we shall in general not be interested in the behaviour of systems having zero and purely imaginary roots, simply considering that the latter correspond to the limits of stability which should not be approached in the design of automatic systems. It is important that by virtue of Liapunov's first two theorems the position of the boundary of stability of a real system is found, exactly from its linearised equations, if, of course, the system is subject to linearisation. These theorems of Liapunov are the mathematical foundation of the entire linear theory of automatic regulation, since, strictly speaking, we are concerned in engineering not with purely linear but with linearised systems (although in what follows we shall always call them for conciseness linear systems).

It is very important to bear in mind that these theorems of Liapunov are valid only when the linearisation is carried out by rule (18.5) i.e. when all the non-linear functions have (at least) finite continuous single-valued derivatives in the neighborhood of the steady state points of the process. Therefore they do not concern stepwise and polygonal functions, and the neglect of such essential non-linearities as dry friction, relay characteristics, zones of insensitivity, etc. may frequently substantially change the position of the boundary of stability. From this there follows the practical importance of taking into account certain forms of non-linearity in calculating an automatic system.

In addition, we remark that these theorems of Liapunov concern only the stability of the system without touching the transient process. Even a smooth form of non-linearity neglected in linearisation can sometimes have a very strong influence on the transient response, i.e. on the dynamic system errors.

19. Types of elements in automatic systems and their characteristics

The types of elements in automatic regulation systems (independently of their design and physical nature) are distinguished by their dynamic properties, i.e. by the form of the differential equation of motion which is most important for the theory of regulation and for technical calculation of closed automatic systems.

Classification of element types. Let us consider different variants of the equations of not higher than second order of elements in standard form (18.9) which are most frequently encountered.

When p is a common factor of the left-hand side, as for example in (18.10), it is necessary to divide it into the entire equation. If an element is encountered in practice with an equation not included in this classification, its dynamic properties may be investigated individually by the same technique.

Let us denote the input and output quantities of the element by x_1 and x_2. Different forms which may be encountered in the left and right-hand parts of the equation of motion of the element are given in the form of a table (see p. 159).

It is assumed that the equation of the element may be represented as an equality between left and right-hand parts taken from any rows of the table. In addition, to the right-hand side of the equation of any element may be added an external perturbation function.

The table also gives the designations of the elements. In general the designation of an element is composed of the two designations corresponding to the left and right-hand parts of its equation. In the structural diagrams of automatic systems the elements are usually characterised by their transfer functions

$$W(p) = \frac{R(p)}{Q(p)},$$

where $R(p)$ and $Q(\mathrm{p})$ are the operational polynomials standing in the right and left-hand parts of the element equation respectively.

For example, if some element in a real system is described by the equation

$$(T_1 p + 1)x_2 = (k + k'p + k''p^2)x_1,$$

TABLE OF ELEMENT TYPES

No	Element designation	Left-hand side of equation	Right-hand side of equation	Element designation	No
1	Ideal	x_2	kx_1	Simple	1
2	Aperiodic	$(T_1 p + 1)x_2$	kpx_1	Differentiating	2
3	Aperiodic of second order $(T_1 \geqslant 2T_2)$	$(T_2^2 p^2 + T_1 p + 1)x_2$	$k\dfrac{x_1}{p}$	Integrating	3
4	Oscillatory $(T_1 < 2T_2)$		$(k + k'p)x_1$	With introduction of derivative	4
5	Harmonically oscillating	$(T_2^2 p^2 + 1)x_2$	$\left(x + k_1\dfrac{1}{p}\right)x_1$	With introduction of integral	5
6	Unstable aperiodic	$(T_1 p - 1)x_2$	$\left(k + k'p + k_1\dfrac{1}{p}\right)x_1$	With introduction of derivative and integral	6
7	Unstable oscillatory $(T_1 < 2T_2)$	$(T_2^2 p^2 - T_1 p + 1)x_2$	$(k + k'p + k''p^2)x_1$	With introduction of two derivatives	7
8	Unstable aperiodic of second order $(T_1 \geqslant 2T_2)$		$\left(k + k'p + k''p^2 + k_1\dfrac{1}{p}\right)x_1$	With introduction of two derivatives and integral	8
9	Unstable aperiodic of second order $(T_1$ and T_2 arbitrary)	$(T_2^2 p^2 + T_1 p - 1)x_2$	$k(x_1 + y + z + ...)$	Summation	9
10		$(T_2^2 p^2 - T_1 p - 1)x_2$	$k(x_1 - x_{o.c})$	With inclusion of feedback (negative)	10

then, according to the table, from its dynamic properties this element is termed an aperiodic element with introduction of two derivatives. The derivatives in the right-hand side of the equation may either be applied to the input of the element or be formed in the given element. In the structural diagram they are denoted as shown in Fig. 94a.

If the equation of the element has the form

$$(T_1 p + 1)x_2 = kx_1 ,$$

the element is termed simple aperiodic (Fig. 94b). The word "simple" in the table next to kx_1 may be omitted since simple elements of all types are encountered most frequently.

An element described by the equation

$$x_2 = kpx_1$$

is termed ideally differentiating (Fig. 94c). An element with the equation

$$(T_2^2 p^2 + T_1 p + 1)x_2 = k\frac{1}{p}x_1 \qquad (T_1 < 2T_2)$$

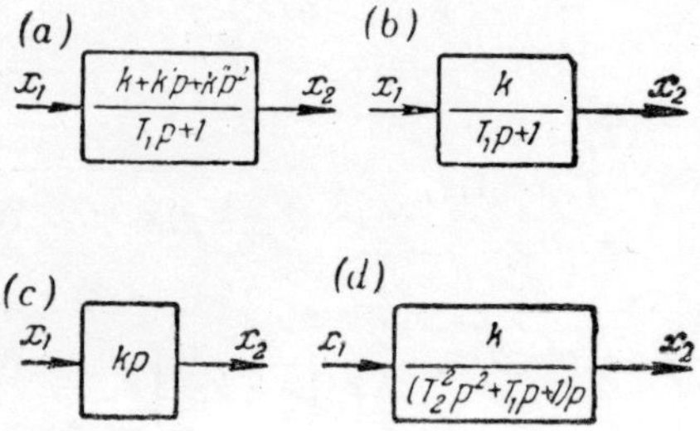

Fig. 94

will be oscillatory integrating. The last equation may be written in the form*

$$(T_2^2 p^2 + T_1 p + 1)px_2 = kx_1 ,$$

which is adopted in denoting the given element in the diagram (Fig. 94d).

All the recommended designations correspond to the actual dynamic properties which these elements have in automatic regulation systems. Let us consider these dynamic properties of all types of elements.

Right-hand side of element equation. The right-hand side of the equation shows to what the given element "reacts" and with what gain factor (or transfer factor) the input quantity is transferred to the output.

The first eight forms of right-hand sides (see table on p. 159) relate to such elements as react respectively:

(1) only to the input quantity itself (simple element according to the table nomenclature);

(2) only to the derivative of the input quantity (differentiating element);

(3) only to the integral of the input quantity (integrating element);

(4) to the input quantity and its derivative (element with introduction of derivative);

(5) to the input quantity and its integral (element with introduction of integral);

* It is expedient to proceed in writing the equation of any integrating element and any element with introduction of the integral so as not to have a fraction with the letter p in the denominator.

(6) to the input quantity, derivative and integral (element with introduction of derivative and integral);

(7) to the input quantity, first and second derivatives (element with introduction of two derivatives);

(8) to the input quantity, the first derivative, second derivative and integral (elements with introduction of two derivatives and integral).

Other types, for example, introduction of the second derivative without the first, different signs for the coefficients k, k', k'', k_1 inside the parenthesis, will not be considered typical. They are rarely encountered. The common minus sign before the right-hand part, which may be encountered frequently, has no influence on the element dynamics.

The last two forms of the right-hand sides presented in the table relate to the following cases:

(1) form 9 includes two or more input quantities x, y, z, etc. which are applied simultaneously in the basic network to the input of a single element (summation element);

(2) form 10—in addition to the quantity x_1, applied at the input of the given element from the fundamental network, a further quantity x_{fb} is applied from the feedback network (element with inclusion of feedback).

Left-hand side of element equation. The left-hand side of the equation containing the output quantity and its derivatives indicates how fast and exactly the given element transmits the signal arriving at its input (in the form of the right-hand side). The absence of derivatives in the left-hand side corresponds to ideal transmission while their presence denotes either non-instantaneous transmission with distortion at the start of the process, having an aperiodic or oscillatory character, or in general the impossibility of transmission as a result of instability of the element.

Let us demonstrate this by construction of the so-called time characteristics (or, in other words, transient functions) for various types of element shown in the table (according to the forms of the left-hand sides of their equations), individually.

Time characteristics (transient functions) of simple elements. By time characteristic of an element we understand the variation of the output quantity as a function of time $x_2 = x_2(t)$, which is obtained when the input quantity is applied in the form of a unit step $x_1 = 1(t)$ (Fig. 95a) with zero initial conditions at the output x_2. The time characteristics are also called the transient functions of the element. Let us consider the time characteristics of simple elements when the left-hand side of the element equation may take various forms and the right-hand side only kx_1.

The ideal element

$$x_2 = kx_1$$

transmits instantaneously and without distortion to the output x_2 any value taken on by the input quantity x_1. Its time characteristic is shown in Fig. 95b.

The aperiodic element

$$(T_1 p + 1)x_2 = kx_1$$

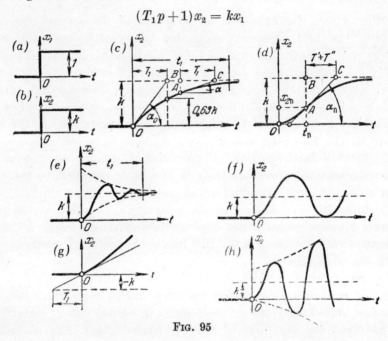

FIG. 95

with the initial condition $x_2 = 0$ (for $t \leqslant 0$) and with a unit step of the input quantity gives at the output

$$x_2 = k(1 - e^{-\frac{1}{T_1}}). \tag{19.1}$$

This time characteristic is shown in Fig. 95c. We have already considered this solution in Section 18. In particular, the time t_1 for establishing the value of $x_2 = k$ to within 5 per cent or 1 per cent was calculated there:

$$t_1 = 3T_1 \quad \text{and} \quad t_1 = 4 \cdot 6T_1. \tag{19.2}$$

We note that the derivative at any point A (Fig. 95c), taking into account (19.1), will be:

$$\dot{x}_2 = \frac{k}{T_1} e^{-\frac{1}{T_1}} = \frac{k - x_2}{T_1}. \tag{19.3}$$

But since in Fig. 95c we have

$$AB = k - x_2 \quad \text{and} \quad \tan \alpha = \dot{x}_2,$$

then from (19.3) the tangent at any point A of the exponential (including the origin of coordinates) intercepts on the straight line $x_2 = k$ a segment BC, equal to the time constant T_1 of the given circuit.

It is obvious that the larger the time constant, the more slowly the establishment of the output quantity $x_2 = k$ proceeds. The constancy of the length of projection of the tangent on the line $x_2 = k$ characterises "uniformity of attenuation" which is a property of the exponential. This property is employed in determining the time constant T_1 from experimentally recorded curves of the transient response $x_2(t)$ of the element. In place of plotting the tangent, which may be connected with substantial error, sometimes T_1 is defined as the time during which the output quantity x_2 takes on the value $x_2 = 0.63k$ which corresponds to the point $t = T_1$, since here from (19.1) we have

$$x_2 = k(1 - e^{-1}) \approx 0.63k,$$

Frequently such an element is called, instead of aperiodic, inertial, single-capacitance or relaxation, attempting to express by these terms the dynamic properties of the element which have been described above. In further discussion we shall retain the first designation (aperiodic element).

A second-order aperiodic element is described by the equation

$$(T_2^2 p^2 + T_1 p + 1)x_2 = kx_1$$

under the condition $T_1 \geqslant 2T_2$. Its time characteristic (Fig. 95d) is obtained by solving this equation for $x_1 = 1(t)$ with initial conditions $x_2 = \dot{x}_2 = 0$ at $t = 0$. The roots of the characteristic equation will be here real and the solution may be represented in the form

$$x_2 = k\left(1 - \frac{T'}{T' - T''} e^{-\frac{t}{T'}} + \frac{T''}{T' - T''} e^{-\frac{t}{T''}}\right), \qquad (19.4)$$

where T' and T'' denote the time constants of the component exponentials having the values

$$T' = \frac{2T_2^2}{T_1 - \sqrt{T_1^2 - 4T_2^2}}, \qquad T'' = \frac{2T_2^2}{T_1 + \sqrt{T_1^2 - 4T_2^2}}.$$

Calculating the first and second derivatives from (19.4), we find for the point of inflection of the curve the following values:

$$x_{2i} = k\left(1 - \frac{T' + T''}{T'} e^{-\frac{t_i}{T'}}\right),$$

$$\tan \alpha_i = \dot{x}_{2i} = \frac{k}{T'} e^{-\frac{t_i}{T'}} = \frac{k - x_{2i}}{T' + T''}$$

i.e. the tangent at the point of inflection intercepts on the straight line $x_2 = k$ the segment BC, equal to the sum of time constants $T' + T''$ (Fig. 95*d*).

In the limiting case when $T_1 = 2T_2$, the time characteristic will be

$$x_2 = k\left[1 - \left(1 + \frac{t}{T_2}\right)e^{-\frac{t}{T_2}}\right].\qquad(19.5)$$

This has the same form (Fig. 95*d*), where the point of inflection A is defined by the coordinates

$$t_i = T_2; \quad x_{2i} = k\left(1 - \frac{2}{e}\right) = 0{\cdot}264k; \quad \dot{x}_{2i} = \frac{k}{T_2 e} = 0{\cdot}368\,\frac{k}{T_2}.$$

Sometimes the second-order aperiodic element is termed the two-capacitance circuit.

An oscillatory element is described by the equation

$$(T_2^2 p^2 + T_1 p + 1)x_2 = kx_1$$

under the condition $T_1 < 2T_2$. The characteristic equation here has complex roots and the time characteristic takes the form

$$x_2 = k\left[1 - e^{-\frac{t}{T'}}\left(\cos\omega t + \frac{1}{T'\omega}\sin\omega t\right)\right],\qquad(19.6)$$

where

$$T' = \frac{2T_2^2}{T_1}, \qquad \omega = \frac{\sqrt{4T_2^2 - T_1^2}}{2T_2^2}.\qquad(19.7)$$

It is represented in Fig. 95*e*. The quantity T' is the time constant of the exponential envelope (broken line in Fig. 95*e*), and ω is the angular frequency of oscillation. The non-idealness of the given element is expressed, consequently, in the oscillatory character of establishment of the output quantity. The establishment time (to 5 per cent) by analogy to (19.2) will be here $t_1 = 3T'$.

An harmonically oscillating element

$$(T_2^2 p^2 + 1)x_2 = kx_1$$

has a time characteristic (Fig. 95*f*) in the form of an unattenuated harmonic oscillation with constant amplitude, i.e.

$$x_2 = k\left(1 - \cos\frac{t}{T_2}\right).$$

For an unstable aperiodic element

$$(T_1 p - 1)x_2 = kx_1$$

the time characteristic (Fig. 95*g*) will be:

$$x_2 = k(e^{\frac{t}{T_1}} - 1).\qquad(19.9)$$

Here in general a definite value will not be established at the output.

An unstable oscillatory element

$$(T_2^2 p^2 - T_1 p + 1)x_2 = kx_1 \qquad (T_1 < 2T_2)$$

has the time characteristic

$$x_2 = k\left[1 - e^{\frac{t}{T'}}\left(\cos \omega t - \frac{t}{T'\omega}\sin \omega t\right)\right], \qquad (19.10)$$

shown in Fig. 95h. We have here divergent oscillations.

Unstable second-order aperiodic elements may have in the left-hand side of the equation one of three expressions: (8), (9), (10),

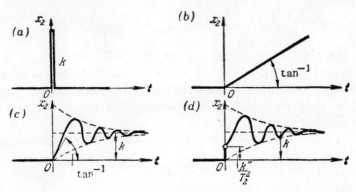

FIG. 96

presented in the table of typical elements. Here, as in the case of Fig. 95g, we obtain unbounded aperiodic deviation of the output quantity from the steady state value.

Time characteristics of non-simple elements. Let us find certain time characteristics (transient functions) of other elements—non-simple—for which the right-hand sides of the equations, in distinction to the above simple elements, do not contain kx_1 or not only kx_1.

An ideal differentiating element

$$x_2 = kpx_1$$

with the input $x_1 = 1(t)$ gives at the output an instantaneous impulse $x_2 = k'1'(t)$, which consequently is the time characteristic of the given circuit (Fig. 96a).

The ideal integrating element

$$x_2 = k\frac{x_1}{p} \qquad \text{or} \qquad px_2 = kx_1$$

has a time characteristic (for $x_1 = 1(t)$) in the form of a straight line $x_2 = kt$ (Fig. 96b).

An oscillatory element with introduction of the derivative

$$(T_2^2 p^2 + T_1 p + 1)x_2 = (k + k'p)x_1 \qquad (T_1 < 2T_2)$$

under the force $x_1 = 1(t)$ is described by the equation

$$(T_2^2 p^2 + T_1 p + 1)x_2 = k \qquad (T_1 < 2T_2) \qquad (19.11)$$

with initial conditions from (6.23) in the form

$$x_2 = 0, \qquad \dot{x}_2 = \frac{k'}{T_2^2} \qquad \text{at} \quad t = +0 \qquad (19.12)$$

(directly after the step). The time characteristic of the given element (Fig. 96c), defined by solution of this equation, will be:

$$x_2 = k\left\{1 - e^{-\frac{t}{T'}}\left[\cos \omega t + \left(\frac{1}{\omega T'} - \frac{k'}{k\omega T_2^2}\right)\sin \omega t\right]\right\}, \qquad (19.13)$$

where the time constant of the exponential envelope T' and the frequency of oscillation ω have the values (19.7). This time characteristic (Fig. 96c) differs from that of a simple oscillatory element (Fig. 95e) only in that here at the origin of coordinates there will be an inclined tangent.

An oscillatory element with introduction of two derivatives

$$T_2^2 p^2 + T_1 p + 1)x_2 = (k + k'p + k''p^2)x_1 \qquad (T_1 < 2T_2)$$

has a time characteristic (Fig. 96d)

$$x_2 k = \left\{1 - e^{-\frac{t}{T'}}\left[\left(1 - \frac{k''}{kT_2^2}\right)\cos \omega t + \left(\frac{1}{\omega T'} - \frac{k'}{k\omega T_2^2} + \frac{k''}{k\omega T' T_2^2}\right)\sin \omega t\right]\right\}$$

(T' and ω as before) as the solution of the same equation (19.11), but with other initial conditions, in accordance with (6.23), in the form

$$x_2 = \frac{k''}{T_2^2}, \qquad \dot{x}_2 = \frac{k'}{T_2^2} - \frac{T_1 k''}{T_2^4} \qquad \text{at} \quad t = +0 \qquad (19.14)$$

(directly after the step). Here the time characteristic (Fig. 96d) has not only an inclined tangent at the origin of coordinates but an instantaneous step of the output quantity.

The time characteristics for other compound elements may be obtained analogously.

Amplitude-phase frequency characteristics of simple elements. Let us assume that the input quantity x_1 of the elements is an harmonic oscillation of unit amplitude $x_1 = \sin \omega t$. Then the steady-state forced oscillations of the output quantity x_2 of the element will be defined completely by construction of the amplitude-phase frequency characteristics in accordance with Section 8.

An aperiodic element corresponds to the transfer function

$$W(p) = \frac{k}{T_1 p + 1}.$$

Therefore the expression for its amplitude-phase characteristic (8.16) will take the form

$$W(i\omega) = \frac{k}{T_1 i\omega + 1} = \frac{k(1 - T_1 i\omega)}{(1 + T_1 i\omega)(1 - T_1 i\omega)} = \frac{k}{1 + T_1^2 \omega^2} - i \frac{k T_1 \omega}{1 + T_1^2 \omega^2}.$$

Consequently,

$$U(\omega) = \frac{k}{1 + T_1^2 \omega^2}, \qquad V(\omega) = -\frac{k T_1 \omega}{1 + T_1^2 \omega^2}. \qquad (19.15)$$

It is not difficult to verify that these expressions satisfy the equation of a circle

$$\left(U - \frac{k}{2}\right)^2 + V^2 = \left(\frac{k}{2}\right)^2,$$

which is shown in Fig. 97a; only the lower half of the circle is shown since, from (19.15), to all positive values of ω $(0 \leqslant \omega \leqslant \infty)$ there correspond only negative values of the ordinates V.

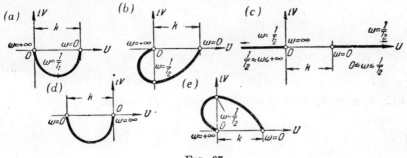

Fig. 97

For a second-order aperiodic element and for an oscillatory element

$$W(p) = \frac{k}{T_2^2 p^2 + T_1 p + 1}.$$

We obtain analogously the expression

$$W(i\omega) = \frac{k}{1 - T_2^2 \omega^2 + T_1 i\omega} = \frac{k(1 - T_2^2 \omega^2 - T_1 i\omega)}{(1 - T_2^2 \omega^2)^2 + T_1^2 \omega^2},$$

from which

$$U = \frac{k(1 - T_2^2 \omega^2)}{(1 - T_2^2 \omega^2)^2 + T_1^2 \omega^2}, \qquad V = -\frac{k T_1 \omega}{(1 - T_2^2 \omega^2) + T_1^2 \omega^2}. \qquad (19.16)$$

Putting $U = 0$, we find the point of intersection of the required curve with the axis iV, namely, for $U = 0$ we have:

$$\omega = \frac{1}{T_2}, \qquad V = -\frac{kT_2}{T_1}.$$

This characteristic is represented in the form of the curve in Fig. 97b.

For an harmonically-oscillatorry element we have:

$$W(p) = \frac{k}{T_2^2 p^2 + 1},$$

and consequently,

$$W(i\omega) = \frac{k}{1 - T_2^2\omega^2}, \qquad U = \frac{k}{1 - T_2^2\omega^2}, \qquad V = 0,$$

which gives two straight lines on the real axis (Fig. 97c):

$$k \leqslant U \leqslant +\infty \qquad \text{with} \qquad 0 \leqslant \omega \leqslant \frac{1}{T_2},$$

$$-\infty \leqslant U \leqslant 0 \qquad \text{with} \qquad \frac{1}{T_2} \leqslant \omega \leqslant +\infty.$$

There corresponds to an unstable aperiodic element an amplitude-phase characteristic in the form of a semi-circle, Fig. 97d, since here

$$W(i\omega) = \frac{k}{T_1 i\omega - 1} = -\frac{kT_1 i\omega + k}{T_1^2 \omega^2 + 1},$$

$$U = -\frac{k}{T_1^2\omega^2 + 1}, \qquad V = -\frac{kT_1\omega}{T_1^2\omega^2 + 1}. \qquad (19.17)$$

For a second-order unstable element we obtain:

$$W(i\omega) = \frac{k}{-T_2^2\omega^2 - T_1 i\omega + 1},$$

$$U = \frac{k(1 - T_2^2\omega^2)}{(1 - T_2^2\omega^2)^2 + T_1^2\omega^2}, \qquad V = \frac{kT_1\omega}{(1 - T_2^2\omega^2)^2 + T_1^2\omega^2},$$

to which there corresponds the curve of Fig. 97e.

Amplitude-phase characteristics of compound elements. Let us consider certain types of elements, not related to the above simple ones.

An ideal differentiating element

$$W(p) = kp$$

---

* The amplitude-phase characteristic defines the steady-state sinusoidal forced oscillation of the element. In an isolated unstable element it cannot in practice occur. Therefore the characteristics are plotted here only theoretically for the later overall calculation of the system in which such elements may enter into the structure.

has the amplitude-phase characteristic

$$W(i\omega) = ki\omega, \quad U = 0, \quad V = k\omega,$$

coinciding with the positive imaginary axis (the line 1 in Fig. 98*a*).

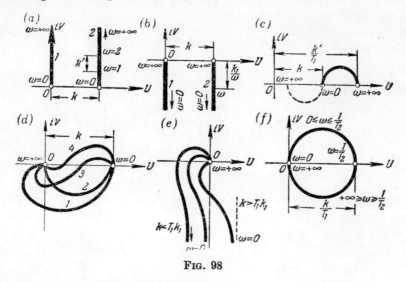

FIG. 98

For the ideally integrating element

$$W(i\omega) = \frac{k}{i\omega} = -i\frac{k}{\omega}, \quad U = 0, \quad V = -\frac{k}{\omega}$$

the characteristic coincides with the negative real axis (the line 1 in Fig. 98*b*).

For an ideal element with introduction of the derivative we obtain the line 2 (Fig. 98*a*), while for an ideal element with introduction of the integral, the line 2 (Fig. 98*b*), since in the latter case

$$W(i\omega) = k + k_1\frac{1}{i\omega}, \quad U = k, \quad V = -\frac{k_1}{\omega}.$$

An aperiodic element with introduction of derivative has the transfer function

$$W(p) = \frac{k + k'p}{T_1 p + 1},$$

from which

$$W(i\omega) = \frac{k + k'i\omega}{1 + T_1 i\omega} = \frac{(k + k'i\omega)(1 - T_1 i\omega)}{1 + T_1^2\omega^2},$$

$$U = \frac{k + k'T_1\omega^2}{1 + T_1^2\omega^2}, \quad V = \frac{(k' - kT_1)\omega}{1 + T_1^2\omega^2}, \quad (19.18)$$

which is represented in Fig. 98*c* in two forms: $kT_1 < k'$—the full line and $kT_1 > k'$—the broken line in the form of semi-circles.

For an oscillatory element with introduction of derivative

$$W(p) = \frac{k + k'p}{T_2^2 p^2 + T_1 p + 1}$$

we obtain

$$W(i\omega) = \frac{k + k'i\omega}{1 - T_2^2\omega^2 + T_1 i\omega} = \frac{(k + k'i\omega)(1 - T_2^2\omega^2 - T_1 i\omega)}{(1 - T_2^2\omega^2)^2 + T_1^2\omega^2},$$

from which we find

$$\left.\begin{array}{l} U = \dfrac{k(1 - T_2^2\omega^2) + k'T_1\omega^2}{(1 - T_2^2\omega^2)^2 + T_1^2\omega^2}, \\[4mm] V = -\dfrac{[kT_1 - k'(1 - T_2^2\omega^2)]\,\omega}{(1 - T_2^2\omega^2)^2 + T_1^2\omega^2} \end{array}\right\} \qquad (19.19)$$

The point $U = 0$ (intersection of the curve with the axis iV) is here defined by the values

$$\omega_U^2 = \frac{k}{kT_2^2 - k'T_1}, \qquad V_U = -\frac{k}{T_1\omega_U} = -\frac{\sqrt{k(kT_2^2 - k'T_1)}}{T_1}.$$

It exists only for $kT_2^2 > k'T_1$. Let us find further the point $V = 0$ (intersection with the U-axis):

$$\omega_V^2 = \frac{1}{T_2^2}\left(1 - \frac{kT_1}{k'}\right), \qquad U_V = \frac{k'}{T_1}.$$

This point exist only for $k' > kT_1$. Therefore four types of amplitude-phase characteristics are possible for an oscillatory element with introduction of the derivative, as shown in Fig. 98d. Of these, curve 1 occurs for

$$kT_2^2 > k'T_1 \quad \text{and} \quad k' < kT_1,$$

curve 2 for

$$kT_2^2 < k'T_1 \quad \text{and} \quad k' < kT_1,$$

curve 3 for

$$kT_2^2 > k'T_1 \quad \text{and} \quad k' > kT_1,$$

curve 4 for

$$kT_2^2 < k'T_1 \quad \text{and} \quad k' > kT_1.$$

From a comparison of the curve in Fig. 97b with the curves of Fig. 98d, it is clearly evident that introduction of the derivative deforms and rotates the amplitude-phase characteristic of the element about the origin of coordinates counterclockwise and the more strongly, the greater the coefficient k' of the derivative (and the smaller the time constant T_2). This will be important for us below.

For an oscillatory element with introduction of the integral we have:

$$W(p) = \frac{kp + k_1}{p(T_2^2 p^2 + T_1 p + 1)},$$

$$W(i\omega) = \frac{k\omega - ik_1}{\omega(1 - T_2^2\omega^2 + T_1 i\omega)},$$

from which

$$U = \frac{k(1 - T_2^2\omega^2) - T_1 k_1}{(1 - T_2^2\omega^2)^2 + T_1^2\omega^2}, \qquad V = -\frac{k_1(1 - T_2^2\omega^2) + T_1 k\omega^2}{\omega[(1 - T_2^2\omega^2)^2 + T_1^2\omega^2]}.$$

For $\omega = 0$ we have:

$$U_0 = k - T_1 k_1, \qquad V_0 = -\infty.$$

For $U = 0$

$$\omega_U^2 = \frac{k - T_1 k_1}{kT_2^2}, \qquad V_U = -\frac{k}{T_1\omega_U} = -\frac{kT_2}{T_1}\sqrt{\frac{k}{k - T_1 k_1}}.$$

For $V = 0$

$$\omega_V^2 = \frac{k_1}{k_1 T_2^2 - T_1 k}, \qquad U_V = -\frac{k_1}{T_1\omega_V^2} = -\left(\frac{k_1 T_2^2}{T_1} - k\right).$$

As a result of this we obtain in Fig. 98e three variants of the amplitude-phase characteristics for this element.

Here it is evident that introduction of the integral, in contrast to the derivative, deforms and rotates the amplitude-phase characteristics of the element clockwise and the more strongly, the greater the coefficient k_1 of the integral (and the greater the time constant T_2).

For an oscillatory differentiating element, when

$$W(p) = \frac{kp}{T_2^2 p^2 + T_1 p + 1},$$

we obtain the amplitude-phase characteristic in the form of a complete circle of radius $k/2T_1$ (Fig. 98f), so that here the expressions

$$U = \frac{kT_1\omega^2}{(1 - T_2^2\omega^2)^2 + T_1^2\omega^2}, \qquad V = \frac{k(1 - T\omega^2)\omega}{(1 - T_2^2\omega^2)^2 + T_1^2\omega^2}$$

satisfy the equation of a circle

$$\left(U - \frac{k}{2T_1}\right)^2 + V^2 = \left(\frac{k}{2T_1}\right)^2,$$

which is easily verified by substitution.

It is possible by an analogous method to plot the amplitude-phase characteristics for any other possible combinations of left and right-hand parts of the element equation.

Logarithmic frequency characteristics of simple elements. Let us consider two types of simple element: aperiodic and oscillatory.

An aperiodic element, as is evident from the expression for its amplitude-phase characteristics, has the following amplitude frequency characteristic:

$$A(\omega) = \frac{k}{\sqrt{T_1^2\omega^2 + 1}}.$$

The logarithmic amplitude characteristic from Section 8 will be:

$$A_l(\omega) = 20\log k - 20\log\sqrt{T_1^2\omega^2 + 1}. \qquad (19.20)$$

We have approximately

$$\left.\begin{array}{ll}
\sqrt{T_1^2\omega^2 + 1} \approx 1 \quad \text{and} \quad A_l(\omega) \approx 20\log k & \text{for } \omega \ll \dfrac{1}{T_1} \\[2mm]
\sqrt{T_1^2\omega^2 + 1} = \sqrt{2} \;\text{and}\; A_l(\omega) = 20\log k - 3 & \text{for } \omega = \dfrac{1}{T_1} \\[2mm]
\sqrt{T_1^2\omega^2 + 1} \approx T_1\omega \;\text{and}\; A_l(\omega) \approx 20\log k - 20\log T_1\omega & \text{for } \omega \gg \dfrac{1}{T_1}
\end{array}\right\} \quad (19.21)$$

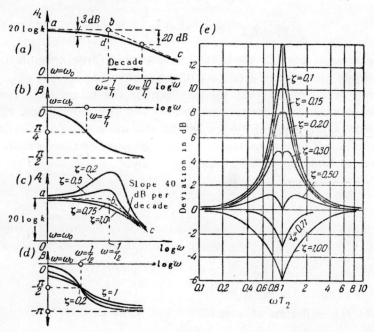

FIG. 99

The first of these expressions gives the horizontal straight line *ab* (Fig. 99a), the second gives the point *d* while the third the inclined line *bc*. Let us calculate its slope, measuring in decibels per decade or in decibels per octave. The decibel is the designation of the unit of measurement along the axis of ordinates for the quantity $A_1 = 20\log A$. Decade is the term of a segment along the axis of abscissae $\lg \omega$, corresponding to a change of frequency ω by a factor of ten. An octave is a section along the axis $\log \omega$, corresponding to a change of ω by a factor of two. Since for the line bc we have $A_l(\omega) = 20 \log k - 20 \log T_1 \omega$, in a single decade we will have:

$$A_l(10\omega) = 20 \log k - 20 \log T_1 10\omega = 20 \log k - 20 \log T_1 \omega - 20 \log 10$$
$$= A_l(\omega) - 20 \ .$$

Consequently, the ordinate of the line bc decreases by 20 units, i.e. by 20 dB, with increase of abscissa by one decade (Fig. 99a). This is called a slope of 20 dB per decade. If along the axis of abscissae we take an octave, we obtain

$$A_l(2\omega) = 20 \log k - 20 \log T_1 2\omega = 20 \log k - 20 \log T_1 \omega - 20 \log 2$$
$$= A_l(\omega) - 6 \cdot 02 \ .$$

Consequently, a slope of 20 dB per decade is equivalent to a slope of approximately 6 dB per octave.

Thus, a logarithmic amplitude characteristic of an aperiodic (inertial) element is represented approximately by two straight lines: one horizontal ab and the other inclined bc with a slope of 20 dB per decade, where the point of intersection b is defined by the frequency $\omega = 1/T_1$. If it is required to represent a given characteristic more exactly, then it is necessary to lay out from the point of intersection a segment $bd = 3$ dB downwards and to plot through the point d a curve asymptotically approaching the lines ab and bc. When necessary to obtain a high precision, it is possible to calculate a further point on each branch of the curve. The polygonal curve abc is termed the asymptotic logarithmic characteristic.

The phase-frequency characteristic of an aperiodic element from (8.18) and (19.15) will be:

$$\beta(\omega) = \tan^{-1} \frac{V}{U} = -\tan^{-1} T_1 \omega \ ,$$

which is shown in Fig. 99b.

We note that along the axis of abscissae of the logarithmic characteristics the values of ω do not begin from zero, since $\log \omega 0 = -\infty$, but from some value $\omega = \omega_0$, which may be taken differently in different problems.

For an oscillatory element we have from the expression $W(i\omega)$:

$$A(\omega) = \frac{k}{\sqrt{T_1^2 \omega^2 + (1 - T_2^2 \omega^2)^2}}, \qquad T_1 < 2T_2 \ ,$$

$$A_l(\omega) = 20 \log k - 20 \log \sqrt{T_1^2 \omega^2 + 1(1 - T_2^2 \omega^2)^2}.$$

$$(19.22)$$

From this we obtain

$$\left.\begin{aligned}
A_l(\omega) &\approx 20\log k & \text{for} \quad &\omega \ll \frac{1}{T_2}, \\
A_l(\omega) &\approx 20\log k - 20\log T_2^2\omega^2 & \text{for} \quad &\omega \gg \frac{1}{T_2},
\end{aligned}\right\} \qquad (19.23)$$

where the first relation gives the horizontal line *ab* (Fig. 99c) while the second the line *bc* with the slope of 40 dB per decade or approximately 12 dB per octave. The point of intersection *b* corresponds to the frequency $\omega = 1/T_2$.

However, for an oscillatory element the true logarithmic amplitude characteristic may differ strongly from the asymptotic characteristic *abc*. This is shown in Fig. 99c where we put

$$\zeta = \frac{T_1}{2T_2} \; (\zeta \leqslant 1).$$

In Fig. 99e a graph is given of the deviation of the true characteristic from the asymptotic for various values of ζ. From this graph it is evident that the asymptotic characteristic corresponds to the true one to within 3 dB only for

$$0{\cdot}38 \leqslant \zeta \leqslant 0{\cdot}71.$$

If $\zeta < 0{\cdot}38$, the maximum deviation will be equal to $20\log 2\zeta\sqrt{1-\zeta^2}$ at values $\omega T_2 = \sqrt{1 \pm 2\zeta^2}$. If $\zeta > 0{\cdot}71$, the maximum deviation is equal to $20\log 2\zeta$ at $\omega T_2 = 1$.

Starting from this, it is recommended to plot the logarithmic amplitude characteristic for an oscillatory element either using the graph of Fig. 99e or directly using formulae (19.22) in the interval of frequencies *

$$\omega_I < \omega < \omega_{II},$$

where ω_I is defined as the smallest of the real values

$$T_2\omega_I = \sqrt{(1-2\zeta^2) + \sqrt{(1-2\zeta^2)^2 + 1}},$$
$$T_2\omega_I' = \sqrt{(1-2\zeta^2) + \sqrt{(1-2\zeta^2)^2 - 0{\cdot}5}},$$

while ω_{II} from

$$T_2\omega_{II} = \sqrt{(2\zeta^2-1) + \sqrt{(2\zeta^2-1)^2 + 1}} = \frac{1}{T_2\omega_I},$$

$$T_2\omega_{II}' = \sqrt{2(1-2\zeta^2) + \sqrt{4(1-2\zeta^2)^2 - 2}} = \frac{1}{T_2\omega_I'}.$$

---

* According to V. V. Solodovnikov.

The phase-frequency characteristic of an oscillatory element according to (19.16) will be (Fig. 99d):

$$\beta(\omega) = \tan^{-1}\frac{V}{U} = -\tan^{-1}\frac{T_1\omega}{1-T_2^2\omega^2}.$$

A second-order aperiodic element may always be divided into two first-order aperiodic elements, for each of which it is possible to plot the characteristics, employing Fig. 99a and b.

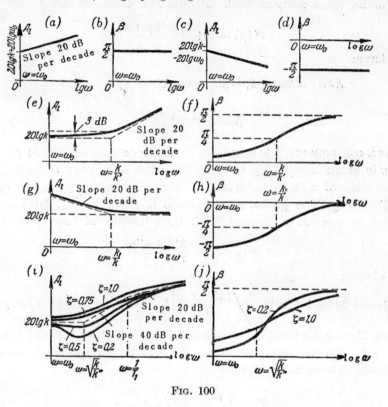

Fig. 100

Logarithmic frequency characteristics of non-simple elements. Let us consider certain types of element of this category.

For an ideally differentiating element we have $W(i\omega) = ki\omega$, from which

$$A_l(\omega) = 20\log k + 20\log\omega, \qquad \beta = \frac{\pi}{2},$$

which is represented by a straight line with a slope of 20 decibels per decade (Fig. 100a) and a horizontal line (Fig. 100b).

For an ideal integrating element (Fig. 100c and d) there will be:

$$A_l(\omega) = 20\log k - 20\log\omega, \qquad \beta = \frac{\pi}{2}.$$

For an ideal element with introduction of derivative

$$W(p) = k + k'p$$

we obtain:

$$A_l(\omega) = 20\log k + 20\log \sqrt{1 + \left(\frac{k'}{k}\,\omega\right)^2}\,, \qquad \beta = \tan^{-1}\frac{k'\omega}{k}\,.$$

Comparing this with (19.20), we obtain by analogy the graphs A_l and β (Fig. 100*e* and *f*).

For an ideal element with introduction of the integral

$$W(p) = k + \frac{k_1}{p} = \frac{kp + k_1}{p}$$

we have:

$$A_l(\omega) = 20\log k_1 - 20\log \omega + 20\log \sqrt{\left(\frac{k}{k_1}\,\omega\right)^2 + 1}\,,$$

$$\beta = -\tan^{-1}\frac{k_1}{k\omega}\,.$$

As a consequence it is necessary to construct the amplitude characteristic of an integrating element from the amplitude characteristic of an element with introduction of derivative, which gives the curve of Fig. 100*g*. The phase characteristic is given in Fig. 100*h*.

For an aperiodic element with introduction of two derivatives

$$W(p) = \frac{k + k'p + k''p^2}{T_1 p + 1}$$

we obtain:

$$A_l(\omega) = 20\log k + 20\log \sqrt{\left(\frac{k'}{k}\,\omega\right)^2 + \left[1 - \frac{k''}{k}\,\omega^2\right]^2} - 20\log \sqrt{T_1^2\omega^2 + 1}\,,$$

where the second term is defined as for an oscillatory element (19.22), but with reversed sign, while the third as for an aperiodic element, where it is necessary to put:

$$T_2 = \sqrt{\frac{k''}{k}}\,, \qquad \zeta = \frac{k'}{2k''}\,; \tag{19.24}$$

as the result we obtain the logarithmic amplitude characteristic in the form of Fig. 100*i*. The phase-frequency characteristic of this element will be:

$$\beta = \tan^{-1}\frac{k'\omega}{k - k''\omega^2} - \tan^{-1}T_1\omega\,,$$

i.e. it is necessary to take the phase characteristic of the oscillatory element with reversed sign (in the notation of (19.24)) and to add the characteristic of an aperiodic element with the same negative sign (Fig. 100*j*).

The logarithmic frequency characteristics are constructed analogously for other types of element.

General remarks. All the characteristics presented in the present paragraph clearly illustrate the dynamic properties of different individually taken elements of an automatic system. The processes occuring in them, as already discussed, change radically when they are included in closed automatic systems. But to find the latter it is necessary to know the dynamic equations or the characteristics of all elements of which the system consists.

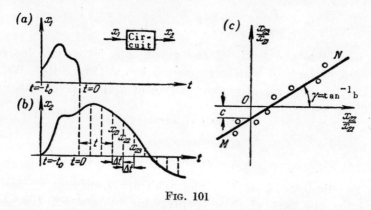

FIG. 101

In individual cases, if it is not possible to construct the dynamic equation of some element in a real system, it is possible on the basis of the above materials to match these equations from experimentally recorded time or frequency characteristics. It frequently happens that the form of the element equation is approximately known but it is difficult to calculate the numerical values of its coefficients theoretically. Then the above material permits finding these from the experimental characteristics and, incidentally, to verify if the adopted form of the element equation is successful (since to each form of equation there corresponds a definite form of time and amplitude-phase characteristics).

Let us discuss one procedure for determining the coefficients of the element equation from experimental data, proposed by Ia. Z. Tsypkin. We apply to the input of the element an arbitrary force $x_1(t)$ and then remove it (Fig. 101a). We plot during this period (for example, using an oscillograph) the variation of the output quantity, x_2 (Fig. 101b). We shall consider only that part of the graph $x_t(t)$, occuring after removal of the input quantity ($x_1 = 0$). Therefore the time t will be read, as shown in Fig. 101a and b, from the instant of removing the input force.

Let us assume that the element may be described by a second-order equation with a simple right-hand part

$$(T_2^2 p^2 + T_1 p + 1) x_2 = k x_1; \qquad (19.25)$$

it is required to find the values of T_1, T_2. (The transfer factor k is taken from the experimentally recorded static characteristic of the element).

The solution of equation (19.25) has the form

$$x_2 = C_1 e^{z_1 t} + C_2 e^{z_2 t} , \qquad (19.26)$$

where

$$z_{1,2} = -\alpha \pm i\omega , \qquad (19.27)$$

$$\alpha = \frac{T_1}{2T_2^2}, \qquad \omega = \sqrt{\alpha^2 - \omega_0^2}, \qquad \omega_0^2 = \frac{1}{T_2^2} . \qquad (19.28)$$

Let us divide the t-axis of the graph $x_2(t)$ into equal intervals, the length of each of which is denoted by Δt (Fig. 101b). We also denote by x_{21}, x_{22}, x_{23} any three adjacent ordinates of the graph $x_2(t)$. Then

$$x_{21} = C_1 e^{z_1 t} + C_2 e^{z_1 t} ,$$
$$x_{22} = C_1 e^{z_1(t+\Delta t)} + C_2 e^{z_2(t+\Delta t)} ,$$
$$x_{23} = C_1 e^{z_1(t+2\Delta t)} + C_2 e^{z_2(t+2\Delta t)} .$$

Let us eliminate from this the arbitrary constants C_1 and C_2, multiplying the first of these expressions by $e^{(z_1+z_2)\Delta t}$, the second by $-(e^{z_1\Delta t} + e^{z_2\Delta t})$, and then add all three equations. The result is:

$$x_{23} - (e^{z_1\Delta t} + e^{z_2\Delta t}) x_{22} + e^{(z_1+z_2)\Delta t} x_{21} = 0$$

or

$$\frac{x_{23}}{x_{21}} = b \frac{x_{22}}{x_{21}} - c , \qquad (19.29)$$

where

$$b = e^{z_1\Delta t} + e^{z_2\Delta t} , \qquad c = e^{(z_1+z_2)\Delta t} . \qquad (19.30)$$

The expression (19.29) is the equation of the straight line shown in Fig. 101c.

From this we have the following recommendation. It is necessary to measure all ordinates on the experimentally recorded graph $x_2(t)$ at intervals Δt (Fig. 101b). Then for each triplet of neighbouring ordinates it is necessary to calculate the ratios x_{22}/x_{21} and x_{23}/x_{21} each time plotting corresponding points in a plane (Fig. 101c). After this it is necessary to plot the inclined line MN to pass close to all the points (if this is possible, then the given element is actually described by equation (19.25)).

Further we measure in Fig. 101c the segment c and the angle γ, determining also $b = \tan\gamma$. Then, employing the formulae

$$\cosh(\omega\Delta t) = \frac{b}{2\sqrt{c}}, \qquad \alpha = -\frac{\ln c}{2\Delta t}, \qquad (19.31)$$

following from (19.30) and (19.27), we find the values $(\omega\Delta t)$ and α. Knowing the latter, we calculate the required coefficients T_2^2 and T_1

of the element equation (19.25) from the formulae

$$T_2^2 = \frac{1}{\alpha^2 - \omega^2}, \qquad T_1 = 2\alpha T_2^2, \qquad (19.32)$$

which follow from (19.28).

If the straight line MN in Fig. 101*c* passes through the origin of coordinates, i.e. $c = 0$, this will signify that the given element is described by a first-order equation

$$(Tp + 1)x_2 = kx_1,$$

where

$$T = -\frac{\Delta t}{\ln b}.$$

For stable circuits the straight line MN always lies below the bisectrix of the coordinate axes.

20. Transformation of equations and frequency characteristics of single-tuned systems

In constructing the dynamic equations of automatic systems, as we shall see below in specific examples, we first construct the equations of individual elements. Then, most frequently, we transform them to a single system equation in the form (5.6). The same is sometimes done with amplitude-phase characteristics of the elements to obtain the overall amplitude-phase characteristics of the system. Here we shall derive certain formulae by the aid of which it is possible to carry out these transformations easily.

In transforming two differential equations

$$Q_2(p)x_2 = R_2(p)x_1, \qquad Q_3(p)x_3 = R_3(p)x_2$$

to a single one we employ the following symbolic operation. Let us multiply the left-hand part of the equation and "cancel" all equations by the common factor x_2. As a result we obtain a single differential equation

$$Q_2(p)Q_3(p)x_3 = R_2(p)R_3(p)x_1,$$

which, after carrying out the operations of multiplication of polynomials in the left and right-hand sides, takes the ordinary form:

$$Q(p)x_3 = R(p)x_1.$$

This algebraic operation is the simplest method of eliminating variables from differential equation. Its validity may be verified in the following way. Let there be, for example, two differential equations

$$a_0\ddot{x}_2 + a_1\dot{x}_2 + a_2x_2 = b_0\dot{x}_1 + b_1x_1, \qquad c_0\dot{x}_3 + c_1x_3 = d_0\dot{x}_2,$$

i.e.

$$Q_2(p) = a_0 p^2 + a_1 p + a_2, \quad R_2(p) = b_0 p + b_1, \quad Q_3(p) = c_0 p + c_1,$$
$$R_3(p) = d_0 p.$$

To eliminate the variable x_2 from these two equations it is necessary to solve for x_2 in the second equation and substitute it in the first. We first differentiate the first equation and multiply by d_0:

$$a_0 d_0 \dddot{x}_2 + a_1 d_0 \ddot{x}_2 + a_2 d_0 \dot{x}_2 = b_0 d_0 \ddot{x}_1 + b_1 d_0 \dot{x}_1.$$

We then substitute here from the second equation:

$$a_0 (c_0 \dddot{x}_3 + c_1 \ddot{x}_3) + a_1 (c_0 \ddot{x}_3 + c_1 \dot{x}_3) + a_2 (c_0 \dot{x}_3 + c_1 x_3) = b_0 d_0 \ddot{x}_1 + b_1 d_0 \dot{x}.$$

or finally

$$a_0 c_0 \dddot{x}_3 + (a_0 c_1 + a_1 c_0) \ddot{x}_3 + (a_1 c_1 + a_2 c_0) \dot{x}_3 + a_2 c_1 x_3 = b_0 d_0 \ddot{x}_1 + b_1 d_0 \dot{x}_1,$$

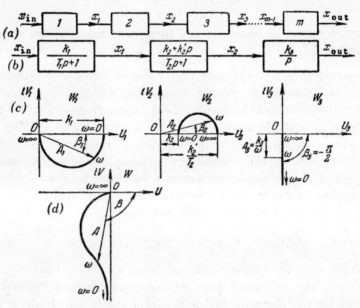

FIG. 102

from which the validity of the above algebraic operation becomes obvious. It is valid for any order and any number of equations. Its great practical advantage in application is without doubt.

Let us first describe the single equation and overall amplitude-phase characteristics obtained for the simplest open network of elements.

Open network. Let us consider an open system, consisting of m elements of directed action connected in series (Fig. 102a).

Let the network contain elements of arbitrary types, including those with introduction of derivatives and integrals and with feedback (which will be considered in Section 21) but excluding summation. We now write the element equations in the following general form:

$$\left. \begin{array}{l} 1 \text{ circuit } \ldots \; Q_1(p)x_1 = R_1(p)x_{\text{in}}\,, \\ 2 \text{ circuit } \ldots \; Q_2(p)x_2 = R_2(p)x_1\,, \\ 3 \text{ circuit } \ldots \; Q_3(p)x_3 = R_3(p)x_2\,, \\ \cdots\cdots\cdots\cdots\cdots\cdots\cdots\cdots \\ g\text{th circuit } \ldots \; Q_m(p)x_{\text{out}} = R_m(p)x_{m-1}\,. \end{array} \right\} \tag{20.1}$$

Here $Q_i(p)$ and $R_i(p)$ denote arbitrary polynomials in p, not only those shown in the table of Section 19. It is not necessary to reduce the equations (20.1) to the tabulated form. In particular cases $Q_i(p)$ and $R_i(p)$ may be equal to unity or to an arbitrary constant. For elements involving an integral it is more convenient to write the equation eliminating p from the denominator.

Multiplying all left and all right-hand sides of the equations (20.1), we arrive at a single equation of the open network (Fig. 102*a*) in the form

$$Q(p)x_{\text{out}} = R(p)x_{\text{in}}\,, \tag{20.2}$$

where

$$\left. \begin{array}{l} Q(p) = Q_1(p)\,Q_2(p)\ldots Q_m(p)\,, \\ R(p) = R_1(p)\,R_2(p)\ldots R_m(p)\,. \end{array} \right\} \tag{20.3}$$

The transfer function of this open network will be:

$$W(p) = \frac{R(p)}{Q(p)} = \frac{R_1(p)\,R_2(p)\ldots R_m(p)}{Q_1(p)\,Q_2(p)\ldots Q_m(p)}$$

or

$$W(p) = W_1(p)\,W_2(p)\ldots W_m(p)\,, \tag{20.4}$$

where $W_1(p), W_2(p), \ldots, W_m(p)$ are the transfer functions of individual elements. The amplitude-phase characteristic of the open network of series connected elements will consequently be

$$W(i\omega) = W_1(i\omega)\,W_2(i\omega)\ldots W_m(i\omega)\,, \tag{20.5}$$

i.e. it will be equal to the product of amplitude-phase characteristics of the individual elements. It is calculated by the rule of multiplication of complex numbers, namely, if each of the characteristics (20.5) is represented in the form $W_k = A_k e^{i\beta_k}$, then

$$A = A_1 A_2 \ldots A_m\,, \qquad \beta = \beta_1 + \beta_2 + \ldots + \beta_m\,, \tag{20.6}$$

where A_k and β_k denote the amplitudes and phases taken from the corresponding amplitude-phase characteristics at a common frequency ω.

For example, let, the open network of series-connected elements consist of three elements: a simple aperiodic, aperiodic with introduction of derivative and ideal integrating (Fig. 102*b*). It is possible to adopt one of the following methods for finding the overall amplitude-phase characteristic of the open network.

Graphic method. The amplitude-phase characteristics of individual elements (Fig. 102c) are taken complete from Figs. 97 and 98 or are obtained experimentally. Taking points corresponding to single (arbitrary) values of ω on all these characteristics, we find from the drawing (Fig. 102c) the amplitudes and phases A_1, β_1, A_2, β_2, A_3, β_3, from (20.6)

$$A = A_1 \cdot A_2 \cdot A_3 , \qquad \beta = \beta_1 + \beta_2 + \beta_3 ,$$

we obtain from the angle β and the magnitude A, as shown in Fig. 102d, the corresponding point of the overall amplitude-phase characteristic of the open network $W(i\omega)$. In the same manner we find several further points, which we join by a smooth curve. In particular as is evident from the drawing, the origin and end of the curve are defined by the following data:

$$A_{\omega=0} = k_1 \cdot k_2 \cdot \infty = \infty , \qquad \beta_{\omega=0} = 0 + 0 - \frac{\pi}{2} = -\frac{\pi}{2} ,$$

$$A_{\omega=\infty} = 0 \cdot \frac{k_2'}{T_2} \cdot 0 = 0 , \qquad \beta_{\omega=\infty} = -\frac{\pi}{2} + 0 - \frac{\pi}{2} = -\pi .$$

Analytic method. We have

$$W_1(i\omega) = \frac{k_1}{T_1 i\omega + 1} , \qquad W_2(i\omega) = \frac{k_2 + k_2' i\omega}{T_2 i\omega + 1} , \qquad W_3(i\omega) = \frac{k_3}{i\omega} .$$

Let us denote by A' and β' the moduli and arguments of the numerator, and by A'' and β'' the denominator. In the above expressions $W_1(i\omega)$, $W_2(i\omega)$, $W_3(i\omega)$, we have respectively:

$$A_1' = k_1 , \qquad \beta_1' = 0 , \qquad A_1'' = \sqrt{T_1^2\omega^2 + 1} , \qquad \beta_1'' = \tan^{-1} T_1\omega ,$$

$$A_2' = \sqrt{k_2^2 + (k_2'\omega)^2} , \qquad \beta_2' = \tan^{-1}\frac{k_2'\omega}{k_2} , \qquad A_2'' = \sqrt{T_2^2\omega^2 + 1} ,$$

$$\beta_2'' = \tan^{-1} T_2\omega ,$$

$$A_3' = k_3 , \qquad \beta_3' = 0 , \qquad A_3'' = \omega , \qquad \beta_3'' = \frac{\pi}{2} .$$

Considering formula (20.5), we obtain for the amplitude-phase characteristic of the entire open network $W(i\omega)$:

$$\left. \begin{aligned} A &= \frac{A_1' \cdot A_2' \cdot A_3'}{A_1'' \cdot A_2'' \cdot A_3''} = \frac{k_1 k_3 \sqrt{k_2^2 + (k_2'\omega)^2}}{\omega\sqrt{(T_1^2\omega^2 + 1)(T_2^2\omega^2 + 1)}} , \\ \beta &= \beta_1' - \beta_1'' + \beta_2' - \beta_2'' + \beta_3' - \beta_3'' \\ &= -\left(\tan^{-1} T_1\omega - \tan^{-1}\frac{k_2'\omega}{k_2} + \tan^{-1} T_2\omega + \frac{\pi}{2} \right). \end{aligned} \right\} \qquad (20.7)$$

Assigning various values of ω, we calculate from this formula pairs of values A and β from which we construct the amplitude-phase characteristic of the entire open network $W(i\omega)$ in accordance with Fig. 102d.

Use of logarithmic frequency characteristic. From relations (20.6) we obtain the following formulae for constructing the logarithmic frequency characteristics of an open network of series connected elements:

$$A_l = 20\log A = A_{l_1} + A_{l_2} + \ldots + A_{l_m}, \qquad \beta = \beta_1 + \beta_2 + \ldots + \beta_m,$$

where A_{l_1}, A_{l_2}, ..., A_{l_m} are the logarithmic amplitude characteristics of the individual elements.

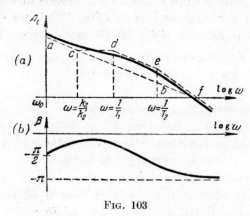

Fig. 103

For the same example of open network (Fig. 102b) we obtain:

$$A_l = 20\log k_1 k_2 k_3 - 20\log \sqrt{T_1^2 \omega^2 + 1} - 20\log \sqrt{T_2^2 \omega^2 + 1}$$
$$+ 20\log \sqrt{1 + \left(\frac{k_2'}{k_2}\right)^2 \omega^2} - 20\log \omega,$$

$$\beta = -\tan^{-1} T_1\omega - \tan^{-1} T_2\omega + \tan^{-1} \frac{k_2'\omega}{k_2} - \frac{\pi}{2}.$$

Plotting the characteristic A_1 consists of the following (Fig. 103a). Along the axis of abscissae we mark off the abscissae of the points of intersection of the asymptotic characteristics. For a given expression A_1, as is clear from Section 19, these points will be:

$$\omega = \frac{1}{T_1}, \qquad \omega = \frac{1}{T_2}, \qquad \omega = \frac{k_2}{k_2'}.$$

Their relative positions may vary in dependence on the specific values of the parameters. In addition, we denote an arbitrary point ω_0, which serves as the origin of coordinates of the graph.

From the point a (Fig. 103a) with ordinate equal to $20\log k_1 k_2 k_3$ $-20\log\omega_0$, we plot the straight line ab with a slope of 20 dB per decade. This line corresponds to the first and last component $(20\log k_1 k_2 k_3 - 20\log\omega)$ in the given expression A_1. To it we shall add the remaining components according to the order of the previously plotted abscissae of the break points.

The component $20\log\sqrt{1+(k_2'/k_2)^2\omega^2}$ from Fig. 100e to the break point has a zero slope and after this point a slope of 20 dB per decade upwards. Adding to the slope of the straight line ab (Fig 103a), we obtain the horizontal section cd. The component $-20\log\sqrt{T_1^2\omega^2+1}$ also has a zero slope to the point of break according to Fig. 99a and after this point a slope of 20 dB per decade downwards. Adding to the slope of the straight line cd (Fig. 103a), we obtain the new inclined segment de with slope 20 dB per decade. The component $-20\log\sqrt{T_2^2\omega^2+1}$ increases the slope of the characteristic after the point e, which gives the straight line ef with a slope of 40 dB per decade.

In accordance with Figs. 100e and 99a, the true logarithmic amplitude characteristic (full-line curve in Fig. 103a) first passes somewhat higher and then lower than the asymptotic characteristic $acdef$. The simplicity of the construction is obvious.

In the described construction an accumulation of errors occurs. The most exact characteristic in this case is obtained if the true values A_1 are calculated at the break points and then the points obtained joined by straight lines.

Employing the material of Section 19, by algebraic addition of the corresponding phase characteristics we also obtain the logarithmic phase-frequency characteristic of the given open network (Fig. 103b).

The use of experimental frequency characteristics. Frequency characteristics of any form may be obtained experimentally (Section 8). Therefore in those cases when it is difficult to set up the differential equation of some real part of the system, this need not be done but, constructing an operating model of it or taking a complete element in its natural form, record from it the frequency characteristics experimentally. As a result we shall have some of the element characteristics plotted by calculation from the equations and some of the characteristics obtained experimentally. Multiplying or adding them all, as shown above, we find the frequency characteristics of the entire open network (and then, as we shall see below, for the closed system).

Closed single-loop system with perturbation. In the general form (Fig. 104) such a system is defined by the following equations:

$$Q_1(p)\,x_1 = R_1(p)\,x_m + S_1(p)f(t)\,,$$
$$Q_2(p)\,x_2 = -\,R_2(p)\,x_1\,,$$
$$Q_3(p)\,x_3 = R_3(p)\,x_2\,,$$
$$\cdots\cdots\cdots\cdots\cdots\cdots$$
$$Q_m(p)\,x_m = R_m(p)\,x_{m-1}\,. \tag{20.8}$$

Elements 1, 2 and m may represent, for example, the following: the regulated object, the sensitive element (including the measurement of derivatives and integrals, if they are introduced into the

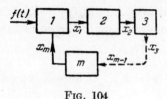

FIG. 104

regulation function and enter into $R_2(p)$) and the regulating organ, where $f(t)$ will be an arbitrary variation of the load on the object. The signs of the right-hand sides of equations (20.8) in general may be arbitrary, but if by $Q_i(p)$ and $R_i(p)$ are understood operational polynomials with positive coefficients, as a rule the total number of element equations with minus signs at the right will be odd (for the reason for this see Section 27).

Let us transform the system of equations (20.8) to a single equation.

From formulae (20.2) and (20.3) the equation of the network of elements from the second to the mth elements inclusive may be written in the form

$$Q_2(p)\,Q_3(p)\,\ldots\,Q_m(p)\,x_m = -\,R_2(p)\,R_3(p)\,\ldots\,R_m(p)\,x_1\,. \tag{20.9}$$

Then, multiplying the first of equations (20.8) by $Q_2(p)\,\ldots\,Q_m(p)$ and employing (20.9), we will have:

$$Q_1(p)\,Q_2(p)\,\ldots\,Q_m(p)\,x_1$$
$$= -\,R_1(p)\,R_2(p)\,\ldots\,R_m(p)\,x_1 + Q_2(p)\,\ldots\,Q_m(p)\,S_1(p)f(t)\,,$$

from which we obtain the required equation of the closed system in the form

$$L(p)\,x_1 = S(p)f(t)\,, \tag{20.10}$$

where

$$L(p) = Q(p) + R(p)\,, \qquad S(p) = \frac{Q(p)\,S_1(p)}{Q_1(p)}\,, \tag{20.11}$$

and $Q(p)$ and $R(p)$ are defined by formulae (20.3).

The static error of the system is defined by the formula

$$\Delta_{st} = \frac{S(0)}{L(0)} f^0 .$$

We recall that in such a "single-loop" system there may be not only "simple" elements but also compound elements with introduction of derivative and integrals included in $R_1(p)$. In a particular case, if the system consists of "simple" elements where the right-hand sides of these equations (table in Section 19) contain only kx_i, then $R_1(p) = k_1$, $R_2(p) = k_2$, ..., $R_m(p) = k_m$ (the transfer factors or gain factors of the elements) and in the equation of the system (20.10) we will have:

$$L(p) = Q(p) + k , \quad \text{where} \quad k = k_1 k_2 ... k_m . \qquad (20.12)$$

The quantity k is termed the overall transfer factor (or overall gain factor).

The transfer function (see Section 8) for the closed single-loop system with perturbation, according to the above formulae, will be:

$$W_f(p) = \frac{S(p)}{L(p)} = \frac{Q(p) S_1(p)}{Q_1(p)[Q(p) + R(p)]} .$$

If we divide the numerator and denominator by $Q(p)$, we obtain

$$W_f(p) = \frac{W_1^f(p)}{1 + W(p)} , \qquad (20.13)$$

where

$$W_1^f(p) = \frac{S_1(p)}{Q_1(p)} \quad \text{and} \quad W(p) = \frac{R(p)}{Q(p)} \qquad (20.14)$$

are the additional transfer function of the element 1 with respect to the perturbation (see the first of equations (20.8)) and the transfer function of the open loop, consisting of the same elements $1, 2, 3, ..., m$ as in the given closed system, respectively.

Consequently, the amplitude-phase characteristic of a closed single-loop with perturbation will be:

$$W_f(i\omega) = \frac{W_1^f(i\omega)}{1 + W(i\omega)} , \qquad (20.15)$$

where $W^f(i\omega)$ is the additional amplitude-phase characteristic of element I with respect to the perturbation while $W(i\omega)$ is the amplitude-phase characteristic of the corresponding open network. We already know how to find the latter from the above, while the first, i.e.

$$W_1^f(i\omega) = \frac{S_1(i\omega)}{Q_1(i\omega)},$$

is either calculated, if the element equation $Q_1(p)x_1 = R_1(p)x_m + S_1(p)f$ is given, or taken experimentally according to the scheme of Fig. 105b.

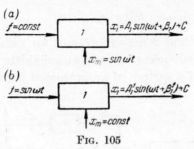

(a)

f=const → [1] → $x_1 = A_1 \sin(\omega t + \beta_1) + C$

$x_m = \sin \omega t$

(b)

f=sin ωt → [1] → $x_1 = A_1' \sin(\omega t + \beta_1') + C$

$x_m = \text{const}$

Fig. 105

Let the characteristic $W_1^f(i\omega)$ have the amplitude A_1^f and the phase β_1^f (Fig. 106a) while the characteristic $W(i\omega)$ has the following coordinates (Fig. 106b):

$$W(i\omega) = U(\omega) + iV(\omega).$$

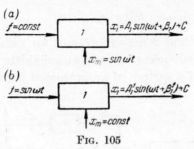

Fig. 106

Then the modulus A'' and the argument β'' of the denominator (20.15) will be:

$$A'' = \sqrt{[1 + U(\omega)]^2 + [V(\omega)]^2}, \qquad \beta'' = \tan^{-1}\frac{V(\omega)}{1 + U(\omega)}.$$

Therefore the amplitude A_f and the phase β_f of the characteristic of the given closed system is found as

$$A_f = \frac{A_1^f}{A''}, \qquad \beta_f = \beta_1' - \beta''. \tag{20.16}$$

The amplitude-phase characteristic is plotted from these expressions (Fig. 106c).

Graphically it is constructed by taking the values A_1^f, β_1^f from the drawing (Fig. 106a) and the values A'', β'' as shown in Fig. 106b for the same values of ω, with subsequent utilisation of formulae (20.16), and drawing the required curve according to Fig. 106c.

Closed single-loop system with command signal. In the general form (Fig. 107) such a system is defined by the equations

$$Q_1(p)x_1 = R_1(p)x_m + S_1(p)f(t) ,$$
$$Q_2(p)x_2 = R_2(p)x_1 ,$$
$$x = y(t) - x_2 \quad \text{(circuit } ED) ,$$
$$Q_3(p)x_3 = R_3(p)x ,$$
$$\cdots \cdots \cdots \cdots \cdots \cdots \cdots \cdots \cdots \cdots$$
$$Q_m(p)x_m = R_m(p)x_{m-1} . \qquad (20.17)$$

Here elements 1 and 2 may represent, for example: the controlled object and the feedback of a servomechanism or the object and sensitive element of a system of programmed regulation, respectively,

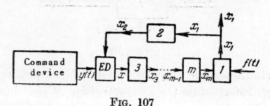

Fig. 107

while the element *ED* is the error detector. The symbol x denotes the error magnitude, the symbol x_1 the output (regulated) quantity of the system, while $y(t)$ is the input (command) quantity. The introduction of derivatives and integrals into the regulation function is defined by the right-hand sides of $R_i(p)$ of the equations.

Let us first find the common equation of the system with respect to the error x. Multiplying the third of equations (20.17) by $Q_2(p)$ and employing the second, we obtain:

$$Q_2(p)x = Q_2(p)y(t) - R_2(p)x_1 . \qquad (20.18)$$

For the network of elements from the third to the mth, from formulae (20.2) and (20.3) we have:

$$Q_3(p) \ldots Q_m(p)x_m = R_3(p) \ldots R_m(p)x . \qquad (20.19)$$

Multiplying the first of equations (20.17) by $Q_3(p) \ldots Q_m(p)$ and employing (20.19), and then multiplying the result by $R_2(p)$ and employing equation (20.18), we find the single equation for the closed system with respect to the error:

$$L(p)x = N(p)y(t) + S(p)f(t) , \qquad (20.20)$$

where

$$L(p) = Q(p) + R(p) , \quad N(p) = Q(p) ,$$
$$S(p) = \frac{Q(p)S_1(p)R_2(p)}{Q_1(p)Q_2(p)} , \qquad (20.21)$$

while $Q(p)$ and $R(p)$ are defined from formulae (20.3).

If $f = 0$ (i.e. the object has a constant load), which frequently occurs in servomechanisms, then equation (20.20) takes the form

$$[Q(p) + R(p)]x = Q(p)y(t) , \qquad (20.22)$$

while if, in addition, all the elements are "simple" (without derivatives and integrals in the right-hand sides), the system equation will be:

$$[Q(p) + k]x = Q(p)y(t) ,$$

where k is calculated from formula (20.12).

If we derive in a similar way the equation of the closed system with respect to the regulated quantity x_1, we obtain:

$$L(p)x_1 = N(p)y(t) + S(p)f(t) ,$$

where

$$\left. \begin{array}{ll} L(p) = Q(p) + R(p) , & N(p) = \dfrac{R(p)Q_2(p)}{R_2(p)} , \\[3mm] S(p) = \dfrac{Q(p)S_1(p)}{Q_1(p)} , & \end{array} \right\} \qquad (20.23)$$

while with respect to the quantity x_2

$$L(p)x_2 = N(p)y(t) + S(p)f(t) ,$$

where

$$\left. \begin{array}{ll} L(p) = Q(p) + R(p) , & N(p) = R(p) , \\[3mm] S(p) = \dfrac{Q(p)S_1(p)R_2(p)}{Q_1(p)Q_2(p)} . & \end{array} \right\} \qquad (20.24)$$

The various cases considered of writing the equations of a closed single-loop system with command input correspond to different amplitude-phase characteristics. Thus, from (20.21) we obtain with respect to the error x the following amplitude-phase characteristicts of the closed system:

$$W_f^x(i\omega) = \frac{S(i\omega)}{L(i\omega)} = \frac{-QS_1R_2}{Q_1Q_2(Q+R)} = -\frac{W_2(i\omega)W_1'(i\omega)}{1+W(i\omega)} , \qquad (20.25)$$

$$W_y^x(i\omega) = \frac{N(i\omega)}{L(i\omega)} = \frac{Q(i\omega)}{Q(i\omega)+R(i\omega)} = \frac{1}{1+W(i\omega)} \qquad (20.26)$$

(the first of these differs from (20.15) by the factor $W_2(i\omega)$, constituting the characteristic of the feedback circuit 2).

The amplitude-phase characteristics of the closed system with respect to the regulated quantity x_1 from (20.23) will be here:

$$W_f^{x_1}(i\omega) = \frac{QS_1}{Q_1(Q+R)} = \frac{W_1'(i\omega)}{1+W(i\omega)} , \qquad (20.27)$$

$$W_y^{x_1}(i\omega) = \frac{RQ_2}{R_2(Q+R)} = \frac{W(i\omega)}{W_2(i\omega)[1+W(i\omega)]} , \qquad (20.28)$$

while with respect to the quantity x_2, form (20.24):

$$W_y^{x_2} = \frac{R(i\omega)}{Q(i\omega) + R(i\omega)} = \frac{W(i\omega)}{1 + W(i\omega)} . \qquad (20.29)$$

The plotting of all these frequency characteristics of a closed system is carried out similarly to the above, if the amplitude-phase characteristic of the corresponding open system $W(i\omega)$ is known. We note, in addition, that there are special circle diagrams (Reference 11) for plotting the characteristics (20.26) and (20.29).

21. Transformation of the equations and frequency characteristics of multi-loop systems

Let us consider several simple examples of multi-loop systems.
Element with negative feedback.—We first obtain the equation and amplitude-phase frequency characteristic for an arbitrary element with feedback (108). Let the equation of the element and the feedback have the forms

$$\left.\begin{array}{l} Q_c(p)x_{\text{out}} = R_c(p)(x_{\text{in}} - x_{fb}) , \\ Q_{fb}(p)x_{fb} = R_{fb}(p)x_{\text{out}} . \end{array}\right\} \qquad (21.1)$$

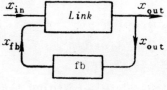

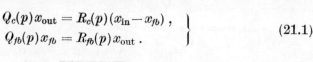

FIG. 108

Multiplying the first of equations (21.1) by $Q_{fb}(p)$ and substituting the second in it, we obtain the equation in the form

$$[Q_c(p)Q_{fb}(p) + R_c(p)R_{fb}(p)]x_{\text{out}} = R_c(p)Q_{fb}(p)x_{\text{in}} . \qquad (21.2)$$

Its transfer function will be:

$$W_c^{fb}(p) = \frac{R_c Q_{fb}}{Q_c Q_{fb} + R_c R_{fb}} = \frac{W_c(p)}{1 + W_c(p) W_{fb}(p)} , \qquad (21.3)$$

where

$$W_c(p) = \frac{R_c(p)}{Q_c(p)} , \qquad W_{fb}(p) = \frac{R_{fb}(p)}{Q_{fb}(p)}$$

is the transfer function of the element with feedback.

The amplitude-phase characteristic of an element with feedback will be, as a result:

$$W_c^{fb}(i\omega) = \frac{W_c(i\omega)}{1 + W_c(i\omega) W_{fb}(i\omega)} = \frac{1}{M_c(i\omega) + W_{fb}(i\omega)} , \qquad (21.4)$$

where

$$M_c = \frac{1}{W_c(i\omega)} = \frac{Q_c(i\omega)}{R_c(i\omega)};$$

M_c is termed the inverse amplitude-phase characteristic of the element.

For example, let there be an oscillatory element with introduction of integral (see table in Section 19), included in a feedback loop in the form of an aperiodic element. From Section 19 we take the corresponding amplitude-phase characteristics (Fig. 109a and b) and, by the rules of Section 20, we find first the product $W_c W_{fb}$ (Fig. 109c) and then W^{fb} (Fig. 109d).

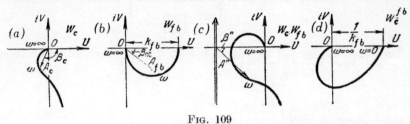

Fig. 109

From equation (21.2) it is easy to follow the influence of various forms of feedback on the properties of different types of element. We shall consider only two cases.

Let us take the element with introduction of integral (or integrating element, where the polynomial $Q_c(p)$ does not have a constant term while $R_c(p)$ has one. We shall include it in a stiff feedback, i.e. one for which $Q_{fb}(p)$ and $R_{fb}(p)$ both have constant terms in the equation. Then, as is evident from formula (21.2), the element (taken together with feedback) loses its integrating properties, since a constant term appears in the left-hand side of the equation equal to the product of constant terms of $R_c(p)$ and $R_{fb}(p)$. As a simple example: given equation (21.1) in the form:

$$p x_{\text{out}} = k_1(x_{\text{in}} - x_{fb}), \qquad x_{fb} = k_2 x_{\text{out}};$$

the equation of the element together with the feedback from (21.2) will be:

$$(p + k_1 k_2) x_{\text{out}} = k_1 x_{\text{in}}$$

or

$$(Tp + 1) x_{\text{out}} = k x_{\text{in}} \qquad T = \frac{1}{k_1 k_2}, \qquad k = \frac{1}{k_2},$$

i.e. the integrating element with an ideal stiff feedback changes to aperiodic.

Let us now take again an integrating element. But we shall include it in a transient feedback for which the equation $Q_{fb}(p)$ has a constant term, while $R_{fb}(p)$ does not have one. Then, as is evident from (21.2), the integrating property of the element (with feedback) is preserved. For example,

$$px_{out} = k_1(x_{in} - x_{fb}), \qquad (Tp+1)x_{fb} = k_2 px_{out}$$

the equation of the element together with feedback will be:

$$(Tp+1+k_1 k_2)px_{out} = (Tp+1)k_1 x_{in}$$

(the aperiodic element with introduction of integral). This property is utilised in designing astatic systems (see Section 11 and Section 14).

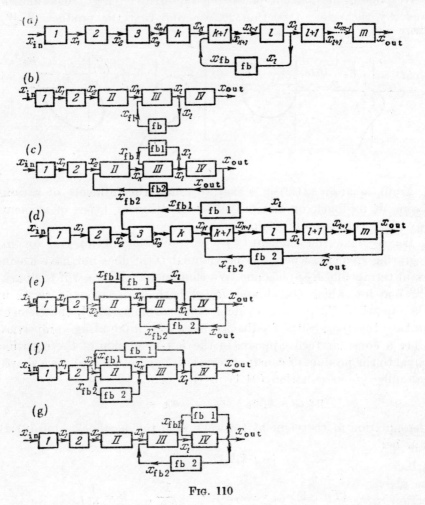

FIG. 110

Open network with negative feedback. Let feedback (Fig. 110a) be connected to the above open network (Fig. 102a) at an arbitrary point. The equations of all the elements except the $(k+1)$st are written in the form (20.1) while for the $(k+1)$st element we have:

$$Q_{k+1}(p)x_{k+1} = R_{k+1}(p)(x_k - x_{fb}), \tag{21.5}$$

where the feedback equation is added

$$Q_{fb}(p)x_{fb} = R_{fb}(p)x_l. \tag{21.6}$$

Individual portions of the network consisting of series connected elements are joined in "blocks" II, III and IV (Fig. 110b), the equations of which from (20.2), (20.3) and (21.2) will be:

$$\begin{aligned} Q_{II}(p)x_k &= R_{II}(p)x_2, \\ [Q_{III}(p)Q_{fb}(p) + R_{III}(p)R_{fb}(p)]x_l &= R_{III}(p)Q_{fb}(p)x_k, \\ Q_{IV}(p)x_{out} &= R_{IV}(p)x_l, \end{aligned} \right\} \tag{21.7}$$

where

$$\begin{aligned} Q_{II}(p) &= \prod_{i=3}^{k} Q_i(p), & R_{II}(p) &= \prod_{i=3}^{k} R_i(p), \\ Q_{III}(p) &= \prod_{i=k+1}^{l} Q_i(p), & R_{III}(p) &= \prod_{i=k+1}^{l} R_i(p), \\ Q_{IV}(p) &= \prod_{i=l+1}^{m} Q_i(p), & R_{IV}(p) &= \prod_{i=l+1}^{m} R_i(p) \end{aligned} \right| \tag{21.8}$$

(π is the symbol for the product). Considering now the block III together with feedback as a single element with a complex equation (the second of (21.7)), we may employ formulae (20.2) and (20.3) to obtain a single equation for the entire open network (Fig. 110b)

$$Q(p)x_{out} = R(p)x_{in}, \tag{21.9}$$

where

$$\begin{aligned} Q(p) &= Q_1 Q_2 Q_{II} Q_{IV}(Q_{III} Q_{fb} + R_{III} R_{fb}), \\ R(p) &= R_1 R_2 R_{II} R_{III} R_{IV} Q_{fb}. \end{aligned} \right\} \tag{21.10}$$

The amplitude-phase characteristic of such an open network (Fig. 110b) will be:

$$W(i\omega) = \frac{R(i\omega)}{Q(i\omega)} = \frac{W_1 W_2 W_{II} W_{III} W_{IV}}{1 + W_{III} W_{fb}}. \tag{21.11}$$

Open network with two negative feedbacks. Let us consider here four different cases. The network equation when the second feedback includes the first completely (Fig. 110c) is easily obtained from the above, specifically, applying formulae (21.9) and (21.10) to the section of the network II, III, IV and feedback 1 (Fig. 110c), we find for it the equation

$$Q'(p)x_{out} = R'(p)(x_2 - x_{fb2}), \tag{21.12}$$

where

$$\begin{aligned} Q'(p) &= Q_{II} Q_{IV}(Q_{III} Q_{fb4} + R_{III} R_{fb1}), \\ R'(p) &= R_{II} R_{III} R_{IV} Q_{fb1}. \end{aligned} \right\} \tag{21.13}$$

Considering this now as a single element and applying (21.9) and (21.10) to the entire network with feedback 2, we obtain the equation for the entire open network

$$Q(p)x_{\text{out}} = R(p)x_{\text{in}} \qquad (21.14)$$

where

$$Q(p) = Q_1 Q_2 (Q'Q_{fb2} + R'R_{fb2}) , \qquad R(p) = R_1 R_2 R' Q_{fb}$$

and after substitution of (21.13)

$$\left.\begin{aligned} Q(p) &= Q_1 Q_2 (Q_{\text{II}} Q_{\text{III}} Q_{\text{IV}} Q_{fb1} Q_{fb2} \\ &\quad + Q_{\text{II}} R_{\text{III}} Q_{\text{IV}} R_{fb1} Q_{fb2} + R_{\text{II}} R_{\text{III}} R_{\text{IV}} Q_{fb1} R_{fb2}) , \\ R(p) &= R_1 R_2 R_{\text{II}} R_{\text{III}} R_{\text{IV}} Q_{fb1} Q_{fb2} . \end{aligned}\right\} \qquad (21.15)$$

The amplitude-phase characteristic of this open network will be:

$$W(i\omega) = \frac{R(i\omega)}{Q(i\omega)} = \frac{W_1 W_2 W_{\text{II}} W_{\text{III}} W_{\text{IV}}}{1 + W_{\text{III}} W_{fb1} + W_{\text{II}} W_{\text{III}} W_{\text{IV}} W_{fb2}} . \qquad (21.16)$$

The numerator of this formula contains the amplitude-phase characteristics of all the series-connected blocks (Fig. 110c) and the denominator, unity with two terms (from the number of feedbacks), in each of which the feedback characteristic is multiplied by the characteristic of the block included by it.

As the second example we shall consider one where the feedbacks partially overlap each other (Fig. 110e). In this case the equations of all the elements have the above form (20.1), except the third and $(k+1)$st for which we have:

$$\left.\begin{aligned} Q_3(p)x_3 &= R_3(p)(x_2 - x_{fb1}) , \\ Q_{k+1}(p)x_{k+1} &= R_{k+1}(p)(x_k - x_{fb2}) , \end{aligned}\right\} \qquad (21.17)$$

where two feedback equations are added:

$$\left.\begin{aligned} Q_{fb1}(p)x_{fb1} &= R_{fb1}(p)x_l , \\ Q_{fb2}(p)x_{fb2} &= R_{fb2}(p)x_{\text{out}} . \end{aligned}\right\} \qquad (21.18)$$

Joining the sections of the network of series-connected elements into blocks (Fig. 110e), we write the equations of the blocks:

$$\left.\begin{aligned} Q_{\text{II}}(p)x_k &= R_{\text{II}}(p)(x_2 - x_{fb1}) , \\ Q_{\text{III}}(p)x_l &= R_{\text{III}}(p)(x_k - x_{fb2}) , \\ Q_{\text{IV}}(p)x_{\text{out}} &= R_{\text{IV}}(p)x_l , \end{aligned}\right\} \qquad (21.19)$$

where $Q_{\text{II}}, Q_{\text{III}}, Q_{\text{IV}}, R_{\text{II}}, R_{\text{III}}, R_{\text{IV}}$ are defined by the above formulae (21.8). Multiplying the first equation (21.19) by Q_{fb1} and the second by Q_{fb2}, we eliminate x_{fb1} and x_{fb2} using (21.18). Multiplying again both of them by R_{IV}, we eliminate x_l, using the third of equations (21.19). Then the first of the two equations obtained is multiplied by $Q_{fb2} R_{\text{III}}$ with the use of which we eliminate x_k. As a result we shall have a single equation for the entire open network (Fig. 110*d*) and *e*) in the form

$$Q(p)x_\text{out} = R(p)x_\text{in} , \qquad (21.20)$$

where

$$\left.\begin{aligned}
Q(p) &= Q_1Q_2(Q_{II}Q_{III}Q_{IV}Q_{fb1}Q_{fb2} \\
&\quad + R_{II}R_{III}Q_{IV}R_{fb1}Q_{fb2} + Q_{II}R_{III}R_{IV}Q_{fb1}R_{fb2}) , \\
R(p) &= R_1R_2R_{II}R_{III}R_{IV}Q_{fb1}Q_{fb2} .
\end{aligned}\right\} \qquad (21.21)$$

The amplitude-phase characteristic of this open network will be:

$$W(i\omega) = \frac{R(i\omega)}{Q(i\omega)} = \frac{W_1W_2W_{II}W_{III}W_{IV}}{1 + W_{II}W_{III}W_{fb1} + W_{III}W_{IV}W_{fb2}} , \qquad (21.22)$$

where the same principle is observed for constructing the formulae as in (21.16).

The same principle is valid even for the case where both feedbacks are connected to the same element (Fig. 110*f*). In this case the equation of the open network takes on the same form (21.20), where

$$\begin{aligned}
Q(p) &= Q_1Q_2Q_{IV}(Q_{II}Q_{III}Q_{fb1}Q_{fb2} + R_{II}R_{III}R_{fb1}Q_{fb2} \\
&\quad + R_{II}Q_{III}Q_{fb1}R_{fb2}) , \\
R(p) &= R_1R_2R_{II}R_{III}R_{IV}Q_{fb1}Q_{fb2} .
\end{aligned} \qquad (21.23)$$

The amplitude-phase characteristic of such an open element will be:

$$W(i\omega) = \frac{R(i\omega)}{Q(i\omega)} = \frac{W_1W_2W_{II}W_{III}W_{IV}}{1 + W_{II}W_{III}W_{fb1} + W_{II}W_{fb2}} . \qquad (21.24)$$

Where both feedbacks originate at the output of a single elements (Fig. 110*g*) we obtain in exactly the same way the equation of the open network (21.20) in which

$$\left.\begin{aligned}
Q(p) &= Q_1Q_2Q_{II}(Q_{III}Q_{IV}Q_{fb1}Q_{fb2} + Q_{III}R_{IV}R_{fb1}Q_{fb2} \\
&\quad + R_{III}R_{IV}Q_{fb1}R_{fb2}) , \\
R(p) &= R_1R_2R_{II}R_{III}R_{IV}Q_{fb1}Q_{fb2}
\end{aligned}\right\} \qquad (21.25)$$

and the amplitude-phase characteristic of the open network

$$W(i\omega) = \frac{R(i\omega)}{Q(i\omega)} = \frac{W_1W_2W_{II}W_{III}W_{IV}}{1 + W_{IV}W_{fb1} + W_{III}W_{IV}W_{fb2}} . \qquad (21.26)$$

Open network with branching. Let an open network be composed of certain blocks of elements with branching (Fig. 111). The equations of the blocks have the form

$$Q_1(p)x_1 = R_1(p)x_\text{in} , \qquad Q_2(p)x_2 = R_2(p)x_1 ,$$
$$Q_{II}(p)x_k = R_{II}(p)x_2 , \qquad Q_{III}(p)x_l = R_{III}(p)x_2 ,$$
$$Q_{IV}(p)x_\text{out} = R_{IV}(p)(x_k + x_l) .$$

14

From this we find the equation of the open network.

$$Q(p)x_{\text{out}} = R(p)x_{\text{in}} \tag{21.27}$$

where

$$\left. \begin{aligned} Q(p) &= Q_1 Q_2 Q_{\text{II}} Q_{\text{III}} Q_{\text{IV}}, \\ R(p) &= R_1 R_2 R_{\text{IV}}(R_{\text{II}} Q_{\text{III}} + Q_{\text{II}} R_{\text{III}}). \end{aligned} \right\} \tag{21.28}$$

The amplitude-phase characteristic of this open network will be

$$W(i\omega) = \frac{R(i\omega)}{Q(i\omega)} = W_1 W_2 W_{\text{IV}}(W_{\text{II}} + W_{\text{III}}), \tag{21.29}$$

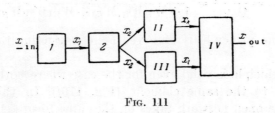

Fig. 111

i.e. the amplitude-phase characteristics of the parallel-connected blocks are added.

It is similarly easily possible to derive formulae for various other complex open-network systems.

Here, as in Section 20, experimentally obtained frequency characteristics of the elements may be used in all cases in place of calculating them from the differential equations.

Closed systems with additional feedbacks and with branching. In Fig. 112 are represented six different structural diagrams of closed systems, with perturbation f (for example, automatic regulation systems), and six different structural diagrams for closed systems in which the command y is introduced (for example, servomechanisms or program-controlled systems). Here such closed systems are taken to which correspond the six forms of open networks with negative feedback and with branching considered above. The introduction into the regulation function of derivatives and integrals is defined by the right-hand sides $R_i(p)$ of the regulator element equations.

The equations of all the elements remain the same as for the open networks (with substitution of the index "out" by m), except the first (regulated object), for which we have

$$Q_1(p)x_1 = R_1(p)x_m + S_1(p)f(t), \tag{21.30}$$

and the element ED (error detector)

$$x = y(t) - x_2. \tag{21.31}$$

It is assumed, as before, that in regulation systems an odd number of elements (most frequently one) of the basic loop has a minus sign before the right-hand sides of the equations; in the presence of the command signal the necessary minus sign is given by relation

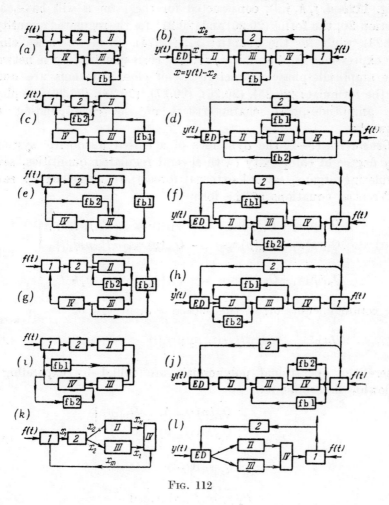

FIG. 112

(21.31). The equations of all open networks here, as in Section 20, have been reduced to a single form $Q(p)x_{out} = R(p)x_{in}$, where the operational polynomials $Q(p)$ and $R(p)$ have differing expressions for different networks.

In this connection the equations of all open systems with perturbations (Fig. 112a, c, e, g, i, k) are brought to the forms (20.10) and (20.11), as in Section 20, but only now the expressions $Q(p)$ and $R(p)$ must be taken from the formulae for the corresponding open networks (21.10), (21.15), (21.21), (21.23), (21.25) or (21.28). The amplitude-phase characteristic of the closed system will also have the form (20.15), where $W(i\omega)$ is the characteristic corresponding to the open network: (21.11), (21.16), (21.22), (21.24), (21.26) or (21.29).

The equations of all closed systems with command signals (Fig. 112b, d, f, h, j, l), constructed for the error x will have, as in Section 20, the forms (20.20) and (20.21), for the regulated quantity x_1, (20.23), while for the quantity x_2, (20.24). In all cases we employ the expressions $Q(p)$ and $R(p)$ for the corresponding open networks. The amplitude-phase characteristics of closed systems are defined by the formulae: (20.25), (20.26), (20.27), (20.28), (20.29), employing the amplitude-phase characteristics of the corresponding open networks.

General case.—If the dynamics of a closed automatic system of any degree of complexity (with several regulated quantities, several regulating organs, several external forces) are described by several differential equations of the form

$$\left.\begin{aligned}
Q_{11}(p)x_1 + Q_{12}(p)x_2 + \ldots + Q_{1n}(p)x_n &= P_1(p)f_1(t)\,, \\
Q_{21}(p)x_1 + Q_{22}(p)x_2 + \ldots + Q_{2n}(p)x_n &= P_2(p)f_2(t)\,, \\
\ldots\ldots\ldots\ldots\ldots\ldots\ldots\ldots\ldots\ldots\ldots \\
Q_{n1}(p)x_1 + Q_{n2}(p)x_2 + \ldots + Q_{nn}(p)x_n &= P_n(p)f_n(t)\,,
\end{aligned}\right\}
\quad (21.32)$$

the common equation of this closed system will be:

$$L(p)x_1 = S_1(p)f_1(t) + S_2(p)f_2(t) + \ldots + S_n(p)f_n(t)\,, \quad (21.33)$$

where the operational polynomials are found by expanding the following determinants:

$$L(p) = \begin{vmatrix}
Q_{11}(p) & Q_{12}(p) & \ldots & Q_{1n}(p) \\
Q_{21}(p) & Q_{22}(p) & \ldots & Q_{2n}(p) \\
\ldots & \ldots & \ldots & \ldots \\
Q_{n1}(p) & Q_{n2}(p) & \ldots & Q_{nn}(p)
\end{vmatrix}\,, \quad (21.34)$$

$$\begin{aligned}
S_1(p) &= P_1(p)\,A_{11}(p)\,, \\
S_2(p) &= P_2(p)\,A_{21}(p)\,, \\
&\ldots\ldots\ldots\ldots \\
S_n(p) &= P_n(p)\,A_{n1}(p)\,,
\end{aligned}$$

where $A_{11}(p)$, $A_{21}(p)$, ..., $A_{n1}(p)$ are the algebraic complements of the elements of the first column of the determinant (21.34).

The static error of the system of each of the external forces is defined by the formula

$$\Delta_{st} = \frac{S_i(0)}{L(0)}f_{i\max}^0 \quad (i = 1, 2, \ldots, n)\,. \quad (21.35)$$

The amplitude-phase characteristics of a closed system defining its forced oscillations with sinusoidal variation of each of the external forces individually will be:

$$
\left.
\begin{aligned}
W_{f1}(i\omega) &= \frac{S_1(i\omega)}{L(i\omega)}\,, \\[2mm]
W_{f2}(i\omega) &= \frac{S_2(i\omega)}{L(i\omega)}\,, \\[2mm]
&\cdots\cdots\cdots\cdots \\[2mm]
W_{fn}(i\omega) &= \frac{S_n(i\omega)}{L(i\omega)}\,.
\end{aligned}
\right\}
\qquad (21.36)
$$

The material of this chapter, which has a general auxiliary character, will be used to a large extent further in examples. However, independently of this, from the general formulae already obtained it is possible to make a substantial number of useful concrete conclusions about the dynamic and static properties of various automatic systems.

CHAPTER VI

SETTING UP THE EQUATIONS OF ORDINARY LINEAR AUTOMATIC REGULATION SYSTEMS

22. Equations for an automatic engine-speed regulation system

Let us derive the equations for a system for the automatic regulation of the speed of an engine with a centrifugal regulator. Aside from the standard form of equations adopted in contemporary regulation theory described in Section 18, let us also write them in another form—the dimensionless form, in which they appeared at the start of this century. This form of notation is also encountered in contemporary regulation theory literature.

The basic arrangement of the system (Fig. 78) consists of the engine 1 (regulated object), centrifugal mechanism 2 (sensitive element), the gate valve 3, the hydraulic motor 4 (the last two constitute an amplifier) and the regulating gate valve 5 (regulating organ). There is an additional transient feedback in the system in the form of an isodromic device consisting of the oil damper D and the spring S.

In addition, there is the adjustment of the system for a definite number of revolutions per minute, for example using the handle E, manually adjustable to a definite position. The adjustment may also be carried out in advance by increasing or reducing the tension of the spring in the centrifugal mechanism 2.

The role of the external perturbation on the system is played in the present case by variations of the engine-shaft load.

We shall write the equations for all the elements of the system in their complete form and we shall also analyse several simpler variants in the form of particular cases.

Equations of the regulated object (engine). The equation of rotation of the engine shaft together with all other masses which move with the shaft will be:

$$J \frac{d\omega}{dt} = M_{dv} - M_r - M_l, \tag{22.1}$$

where J is the moment of inertia of the entire moving mass reduced to the engine shaft, ω is the angular velocity of the engine shaft,

M_{dr} is the driving moment on the engine shaft, M_r and M_l are the resistive and load moments reduced to the engine shaft.

The driving moment M_{dr} depends mainly on the magnitude of the energy applied to the engine, i.e. on the position of the regulation organ 5 and sometimes also on the angular velocity of the shaft ω. Consequently,

$$M_{dr} = M_{dr}(x) \quad \text{or} \quad M_{dr} = M_{dr}(x, \omega) , \qquad (22.2)$$

where x is the coordinate of the regulating organ.

The actual form of function (22.2) will differ for different regulated objects and may be taken from the theory of the corresponding engines in the form of a formula or from experimental characteristics in the form of graphs (for example, Fig. 113*a*, *b*).

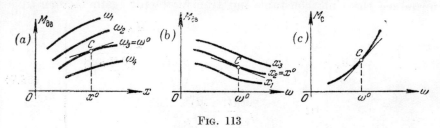

Fig. 113

The resistive and load moments usually have the form

$$M_r = M_r(\omega) , \quad M_l = M_l(t) . \qquad (22.3)$$

The function $M_r(\omega)$ is also given by a formula or graph (Fig. 113*c*). The quantity M_l is independent of the system under consideration and may vary arbitrarily with connection, disconnection or variation of the operating regime of the load served by the engine.

Substituting (22.2) and (22.3) in equation (22.1), we obtain

$$J\dot{\omega} - M_{dr}(x, \omega) + M_r(\omega) = - M_l(t) . \qquad (22.4)$$

The functions M_{dr} and M_r which are non-linear with respect to x and ω may be linearised in the vicinity of the investigated steady-state.

Let, for example, the steady-state operation of the engine be defined by certain constant values $\omega = \omega^0$, $x = x^0$, $M_l = M_l^0$. Let us introduce the deviations

$$\Delta\omega = \omega - \omega^0 , \quad \Delta x = x - x^0 . \qquad (22.5)$$

Comparing (22.4) with the general formula (18.1) we conclude that in the present case

$$F = J\dot{\omega} - M_{dr}(x, \omega) + M_r(\omega) ,$$
$$x_1 = x , \quad x_2 = 0 , \quad x_3 = \omega .$$

Therefore in accordance with formula (18.5) equation (22.4) in linearised form will be:

$$J\Delta\dot{\omega} + \left[\left(\frac{\partial M_r}{\partial\omega}\right)^0 - \left(\frac{\partial M_{dr}}{\partial\omega}\right)^0\right]\Delta\omega - \left(\frac{\partial M_{dr}}{\partial x}\right)^0\Delta x = -[M_l(t) - M_l^0]\,, \qquad (22\,6)$$

where

$$\left(\frac{\partial M_{dr}}{\partial x}\right)^0\,, \qquad \left(\frac{\partial M_{dr}}{\partial\omega}\right)^0\,, \qquad \left(\frac{\partial M_r}{\partial\omega}\right)^0$$

are partial derivatives of the functions (22.2) and (22.3) with $\omega = \omega^0$ and $x = x^0$. Graphically they may be obtained as the slopes of the tangents at the points C in Fig. 113a, b, c (taking into account the scale of the drawing).

To reduce this equation to the standard from of Section 18 we introduce the time constant and transfer factor (gain factor):

$$\left. \begin{array}{c} T_1 = \dfrac{J}{\left|\left(\dfrac{\partial M_r}{\partial\omega}\right)^0 - \left(\dfrac{\partial M_{dr}}{\partial\omega}\right)^0\right|}\,, \qquad k_1 = \dfrac{\left(\dfrac{\partial M_{dr}}{\partial x}\right)^0}{\left|\left(\dfrac{\partial M_r}{\partial\omega}\right)^0 - \left(\dfrac{\partial M_{dr}}{\partial\omega}\right)^0\right|}\,, \\[6mm] f(t) = \dfrac{M_l(t) - M_l^0}{\left|\left(\dfrac{\partial M_r}{\partial\omega}\right)^0 - \left(\dfrac{\partial M_{dr}}{\partial\omega}\right)^0\right|}\,. \end{array} \right\} \qquad (22.7)$$

With this notation the parameters T_1 and k_1 will be positive numbers.

In the most frequently encountered case when

$$\left(\frac{\partial M_r}{\partial\omega}\right)^0 - \left(\frac{\partial M_{dr}}{\partial\omega}\right)^0 > 0\,, \qquad (22.8)$$

the equation of the regulated object (22.6) will be:

$$(T_1 p + 1)\Delta\omega = k_1\Delta x - f(t)\,, \qquad (22.9)$$

i.e. the object represents an aperiodic element with time constant T_1 proportional to the moment of inertia J and with gain factor proportional to the slope of the characteristic $M_{dr}(x)$. For the dynamic properties of such an element see Section 19.

In the less frequent case, when

$$\left(\frac{\partial M_r}{\partial\omega}\right)^0 - \left(\frac{\partial M_{dr}}{\partial\omega}\right)^0 < 0\,, \qquad (22.10)$$

we obtain the equation

$$(T_1 p - 1)\Delta\omega = k_1\Delta x - f(t)\,, \qquad (22.11)$$

i.e. the object represents an unstable aperiodic element.

If, finally,

$$\left(\frac{\partial M_r}{\partial\omega}\right)^0 - \left(\frac{\partial M_{dr}}{\partial\omega}\right)^0 = 0 \quad \text{or} \quad M_r = 0\,, \quad M_{dr} = M_{dr}(x)\,, \qquad (22.12)$$

then the equation of the regulated object (22.6) takes the form

$$p\Delta\omega = k_1'\Delta x - f_1(t) , \qquad (22.13)$$

where

$$k_1' = \frac{1}{J}\left(\frac{\partial M_{dr}}{\partial x}\right)^0 , \qquad f_1(t) = \frac{M_l(t) - M_l^0}{J} . \qquad (22.14)$$

In this case the object appears neutral and represents an integrating element.

We shall now write the equation of the regulated object (22.6) in the other (dimensionless) form.

Each term of equation (22.6) and (22.1) has the dimensions of a moment. We note that each motor or engine has some nominal calculated regime defined by the nominal driving moment M_n and the nominal angular velocity ω_n. To eliminate dimensions we divide equation (22.6) by M_n.

We shall also introduce the conventional nominal quantity x_n:

$$x_n = \frac{M_n}{\left(\dfrac{\partial M_{dr}}{\partial x}\right)^0} . \qquad (22.15)$$

Then equation (22.6) may be rewritten in the form

$$\frac{J\omega_n}{M_n}\frac{\Delta\dot\omega}{\omega_n} + \left[\left(\frac{\partial M_r}{\partial\omega}\right)^0 - \left(\frac{\partial M_{dt}}{\partial\omega}\right)^0\right]\frac{\omega_n}{M_n}\frac{\Delta\omega}{\omega_n} = \frac{\Delta x}{x_n} - \frac{M_{dt}(t) - M_{dt}^0}{M_n} .$$

Introducing now the dimensionless relative deviation

$$\varphi = \frac{\Delta\omega}{\omega_n} , \qquad \xi = \frac{\Delta x}{x_n} , \qquad (22.16)$$

we obtain from the preceding the required equation of the regulated object in dimensionless deviations

$$T_a\dot\varphi + \beta\varphi = \xi - \psi(t) , \qquad (22.17)$$

where we have introduced the notation:

$$\left.\begin{aligned} \beta &= \left[\left(\frac{\partial M_r}{\partial\omega}\right)^0 - \left(\frac{\partial M_{dr}}{\partial\omega}\right)^0\right]\frac{\omega_n}{M_n} , \\ T_a &= \frac{J\omega_n}{M_n} , \qquad \psi(t) = \frac{M_l(t) - M_l^0}{M_n} . \end{aligned}\right\} \qquad (22.18)$$

The coefficient T_a has the dimensions of time and is termed the acceleration time of the engine. This is the time in which the engine accelerates from a state of rest to the nominal angular velocity in the absence of resistance and with constant driving moment equal to nominal. In fact, from equation (22.1) with $M_{dr} = M_n$, $M_r = M_1 = 0$, $0 \leqslant t \leqslant T_2$, $0 \leqslant \omega \leqslant \omega$, we have:

$$J \int_0^{\omega_n} d\omega = M_n \int_0^{T_a} dt \, ,$$

from which after integration we obtain the value T_a given in formula (22.18).

The quantity β (see formula (22.18)) is termed the self-regulation factor. The significance of this term consists in that for $\beta > 0$ we have case (22.8), i.e. a stable object (22.9), which, from Section 19, by itself, without regulator, always comes to some steady-state the more rapidly and with less static deviation, the greater β. The task of the regulator will consist in this case in substantially accelerating the transient process in the system and making the static deviation of the regulated quantity practically negligible (i.e. sufficiently small).

For $\beta < 0$ ("negative self-regulation") we have case (22.10), i.e. an unstable object (22.11), while for $\beta = 0$ (object without self-regulation) we arrive at case (22.12), i.e. to the neutral object (22.13). In these two cases the principal problem of regulation consists in establishing a stable system as well as in achieving a good transient response and small static error.

The equation of the sensitive element (centrifugal mechanism). Let us denote by y the coordinate of the sleeve B of the centrifugal mechanism (Fig. 78), read downwards. The equation of motion of the sleeve will be:

$$m_1 \ddot{y} = -F_b + F_s - F_r \, , \tag{22.19}$$

where m_1 is the mass of the sleeve and all the parts of the centrifugal mechanism moving with it, reduced to the sleeve, y is the coordinate of the sleeve, F_b is the force, reduced to the sleeve, arising from the centrifugal force of the bobs, F_s is the spring force, F_r is the resistance force realised conventionally in the diagram of Fig. 78 by a damper.

For these forces we have the following relations:

$$\left. \begin{array}{l} F_b = a_1 \omega^2 + a_2 \, , \\ F_s = F_1 - c_1 y \, , \\ F_r = c_2 \dot{y} \, , \end{array} \right\} \tag{22.20}$$

where the coefficients a_1, a_2, c_1, c_2 depend on the design and dimensions of the centrifugal mechanism, F_1 is the force of the precompressed spring (in the position $y = 0$).

Only the component $a_1 \omega$ is here non-linear. After substituting (22.20) in equation (22.19) and linearising it in accordance with Section 18 close to the steady-state $\omega = \omega^0$, $y = y^0$ we obtain:

$$c_1 \Delta y + c_2 \Delta \dot{y} + m_1 \Delta \ddot{y} + 2a_1 \omega^0 \Delta \omega = 0 \, , \tag{22.21}$$

where $\Delta y = y - y^0$ and, in accordance with (22.19) and (22.20), the steady-state value y^0 (sleeve position) is defined in the following manner:

$$c_1 y^0 = F_1 - a_2 - a_1(\omega^0)^2 . \tag{22.22}$$

From (22.21) we obtain the following equation of the sensitive element in standard form (Section 18):

$$(T_4^2 p^2 + T_2 p + 1)\Delta y = -k_2 \Delta \omega , \tag{22.23}$$

where

$$k_2 = \frac{2a_1\omega^0}{c_1}, \qquad T_2 = \frac{c_2}{c_1}, \qquad T_4^2 = \frac{m_1}{c_1} . \tag{22.24}$$

Here it is evident on which design parameters of the centrifugal mechanism the transfer factor k_2 and the time constants T_2 and T_4 of the sensitive element of the regulator depend.

Thus, the sensitive element constitutes either an oscillatory system if $T_2 < 2T_4$, or is second-order aperiodic (see Section 19 for their dynamic properties). If we neglect the resistance ($c_2 = 0$), we obtain the equation

$$(T_4^2 p^2 + 1)\Delta y = -k_2 \Delta \omega \tag{22.25}$$

of harmonic oscillator. If it is necessary to consider the resistance, but it is possible to neglect the mass ($m_1 \approx 0$), then equation (22.23) takes the aperiodic form

$$(T_2 p + 1)\Delta y = -k_2 \Delta \omega . \tag{22.26}$$

Finally, if we neglect the mass and the resistance, we obtain the equation of an ideal sensitive element:

$$\Delta y = -k_2 \Delta \omega \tag{22.27}$$

Let us now introduce the relative deviation

$$\eta = \frac{\Delta y}{y_n} , \tag{22.28}$$

where y_n is some constant having the dimensions of y, defined below. We then obtain the equation of the sensitive element in the dimensionless form

$$T_r^2 \ddot{\eta} + T_k \dot{\eta} + \delta\eta = -\varphi , \tag{22.29}$$

where we put

$$
\left.
\begin{aligned}
T_r^2 &= \frac{m_1 y_n}{2a_1\omega^0\omega_n} \approx \frac{m_1 y_n}{2a_1\omega_n^2}, \\[2mm]
T_k &= \frac{c_2 y_n}{2a_1\omega^0\omega_n} \approx \frac{c_2 y_n}{2a_1\omega_n^2}, \\[2mm]
\delta &= \frac{c_1 y_n}{2a_1\omega^0\omega_n} \approx \frac{c_1 y_n}{2a_1\omega_n^2},
\end{aligned}
\right\} \tag{22.30}
$$

Approximate equalities are written for those cases where we may take $\omega^0\omega_n \approx \omega_n^2$ (this is usually the case).

The quantities T_r and T_k, having the dimensions of time, are termed the mass and damping constants while δ is the non-uniformity coefficient of the sensitive element. They depend on the choice of y_n and ω_n while the time constants and transfer factor (22.24) did not depend on the choice of these quantities.

Analogously to the above, the simplified forms of equation (22.29) will be:

sensitive element without resistance

$$T_r^2 \ddot{\eta} + \delta\eta = -\varphi ,$$

sensitive element without mass

$$T_k \dot{\eta} + \delta\eta = -\varphi , \qquad (22.31)$$

sensitive element without mass and resistance (ideal)

$$\delta\eta = -\varphi . \qquad (22.32)$$

Slide valve equation. Let Z denote the coordinate of the point A of the lever ABC, connected with the isodromic device $D–S$ (Fig. 78), s the coordinate of the point C connected with the slide valve rod and q the coordinate of the point E, connecting the body of the slide valve with the handle of the adjuster. The directions of reading all these coordinates are shown in Fig. 78. Their origins are taken such that for $y = 0$ and $s = 0$ the coordinate z is also equal to zero.

If the point A is fixed and $z = 0$, the position of the point C is defined by the formula

$$s_1 = \frac{AC}{AB} y ;$$

if the point B is fixed and $y = 0$, then at the point C we obtain:

$$s_2 = -\frac{BC}{AB} z .$$

Therefore for arbitrary shifts of the two points A and B the position of C will be defined by the coordinate

$$s = s_1 + s_2 = \frac{AC}{AB} y - \frac{BC}{AB} z . \qquad (22.33)$$

The magnitude of the slide-valve openings will be:

$$\Delta s = s - q \qquad (22.34)$$

(with suitable choice of origin of the coordinate q). From (22.33), we obtain:

$$\Delta s = \frac{AC}{AB} y - \frac{BC}{AB} z - q . \qquad (22.35)$$

We shall consider that the shift of the point E from the handle of the adjuster, q, is established and remains constant in the interval of time considered. In the steady-state we have:

$$y = y^0, \quad z = z^0, \quad \Delta s = 0,$$

which follows from the fact that the piston of the servomotor 4 obviously cannot remain in place with $\Delta s \neq 0$, i.e. with the slide valve open. The steady-state value z is defined in accordance with (22.35) by the formula

$$z^0 = \frac{AC}{BC} y^0 - \frac{AB}{BC} q. \tag{22.36}$$

Comparing this with (22.35), we obtain the equation of the slide-valve in deviations (in standard form)

$$\Delta s = k_3(\Delta y - \Delta y_{fb}), \tag{22.37}$$

where

$$k_3 = \frac{AC}{AB}, \quad \Delta y_{fb} = \frac{BC}{AC} \Delta z, \quad \Delta z = z - z^0. \tag{22.38}$$

This is an ideal element with introduction of feedback (see Table in Section 19).

If there is no feedback in the system, i.e. the point A is fixed (for example, Fig. 18), the equation of the slide valve will be:

$$\Delta s = k_3 \Delta y. \tag{22.39}$$

Let us now introduce certain nominal values:

$$s_n = \frac{BC}{AB} z_n, \quad y_n = \frac{BC}{AC} z_n \tag{22.40}$$

(where z_n will be defined below) and the relative deviations

$$\sigma = \frac{\Delta s}{s_n}, \quad \zeta = \frac{\Delta z}{z_n}. \tag{22.41}$$

Then in place of (22.37), the equation of the slide valve in dimensionless form will be

$$\sigma = \eta - \zeta, \tag{22.42}$$

and in the absence of feedback

$$\sigma = \eta. \tag{22.43}$$

The equation of the regulating organ drive. A fairly exact equation of the hydraulic drive 4 (Fig. 78) has a complex non-linear form because of the complex dependency between the motion of the slide valve rod, the area of the opening, the quantity of working fluid flowing, its force on the piston of the motor and the mass of the moving portions of the drive. Basically the quantity of fluid flowing per unit time also depends on the size of the opening in the slide valve Δs and, if we neglect its mass, imparts a definite velocity u to the piston of the hydraulic motor. Let (Fig. 114a)

$$\dot{u} = F(\Delta s) \, ,$$

where $\dot{u} = 0$ when $\Delta s = 0$ In the linear form (Fig. 114b) this gives:

$$\dot{u} = c\Delta s \quad \text{or} \quad \Delta u = c\Delta s \, .$$

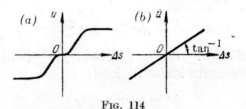

Fig. 114

The transmission to the regulating organ 5 (gate valve) is described by the equation (see Fig. 78)

$$x = \frac{LM}{MN} u \quad \text{or} \quad \Delta x = \frac{LM}{MN} \Delta u \, . \tag{22.44}$$

From the above equations we obtain the following equation for the regulating organ drive (in standard form):

$$p\Delta x = k_4 \Delta s \, , \quad \text{where} \quad k_4 = \frac{LM}{MN} c \, , \tag{22.45}$$

which represents an integrating element.

Introducing the known x_n and s_n we obtain the equation of the hydraulic motor in dimensionless form

$$T_s \dot{\xi} = \sigma \, , \quad \text{where} \quad T_i = \frac{MN}{LM} \frac{x_n}{c s_n} \tag{22.46}$$

The quantity T_s, having the dimensions of time, is termed the hydraulic motor constant.

The equation of motion of the regulating organ will not be given separately since it is implicit in the above work.

Feedback equation. The equation of motion of the damper piston* D (and together with it the point A, Fig. 78) will be:

$$m_2 \ddot{z} = F_s + F_d \, , \tag{22.47}$$

where m_2 is the mass of the damper piston, F_s is the spring force, F_d is the damper force, with

$$F_s = F_3 + c_3 z \, , \quad F_d = c_4(\dot{z} - \dot{u}) \, , \tag{22.48}$$

* It is also termed stroke regulator.

and F_3 is the pre-compression force of the spring (in the position $z = 0$), c_3 is the stiffness of the spring, c_4 is a proportionality factor, $(\dot{z} - \dot{u})$ is the relative velocity of the piston in the damper cylinder. In the steady-state from (22.47) and (22.48) we have:

$$F_3 + c_3 z^0 = 0 \ . \tag{22.49}$$

Neglecting the small mass of the piston m and letting $\dot{u} = \Delta \dot{u}$, $\dot{z} = \Delta \dot{z}$ in the transient process we obtain from the same equations:

$$c_3 \Delta z + c_4 \Delta \dot{z} = c_4 \Delta \dot{u} \ . \tag{22.50}$$

Introducing Δy_{fb} from (22.38) and Δx from (22.44), we derive the equation of transient (isodromic) feedback in standard form

$$(T_5 p + 1) \Delta y_{fb} = k_5' p \Delta x \ , \tag{22.51}$$

where

$$T_5 = \frac{c_4}{c_3}, \qquad k_5' = \frac{c_4}{c_3} \frac{BC \cdot MN}{AC \cdot LM} \ ; \tag{22.52}$$

this is an aperiodic differentiating element (see Section 19).

If we eliminate the damper D and join the point A with the piston 4 (Fig. 78) using a rigid rod, we obtain a system with stiff feedback (Fig. 74). Here, obviously, the displacements $\Delta z = \Delta u$ will be rigidly coupled, from which, employing (22.38) and (22.44), we obtain the equation of stiff feedback

$$\Delta y_{fb} = k_5 \Delta x \ , \qquad \text{where} \qquad k_5 = \frac{BC \cdot MN}{AC \cdot LM} \tag{22.53}$$

(an ideal element).

To write the feedback equation in dimensionless form we represent (22.50) in the form

$$\frac{c_4}{c_3} \frac{\Delta \dot{z}}{z_n} + \frac{\Delta z}{z_n} = \frac{MN}{LM} \frac{c_4 x_n}{c_3 z_n} \frac{\Delta \dot{x}}{x_n} \ . \tag{22.54}$$

The quantity z_n above has already appeared in formula (22.40), but has remained undefined. We shall define this conventional nominal quantity z_n in the following manner:

$$z_n = \frac{MN}{LM} x_n \ , \tag{22.55}$$

where x_n is calculated according to (22.15); the quantities y_n and s_n are then defined by relation (22.40).

Thus we obtain from (22.54) the equation of transient (isodromic) feedback in dimensionless form

$$T_i \dot{\zeta} + \zeta = T_i \dot{\xi} \ , \qquad \text{where} \qquad T_i = \frac{c_4}{c_3} \ , \tag{22.56}$$

and the equation of stiff feedback will be:

$$\zeta = \xi .$$

Overall system equation. We have thus obtained a number of equations for the elements of several variants of the automatic engine velocity regulation system. Different combinations of these equations with each other will describe different systems.

For example, if there is a regulated object without self-regulation, fitted with a regulator with stiff feedback, the equation of the automatic regulation system in the two forms will be:

$$
\left.
\begin{aligned}
p\Delta\omega &= k_1'\Delta x - f(t) , \\
(T_4^2 p^2 + T_2 p + 1)\Delta y &= -k_2\Delta\omega , \\
\Delta s &= k_3(\Delta y - \Delta y_{fb}) , \\
p\Delta x &= k_4\Delta s , \\
\Delta y_{fb} &= k_5\Delta x ,
\end{aligned}
\right|
\left.
\begin{aligned}
T_a\dot\varphi &= \xi - \psi(t) , \\
T_r^2\ddot\eta + T_k\dot\eta + \delta\eta &= -\varphi , \\
\sigma &= \eta - \zeta , \\
T_s\dot\xi &= \sigma , \\
\zeta &= \xi ,
\end{aligned}
\right\}
\quad (22.57)
$$

or, if we combine the last three equations, then

$$
\left.
\begin{aligned}
p\Delta\omega &= k_1'\Delta x - f(t) , \\
(T_4^2 p^2 + T_2 p + 1)\Delta y &= -k_2\Delta\omega , \\
(p + k_3 k_4 k_5)\Delta x &= k_3 k_4 \Delta y;
\end{aligned}
\right|
\left.
\begin{aligned}
T_a\dot\varphi &= \xi - \psi(t) , \\
T_r^2\ddot\eta + T_k\dot\eta + \delta\eta &= -\varphi , \\
T_s\dot\xi + \xi &= \eta;
\end{aligned}
\right\}
\quad (22.58)
$$

this is an example of how stiff feedback changes an integrating element into an aperiodic one.

From (20.10) and (20.11) the general equation of the entire closed system in this case will be:

$$L(p)\Delta\omega = -S(p)f(t) , \qquad (22.59)$$

where

$$
\left.
\begin{aligned}
L(p) &= (T_4^2 p^2 + T_2 p + 1)(p + k_3 k_4 k_5)p + k_1' k_2 k_3 k_4 , \\
S(p) &= (T_4^2 p^2 + T_2 p + 1)(p + k_3 k_4 k_5) .
\end{aligned}
\right\}
\quad (22.60)
$$

Similarly, starting from the real properties of the investigated system, it is possible to take any other combinations of the equations derived in this section.

In example (22.60) the system is static, since the polynomial $S(p)$ contains a constant term, where the static error of the system on the linear segment

$$\Delta\omega_{st} = \frac{S(0)}{L(0)}f^0 = \frac{k_5}{k_1' k_2}f^0 \qquad (22.61)$$

is proportional to the feedback transfer factor k_5.

But the deviations of the load f^0 may be large and the characteristics of the object non-linear. Therefore (22.61) must be considered only as a qualitative result. We shall derive a more exact static characteristic for the given automatic regulation system. For the engine as the object of velocity regulation it is necessary to know the static characteristics $\omega^0(x^0)$, i.e. the dependence of angular velocity on the position of the regulating organ in the steady-states for various loads. For an object with self-regulation, on the basis of the graphs of Fig. 113 and formula (22.1) with $d\omega/dt = 0$, this static characteristic takes on the form of Fig. 115a.

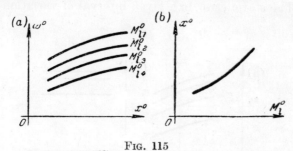

Fig. 115

In the case of an object without self-regulation (22.12) the quantity ω does not enter into the equation of the static characteristic. We may plot only an auxiliary characteristic—the dependence of the position of the regulating organ x^0 on the load magnitude M_1^0 (Fig. 115b). The angular velocity ω^0 may have an arbitrary value, i.e. the engine is indifferent to the magnitude of ω (neutral object). The angular velocity ω becomes defined only in the presence of an appropriate regulator.

It is further necessary to assemble the static characteristic of the regulator, which should express the dependence of the regulating force x^0 on the value of the regulated quantity ω^0 in different steady-states.

If the regulator has stiff feedback (Fig. 74), then, on the basis of (22.19), (22.20), (22.36), (22.44), we write:

$$c_1 y^0 = F_1 - a_1(\omega^0)^2 - a_2 \,,$$

$$\frac{AC}{AB} y^0 = \frac{BC}{AB} z^0 + q \,, \qquad \Delta s = 0 \,,$$

$$x^0 = \frac{LM}{MN} u^0 \,, \qquad z^0 = u^0 \,.$$

Eliminating y^0, z^0, u^0, from this, we find:

$$(\omega^0)^2 = -\frac{c_1}{a_1} \frac{AB}{AC} q + \frac{F_1 - a_2}{a_1} - \frac{c_1}{a_1} \frac{BC}{AC} \frac{MN}{LM} x^0 \,. \qquad (22.62)$$

The quantity x^0 depends on the load M_1^0 in accordance with the characteristics of the object (Fig. 115). Therefore, in the given system the regulated angular velocity cannot be strictly constant, and will vary with the load M_1; obviously, to obtain the smallest possible static error of the system the parameters of the regulator should be selected so that the coefficient of x^0 in (22.62) is as small as possible.

The static characteristics of the overall automatic regulation system $\omega^0(M_1^0)$ for various constant adjustments q (Fig. 116a) are obtained by eliminating x^0 from equation (22.62) using the graph (Fig. 115). The static error in a given interval of variation of the load

$$M_{l\,min}^0 \leqslant M_l^0 \leqslant M_{l\,max}^0$$

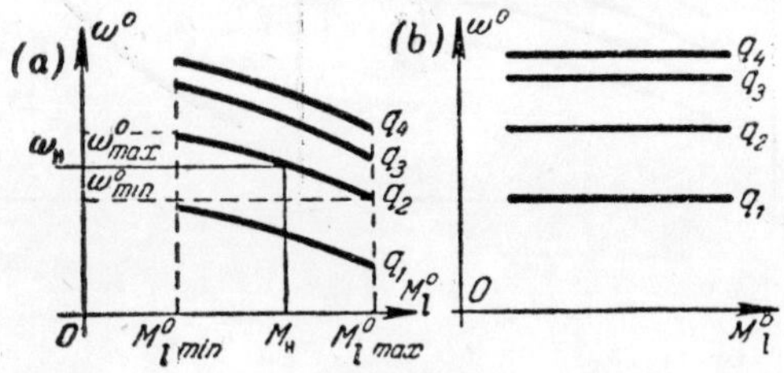

Fig. 116

with given adjustment q is defined from the static characteristic (Fig. 116a) as

$$\Delta_{st}\% = \frac{\omega_{max}^0 - \omega_{min}^0}{\omega_n} 100\% .$$

By analogous calculations it is easily verified that in the presence of transient feedback (Fig. 78) the system becomes astatic and the angular velocity ω does not depend on the magnitude of the load but is defined only by the adjustment of the system (Fig. 116b).

23. Equations of an automatic pressure regulation system

Let us construct the equations of a system for the automatic regulation of air pressure in a certain chamber. The schematic diagram of the system is shown in Fig. 117, where 1 is the chamber (regulated object), 2 is a membrane pressure gauge (sensitive element), 3 is a jet, 4 is a spring, 5 is a distributor, 6 is a pneumatic motor (elements 3, 5, 6 comprise the amplifier), 7 is a stiff feedback, 8 is a valve (regulating organ). The regulated quantity is the pressure p_c in the chamber 1.

The equation of the regulated object. Let us denote by g_{in} the quantity of air admitted in one second g_{out} the quantity of air released in 1 second, G_c the quantity of air in the chamber (by weight).

Obviously, the difference between the input and output is the increment to the quantity of air in the chamber, i.e.

$$(g_{in} - g_{out})\, dt = dG_c . \tag{23.1}$$

The steady-state will occur with $g_{in} = g_{out}$, when $C_c = \text{const} = G_c^0$.

Let V_c, θ_c, R, p_c be respectively the volume, temperature, gas constant and air pressure in the chamber, then, employing the fundamental law of gas physics, we may write

$$p_c V_c = G_c R \theta_c$$

or

$$G_c = \frac{p_c V_c}{R \theta_c}. \tag{23.2}$$

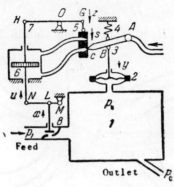

FIG. 117

If the temperature θ_c is constant (as a result of the presence of thermal insulation or a special separate automatic regulator, not considered here), we obtain from (23.1) and (23.2):

$$\frac{V_c}{R\theta_c} \frac{dp_c}{dt} = g_{\text{in}} - g_{\text{out}}. \tag{23.3}$$

The quantity of air supplied per second g_{in} depends on the coordinates of the regulating valve position x, on the pressure in the chamber p_c and, in general, also on the pressure p_1 and the temperature θ_1 of the air supplied. The quantity of air released per second g_{out} depends on the air pressure in the chamber p_c and the external pressure p_0, as well as on the cross section q of the air outlet from the chamber. In other words,

$$\left. \begin{aligned} g_{\text{in}} &= f_1(x,\ p_c,\ p_1,\ \theta_1)\ , \\ g_{\text{out}} &= f_2(p_c,\ p_c,\ q)\ . \end{aligned} \right\} \tag{23.4}$$

Equation (23.3) takes the form

$$\frac{V_c}{R\theta_c} \dot{p}_c - g_{\text{in}}(x,\ p_c,\ p_1,\ \theta_1) + g_{\text{out}}(p_c,\ p_0,\ q) = 0\ .$$

Denoting the entire left-hand part of this equation by F, by analogy with (18.1) and (18.5) we obtain after linearisation

$$\frac{V_c}{R\theta_c} \Delta \dot{p}_c - \left(\frac{\partial g_{\text{in}}}{\partial x}\right)^0 \Delta x - \left(\frac{\partial g_{\text{in}}}{\partial p_c}\right)^0 \Delta p_c - \left(\frac{\partial g_{\text{in}}}{\partial p_1}\right)^0 \Delta p_1 - \left(\frac{\partial g_{\text{in}}}{\partial \theta_1}\right)^0 \Delta \theta_1 +$$

$$+ \left(\frac{\partial g_{\text{out}}}{\partial p_c}\right)^0 \Delta p_c + \left(\frac{\partial g_{\text{out}}}{\partial p_0}\right)^0 \Delta p_0 + \left(\frac{\partial g_{\text{out}}}{\partial q}\right)^0 \Delta q = 0\ , \tag{23.5}$$

where Δp_c, Δx, ..., are the deviations of the variables p_c, x, ..., from the defined steady-state values p_c^0, x^0, ... The steady-state of the system, from (23.1), (23.2) and (23.4), is defined by the following equations:

$$G_c^0 = \frac{V_c}{R\theta_c}\, p_c^0, \qquad g_{\text{in}}^0 = g_{\text{out}}^0, \\ g_{\text{in}}^0 = f_1(x^0, p_c^0, p_1^0, \theta_1^0), \\ g_{\text{out}}^0 = f_2(p_c^0, p_0^0, q^0),$$

(23.6)

where the values V_c, R, θ_c, p_1, θ_1, p_0, q should be given.

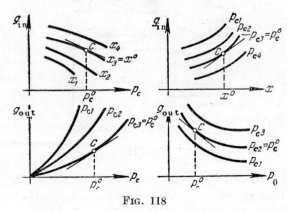

FIG. 118

If Δp_1, $\Delta\theta_1$, Δq and Δp_0 are arbitrary perturbing functions, independent of our system (external conditions), then from (23.5) we obtain:

$$\frac{V_c}{R\theta_c}\Delta\dot{p}_c + \left[\left(\frac{\partial g_{\text{out}}}{\partial p_c}\right)^0 - \left(\frac{\partial g_{\text{in}}}{\partial p_c}\right)^0\right]\Delta p_c = \left(\frac{\partial g_{\text{in}}}{\partial x}\right)^0 \Delta x + f_1(t),$$

(23.7)

where

$$f_1(t) = \left(\frac{\partial g_{\text{in}}}{\partial p_1}\right)^0 \Delta p_1 + \left(\frac{\partial g_{\text{in}}}{\partial \theta_1}\right)^0 \Delta\theta_1 - \left(\frac{\partial g_{\text{out}}}{\partial p_0}\right)^0 \Delta p_0 - \left(\frac{\partial g_{\text{out}}}{\partial q}\right)^0 \Delta q .$$

The coefficients

$$\left(\frac{\partial g_{\text{in}}}{\partial p_c}\right)^0, \quad \left(\frac{\partial g_{\text{out}}}{\partial p_0}\right)^0, \quad \left(\frac{\partial g_{\text{in}}}{\partial p_c}\right)^0, \quad \left(\frac{\partial g_{\text{out}}}{\partial x}\right)^0$$

and others may be defined, for example, as the slopes of the experimental static characteristics at the points C (Fig. 118), corresponding to the steady-state ($p_c = p_c^0$, $x = x^0$, $p_0 = p_0^0$). These coefficients may also be determined theoretically.

Let p_n and g_n denote certain relative nominal values of the pressure in the chamber and the quantity of air supplied per second, for which the given system has been calculated.

To reduce to dimensionless form we divide the entire equation (23.7) by g_n and, in addition, the left-hand side is multiplied and divided by p_n and the right-hand side by x_n, where x_n denotes some relative nominal value having the dimensions of the coordinate of the regulating valve x, namely:

$$x_n = \frac{g_n}{\left(\dfrac{\partial g_{in}}{\partial x}\right)^0}. \tag{23.8}$$

Then, introducing the relative deviation

$$\varphi = \frac{\Delta p_c}{p_n}, \qquad \xi = \frac{\Delta x}{x_n}, \tag{23.9}$$

we obtain the equation of the regulated object (chamber) in dimensionless form

$$T_a \dot\varphi + \beta\varphi = \xi + \psi(t), \tag{23.10}$$

where

$$\left.\begin{array}{l} T_a = \dfrac{V_c p_n}{R\theta_c g_n}, \\[2mm] \beta = \left[\left(\dfrac{\partial g_{out}}{\partial p_c}\right)^0 - \left(\dfrac{\partial g_{in}}{\partial p_c}\right)^0\right]\dfrac{p_n}{g_n}, \\[2mm] \psi(t) = \dfrac{f_1(t)}{g_{in}}. \end{array}\right\} \tag{23.11}$$

This equation coincides with (22.17) except for the sign of ψ. The quantity β is the self-regulation coefficient of the object. The quantity T_a is termed here the filling time. This is the time required for filling the chamber with air from zero to a nominal pressure p_n in the absence of outlet and leakage and with constant supply, equal to the nominal g_n. In fact, integrating equation (23.3) with $g_{in} = g_n, g_{out} = 0, 0 \leqslant p_c \leqslant p_n, 0 \leqslant t \leqslant T_a$, we obtain

$$\frac{V_c}{R\theta_c} \int\limits_0^{p_n} dp_c = g_n \int\limits_0^{T_a} dt,$$

which leads to the formula written above for T_a.

The time constant T_1 and the transfer factor k_1 of the regulated object as an aperiodic element are defined from the standard form of the equation

$$(T_1 p + 1)\varphi = k_1\xi + f(t), \tag{23.12}$$

where

$$T_1 = \frac{T_a}{\beta}, \qquad k_1 = \frac{1}{\beta}, \qquad f(t) = \frac{f_1(t)}{g_n\beta}. \tag{23.13}$$

Equation of the sensitive element. The equation of motion of the membrane coupling rod is written in the form

$$m\ddot y = -P + F_m + F_f + F_s, \tag{23.14}$$

where m is the reduced mass of the parts moving together with the coupling rod, y is the coordinate of the coupling rod (for direction of reading see (Fig. 117), P is the air pressure in the chamber on the membrane, F_m is the spring force of the membrane itself, F_f is the resistive force (friction), F_s is the spring force 4. Here

$$P = q_m p_c , \qquad F_m = c_2'(y - y_1) , \qquad F_f = - c_3 \dot{y} , \qquad F_s = F_1 - c_1 y ,$$

where q_m is the membrane area, y_1 is the coupling rod coordinate corresponding to the unstressed state of the membrane c_2' is a coefficient of proportionality, F_1 is the pre-compression force of the spring in the position $y = 0$. Dividing (23.14) by q_m and putting $c_2'/q_m = c_2$, we obtain:

$$\frac{m}{q_m} \ddot{y} + p_c - c_2(y - y_1) + \frac{c_3}{q_m} \dot{y} - \frac{F_1}{q_m} + \frac{c_1}{q_m} y = 0 , \qquad (23.15)$$

where c_2 is the stiffness of the membrane, measured in units of force divided by the units of area and length (for example, kg/cm²·cm). It may be found theoretically (Reference 47) or experimentally.

In an arbitrary steady-state the system of equations (23.15) has the form

$$p_c^0 - c_2(y^0 - y_1) - \frac{F_1}{q_m} + \frac{c_1}{q_m} y^0 = 0 . \qquad (23.16)$$

Let us subtract this from (23.14) taking into account that $\dot{y} = \Delta \dot{y}$, where $\Delta y = y - y^0$, and introduce the relative deviation (23.9) and

$$\eta - \frac{\Delta y}{y_n} , \qquad (23.17)$$

where y_n is some nominal value, the magnitude of which is defined below in deriving the feedback equation. As a result we obtain the equation of the sensitive element in dimensionless form

$$T_r^2 \ddot{\eta} + T_k \dot{\eta} + \delta \eta = - \varphi , \qquad (23.18)$$

where

$$T_r^2 = \frac{m}{q_m} \frac{y_n}{p_n} , \qquad T_k = \frac{c_3}{q_m} \frac{y_n}{p_n} , \qquad \delta = \left(\frac{c_1}{q_m} - c_2 \right) \frac{y_n}{p_n} . \qquad (23.19)$$

In standard form this equation takes the form

$$(T_3^2 p^2 + T_2 p + 1) \eta = - k_2 \varphi , \qquad (23.20)$$

where

$$T_3^2 = \frac{T_r^2}{\delta} = \frac{m}{c_1 - c_2 q_m} , \qquad T_2 = \frac{T_k}{\delta} = \frac{c_3}{c_1 - c_2 q_m} ,$$

$$k_2 = \frac{1}{\delta} = \frac{p_n q_m}{y_n (c_1 - c_2 q_m)} . \qquad (23.21)$$

Equation of the distributor 5 together with the jet tube 3. The origin of coordinates s and z (Fig. 117) is so chosen that, for $y = 0$ and a neutral position of the jet tube with respect to the openings in the distributor $s = z = 0$. Then, as is evident from the diagram (Fig. 117), the size of the distributor opening will be

$$ s - z = \frac{CA}{BA} y - z . \tag{23.22} $$

In the steady-state the tube must be in the neutral position $(s - z = 0)$, since otherwise the piston of the pneumatic drive 6 would move. From this we have for the steady-state

$$ z^0 = \frac{CA}{BA} y^0 . $$

Subtract this from (23.22) and introduce the relative deviations

$$ \sigma = \frac{s - z}{s_n} , \quad \zeta = \frac{\Delta z}{z_n} , \tag{23.23} $$

where the relative nominal values s_n and g_n are taken in the following manner:

$$ s_n = z_n = \frac{CA}{BA} \cdot y_n . \tag{23.24} $$

As a result we obtain the required equation

$$ \sigma = \eta - \zeta . \tag{23.25} $$

The equation of the pneumatic drive. The drive 6 (Fig. 117) and the transmission from it to the regulating organ 8 here is similar to the above (Section 22), with the replacement of oil by compressed air as the working fluid. Therefore the approximate equation of the pneumatic drive together with the transmission to the regulating organ will be the same:

$$ T_s \dot{\zeta} = \sigma , \tag{23.26} $$

where

$$ T_s = \frac{MN}{LM} \frac{x_n}{c s_n} , \tag{23.27} $$

and the coefficient c characterises the relation $\dot{u} = c(s - z)$ between the size of opening in the distributor of the jet tube $(s - z)$ and the velocity of the piston $\dot{u}$.

Feedback equation. For stiff feedback 7 we obtain easily the relationship (see Fig. 117)

$$ z = \frac{OG}{OH} u = \frac{OG \cdot MN}{OH \cdot LM} x . \tag{23.28} $$

From this in relative variables (23.23) and (23.9) we obtain the equation of stiff feedback

$$\zeta = \xi , \qquad (23.29)$$

if the nominal value z_n is taken in the form

$$z_n = \frac{OG \cdot MN}{OH \cdot LM} \cdot x_n . \qquad (23.30)$$

This condition eliminates the arbitrary character of the choice of y_n. discussed in introduction of expression (23.17). In essence, now x_n is taken from (23.8), z_n from (23.30), s_n and y_n from (23.24).

Overall system equation. Thus, collecting all the final results, we write the equations of the system for automatic regulation of air pressure in the chamber (Fig. 117) in dimensionless form:

$$\left.\begin{aligned}
T_a\dot{\varphi} + \beta\varphi &= \xi + \psi(t) , \\
T_r^2\ddot{\eta} + T_k\dot{\eta} + \delta\eta &= -\varphi , \\
\sigma &= \eta - \zeta , \\
T_s\dot{\xi} &= \sigma , \\
\zeta &= \xi ,
\end{aligned}\right\} \qquad (23.31)$$

or otherwise in standard form (after combining the last three equations):

$$\left.\begin{aligned}
(T_1 p + 1)\varphi &= k_1\xi + f(t) , \\
(T_3^2 p^2 + T_2 p + 1)\eta &= -k_2\varphi , \\
(T_s p + 1)\xi &= \eta .
\end{aligned}\right\} \qquad (23.32)$$

From this in accordance with (20.10) and (20.11) we obtain the equation of the given automatic regulation system in the form

$$L(p)\varphi = S(p)f(t) , \qquad (23.33)$$

where

$$\left.\begin{aligned}
L(p) &= (T_1 p + 1)(T_3^2 p^2 + T_2 p + 1)(T_s p + 1) + k_1 k_2 , \\
S(p) &= (T_3^2 p^2 + T_2 p + 1)(T_s p + 1) .
\end{aligned}\right\} \qquad (23.34)$$

Just as has been done here, it is possible to reduce equations of other systems to a single dimensionless form. At the present time, however, the standard form is used more frequently, and we shall retain it in, and after, chapter V.

24. Equations of an automatic voltage regulation system

Let us consider the composition and linearisation of the equations of an automatic voltage regulation system for a shunt dynamo (carbon-pile regulator).

The schematic diagram is shown in Fig. 119. The regulated quantity is the voltage V applied to the power line at the shunt-dynamo terminals 1. It proceeds to the electromagnet 2 (sensitive element), the armature of which, 3, depending on the magnitude of V, exerts a certain pressure on the carbon pile 4 (regulating organ). A change in this pressure causes a change in the electrical resistance of the pile r. This latter causes a change of current in the field circuit 5 and consequently the necessary change in the regulated quantity V (eliminating its deviation). This is a direct-acting regulation system (according to Polzunov's principle, Fig. 10).

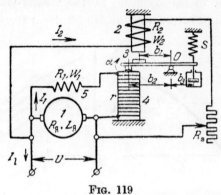

Fig. 119

The series resistance R_s (Fig. 119) serves for adjusting the system with the aid of a constant setting of the slide to the required value of the regulated quantity V, which is to be maintained constant. Adjustment may also be carried out by changing the spring force s.

The equation of the regulated object (dynamo). The voltage V depends, firstly, on the field current, secondly, on the mains load and, thirdly, on the angular velocity of the dynamo armature.

The first of these relationships is defined by the equation of the field circuit

$$V = I_1(R_1 + r) + L_1 \frac{dI_1}{dt}, \qquad (24.1)$$

where I_1 and R_1 are the current and the resistance of the field circuit (Fig. 119), r is the carbon pile resistance, L_1 is a coefficient having the dimensions of inductance and defined by the design of the dynamo armature, but dependent also on the angular velocity of the armature, i.e.

$$L_1 = L_1(n), \qquad (24.2)$$

where n is the number of revolutions per minute of the dynamo armature.

Let the steady-state dynamo operation be characterised by certain constant values V^0, I^0, r^0, n^0. The equation of the steady-state process from (24.1) will be:

$$V^0 = I_1^0(R_1 + r^0). \qquad (24.3)$$

The linearised equation of the field circuit (24.1) (according to Section 18) takes the form

$$\Delta V = (R_1 + r^0)\Delta I_1 + I_1^0 \Delta r + L_1^0 \dot{\Delta I_1}\,, \qquad (24.4)$$

where

$$L_1^0 = L_1(n^0)\,. \qquad (24.5)$$

To establish the voltage dependence on the load current I_1 and on the number of revolutions per minute n let us take the static load characteristic of the dynamo at the steady-state values $n = n^0$ and $I_1 = I_1^0$ (Fig. 120a) as well as the static external characteristic

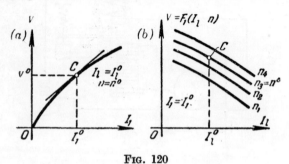

FIG. 120

of the dynamo $V = F_1(I_1, n)$, expressing the relationship of voltage V on the load current I_1 and the number of revolutions per minute n in the steady-state value of the field current $I_1 = I_1^0$ (Fig. 120b). This static characteristic $V = F_1(I_1, n)$ may be obtained by simple plotting of a series of load characteristics Fig. 120a, recorded at various constant of I_1 and n.

Considering the smallness of variation $I_1 = I_1^0 + \Delta I_1$ in the regulation process, we may write:

$$V = F_1(I_l, n) + \left(\frac{\partial U}{\partial I_1}\right)^0 \Delta I_1\,, \qquad (24.6)$$

where $\left(\frac{\partial V}{\partial I_1}\right)^0$ represents geometrically the slope of the tangent to the load characteristic (Fig. 120a) at the point C, corresponding to the steady-state. Here, as usual, we neglect the armature inductance, and the armature reaction is considered lumped in the load characteristic. Let us introduce for conciseness the notation

$$R_u^0 = \left(\frac{\partial V}{\partial I_1}\right)^0\,, \qquad (24.7)$$

with which (24.6) takes the form

$$V = F_1(I_l, n) + R_u^0 \Delta I_1\,.$$

From this we obtain: for the deviation $\Delta V = V - V^0$

$$\Delta V = R_u^0 \Delta I_1 + F_1(I_l, n) - V^0\,, \qquad (24.8)$$

where
$$V^0 = F_1(I^0_l, n^0),\qquad(24.9)$$
which corresponds to the point C in Fig. 120a.

Expressing from (24.8) the quantity ΔI_1 and substituting it in the field circuit equation (24.4), we find:

$$\Delta V = \frac{R_1 + r^0}{R^0_u}\,\Delta V + I^0_1 \Delta r + \frac{L^0_1}{R^1_u}\,\dot{\Delta V} - \frac{L^0_1}{R^0_u}\frac{d}{dt}[F_1(I_l, n) - V^0] -$$
$$- \frac{R_1 + r^0}{R^0_u}[F_1(I_l, n) - V^0].$$

Bringing this to standard form, we obtain the following equation for the regulated object (dynamo):

$$(T_1 p + 1)\Delta V = -k_1 \Delta r + (b_0 p + b) f(t),\qquad(24.10)$$
and
$$T_1 = \frac{L^0_1}{R_1 + r^0 - R^0_u},\qquad k_1 = \frac{I^0_1 R^0_u}{R_1 + r^0 - R^0_u},$$
$$b_0 = T_1,\qquad b = \frac{R_1 + r^0}{R_1 + r^0 - R^0_u},\qquad \left.\right\}\qquad(24.11)$$
$$f(t) = F_1(I_l, n) - V^0,\qquad(24.12)$$

where $I_1 = I_1(t)$, $n = n(t)$.

Here it is assumed that during the regulation process the load current may vary arbitrarily in time $I_1 = I_1(t)$ and the number of revolutions per minute $n = n(t)$, i.e. equation (24.10) is constructed for a regulation process with arbitrarily varying external perturbations.

For the transient process with steady-state external conditions, where from (24.12) and (24.9) we have $f(t) = 0$, the equation of the regulated object will be:

$$(T_1 p + 1)\Delta V = -k_1 \Delta r.\qquad(24.13)$$

Thus, the regulated object in the given system is an aperiodic element.

The equation of the sensitive element (electromagnet with armature). Let us first consider the process in the electromagnet circuit and then the electromagnet armature motion.

The process in the electromagnet circuit 2 (Fig. 119) is described by the equation

$$W_2 \frac{d\Phi_2}{dt} + (R_2 + R_s) I_2 = V,\qquad(24.14)$$

where R_2 and N_2 are the resistance and the number of turns in the electromagnet winding, R_a is the series rheostat resistance for adjusting the system, I_2 and Φ_2 are the electromagnet current and flux. The quantity Φ_2 depends on the ampere-turns of the coil AW_2 and on the gap δ. For a given number of turns N_2 we have $\Phi_2 = \Phi_2(I_2, \delta)$, which is represented graphically in Fig. 121.

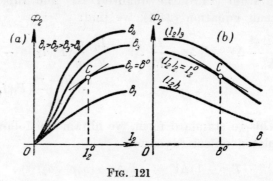

FIG. 121

The gap depends on the angle of rotation of the armature α (read from the attracted side, Fig. 119). For small α we have:

$$\delta = \delta_1 - b_1\alpha , \tag{24.15}$$

where by δ_1 is denoted the gap at $\alpha = 0$ and by b_1 the arm (Fig. 119). Obviously,

$$N_2\frac{d\Phi_2}{dt} = N_2\frac{\partial\Phi_2}{\partial I_2}\frac{dI_2}{dt} + N_2\frac{\partial\Phi_2}{\partial\delta}\frac{d\delta}{dt} = N_2\frac{\partial\Phi_2}{\partial I_2}\frac{dI_2}{dt} + N_2 b_1\left(-\frac{\partial\Phi_2}{\partial\delta}\right)\frac{d\alpha}{dt}$$

or

$$N_2\frac{d\Phi_2}{dt} = L_2\frac{dI_2}{dt} + \Gamma_2\frac{d\alpha}{dt} , \tag{24.16}$$

where we put

$$L_2 = N_2\frac{\partial\Phi_2}{\partial I_2} , \qquad \Gamma_2 = N_2 b_1\left(-\frac{\partial\Phi_2}{\partial\delta}\right) . \tag{24.17}$$

Both partial derivatives are defined graphically as the slopes of the tangents to the curves $\Phi_2 = \Phi_2(I_2)$ and $\Phi_2 = \Phi_2(\delta)$ in Fig. 121 (with respect to the scale of the drawing). The second of these partial derivatives is negative and therefore the minus sign before it in formula (24.17) gives $\Gamma_2 > 0$.

As a result of substituting (24.16) equation (24.14) takes the form

$$L_2\frac{dI_2}{dt} + (R_2 + R_s)I_2 = V - \Gamma_2\frac{d\alpha}{dt} . \tag{24.18}$$

In the steady-state we have:

$$(R_2 + R_s)I_2^0 = V^0 . \tag{24.19}$$

Introducing the deviations $\Delta I_2 = I_2 - I_2^0$, $\Delta\alpha = \alpha - \alpha^0$, $\Delta V = V - V^0$ and subtracting (24.19) from (24.18), we obtain the equation of the electromagnet circuit in deviations

$$(T_2 p + 1)\Delta I_2 = k_2(\Delta V - \Gamma_2^0 p \Delta \alpha),\qquad (24.20)$$

where

$$T_2 = \frac{L_2^0}{R_2 + R_s}, \qquad k_2 = \frac{1}{R_2 + R_s}, \qquad (24.21)$$

and the quantities L_2^0 and Γ_2^0 are defined at the points C (Fig. 121), corresponding to the steady-state: $I_2 = I_2^0$ and $\delta^0 = \delta_1 - b_1 \alpha^0$.

The dynamics of motion of the electromagnet armature 3 (Fig. 119) are described by the equation

$$J\ddot{\alpha} = F_2 b_1 - F_s b_3 + F b_2 - M_f, \qquad (24.22)$$

where J is the moment of inertia of the armature with respect to its axis of rotation, F_2 is the tractive force of the electromagnet,

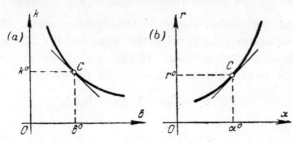

Fig. 122

F is the reaction of the carbon pile (equal to the pressure of the armature on the pile), F_s is the spring tension, b_1, b_2, b_3 are arms (Fig. 119), M_f is the friction resistance to the motion of the armature. Then

$$F_s = F_1 + c_1 b_3 \alpha, \qquad F = F_0 - c_2 b_2 \alpha - c_2' b_2 \dot{\alpha}, \qquad M_f = c_3 \dot{\alpha}, \qquad (24.23)$$

where F_1 is the preliminary spring tension (at $\alpha = 0$), c_1 is the spring stiffness, F_0 is the pre-compression of the pile (at $\alpha = 0$), c_2 is the elastic coefficient of the pile stiffness, c_3 and c_2' are coefficients of proportionality of the "viscous" friction, b_2 and b_3 are arms (Fig. 119).

For an arbitrary given gap δ the tractive force of the electromagnet will be:

$$F_2 = k I_2^2, \qquad (24.24)$$

where the coefficient k depends on the design of the armature and the magnitude of the gap δ. It may be found experimentally and represented for a given design in the form of a graph $k = k(\delta)$ (Fig. 122a).

In the steady-state from (24.22) (24.23) and (24.24) we have:

$$b_1 k^0 (I_2^0)^2 = F_1 b_3 - F_0 b_2 + (c_1 b_3^2 + c_2 b_2^2)\alpha^0, \qquad (24.25)$$

where k^0 is defined from the graph (Fig. 122a) at $\delta^0 = \delta_1 - b_1 \alpha^0$ (from (24.15)).

Substituting (24.23) and (24.24) in equation (24.22) and linearising it in accordance with (18.5), we find the equation of motion of the electromagnet armature in deviations:

$$J\Delta\ddot{\alpha} + (c_3 + c_2'b_2^2)\,\Delta\dot{\alpha} + (c_1 b_3^2 + c_2 b_2^2)\,\Delta\alpha$$
$$= b_1 k^0 2 I_2^0 \Delta I_2 + b_1 (I_2^0)^2 \left(\frac{\partial k}{\partial \delta}\right)^0 \Delta\delta . \qquad (24.26)$$

Noting that in Fig. 122a $\dfrac{\partial k}{\partial \delta} < 0$, we introduce the notation

$$c_4 = -\left(\frac{\partial k}{\partial \delta}\right)^0 \cdot (I_2^0)^2 , \qquad c_5 = 2 I_2^0 k^0 , \qquad (24.27)$$

where k^0 and $\left(\dfrac{\partial k}{\partial \delta}\right)^0$ are taken from the graph (Fig. 122a) at the point C, corresponding the steady-state of the system when $\delta^0 = \delta_1 - b_1 \alpha^0$.

Bringing equation (24.26) with the notation (24.27) to standard form, and taking into account (24.15), we obtain the equation of motion of the electromagnet armature in the form

$$(T_4^2 p^2 + T_3 p + 1)\,\Delta\alpha = k_3 \Delta I_2 , \qquad (24.28)$$

where

$$\left.\begin{aligned}
T_4^2 &= \frac{J}{c_1 b_3^2 + c_2 b_2^2 - c_4 b_1^2} , \\[2mm]
T_3 &= \frac{c_3 + c_2' b_2^2}{c_1 b_3^2 + c_2 b_2^2 - c_4 b_1^2} , \\[2mm]
k_3 &= \frac{c_5 b_1}{c_1 b_3^2 + c_2 b_2^2 - c_4 b_1^2} .
\end{aligned}\right\} \qquad (24.29)$$

Thus the dynamics of the sensitive element of the given automatic regulation system are described by two differential equations: (24.20) and (24.28). In equation (24.20) are two "input" quantities ΔV and $\Delta\alpha$, but the latter is the "output" in the second equation (24.28). Consequently, the sensitive element of the given regulator may represent an assembly of two elements (aperiodic and oscillatory) with transient feedback, expressed by the presence of the term $-\Gamma_2^0 p \Delta\alpha$, shown in the schematic diagram (Fig. 123). Physically this transient feedback is a result of the dependence of the electromagnet flux on the armature motion, where the feedback transfer factor Γ_2^0 is defined from (24.17) by the slope of the characteristic $\Phi_2(\delta)$ (Fig. 121b).

The single equation of the sensitive element from formulae (21.9) and (21.10), derived for the open network with feedback, will be:

$$[(T_2 p + 1)(T_4^2 p^2 + T_3 p + 1) + k_2 k_3 \Gamma_2^0 p]\,\Delta\alpha = k_2 k_3 \Delta V . \qquad (24.30)$$

Simplified forms of the equation of the sensitive element are possible:

(1) if we neglect the moment of inertia of the electromagnet armature J, i.e. the quantity T_4, we obtain

$$(T_2 T_3 p^2 + T_2' p + 1)\Delta\alpha = k_2 k_3 \Delta V , \qquad (24.31)$$

where

$$T_2' = T_2 + T_3 + k_2 k_3 \Gamma_2^0 \qquad (24.32)$$

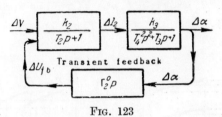

FIG. 123

(an oscillatory element for $T_2' < 2\sqrt{T_2 T_3}$ or a second-order aperiodic element for $T_2' \geqslant 2\sqrt{T_2 T_3}$);

(2) neglecting, in addition, the viscous resistance ($T_3 \approx 0$) gives the equation of the sensitive element

$$(T_2'' p + 1)\Delta\alpha = k_2 k_3 \Delta V , \qquad T_2'' = T_2 + k_2 k_3 \Gamma_2^0 \qquad (24.33)$$

(aperiodic element);

(3) neglecting the moment of inertia of the armature ($T_4 \approx 0$), viscous resistance ($T_3 \approx 0$) and the influence of a small shift of the armature on the process in the electromagnet ($\Gamma_2 = c_4 = 0$), we obtain the equation

$$(T_2 p + 1)\Delta\alpha = k_2 k_3' \Delta V , \qquad (24.34)$$

where

$$k_3' = \frac{c_5 b_1}{c_1 b_3^2 + c_2 b_2^2} \qquad (24.35)$$

(aperiodic element).

The equation of the regulating organ (carbon pile). The dependence of the electrical resistance r of the carbon pile on the pressure F or, which is analogous to this, on the angle of rotation of the armature α, is determined experimentally and given in the form of a graph in Fig. 122*b*. Let the steady-state correspond to a certain point $C(\alpha^0, r^0)$. The deviation of the magnitude of the resistance in the transient process will be:

$$\Delta r = k_4 \Delta\alpha , \qquad (24.36)$$

where the transfer factor

$$k_4 = \left(\frac{\partial r}{\partial \alpha}\right)^0 \qquad (24.37)$$

is defined as the slope at the point C (Fig. 122*b*).

Overal system equation. In complete form the equation of the overall automatic voltage regulation system is composed of (24.10), (24.30) and (24.36). These equations are simplified by substitution of (24.30) by (24.31), (24.33) or (24.34). If we take expression (24.31), then from formulae (20.10) and (20.11) the overall system equation will be:

$$L(p)\Delta V = S(p)f(t) , \qquad (24.38)$$

where

$$\left.\begin{array}{l} L(p) = (T_1 p + 1)(T_2 T_3 p^2 + T_2' p + 1) + k_1 k_2 k_3 k_4 , \\ S(p) = (b_0 p + b)(T_2 T_3 p^2 + T_2' p + 1) . \end{array}\right\} \qquad (24.39)$$

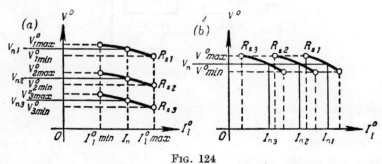

FIG. 124

The static error of the system on the linear portion will be:

$$\Delta V_{st}^1 = \frac{b}{1 + k_1 k_2 k_3 k_4} f^0 , \qquad (24.40)$$

where the coefficients b, k_1, k_2, k_3, k_4 were defined above through the various parameters of the circuits in the system.

The complete static characteristic of the system is determined on the basis of the non-linear characteristics of the object and regulator element (similarly to Section 22) and take the form of Fig. 124. We give there two different presentations of the system adjustment by means of resistance R_s: (a) at various nominal potentials for the same load range, (b) for various load ranges at a common nominal potential.

25. Equations of automatic aircraft-course regulator

Without considering modern complex autopilot systems, let us consider the equations of an automatic aircraft-course regulation system (with a course autopilot) from the simplified schematic diagram (Fig. 125).

The regulated object is the aircraft, the regulator is the course autopilot, conventionally represented in Fig. 125 adjacent to the body of the aircraft, while the regulated quantity is the angle of rotation ψ of the aircraft axis read from the required course direction.

The sensitive elements of the course autopilot are the free gyro-scope 2 installed in the aircraft, measuring the angle of rotation ψ and the rate gyroscope 3, measuring the first and second derivatives with respect to time $\dot{\psi}$ and $\ddot{\psi}$ of the angle of rotation ψ (i.e. the angular velocity and angular acceleration of the aircraft about the vertical axis).

From the sensitive elements the current proceeds through the potentiometers 4, 5, 6 to the control winding of the differential

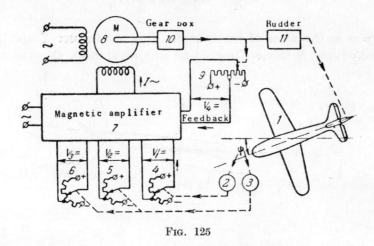

FIG. 125

magnetic amplifier 7. In the magnetic amplifier summation and amplification of these three signals takes place. The resulting alter-nating current is applied to one of the windings of the reversing at electric motor 8 which, through the gear box 10, rotates the rudder 11 (regulating organ). The rudder acts on the aircraft, thus closing the regulating loop.

There may also be an additional negative feedback 9, in which the rheostat slide shifts together with the rudder rotation and the voltage taken from the rheostat goes to a fourth control winding of the magnetic amplifier.

Equation of the regulated object. Considering only small deviations of the aircraft from rectilinear horizontal flight, we shall consider that the motion of the aircraft in the horizontal plane (with respect to course) in the first approximation is independent of its motion in the vertical plane (pitch) and of banking in a more general treatment the course and banking are not separated). We shall construct firstly, two equations of motion of the center of gravity of the aircraft, projected on the tangent to the trajectory (i.e. in the direction of the velocity V) and on the normal to the trajectory, i.e. in the direction n, perpendicular to the velocity V (Fig. 126), secondly, the equation

16

of rotation of the aircraft about the vertical axis passing through its center of gravity (perpendicular to the drawing). These three equations are:

$$m\frac{dV}{dt} = T - X,$$
$$m\frac{V^2}{R} = Z - Z_\pi,$$
$$J\frac{d\omega}{dt} = M_\pi - M_a - M_r,$$

(25.1)

where m is the mass of the aircraft, T is the thrust, X and Z are the aerodynamic forces (frontal and side resistance), R is the radius

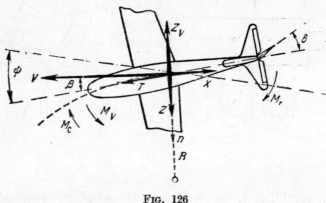

FIG. 126

of curvature of the trajectory, J and ω are the moments of inertia and the angular velocity of the aircraft with respect to the vertical axis, Z_p and M_p are the perturbing force and moment (arising, for example, from inexact correspondance between the true direction of the thrust and the calculated, or arising from wind), M_a is the aerodynamic resistive moment against the rotation of the aircraft, M_r is the rudder moment.

For simplicity the velocity of the V will be considered constant. Therefore the first of equations (25.1) gives only $T = X$ (the thrust should be equal to the drag) and drops out of further consideration.

The second of equations (25.1) will be transformed, noting that V/R is the angular velocity of rotation of the vector V in the motion of the aircraft over a curvilinear trajectory (broken line in Fig. 126). The angle between the velocity and a fixed direction, as is evident from the figure (Fig. 126), is equal to $\psi-\beta$. Consequently,

$$\frac{V}{R} = \frac{d(\psi - \beta)}{dt},$$

(25.2)

where ψ is the angle of yaw, β is the angle of slide. The angular velocity of rotation of the aircraft itself will be:

$$\omega = \frac{d\psi}{dt}.$$

The aerodynamic forces and moments Z, M_a, and M_r are, generally speaking, non-linear functions of a number of variable coordinates of the aircraft in flight. We shall consider only the following principle relations (aerodynamic characteristics of the aircraft):

$$Z = Z(\beta), \qquad M_a = M_a(\psi, \beta), \qquad M_r = M_r(\delta),$$

where δ is the angle of deviation of the rudder from the neutral position.

The perturbing forces and moments Z_p and M_p are arbitrary functions of time,

$$M_p = M_p(t), \qquad Z_p = Z_p(t),$$

independent of the automatic regulation system under consideration.

Equations (25.1), considering (25.2), are written in the form

$$\left.\begin{aligned} J\ddot{\psi} + M_a(\psi, \beta) + M_r(\delta) &= M_p(t), \\ mV\dot{\beta} + Z(\beta) - mV\dot{\psi} &= Z_p(t). \end{aligned}\right\} \tag{25.3}$$

Let the steady-state flight be defined by certain values $\psi = \psi^0$, $\beta = \beta^0$, $\delta = \delta^0$. In view of the smallness not only of the deviations $\Delta\psi = \psi - \psi^0$, $\Delta\beta = \beta - \beta^0$, $\Delta\delta = \delta - \delta^0$, but of the steady-state values themselves ψ^0, β^0, δ^0, linearisation of the aircraft equations (23.3) is frequently carried out in the total quantities ψ, β, δ rather than in deviations, specifically:

$$\left.\begin{aligned} J\ddot{\psi} + M_a^{\dot{\psi}}\dot{\psi} + M_a^{\beta}\beta + M_r^{\delta}\delta &= M_p(t), \\ mV\dot{\beta} + Z^{\beta}\beta - mV\dot{\psi} &= Z_p(t), \end{aligned}\right\} \tag{25.4}$$

where we introduce the notation

$$M_a^{\dot{\psi}} = \left(\frac{\partial M_a}{\partial \psi}\right)^0, \qquad M_a^{\beta} = \left(\frac{\partial M_a}{\partial \beta}\right)^0, \qquad M_r^{\delta} = \left(\frac{\partial M_r}{\partial \delta}\right)^0, \qquad Z^{\beta} = \left(\frac{\partial Z}{\partial \beta}\right)^0,$$

and the partial derivatives (slope of the aerodynamic characteristics) are taken at $\psi = \dot{\psi} = \beta = \delta = 0$.

The steady-state flight $(\psi^0, \beta^0, \delta^0)$ for given constant perturbing moments and forces M_p^0 and Z_p^0 are defined from (25.3) with respect to non-linearity of the aerodynamic characteristics by the equations

$$M_a(0, \beta^0) + M_r(\delta^0) = M_p^0, \qquad Z(\beta^0) = Z_p^0, \tag{25.5}$$

and from (25.4) in linearised form, by the equations

$$M_a^\beta \beta^0 + M_r^\delta \delta^0 = M_p^0 , \quad Z^\beta \beta^0 = Z_p^0 .$$

This signifies that because of the presence of constant magnitudes of perturbing forces M_p^0 and Z_p^0 the steady-state rectilinear flight will take place with a certain constant slide angle β^0 at constant deviation of the rudder position δ^0.

The equations of the aircraft (25.3) or (25.4) in deviations will be:

$$\left. \begin{array}{l} J\Delta\dot\psi + M_a^{\dot\psi}\Delta\psi + M_a^\beta\Delta\beta + M_r^\delta\Delta\delta = M_p - M_p^0 , \\ mV\Delta\dot\beta + Z^\beta\Delta\beta - mV\Delta\psi = Z_p - Z_p^0 , \end{array} \right\} \quad (25.6)$$

where the coefficients $M_s^{\dot\psi}, M_s^\beta, M_r^\delta, Z^\beta$ may have the previous values. But it is more correct to take them as the slopes of the tangents to the corresponding aerodynamic characteristics at the points of steady-state flight ($\beta^0, \delta^0, \dot\psi = 0$).

Reducing this to standard form (Section 18), we find the equation of the regulated object (equation of perturbed motion of the aircraft) in the form

$$\left. \begin{array}{l} (T_1 p + 1)p\Delta\psi = -k_1\Delta\delta - k_2\Delta\beta + f_1(t) , \\ (T_2 p + 1)\Delta\beta = T_2 p\Delta\psi + f_2(t) , \end{array} \right\} \quad (25.7)$$

or after eliminating the quantities $\Delta\beta$;

$$[(T_1 p + 1)(T_2 p + 1) + k_2 T_2]p\Delta\psi$$
$$= -k_1(T_2 p + 1)\Delta\delta + (T_2 p + 1)f_1 - k_2 f_2 , \quad (25.8)$$

where

$$\left. \begin{array}{llll} T_1 = \dfrac{J}{M_a^{\dot\psi}}, & T_2 = \dfrac{mV}{Z^\beta}, & k_1 = \dfrac{M_r^\delta}{M_a^{\dot\psi}}, & k_2 = \dfrac{M_a^\beta}{M_a^{\dot\psi}}, \\[3mm] f_1(t) = \dfrac{M_p(t) - M_p^0}{M_a^{\dot\psi}}, & f_2(t) = \dfrac{Z_p(t) - Z_p^0}{Z^\beta}. \end{array} \right\} \quad (25.9)$$

The fact that $\Delta\varphi$ itself does not enter into the aircraft equation (25.8) but only the angular velocity $p\Delta\psi$ indicates the neutrality of the aircraft to the course direction (this is a result of the independence of the aerodynamics characteristics of the angle ψ itself). In this case the aircraft represents an oscillatory element with introduction of integral (see Section 19) or a second-order aperiodic element with introduction of integral, depending on the corresponding coefficients.

To simplify the problem the motion of the aircraft is sometimes studied more coarsely, without taking into account the slip ($\beta = 0$). Then the equation of the regulated object takes the form

$$(T_1 p + 1)p\Delta\psi = -k_1\Delta\delta + f_1(t) \quad (25.10)$$

(aperiodic integrating element). The aircraft described by this approximate equation is termed a neutral aircraft in the literature.

Equations of the sensitive elements. The free gyroscope 2 and the rate gyroscope 3 (see Fig. 125) will be considered ideal, assuming that by the use of special corrections we have succeeded in obtaining without distortion an angle proportional to the angle ψ of rotation of the aircraft on the slider 4 connected with the free gyroscope, and on the sliders 5 and 6, connected with the rate gyroscope, angles

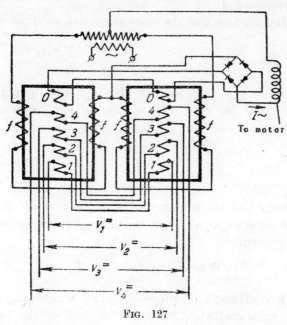

FIG. 127

proportional to the angular velocity $\dot\psi$ and the angular acceleration $\ddot\psi$. As a result the equations of the sensitive elements take the form

$$V_1 = k_3\psi\,, \qquad V_2 = k_3'\dot\psi\,, \qquad V_3 = k_3''\ddot\psi\,,$$

or in deviations from the steady-state values:

$$\Delta V_1 = k_3\Delta\psi\,, \qquad \Delta V_2 = k_3'p\Delta\psi\,, \qquad \Delta V_3 = k_3''p^2\Delta\psi\,, \qquad (25.11)$$

where in the steady-state

$$V_1^0 = k_3\psi^0\,, \qquad V_2^0 = V_3^0 = 0\,. \qquad (25.12)$$

Equation of the magnetic amplifier. The circuit of the differential magnetic amplifier with positive feedback is given in Fig. 127. It has four pairs of control windings 1, 2, 3, 4 and a pair of windings for the internal positive feedback 0. Windings 1, 2, 3 are connected with the sensitive elements of the autopilot and winding 4 is connected in the negative-feedback circuit from the rudder.

The dependence of the total change of the constant components of the magnetic flux Φ as a function of the magnitude of the magnetising mmf is expressed for the given circuit in the form

$$\Phi = \gamma(I_1 N_1 + I_2 N_2 + I_3 N_3 + I_4 N_4 + I_0 N_0), \qquad (25.13)$$

where the components in the parentheses denote the ampere-turns of the windings $1, 2, 3, 4$ and the internal feedback of the amplifier 0 respectively. The quantity γ is a coefficient of proportionality determined experimentally.

For the circuits of each of the pairs of control windings it is possible to write:

$$I_1 = \frac{V_1}{R_1} - \frac{N_1}{R_1}\frac{d\Phi}{dt}, \qquad I_2 = \frac{V_2}{R_2} - \frac{N_2}{R_2}\frac{d\Phi}{dt}, \dots \qquad (25.14)$$

Let us denote the gain factors of the magnetic amplifier with respect to current for each of the pairs of control windings (with the remaining disconnected) by q_1, q_2, q_3, q_4, i.e.

$$\frac{I}{I_1} = q_1, \qquad \frac{I}{I_2} = q_2, \dots \qquad (25.15)$$

Neglecting delay in the alternating-current circuit we assume that the current I at the output of the magnetic amplifier is proportional to the total change of the constant components of magnetic-flux Φ. Consequently,

$$\Phi = \frac{I}{\alpha} \quad \text{and} \quad I_0 = I, \qquad (25.16)$$

where α is a coefficient of proportionality which may be defined through the gain coefficients (25.15) for each of the four pairs of control windings individually, with the remaining control windings disconnected. In accordance with (25.13), (25.16) and (25.15) we obtain:

$$\left.\begin{aligned}
\alpha &= \frac{I}{\gamma(I_1 N_1 + I N_0)} = \frac{q_1}{\gamma(N_1 + q_1 N_0)}, \\
\alpha &= \frac{I}{\gamma(I_2 N_2 + I N_0)} = \frac{q_2}{\gamma(N_2 + q_2 N_0)}, \dots
\end{aligned}\right\} \qquad (25.17)$$

Further, substituting in equation (25.13) the quantities (25.14) and (25.16), we find:

$$\gamma \sum_{i=1}^{4} \frac{N_i^2}{R_i(1 - \gamma\alpha N_0)}\frac{dI}{dt} + I = \gamma \sum_{i=1}^{4} \frac{\alpha U_i N_i}{R_i(1 - \gamma\alpha N_0)}.$$

Then the quantity α in each of the four components in the left and right-hand sides of this equality is replaced by the corresponding expressions (25.17). As a result we obtain the following dynamic equation of the magnetic amplifier:

$$T_3\frac{dI}{dt} + I = k_4 V_1 + k_5 V_2 + k_6 V_3 + k_7 V_4, \qquad (25.18)$$

or in deviations:

$$(T_3 p + 1)\Delta I = k_4 \Delta V_1 + k_5 \Delta V_2 + k_6 \Delta V_3 + k_7 \Delta V_4 , \qquad (25.19)$$

where

$$
\left.
\begin{aligned}
T_3 &= \gamma \sum_{i=1}^{4} \frac{N_i + q_i N_O}{R_i}\, N_i , \\
k_4 &= \frac{q_1}{R_1}, \quad k_5 = \frac{q_2}{R_2}, \quad k_6 = \frac{q_3}{R_3}, \quad k_7 = \frac{q_4}{R_4}.
\end{aligned}
\right\} \qquad (25.20)
$$

The magnetic amplifier thus represents in the present case an aperiodic summation circuit with time constant T_3 and gain coefficients k_4, k_5, k_6, k_7.

In the steady-state, considering (25.12) and (25.18), we have:

$$I^0 = k_4 V_1^0 + k_7 V_4^0 . \qquad (25.21)$$

Equation of the regulating organ drive. The drive consists of an electric motor and gear reduction with transmission to the aircraft rudder (regulating organ). One of the windings of the motor (Fig. 125) is fed by alternating current from the output circuit of the magnetic amplifier and the second from an external source. The relation between the angle of rotation δ of the rudder and the current in the first winding is written in the form

$$J\ddot{\delta} + k'\dot{\delta} = k''\dot{I} ,$$

where J and $k'\dot{\delta}$ are the moment of inertia of the entire mass rotated by the motor and the entire resistance moment reduced to the axis of the rudder, $k''I$ is the rotating moment, k' and k'' are given coefficients. Dividing these equations by k' and passing to deviations, we obtain the equation of the regulating organ drive in the form

$$(T_4 p + 1) p \Delta\delta = k_8 \Delta I , \qquad (25.22)$$

where

$$T_4 = \frac{J}{k'}, \quad k_8 = \frac{k''}{k'} . \qquad (25.23)$$

It is not necessary to set up separate equations for the regulating organ since its motion has already been taken into account here.

Feedback equation. The feedback consists of the potentiometer 9 (Fig. 125), the slider of which is rigidly coupled to the shaft of the reduction gear. Therefore the voltage taken from it V_4 is proportional to the angle of rotation of the rudder δ. Consequently, the feedback equation will be:

$$\Delta V_4 = -k_9 \Delta\delta , \qquad (25.24)$$

where in the steady-state

$$V_4^0 = -k_9 \delta^0 . \qquad (25.25)$$

The voltage V_4 is applied to the fourth control winding 4 of the magnetic amplifier and was taken into account in its equation (25.19).

Overal system equation. The equation of the closed automatic course regulation system (aircraft and course autopilot) thus consists of (25.8) (or (25.10)), (25.11), (25.19). (25.22) and (25.24).

Let us write the equations of the entire course autopilot individually. Substituting (25.11), (25.22) and (25.24) in equation (25.19), we obtain the equation of the course autopilot in the form

$$[(T_3 p + 1)(T_4 p + 1)p + k_{fb}]\Delta\delta = (k_\psi + k_{\dot\psi} p + k_{\ddot\psi}p^2)\Delta\psi , \quad (25.26)$$

where we have put

$$k_\psi = k_3 k_4 k_8 , \quad k_{\dot\psi} = k_3' k_7 k_8 , \quad k_{\ddot\psi} = k_3'' k_6 k_8 , \quad k_{fb} = k_7 k_8 k_9 . \quad (25.27)$$

In the regulation function (see Section 14 and Section 15) here, as we see, in addition to the deviation magnitude $\Delta\psi$ we have introduced also its first and second derivatives. In the absence of feedback $(k_7 = k_9 = 0)$ the autopilot equation will be:

$$(T_3 p + 1)(T_4 p + 1)p\Delta\delta = (k_\psi + k_{\dot\psi} p + k_{\ddot\psi} p^2)\Delta\psi , \quad (25.28)$$

i.e. the integral of the deviation enters into the regulation function, eliminating the static error of the system with respect to the angle ψ.

In fact, in the presence of stiff feedback the equation of the entire system (aircraft with autopilot) from (25.8), (25.26), (20.10) and (20.11) takes the form

$$L(p)\Delta\psi = S_1(p)f_1(t) - S_2(p)f_2(t) , \quad (25.29)$$

where

$$\left.\begin{aligned}
L(p) &= [(T_1 p + 1) \times (T_2 p + 1) + k_2 T_2] \\
&\quad [(T_3 p + 1)(T_4 p + 1)p + k_{fb}]p + \\
&\quad + k_1(T_2 p + 1)(k_\psi + k_{\dot\psi} p + k_{\ddot\psi} p^2) , \\
S_1(p) &= (T_2 p + 1)[(T_3 p + 1)(T_4 p + 1)p + k_{fb}] , \\
S_2(p) &= k_2[(T_3 p + 1)(T_4 p + 1)p + k_{fb}] .
\end{aligned}\right\} \quad (25.30)$$

From (21.35) the static error of the system with respect to each of the perturbations will be:

$$\Delta\psi_{st1} = \frac{k_{fb}}{k_1 k_\psi} f_{1max}^0 ; \quad \Delta\psi_{st2} = \frac{k_2 k_{fb}}{k_1 k_\psi} f_{2max}^0 ; \quad (25.31)$$

it drops out in the absence of stiff feedback 9, introduced into the circuit in Fig. 125, since without it $k_{fb} = k_7 k_8 k_9 = 0$.

26. Equations of a servomechanism

Let us consider a servomechanism, the schematic diagram of which is shown in Fig. 128. The command device is a handwheel, rotated from without according to an arbitrary function $\alpha = \alpha(t)$.

This angle of rotation should be reproduced by the control object with change of scale factor: $k_0\alpha(t)$.

The error detector *ED* is here a mechanical differential, the output shaft of which gives the difference of angles of rotation of the input device shaft and the feedback shaft (i.e. the error angle γ). The mechanical feedback shaft may be replaced by an electrical one using selsyns, as in Fig. 21.

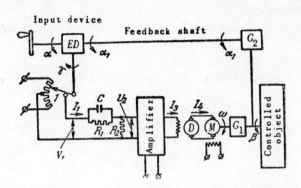

FIG. 128

The error angle, obtained by means of the rheostat 1, is transformed to the error voltage V_1. The electric circuit consisting of the capacitance C and the resistances R_1 and R_2 is a differentiating device. As a result, a voltage V_2 is applied to the input of the dc amplifier equal to the sum of two terms, proportional respectively to the error angle and its first derivative with respect to time.

The amplified current I_3 passes through the field winding of generator G (its drive is not shown in the circuit). The armature circuit of the generator is connected in series with the armature circuit of the motor M with independent excitation. The motor rotates the controlled object through a gear reduction P_1.

Equation of the controlled object with motor. Let us denote β (Fig. 128) the angle of rotation actually obtained at the control object (regulated quantity). The differential equation of rotation of the object is written in the form

$$J\ddot{\beta} = M_r - M_f - M_l, \tag{26.1}$$

where J is the moment of inertia of the entire mass rotating together with the shaft, reduced to the shaft, M_r is the rotating moment at the shaft of the object from the drive side, M_f is the moment of the friction force and resistance, M_l is the moment of the external load on the object.

The rotating moment on the dc electric motor shaft with independent excitation is:

$$M'_r = \frac{p_1 N \Phi}{p_2 20\pi} I_4 \,,$$

where p_1 is the number of pole pairs, p_2 is the number of parallel pairs of branches of the armature winding, N is the number of conductors in the armature winding, Φ is the field flux, I_4 is the current in the armature.

Since the reduction gear P_1 is characterised by the relation

$$\beta = k_r \omega \qquad (26.2)$$

(k_r is the transfer ratio of the reduction box, $k_r < 1$), we obtain:

$$M_r = \frac{1}{k_r} M'_r = c_1 I_4 \,, \qquad (26.3)$$

where

$$c_1 = \frac{p_1 N \Phi}{p_2 k_r 20\pi} \,.$$

The friction and resistance moments

$$M_f = c_2 \beta \,. \qquad (26.4)$$

The moment of the external load on the object

$$M_l = M_l(t) \,, \qquad (26.5)$$

which plays the role of an external perturbation.

Substituting (26.3), (26.4) and (26.5) in equation (26.1), we obtain the required equation of the controlled object with motor:

$$(T_1 p + 1) p \beta = k_1 I_4 - f(t) \,, \qquad (26.6)$$

where

$$T_1 = \frac{J}{c_2}, \qquad k_1 = \frac{c_1}{c_2}, \qquad f(t) = \frac{M_l(t)}{c_2} \qquad (26.7)$$

(aperiodic integrating element).

Feedback equation. Considering the required scale constant k_0 of the forward circuit of the system, let us introduce into the feedback loop a reduction gear P_2, such that (see Fig. 128)

$$\alpha_1 = \frac{1}{k_0} \beta \,. \qquad (26.8)$$

Equation of the error detector. At the output shaft of the differential *ED*, the angle of rotation γ is equal to the difference of angles of rotation of the two input shafts α and α_1, i.e.

$$\gamma = \alpha - \alpha_1 \,, \qquad (26.9)$$

where γ is termed the error angle.

Potentiometer equation. We shall consider that the voltage V_1 taken from the rheostat is proportional to the angle of rotation γ of its slider, i.e.

$$V_1 = k_2\gamma, \tag{26.10}$$

where k_2 is the transfer or gain factor of the potentiometer, V_1 is the error voltage.

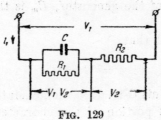

Fig. 129

Equation of the differentiating device. This device consists of the network CR_1R_2 (Fig. 128), which is shown separately (Fig. 129). Writing the obvious equality

$$I_1 = C\frac{d(V_1-V_2)}{dt} + \frac{V_1-V_2}{R_1} = \frac{V_2}{R_2},$$

we obtain from this the required differential equation of the device

$$(T_2p+1)V_2 = (k_3+k_3'p)V_1, \tag{26.11}$$

where

$$\left.\begin{aligned} T_2 &= k_3' = \frac{CR_1R_2}{R_1+R_2}, \\ k_3 &= \frac{R_2}{R_1+R_2}. \end{aligned}\right\} \tag{26.12}$$

This is an aperiodic element with introduction of derivative. Using this, the derivative is introduced into the regulation function. The time constant T_2 indicates the non-idealness ("inertia") of the given device. A second type of differentiating device has been given, for example, in Fig. 89c.

Equation of the amplifier and generator field circuit. Denoting by L_3 and R_3 the inductance and resistance of the generator field winding (Fig. 128) and by R_i the anode resistance of the amplifier tube, we may write the equation

$$L_3\frac{dI_3}{dt} + (R_i+R_3)I_3 = qV_2, \tag{26.13}$$

where q is the gain factor. From this, after division by (R_i+R_3), we obtain:

$$(T_3p+1)I_3 = k_4V_2, \tag{26.14}$$

where

$$T_3 = \frac{L_3}{R_i+R_3}, \qquad k_4 = \frac{q}{R_i+R_3}. \tag{26.15}$$

Equation of the armature circuit. The generator and motor armatures comprise a single circuit. Let L_4 and R_4 denote its total inductance and resistance. Then

$$L_4 \frac{dI_4}{dt} + R_4 I_4 = E_g - E_m , \qquad (26.16)$$

where E_g is the emf of the generator, E_m is the counter-emf of the motor.

It may be assumed that

$$E_g = k_g J_3 ,$$

since in the given circuit (Fig. 128) the generator operates in a rectilinear (non-saturated) portion of the characteristic.

The counter-emf of the motor is proportional to the angular velocity of the motor shaft i.e., taking into account (26.2)

$$E_m = k_m \omega = \frac{k_m}{k_r} \beta .$$

Substituting the expressions for E_g and E_m in equation (26.16), we obtain:

$$(T_4 p + 1) I_4 = k_5 I_3 - k_6 p\beta , \qquad (26.17)$$

where

$$T_4 = \frac{L_4}{R_4}, \qquad k_5 = \frac{k_g}{R_4}, \qquad k_6 = \frac{k_m}{k_r R_4} . \qquad (26.18)$$

We note that in equation (26.17) aside from the input quantity I_3 taken from the preceding circuit (generator field winding (26.14)), there is a further input quantity $p\beta$, which is equivalent to one taken from the last circuit of the system (from the output of the reduction gear P_1). As a result of the appearance of the motor counter-emf the term $k_6 p\beta$ has appeared in equation (26.17), and this represents an additional negative and transient feedback.

The overall system equation. From the above equations the structural block diagram of the system is represented in Fig. 130, where the transfer function of each element is given. In accordance with the interpretation of the counter-emf as an additional transient feedback, equation (26.17) is divided into two parts:

$$(T_4 p + 1) I_4 = k_5 (I_3 - I_{fb}) , \qquad I_{fb} = \frac{k_6}{k_5} p\beta , \qquad (26.19)$$

i.e. the effect of the counter emf is reduced conventionally to an additional opposing current in the field circuit, proceeding from the feedback to the shaft of the object and proportional to the derivative of the quantity β.

To obtain the equation of the entire system let us write first the equation of the block enclosed in broken line (Fig. 130), considering it as a separate servomechanism with external signal I_2 and regulated quantity β. According to formulae (20.23) we obtain for this block the equation

$$[(T_1 p + 1)(T_4 p + 1) + k_1 k_6] p \beta = k_1 k_5 I_3 - (T_4 p + 1) f(t) . \quad (26.20)$$

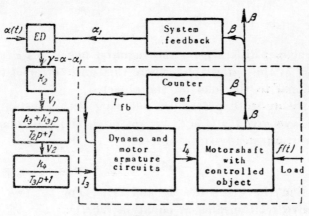

FIG. 130

Considering now the entire block enclosed by broken line (Fig. 130) as a single element 1 with equation (26.20), by the same formulae (20.23) we find the equation of the entire servomechanism in the form

$$L(p) \beta = N(p) \alpha(t) - S(p) f(t) , \quad (26.21)$$

where

$$
\left.
\begin{aligned}
L(p) &= [(T_1 p + 1)(T_4 p + 1) + k_1 k_6] \times \\
&\quad \times p(T_2 p + 1)(T_3 p + 1) + k_1(k + k'p) , \\
N(p) &= k_0 k_1(k + k'p) , \\
S(p) &= (T_2 p + 1)(T_3 p + 1)(T_4 p + 1);
\end{aligned}
\right\}
\quad (26.22)
$$

with

$$k = \frac{k_2 k_3 k_4 k_5}{k_0} , \qquad k' = \frac{k_2 k_3' k_4 k_5}{k_0} , \quad (26.23)$$

the overall transfer factors of the system with respect to angle and with respect to derivative respectively. It is easily seen that relationship (7.18) is fundamental for the servomechanism, i.e. $c_v = k_0 a_n$, is here satisfied, since the polynomial $N(p)$ has a constant term $c_v = k_0 k_1 k$, while the polynomial $L(p)$, the constant term $a_n = k_1 k$.

If the equation of the system is written with respect to the error γ, then from (20.21) we obtain:

$$L(p) \gamma = N_\gamma(p) \alpha(t) + S_\gamma(p) f(t) , \quad (26.24)$$

where

$$N_\gamma(p) = [(T_1 p + 1)(T_4 p + 1) + k_1 k_6] p (T_2 p + 1)(T_3 p + 1), \\ S_\gamma(p) = (T_2 p + 1)(T_3 p + 1)(T_4 p + 1) \frac{1}{k_0}. \qquad\qquad (26.25)$$

In the fixed stationary state ($\alpha = \text{const} = \alpha$, $\beta = \text{const} = \beta$) we have:

$$\beta^0 = k_0 \alpha^0 - \frac{f^0}{k_1 k}, \qquad \gamma^0 = \frac{f^0}{k_1 k k_0}, \qquad (26.26)$$

i.e. the angle β differs from the required one $\beta = k_0 \alpha$ (mentioned at the start of the paragraph), where this static error of the system is proportional to the load on the object.

In the steady-state process of following with constant velocity, when we have given $\alpha = \omega_\alpha t$, i.e. $p\alpha = \omega_\alpha$ and $f = \text{const} = f^0$, we obtain a certain steady-state process

$$\beta = \omega_\beta t - \Delta\beta_{sd}, \qquad p\beta = \omega_\beta.$$

Let us find the quantities ω_β and $\Delta\beta_{sd}$. For this we substitute all the above relationships in equation (26.21):

$$[(1 + k_1 k_6) p + k_1 (k + k'p)]\beta = k_0 k_1 (k + k'p)\alpha - f^0$$

or

$$[(1 + k_1 k_6) + k_1 k']\omega_\beta + k_1 k (\omega_\beta t - \Delta\beta_{sd}) = k_0 k_1 k \omega_\alpha t + k_0 k_1 k' \omega_\alpha - f^0.$$

Equating coefficients for t, we find:

$$\omega_\beta = k_0 \omega_\alpha, \qquad (26.27)$$

i.e. the response velocity exactly follows the command. Equating all remaining terms taking into account (26.27), we obtain:

$$\Delta\beta_{sd} = \frac{(1 + k_1 k_6) k_0 \omega_\alpha + f^0}{k_1 k}. \qquad (26.28)$$

This is the stationary dynamic error of the system during following with constant velocity, representing the divergence of the angle of rotation of the controlled object from the required one, with one part proportional to the velocity, the other to the load.

If the load $f^0 = 0$, then from (26.28) and (26.27) we have the error expression

$$\Delta\beta_{sd} = \frac{\omega_\beta}{D}, \qquad \text{where} \quad D = \frac{k_1 k}{1 + k_1 k_6}, \qquad (26.29)$$

and we term the quantity D the "quality" of the servomechanism. The greater it is, the less the stationary dynamic error at constant velocity (per unit velocity).

CHAPTER VII

STABILITY CRITERIA FOR ORDINARY LINEAR SYSTEMS

27. Preliminary information

It was shown above (in Section 7) that for ordinary linear systems to be stable it is necessary and sufficient that all the roots of the characteristic equation of the given system have negative real parts (or, geometrically, that all roots be located to the left of the imaginary axis in the complex root plane). In Section 18 this proposition was extended to linearised systems.

Therefore by calculating the roots of the characteristic equation it is always possible to determine whether the given system is stable or not. But there is no necessity to calculate the roots completely only to determine the stability of the system. On the other hand, such a method of studying stability is rarely convenient since we have only numerical methods to calculate the roots of equations of higher than fourth order, general formulae in algebraic form do not exist, as a result of which it is necessary to give all the coefficients of the equation in numerical form (see Section 39). But even for equations of the third and forth degree the general formulae for the roots are very cumbersome. This makes the solution of the problem difficult when the parameters of the system are to be chosen from a broad range according to the condition of stability of the system.

Therefore so-called stability criteria have been developed, which permit consideration of the stability or instability of a dynamic system without recourse to calculating the roots of the characteristic equation, when this is for any reason undesirable. Before describing the existing stability criteria, we shall present here certain preliminary remarks.

Obtaining the characteristic equation of the system. The differential equation of motion of an automatic regulation system (and servomechanism) was written in the following general form:

$$L(p)x = S(p)f(t) + N(p)y(t), \qquad (27.1)$$

where x is the deviation of the regulated quantity, $f(t)$ is the external perturbation on the object, $y(t)$ is the external command signal on the regulator. In chapters V and VI we have obtained expressions for the operational polynomials $L(p)$, $S(p)$, $N(p)$ for various systems in the general form and in specific examples.

The characteristic equation of a closed automatic system from (27.1) will be

$$L(z) = 0 \qquad (27.2)$$

or

$$Q(z) + R(z) = 0 , \qquad (27.3)$$

where Q and R are operational polynomials of the left and right-hand sides of the equations of the corresponding open network (see Sections 20 and 21) or, which is the same thing, the numerator and the denominator of the transfer function of the open network.

Consequently, methods of obtaining the characteristic equation of the system are the same as the methods of obtaining the left-hand side $L(p)$ of the differential equation of the closed system, described in chapters V and VI, only substituting p by z.

The characteristic equation of the linear system is independent of the variable with respect to which the differential equation of the system is constructed and the perturbations and input signals introduced into this system. The right-hand side of equation (27.1), i.e. the operational polynomials $S(p)$ and $N(p)$ change substantially, firstly, when the variable x is not the regulated quantity but some other variable in the given system and, secondly, when the point of introduction of the perturbation $f(t)$ or the command $y(t)$ acting on the system is changed.

Necessary stability condition. We shall demonstrate that a necessary (but not sufficient) condition for stability of an ordinary linear system of arbitrary order is that all coefficients of the characteristic equation of the given system be positive.

Given the characteristic equation

$$a_0 z^n + a_1 z^{n-1} + \ldots + a_{n-1} z + a_n = 0 \qquad (a_0 > 0) . \qquad (27.4)$$

Here and below we shall everywhere introduce the condition $a_0 > 0$ for concreteness. It does not introduce any restriction, as in those cases where the equation has $a_0 < 0$, the required condition $a_0 > 0$ may always be satisfied by simple reversal of signs for all terms in the equation.

Let it be given that the system is stable, i.e. that all roots of the above characteristic equation have negative real parts, namely,

$$z_1 = -|\alpha_1|; \quad z_{2,3} = -|\alpha_2| \pm i\omega_2, \ldots, z_n = -|\alpha_n| . \qquad (27.5)$$

It is required to prove that all coefficients of the characteristic equation are always positive.

It is known from algebra that equation (27.4) may be represented in the form

$$a_0(z - z_1)(z - z_2)\ldots(z - z_n) = 0 . \tag{27.6}$$

Substituting here (27.5), we obtain:

$$a_0(z + |\alpha_1|)(z + |\alpha_2| - i\omega_2)(z + |\alpha_2| + i\omega_2)\ldots(z + |\alpha_n|) = 0$$

or

$$a_0(z + |\alpha_1|)[(z + |\alpha_2|)^2 + \omega_2^2]\ldots(z + |\alpha_n|) = 0 . \tag{27.7}$$

This equation may be brought to the form (27.4) by expanding and eliminating parentheses. It is obvious that since $a_0 > 0$ and all the factors not explicitly written in (27.7) may be expressed only by one of the two forms given here, in expanding and multiplying nowhere can negative numbers or zeros be obtained, i.e. all coefficients of equation (27.4) are always positive if the system is stable. But this was to be proved.

We shall now prove the following three propositions.

1. The necessary condition of stability, the positiveness of the coefficients of the characteristic equation, is at the same time a sufficient condition for stability only for systems of first and second order.

In fact, the first-degree characteristic equation

$$a_0 z + a_1 = 0$$

has a single root

$$z_1 = -\frac{a_1}{a_0},$$

while the second-degree characteristic equation

$$a_0 z^2 + a_1 z + a_2 = 0$$

has two roots

$$z_{1,2} = \frac{-a_1 \pm \sqrt{a_1^2 - 4a_0 a_2}}{2a_0} .$$

It is easily seen that in both cases (with $a_0 > 0$) the simple requirement of positiveness of the coefficients of the characteristic equation is necessary and sufficient to ensure negativeness of the real roots and the real parts of the complex roots, which means the stability of the system.

2. Necessary condition for stability—the positiveness of the coefficients of the characteristic equation—for systems of third and higher orders ensures negativeness only of the real roots, but does not ensure negativeness of the real parts of the complex roots

(and is therefore insufficient for stability of systems of higher than second order).

Actually, if there are real roots in the characteristic equation (27.4), then with positive coefficients all these roots will be negative, since no positive number or zero can cause the left-hand side of equation (27.4) to vanish in the presence of positive coefficients, but this signifies that they cannot be its roots.

If in equation (27.4) (higher than second degree) there are complex roots $z_{2,3}$, then, for example, in the case where their real parts are positive we obtain in place of (27.7):

$$a_0(z + |\alpha_1|)[(z - |\alpha_2|)^2 + \omega_2^2]...(z + |\alpha_n|) = 0$$

or

$$a_0[z^3 + (|\alpha_1| - 2|\alpha_2|)z^2 + (\alpha_2^2 + \omega_2^2 - 2|\alpha_1| \cdot |\alpha_2|)z +$$
$$+ |\alpha_1|(\alpha_2^2 + \omega_2^2)]...(z + |\alpha_n|) = 0 .$$

It is easy to see that with certain relations between the numbers α_1, α_2, ω_2 the coefficients of the equation in the present case may be positive while the system is unstable.

Consequently, in the presence of only positive coefficients in the characteristic equation of higher than second degree the presence of positive real parts of the complex roots is not excluded, i.e. the possibility of instability of the system is not excluded.

3. Above (Section 20) we mentioned without proof the desirability that in the equations of a single-loop automatic regulation system there be an odd number of right-hand sides of the circuit equations with minus signs, if by $Q_i(p)$ and $R_i(p)$ are understood operational polynomials with positive coefficients. We shall now explain this rule.

In essence, in obtaining the equations of the closed system the expression $R(p)$ was transferred from the right-hand side to the left with change of sign. Therefore an odd number of system equations with minus sign at the right give a minus sign before the expression $R(p)$ before its transfer to the left-hand side and a plus sign after transfer. But this in turn ensures satisfaction of the necessary condition of stability—the positiveness of the coefficients of the characteristic equation (27.3).

If the system is multi-loop, this rule should be satisfied by the equations of individual blocks after reducing the system to a single-loop equivalent.

In servomechanisms the same requirement is ensured by the presence of a minus sign before x_2 in the third equation (20.17), i.e. in the equation of the error detector.

The Mikhailov curve and its relation to the sings of the real parts of the polynomial roots. Below in different studies connected with the stability of automatic regulation systems a large role will be played by the so-called Mikhailov curve. We shall therefore here consider the general concept of this curve.

Let there be given some polynomial of arbitrary degree n:

$$L(z) = a_0 z^n + a_1 z^{n-1} + \ldots + a_{n-1} z + a_n . \qquad (27.8)$$

Substituting in this the purely imaginary value $z = i\omega$, we obtain:

$$L(i\omega) = X(\omega) + iY(\omega) , \qquad (27.9)$$

where

$$\left. \begin{aligned} X(\omega) &= a_n - a_{n-2}\omega^2 + a_{n-4}\omega^4 - \ldots , \\ Y(\omega) &= a_{n-1}\omega - a_{n-3}\omega^3 + a_{n-5}\omega^5 - \ldots \end{aligned} \right\} \qquad (27.10)$$

From (27.9) and (27.10) the quantity $L(i\omega)$ may be represented in the complex plane (X, iY) in the form of a vector for a given value of ω (Fig. 131a). If we vary the parameter ω in the interval $0 \leqslant \omega \leqslant +\infty$, the tip of this vector describes a certain curve, each point of which corresponds to a definite value of ω.

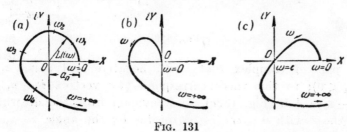

FIG. 131

The graph of the function $L(i\omega)$ obtained in this way, plotted in the complex plane (X, iY) as the parameter varies in the interval $0 \leqslant \omega \leqslant +\infty$, is termed the Mikhailov curve for the polynomial $L(z)$.

It is found that the signs of the real parts of the roots of the given polynomial may be decided from the shape of the Mikhailov curve. This was proved by A. V. Mikhailov in 1936.

Denoting the roots of the polynomial $L(z)$ by $z_1, z_2, \ldots, z_n$, we may write its expression (27.8) in the form

$$L(z) = a_0(z - z_1)(z - z_2) \ldots (z - z_n) . \qquad (27.11)$$

Then the expression for the Mikhailov curve will be:

$$L(i\omega) = a_0(i\omega - z_1)(i\omega - z_2) \ldots (i\omega - z_n) . \qquad (27.12)$$

Let us consider four types of positions of a single root or pair of roots of this polynomial in the complex root plane $(\alpha, i\omega)$:

(1) the negative real root $z_1 = \alpha_1 < 0$ (Fig. 132a); from the rule for vector subtraction we find that the complex number $(i\omega - z_1)$ represents a vector AB; if we let $0 \leqslant \omega \leqslant +\infty$, the point B traverses

the entire positive portion of the imaginary axis, where the vector AB becomes constantly longer, rotating about the point A counter-clockwise by the angle

$$\varphi_1 = +\frac{\pi}{2};\qquad(27.13)$$

(2) positive real root $z_1 = \alpha_1 > 0$; to this there corresponds the vector $i\omega - z_1 = AB$ (Fig. 132b), which for $0 \leqslant \omega \leqslant +\infty$ rotates clockwise by the angle

$$\varphi_1 = -\frac{\pi}{2};\qquad(27.14)$$

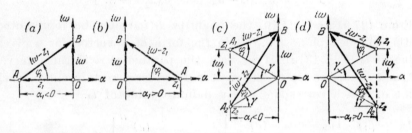

FIG. 132

(3) a pair of complex roots with negative real parts $z_{1,2} = \alpha_1 \pm i\omega_1(\alpha_1 < 0)$; to this there correspond two vectors $i\omega - z_1 = A_1B$ and $i\omega - z_2 = A_2B$ (Fig. 132c). As is evident from the drawing, the first of these with $0 \leqslant \omega \leqslant +\infty$ rotates by the angle

$$\varphi_1 = +\frac{\pi}{2} + \gamma,\qquad(27.15)$$

the second by the angle

$$\varphi_2 = +\frac{\pi}{2} - \gamma;\qquad(27.16)$$

(4) finally, to the pair of complex roots with positive real parts $z_{1,2} = \alpha_1 \pm i\omega_1(\alpha_1 > 0)$ there correspond two vectors $i\omega - z_1 = A_1B$ and $i\omega - z_2 = A_2B$ (Fig. 132d), where the first of these with $0 \leqslant \omega \leqslant +\infty$ rotates by the angle

$$\varphi_1 = -\left(\frac{\pi}{2} + \gamma\right),\qquad(27.17)$$

and the second by the angle

$$\varphi_2 = -\left(\frac{\pi}{2} - \gamma\right).\qquad(27.18)$$

Let us now calculate the angle of rotation of the vector $L(i\omega)$ with $0 \leqslant \omega \leqslant +\infty$. It is well known that in multiplication of complex numbers the arguments are added. Therefore the required angle of rotation φ of the vector $L(i\omega)$, from (27.12), will be equal to the sum of rotations of the vectors $(i\omega - z_1)$, $(i\omega - z_2)$, ..., $(i\omega - z_n)$, i.e.

$$\varphi = \varphi_1 + \varphi_2 + ... + \varphi_n .$$

From formulae (27.13)–(27.18) it is clear that in this sum to each of the real roots there will correspond a component $+\pi/2$ or $-\pi/2$ (the signs are opposite to the signs of the roots), and to each pair of complex roots will correspond a component $+2\pi/2$ or $-2\pi/2$ (the signs are opposite to the signs of the real parts of the pairs of roots).

From this there follows that if the nth-degree polynomial $L(z)$ (27.8) has m roots with positive real parts (both complex and real), and the remaining $(n-m)$ with negative, the rotation of the vector $L(i\omega)$ with $0 \leqslant \omega \leqslant +\infty$ will be:

$$\varphi = (n-m)\frac{\pi}{2} - m\frac{\pi}{2} = (n-2m)\frac{\pi}{2} . \qquad (27.19)$$

This very important relationship will be widely used below.

In deriving formula (27.19) we did not consider three particular cases: a zero root, an infinite root and purely imaginary roots. In the case of a zero root the constant term a_n of the polynomial (27.8) vanishes; therefore the Mikhailov curve begins at the origin of coordinates (Fig. 131b).

An infinite root ($z = \infty$) of the polynomial (27.8) may be considered as a zero root for the variable $1/z$ of the polynomial

$$a_0 + a_1 \frac{1}{z} + ... + a_{n-1}\frac{1}{z^{n-1}} + a\frac{1}{z^n};$$

and therefore an infinite root is obtained when the coefficient a_0 vanishes for the highest-order term of the polynomial $L(z)$ (27.8), which corresponds to change of sign of a_0 (with all remaining coefficients positive).

In the case of a pair of purely imaginary roots $z = \pm i\omega_0$ the polynomial (27.8) vanishes with the substitution $z = i\omega_0$; therefore the Mikhailov curve (27.9) passes through the origin of coordinates at that point which corresponds to the value $\omega = \omega_0$ (Fig. 131c); therefore in this case the Mikhailov curve not only indicates the presence of a pair of purely imaginary roots of the polynomial, but their values as well.

Thus, from the Mikhailov curve $L(i\omega)$, plotted for a given polynomial $L(z)$, the number of roots having positive or negative real parts may be determined, and also if there are purely imaginary roots and, if so, their value. In other words, the position of the Mikhailov curve with respect to the origin of coordinates defines the distribution of roots of the polynomial with respect to the imaginary axis in the root plane.

To the extent that it is important only to determine the position of the Mikhailov curve with respect to the origin of coordinates, it is not necessary to plot it exactly. In point-by-point plotting from (27.10) may be used either the numerical tables of K. P. Ivanov (Reference 31) or the method of calculating the values of the polynomial given in Section 39.

Example 1. The polynomial is given

$$L(z) = z^5 + 2z^4 + 2z^3 + 46z^2 + 89z + 260; \qquad (27.20)$$

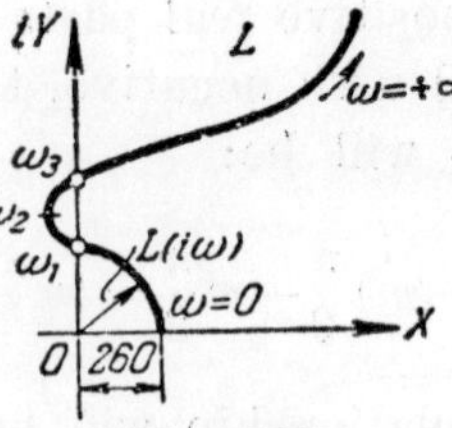

FIG. 133

and it is required to determine the number of roots with positive real parts. The equation of the Mikhailov curve for this polynomial will be:

$$L(i\omega) = i\omega^5 + 2\omega^4 - 2i\omega^3 - 46\omega^2 + 89i\omega + 260 ,$$

where

$$X(\omega) = 2\omega^4 - 46\omega^2 + 260 ,$$

$$Y(\omega) = \omega^5 - 2\omega^3 + 89\omega ,$$

and also

$$\frac{dY}{dX} = \frac{\dfrac{dY}{d\omega}}{\dfrac{dX}{d\omega}} = \frac{5\omega^4 - 6\omega^2 + 89}{\omega(8\omega^2 - 92)} .$$

From this we find $X = 260$, $Y = 0$ at $\omega = 0$ and two points of intersection of the curve with the Y-axis by solution of the biquadratic equation $X(\omega) = 2\omega^4 - 46\omega^2 + 260 = 0$, which gives:

$$\omega_1 = \sqrt{10} = 3 \cdot 162; \qquad \omega_3 = \sqrt{13} = 3 \cdot 606 .$$

From the expression for dY/dX we find three points at which the curve has vertical tangents:

$$\omega = 0; \qquad \omega_2 = \frac{1}{2}\sqrt{46} = 3 \cdot 391 \quad \text{and} \quad \omega = \infty .$$

From these data alone without detailed plotting, the course of the required Mikhailov curve may be approximately sketched

(Fig. 133), and it is clear that the vector $L(i\omega)$ with $0 \leqslant \omega \leqslant +\infty$ passes through a total angle of $\varphi = \pi/2$. Consequently, we have from (27.19) $n - 2m = 1$ and

$$m = \frac{n-1}{2} = 2,$$

i.e. two roots of polynomial (27.20) have positive real parts (lie to the right of the imaginary axis in the root plane).

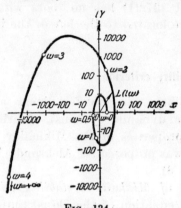

FIG. 134

Example 2. Given the polynomial

$$L(z) = z^7 + 7z^6 + 23z^5 + 37z^4 + 56z^3 + 36z^2 + 12z + 4 . \quad (27.21)$$

In this case we have:

$$X(\omega) = -7\omega^6 + 37\omega^4 - 36\omega^2 + 4 ,$$
$$Y(\omega) = -\omega^7 + 23\omega^5 - 56\omega^3 + 12\omega$$

and

$$\left(\frac{dY}{dX}\right)_{\omega=0} = -\infty \quad \text{and} \quad \left(\frac{dY}{dX}\right)_{\omega=+\infty} = \infty .$$

Let us plot the required Mikhailov curve point-by-point. The calculation will be carried out in the following order.

ω	12ω	$-36\omega^2$	$-56\omega^3$	$37\omega^4$	$23\omega^5$	$-7\omega^6$	$-\omega^7$	$X(\omega)$	$Y(\omega)$
0	0	0	0	0	0	0	0	4	0
0·5	6	−9	−7	2·31	0·719	−0·109	−0·008	−2·80	−0·289
1	12	−36	−56	37	23	−7	−1	−2	−22
2	24	−144	−448	592	736	−448	−128	4	184
3	36	−324	−1512	2997	5589	−5103	−2187	−2426	1926
4	48	−576	−3584	9472	23,552	−28,672	−16,384	−19,772	−3632
$+\infty$	—	—	—	—	—	—	—	$-\infty$	$-\infty$

The curve plotted from these numerical values is shown in Fig. 134, where for clarity different scales are adopted, namely: along both coordinate axes in the interval from -10 to 10 a linear scale is used while from 10 to the end a logarithmic scale (in all four directions).

The vector $L(i\omega)$ for $0 \leqslant \omega \leqslant +\infty$ completes here (Fig. 134) a rotation by the angle $\varphi = 7\pi/2$. Therefore from (27.19) we have $n - 2m = 7$ and

$$m = \frac{n-7}{2} = 0 \,,$$

i.e. the polynomial (27.21) has no roots with positive real part, and all the roots are located to the left of the imaginary axis in the root plane.

28. Mikhailov's stability criterion

Mikhailov's stability criterion for linear automatic regulation systems (and other dynamic systems) of arbitrary order follows directly from the properties of the Mikhailov curve, expressed by formula (27.19). It was proposed by Aleksandr Vasil'evich Mikhailov in 1936 (Reference 8).

First formulation of Mikhailov's stability criterion. Let there be given a differential equation of the closed automatic system (27.1). We may then write its characteristic equation in the form (27.2) or (27.3). The expression for the Mikhailov curve of this equation will be:

$$L(i\omega) \quad \text{or} \quad Q(i\omega) + R(i\omega) \,. \tag{28.1}$$

For stability of the system it is necessary and sufficient (Section 7) that all roots of the characteristic equation $L(z) = 0$ have negative real parts, i.e. in formula (27.19) for the polynomial $L(z)$ we should have $m = 0$.

From this we derive the following formulation of Mikhailov's criterion.

For stability of an nth-order linear system it is necessary and sufficient that the vector $L(i\omega)$ with $0 \leqslant \omega \leqslant +\infty$ complete a rotation by the angle

$$\varphi = n \frac{\pi}{2} \,, \tag{28.2}$$

if $L(z)$ denotes the nth-degree polynomial representing the left-hand side of the characteristic equation of the given system.

In accordance with this stability criterion it is necessary to plot the approximate Mikhailov curve $L(i\omega)$ for the polynomial $L(z)$ (i.e. for the left-hand side of the characteristic equation of the system) according to the rule given in Section 27, and to find the angle of rotation φ of the vector $L(i\omega)$, starting from the origin of coordinates, when its tip traverses the entire Mikhailov curve.

If it is found that $\varphi = n\pi/2$, the system is stable, if $\varphi < n\pi/2$, unstable. For example, the curve in Fig. 131a corresponds to a fourth-order stable system, in Fig. 133 fifth-order unstable system, and in Fig. 134 a seventh-order stable system.

Let us consider what forms may be taken on by the Mikhailov curve for stable and unstable systems. We limit ourselves only to polynomials with positive coefficients since, if this necessary condition is not satisfied, there is no significance in investigating stability.

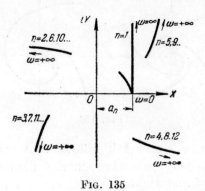

FIG. 135

From formula (27.10) for the coordinates of the Mikhailov curve

$$X(\omega) = a_n - a_{n-2}\omega^2 + a_{n-4}\omega^4 - \ldots , \quad \Bigg\}$$
$$Y(\omega) = a_{n-1}\omega - a_{n-3}\omega^3 + a_{n-5}\omega^5 - \ldots \quad \Bigg\} \qquad (28.3)$$

and from the formulae for its derivatives

$$\frac{dX}{d\omega} = -2a_{n-2}\omega + 4a_{n-4}\omega^3 - \ldots , \quad \Bigg\} \qquad \frac{dY}{dX} = \frac{\dfrac{dY}{d\omega}}{\dfrac{dX}{d\omega}} \qquad (28.4)$$
$$\frac{dY}{d\omega} = a_{n-1} - 3a_{n-3}\omega^2 + 5a_{n-5}\omega^4 - \ldots , \quad \Bigg\}$$

there follow the general properties of the Mikhailov curve given below for polynomials with positive coefficients.

1. The origin of the curve ($\omega = 0$) is always located on the real X-axis at a distance a_n from the origin of coordinates, has a vertical tangent and is concave to the left (Fig. 135). This follows from the fact that from (28.3) the quantity X decreases while Y increases for small positive ω.

2. The end of the curve ($\omega = +\infty$) is always located at infinity (from (28.3)) with vertical or horizontal tangent (from (28.4)) depending on the degree n of the polynomial, as shown in Fig. 135.

3. The total number of points of intersection with the coordinate axes, i.e. the points $Y = 0$ and the points $X = 0$ may not exceed n, including the initial point $\omega = 0$, in accordance with the maximum

possible number of positive roots of the expressions $Y(\omega) = 0$ and $X(\omega) = 0$ (28.3).

4. The total number of points with vertical and horizontal tangents i.e. the points $dX/d\omega = 0$ and the points $dY/d\omega = 0$ may not exceed n, including the points $\omega = 0$ and $\omega = +\infty$, in accordance with the maximum possible number of positive roots of the expressions given for $dX/d\omega$ and $dY/d\omega$ (28.4).

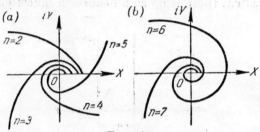

FIG. 136

5. From properties 3 and 4 it follows that the Mikhailov curve with $0 \leqslant \omega \leqslant +\infty$ may pass through not more than n quadrants about the origin of coordinate.

6. If the curve passes through n quadrants in succession, then, in accordance with property 4, it has a monotonic spiral shape.

On the basis of this first formulation of Mikhailov's criterion, (28.2) may be expressed otherwise.

For stability of an nth-order linear system it is necessary and sufficient that the Mikhailov curve plotted for the characteristic equation of the given system pass through n quadrants in succession counterclockwise, circling the origin of coordinates (Fig. 136).

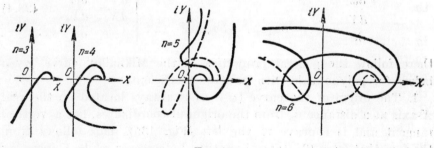

FIG. 137

It cannot pass through more than n quadrants. Therefore instability of the system is reflected here by the Mikhailov curve completely avoiding some quadrant, i.e. violating the sequence of passing through them (Fig. 137).

Second formulation of Mikhailov's stability criterion. The sequence of passing the quadrants shows that the curve alternately intersects the cordinate axes. Consequently, the coordinates $X(\omega)$ and $Y(\omega)$ of the Mikhailov curve alternately vanish for a stable system.

From this follows the second formulation of Mikhailov's stability criterion.

For stability of the linear nth-order system it is necessary and sufficient that all roots of the two equations (28.3) taken separately.

$$X(\omega) = 0, \qquad Y(\omega) = 0 \qquad\qquad (28.5)$$

be real and alternating with each other or, in other words that the curves $X(\omega)$ and $Y(\omega)$ defining the real and imaginary parts of the expression for the Mikhailov curve for $0 \leqslant \omega \leqslant +\infty$ intersect the axis of abscissae ω a total of n times (including the point $\omega = 0$) and that these points of intersection alternate.

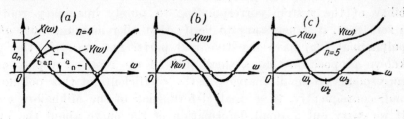

FIG. 138

In Fig. 138a is shown an example of this criterion being satisfied (stable system), while in Fig. 138b it is not satisfied (unstable system) for a fourth-order system. In Fig. 138c are shown curves of $X(\omega)$ and $Y(\omega)$ for an unstable fifth-order system with characteristic equation $L(z) = 0$, where $L(z)$ is the polynomial (27.20) for which the Mikhailov curve has the form of Fig. 133.

Limit of stability. As was seen in Section 7, the limit of stability in the root plane is the imaginary axis $i\omega$, as the boundary between roots with negative and positive parts. Passage of the system to the region of instability is connected with passage of the roots through the purely imaginary values $z_{1,2} = \pm i\omega$ or through the origin $z = 0$ (i.e. $\omega = 0$) or through infinity $z = \infty (\omega = \infty)$.

The requirement of the presence of a purely imaginary root $z = i\omega$ in the characteristic equation of the system $L(z) = 0$ is equivalent to equating to zero the expression for the Mikhailov curve $L(i\omega)$ for the given system, i.e.

$$L(i\omega) = 0. \qquad\qquad (28.6)$$

Graphically this denotes passage of the Mikhailov curve $L(i\omega)$ through the origin of coordinates. In Fig. 139 are shown four examples of the passage of the Mikhailov curve through the origin of coordinates, where the graphs *a* and *b* correspond to incidence on the origin of coordinates of a point of the curve with arbitrary value $\omega = \omega_0$ (purely imaginary roots $z = \pm i\omega$), while for curves c and d the point with $\omega = 0$ (zero root $z = 0$). We shall discuss the infinite root at the end of this section.

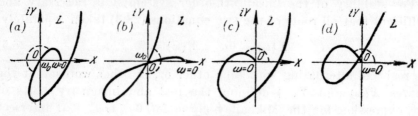

Fig. 139

However, aside from this, from the definition of the limit of stability of the system corresponding to purely imaginary roots or a zero root, it is necessary to verify that all remaining roots of the polynomial $L(z)$ have negative real parts. Let us apply the well-known proposition that a small shift of the roots of a polynomial corresponds to small changes in the coefficients of this polynomial and, consequently, to a small deformation of the Mikhailov curve. If we carry out a small deformation of the curve about the origin of coordinates, as shown in broken line in Fig. 139, then in cases a and c the Mikhailov stability criterion is satisfied while in cases b and d not satisfied (regardless of the side to which we have deformed the curve about the origin of coordinates).

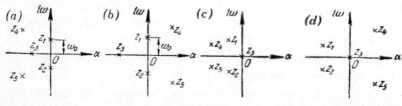

Fig. 140

This signifies that with small shifts of the roots stable systems are obtained in cases a and c while in cases b and d unstable. From this it follows that in cases a and c all remaining roots of the polynomial $L(z)$ except the purely imaginary $z_{1,2} = \pm i\omega_0$ or zero $z_3 = 0$ lie to the left of the imaginary axis in the root plane as shown in Fig. 140a and c. In cases b and d the presence of purely imaginary roots $z_{1,2} = \pm i\omega$ or a zero root $z_3 = 0$ does not correspond to the limit of stability since here two roots are found to the right of the imaginary axis (Fig. 140b and d). This is found on the basis formula (27.19) by simply finding the angle of rotation of the vector $L(i\omega)$

as its tip traverses the entire Mikhailov curve (with the above small deformation at the origin of coordinates).

The limit of stability of the system (corresponding to purely imaginary roots and zero root) is thus defined by passage of the Mikhailov curve through the origin of coordinates, when by a small deformation of the curve at the origin of coordinates it is possible to satisfy the Mikhailov stability criterion.

We note that the value of the parameter $\omega = \omega_0$ which corresponds to the point of the Mikhailov curve incident on the origin of coordinates (Fig. 139a) has the physical significance of the frequency of undamped self-oscillation of the system, when it is located on the boundary of stability. This follows from the fact that the characteristic equation of the system has a pair of purely imaginary roots $\pm i\omega_0$, to which there corresponds a purely sinusoidal term of the solution $x_t(t)$.

Analytically the boundary of stability of the system in the Mikhailov criterion is represented by expression (28.6) or, if we separate the real and imaginary parts, then by equations

$$X(\omega) = 0 , \qquad Y(\omega) = 0 , \tag{28.7}$$

where both of these equations should be satisfied simultaneously for a given value of ω (we denote it as before by ω_0). Expression (28.6) or (28.7) is the condition for the presence of a pair of purely imaginary roots $z = \pm i\omega_0$ in the characteristic equation (in particular zero, if $\omega_0 = 0$). But, in addition, it is necessary to verify that here all remaining roots of the characteristic equation will have negative real parts. For this the polynomial obtained after division

$$\frac{L(z)}{z^2 + \omega_0^2} , \tag{28.8}$$

should satisfy the stability criterion, since the factor $(z^2 + \omega_0^2)$ corresponds to purely imaginary roots (or to the zero root $\omega_0 = 0$), and the result of division (28.8) corresponds to all the remaining roots.

Let us now consider the case of an infinite root. As was explained in Section 27, an infinite root ($z = \infty$) corresponds to vanishing of the coefficient a_0 of the highest-order term of the characteristic equation

$$a_0 z^n + a_1 z^{n-1} + \ldots + a_{n-1} z + a_n = 0 . \tag{28.9}$$

This condition

$$a_0 = 0$$

as the limit of stability of the system, represents the boundary between the positive and negative values a_0 (where all remaining coefficients of the equation remain positive). In the expression for the Mikhailov curve with change of sign of a_0 only the sign of the component $a_0(i\omega)^n$ changes. If n is even, then this component enters into formulae (28.3) in the expression for $X(\omega)$, but, if n is odd, then into the expression for $Y(\omega)$. Consequently, change of the value of a_0 changes the value of one of the coordinates of the Mikhailov curve, namely that along which the end of the curve passes to infinity (Figs. 135 and 136). For example, in the case of a stable fourth-order system ($n = 4$) with reduction of a_0 the Mikhailov curve is deformed as shown in Fig. 141, where at the moment when the quantity a_0 changes sign from positive to negative the

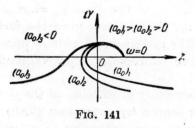

Fig. 141

end of the Mikhailov curve passes over to the opposite side and the system becomes unstable. This is an illustration of passage to the region of instability through the infinite root in the characteristic equation of the system.

Below it will be seen that an infinite root plays a smaller role in determining the limits of stability than purely imaginary and zero roots. But we may return to the concept of infinite root in another question—in reduction of the order of the differential equation of the given system through neglecting some of its parameters having small values in comparison with the magnitudes of other similar parameters (this most frequently concerns small time constants). In essence, reduction of the order of the equation by unity is equivalent to vanishing of the coefficient of the highest-order term of the characteristic equation, which in turn is equivalent to passage of one root to infinity.

29. Algebraic stability criteria

As was explained in Section 27, for stability of a first or second-order linear system it was necessary and sufficient that all coefficients of the characteristic equation be positive.

For a third and higher-order system it was demonstrated that positiveness of all coefficients of the characteristic equation ensures negativeness only of its real roots but does not ensure negativeness of the real parts of the complex roots. It was found that to ensure the last condition in the case of third and fourth-order systems it was necessary to satisfy one additional relationship between the coefficients of the characteristic equation (aside from their positiveness). In the case of fifth and higher order systems there will be two and more additional relations.

Let us derive these additional relations individually for third, fourth, fifth and sixth-order systems, and then give a general formulation of the Hurwitz and Routh stability criteria for systems of any order.

Vyshnegradskii's stability criterion for a third-order system. The founder of the theory of automatic regulation I. A. Vyshnegradskii, in investigating a given third-order automatic regulation system in 1876 proposed a stability criterion having general value for arbitrary dynamic systems described by ordinary third-order* linear differential equations.

Let us derive this stability criterion from the proof in Section 28 of the Mikhailov stability criterion.

The characteristic equation of the third-order system will be:

$$a_0z^3 + a_1z^2 + a_2z + a_2 = 0 . \qquad (29.1)$$

Let us assume that all coefficients of this equation are positive, which is, as proved in Section 27, a necessary condition for stability.

From the general properties of the Mikhailov curve (Section 28) it is clear that for the third-degree polynomial

$$L(z) = a_0z^3 + a_1z^2 + a_2z + a_3$$

with positive coefficients the Mikhailov curve may have only two types of positions relative to the origin of coordinates (Fig. 142). The expression of this curve will be:

$$L(i\omega) = -a_0i\omega^3 - a_1\omega^2 + a_2i\omega + a_3 ,$$

i.e.

$$X(\omega) = a_3 - a_1\omega^2 ,$$
$$Y(\omega) = (a_2 - a^0\omega^2)\,\omega .$$

The stability or instability of the system depends exclusively on whether the point A of the Mikhailov curve (Fig. 142) is to the left or to the right of the origin of coordinates. The abscissa of the point A is determined by equating the coordinate Y to zero. Then from the formulae written for the X- and Y-coordinates we obtain:

$$\omega_A^2 = \frac{a_2}{a_0} , \qquad X_A = -a_1\frac{a_2}{a_0} + a_3 = \frac{-a_1a_2 + a_0a_3}{a_0} ,$$

---

* There is evidence that this was already done by him in 1871–1872.

where for stability of the system $X_A < 0$ (Fig. 142). From this there follows the following formulation of Vyshnegradskii's stability criterion.

For stability of a third-order linear system it is necessary and sufficient:

(1) that all coefficients of the characteristic equation be positive, i.e.

$$a_1 > 0 , \ a_2 > 0 , \ a_3 > 0 \qquad (\text{with } a_0 > 0); \tag{29.2}$$

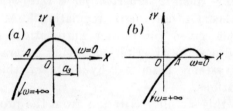

Fig. 142

(2) that the product of the middle coefficients of the characteristic equation be greater than the product of the extreme coefficients, i.e.

$$a_1 a_2 > a_0 a_3 . \tag{29.3}$$

The limit of stability from Section 28 is defined here by incidence at the origin of coordinates of either the point A or the point $\omega = 0$ (Fig. 142), which gives either

$$a_1 a_2 = a_0 a_3 \tag{29.4}$$

(the presence of a pair of purely imaginary roots), or

$$a_3 = 0 \tag{29.5}$$

(the presence of a zero root) with all remaining coefficients positive, or, finally,

$$a_0 = 0 \tag{29.6}$$

(the presence of an infinite root).

Vyshnegradskii's hyperbola. The limit of stability (29.4) was represented graphically by Vyshnegradskii on the so-called parametric plane in the following manner.

Through division by a_3 and introduction of the new variable

$$u = \sqrt[3]{\frac{a_0}{a_3}} z \qquad (a_0 > 0 , \ a_3 > 0) \tag{29.7}$$

equation (29.1) is reduced to the so-called normalised form:

$$u^3 + A u^2 + B u + 1 = 0 , \tag{29.8}$$

where the dimensionless coefficients

$$A = \frac{a_1}{\sqrt[3]{a_0^2 a_3}}, \qquad B = \frac{a_2}{\sqrt[3]{a_0 a_3^2}} \qquad (29.9)$$

are termed Vyshnegradskii parameters.

Applying condition (29.4) to equation (29.8), we obtain the limit of stability in the form

$$AB = 1 \quad \text{with} \quad A > 0, \; B > 0. \qquad (29.10)$$

In the parametric plane A and B (Fig. 143) this equality is represented in the form of a hyperbola, termed the Vyshnegradskii hyperbola. The Vyshnegradskii stability criterion for equation (29.8) is written in the form

$$A > 0, \; B > 0, \; AB > 1. \qquad (29.11)$$

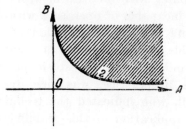

FIG. 143

The region of stability therefore lies above and to the right of the hyperbola (29.10), which is proved in Fig. 143. The region between the hyperbola and the coordinate axis for which

$$A > 0, \; B > 0, \; AB < 0,$$

as well as all quadrants of the plane except the first, do not satisfy the stability criterion (29.11). Consequently, to the left and below the hyperbola is the region of instability.

Contradiction between static precision and dynamic stability. The differential equation of the third-order system has the form

$$a_0 \dddot{x} + a_1 \ddot{x} + a_2 \dot{x} + a_3 x = f_1(t), \qquad (29.12)$$

where x is the increment to the regulated quantity while $f_1(t)$, from Chapters V and VI, is expressed by the perturbation on the object $f(t)$ and its derivatives.

If, for example,

$$f_1(t) = b_0 \ddot{f}(t) + b_1 \dot{f}(t) + b_2 f(t), \qquad (29.13)$$

then in the steady-state, where a certain constant value $f = \text{const} = f^0$ occurs, we obtain a static deviation of the regulated quantity (static error of the system)

$$x^0 = \frac{b_2 f^0}{a_3} \, . \qquad (29.14)$$

If

$$f_1(t) = b_0 \dot{f}(t) + b_1 \dot{f}(t) \qquad (29.15)$$

(i.e. the incremental load f does not enter into the equation), then static error is absent from the above steady state:

$$x^0 = 0 \quad \text{with arbitrary} \quad f^0 = \text{const} \, . \qquad (29.16)$$

The first case corresponds to static systems and the second to astatic.

Starting only from the static calculation (29.14), at first glance it appears possible to obtain any degree of precision of regulation by simply increasing the coefficient a_3. However, if the system is not checked for stability with increase of a_3 it is possible to obtain in general a system incapable of operating with divergent or poorly attenuating transients because of violation of condition (29.3) or because of appreciable approach to its boundary).

This "contradiction" between the static precision and dynamic stability, observable in practice, was first resolved in 1876 by I. A. Vyshnegradskii, who indicated the technical solution of this "contradiction" by application of this stability criterion.

On the other hand, consideration of the suitability of a system only from the stability criterion (29.3) may easily lead to a system which in practice does not fulfil the task of regulation due to a large static error (29.14).

The Hurwitz stability criterion for a fourth-order system. A. Stodola, developing the ideas of I. A. Vyshnegradskii and encountering the necessity of investigating the stability of systems of higher than third order, put this problem to the mathematician Hurwitz. The latter developed an algebraic criterion of stability for ordinary linear systems or arbitrary order in 1893, evidently not knowing that this had already been done previously, although in a somewhat different form, by Routh. We shall give the general formulation of their criteria below, and shall consider one important case—a fourth-order system starting from Mikhailov's criterion.

The characteristic equation of the system has the form

$$a_0 z^4 + a_1 z^3 + a_2 z^2 + a_3 z + a_4 = 0 \, . \qquad (29.17)$$

For the polynomial

$$L(z) = a_0 z^4 + a_1 z^3 + a_2 z^2 + a_3 z + a_4$$

with positive coefficients the Mikhailov curve, in accordance with its general properties (Section 28), may have various positions with respect to the origin of coordinates, but in all cases the stability (Fig. 144a) on instability (Fig. 144b) are here defined by whether the point A lies to the left or to the right of the origin of coordinates.

For the given polynomial the expression for the Mikhailov curve will be:

$$L(i\omega) = a_0\omega^4 - a_1 i\omega^3 - a_2\omega^2 + a_3 i\omega + a_4,$$

from which

$$X(\omega) = a_0\omega^4 - a_2\omega^2 + a_4, \qquad Y(\omega) = -a_1\omega^3 + a_3\omega.$$

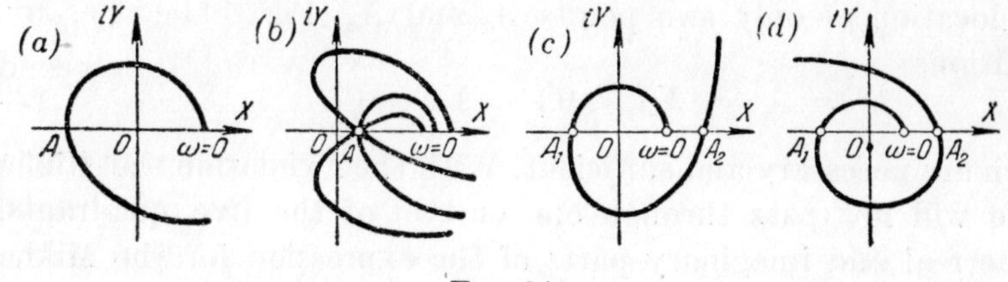

Fig. 144

For the point A (Fig. 144) we obtain according to these formulae from the condition $Y_A = 0$:

$$\omega_A^2 = \frac{a_3}{a_1}, \qquad X_A = a_0\frac{a_3^2}{a_1^2} - a_2\frac{a_3}{a_1} + a_4 = \frac{-a_3(a_1a_2 - a_0a_3) + a_4a_1^2}{a_1^2}.$$

But since for stability of the system we require $X_A < 0$ (Fig. 144a), we arrive at the following formulation of the stability criterion.

For the stability of a fourth-order linear system it is necessary and sufficient:

(1) that all coefficients of the characteristic equation be positive: i.e.

$$a_1 > 0, \ a_2 > 0, \ a_3 > 0, \ a_4 > 0 \qquad (\text{with } a_0 > 0);$$

(2) that the inequality

$$a_3(a_1a_2 - a_0a_3) - a_4a_1^2 > 0 \qquad (29.18)$$

be satisfied.

The limit of stability is defined by incidence on the origin of coordinates of the point A or the point $\omega = 0$ of the Mikhailov curve, which corresponds either to the condition

$$a_3(a_1a_2 - a_0a_3) - a_4a_1^2 = 0 \qquad (29.19)$$

(the presence of a pair of purely imaginary roots) with all positive coefficients, or

$$a_4 = 0$$

(the presence of a zero root) with satisfaction of the remaining stability conditions, or, finally,

$$a_0 = 0$$

(the presence of an infinite root).

The Hurwitz stability criterion for a fifth-order system. The characteristic equation will be:

$$a_0 z^5 + a_1 z^4 + a_2 z^3 + a_3 z^2 + a_4 z + a_5 = 0 .$$

From the Mikhailov criterion the system will be stable if the Mikhailov curve successively passes through five quadrants (Fig. 144c). This, in turn, as is evident from the general properties of the Mikhailov curve with positive coefficients (Section 28), is ensured by a correct location of only two points A_1 and A_2 (Fig. 144c), i.e. by the conditions

$$X_{A_1} < 0 , \qquad X_{A_2} > 0 , \qquad (29.20)$$

which are necessary and sufficient. With their violation the Mikhailov curve will not pass through one or two of the five quadrants.

The real and imaginary parts of the expression for the Mikhailov curve for a fifth-degree polynomial will be:

$$X(\omega) = a_5 - a_3 \omega^2 + a_1 \omega^4 ,$$
$$Y(\omega) = (a_4 - a_2 \omega^2 + a_0 \omega^4)\, \omega .$$

Putting $Y(\omega) = 0$, we find the values of ω^2 at the points A_1 an A_2:

$$\omega^2_{A_2,\, A_1} = \frac{a_2 \pm \sqrt{a_2^2 - 4 a_0 a_4}}{2 a_0} .$$

Substituting this in the expression for $X(\omega)$, after reducing similar terms, we find:

$$X_{A_1} = \frac{1}{4 a_0^2}\left\{ a_2(a_1 a_2 - a_0 a_3) - 2 a_0(a_1 a_4 - a_0 a_5) - (a_1 a_2 - a_0 a_3)\sqrt{a_2^2 - 4 a_0 a_4} \right\} ,$$

$$X_{A_2} = \frac{1}{4 a_0^2}\left\{ a_2(a_1 a_2 - a_0 a_3) - 2 a_0(a_1 a_4 - a_0 a_5) + (a_1 a_2 - a_0 a_3)\sqrt{a_2^2 - 4 a_0 a_4} \right\} .$$

The difference here is only in the signs of the last terms. From this it is evident that the conditions (29.20) will be satisfied if, firstly, these last terms are positive, i.e. if

$$a_1 a_2 - a_0 a_3 > 0 ,$$

and, secondly, if

$$|a_2(a_1 a_2 - a_0 a_3) - 2 a_0(a_1 a_4 - a_0 a_5)| < (a_1 a_2 - a_0 a_3)\sqrt{a_2^2 - 4 a_0 a_4} .$$

Squaring both sides of this inequality (which is valid, since they are both positive) and reducing similar terms, we obtain the result:

$$(a_1 a_4 - a_0 a_5)^2 - (a_1 a_2 - a_0 a_3)(a_3 a_4 - a_2 a_5) < 0 .$$

Thus, we come to the following formulation of the stability criterion. For stability of a fifth-order linear system it is necessary and sufficient:

(1) that all coefficients of the characteristic equation be positive, i.e.

$$a_1 > 0, \, a_2 > 0, \, ..., \, a_5 > 0 \quad \text{(with } a_0 > 0\text{)};$$

(2) that there be simultaneously satisfied two inequalities:

$$\left. \begin{array}{l} a_1 a_2 - a_0 a_3 > 0 \, , \\ (a_1 a_2 - a_0 a_3)(a_3 a_4 - a_2 a_5) - (a_1 a_4 - a_0 a_5)^2 > 0 \, . \end{array} \right\} \qquad (29.21)$$

The limit of stability is defined either by the equality

$$(a_1 a_2 - a_0 a_3)(a_3 a_4 - a_2 a_5) - (a_1 a_4 - a_0 a_5)^2 = 0$$

(purely imaginary roots) with satisfaction of the remaining conditions, or $a_5 = 0$ (zero root), or $a_0 = 0$ (infinite root).

The Hurwitz stability criterion for a sixth-order system. The characteristic equation has the form

$$a_0 z^6 + a_1 z^5 + a_2 z^4 + a_3 z^3 + a_4 z^2 + a_5 z + a_6 = 0 \, .$$

In accordance with the Mikhailov criterion and the general properties of the Mikhailov curve with positive coefficients, in the case $n = 6$ (Fig. 144*d*) the stability conditions remain in the form (29.20). The real and imaginary parts of the expression for the Mikhailov curve are here:

$$X(\omega) = a_6 - a_4 \omega^2 + a_2 \omega^4 - a_0 \omega^6 \, ,$$
$$Y(\omega) = (a_5 - a_3 \omega^2 + a_1 \omega^4) \, \omega \, .$$

From the condition $Y = 0$ we find:

$$\omega^2_{A_2, \, A_1} = \frac{a_3 \pm \sqrt{a_3^2 - 4 a_1 a_5}}{2 a_1} \, .$$

Substitution of these values in the expression $X(\omega)$ after reduction of similar terms gives:

$$X_{A_1} = \frac{1}{8 a_1^3} \{ 2 a_1^3 a_6 + (a_3^2 - 2 a_1 a_5)(a_1 a_2 - a_0 a_3) - a_1 a_3(a_1 a_4 - a_0 a_5) -$$
$$- [a_3(a_1 a_2 - a_0 a_3) - a_1(a_1 a_4 - a_0 a_5)] \sqrt{a_3^2 - 4 a_1 a_5} \, ,$$

$$X_{A_2} = \frac{1}{8 a_1^3} \{ 2 a_1^3 a_6 + (a_3^2 - 2 a_1 a_5)(a_1 a_2 - a_0 a_3) - a_1 a_3(a_1 a_4 - a_0 a_5) +$$
$$+ [a_3(a_1 a_2 - a_0 a_3) - a_1(a_1 a_4 - a_0 a_5)] \sqrt{a_3^2 - 4 a_1 a_5} \} \, .$$

For the first of these expressions to be negative and the second positive, from (29.20) it is necessary, firstly, that

$$[a_3(a_1 a_2 - a_0 a_3) - a_1(a_1 a_4 - a_0 a_5)] > 0$$

and, secondly

$$[2a_1^3 a_6 + (a_3^2 - 2a_1 a_5)(a_1 a_2 - a_0 a_3) - a_1 a_3(a_1 a_4 - a_0 a_5)]|$$
$$< [a_3(a_1 a_2 - a_0 a_3) - a_1(a_1 a_4 - a_0 a_5)] \sqrt{a_3^2 - 4a_1 a_5}.$$

Squaring both sides of the last inequality and reducing similar terms, we come to the expression

$$a_1^3 a_6^2 - (a_1 a_2 - a_0 a_3)[a_5(a_4 a_3 - a_2 a_5) + a_6(2a_1 a_5 - a_3^2)] -$$
$$- (a_1 a_4 - a_0 a_5)[a_1 a_3 a_6 - a_5(a_1 a_4 - a_0 a_5)] < 0.$$

We thus obtain the following formulation of the stability criterion.

For stability of a sixth-order linear system it is necessary and sufficient:

(1) that all coefficients of the characteristic equation be positive, i.e.

$$a_1 > 0, \ a_2 > 0, \ ..., \ a_6 > 0 \quad \text{(with } a_0 > 0 \text{)};$$

(2) that there be simultaneously satisfied two inequalities:

$$\left. \begin{aligned} a_3(a_1 a_2 - a_0 a_3) - a_1(a_1 a_4 - a_0 a_5) &> 0, \\ (a_1 a_2 - a_0 a_3)[a_5(a_4 a_3 - a_2 a_5) + a_6(2a_1 a_5 - a_3^2)] + \quad & \\ + (a_1 a_4 - a_0 a_5)[a_1 a_3 a_6 - a_5(a_1 a_4 - a_0 a_5)] - a_1^3 a_6^2 &> 0. \end{aligned} \right\} \quad (29.22)$$

At the limit of stability the last of the inequalities becomes an equality (appearance of purely imaginary roots) with the remaining inequalities satisfied. The zero root is obtained with $a_6 = 0$ and the infinite root with $a_0 = 0$.

General formulation of the Hurwitz criterion. Above we have derived expressions for the Hurwitz criterion for systems up to sixth-order inclusive on the basis of the Mikhailov criterion proved in the preceding sections. With further increase of order of the system the Hurwitz inequalities will become very complicated and their number will increase. Thus, for seventh and eighth-order systems not two but three additional inequalities will be required, since the Mikhailov curve will have not two (such as A_1 and A_2 in Fig. 144), but three points of intersection with the X-axis, where the quantity ω_A from the condition $Y = 0$ will be defined not by a bi-quadratic but by a bi-cubic equation.

To derive the algebraic stability conditions of a system of higher than sixth-order it is necessary to turn to the following general formulation of the Hurwitz criterion.

For stability of an nth-order linear system it is necessary and sufficient that the n determinants composed of the coefficients $a_0, a_1, ..., a_n$ of the characteristic equation of the given system

$$a_0 z^n + a_1 z^{n-1} + ... + a_{n-1} z + a_n = 0,$$

be positive, where these determinants are taken as the principle minors of the following square matrix:

$$
\begin{vmatrix}
a_1 & a_3 & a_5 & a_7 & \dots & 0 & 0 & 0 \\
a_0 & a_2 & a_4 & a_6 & \dots & 0 & 0 & 0 \\
0 & a_1 & a_3 & a_5 & \dots & 0 & 0 & 0 \\
0 & a_0 & a_2 & a_4 & \dots & 0 & 0 & 0 \\
\hdotsfor{8} \\
0 & 0 & 0 & 0 & \dots & a_{n-2} & a_n & 0 \\
0 & 0 & 0 & 0 & \dots & a_{n-3} & a_{n-1} & 0 \\
0 & 0 & 0 & 0 & \dots & a_{n-4} & a_{n-2} & a_n
\end{vmatrix}
\tag{29.23}
$$

Let us consider the rule of composition of the matrix (29.23). In the first row all the coefficients of the characteristic equation with odd indices are written, after which enough zeros are written so that the row will have a total of n elements (where n is the degree of the characteristic equation). In the second row we write all the coefficients of the characteristic equation with even indices, beginning with a_0, in the same manner.

The third and fourth rows constitute the first two rows, shifted to the right by one element. The fifth and sixth are the same rows, shifted by a further element to the right, etc. A total of n rows should be written in this manner.

The first determinant, the positiveness of which is here required, will be:

$$ \Delta_1 = a_1 > 0 , $$

the second,

$$
\Delta_2 =
\begin{vmatrix}
a_1 & a_3 \\
a_0 & a_2
\end{vmatrix} > 0 ,
$$

the third,

$$
\Delta_3 =
\begin{vmatrix}
a_1 & a_3 & a_5 \\
a_0 & a_2 & a_4 \\
0 & a_1 & a_3
\end{vmatrix} > 0
$$

etc. These are termed the Hurwitz determinants. We note that the last determinant Δ_n constitutes the entire matrix. If it is expanded in elements of the last column, it is immediately evident that

$$ \Delta_n = a_n \Delta_{n-1} . $$

Consequently, the requirement of positiveness of the last, nth determinant always reduces to the requirement of positiveness of the constant term a_n of the characteristic equation of the system. The limit of stability is defined either by the condition

$$ \Delta_{n-1} = 0 \tag{29.24} $$

(the presence of a pair of purely imaginary roots) with satisfaction of the positiveness of all remaining determinants, or

$$a_n = 0$$

(the presence of a zero root) with satisfaction of all the remaining stability conditions, or, finally, $a_0 = 0$ (infinite root).

It is easy to verify that the limits of stability (29.4) and (29.5) are particular cases of the expressions ($\Delta_{n-1} = 0$ and $a_n = 0$ with $n = 3$, and the boundary of stability (29.19) with $n = 4$.

The stability criteria for third, fourth, fifth and sixth-order systems, considered above, are also obtained from (29.23) with $n = 3$, $n = 4$, $n = 5$ and $n = 6$. Let us demonstrate this, for example, for a fourth-order system. Here the matrix (29.23) takes the form

$$\begin{vmatrix} a_1 & a_3 & 0 & 0 \\ a_0 & a_2 & a_4 & 0 \\ 0 & a_1 & a_3 & 0 \\ 0 & a_0 & a_2 & a_4 \end{vmatrix}$$

Therefore the Hurwitz criterion is expressed in the form of the following four inequalities

$$\Delta_1 = a_1 > 0 \,,$$

$$\Delta_2 = \begin{vmatrix} a_1 & a_3 \\ a_0 & a_2 \end{vmatrix} = a_1 a_2 - a_0 a_3 > 0 \,,$$

$$\Delta_3 = \begin{vmatrix} a_1 & a_3 & 0 \\ a_0 & a_2 & a_4 \\ 0 & a_1 & a_3 \end{vmatrix} = a_3(a_1 a_2 - a_0 a_3) - a_4 a_1^2 > 0 \,,$$

$$\Delta_4 = a_4 \Delta_3 > 0 \,.$$

The last of them from the condition $\Delta_3 > 0$ reduce to

$$a_4 > 0 \,.$$

But if $a_4 > 0$, for satisfaction of the preceding inequalities in the determinant Δ_3 we should have at least

$$a_3(a_1 a_2 - a_0 a_3) > 0 \,,$$

which may be written in the form $a_3 \Delta_2 > 0$; but this from the condition $\Delta_2 > 0$ reduces to

$$a_3 > 0 \,.$$

We therefore require in the determinant Δ_2, taking into account the condition $a_0 > 0$, at least $a_1 a_2 > 0$, which in accordance with the first condition ($a_1 > 0$) reduces to

$$a_2 > 0 \,.$$

We have thus obtained the already known requirement of positiveness of all coefficients of the characteristic equation. It is further obvious that with $a_3 > 0$ and $a_4 > 0$ the condition $\Delta_3 > 0$ may be satisfied only if $a_1 a_2 - a_0 a_3 > 0$. Therefore the condition $\Delta_2 > 0$ is superfluous, since it is automatically satisfied if we satisfy $\Delta_3 > 0$, i.e. (29.18), which was to be proved.

The Routh stability criterion. For a high-order system, with parameters-given numerically, the following criterion of Routh for verifying the stability of the system may be convenient.

The characteristic equation of an nth-degree system is given with numerical coefficients. We calculate according to the following scheme, containing $(n+1)$ lines:

a_0		a_2		a_4		a_6	
a_1		a_3		a_5		a_7	
$b_1 = \dfrac{a_1 a_2 - a_0 a_3}{a_1}$		$b_2 = \dfrac{a_1 a_4 - a_0 a_5}{a_1}$		$b_3 = \dfrac{a_1 a_6 - a_0 a_7}{a_1}$		$b_4 = \dfrac{a_1 a_8 - a_0 a_9}{a_1}$	
$c_1 = \dfrac{b_1 a_3 - a_1 b_2}{b_1}$		$c_2 = \dfrac{b_1 a_5 - a_1 b_3}{b_1}$		$c_3 = \dfrac{b_1 a_7 - a_1 b_4}{b_1}$		$c_4 = \dfrac{b_1 a_9 - a_1 b_5}{b_1}$	
$d_1 = \dfrac{c_1 b_2 - b_1 c_2}{c_1}$		$d_2 = \dfrac{c_1 b_3 - b_1 c_3}{c_1}$		$d_3 = \dfrac{c_1 b_4 - b_1 c_4}{c_1}$		$d_4 = \dfrac{c_1 b_5 - b_1 c_5}{c_1}$	
...		...		...		...	

For the system to be stable it is necessary and sufficient that all numbers in the first column of the matrix $(a_1, b_1, c_1, d_1, ...)$, be positive, if $a_0 > 0$. This corresponds to positiveness of the Hurwitz determinants.

For example, the characteristic equation is given

$$z_5 + 2z^4 + 2z^3 + 46z^2 + 89z + 260 = 0 .$$

We write according to the above procedure $(n+1)$ lines:

1;   2;   89;
2;   46;   260;
—1;   — 1·95 (after division by 21);
1;   6.18 (after division by 42.1);
4·23;
6·18.

This system is unstable since the first elements are not positive in all rows. Instability of this system was also evident from the Mikhailov curve plotted for it in example 1 of Section 27.

30. Frequency stability criterion

All the above presented stability criteria are applicable when the characteristic equation of the entire system is known, with coefficients expressed in a definite manner through the parameters of the circuits of the system.

In practice there exist cases where for certain elements of the system it is difficult to construct sufficiently reliable differential equations, but it is easy to construct an operating model of an individual circuit or simply to take it in finished form. In these cases we use experimental recording of the frequency characteristics and the frequency criterion, permitting determination of stability of a closed automatic system from the frequency characteristics of its circuits.

In other words, the frequency method permits judging the behaviour of a closed system in the transient state (stability) from the properties of its open network in steady-state forced sinusoidal oscillations (frequency characteristics). These may be determined experimentally for the individual elements.

The frequency criterion of stability applied to amplifier theory is due to Nyquist (1932). In 1936 it was first introduced into the theory of automatic regulation by A. V. Mikhailov, who proved mathematically and showed on concrete systems the applicability of this criterion to an arbitrary closed automatic system.

Opening of the system. Eliminating external perturbations, we open the automatic regulation system in an arbitrary manner, but in such a way that at the point of opening of the closed system the interaction between the separated circuits is expressed by only a single variable. This variable breaks up into two: the input and output quantities of the open network (Fig. 145a). The open network itself may have a structure of arbitrary complexity.

For example, the open network for an engine speed regulation system (Fig. 78) may be taken in the form shown in Fig. 145b. In this case the circuit was opened at the input to the regulator, where φ in the closed system denoted the relative change of the regulated quantity (angular velocity, see Section 22). Now, in the open network, it has separated into two quantities: (1) φ_{in}, an arbitrarily given relative change of angular velocity at the input to the centrifugal mechanism, (2) φ_{out} obtained at this angular velocity at the output of the regulated object (which in the closed system was measured by the centrifugal mechanism).

For the open network we shall adopt the convention of not introducing minus signs in the right-hand sides of the circuit equations, as was done for the closed system (see formulae (20.8), (22.58),

(25.8)). For the open network this constitutes only an insignificant change of polarity of connection or direction of reading variables (while in the closed system this was necessary in principle for satisfying the regulation problem).

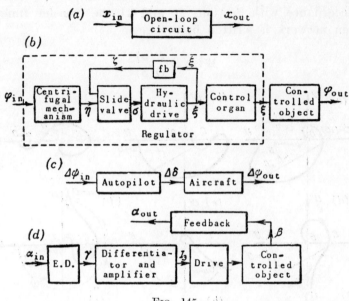

FIG. 145

Thus, if the equation of the closed velocity regulation system has the form (22.58), the equations of the corresponding open network (Fig. 145*b*) will be:

$$\left. \begin{array}{l} (T_r^2 p^2 + T_k p + \delta)\eta = \varphi_{\text{in}} , \\ (T_s p + 1)\xi = \eta , \\ T_a p \varphi_{\text{out}} = \xi . \end{array} \right\} \tag{30.1}$$

Analogously, for a system for the automatic regulation of aircraft course (Fig. 125) the open network may be represented in the form shown in Fig. 145*c*. Its equations, in accordance with (25.26) and (25.8) will be:

$$\left. \begin{array}{l} [(T_3 p + 1)(T_4 p + 1)p + k_{\text{bf}}]\Delta\delta = (k_\psi + k_{\dot\psi} p + k_{\ddot\psi} p^2)\Delta\psi_{\text{in}} , \\ [(T_1 p + 1)(T_2 p + 1) + k_2 T_2]p\Delta\psi_{\text{out}} = k_1(T_2 p + 1)\Delta\delta . \end{array} \right\} \tag{30.2}$$

For a servomechanism (Fig. 128) the open network is shown in Fig. 145*d*, where $\gamma = \alpha_{\text{in}}$ and $\alpha_1 = \alpha_{\text{out}}$. Its equations, from (26.10), (26.11), (26.14) and (26.20), taking into account (26.8) will be:

$$\left. \begin{array}{l} (T_2 p + 1)(T_3 p + 1)I_3 = (k_3 + k_3' p)k_2 k_4 \alpha_{\text{in}} , \\ [(T_1 p + 1)(T_4 p + 1) + k_1 k_6]k_0 p \alpha_{\text{out}} = k_1 k_5 I_3 . \end{array} \right\} \tag{30.3}$$

The frequency characteristics for the open networks are constructed in accordance with the discussions in Sections 20 and 21 on the basis of either the differential equations (transfer functions) or the experimentally seconded frequency characteristics of certain elements and the equations (transfer functions) of the remaining.

In accordance with Sections 20 and 21 the transfer function of the open network is written in the form

$$W(p) = \frac{R(p)}{Q(p)}, \tag{30.4}$$

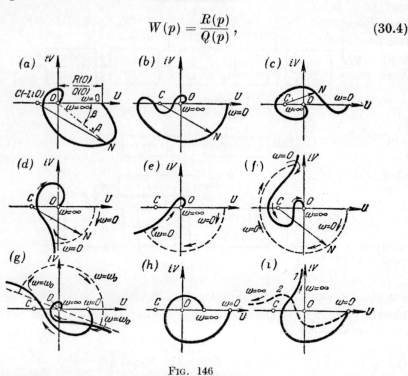

Fig. 146

where Q and R are operational polynomials having differing expressions for different systems, where the degree of the polynomial R for all real systems is usually lower than the degree of the polynomial Q, but in rare cases the opposite may be encountered which we shall also take into consideration.

The amplitude-phase frequency characteristic of the open network will be:

$$W(i\omega) = \frac{R(i\omega)}{Q(i\omega)}. \tag{30.5}$$

Possible forms of this curve for various networks are shown in Fig. 146. The curves a, b, c correspond to the case where the degree of R is lower than the degree of Q (therefore $W_{\omega=\infty} = 0$) and the polynomials Q and R have positive constant terms, i.e. $R(0) \neq 0$ and $Q(0) \neq 0$.

If the denominator $Q(p)$ of the transfer function of an open network (30.4) has a zero root, i.e. p may be factored out of the denominator $Q(p) = pQ_1(p)$, where $Q_1(p)$ has a positive constant term, the amplitude-phase characteristic of the open network will be:

$$W(i\omega) = \frac{R(i\omega)}{i\omega Q_1(i\omega)} = -i\,\frac{R(i\omega)}{\omega Q_1(i\omega)}\,,$$

and as $\omega \to 0$ it passes to infinity in the direction of the negative imaginary axis (Fig. 146d). Similarly, with a double zero root in the denominator the transfer function of the open network, when $Q(p) = p^2 Q_1(p)$ and a triple zero root, when $Q(p) = p^3 Q_1(p)$, we have respectively:

$$W(i\omega) = -\frac{R(i\omega)}{\omega^2 Q_1(i\omega)}\,, \qquad W(i\omega) = i\,\frac{R(i\omega)}{\omega^3 Q_1(i\omega)}\,,$$

which indicates the passing of the curve to infinity as $\omega \to 0$ towards the negative real axis (Fig. 146e) and the side of the positive imaginary axis (Fig. 146f) respectively.

If $Q(p)$ has a pair of purely imaginary roots $p = \pm i\omega$, i.e. if

$$Q(p) = (p^2 + \omega_0^2)Q_1(p)\,,$$

expression (30.5) becomes infinite at $p = i\omega_0$, changing sign (Fig. 146g).

The case of equal degrees of polynomials R and Q is shown in Fig. 146h, and in Fig. 146i the case where the degree of R is higher than the degree of Q (curve 1, higher by unity, curve 2, higher by two).

We note that the differential equation of the open network $Q(p)x_{out} = R(p)x_{in}$ corresponds to the characteristic equation of the open network

$$Q(z) = 0\,, \tag{30.6}$$

while the characteristic equation of the closed system (27.3) has the form

$$Q(z) + R(z) = 0\,. \tag{30.7}$$

Consequently, their roots will be different, signifying that the dynamic properties of the open network and closed system, consisting of the same elements, will be completely different. In particular, it is possible that a stable open network will correspond to an unstable closed system while an unstable open network may become stable in the closed state.

First formulation of the frequency stability criterion. We mark the point C on the real axis (Fig. 146) with the coordinates $(-1, i0)$ and plot from it the vector CN to an arbitrary point N of the amplitude-phase characteristic $W(i\omega)$ of the open network. Then the most general formulation of the frequency stability criterion will be as follows.

For stability of a closed linear automatic system it is necessary and sufficient that with motion of the point N along the entire amplitude-phase characteristic of the corresponding open network $(0 \leqslant \omega \leqslant +\infty)$ the vector CN rotates by the angle

$$\varphi_{CN} = (n - n_1 + 2m) \frac{\pi}{2}, \tag{30.8}$$

where n and n_1 are the degrees of the characteristic equations of the closed system $(Q(z) + R(z) = 0)$ and the open network $(Q(z) = 0)$, m is the number of roots with positive real parts in the characteristic equation of the open network (in case the latter is unstable). The proof is given below.

In calculating the angle of rotation of the vector CN and in employing formula (30.8) it is necessary to traverse an arc at infinity in those cases where $Q(p)$ has zero and purely imaginary roots (broken line in Fig. 146, e, f, g).

The frequency stability criterion is not usually applied in such a general formulation but in a simpler one. In essence, the degree of the polynomial $R(z)$ is usually lower in real systems than that of $Q(z)$. Therefore the degrees of equations (30.6) and (30.7) are the same, i.e. $n = n_1$. Then from (30.8)

$$\varphi_{CN} = m\pi. \tag{30.9}$$

An open network is frequently stable or neutral (on the boundary of stability), i.e. $m = 0$ and

$$\varphi_{CN} = 0. \tag{30.10}$$

Consequently, for cases where the degree of the polynomial $Q(p)$ in the transfer function of the open network (30.4) is greater than (or at least equal to) the degree of the polynomial $R(p)$ the frequency stability criterion is formulated as follows (and always used in practical cases):

If the open network is stable or neutral*, then for the corresponding closed system to be stable it is necessary and sufficient that the amplitude-phase frequency characteristic of the closed network not enclose the point C with the coordinates $(-1, i0)$. All the curves in Fig. 146, for example, satisfy this criterion except the curves c, i, relating to other cases ($m \neq 0$ and $n_1 \neq n$).

---

* In other words, if there are no roots with positive real parts in the characteristic equation of the open network $(Q(z) = 0)$, but there may be zero or purely imaginary roots.

If the open network is unstable, then for stability of the corresponding closed system it is necessary and sufficient that the amplitude-phase frequency characteristic of the open network encircle the point C with the coordinates $(-1, i0)$ by the angle $m\pi$ (counterclockwise), where m is the number of roots with positive real parts in the characteristic equation of the open network $(Q(z) = 0)$; see, for example, the curve in Fig. 146c, where $m = 2$.

Consequently, for correct application of the frequency criterion it is necessary to know whether the open network is stable or unstable and to know the number m. For single-loop systems this is immediately evident from the circuit equations. In other cases it is first necessary either to determine the roots of the polynomial $Q(z)$ or

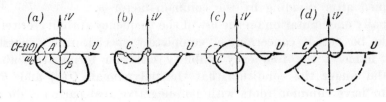

FIG. 147

to plot the Mikhailov curve $Q(i\omega)$ which, from Section 17, shows the number of roots with positive real part, if present. When, for certain elements, the amplitude-phase characteristic is recorded experimentally, the stability of these is evident from the experiment. But a preliminary investigation of the stability of the remaining parts of the open network is necessary.

When the conditions stated in the formulation of the frequency criterion are not satisfied, the closed system will be unstable.

The limit of stability for the closed system corresponds to the case where the amplitude-phase characteristic of the corresponding open network passes through the point C with coordinates $(-1. i0)$ with the condition that the stability criterion will be satisfied by a small deformation of the curve close to the point C (Fig. 147). Thus, if the degree of R is smaller (or equal to) the degree of Q and the open network is stable or neutral, the limit of stability of the closed system is defined by the amplitude-phase characteristic of the open network passing through the point C without encircling it.

This circumstance may be given the following physical interpretation. Let us denote the negative of ω corresponding to the point C of the amplitude-phase characteristic by ω_c. At this point we have $A = 1$, $\beta = -\pi$ (Fig. 147a). Consequently, at the frequency of the input oscillation $\omega = \omega_c$ the forced oscillations at the output of the open network have the same amplitude as at the input but with a phase shift of $-\pi$. If such a system is closed (with reversed polarity, according to the condition), the output oscillation agrees exactly with the input and there is no obstacle to continuation of the oscillation at frequency $\omega = \omega_c$ in the closed system in the form of an undamped free oscillation with constant amplitude. The possibility of this taking place indicates, as is well known (Section 7), that the closed system is at the boundary of stability.

This stability boundary corresponds to the presence of a pair of purely imaginary roots $\pm i\omega_c$ in the characteristic equation. The second boundary of stability, corresponding to a zero root in the characteristic equation is found simply by the fact that either $R(0) = Q(0) = 0$ or $R(0) = -Q(0)$, where in the first case the stability criterion must be observed for the transfer function $R_1(p)/Q_1(p)$, obtained after dividing by the common factor p.

Finally one limitation on the use of the frequency stability criterion should be noted, concerning a completely special, rarely possible case, namely: the frequency stability criterion formulated above is valid under the condition that the polynomials $Q(p)$ and $R(p)$ do not have common roots with non-negative real part, i.e. do not have common factors corresponding to such roots.

This limitation is explained in the following manner. Let us assume that $Q(p)$ and $R(p)$ have the form, for example,

$$\left. \begin{array}{l} Q(p) = Q_1(p)(1 - T_1 p) \,, \\ R(p) = R_1(p)(1 - T_1 p) \,. \end{array} \right\} \tag{30.11}$$

Then the amplitude-phase characteristic of the open network will be:

$$W(i\omega) = \frac{R(i\omega)}{Q(i\omega)} = \frac{R_1(i\omega)}{Q_1(i\omega)} \,,$$

since the factor $(1 - T_1 p)$ is cancelled.

The same characteristic will obviously occur for another open network, in which

$$\left. \begin{array}{l} Q(p) = Q_1(p) \,, \\ R(p) = R_1(p) \,. \end{array} \right\} \tag{30.12}$$

The open network (30.11) corresponds to the closed system with characteristic equation

$$[Q_1(z) + R_1(z)](1 - T_1 z) = 0 \,, \tag{30.13}$$

and the open network (30.12) to the closed system

$$Q_1(z) + R_1(z) = 0 \,. \tag{30.14}$$

Let the second closed system be stable. Then the first closed system in accordance with (30.13) will be unstable since its characteristic equation has a positive root

$$z_1 = \frac{1}{T_1}.$$

But since the amplitude-phase characteristic of the open network for this first system is the same as for the second system, the frequency stability criterion gives for both systems one and the same result, namely: "stable system", which is invalid for the first system.

This indicates that the frequency stability criterion in calculating the stability of a system according to the equations (or, what is the same, from the transfer functions of the circuits) may be more

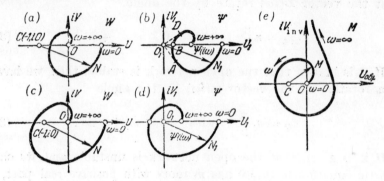

FIG. 148

complicated than the Mikhailov criterion and more laborious. Therefore its application is preferable in those cases where for some of the elements of the system the equations and transfer functions are unknown and experimentally recorded frequency characteristics are given, or when the plotting of the frequency characteristics is necessary in any case for a subsequent calculation of the forced oscillations of the system, or when it is desired to employ frequency methods for other special reasons.

Proof of the first formulation of the frequency stability criterion. Let us consider the function

$$\Psi(i\omega) = 1 + W(i\omega). \qquad (30.15)$$

The function $W(i\omega)$ constitutes the amplitude-phase characteristic of an open network (for example, Fig. 148a). The function $\Psi(i\omega)$ will obviously be represented by the same curve, but shifted by unity to the right (for example, Fig. 148b).

Substituting in formula (30.15) the expression $W(i\omega)$ from (30.5), we obtain:

$$\Psi(i\omega) = \frac{Q(i\omega) + R(i\omega)}{Q(i\omega)} = \frac{L(i\omega)}{Q(i\omega)}, \qquad (30.16)$$

where the numerator represents the expression for the Mikhailov curve (28.1) of a closed system. It corresponds to the characteristic equation of the closed system $Q(z) + R(z) = 0$. The denominator of expression (30.16) corresponds to the characteristic equation of the open network $Q(z) = 0$.

As already mentioned, the degrees of both characteristic equations are usually the same. But to prove the general formulation of the frequency criterion we shall assume that they are different and denote them respectively by n and n_1.

The closed system should be stable. Starting from this, in accordance with the Mikhailov criterion (28.2) we should require that the vector $L(i\omega)$ rotate by the angle

$$\varphi_L = n \frac{\pi}{2} \quad \text{with} \quad 0 \leqslant \omega \leqslant +\infty . \tag{30.17}$$

If it is known that the open network is stable, then we have for it a rotation of the vector $Q(i\omega)$ by the angle

$$\varphi_Q = n_1 \frac{\pi}{2} \quad \text{with} \quad 0 \leqslant \omega \leqslant +\infty . \tag{30.18}$$

If it is given that the open network is unstable and its characteristic equation $Q(z) = 0$ has m roots with positive real part, then from (27.19) we obtain a rotation of the vector $Q(i\omega)$ by the angle

$$\varphi_Q = (n_1 - 2m) \frac{\pi}{2} \quad \text{with} \quad 0 \leqslant \omega \leqslant +\infty . \tag{30.19}$$

Let us now turn to the vector $\Psi(i\omega)$ (Fig. 148*b*), representing the ratio of two complex numbers $L(i\omega)$ and $Q(i\omega)$ in accordance with (30.16). Since in the division of complex numbers their arguments are subtracted, with variation of ω from 0 to $+\infty$ the vector $\Psi(i\omega)$ should rotate by an angle equal to the difference of angles of rotation of the vectors $L(i\omega)$ and $Q(i\omega)$, i.e.

$$\varphi_\Psi = \varphi_L - \varphi_Q . \tag{30.20}$$

In the general case, from (30.17) and (30.19) this will be:

$$\varphi_\Psi = (n - n_1 + 2m) \frac{\pi}{2} . \tag{30.21}$$

In particular cases we find: with $n_1 = n$

$$\varphi_\Psi = mz , \tag{30.22}$$

and with $n_1 = n$ and $m = 0$

$$\varphi_\Psi = 0 . \tag{30.23}$$

If we pass from the function $\Psi(i\omega)$ (Fig. 148b) to the function $W(i\omega)$ (Fig. 148a), then the entire curve is shifted by unity to the left and the role of the vector $\Psi(i\omega) = O_1N_1$ will be played by the vector CN, the origin of which lies at the point C with coordinates $(-1, i0)$. Therefore the results of (30.21), (30.22), (30.23) relate without change to the vector CN. This proves the above general form of the frequency stability criterion (30.8) and its particular cases (30.9) and (30.10).

On the application of inverse amplitude-phase characteristics. In the denominator of expression (30.5), the amplitude-phase characteristic of the open network $W(i\omega)$, there is the polynomial $Q(i\omega)$, corresponding to the left-hand side of the equation of the open network $Q(p) = 0$. When $Q(p)$ has a high degree, the expression $W(i\omega)$ becomes very cumbersome after elimination of the imaginary part of the denominator. The polynomial $R(i\omega)$ usually has a low degree. It is therefore easier analytically to construct not $W(i\omega)$ but the inverse quantity

$$M(i\omega) = \frac{1}{W(i\omega)} = \frac{Q(i\omega)}{R(i\omega)};$$

such an inverse amplitude-phase characteristic (Fig. 148e) is used sometimes. Now the formulation of the stability criterion changes. As above it is easily proved that for stability of a closed system it is now required that vector CM with motion of the point M over the curve $(0 \leqslant \omega \leqslant +\infty)$ rotate by the angle

$$\varphi_{CM} = (n - n_2 + 2m_2) \frac{\pi}{2}, \tag{30.24}$$

where n is the degree of the characteristic equation of the closed system $(Q(z) + R(z) = 0)$, n_2 is the degree of the polynomial $R(z)$ while m_2 is the number of its roots with positive real part.

It has meaning to employ this way of simplifying the construction when it is desired to employ experimentally recorded frequency characteristics. Theoretically this represents a step towards using the Mikhailov criterion. For the maximum simplification (when calculating from the equations) the Mikhailov criterion should be used directly (Section 28), since the analytic plotting of the Mikhailov curve is simpler than plotting of the amplitude-phase characteristic including the inverse.

Second formulation of the frequency stability criterion. The first formulation of the frequency stability criterion considered above may be restated with application to the logarithmic amplitude and phase frequency characteristics of the open network. The construction of these characteristic was discussed in Section 20, where for individual elements we may also employ experimentally given characteristics instead of the equations.

Let us take only the simplest, most widespread case, where the open network is stable or neutral and the degree of R is less than the degree of Q. In this case, from the first formulation of the frequency criterion it follows that the real U-axis either should not at all intersect the curve to the left of the point $C(-1, i0)$, as in Fig. 146a, d, e, g, h, or it should intersect an even number of times to the left of the point C (Fig. 146b, f). This signifies that with $\beta = -\pi, \beta = -3\pi, \beta = -5\pi, \ldots$ either $A > 1$ should not occur or values $A > 1$ are admitted an even number of times with the corresponding direction of variation of β at these points. From this we obtain the following formulation of the frequency criterion.

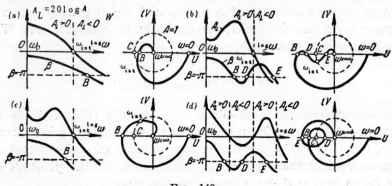

Fig. 149

If the open network is stable or neutral and the degree of R is less than the degree of Q, then for the stability of the closed system it is necessary and sufficient that the number of real roots of each of the equations $\beta(\omega) = -\pi, \beta(\omega) = -3\pi, \beta(\omega) = -5\pi, \ldots$ be even or in that interval of frequencies ω for which the logarithmic amplitude characteristic $A_l(\omega) = 20\log A(\omega)$ is positive, zero and at the given points the derivative $d\beta/d\omega$ alternate sign. In other words, the curve $\beta(\omega)$ should either intersect an even number of times with the lines $\beta = -\pi, \beta = -3\pi, \beta = -5\pi, \ldots$, or not intersect them at all on those segments where the curve $A_l(\omega)$ lies above the axis of abscissae, and the slope of the curve at these points of intersection should alternate in sign. Here, as is evident from Fig. 146f, the branch $A = \alpha$ should be taken into consideration at $\omega = 0$, as shown in Fig. 146f by broken line.

In Fig. 149a and b are shown cases where this stability criterion is satisfied, i.e. the corresponding closed system will be stable. In Fig. 149c the requirement of an even number of points $\beta = -\pi$ with $A_l > 0$ is not satisfied, while in Fig. 149d the requirement of sign alternation of the slope of the tangent at two points $\beta = -\pi$ with $A_l > 0$ is not satisfied. In both these cases the closed system will be unstable. For comparison with the first formulation of the frequency criterion in all cases the amplitude-phase characteristics of the open networks are shown in Fig. 149.

In a similar manner it would be possible to restate the frequency stability criterion for cases where the open network is unstable or when the degree of R is greater than the degree of Q.

31. Width of stability region and stability reserve

Using the above stability criteria it is possible to solve two fundamental problems: (1) to verify the stability of a system with given structure and given parameters, (2) to select the structure of a system and numerical values of its parameters, starting from the requirement of stability of the system.

The conditions of system stability should be satisfied simultaneously with the requirement of small static errors discussed previously. Ordinarily it is possible to satisfy the stability conditions and the condition of smallness of static error in a fairly wide range of numerical values of the system parameters. The width of this stability region depends to a large degree on the structure of the system, on the presence of auxiliary feedback, on the introduction of derivatives into the regulation function, etc.

But all this is only the first step in calculating an automatic system. Further it will be necessary to judge the quality of the transient response and to take into account, if necessary, continuously acting perturbations (transient, stationary and additional dynamic errors).

To carry out these last stages of the calculation and to provide freedom to manipulate the values of the system parameters to satisfy various technical requirements, it is advantageous to have a wider stability region.

Determination of the limits of the stability region was described in presenting each of the stability criteria. This question will be developed in the next chapter and examples presented for finding the boundaries and stability regions for concrete automatic systems. In Chapters IX and X the most advantageous location within these stability regions will be found, starting from various criteria for quality of the regulation process.

Meanwhile we shall only mention that it is not possible to select the system parameters too close to the stability boundary. A certain stability reverse in the system is necessary for the following reasons:

(1) in constructing the equations of the regulated objects and other elements of the automatic system certain (sometimes very

coarse) idealisations of the actual phenomena are adopted. Only the principle ones are taken, the corresponding fundamental laws of mechanics, heat engineering or electrical engineering are applied and a mass of secondary factors is omitted;

(2) the approximation of the element equations is aggravated in their linearisation;

(3) the system parameters entering into the coefficients of the equations (masses, moments of inertia, capacitances, resistances, gain factors, time constants), are defined with more or less appreciable errors; it is well known, for example, that the inaccuracy of knowing the aerodynamic coefficients of an aircraft on the basis of wind tunnel tests sometimes reaches 10 per cent;

(4) if equations are not employed but experimentally taken characteristics, there is sometimes an unavoidable error both in the method of experiment itself and in the technique of carrying out and processing the results;

(5) when an automatic system is calculated there is most frequently in view not the production of a single model but a larger or smaller series; in this series the parameters of the individual units cannot be exactly the same; there is always a random scatter of the parameters for various units as a result of the technical tolerances on the manufacture of parts, etc.;

(6) in the operation of each given model there can also occur certain variations of the parameters having a random character (deformations, instability, changes of temperature, etc.).

This signifies that having determined the stability of the system we cannot be certain that the real system will correspond exactly to that point of the stability region which we have found by calculation (even when recourse has been had to experiments). The first three reasons alone are enough to make it diverge substantially from the calculated position, not to speak of the scatter in a series of units and of the possible variation in the course of time of the operation of the system. Consequently, if the calculated state was too close to the limit of stability, the real system may become unstable because of the above reasons.

The stability reserve provides for this drift of the calculated parameters of the system from the values corresponding to the limit of stability, so as to provide safe operation of each real model of the given system at least in the region of stability (taking into account all the above causes of deviation of the actual system from the calculated). Of course, the stability reserve does not express anything about the quality of the regulation process, which requires further special investigation.

The form in which the stability reserve of the system is given depends on which stability criterion is employed.

When using the first formulation of the Mikhailov criterion the stability reserve of the system is expressed in the requirement that the Mikhailov curve be distant from the origin of coordinates at all points by not less than a given quantity r, i.e. satisfying the stability criterion, the Mikhailov curve should also not pass within a forbidden circle of given radius r about the origin of coordinates (Fig. 150a) or

$$|L(i\omega)| \geqslant r \quad \text{with} \quad 0 \leqslant \omega \leqslant +\infty.$$

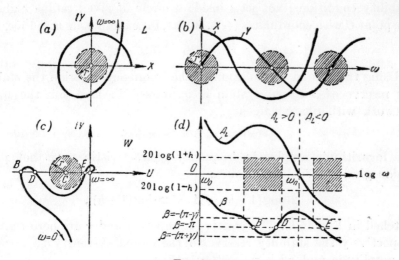

Fig. 150

In applying the second formulation of the Mikhailov criterion the necessary stability reserve of the system is expressed in that the curve $X(\omega)$, satisfying the stability criterion, in addition not pass inside circles of given radius r about the points of intersection of the curve $Y(\omega)$ with the ω-axis (Fig. 150b).

In using algebraic stability criteria, expressed in the form of inequalities, the stability reserve of the system will consist in these inequalities being sufficiently far from the corresponding equalities. For example, aside from the essential positiveness of all coefficients of the characteristic equation for a third-order system (Vyshnegradskii's criterion), we require:

$$a_1 a_2 - a_0 a_3 > \varepsilon,$$

where ε is a given positive quantity defining the stability reserve: for a fourth-order system (Hurwitz criterion):

$$a_3(a_1 a_2 - a_0 a_3) - a_4 a_1^2 > \varepsilon.$$

In the general algebraic form the stability reserve is expressed in the analogous requirement either for the Hurwitz determinants

$$\Delta_1 > \varepsilon, \ \Delta_2 > \varepsilon, \ ..., \ \Delta_{n-1} > \varepsilon, \ a_n > \varepsilon \ ,$$

or the elements of the first column in the Routh calculation scheme

$$a_1 > \varepsilon, \ b_1 > \varepsilon, \ c_1 > \varepsilon, \ d_1 > \varepsilon, \ ...$$

With the first formulation of the frequency criterion the stability reserve of a closed system is expressed in the requirement that the amplitude-phase characteristic of the open network, satisfying the stability conditions, not pass inside a circle of given radius r about the point C with coordinates $(-1, i0)$, as, for example, in Fig. 150c, i.e.

$$|W(i\omega)+1| \geqslant r \quad \text{with} \quad 0 \leqslant \omega \leqslant +\infty .$$

Using the second formulation of the frequency criterion the stability reserve of a closed system is expressed in that for the open network with phase values

$$-(\pi-\gamma) \leqslant \beta \leqslant -(\pi+\gamma)$$

the logarithmic amplitude frequency characteristic must not pass inside given "forbidden" zones:

$$20\log(1-h) \leqslant A \leqslant 20\log(1+h) \ ,$$

hatched in Fig. 150d. The positive numbers h and γ are here termed respectively the stability reserves of the closed system with respect to amplitude and with respect to phase.

Finally, if the stability region is plotted according to any of the stability criteria in the plane of any arbitrary parameters of the system (see Chapter VIII), then to ensure the necessary stability reserve of the system it is required that the point corresponding to the numerical values of the parameters of the given system be located inside the stability region not closer to the stability boundary than a given distance. For example, for a third-order system—inside the hatched region in Fig. 143 not closer than a given distance from the Vyshnegradskii hyperbola.

In certain special cases in connection with the above causes for the difference of equations and parameters of actual systems from the calculated ones there may sometimes be value in separating the stability boundaries into "safe" and "unsafe", as is done in the books of N. N. Bautin (Reference 14) and A. I. Lur'e (Reference 20) using the nonlinear Liapunov theory.

CHAPTER VIII

CHOICE OF STRUCTURE AND PARAMETERS OF ORDINARY LINEAR AUTOMATIC REGULATION SYSTEMS FROM THE STABILITY CONDITION

32. Use of the Vyshnegradskii stability criterion

Let us consider examples of application of the Vyshnegradskii stability criterion to the study of stability of certain concrete automatic systems and to the choice of parameters in designing the systems, starting from the stability condition.

Automatic pressure regulation system. The equation of this system (23.31) is of the fourth order. Neglecting the mass of the sensitive element $(T_r = 0)$, which in this case (Fig. 117) is really small, we obtain a third-order system and the third-degree characteristic equation for it in the form

$$T_a T_k T_s z^3 + (T_a T_s \delta + T_a T_k + \beta T_k T_s) z^2 + (T_a \delta + T_k \beta + T_s \beta \delta) z + \\ + (\beta \delta + 1) = 0 . \qquad (32.1)$$

We note that T_a, T_c, T_s, δ are positive numbers while β from (23.11) may in general be even negative. Therefore to satisfy the necessary stability condition positiveness of all coefficients—it is necessary that

$$T_a T_k T_s > 0 , \quad T_a T_s \delta + T_a T_k + \beta T_k T_s > 0 , \\ T_a \delta + T_k \beta + T_s \beta \delta > 0 , \quad \beta \delta + 1 > 0 . \Bigg\} \qquad (32.2)$$

Equation (29.3) of the Vyshnegradskii stability criterion now takes the form

$$(T_a T_s \delta + T_a T_k + \beta T_k T_s)(T_a \delta + T_k \beta + T_s \beta \delta) > T_a T_k T_s (\beta \delta + 1)$$

or

$$\left| \left(\frac{\beta T_s}{T_a} + \frac{\delta T_s}{T_k} + 1 \right) \left(\frac{T_a}{\beta T_s} + \frac{T_k}{\delta T_s} + 1 \right) > \left(1 + \frac{1}{\beta \delta} \right) . \qquad (32.3)$$

To estimate the static error of the system we employ formula (7.16), which in this case gives

$$\varphi_{st} = \frac{\delta}{1 + \beta \delta} \psi^0 , \qquad (32.4)$$

where ψ^0 is caused, as is evident from (23.11), by change of the steady-state external conditions of operation of the system while φ_{st} is the relative increment of the regulated pressure in the chamber (see formula (23.9)), constituting the static error (since ideally the pressure in the chamber should be a constant independent of external conditions).

To reduce the static error of the system (32.4) it is necessary to reduce δ (for given β), but in such manner as not to disturb the stability condition (32.3). For convenience of calculation it is useful

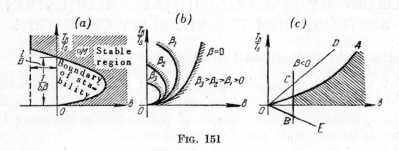

FIG. 151

to plot the stability region in the parameter plane $(\delta, T_c/T_s)$, considering that the quantities T_a/T_s and β are given (let $\beta > 0$). The equation of the stability boundary (29.4) from (32.3) will be

$$b\left(\frac{T_k}{T_s}\right)^2 + \left(ab\delta - \frac{1}{\beta}\right)\frac{T_k}{T_s} + a\delta^2 = 0, \qquad (32.5)$$

where we put

$$a = 1 + \frac{T_a}{\beta T_s}, \qquad b = 1 + \frac{\beta T_s}{T_a}. \qquad (32.6)$$

This stability boundary is represented by the curve in Fig. 151a. The other stability boundaries (29.5) and (29.6) will be

$$\delta = -\frac{1}{\beta}, \qquad \text{and} \qquad T_k = 0.$$

These two boundaries are, respectively: a vertical straight line to the left of the axis of ordinates and a horizontal straight line coinciding with the axis of abscissae.

To find on which side of these boundaries the stability region lies, an arbitrary point may be chosen, for example M (Fig. 151a), and, substituting its coordinates δ and T_c/T_s in both parts of inequality (32.3), we examine if it is satisfied or not. If so, then the stability region lies on that side of the boundary where the point M has been chosen; if not, the opposite. The stability region for the present problem is hatched in Fig. 151a.

Thus, the regulator parameters δ, T_c and T_s are chosen, firstly, so that static error (32.4) does not exceed a given limit, which is ensured by a sufficiently small value of δ. The latter is defined by the stiffness of the spring c_1 and membrane c_2 according to formula (23.19). Secondly, in choosing the parameters it is necessary to ensure stability of the system according to the graph in Fig. 151a. The quantity T_c depends on the damping factor in the sensitive element c_3 in accordance with formula (23.19) and the quantity T_s on the properties of the pneumatic drive (23.27).

Thus, these parameters may be chosen in designing the system, simultaneously considering the stability and the admissible static error (subsequently it will be necessary to consider the dynamic errors also). From Fig. 151a and from formula (32.4) it is evident that the static error of the system may be reduced without limit if we take

$$\frac{T_k}{T_s} > \frac{1}{b\beta} \, .$$

But this is possible only when the regulated object has a sufficiently large self-regulation coefficient β. With decrease of the latter the stability region shifts towards larger values of δ (Fig. 151b) and the static error of the system increases (32.4). The graph of Fig. 151b may be considered as a plot of the stability region in three parameters (δ, T_c/T_s, β).

In the limiting case $\beta = 0$ (neutral regulated object without self-regulation), when the stability boundary (32.5) takes the form (Fig. 151b)

$$\frac{T_k}{T_s} = \frac{\delta^2}{\dfrac{T_s}{T_a} - \delta} \, ,$$

we obtain the greatest static error. In addition, in distinction to objects with high self-regulation, now, to reduce the static error, it is inexpedient to increase T_c/T_s.

If the regulated object is unstable ($\beta < 0$), where we assume

$$|\beta| < \frac{T_a}{T_s}, \quad (\beta < 0) \, , \tag{32.7}$$

then from the equation for the stability boundary (32.5) we obtain the curve OA (Fig. 151c). However in this case it is necessary to consider also satisfaction of condition (32.2) for the positiveness of the coefficients in the characteristic equation. The corresponding stability boundaries with the notation of (32.6) may be written in the form

$$\frac{T_k}{T_s} = 0 \, , \quad \frac{T_k}{T_s} = -\frac{\delta}{b} \, , \quad \frac{T_k}{T_s} = -a\delta \, , \quad \delta = -\frac{1}{\beta} \, ,$$

where in accordance with condition (32.7) $\beta < 0$, $a < 0$, $b > 0$. These four equalities give the straight lines $O\delta$, OE, OD and BC (Fig. 151c). From them the boundaries of the stability region are only the straight lines $O\delta$ and BC, which corresponds to (29.6) and (29.5). The latter (BC) substantially limits the possibility of reducing the static error (32.4).

We shall now clarify the role of the additional feedback 7 (Fig. 117). If this feedback is removed ($\zeta = 0$), there will be no static error (an astatic system is obtained) while the characteristic equation (with the previous condition $T_r = 0$), in place of (32.1), takes the form

$$T_a T_k T_s z^3 + (T_a T_s \delta + \beta T_k T_s) z^2 + \beta \delta T_s z + 1 = 0 .$$

Therefore in place of (32.2) and (32.3) the stability condition will be:

$$T_a T_k T_s > 0 , \qquad T_a T_s \delta + \beta T_k T_s > 0 , \qquad \beta \delta T_s > 0$$

$$\left(\frac{T_s}{T_k} \delta + \frac{T_s}{T_a} \beta \right) \beta \delta > 1 .$$

From this it is evident that without additional feedback the given system may be made stable (with the necessary reserve) only if the regulated object has a sufficiently positive value of self-regulation β. For a neutral ($\beta = 0$) or unstable ($\beta < 0$) object it cannot be made stable for any values of the parameters. Consequently, the feedback has a beneficial effect on the stability of the system.

Servomechanism. If we consider that in the circuit shown in Fig. 128 the time constants of the electric drive circuits (motor-generator) are small ($T_3 \ll 1$ and $T_4 \ll 1$), then in the first (and in practice sometimes sufficient) approximation it is possible to take $T_3 = T_4 = 0$. In this case the characteristic equation of the system, which in accordance with (26.22) is of fifth degree in the complete form, is a third-degree equation

$$T_1 T_2 z^3 + [T_1 + (k_1 k_6) T_2] z^2 + (1 + k_1 k_6 + k_1 k') z + k_1 k = 0 .$$

Since all the coefficients are positive, according to the Vyshne-gradskii criterion (29.3) there is only one stability condition

$$[T_1 + (1 + k_1 k_6) T_2][1 + k_1 k_6 + k_1 k'] > T_1 T_2 k_1 k ,$$

or, dividing by $T_1 T_2 k_1 k$ and taking into account (26.23),

$$\left(\frac{1}{T_2} + \frac{1 + k_1 k_6}{T_1} \right) \left(\frac{1 + k_1 k_6}{k_1 k} + \frac{k_3'}{k_3} \right) > 1 . \tag{32.8}$$

Here the beneficial effect of the introduction of derivative on the system stability is evident, since from (26.11) the derivative is here introduced with coefficient k_3' and its introduction into condition

(32.8) increases the left-hand side of the inequality, i.e. facilitates satisfaction of this stability condition and broadens the region of stability of the system.

The presence of the coefficient k_6 in condition (32.8) is also useful for stability; it arises because of the presence of the counter-emf of the motor, as is evident from formulae (26.16) and (26.17), which in the present case plays the role of an additional transient feedback (see circuit of Fig. 130).

Increase of any of the time constants here in accordance with (32.8) has a negative influence on the stability, as has increase of the overall gain factor k (26.23).

From the adverse influence of the time constant T_2 on the stability of the system it is necessary to conclude that the electrical differentiation circuit shown in Figs. 128 and 129 is not completely successful. In fact, if we increase the coefficient k_3' useful for stability, simultaneously, as is evident from (26.12), it will be necessary to increase the adverse time constant T_2. Thus, from a simple application of the Vyshnegradskii criterion the important practical conclusion follows on the desirability of changing the diffferentiation device of Fig. 128. It should be designed so that the useful quantity k_3' may be increased while the adverse T_2 decreased in required limits. An example of such a differentiation device is, from (15.2), a tachogenerator in the circuit of Fig. 89c.

Let us consider the static calculation.

With a constant given angle α at the output of the system we have a static error (26.26) proportional to the load on the object, so that with zero load ($f = 0$) the system in this state will not give an error in the magnitude of the angle.

In steady-state following with constant velocity, according to (26.27) and (26.28) the system has no error in the magnitude of the velocity but has a stationary dynamic angular error dependent not only on the load but on the velocity of following.

In this example the contradiction between the precision and stability of the system is also clearly evident. Actually, increase of the coefficient

$$\frac{1 + k_1 k_6}{k_1 k} \tag{32.9}$$

is useful for stability, in accordance with (32.8), but is inadmissible because of increase of error (26.28). From this it is evident that with introduction of the derivative, i.e. with introduction of k_3', without disturbing stability (32.8) we may choose a sufficiently small coefficient (32.9) to obtain a small stationary dynamic error (26.28).

Consequently, the differentiating device in the given system is useful also because of the fact that although it does not influence the magnitude of static and stationary dynamic errors directly it permits applying measures for their reduction.

Let us now pose the problem of choosing the parameters of the differentiating device k_3 and k_3' (defined by the quantities C, R_1, R_2 according to formulae (26.12)) from the stability and precision conditions simultaneously, under the assumption that all remaining parameters of the system are given.

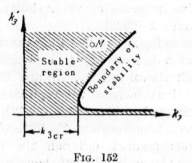

Fig. 152

For this we plot the stability region in the parameter plane (k_3, k_3'). The limit of stability from (32.8), taking into account the equality $T_2 = k_3'$ (26.12), will be

$$k_3 = \left(\frac{1}{k_3'} + a\right)(k_3' + b),\qquad (32.10)$$

where

$$a = \frac{1 + k_1 k_6}{T_1}, \quad b = \frac{1 + k_1 k_6}{k_1 k_2 k_4 k_5} k_0.$$

Graphically this is represented in the plane (k_3, k_3') in the form of a curve (Fig. 152). To decide on which side of the curve the stability region lies, it is sufficient to recall that increase of k_3, and therefore also k (26.23), weakens inequality (32.8). The stability region therefore lies to the left of the boundary of stability. It is shown hatched in Fig. 152. Since all parameters of the system and all coefficients of the equation are known to be positive, we shall not seek the other boundaries of stability ((29.5) and (29.6)) or investigate the other quadrants of the parameter plane.

Thus, wishing to take the quantity k_3 sufficiently large on the basis of the condition of smallness of stationary error of the system (26.28), we shall always choose the values k_3 and k_3' in such manner that in the diagram of Fig. 152 the point M with coordinates (k_3, k_3') lies within the stability region. From the diagram it is evident that if k_3 is taken in the interval $0 < k_3 < k_{3cr}$, where $k_{3cr} = (1 + \sqrt{ab})^2$, the system is stable for arbitrary k_3'. If $k_3 \geqslant k_{3cr}$, then it is absolutely necessary to have a special choice of k_3' as shown in the diagram of Fig. 152.

Voltage regulation system. Let us take the case where in the system considered in Section 24 we may consider $T_4 \ll T_3$. From (24.29) this signifies that the armature of the electromagnet has a negligible moment of inertia while the damping factor $c_3 + c_2' b_2^2$ is sufficiently large. Then in the equation of motion of the armature (24.28) we may put $T_4 = 0$ as a result of which the characteristic equation of the system, in accordance with (24.39), is of third degree:

$$T_1 T_2 T_3 z^3 + (T_1 T_2' + T_2 T_3) z^2 + (T_1 + T_2') z + (1 + k_1 k_2 k_3 k_4) = 0 , \quad (32.11)$$

where, from (24.32)

$$T_2' = T_2 + T_3 + k_2 k_3 \Gamma_2^0 . \tag{32.12}$$

The necessary condition of stability—the positiveness of the coefficients—is satisfied. The second condition (29.3) of the Vyshnegradskii stability criterion takes the form

$$(T_1 T_2' + T_2 T_3)(T_1 + T_2') > T_1 T_2 T_3 (1 + k_1 k_2 k_3 k_4) ,$$

from which

$$k_1 k_2 k_3 k_4 < \left(\frac{1}{T_1} + \frac{T_2'}{T_2 T_3} \right) (T_1 + T_2') - 1 . \tag{32.13}$$

From this inequality and (32.12) we conclude that increase of the transient feedback coefficient in the sensitive element Γ_2^0 (see formulae (24.30) and (24.17) and Fig. 121 and Fig. 123), i.e. increase of intensity of change of flux of the electromagnet Φ_2 in dependence on the magnitude of change of the gap δ (increase of the slope of the graph of Fig. 121*b*), is useful from the point of view of system stability since it increases the right-hand side of inequality (32.13).

Increase of the remaining gain factors (transfer factors) k_2 (24,21), k_3 (24.29), k_4 (24.37) has a negative influence on the system stability, weakening inequality (32.13). However, we are interested in increasing these coefficients k_2, k_3, k_4 from the point of view of reducing the static error of the system (24.40).

The feedback factor in the sensitive element Γ_2^0 has no effect on the static precision since, it has a coefficient p in equation (24.20) (i.e. because this feedback is transient).

33. Employment of the Hurwitz stability criterion

The use of the Hurwitz criterion and the procedure for selecting the system parameters from the stability condition remain here in general the same as for the Vyshnegradskii criterion, but with more complicated calculations, the magnitude of which sharply increases with increase in the degree of the characteristic equation. For a fourth-order system, where the stability condition consists of a single inequality (29.18) in addition to positiveness of the coefficients, the entire method of plotting the stability region in the parameter plane remains completely the same as for a third-order system considered in Section 32.

For fifth and sixth-order systems, where there are two inequalities (29.21) and (29.22), the following features arise in the method of plotting the stability region. The boundary of stability is obtained by equating the left-hand side of the second of inequalities (29.21) or (29.22) to zero, under the condition that the first of these inequalities is satisfied and that all coefficients are positive. Therefore the curve plotted in the parameter plane from the second of the inequalities may have superfluous branches on which the first inequality is not satisfied. These superfluous branches must be eliminated by simple verification of satisfaction of the first inequality (this verification may be done merely for a single point on each branch of the curve). In addition, as before, it is necessary to mark the boundaries of stability $a_n = 0$ and $a_0 = 0$.

The same occurs also for systems of higher than sixth order, where the stability boundary has expression (29.24) as well as $a_n = 0$ and $a_0 = 0$, where the number of excess branches of the curve (29.24) in the parameter plane will increase with increase of the number of additional inequalities (positiveness of the Hurwitz determinants) which are to be satisfied. It is possible to proceed otherwise.

Plotting all branches of the curve (29.24) and the lines $a_n = 0$ and $a_0 = 0$, it is necessary to find among them a region where the stability criterion is satisfied, which is verified by a single point inside each region. This test is most easily carried out by the Routh calculation scheme given in Section 29.

The system aircraft—course autopilot. Let us take the simplified equations of the system, when the time constants of the magnetic amplifier T_3 and drive T_4 are neglected, i.e. the autopilot is considered ideal. This is admissible in practice only in a preliminary approximate analysis of the system. In the given case from the complete equation (25.29), putting $T_3 = T_4 = 0$, we obtain the simplified characteristic equation of the system in the form

$$T_1 T_2 z^4 + (T_1 T_2 k_{fb} + T_1 + T_2 + k_1 k_{\ddot\psi} T_2) z^3 +$$
$$+ [(T_1 + T_2) k_{fb} + k_2 T_2 + 1 + k_1 k_{\ddot\psi} + k_1 k_{\dot\psi} \cdot T_2] z^2 + \qquad (33.1)$$
$$+ [(k_2 T_2 + 1) k_{fb} + k_1 k_{\dot\psi} + k_1 k_\psi T_2] z + k_1 k_\psi = 0 ,$$

where the abbreviated notation (25.27) is introduced.

All coefficients of the characteristic equation (33.1) are positive. Therefore there remains only to write the stability condition (29.18), which from (33.1) takes the form

$$
\begin{aligned}
&[(k_2 T_2+1)k_{fb}+k_1 k_{\dot\psi}+k_1 k_\psi T_2]\{(T_1 T_2 k_{fb}+T_1+T_2+\\
&+k_1 k_{\ddot\psi}T_2)[(T_1+T_2)k_{fb}+k_2 T_2+1+k_1 k_{\ddot\psi}+k_1 k_{\dot\psi}T_2]-\\
&-T_1 T_2[(k_2 T_2+1)k_{fb}+k_1 k_{\dot\psi}+k_1 k_\psi T_2]\}-k_1 k_\psi(T_1 T_2 k_{fb}+\\
&+T_1+T_2+k_1 k_{\ddot\psi}T_2)^2>0\,.
\end{aligned}
\tag{33.2}
$$

By considering the coefficients of the characteristic equation (33.1) and the stability condition (33.2) it is evident how the stability of the system is influenced by the coefficients k_ψ, $k_{\dot\psi}$ and $k_{\ddot\psi}$, appearing with introduction into the autopilot of sensitive elements measuring the angle of deviation of the aircraft axis from the course ψ and its first and second derivatives, and the coefficient k_{fb} characterising the feedback.

If the autopilot has no feedback, i.e.

$$
k_{fb}=0\,,\quad k_\psi\neq0\,,\quad k_{\dot\psi}\neq0\,,\quad k_{\ddot\psi}\neq0\,,
\tag{33.3}
$$

the stability condition (33.2) will be

$$
\begin{aligned}
&k_1(k_{\dot\psi}+k_\psi T_2)[(T_1+T_2+k_1 k_{\ddot\psi}T_2)(k_2 T_2+1+k_1 k_{\ddot\psi}+k_1 k_{\dot\psi}T_2)-\\
&-T_1 T_2 k_1(k_{\dot\psi}+k_\psi T_2)]-k_1 k_\psi(T_1+T_2+k_1 k_{\ddot\psi}T_2)^2>0\,.
\end{aligned}
\tag{33.4}
$$

If in addition the autopilot lacks an element reacting to the second derivative of ψ, i.e.

$$
k_\psi\neq0\,,\quad k_{\dot\psi}\neq0\,,\quad k_{\ddot\psi}=0\,,\quad k_{fb}=0\,,
\tag{33.5}
$$

the stability condition (33.2) takes the form

$$
\begin{aligned}
&(k_{\dot\psi}+k_\psi T_2)[(T_1+T_2)(k_2 T_1+1)+k_1 T_2^2(k_{\dot\psi}-T_1 k_\psi)]-\\
&-k_\psi(T_1+T_2)^2>0\,.
\end{aligned}
\tag{33.6}
$$

Further in the absence of an element reacting to the first derivative of the angle ψ, i.e. with

$$
k_\psi\neq0\,,\quad k_{\dot\psi}=0\,,\quad k_{\ddot\psi}=0\,,\quad k_{fb}=0\,,
\tag{33.7}
$$

we find from (33.2):

$$
T_2[(T_1+T_2)(k_2 T_2+1)-T_1 T_2^2 k_1 k_\psi]-(T_1+T_2)^2>0\,.
\tag{33.8}
$$

Finally, in the presence of feedback but in the absence of elements reacting to ψ and $\ddot\psi$, i.e. with

$$
k_{fb}\neq0\,,\quad k_\psi\neq0\,,\quad k_{\dot\psi}=0\,,\quad k_{\ddot\psi}=0\,,
\tag{33.9}
$$

the stability condition (33.2) will be

$$[(k_2T_2+1)k_{fb}+k_1k_\psi T_2]\{(T_1T_2k_{fb}+T_1+T_2)[(T_1+T_2)k_{fb}+$$
$$+k_2T_2+1]-T_1T_2[(k_2T_2+1)k_{fb}+k_1k_\psi T_2]\}-$$
$$-k_1k_\psi(T_1T_2k_{fb}+T_1+T_2)^2>0 . \qquad (33.10)$$

Let us first consider the stability of the system under condition (33.7), when the autopilot has no feedback and reacts only to the angle ψ. In this case, as is evident from (33.8), the autopilot does not in general contribute to the stable operation of the system since the parameter k_ψ has only a negative influence on stability, weakening inequality (33.8). Consequently, in principle, the course autopilot based on (33.7) cannot in general be constructed.

Therefore the simplest course autopilot which gives the possibility of favorably influencing the stability of the system is either an autopilot with introduction of the derivative of φ without feedback or an autopilot with introduction of feedback without the derivatives of ψ. Frequently, however, when a sufficiently wide stability region is achieved and the quality of the regulation process remains insufficient, in the second case there is sometimes introduced $\dot\psi$ and in the first $\ddot\psi$.

Let us solve the problem of choice of coefficients $k_{\dot\psi}$ and k_ψ from the stability condition when constructing an autopilot according to (33.5). For this we plot the stability region in the plane of the two parameters k_ψ, $k_{\dot\psi}$), considering all the remaining parameters (T_1, T_2, k_1, k_2) as given.

The stability boundary (29.19) is defined by substitution in formula (33.6) of an equality sign for the inequality sign. As a result we obtain the equation

$$(k_{\dot\psi}+T_2k_\psi)(a+T_2^2k_{\dot\psi}-T_1T_2^2k_\psi)-bk_\psi=0 , \qquad (33.11)$$

where

$$a=\frac{1}{k_1}(T_1+T_2)(k_2T_2+1) , \qquad b=\frac{1}{k_1}(T_1+T_2)^2 ,$$

and the other two boundaries of stability $a_4=0$ and $a_0=0$ from (33.1) will be

$$k_\psi=0 , \qquad T_1T_2=0 \qquad (33.12)$$

(the last of these is without significance since it does not include the autopilot parameters of present interest).

The stability boundaries plotted according to equations (33.11) and (33.12) are shown in Fig. 153a. From the fact that increase of $k_{\dot\psi}$ strengthens inequality (33.6), expressing the stability condition, we conclude that the stability region in Fig. 153a lies above the given curve.

The diagram obtained shows that with any value of k_ψ the quantity $k_{\dot\psi}$ must necessarily be present and have such a value that the point M with the coordinates $(k_\psi, k_{\dot\psi})$ lies above the stability boundary in the diagram (Fig. 153a). In accordance with Section 25 this system is astatic.

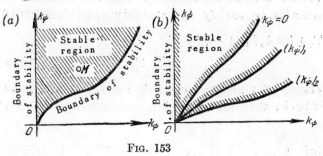

FIG. 153

It is possible to consider the choice of parameters k_ψ and k_{fb} for an autopilot according to (33.9) in an analogous manner, but here the choice of parameters must be compatible with obtaining the permissible static error (25.31).

Let us also consider case (33.3). By comparison with the above case, for which the diagram of Fig. 153a is plotted, a new parameter $k_{\ddot\psi}$ has been added. Consequently, three parameters are to be chosen: k_ψ, $k_{\dot\psi}$, $k_{\ddot\psi}$. In this case, as before, we shall plot the stability boundary in the plane of the two parameters $(k_\psi, k_{\dot\psi})$ for various given values of $k_{\ddot\psi}$.

In accordance with (33.4) the equation of the boundary of stability will here have the same form as (33.11) but with coefficients dependent on $k_{\ddot\psi}$, namely:

$$(k_{\dot\psi} + T_2 k_\psi)(A + C k_{\dot\psi} - T_1 T_2^2 k_\psi) - B k_\psi = 0 \, ,$$

where

$$A = \frac{1}{k_1}(T_1 + T_2)(k_2 T_2 + 1) + (T_1 + k_2 T_2^2 + 2 T_2) k_{\ddot\psi} + T_2 k_1 k_{\ddot\psi}^2 \, ,$$

$$B = \frac{1}{k_1}(T_1 + T_2 + k_1 k_{\ddot\psi} T_2)^3 \, , \qquad C = (1 + k_1 k_{\ddot\psi}) T_2^2 \, .$$

The corresponding stability boundaries in the form of curves $k_{\dot\psi} = f(k_\psi)$ for various given values of $k_{\ddot\psi}$ are represented in Fig. 153b. The region of stability in each individual case lies above the curve, as shown hatched in Fig. 153b. Introduction of the second derivative of ψ, as we see, broadens the region of stability. The given system is also astatic; the static error (25.31) appears in it with introduction of stiff feedback.

System for automatic regulation of engine angular velocity. Let there be an object without self-regulation and a regulator with stiff feedback (Fig. 74). Then the characteristic equation of the system from (22.60) will be:

$$T_4^2 z^4 + (T_2 + k_3 k_4 k_5 T_4^2) z^3 + (1 + k_3 k_4 k_5 T_2) z^2 + k_3 k_4 k_5 z + k_1' k_2 k_3 k_4 = 0 \quad (33.13)$$

The positiveness of all coefficients of the equation is respected. There remains to satisfy the stability condition (29.18), namely:

$$k_5[(T_2 + k_3 k_4 k_5 T_4^2)(1 + k_3 k_4 k_5 T_2) - T_4^2 k_3 k_4 k_5] -$$
$$- k_1' k_2 (T_2 + k_3 k_4 k_5 T_4^2)^2 > 0 . \quad (33.14)$$

For choice of transfer factors k_2 and k_5 (sensitive element and stiff feedback) with all remaining parameters of the system given,

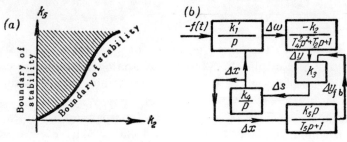

F IG. 154

we plot the stability region in the plane k_2, k_5. The stability boundaries (29.19) and $a_4 = 0$ in the present case, in accordance with (33.14) and (33.13), will be

$$k_2 = \frac{1 + T_2 k_3 k_4 k_5 + T_4^2 k_3^2 k_4^2 k_5^2}{k_1'(T_2 + T_4^2 k_3 k_4 k_5)^2} T_2 k_5 , \quad (33.15)$$

$$k_2 = 0 . \quad (33.16)$$

These stability boundaries are shown in Fig. 154a. The stability region lies between them. As we see, the feedback is obligatory to provide stability. From the point of view of system stability it is useful to increase the transfer factor of the feedback, but the transfer factor of the sensitive element k_2 cannot be strongly increased. However with increase of k_5 and reduction of k_2 the static error of the system (22.61) is increased. Consequently, in choosing the system parameters it is necessary to consider these contradictions between the simultaneous requirements of static precision and stability.

Analogously it is possible to investigate the stability of an automatic velocity regulation system with isodromic transient feedback (Fig. 78), when the system has no static error. In this case the previous feedback equation (22.53) is replaced by a new one (22.51). The structural diagram of the system in accordance with the equations of Section 22 has the form shown in Fig. 154b. Therefore the differential equation of the overall system from formulae (21.10), (20.11) and (20.10) is written in the form

$$[Q(p) + R(p)]\Delta\omega = -S(p)f(t) , \qquad (33.17)$$

where

$$\begin{aligned}
Q(p) &= (T_4^2 p^2 + T_2 p + 1)(T_5 p + 1 + k_3 k_4 k_5') p^2 , \\
R(p) &= k_1' k_2 k_3 k_4 (T_5 p + 1) , \\
S(p) &= (T_4^2 p^2 + T_2 p + 1)(T_5 p + 1 + k_3 k_4 k_5') p .
\end{aligned} \right\} \qquad (33.18)$$

From this the characteristic equation of the system $Q(z) + R(z) = 0$ will be:

$$a_0 z^5 + a_1 z^4 + a_2 z^3 + a_3 z^2 + a_4 z + a_5 = 0 , \qquad (33.19)$$

where

$$\begin{aligned}
a_0 &= T_4^2 T_5 , & a_1 &= (1 + k_3 k_4 k_5') T_4^2 + T_2 T_5 , \\
a_2 &= (1 + k_3 k_4 k_5') T_2 + T_5 , & a_3 &= 1 + k_3 k_4 k_5' , \\
a_4 &= k_1' k_2 k_3 k_4 T_5 , & a_5 &= k_1' k_2 k_3 k_4 .
\end{aligned} \right\} \qquad (33.20)$$

Aside from positiveness of the coefficients, which is satisfied, from the Hurwitz stability criterion we require here the satisfaction of two inequalities (29.21) in which it is necessary to substitute the values of the coefficients (33.20). Substituting in the second of inequalities (29.21) the inequality sign by an equality sign and adding the formulae $a_5 = 0$ and $a_0 = 0$, we obtain the boundaries of stability, where it will be necessary to omit the excess branches of the curve on which the first of inequalities (29.21) is not satisfied. In the result we will obtain the stability region in the plane of any two parameters, for example k_2 and k_5. The stability region among the curves plotted is established finally by verifying the satisfaction of the stability criterion at any one point inside this region.

34. Utilisation of the Mikhailov stability criterion

The Mikhailov criterion differs from the Vyshnegradskii and Hurwitz criteria from the point of view of plotting the stability region of the system in the following. In the Vyshnegradskii and Hurwitz criteria the stability boundary is expressed in explicit form as relation between the parameters of the system (compare Sections 32 and 33). In the Mikhailov criterion the stability boundary (28.6) or (28.7) is expressed through the auxiliary parameter ω, as a result of which the stability boundary equation will not be obtained in explicit form as before, but in parametric form in terms of ω. In addition, it is important to note that here the choice of system structure is possible by combination and superposition of Mikhailov curves taken for individual blocks and loops of the system. In the process

of construction it is possible to verify how the individual parameters
of the system elements are to be changed for the Mikhailov curve
to lie in the plane (X, iY) in a more desirable manner about the
origin of coordinates.

Expressions (28.6) and (28.7) may be used to plot the stability
boundaries in the plane of the system parameters directly (in parametric form in terms of ω), without plotting the Mikhailov curves.
Here the parameter ω, as already remarked in Section. 28, has the
physical significance of the frequency of harmonic oscillation of the

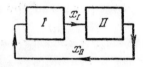

FIG. 155

system at the boundary of stability. The stability boundaries corresponding to zero and infinite roots are obtained from (28.6) or (28.7)
as singular lines with $\omega = 0$ and $\omega = \infty$.

Let us consider different methods of plotting the stability
boundaries of the system employing the Mikhailov criterion.

*Choice of structure and system parameters from the Mikhailov
curve.* Most frequently in the overall network of an automatic system
there are one or two elements where it is possible to vary the parameters
over wide limits while it is undesirable or even impossible to change
the parameters of the remaining elements. In these cases the system
may be divided structurally into two blocks: I and II (Fig. 155),
of which the first (I) includes all the elements where the parameters
may not be varied while the second (II) contains those for which
it is possible to vary the parameters, i.e. to choose their values
from the stability condition of the closed system.

Let the equations of these blocks of the system be of arbitrary
order, given in the form

$$Q_I(p)x_I = -R_I(p)x_{II}, \tag{34.1}$$

$$Q_{II}(p)x_{II} = R_{II}(p)x_I \tag{34.2}$$

(the degrees of the polynomials Q and R are in general arbitrary,
but frequently $R_I = k_I$, $R_{II} = k_{II}$, where k_I and k_{II} are constants).

Eliminating x_{II} and then substituting z for p, we obtain the characteristic equation of the closed system in the form

$$Q_I(z)Q_{II}(z) + R_I(z)R_{II}(z) = 0$$

and the equation for the Mikhailov curve for the entire closed system
in the form

$$L(i\omega) = Q_I(i\omega)Q_{II}(i\omega) + R_I(i\omega)R_{II}(i\omega). \tag{34.3}$$

Since the parameters of block I of the system are assumed invariable, all the coefficients of the operational polynomials $Q_I(p)$ and $R_I(p)$ in equations (34.1) are also invariable. Therefore we may plot fully defined auxiliary Mikhailov curves $Q_I(i\omega)$ and $R_I(i\omega)$ (for example, Fig. 156a) individually for the left and right-hand sides of equation (34.1) for the first block of the system.

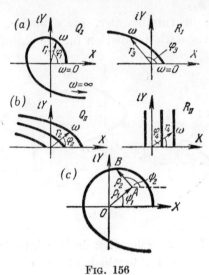

FIG. 156

Then, assigning various practically possible values for the required parameters, entering into the coefficients of equation (34.2), we obtain several alternative auxiliary Mikhailov curves $Q_{II}(i\omega)$ and $R_{II}(i\omega)$ (for example, Fig. 156b) for the second block of the system.

If in equations (34.1) and (34.2) we have $R_I = k_I$ and $R_{II} = k_{II}$, then generally it is not necessary to plot the curves R_I and R_{II}.

Further, for each alternative we find the Mikhailov curve (34.3) from the rule of multiplication and addition of complex numbers and we select the best of them. For the construction we mark on all curves (Fig. 156a and b) points with the same values of ω and take from the drawings the corresponding magnitudes of $r_1, \varphi_1, r_2, \varphi_2, r_3, \varphi_3, r_4, \varphi_4$. Then the vector OA (Fig. 156c) will correspond to the first component in formula (34.3) with

$$\rho_1 = r_1 r_2, \qquad \psi_1 = \varphi_1 + \varphi_2,$$

and to the second component the vector AB, where

$$\rho_2 = r_3 r_4, \qquad \psi_2 = \varphi_3 + \varphi_4.$$

The point B obtained (Fig. 156c) is the point on the required Mikhailov curve of the closed system corresponding to the given value of ω. Carrying this out for other values of ω, we obtain the entire curve. In view of the simplicity of the general properties of the Mikhailov curve of any order (Section 28) it is sufficient to have only a few points to judge the position of the Mikhailov curve with respect to the origin of coordinates from the point of view of satisfying the stability criterion.

The construction is substantially simplified in the cases where $R_I = k_I$ or $R_{II} = k_{II}$.

Let us analyse in this manner, for example, the effect of the derivative in the regulation function on the stability of the system.

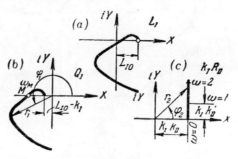

Fig. 157

Let us assume, for example, that before introduction of the derivative the closed system described by the characteristic equation

$$Q_I(z) + k_I = 0 ,$$

was unstable. Let its Mikhailov curve

$$L_I(i\omega) = Q_I(i\omega) + k_I \qquad (34.4)$$

have the form of Fig. 157a. Similar phenomena may occur, for example, for the aircraft with course autopilot if in equation (25.29) we put $k_{fb} = k_{\dot\psi} = k_{\ddot\psi} = 0$.

Opening the given system I, we introduce into it the new element II (Fig. 155) with introduction of derivative. Then for the blocks I and II of the new system we have the equations

$$Q_I(p)x_I = -k_I x_{II} ,$$

$$x_{II} = R_{II}(p)x_I ,$$

where

$$R_{II}(p) = (k_{II} + k'_{II}p)x_I , \qquad (34.5)$$

while the characteristic equation of the entire new closed system (Fig. 155) we be

$$Q_I(z) + k_I R_{II}(z) = 0 .$$

The new Mikhailov curve of the closed system will have the form

$$L(i\omega) = Q_I(i\omega) + k_I R_{II}(i\omega) , \qquad (34.6)$$

where according to (34.4) and (34.5) we have

$$Q_I(i\omega) = L_I(i\omega) - k_I \; , \; \Big\}$$
$$R_{II}(i\omega) = k_{II} + ki'_{II}\omega \; . \; \Big\}$$

$$(34.7)$$

In Fig. 157*b* and *c* are shown the curves $Q_I(i\omega)$ and $k_I R_{II}(i\omega)$ following from these equations. Here the curve $Q_I(i\omega)$ differs from the given Mikhailov curve $L_I(i\omega)$ (Fig. 157*a*) only by a shift to the left by the value k_I.

The Mikhailov curve $L(i\omega)$ for the new system, according to (34.6), is obtained by geometric addition of the vectors Q_I and $k_I R_{II}$, as shown in Fig. 158. Here it is quite clear what value should be taken

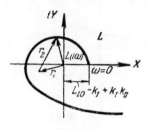

FIG. 158

for the coefficients k_{II} and k_{II} of the additional element with introduction of derivative in order to obtain a stable system with the desired form of the Mikhailov curve $L(i\omega)$.

In designing automatic systems it is possible in a similar clear way to evaluate the effects of various types of elements and their parameters on the stability of the system as a whole.

It is also possible to establish in a similar way the criteria for the means which may be used for making the system with a given structure stable. Certain of these special criteria were obtained by M. A. Aizerman using the Mikhailov curves for single-loop systems in the following form:

(a) a single-loop system of "simple" elements, without unstable elements, should not have more than one integrating element;

(b) the same system, but including a single unstable element, should not contain integrating elements;

(c) the same system, containing m harmonically oscillatory elements should have the degree of the characteristic equation greater than $4m$.

When these conditions are not satisfied the single-loop system is structurally unstable, i.e. it cannot be made stable by any choice of parameters. An example of such a system was given in Section 32— a neutral object and the rudder drive without feedback (violation of the first of the above conditions).

Plotting the stability region in a two-parameter plane. Let there be the characteristic equation of a system

$$a_0 z^n + a_1 z^{n-1} + \ldots + a_{n-1} z + a_n = 0 \qquad (34.8)$$

and it is required to plot the stability region of the system in the plane of any two of its parameters α and β (transfer factors, time constants or other quantities). These parameters may in general enter in any manner into the coefficients of the characteristic equation (34.8). We shall construct for it the expression for the

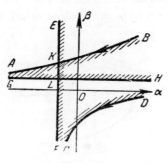

Fig. 159

Mikhailov curve $F(i\omega) = X(\omega) + iY(\omega)$. The parameters α and β enter into the coefficients of the polynomials $X(\omega)$ and $Y(\omega)$ (28.3). Considering all the remaining parameters of the system except α and β constant, we may represent the conditions for the stability boundary in the Mikhailov criterion (28.7) in the form

$$\left. \begin{array}{l} X(\alpha, \beta, \omega) = 0, \\ Y(\alpha, \beta, \omega) = 0 \end{array} \right\} \qquad (34.9)$$

and further, if possible, solve these two equations with respect to α and β in the form

$$\left. \begin{array}{l} \alpha = \alpha(\omega), \\ \beta = \beta(\omega). \end{array} \right\} \qquad (34.10)$$

After eliminating the variable ω it would be possible to obtain an equation $\beta = f(\alpha)$. This last operation, however, is not necessary in practice.

If we now assign differing values of ω in the interval $0 \leqslant \omega \leqslant +\infty$, from equations (34.10) it is possible to construct a curve (or a series of curves) in the plane of parameters α, β (for example, Fig. 159). From the discussion accompanying formula (28.7) it follows that aside from curves bounding the stability region, for example $BKLH$, equations (34.10) may give superfluous curves, lying outside the stability region (AK, CD).

Aside from equations (34.10), defining the stability boundaries, corresponding to the purely imaginary roots of the characteristic equation, there should also be plotted the stability boundary corresponding to zero and infinite roots, for example EF and GH (Fig. 159). These boundaries are defined, as before, by the equations

$$a_n = 0 \quad \text{and} \quad a_0 = 0 . \qquad (34.11)$$

They may be found however in another, as singular lines obtained from equations (34.10) with $\omega = 0$ and $\omega = \infty$. The use of equations (34.11) is frequently simpler.

Ordinarily from the significance of the technical problem it is usually already evident which of the regions, into which the parameter plane (α, β) is divided by curves (34.10) and lines (34.11), is presumably the stability region (as was frequently evident in the examples of Sections 32 and 33). For verification, taking an arbitrary point in this region, it is necessary to plot its Mikhailov curve $\alpha(i\omega)$ or apply the Routh criterion. If the stability criterion is satisfied at a single point, then the entire given region is the required stability region. If not, it is necessary to apply this verification to some other region.

If we plot the Mikhailov curves, taking one point in each of the regions of the parameter plane (Fig. 159), in accordance with Section 27 it may easily be determined from the shape of these curves how many roots of the characteristic equation of the given system have positive real parts in each region. But this is not necessary in solving the regulation problem, it is necessary only to find the stability region as indicated above.

Thus, in distinction to algebraic criteria (Sections 32 and 33), using the Mikhailov criterion the equation of the stability boundaries is obtained in parametric form (34.10) with the auxiliary parameter ω. The auxiliary parameter ω, as was mentioned in Section 28, has fully defined physical significance—it is the frequency of free harmonic oscillation of the system at the given point of the boundary of stability.

This method of plotting the stability region from the Mikhailov criterion was given in general form and with practical applications by A. A. Sokolov in 1940 (Reference 9) and then considered in detail by Yu. I. Neimark in 1948 under the designation D-division (we shall not use this term). It is also known that a similar procedure was applied previously by V. S. Vedrov.

To standardise the procedure for finding the region which presumably is the stability region (after plotting the curves (34.10) and (34.11)), Neimark introduced the following rule for hatching the curves. On each branch of the curve an arrow denotes the direction in which ω increases along the curve and for one point of each branch the sign is found of the Jacobian determinant:

$$\Delta = \begin{vmatrix} \dfrac{\partial X}{\partial \alpha}, & \dfrac{\partial X}{\partial \beta} \\[2mm] \dfrac{\partial Y}{\partial \alpha}, & \dfrac{\partial Y}{\partial \beta} \end{vmatrix}, \qquad (34.12)$$

where the elements are the partial derivatives of the left-hand sides of equations (34.9). If the determinant (34.12) is positive, then the curve should be hatched to the left, traversing it in the direction of the arrow (for example, BA in Fig. 159). If it is negative, then to the right (for example, DC). The singular lines ($a_n = 0$) or $\omega = 0$ and $a_0 = 0$ or $\omega = \infty$), for example the lines EF and GH (Fig. 159) are hatched in agreement with the direction of hatching the curves, as shown at the points $A - G$ and $C - F$.

Having carried out this hatching, we defined the assumed stability region as that region towards which the most hatching is directed (in Fig. 159 that region is $BKLH$). Verification is then carried out, as mentioned above, by applying the Mikhailov stability criterion (or the Routh criterion) to a single arbitrary point in this region.

To simplify the calculations according to formulae (34.9) or (34.10) auxiliary graphs may be plotted (auxiliary Mikhailov curves).

Let us consider two examples. As the first example we shall take a single-loop automatic regulation system consisting of simple elements, described according to (20.12) by the equation

$$Q(z) + k = 0 . \qquad (34.13)$$

Let it be required to find the stability region in the two-parameter plane, one of which is the overall gain factor of the system k and the other the time constant T of one of the aperiodic elements entering into the given system.

Extracting the corresponding polynomial $(Tz + 1)$ from $Q(z)$, we rewrite the characteristic equation (34.13) in the form

$$(Tz + 1)P(z) + k = 0 , \qquad (34.14)$$

where all the coefficients of the polynomial $P(z)$ are given.

The expression for the Mikhailov curve of the given system will be:

$$L(i\omega) = (Ti\omega + 1)P(i\omega) + k . \qquad (34.15)$$

In expression $P(i\omega)$ we separate the real and imaginary parts. Let this be $P(i\omega) = P_1(\omega) + iP_2(\omega)$. Then the real and imaginary parts of the expression for the Mikhailov curve (34.15) take the form

$$\left. \begin{aligned} X(\omega) &= k - \omega TP_2(\omega) + P_1(\omega) , \\ Y(\omega) &= \omega TP_1(\omega) + P_2(\omega) . \end{aligned} \right\} \qquad (34.16)$$

Equating this to zero in accordance with (34.9), we find the parametric equation of the stability boundaries in the form

$$k = -\frac{P_1^2(\omega) + P_2^2(\omega)}{P_1(\omega)}, \qquad T = -\frac{P_2(\omega)}{\omega P_1(\omega)}. \tag{34.17}$$

Now, taking various values of $\omega (0 \leqslant \omega \leqslant +\infty)$, we may plot the curves (34.17) point by point in the parameter plane k and T

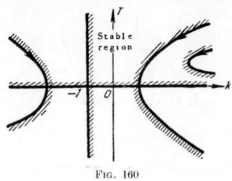

FIG. 160

(Fig. 160). To hatch the curves we employ the sign of the determinant (34.12) which in the present case, in accordance with (34.16), takes the form

$$\Delta = \begin{vmatrix} 1 & -\omega P_2(\omega) \\ 0 & -\omega P_1(\omega) \end{vmatrix} = \omega P_1(\omega).$$

In addition, to find the singular lines ($a_0 = 0$ or $\omega = \infty$ and $a_n = 0$ or $\omega = 0$) from (34.14) we obtain

$$T = 0 \qquad \text{and} \qquad k = -1,$$

since $P_1(0) = 1$ (the constant term of the polynomial $P(z)$), while $P_2(0) = 0$ (includes the common factor ω). These will be the equations of the two singular lines. One of them coincides with the k-axis while the other is parallel to the T-axis (Fig. 160).

From the directions of hatching we find the stability region. For verification let us take any point of the positive T-axis, i.e. let us take $k = 0$, $t > 0$. Then the characteristic equation (34.14) takes the form

$$(Tz + 1) P(z) = 0$$

and the system will be stable if all the roots of the polynomial $P(z)$ have negative real parts. To verify the latter, it is sufficient to plot an auxiliary Mikhailov curve $P(i\omega)$. If, for example, the polynomial $P(z)$ is of fifth degree while the Mikhailov curve is as shown in Fig. 161, this proves that the stability region in Fig. 160 has been correctly found.

As a second example let us consider the system of aircraft with course autopilot for which the stability region was constructed in Section 33. Let the autopilot not have feedback ($k_{fb} = 0$). The characteristic of the equation from (33.1) will be:

$$T_1 T_2 z^4 + (T_1 + T_2 + k_1 k_{\ddot\psi} T_2) z^3 + (k_2 T_2 + 1 + k_1 k_{\ddot\psi} + k_1 k_{\dot\psi} T_2) z^2 +$$
$$+ (k_1 k_{\dot\psi} + k_1 k_\psi T_2) z + k_1 k_\psi = 0 . \qquad (34.18)$$

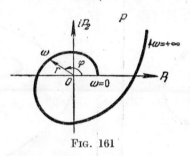

FIG. 161

The real and imaginary parts of the Mikhailov curve expression will be:

$$X(\omega) = k_1 k_\psi - (k_2 T_2 + 1 + k_1 k_{\ddot\psi} + k_1 k_{\dot\psi} T_2)\,\omega^2 + T_1 T_2 \omega^4 ,$$
$$Y(\omega) = (k_1 k_{\dot\psi} + k_1 k_\psi T_2)\,\omega - (T_1 + T_2 + k_1 l_{\ddot\psi} T_2)\,\omega^3 . \qquad (34.19)$$

Let us plot the stability region in the plane of the two parameters k_ψ and $k_{\dot\psi}$ for various values of the third parameter $k_{\ddot\psi}$. For this we equate expressions (34.19) to zero and solve them with respect to the parameters k_ψ and $k_{\dot\psi}$. We obtain

$$k_\psi = \frac{(k_2 T_2 + 1 - k_1 k_{\ddot\psi})\,\omega^2 + (1 + k_1 k_{\ddot\psi})\,T_2^2 \omega^4}{k_1(1 + T_2^2 \omega^2)} ,$$
$$k_{\dot\psi} = \frac{(T_1 - k_2 T_2^2)\,\omega^2 + T_1 T_2^2 \omega^4}{k_1(1 + T_2^2 \omega^2)} . \qquad (34.20)$$

These parametric equations of the stability boundaries in the auxiliary parameter ω are equivalent to the previous equation for the stability boundary. Assigning various values of ω ($0 \leqslant \omega \leqslant \infty$) and calculating from formulae (34.20) the quantities k_ψ and $k_{\dot\psi}$, we obtain the representation in Fig. 153b of the stability boundaries for various values of the coefficient $k_{\ddot\psi}$. Further, in all cases the stability boundary will also include the straight line $k_\psi = 0$ (axis of ordinates), which corresponds to the zero root and is defined by equating the constant term of the characteristic equation (34.18) to zero.

Determination of stability region with respect to a single parameter. Let us denote by α a parameter of the system for which we desire to obtain the stability region. This parameter α enters into the coefficients of the characteristic equation, and thus into the coefficients of the expression for the Mikhailov curve $L(i\omega)$. The expression for the stability boundary according to the Mikhailov criterion (28.6), i.e. the expression $L(i\omega) = 0$ is represented in the form

$$P(i\omega) + \alpha N(i\omega) = 0 , \qquad (34.21)$$

from which

$$\alpha = -G(i\omega) , \quad \text{ahere} \quad G(i\omega) = \frac{P(i\omega)}{N(i\omega)} . \qquad (34.22)$$

Let the polynomials P and N individually be divided into real and imaginary parts in the following manner:

$$\left. \begin{array}{l} P(i\omega) = P_1(\omega) + iP_2(\omega) , \\ N(i\omega) = N_1(\omega) + iN_2(\omega) . \end{array} \right\} \qquad (34.23)$$

Then from (34.22) we obtain

$$G(i\omega) = G_1(\omega) + iG_2(\omega) , \qquad (34.24)$$

where

$$G_1(\omega) = \frac{P_1(\omega) N_1(\omega) + P_2(\omega) N_2(\omega)}{N_1^2(\omega) + N_2^2(\omega)} , \quad G_2(\omega) = \frac{P_2(\omega) N_1(\omega) - P_1(\omega) N_2(\omega)}{N_1^2(\omega) + N_2^2(\omega)} .$$

The values of α corresponding to the stability boundary are defined as the real values satisfying equality (34.22), where among them there may also be superfluous values. Let us plot the curve $G(i\omega)$

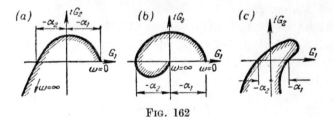

Fig. 162

in the complex plane according to equation (34.24) point by point taking individual values of ω (from $\omega = 0$ to $\omega = +\infty$). Examples of such curves are shown in Fig. 162. The first case occurs when in (34.22) the degree of the numerator is higher than that of the denominator, the second case for the reverse while the third case when the degree of the numerator is higher than that of the denominator but the variable ω may be factored out of the denominator.

The hatching on the curve $G(i\omega)$ is applied to the left-hand side in traversing the curve from $\omega = 0$ to $\omega = +\infty$. The stability region will be the segment of the real axis towards which is directed the majority of hatching. Within the region found in this way the satisfaction of the stability criterion is checked at an arbitrary point, which serves to check the correctness of solution.

Thus, in cases a and c in Fig. 162 the stability region will be

$$\alpha_1 < \alpha < \alpha_2 \ (\alpha_1 < 0, \ \alpha_2 > 0),$$

and in case b

$$0 < \alpha < \alpha_2 \ (\alpha_2 > 0),$$

since from (34.22) the quantity α is a segment of the real axis taken with reversed sign.

For verification let us take the point $\alpha = 0$. Then the expression for the Mikhailov curve from (34.21) takes the form $L(i\omega) = P(i\omega)$. Consequently, if the Mikhailov curve

$$P(i\omega) = P_1(\omega) + iP_2(\omega)$$

in cases a and c (Fig. 162) satisfies the stability conditions (for example, has the form of Fig. 161 for a fifth-degree polynomial), the stability region has been correctly found. In the case of b (Fig. 162) the point $\alpha = 0$ lies on the boundary of the above-found stability region. Therefore its Mikhailov curve $P(i\omega)$ should have (for example, for a polynomial of fifth degree) one of two forms, shown in Fig. 139 (a or c).

Since the curve $P(i\omega)$ would be needed in any case to verify the solution, it is expedient to plot it at the start of the work, employing the graph of $G(i\omega)$ as an auxiliary curve in the construction. It then becomes unnecessary to calculate the quantities G_1 and G_2 mentioned above.

In fact, let us plot from formulae (34.23) two Mikhailov curves: $P(i\omega)$ and $N(i\omega)$ (Fig. 163a and b). Then from (34.22) the modulus and argument of $G(i\omega)$ is found from the rule of division of complex numbers, namely:

$$r = \frac{r_1}{r_2}, \qquad \varphi = \varphi_1 - \varphi_2, \tag{34.25}$$

as shown in Fig. 163c. In this way individual points of the required curve $G(i\omega)$ are found for each value of ω. These points are joined by a smooth curve. In this we obtain immediately both the graph of $G(i\omega)$, defining the stability region, and the curve $P(i\omega)$, necessary for verifying the stability condition in this region.

Let us consider an example. For the velocity regulation system (Fig. 13) we take the following equations:

$$(T_1 p + 1)\Delta\omega = k_1\Delta x,$$
$$(T_4^2 p^2 + T_2 p + 1)\Delta y = -k_2\Delta\omega,$$
$$\Delta x = k_3\Delta y.$$

The characteristic equation of this system will be

$$(T_1 z + 1)(T_4^2 z^2 + T_2 z + 1) + k_1 k_2 k_3 = 0 . \qquad (34.26)$$

Let us find the stability region for the parameter T_2 characterising the damping in the sensitive element (Section 22). All remaining parameters of the system are given.

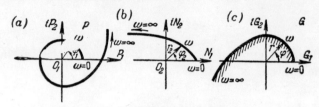

FIG. 163

Solving equation (34.26) with respect to T_2, we obtain

$$T_2 = - \frac{(T_1 z + 1)(T_4^2 z^2 + 1) + k_1 k_2 k_3}{(T_1 z + 1) z} . \qquad (34.27)$$

Let us denote here the numerator by $P(z)$ and the denominator by $N(z)$. Substituting $i\omega$ for z, we will have

$$T_2 = -G(i\omega) ,$$

where

$$G(i\omega) = \frac{P(i\omega)}{N(i\omega)} .$$

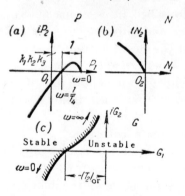

FIG. 164

Separating the real and imaginary parts in numerator and denominator according to (34.27), we find

$$P_1 = 1 + k_1 k_2 k_3 - T_4^2 \omega^2 , \qquad P_2 = T_1 \omega (1 - T_4^2 \omega^2) ,$$
$$N_1 = - T_1 \omega^2 , \qquad N_2 = \omega .$$

On the basis of these expressions we construct the auxiliary Mikhailov curves $P(i\omega)$ and $N(i\omega)$ point by point, assigning various positive values (Fig. 164a and b). We then plot curve $G(i\omega)$, employing formula (34.25). After hatching (Fig. 164c) we determine that the stability region corresponds to the segment of the real axis to the left of the curve $G(i\omega)$. The point of intersection defines the critical value of T_2 with reversed sign, where the stability region will be

$$T_2 > (T_2)_{\text{cr}}[(T_2)_{\text{cr}} > 0].$$

The Mikhailov curve $P(i\omega)$ (Fig. 164a) shows that actually with $T_2 = 0$ the system is unstable.

35. Use of the frequency stability criterion

The choice of structure and parameters of closed automatic systems from the stability condition using the frequency criterion may be carried out from the amplitude-phase characteristic of the open network and its individual blocks, as well as using logarithmic frequency characteristics.

The advantage in employing the frequency criterion appears particularly when in place of the differential equations (or transfer functions) certain circuits or blocks of the system are given in terms of their frequency characteristics, derived, for example, experimentally. In calculating according to the differential equations (or, which is the same, according to the transfer functions), constructed for all circuits of the system, it is convenient to employ also the methods described in Sections 32–34.

Choice of structures and parameters of the system. Let us consider, as in Section 34, that the closed automatic system under investigation is divided into two blocks I and II (Fig. 155) such that block II contains that element (or elements), for which it is necessary to select the parameters from the stability condition. Let block I include all the remaining elements, for which the parameters during the calculation will remain constant.

Let us open the system at the output of block II (this can also be done at the input), as represented in Fig. 165a. Let us write the transfer functions for each of the blocks:

$$W_I(p) = \frac{R_I(p)}{Q_I(p)}, \quad W_{II}(p) = \frac{R_{II}(p)}{Q_{II}(p)}, \quad (35.1)$$

and the expressions for the amplitude-phase characteristics:

$$W_I(i\omega) = \frac{R_I(i\omega)}{Q_I(i\omega)}, \quad W_{II}(i\omega) = \frac{R_{II}(i\omega)}{Q_{II}(i\omega)}. \quad (35.2)$$

The first of these may be plotted (see, for example, the curve of Fig. 165*b*), since all parameters of block I and thus all coefficients of the polynomials Q_I and R_I are given. If the transfer function W_I (35.1) for the block I is not known, we shall assume that the amplitude-phase characteristic is given experimentally, for example, in the form of Fig. 165*b*. If, finally, block I consists of several elements

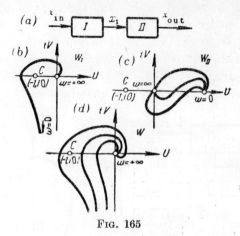

Fig. 165

(as is most frequently the case), where for some blocks the expressions for the transfer functions are known (i.e. their equations), while for others we have experimentally recorded frequency characteristics, we shall assume that according to the rules of Section 20 or Section 21 on the basis of the element characteristics we have obtained the overall amplitude-phase characteristic of block I, for example in the form of Fig. 165*b*.

The characteristic $W_{II}(i\omega)$ of block II may be plotted or recorded experimentally in several alternatives (graphs in Fig. 165*c*), if various possible values are assigned to those parameters of block II which are required to be selected according to the stability condition.

The amplitude-phase characteristic of the entire open-network will be

$$W(i\omega) = W_I(i\omega)\,W_{II}(i\omega)\,. \tag{35.3}$$

Therefore, employing the simple rule of multiplication of characteristics described in Section 20, from the given characteristic $W_I(i\omega)$ and the different alternatives of $W_{II}(i\omega)$ we obtain a corresponding number of alternatives of the overall amplitude-phase characteristic (graph in Fig. 165*d*), from which it will be evident which of the alternatives is the most suitable from the point of view of stability.

We note that in this not only the parameters but the necessary structure of block II may be chosen, starting from the shapes of the given amplitude-phase characteristic $W_I(i\omega)$ of block I. In fact, knowing the amplitude-phase characteristics of individual types of elements (Section 19), it is possible to get a clear picture of how the shape of the curve $W_I(i\omega)$ will change when the characteristics of each of the types of elements are joined to it. Consequently it is possible to determine which type of element block *II* of the system should contain in order that with a given curve $W_I(i\omega)$ the resultant curve $W(i\omega)$ will have a desirable shape from the point of view of stability of the entire closed system.

For example, from Section 19 it is known that introduction of the derivative in the right-hand side of the element equation deforms and rotates the amplitude-phase characteristics clockwise about the origin of coordinates. Therefore the introduction of such an element

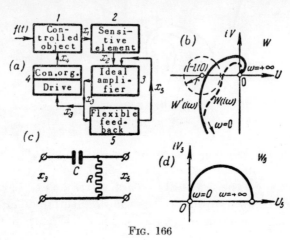

Fig. 166

into block *II* is useful if the given curve $W_I(i\omega)$ encloses the point $(-1, i0)$ (Fig, 165*b*) or, without enclosing it, passes too near to it. Thus the given curve $W_I(i\omega)$ may be deformed into such a resultant curve $W(i\omega)$ which does not enclose the point $(-1, i0)$, if this corresponds to a stable closed automatic system according to the frequency criterion (see Section 30).

For example, let there be an automatic regulation system with the block diagram shown in Fig. 166*a*. The amplitude-phase characteristic of the open network for it, according to (21.11), will take the expression

$$W(i\omega) = W_1(i\omega)\, W_2(i\omega)\, W_4(i\omega)\, \frac{k_3}{1 + k_3 W_5(i\omega)}, \qquad (35.4)$$

where k_3 is the gain factor of the ideal amplifier, $W_1(i\omega)$, $W_2(i\omega)$, $W_4(i\omega)$ are the amplitude-phase characteristics of the regulated object, sensitive element and drive with regulating organ respectively, while $W_5(i\omega)$ is the amplitude-phase characteristic of the transient feedback.

If we eliminate the transient feedback from the system, then the amplitude-phase characteristic of the open network will be

$$W'(i\omega) = W_1(i\omega) \, W_2(i\omega) \, W_4(i\omega) k_3 \,.$$

Let us assume that the characteristic $W'(i\omega)$ has the shape shown by the full line in Fig. 166b. It passes very close to the critical point $(-1, i0)$, not providing the required stability reserve denoted in the form of a circle of given radius r.

It is required to choose the transient feedback so that with its inclusion in the system the amplitude-phase characteristics is deformed as shown in Fig. 166b by the broken line, i.e. will not intersect the "forbidden zone" (circle).

This may be achieved, for example, by transient feedback in the form of an RC-network (Fig. 166c), for which we have

$$W_4(i\omega) = \frac{RCi\omega}{1 + RCi\omega} \,.$$

Since the characteristic $W_5(i\omega)$ is close to zero at low values of ω (Fig. 166d), it has practically no influence on the shape of the lower portion of the characteristic W' (Fig. 166b), but deforms in particular the necessary segment in the required direction.

There exist a number of different procedures which permits the simplest calculations of this type in various simple and complex systems.

We have considered the choice of structure and parameters of an automatic regulation system from the stability condition using the amplitude-phase characteristics, i.e. employing the first formulation of the frequency stability criterion. The calculation is simplified in many cases by using the logarithmic frequency characteristics considered in Section 19 and 20, applying the second formulation of the frequency stability criterion (see Section 30). The general procedure for solving the problem remains as before.

Let the system, for example, be divided into two blocks I and II (Fig. 165a) where all parameters entering into block I are given, and it is required to choose the parameters of block II. The amplitude and phase logarithmic frequency characteristics of the entire open network for the given system will be

$$A_l = A_{ll} + A_{llI} \,, \qquad \beta = \beta_I + \beta_{II} \,, \tag{35.5}$$

where the characteristics A_{ll} and β_I of block I are given, while the characteristics A_{llI} and β_{II} must be taken such that the overall characteristic A_1 and β satisfy the stability criterion with a definite reserve.

312   *The Dynamics of Automatic Control Systems*

Let us assume that the logarithmic characteristics of the first block A_{II} and β_I are given in the form shown in Fig. 149c (i.e. block I taken separately is unstable). To make the closed system as a whole stable, it is necessary to add to the characteristics of Fig. 149c such characteristics A_{II} and β_{II} that the point B be to the right of the point ω_{int}, as in Fig. 149a. For this purpose we take for the block II (Fig. 165a) an ideal element with introduction of derivative, the logarithmic frequency characteristics of which are shown in Fig. 100e and f. Adding the latter according to (35.5) to the characteristics of Fig. 149c we come to the required form of characteristics in Fig. 140a, since in addition both characteristics (A_1 and β) are shifted

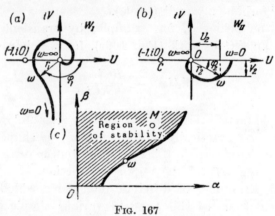

FIG. 167

upwards. The parameters k and k' of the added element may here be taken such that the resultant characteristics A_1 and β satisfy the required stability reserve (see Section 31).

Plotting the stability region in a plane of two parameters. Let it be required to plot the stability region in the plane of parameters a and β entering into block II (which are to be chosen from the stability condition). We take some value of ω. To it there correspond definite points of the amplitude-phase characteristics W_I and W_{II} (Fig. 167), and thus definite values of $r_1, \varphi_1, r_2, \varphi_2$.

The stability boundary of the closed system (Section 30) is defined by passage of the resultant curve $W(i\omega)$, which is found from formula (35.3), through the point $(-1, i0)$. In order that a point of the curve W with a given value of ω be incident on the point $(-1, i0)$, it is obviously necessary that in multiplying W_I and W_{II} there be obtained the vector OC (Fig. 167). For this it is necessary in turn that

$$r_1 r_2 = 1 , \qquad \varphi_1 + \varphi_2 = -\pi . \qquad (35.6)$$

Since the curve W_I is completely given (analytically or experimentally), while the required parameters α and β enter into W_{II}, on the basis of (35.6) we may calculate

$$r_2 = \frac{1}{r_1}, \qquad \varphi_2 = -\pi - \varphi_1, \tag{35.7}$$

and from this (see Fig. 167b)

$$U_2 = r_2 \cos \varphi_2, \qquad V_2 = r_2 \sin \varphi_2. \tag{35.8}$$

But in accordance with equations (35.2) and (35.3) we have a definite expression

$$W_{II}(i\omega) = \frac{R_{II}(i\omega)}{Q_{II}(i\omega)} = U_2(\omega) + iV_2(\omega),$$

where the required parameters α and β enter into the coefficients. Consequently, we know the expressions

$$U_2 = U_2(\alpha, \beta, \omega), \qquad V_2 = V_2(\alpha, \beta, \omega). \tag{35.9}$$

Substituting here the given ω and the values of U_2 and V_2 found from (35.8), we calculate the parameters α and ρ. This gives one point of the stability boundary (Fig. 167c) where ω is the frequency of possible free undamped oscillations of the system at the given point of the stability boundary.

Carrying out similar calculations for various values of ω, we obtain the entire stability boundary. The location of the stability region is established by checking satisfaction of the stability criterion at any point M.

CHAPTER IX

APPROXIMATE CRITERIA OF THE QUALITY OF TRANSIENT RESPONSE IN LINEAR SYSTEMS FROM THE ROOTS OF THE CHARACTERISTIC EQUATION

36. Vyshnegradskii diagram. Aperiodicity and monotonicity of the transient response

Above we have presented methods by which it is possible to find the static error of a system (and simpler forms of stationary dynamic errors) and to investigate the stability of the system. However the investigation of the system stability does not give any indication of the transient response except that it is damped.

The quality of the transient response, some idea of which was given in Section 7 (rate of attenuation, its oscillatory or monotonic character, maximum deviations, frequency of oscillations, etc.), plays a very important role among the other qualitative aspects of operation of an automatic regulation system.

The quality of the transient response with defined external conditions in linear systems is defined by the properties of the solution of the homogeneous differential equation of motion of the closed system $x_l(t)$. It is defined by the values of the roots of the characteristic equation and the arbitrary constants. The values of the roots depend on the coefficients of the equation (i.e. on the structure and parameters of the system), while the arbitrary constants depend on the initial conditions, in which the character of the external force on the system should be reflected (see Section 6). The influence of the latter on the form of the transient response depends to a strong degree on the coefficients of the operational polynomial in the right-hand side of the differential equation of the closed system.

Thus, for a given external force (step, impulse, sinusoidal variation, a force varying with constant velocity, etc.) the curve of the transient is defined, firstly, by the degree and the coefficients (or roots) of the characteristic equation of the closed system and, secondly, by the degree and coefficients (or roots) of the operational polynomial in the right-hand side of the differential equation of the closed system.

If we turn to the concept of system transfer function (see Section 8), where the denominator corresponds to the characteristic equation and the numerator is the operational polynomial of the right-hand side of the differential equation, the above may also be expressed as follows. For a given external force the shape of the transient curve is defined by the locations of the roots of the denominator (which are termed the poles of the transfer function) and the roots of the numerator (termed zeros) of the transfer function of the closed system.

In this chapter we shall consider only the influence of the roots of the characteristic equation (in other words, the denominator of the transfer function of the closed system) on the quality of the transient response and the choice of system parameters, starting from the desired locations of the roots. This is inadequate for a complete judgment of the quality of the transient responses in an automatic regulation system but it already gives very much. This is explained by the fact that the coefficients of the operational polynomial in the right-hand side (i.e. the zeros of the transfer function of the closed system) are defined by the same system parameters as the coefficients of the characteristic equation. After evaluating the quality according to the roots of the characteristic equation it is necessary to plot the transient curves taking into account the right-hand side of the differential equation of the system.

We note the following characteristic property. As already mentioned, the characteristic equation, and thus its roots, will be the same regardless of which of the variables in the regulation system has been used for constructing the differential equation. Only the operational polynomials in the right-hand side of the equation will be different. This is caused by the essential difference of the shapes of the transient curves for various variables in a given system, i.e. with the same locations of the roots of the characteristic equation (see part V). This also illustrates that judgment of the quality of the transient response only from the roots of the characteristic equation is insufficient.

The concepts of oscillatory and monotonic transient responses. The simplest criterion of the shape of transient response is the determination of whether it is oscillatory or not.

A process is termed oscillatory when the deviation of the regulated quantity (from the new steady-state value) changes sign at least twice (Fig. 168a) during the period of damping of the transient (on damping time see Section 7). In an oscillatory process there must necessarily be overshoot, i.e. a deviation x_p of the regulated quantity on a side opposite to the initial deviation.

A transient response is termed monotonic when neither the magnitude of deviation x nor the derivative $\dot{x}$ (i.e. rate of deviation), changes sign during the damping time of the transient (Fig. 168b).

Intermediate forms of transient response are: without overshoot, when x does not change sign but $\dot{x}$ does, and with overshoot when x changes sign once (Fig. 168c).

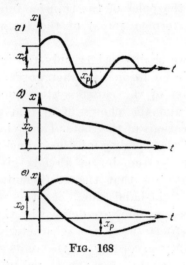

FIG. 168

In a number of closed automatic systems, most frequently in measurement and computation or in certain servomechanisms, or more rarely in regulation, it is desirable to have a rapidly attenuating oscillatory transient response since in this case the new steady-state value of the regulated quantity becomes clear immediately even during the oscillatory process and the mean dynamic error may be made very small. In other cases, mainly in the regulation of machines and automatic control of certain objects, it is desirable to have a monotonic transient response when the regulated object passes smoothly, without oscillation, to the new steady-state (to the new regime with changing load or with readjustment of the system).

A knowledge of the roots of the characteristic equation (or certain of them) is very important for judging the quality of the transient response both directly and for applying other quality criteria described below. In general, it is not possible to obtain a complete picture only from the roots of the characteristic equation in high-order systems, and this applies not only to the shape of transient curve but even as to whether it will be oscillatory or monotonic (if the initial conditions, calculated with respect to the external force, or the operational polynomial in the right-hand side of the equation of the closed system are not employed).

We shall illustrate this, in a case where it is assumed that in all further considerations the system is stable, i.e. all roots of the characteristic equation have negative real parts.

In first and second-order systems the roots of the characteristic equation actually define the character of the transient response. In a first-order system it will always be monotonic:

$$x = C_1 e^{z_1 t} \quad (z_1 < 0) \, .$$

In a second-order system the solution of the homogeneous equation has the form

$$x = C_1 e^{z_1 t} + C_2 e^{z_2 t}$$

and will necessarily be oscillatory (Fig. 168a) for any initial conditions when the roots of the characteristic equation z_1 and z_2 are complex. If they are real, the response will be either monotonic or of an intermediate form (Fig. 168c), depending on the initial rate of deviation.

In third-order systems the question is already more complicated. It was considered by Vyshnegradskii, who constructed a special diagram for this case. In analysing third and higher-order systems it is necessary to abandon the customary concepts about the direct connection between an oscillatory response and the presence of complex roots in the characteristic equation and between the monotonicity of a response and its roots being real. We shall now consider this question.

Vyshnegradskii diagram. The characteristic equation of a third-order system

$$a_0 z^3 + a_1 z^2 + a_2 z + a_3 = 0 \qquad (36.1)$$

by the substitution (29.7) is brought to the form (29.8) with parameters A and B (29.9). The stability region is plotted in the plane of these parameters (Fig. 143). Further, analysing the solution of the cubic equation (29.8), I. A. Vyshnegradskii found in 1876 (Reference 2) that curves plotted in the stability region from the equations

$$\left. \begin{aligned} A^2 B^2 - 4(A^3 + B^3) + 18AB - 27 = 0 \, , \\ 2A^3 - 9AB + 27 = 0 \quad (\text{for} \quad A < 3) , \end{aligned} \right\} \qquad (36.2)$$

demarcate the regions of differing positions of the roots *I*, *II* and *III* (Fig. 169).

The first of equations (36.2) gives two curves *CE* and *CF*, symmetrical with respect to the bisectors of the coordinate axes. The second of equations (36.2) gives the curve *DC*. In the region *III* of the Vyshnegradskii diagram (Fig. 169) all three roots of the characteristic equation are real; in regions *I* and *II* a pair of roots is complex and one is real, with the complex roots being closer to the imaginary axis than the real root in region I and the reverse in region II. This has a substantial influence on the shape of the transient curve. In Fig. 169 within each of the three regions are shown approximate curves of the transient $x(t)$ and the pattern of root distribution z_1, z_2, z_3 in the complex plane z (by crosses). In region IV the system is unstable (divergent oscillations).

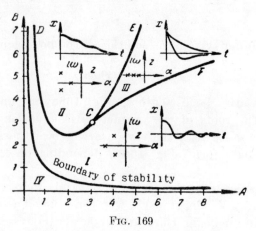

FIG. 169

In Fig. 170 are shown the positions of the roots z_1, z_2, z_3 of the characteristic equation (36.1) the boundaries CD, CE, CF between the regions I, II, III as well as at the point C. All these diagrams

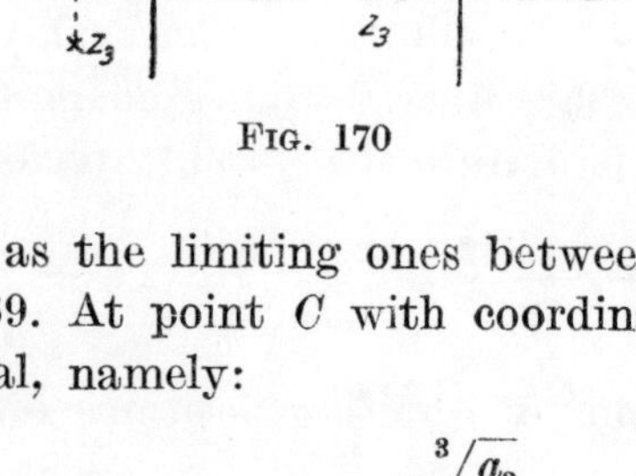

FIG. 170

are easily obtained as the limiting ones between the root position diagrams in Fig. 169. At point C with coordinates $A = B = 3$ all three roots are equal, namely:

$$z_1 = z_2 = z_3 = \sqrt[3]{\frac{a_3}{a_0}}, \qquad (36.3)$$

which follows directly from formulae (29.8) and (29.7).

As established by I. A. Vyshnegradskii, the solution of the homogeneous third-order equation having the form

$$x = C_1 e^{z_1} + C_2 e^{z_2 t} + C_3 e^{z_3 t},$$

with initial conditions corresponding to a step change in the perturbation will be oscillatory only in region *I* while in regions *II* and *III* it will be monotonic. With other initial conditions an oscillatory transient response may be obtained even in the region where all roots are real (*III*).

The Vyshnegradskii diagram may be used in practice to determine the character of root position in a third-order system. For this it is only necessary, having the characteristic equation (36.1), to calculate from formulae (29.9) the coefficients *A* and *B* and to find to which point on the Vyshnegradskii diagram this corresponds. Vice versa, it is possible to choose the parameters of the system so that such coefficients *A* and *B* will be obtained which correspond to a desired character of the root position (taking into account, of course, the requirement of static precision of regulation, as was done in the study of stability in Chapter VIII).

On monotonic and aperiodic processes. Consideration of the Vyshnegradskii diagram shows that even in third-order systems the presence of complex roots of the characteristic equation of the system does not always imply oscillation; the transient response may be monotonic even in the presence of complex roots. At the same time, as is evident from the Vyshnegradskii diagram (Fig. 169), even for a third-order system a monotonic response in the presence of complex roots is in no way a special phenomenon corresponding to some narrow restrictions. The region of monotonic responses with complex roots (*II*) is no narrower than the region of oscillatory responses (*I*), and even as wide as the entire region of real roots (*III*).

In this connection it is necessary to recall the concept of an aperiodic response which always involves the condition that all roots of the characteristic equation shall be real. As is evident from the above, only for the second-order systems does aperiodicity correspond more or less to monotonicity and complex roots to oscillation. In the third and higher-order systems the concept of aperiodicity is in no way connected with the monotonicity of the transient response and may have only an auxiliary significance. In essence, on the one hand, the region of monotonic response in the presence of complex roots is as wide as the entire aperiodic region. On the other hand, even in the aperiodic, region i.e. with all roots real, the transient response may be oscillatory since the sum of several exponentials with differing arbitrary constants

$$x = C_1 e^{z_1 t} + C_2 e^{z_2 t} + \dots + C_n e^{z_n t}$$

may give a finite number of oscillations (similarly to the second-order system where with addition of two exponentials passage through zero is already obtained).

Aperiodicity conditions. Let us present the conditions of aperiodicity, i.e. the realness of all roots of the characteristic equation for their possible utilisation for auxiliary purposes. As shown by A. M. Kats, for all roots of the characteristic equation

$$L(z) = a_0 z^n + a_1 z^{n-1} + \dots + a_{n-1} z + a_n = 0 \qquad (36.4)$$

to be real, it is necessary and sufficient that the polynomial

$$F(z) = L(z^2) + zL'(z^2) = a_0 z^{2n} + n a_0 z^{2n-1} + a_1 z^{2n-2} +$$
$$+ (n-1) a_1 z^{2n-3} + \dots + a_{n-1} z^2 + a_{n-1} z + a_n \qquad (36.5)$$

satisfy the stability criteria. Here by $L'(z^2)$ we denote the derivative $dL(z)/dz$, in which we then substitute z^2 in place of z.

The validity of this condition is proved by application of the second formulation of the Mikhailov stability criterion. In essence, substituting in (36.5) $z = i\omega$, we obtain

$$F(i\omega) = L(-\omega^2) + i\omega L'(-\omega^2) .$$

Therefore if the polynomial $F(z)$ satisfies the stability condition, from the second formulation of the Mikhailov criterion (see Section 28) the expressions $L(-\omega^2)$ and $\omega L'(-\omega^2)$ will have all real and alternating roots for the quantity $-\omega^2$. The realness of all roots of $L(-\omega^2)$ for the quantity $-\omega^2$ is equivalent to realness of all roots of the polynomial $L(z)$ for the quantity z, i.e. the characteristic equation (36.4). The negativeness of these real roots makes the coefficients of this equation positive.

Thus, determination of the aperiodicity condition for the characteristic equation of the system (36.4) consists in applying to expression (36.5) any of the stability criteria (Chapter VII). If it is necessary to plot the aperiodicity region in the plane of any two parameters of the system within the stability region (as in the Vyshnegradskii diagram), it is possible to apply to the polynomial (36.5) any of the methods of plotting the stability boundaries described in Chapter VIII. Here it is possible to employ the Vyshnegradskii criterion (Section 32) (or use directly the Vyshnegradskii diagram), the Hurwitz criterion (Section 33), the Mikhailov criterion (Section 34).

Certain conditions of monotonic transient response. As already discussed, aperiodicity, i.e. realness of all roots of the characteristic equation, is not directly connected with monotonicity of the transient response in higher-order systems than the second. Certain conditions of monotonicity for a third-order system established by I. A. Vyshnegradskii were given above. Following Z. Sh. Blokh, we mention here still other conditions for monotonic transient response, arising also from the positions of the roots of the characteristic equation, but taking into account the initial conditions (the initial condition should here be taken in the form reduced for a given external force according to Section 6).

Necessary (but not always sufficient) criteria for monotonic transient response of a system of arbitrary order n with initial conditions: $t = 0$, $x = x_0 > 0$, $\dot{x} = \dot{x}_0 (\dot{x}_0 < 0)$, $x^{(k)} = x_0^{(k)}$ ($k = 2, 3, ..., n-1$), are the following:

(1) the roots of the characteristic equation (36.4) may be arbitrary (there may be any number of complex roots), but the closest root z_1 to the imaginary axis should be real; the process can also be monotonic with a pair of complex roots $z_{2,3} = \alpha \pm i\omega$ located at the same distance from the imaginary axis as the closest real root to it z_1, i.e. with $\alpha = z_1$;

(2) simultaneously with this the arbitrary constant C_1 corresponding to the term of the solution $C_1 e^{z_1 t}$, where z_1 is the closest root (real) to the imaginary axis, should be positive if the initial deviations x_0 is positive.

In particular, with all roots real (i.e. the condition of aperiodicity) the response is always monotonic with the initial conditions: $t = 0$, $x_0 > 0$, $x_0^{(k)} = 0$ ($k = 1, 2, ..., n-1$). But with these initial conditions, firstly, there exists simultaneously a still wider region of monotonic response in the presence of complex roots located not closer than the real root z_1 to the imaginary axis. Secondly, these particular initial conditions very rarely may correspond to actual transient responses.

With the initial conditions: $t = 0$, $x_0 > 0$, $\dot{x}_0 < 0$, $x_0^{(k)} = 0$ ($k = 2, 3, ..., n-1$), under aperiodic conditions the transient need not always be monotonic. For it to be monotonic in this case it is necessary and sufficient that

$$|\dot{x}|_0 \leqslant \frac{a_n |z_1|}{a_{n-1}|z_1| - a_n} x_0 , \qquad (36.6)$$

where z_1 is a real root closest to the imaginary axis. But simultaneously with this there again exists a still broader region of monotonic responses of complex roots for which (36.6) is the condition bounding from above the permissible absolute value of the initial velocity.

With other more frequently encountered initial conditions the question becomes more complicated and the aperiodicity condition corresponds still less to monotonicity of the response.

For a third-order system (36.1) with initial conditions: $t = 0$, $x_0 > 0$, $\dot{x}_0 < 0$, $\ddot{x}_0 = 0$, a monotonic response will exist with

$$|\dot{x}_0| \leqslant \frac{a_3 |z_1|}{a_2 |z_1| - a_3} x_0 ,$$

if all roots are real while z_1 is the closest of them to the imaginary axis and also with

$$\frac{a_3(a_1 - a_0|z_1|)x_0}{a_3 + a_0|z_1|(a_1 - a_0|z_1|)^2} \leqslant |\dot{x}_0| < \frac{a_3|z_1|x_0}{a_2|z_1| - a_3},$$

if there exists a pair of complex roots located not closer to the imaginary axis than the real root z_1.

In Section 44 will be given the monotonicity conditions derived from the transfer function of a closed system.

In Section 37 we determine the roots nearest to the imaginary axis, which may be used for a rough estimate of the oscillatory or monotonic character of the transient response for certain particular forms of external forces.

37. Degree of stability and its application

The generally employed term "degree of stability" was introduced by Ya. Z. Tsypkin in 1945. However in fact an analogous concept was already employed earlier by I. N. Voznesenskii and G. N. Nikol'-skii (see Section 38).

Concept of degree of stability. The degree of stability is the smallest of the absolute values of the real parts of all roots of the characteristic equation of the system. Geometrically the degree of stability

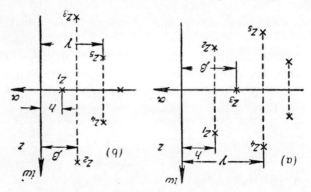

Fig. 171

is the distance h from the imaginary axis to the root of the characteristic equation of a stable system nearest to it (Fig. 171). When the nearest to the imaginary axis is a pair of complex roots (Fig. 171a) the degree of stability is termed oscillatory. When the nearest to the imaginary axis is a real root (Fig. 171b) h is termed the aperiodic degree of stability.

We shall demonstrate that the magnitude of the degree of stability h may serve as an approximate estimate of the rate of attenuation of the transient (although not always reliable).

Let the roots of the characteristic equation of a linear system of arbitrary order, in accordance with Fig. 171a, be the following:

$$
\left.
\begin{aligned}
z_{1,2} &= -h \pm i\omega_1, & h &> 0, \\
z_3 &= -\beta, & \beta &> h, \\
z_{4,5} &= -\gamma \pm i\omega_2, & \gamma &> h,
\end{aligned}
\right\}
\qquad (37.1)
$$

Then the equation of the transient response (i.e. the general solution of the homogeneous differential equation) will have the form

$$
x_t = C_1 e^{-ht}\sin(\omega_1 t + C_2) + C_3 e^{-\beta t} + C_4 e^{-\gamma t}\sin(\omega_2 t + C) + \dots \qquad (37.2)
$$

It is obvious that the rate of attenuation of each of the terms of the solution depends on the quantities h, β and γ respectively, while the absolute magnitude depends on the values of C_i. The greatest of the values h, β, γ corresponds to the most rapid attenuation. Therefore, if the difference in values γ, β and h is substantial, while the difference in values of C_i small, then after a certain period there remains practically only the first term of the solution, which defines the end of the transient process. Under these conditions, the greater the degree of stability h, the more rapidly the entire transient attenuates.

However the magnitude of the degree of stability h frequently cannot serve for an estimate of the rate of attenuation of the transient. For example, if the arbitrary constant C_4 in expression (37.2) is substantially greater than the arbitrary constants C_1 and C_3 the quality of the transient response, including its rate of attenuation, will be principally determined by the third term corresponding to the more remote roots $z_{4,5}$ of the characteristic equation rather than the first term corresponding to the nearest root. Then the degree of stability h gives only an indication of the distance of the system from the boundary of stability from the point of view of the characteristic root distribution.

This is particularly expressed when the root z_3 or the roots $z_{4,5}$ are located close to the roots $z_{1,2}$ (Fig. 171a) and when multiple roots appear. If, for example, the roots $z_{1,2}$ in Fig. 171a are triple, the equation of the transient curve will be:

$$
x_t = (C_1 + C_2 t + C_3 t^2) e^{-ht}\sin(\omega_1 t + C_4) + C_5 e^{-\beta t} + C_6 e^{-\gamma t}\sin(\omega_2 t + C_7) + \dots
$$

The first factor containing t and t^2 reduces the rate of attenuation in comparison with that which would take place for a simple root with the same value of h.

It is clear however that although in the above unfavorable cases the attenuation of the transient is not determined only by the quantity h, nevertheless with other conditions equal the attenuation will frequently be better where the degree of stability h is greater.

In any case determination of the degree of stability gives more than the calculation of the stability of the system and the stability reserve (Section 31). But even the degree of stability does not yet give any concept of the magnitude of the deviation of the regulated quantity during the transient.

Shifted equation. Common to all methods of determining the degree of stability of the system is the preliminary derivation of the so-called shifted equation, which is obtained as follows. Let there exist an automatic regulation system for which the characteristic equation has been obtained in the form

$$a_0 z^n + a_1 z^{n-1} + \ldots + a_{n-1} z + a_n = 0 . \tag{37.3}$$

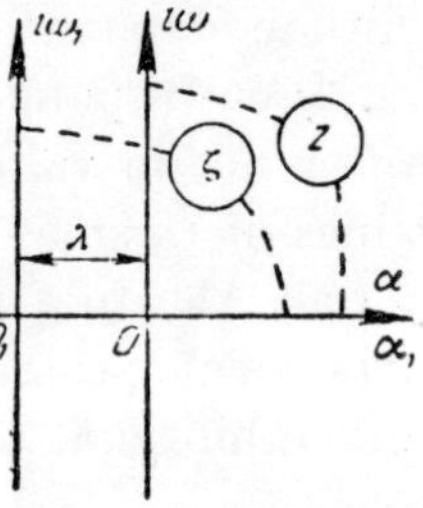

Fig. 172

In the root plane $z = \alpha + i\omega$ (Fig. 172) we shift the imaginary axis to the left by a certain distance λ. We obtain a new plane $\zeta = \alpha_1 + i\omega_1$, where

$$\alpha_1 = \alpha + \lambda , \qquad \omega_1 = \omega .$$

Let us transform the given characteristic equation (37.3) to the new variable ζ. For this we put

$$L(z) = a_0 z^n + a_1 z^{n-1} + \ldots + a_{n-1} z + a_n . \tag{37.4}$$

But $z = \zeta - \lambda$ while the function $L(\zeta - \lambda)$ may be expanded in series

$$L(\zeta - \lambda) = L(-\lambda) + \frac{L'(-\lambda)}{1} \zeta + \frac{L''(-\lambda)}{1 \cdot 2} \zeta^2 + \ldots , \tag{37.5}$$

where primes denote the derivatives with respect to z of the function (37.4). In the present case this series contains a finite number of terms since the last non-zero derivative is $L^{(n)}(-\lambda) = n! a_0$. All derivatives of higher order than n vanish.

Since from (37.4) and (37.3) we have $L(z) = L(\zeta - \lambda) = 0$, equating the finite series (37.5) to zero, we obtain the following equation:

$$a_0 \zeta^n + A_1 \zeta^{n-1} + \ldots + A_{n-1} \zeta + A_n = 0 , \tag{37.6}$$

where

$$A_k = \frac{L^{n-k}(-\lambda)}{(n-k)!} \qquad (k = 1, 2, \ldots, n) . \tag{37.7}$$

This is the shifted equation, corresponding to the shifted root plane ζ (Fig. 172).

For example, let the characteristic equation for a fourth-order system be

$$a_0 z^4 + a_1 z^3 + a_2 z^2 + a_3 z + a_4 = 0 \, .$$

To obtain the shifted equation we first find:

$$\left. \begin{aligned}
L(z) &= a_0 z^4 + a_1 z^3 + a_2 z^2 + a_3 z + a_4 \, , \\
L'(z) &= 4 a_0 z^3 + 3 a_1 z^2 + 2 a_2 z + a_3 \, , \\
L''(z) &= 12 a_0 z^2 + 6 a_1 z + 2 a_2 \, , \\
L'''(z) &= 24 a_0 z + 6 a_1 \, .
\end{aligned} \right\} \tag{37.8}$$

The coefficients of the shifted equation

$$a_0 \zeta^4 + A_1 \zeta^3 + A_2 \zeta^2 + A_3 \zeta + A_4 = 0$$

from (37.7) and (37.8) will be:

$$\left. \begin{aligned}
A_1 &= a_1 - 4 a_0 \lambda \, , \\
A_2 &= a_2 - 3 a_1 \lambda + 6 a_0 \lambda^2 \, , \\
A_3 &= a_3 - 2 a_2 \zeta + 3 a_1 \zeta_2^2 - 4 a_0 \lambda^3 \, , \\
A_4 &= a_4 - a_3 \lambda + a_2 \lambda^2 - a_1 \lambda^3 + a_0 \lambda^4 \, .
\end{aligned} \right\} \tag{37.9}$$

Thus in the general case the coefficients (37.7) of the shifted equation (37.6) are expressed through the coefficients of the initial characteristic equation (37.3) and, in addition, depend on the magnitude of shift λ of the imaginary axis.

It is easy to see that if the magnitude of shift λ (Fig. 172) is exactly equal to the degree of stability h, in Fig. 171a the roots z_1 and z_2 will lie on the shifted imaginary axis $i\omega_1$ while in the case of Fig. 171b the root z_1 will lie at the origin of coordinates 0_1 of the shifted plane ζ. In both cases all the remaining roots will have negative real parts, i.e. will be located to the left of the shifted imaginary axis $i\omega_1$.

In other words, when the magnitude of shift $\lambda = h$, the shifted equation corresponds to a system located at the boundary of stability. This is the basis for calculating the degree of stability h for any linear automatic regulation system.

Degree of stability of third-order system. Let us consider calculation of the degree of stability for a third-order system applying the Vyshnegradskii criterion. The characteristic equation (29.1) by substitution of (29.7) is reduced to the form (29.8) with coefficients A and B (29.9).

The degree of stability in equation (29.8) will be different from that in equation (29.1) since the magnitudes of the degree of stability (being the real parts of the roots) are related by the same relationship (29.7) as the roots of the equation, namely:

$$h = \sqrt[3]{\frac{a_3}{a_0}} \, h_0 \, , \tag{37.10}$$

where h and h_0 denote the degree of stability for equations (29.1) and (29.8) respectively.

Since an equation of the form (29.8) is termed normalised, h_0 may be termed the normalised degree of stability and h the actual degree of stability of the system.

To find h_0, starting from equation (29.8), we calculate the coefficients of the shifted equation

$$\zeta^3 + A_1\zeta^2 + A_2\zeta + A_3 = 0 \qquad (37.11)$$

according to formula (37.7), which gives:]

$$\left.\begin{aligned}
A_1 &= A - 3\lambda, \\
A_2 &= B - 2A\lambda + 3\lambda^2, \\
A_3 &= 1 - B\lambda + A\lambda^2 - \lambda^3.
\end{aligned}\right\} \qquad (37.12)$$

Employing equality (29.4) as the criterion of the presence of purely imaginary roots, we find that an oscillatory degree of stability will occur when the coefficients (37.12) with $\lambda = h_0$ are all positive and satisfy the condition $A_3 = A_1 A_2$, from which

$$B = \frac{1}{A - 2h_0} + 2h_0(A - 2h_0). \qquad (37.13)$$

An aperiodic degree of stability will occur in the presence in the shifted equation (37.11) of a zero root, i.e. when $A_3 = 0$, from which in accordance with (37.12) with $\lambda = h_0$ we obtain

$$B = \frac{1}{h_0} + Ah_0 - h_0^2. \qquad (37.14)$$

Following Ya. Z. Tsypkin and P. V. Bromberg, we construct the diagram of the normalised degree of stability for a third-order system, for which we plot in the Vyshnegradskii diagram (Fig. 169) curves of equal values of degree of stability h_0.

For $h_0 = 0$ we find from (37.13) $B = 1/A$, which corresponds to a Vyshnegradskii hyperbola (limit of stability of the system). For $h_0 = 0.1$, $h_0 = 0.2$, $h_0 = 0.3$, $h_0 = 0.4$, $h_0 = 0.5$ we obtain from formula (37.13) second-order curves in region I of the parameter plane (Fig. 173) and from (37.14) straight lines in regions II and III. These curves and straight lines together form closed contours as shown in Fig. 173. With further increase of $h_0 > 0.5$ the contour progressively contracts, degenerating at $h_0 = 1$ to a single point C with coordinates $A = B = 3$.

The diagram of the normalised degree of stability (Fig. 173) may be used in practice, firstly, to determine the magnitude of the degree of stability for any given third-order system and secondly, to choose the parameters of a third-order automatic regulation system for a desired magnitude of its degree of stability.

For the equation of a real system (29.1) it is necessary to find the Vyshnegradskii parameters A and B from formulae (29.9) and from them the point on the diagram (Fig. 173); from the location of this point on the diagram the normalised magnitude of h_0 is determined and then, from formula (37.10), the actual degree of stability of the system h.

The greatest degree of stability occurs at the point $C(h_0 = 1)$. But here all three roots of the characteristic equation are equal

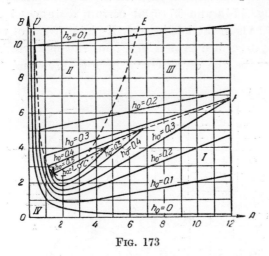

FIG. 173

(see formula (36.3)). But this, as already mentioned, is not always favorable from the point of view of the rate of attenuation of the transient. Therefore in practice there is no sense in choosing the greatest degree of stability—but a point in its vicinity should be chosen (for example, within the contour $h_0 = 0 \cdot 5$), considering simultaneously the other technical requirements on the system.

Example. Let us take the automatic pressure regulation system (Section 23). Its characteristic equation has the form (32.1) if we neglect the mass of the sensitive element. From formulae (29.9) we calculate the Vyshnegradskii parameters:

$$A = \frac{T_a T_s \delta + T_a T_k + \beta T_k T_s}{\sqrt[3]{T_a^2 T_k^2 T_s^2 (\beta \delta + 1)}}, \qquad B = \frac{T_a \delta + T_k \beta + T_s \beta \delta}{\sqrt[3]{T_a T_k T_s (\beta \delta + 1)^2}}.$$

These two relations may serve as the equations for determining any two parameters of the system if those remaining are given. In fact, on the basis of the diagram of Fig. 173 let us assign desired values of A and B, for example $A = 2 \cdot 5$ and $B = 2 \cdot 5$. Then from these formulae we may calculate the required values of δ and T_c for given β, T_a, T_s, i.e. in other words, we may choose the corresponding sensitive element of the system (see Section 23).

It is possible to proceed similarly with a servomechanism and a voltage regulation system or any other described by a third-order equation (such as for example those in Section 32).

Graphical-analytic method for finding the degree of stability for a system of arbitrary order. A second method of calculating the degree of stability, proposed by N. N. Miasnikov in 1948 utilises the Mikhailov stability criterion.

Let us plot straight lines parallel to the imaginary axis in the root plane (Fig. 174*a* and 174*c*) at certain distances $\lambda_1, \lambda_2, \ldots$, from the imaginary axis in the left-hand half-plane. We plot the Mikhailov curve $L(i\omega)$ as described in Section 27 for the characteristic equation (37.3). Let this be the outer curve in Fig. 174*b* and 174*d*.

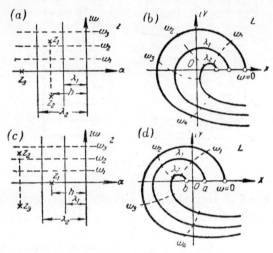

Fig. 174

Then from the shifted equation (37.6) with coefficients (37.7) we plot in exactly the same manner the Mikhailov curves for certain $\lambda = \lambda_1, \lambda = \lambda_2$ (inner curves in Fig. 174*b* and 174*d*). It is then found that points with common values of ω form curves (broken line) perpendicular to the Mikhailov curves at their points of intersection. Thus, in the complex plane L a network of curves is obtained which represents a conformal mapping of a network of straight lines in the root plane z.

If we have a distribution of curves as in Fig. 174*b* it is obvious that for a certain value λ lying between λ_1 and λ_2 the Mikhailov curve passes through the origin of coordinates. This, as we know from Section 27, denotes the presence of a pair of purely imaginary roots in the shifted equation and, consequently, the presence of a pair of complex conjugate roots $z_{1,2}$ in the initial equation. Then, since $\lambda = \lambda_1$ gives a Mikhailov curve corresponding to a stable system while $\lambda = \lambda_2$ an unstable system, its passage through the origin of coordinates for the given $\lambda_1 < \lambda < \lambda_2$ will correspond to the limit of stability (for the shifted equation). Consequently, the given value of $\lambda(\lambda_1 < \lambda < \lambda_2)$ will actually be equal to the required degree of stability h, where the degree of stability is oscillatory.

This value $\lambda = h$ may be found approximately by interpolation, thus: between the curves λ_1 and λ_2 we plot approximately the curve corresponding to them cd through the origin of coordinates O

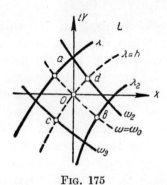

FIG. 175

(Fig. 175), and similarly between the curves ω_2 and ω_3 we mark the curve ab. Measuring the lengths of segments aO, ab, Od, cd, we obtain by linear interpolation

$$h = \lambda_1 + (\lambda_2 - \lambda_1)\frac{aO}{ab}, \\ \omega_0 = \omega_2 + (\omega_3 - \omega_2)\frac{Od}{cd}. \quad \left.\right\} \tag{37.15}$$

Consequently, the closest to the imaginary axis in this case will be the roots

$$z_{1,2} = -h \pm i\omega_0. \tag{37.16}$$

Here we have obtained immediately the complete value of the roots closest to the imaginary axis of the characteristic equation of the system and not only the degree of stability h. The quantity ω_0 will be the frequency of oscillation of the first component in the equation for the transient curve:

$$x = C_1 e^{-ht} \sin(\omega_0 t + C_2) + ..$$

Similarly, if the distribution of curves is that shown in Fig. 174d, for some $\lambda = h$ located between λ_1 and λ_2 the origin of the Mikhailov curve ($\omega = 0$) is incident on the origin of coordinates 0. This signifies that here the shifted equation with $\lambda = h$ will have a zero root.

Verifying that this corresponds just to the boundary of stability for the shifted equation, by interpolation we then obtain:

$$h = \lambda_1 + (\lambda_2 - \lambda_1)\frac{aO}{ab}, \qquad (37.17)$$

where aO and ab are segments shown in Fig. 174d. In this case we have an aperiodic degree of stability; the first term in the equation for the transient curve will be:

$$x = C_1 e^{-ht} + \dots$$

Ordinarily the precision obtained by this approximate interpolation is sufficient. When required, however, it is always easily possible to find the value of h (and ω_0) more exactly by plotting the Mikhailov curve for the shifted equation with λ equal to the interpolated value of h just obtained. Because of the approximateness of interpolation this curve does not pass exactly through the origin of coordinates. A new network of curves is obtained similar to that in Fig. 174 form which by the same method a second interpolation may be carried out, improving the previously found h and ω but for practical calculations this is usually not required.

Plotting loci of equal values of degree of stability. To choose the system parameters for a given degree of stability it is convenient to have a drawing in which inside the region of stability in the plane of any two parameters of the system the loci of equal values of degree of stability are plotted. For a third-order system this has already been done in Fig. 173 using the Vyshnegradskii stability criterion.

For a system of higher order the loci of equal values of degree of stability are conveniently plotted in the parameter plane by construction of the boundaries of stability for the shifted equation (37.6) using the Mikhailov criterion (Section 34) or the Hurwitz criterion (Section 33).

Example using the Hurwitz criterion. For an aircraft with course autopilot without feedback and without introduction of the second derivative, and neglecting the inertia of the autopilot, the characteristic equation from (33.1) will be:

$$a_0 z^4 + a_1 z^3 + a_2 z^2 + a_3 z + a_4 = 0,$$

where

$$a_0 = T_1 T_2, \; a_1 = T_1 + T_2, \qquad a_2 = k_2 T_2 + 1 + k_1 k_\psi T_2, \\ a_3 = k_1 k_\psi + k_1 k_\psi T_2, \qquad\qquad a_4 = k_1 k_\psi. \qquad\qquad (37.18)$$

The region of stability for this case was plotted in Fig. 153a. We now plot inside it the loci of equal values of degree of stability h. For this we write the shifted equation

$$a_0 \zeta^4 + A_1 \zeta^3 + A_2 \zeta^2 + A_3 \zeta + A_4 = 0, \qquad (37.19)$$

where from (37.9) and (37.18) we have:

$$A_1 = T_1 + T_2 - 4T_1T_2h \,,$$

$$A_2 = k_2T_2 + 1 + k_1k_{\dot\psi}T_2 - 3(T_1 + T_2)h + 6T_1T_2h^2 \,,$$

$$A_3 = k_1k_{\dot\psi} + k_1k_\psi T_2 - 2(k_2T_2 + 1 + k_1k_{\dot\psi}T_2)h + 3(T_1 + T_2)h^2 - 4T_1T_2h^3 \,,$$

$$A_4 = k_1k_\psi - (k_1k_{\dot\psi} + k_1k_\psi T_2)h + (k_2T_2 + 1 + k_1k \cdot T_2)h^2 -$$
$$- (T_1 + T_2)h^3 + T_1T_2h^4 \,.$$

We then apply to the shifted equation (37.19) the conditions for the stability boundary from the Hurwitz criterion (29.19), namely:

$$A_3(A_1A_2 - a_0A_3) - A_4A_1^2 = 0 \,, \tag{37.20}$$

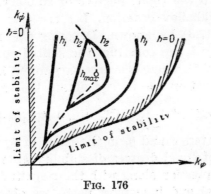

FIG. 176

which corresponds to an oscillatory degree of stability, and

$$A_4 = 0 \tag{37.21}$$

for an aperiodic degree of stability.

Considering the variables k_ψ and $k_{\dot\psi}$ as coordinates of the parameter plane (Fig. 176), from (37.20) and the preceding expressions we obtain:

$$(b_1k_{\dot\psi} + b_2k_\psi + b_3)(b_4k_{\dot\psi} - b_5k_\psi + b_6) + (b_7k_{\dot\psi} - b_8k_\psi - b_9) = 0 \,, \tag{37.22}$$

where

$$b_1 = k_1(1 - 2T_2h) \,, \qquad b_2 = k_1T_2 \,,$$

$$b_3 = -2(k_2T_2 + 1)h + 3(T_1 + T_2)h^2 - 4T_1T_2h^3 \,,$$

$$b_4 = (T_1 + T_2 - 4T_1T_2h)k_1T_2 - k_1T_1T_2(1 + 2T_2h) \,, \qquad b_5 = k_1T_1T_2^2 \,,$$

$$b_6 = (T_1 + T_2 - 4T_1T_2h)[k_2T_2 + 1 - 3(T_1 + T_2)h + 6T_1T_2h^2] +$$
$$+ T_1T_2h[2(k_2T_2 + 1) - 3(T_1 + T_2)h + 4T_1T_2h^2] \,,$$

$$b_7 = hb_8 \,, \qquad b_8 = k_1(T_1 + T_2 - 4T_1T_2h)^2(1 - T_2h) \,,$$

$$b_9 = (T_1 + T_2 - 4T_1T_2h)^2h^2[k_2T_2 + 1 - (T_1 + T_2)h + T_1T_2h^2] \,.$$

From (37.21) we have:

$$k_{\dot\psi} = \frac{1}{h}k_\psi + c \,, \tag{37.23}$$

where

$$c = \frac{k_2 T_2 - 1 - (T_1 + T_2)h + T_1 T_2 h^2}{k_1 (1 - T_2 h)} \, h \, . \qquad (37.24)$$

Assigning various values of the degree of stability h, for each of them from equation (37.23) we obtain in the parameter plane $(k_\psi, k_{\dot\psi})$ loci of equal values of the aperiodic degree of stability in the form of straight lines h_1, h_2 (Fig. 176). Similarly from equation (37.22) we plot the curved lines h_1, h_2 equal to the values of the oscillatory degrees of stability. The broken line in Fig. 176 shows the curves obtained separating the region of aperiodic (to the left) and oscillatory (to the right) degrees of stability.

Use of the Mikhailov criterion. Let the characteristic equation of the system (37.3) be known. Denoting the magnitude of the degree of stability h, we construct the shifted equation (37.6) with the coefficients (37.7), where it is necessary to put $\lambda = h$. Substituting in the shifted equation $\zeta = i\omega$, we obtain the expression

$$L^{sh}(i\omega) = a_0(i\omega)^n + A_1(i\omega)^{n-1} + \ldots + A_{n-1}i\omega + A_n^{\sim} = 0 \, , \qquad (37.25)$$

where the parameters α and β, in the plane of which it is necessary to plot the loci of equal degrees of stability h, enter into the coefficients of this expression along with the magnitude of h. Separating in (37.25) the real and imaginary parts, we obtain two equations in the form

$$\begin{aligned} X^{sh}(\alpha, \, \beta, \, \omega, \, h) &= 0 \, , \\ Y^{sh}(\alpha, \, \beta, \, \omega, \, h) &= 0 \end{aligned} \Bigg\} \qquad (37.26)$$

(which corresponds to finding the boundary of stability (28.7) in the Mikhailov stability criterion).

If possible, we solve equation (37.26) with respect to α and β in the form

$$\begin{aligned} \alpha &= \alpha(\omega, \, h) \, , \\ \beta &= \beta(\omega, \, h) \, . \end{aligned} \Bigg\} \qquad (37.27)$$

Taking a single fixed value of $h = h_1$ and various values of ω, on the basis of (37.27) or (37.26) we plot point by point inside the stability region in the parameter plane (α, β) loci of equal degrees of stability h_1 (Fig. 177). Similarly we plot the lines $h = h_2$, etc. Here the singular lines with $\omega = 0$ correspond to the aperiodic degree of stability, the remaining to oscillatory.

Plotting the loci of equal values of degree of stability within the stability region by any of the above methods, it is possible to choose the parameters of the system, already taken into consideration with the magnitude of the degree of stability and its oscillatory or its aperiodic character (considering simultaneously, as always, the static error and other technical requirements placed on the system).

On the choice of parameters for maximum stability. The choice of system parameters for maximum stability, as the simplest criterion of quality, has been considered by various authors. In particular, if we consider all roots of the characteristic equation real

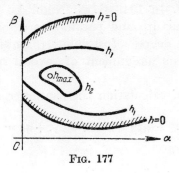

Fig. 177

and equal (the point of greatest value of normalised degree of stability), it will be possible to write in algebraic form a relationship for the choice of parameters for a system of any order (from V. A. Bodner (Reference 51)). In fact, with real and equal roots ($z_1 = z_2 = \ldots = z_n$) the characteristic equation may be written in the form

$$a_0(z - z_1)^n = 0 ,$$

the coefficients of which are therefore defined by the formulae

$$\frac{a_1}{a_0} = \binom{n}{1} z_1 , \quad \frac{a_2}{a_0} = \binom{n}{2} z_1^2 , \ldots, \quad \frac{a_n}{a_0} = \binom{n}{n} z_1^n ,$$

where $\binom{n}{1}, \binom{n}{2}, \ldots, \binom{n}{n}$ are the binomial coefficients. Eliminating z_1, we obtain the relationships

$$
\left.
\begin{aligned}
n^2 a_0 a_2 &= \binom{n}{2} a_1^2 , \\
n^3 a_0^2 a_3 &= \binom{n}{3} a_1^3 , \\
&\cdots\cdots\cdots \\
n^n a_0^{n-1} a_n &= \binom{n}{n} a_1^n ,
\end{aligned}
\right\}
\qquad (37.28)
$$

which may serve for choice of system parameters, since all coefficients here are expressed in a definite manner through the given parameters. The rigorously given conditions for optimum parameters occuring here may sometimes lead to physically unrealisable choice of parameters.

38. Choice of system parameters from the distribution of several roots of the characteristic equation closest to the imaginary axis

Let us consider certain methods for selecting the parameters of automatic regulation systems (and servomechanisms), starting from a desired distribution of several roots of the characteristic equation nearest to the imaginary axis.

Nikol'skii's method. In 1943 G. N. Nikol'skii proposed a method for choosing the structure and parameters of automatic regulation systems for a given degree of stability ("limiting number" in his terminology) and from assignment of several roots of the characteristic equation.

For convenience of calculation the characteristic equation of the system

$$a_0 z^n + a_1 z^{n-1} + \ldots + a_{n-1} z + a_n = 0 \qquad (38.1)$$

is written in the form

$$a_0 z^n + (\beta_1^0 + \beta_1) z^{n-1} + (\beta_2^0 + \beta_2) z^{n-2} + \ldots$$
$$\ldots + (\beta_{n-1}^0 + \beta_{n-1}) z + (\beta_n^0 + \beta_n) = 0 , \qquad (38.2)$$

where the coefficients $a_1, a_2, \ldots, a_n$ are all divided into two components in such manner that the first components $\beta_1^0, \beta_2^0, \ldots, \beta_n^0$ do not contain the transfer factors (gain factors) of the regulator and its elements. Consequently, they contain only the parameters of the regulated object and, in addition, may contain the regulator time constants or those of its individual elements (for an ideal regulator the components $\beta_1^0, \ldots, \beta_n^0$ contain only the parameters of the regulated object).

The second components $\beta_1, \beta_2, \ldots, \beta_n$, termed the additional coefficients of equation (38.2), contain the transfer factors k_1 (gain factors) of the regulator and its elements. A part of the components (first or second) may be zero.

The general problem is posed of choosing the values of transfer factors k_i of the regulator and determining which of them are necessary to provide a given degree of stability and a desired distribution of roots (i.e. what kind of elements should or should not be introduced into the regulator). Put in this way all the coefficients $\beta_1^0, \beta_2^0, \ldots, \beta_n^0$ in equation (38.2) are known numbers and all k_i, entering into the "additions" $\beta_1, \beta_2, \ldots, \beta_n$ are unknown coefficients.

If the desired degree of stability h is given, then all roots of the characteristic equation of the system (38.1) should have the form

$$z_1 = -h + \zeta_1 , \ z_2 = -h + \zeta_2 , \ \ldots, \ z_n = -h + \zeta_n , \qquad (38.3)$$

where $\zeta_1, \zeta_2, \ldots, \zeta_n$ are arbitrary numbers with non-positive real parts. In other words, all roots z should be located to the left of the imaginary axis shifted by the given quantity $\lambda = h$ (Fig. 172) or, at least, located on it.

This signifies that the shifted equation (37.6) should satisfy the stability criterion or be located on the boundary of stability.

Since the degree of stability h is the distance to the root nearest to the imaginary axis, in formulae (38.3) it is necessary to put either

$$\zeta_1 = 0 , \qquad (38.4)$$

or

$$\zeta_{1,2} = \pm i\omega_0 , \qquad (38.5)$$

where ω_0 is an arbitrary positive number (frequency of the first component in the equation for the transient curve).

If the system is of higher order than fourth, it may be difficult to use condition (38.5); for these systems only condition (38.4) is taken. For third and fourth-order systems it is possible to use either of conditions (38.4) or (38.5).

With condition (38.4) the characteristic equation (38.1) has a root $z = -h$, as a result of which we may write:

$$a_0(-h)^n + a_1(-h)^{n-1} + \ldots + a_{n-1}(-h) + a_n = 0 . \qquad (38.6)$$

In this equation everything is given including h, except the required transfer factors of the regulator entering into certain of the coefficients $a_1, \ldots, a_n$. If we need to determine only a single transfer factor, it is immediately defined from equation (38.6). But it is still necessary to ensure negativeness of the real parts for all remaining ζ_i. For this, since (38.6) in accordance with (37.7) is equivalent to the condition $A_n = 0$, it is necessary to verify whether the stability condition is observed for the shifted equation, the degree of which is lower by unity, i.e. the equation

$$a_0\zeta^{n-1} + A_1\zeta^{n-2} + \ldots + A_{n-2}\zeta + A_{n-1} = 0 . \qquad (38.7)$$

Verification of the stability conditions may be carried out in any way (by the Vyshnegradskii, Routh, Hurwitz or Mikhailov conditions).

When the stability conditions are satisfied the assumed structure of the system is possible, and vice versa. When it is not possible it is necessary either to be satisfied with a lower degree of stability than required (if this is permissible) or, retaining the assigned degree of stability h, to abandon the simple case (selection of only a single transfer factor) and go over to the more complicated case considered below of choosing two or several transfer factors (in practice this may sometimes require, for example, complication of the system by the introduction of new elements).

For third and fourth-order systems, aside from the above, the following method of solving the problem from the choice of a single transfer factor of the regulator is also possible. Let us assume condition (38.5). Then for the shifted equation (37.6), in which $\lambda = h$, we have from (29.4) and (29.19)

$$A_1 A_2 = a_0 A_3 \quad \text{or} \quad A_3(A_1 A_2 - a_0 A_3) - A_4 A_1^2 = 0 , \qquad (38.8)$$

respectively for the third and fourth-order systems. In equation (38.8) there is a single unknown transfer factor present, which is defined from it. In addition, it is required that all coefficients of the shifted equation be positive.

If the form with choice of a single transfer factor is found impossible, we pass to the choice of two transfer factors of the regulator. For this (in a system of arbitrary order) we put

$$\zeta_1 = 0 , \quad \zeta_2 = 0 . \qquad (38.9)$$

Then to condition (38.6) is added $A_{n-1} = 0$, which, from (37.7) where $\lambda = h$, will be:

$$na_0(-h)^{n-1} + (n-1)a_1(-h)^{n-2} + \ldots + a_{n-1} = 0 , \qquad (38.10)$$

where h is given.

From the system of two equations (38.6) and (38.10) two unknown transfer factors are determined. After their calculation it is necessary to verify satisfaction of the stability condition for the shifted equation, the degree of which is lower by two, namely:

$$a_0 \zeta^{n-2} + A_1 \zeta^{n-3} + \ldots + A_{n-3}\zeta + A_{n-2} = 0 . \qquad (38.11)$$

It is possible to achieve the necessary degree of stability h not only by the number of new elements introduced into the system but by substitution of new elements for others. Therefore if in the given element the stability condition for equation (38.11) is not satisfied, other possible alternative structures of the system should be tested.

Condition (38.9) signifies that the closest root to the imaginary axis is the double real root $z_1 = z_2 = -h$. When the order of the system is not higher than fifth, it is also possible to employ another method for choosing two transfer factors of the regulator, namely, in place of condition (38.9) to assume the following:

$$\zeta_1 = 0 , \quad \zeta_{2,3} = \pm i\omega_0 . \qquad (38.12)$$

Then to determine the two required transfer factors there will be two equations: the first, (38.6) and the second, one of (38.8) for systems of fourth and fifth order, respectively, where it is composed for expression (38.7).

If we do not succeed in constructing a system with two required transfer factors of the regulator for a given degree of stability, we introduce a third. With choice of three transfer factors of the regulator it is possible, as above, to test the condition

$$\zeta_1 = \zeta_2 = \zeta_2 = 0 .$$

But if the presence of a triple root is undesirable, it is possible to apply either

$$\zeta_1 = 0 , \ \zeta_2 = 0 , \ \zeta_3 = -\varepsilon \quad (\varepsilon > 0) , \tag{38.13}$$

or

$$\zeta_1 = 0 , \ \zeta_{2,3} = \pm i\omega_0 , \ \zeta_4 = -\varepsilon , \tag{38.14}$$

or

$$\zeta_1 = 0 , \ \zeta_2 = 0 , \ \zeta_{3,4} = \pm i\omega_0 . \tag{38.15}$$

Condition (38.13) is convenient for systems of any order. To choose the three transfer factors of the regulator it is necessary to add to the two previous conditions (38.6) and (38.10), from (38.11), the following (ε is preassigned):

$$a_0(-\varepsilon)^{n-2} + A_1(-\varepsilon)^{n-1} + \ldots + A_{n-2} = 0 , \tag{38.16}$$

where it is necessary to verify satisfaction of the stability condition for the equation obtained by dividing (38.11) by $(\zeta + \varepsilon)$.

Condition (38.14), analogously to (38.12), is applied for systems of not higher than fifth order. In this case the following three equations are used to determine the three transfer factors: (38.6), one of (38.8), composed for (38.7), and (38.16).

Finally, condition (38.15) may be applied for fifth and sixth-order systems where in choosing three transfer factors of the regulator equations (38.6), (38.10) and one of (38.8), composed for the expression (38.11), are used.

In all cases satisfaction of the individual conditions in numerical calculations is facilitated by using the appropriate auxiliary graphical constructions.

Above we were everywhere concerned with the choice of transfer factors of the regulator, but it is completely obvious that this method may be applied in the same form to choose various other parameters of the system including the time constants.

In applying this method (as in all the preceding, starting from the stability condition) the choice of parameters from the given conditions should always simultaneously be accompanied by consideration of the static (and stationary) system errors.

We remark that the simplest choice of m different system parameters is obtained from the condition of equality and realness of the roots of the characteristic equation nearest to the imaginary axis, i.e.

$$\zeta_1 = \zeta_2 = \ldots = \zeta_m = 0 ,$$

which gives equations of the form (38.6), (38.10), etc., for the calculation of m. Several authors have used this approach. However multiple roots give more drawn-out processes in comparison with those with separated roots and the same degree of stability. When basing the calculation on the equality and realness of all roots it is therefore better not to preassign the quantity h but to employ a system of formulae (37.28) for the choice of parameters.

Nikol'skii's method discussed above permits the roots to be different. It may be developed further in this direction if we use shifted equations of the form (37.6) for two or several $\lambda = h$, $\lambda = \lambda_1$, $\lambda = \lambda_2$ in place of the single preassigned $\lambda = h$. But this makes the calculation more complicated.

The Popov-Sokolov method. The following method, developed by T. N. Sokolov, is based on a work of V. K. Popov (1947). The best case is considered to be that in which a pair of complex roots of the characteristic equation of the system is closest to the imaginary axis. Then the characteristic equation (38.1) of arbitrary degree n is represented in the form (the coefficients are unknown)

$$\varphi(z)(z^2 + \beta_1 z + \beta_2) = 0 , \qquad (38.17)$$

where $\varphi(z)$ is a polynomial of degree $(n-2)$ while the quadratic expression in parentheses corresponds to the pair of complex roots closest to the imaginary axis, which will have the expression.

$$z_{1,2} = -\frac{\beta_1}{2} \pm i \sqrt{\beta_2 - \frac{\beta_1^2}{4}} \qquad (38.18)$$

(the numbers β_1 and β_2 are as yet unknown).

We shall consider the above trinomial as basic, defining in general outlines the form of the entire transient process (for this all the remaining roots should be remote from the above). As is evident from (38.18), the time constant T characterising the attenuation of the basic part of the transient as well as the fundamental natural frequency ω and period θ will be:

$$T = \frac{2}{\beta_1} , \qquad \omega = \sqrt{\beta_2 - \frac{\beta_1^2}{4}} , \qquad \theta = \frac{2\pi}{\omega} . \qquad (38.19)$$

The decrement ratio of the basic term in the transient response (i.e. the ratio of successive amplitudes over a period) will be

$$e^{-\frac{\theta}{T}} . * \qquad (38.20)$$

---

* Editor's note. (38.20) is the reciprocal of the usual damaging factor in Western literature $C^{\theta/T}$.

The attenuation will be the stronger, the smaller is T (i.e. the greater the degree of stability $\beta_1/2$), while the number of oscillations in the process will be smaller, the smaller the decrement, i.e. the greater the ratio θ/T. For example,

$$e^{-\frac{\theta}{T}} = 0.018 \quad \text{with} \quad \frac{\theta}{T} = 4; \qquad (38.21)$$

this signifies that even after a single period the amplitude of oscillation in the transient is only 1.8 per cent of the initial peak, i.e. practically the oscillation has not succeeded in developing since after a single period it may already be considered as damped out.

From (38.19) condition (38.21) leads to

$$\beta_2 = \frac{\pi^2 + 4}{16} \beta_1^2, \qquad (38.22)$$

where the roots (38.18) may be represented in the form

$$z_{1,2} = \frac{\beta_1}{2}\left(-1 \pm i\frac{\pi}{2}\right).$$

Developing this method further, T. N. Sokolov (Reference 22) proposes estimating the entire transient response not from two but from three roots closest to the imaginary axis, considering the third root to be real. The characteristic equation (38.1) is represented in the form

$$\varphi_1(z)(z + \beta_3)(z^2 + \beta_1 z + \beta_2) = 0,$$

where $\varphi_1(z)$ is a polynomial of degree $(n - 3)$. Two roots will have the values (38.18) and the third, $z_3 = -\beta_3$.

Relations (38.19) and (38.22) remain as before, and in addition it is considered expedient to put

$$\beta_3 = \frac{\beta_1}{2}. \qquad (38.23)$$

Aside from the choice of roots of the characteristic equation closest to the imaginary axis an estimate should also be made of the static error of the system for the regulated quantity (and in servomechanisms, the stationary dynamic error with constant velocity or constant acceleration).

We shall illustrate the method of determining the system parameters based on these considerations, following T. N. Sokolov (since the method requires individual approach to each structure taking into account the physical realisability of the requirements placed on the transient response).

Let us consider a servomechanism with the structure shown in Fig. 178. Here $y(t)$ is a preassigned quantity, x_1 is the regulated quantity. The system has differentiating D and integrating I elements

23

and transient feedback, in which the input quantity is $\dot{x}_1$ and the output V_4. Let us construct the system equations.

The equation of the drive with the regulated object will be

$$(T_1 p + 1) p x_1 = k_1 V_2 ,$$

where T_1 is the electromechanical constant of the drive.

Further we have

$$V_1 = k_0(y - x_1) .$$

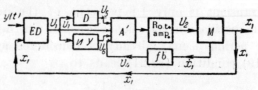

FIG. 178

At the output of the amplifier the voltage will be $V_1 + V_6 + V_5 - V_4$, while at the output, V_2; consequently,

$$(T_2 p + 1) V_2 = k_2(V_1 + V_6 + V_5 - V_4) ,$$

where T_2 is a time constant, k_2 is the overall gain factor of the vacuum tube and rotary amplifiers.

We have for the feedback (Fig. 178) the equation

$$(T_3 p + 1) V_4 = k_3 p^2 x_1 .$$

At the output of the integrator

$$V_6 = k_6 \frac{1}{p} V_1 .$$

At the output of the differentiating element

$$V_5 = k_5 p V_1 .$$

Let us write this in the form of a single system equation for the error magnitude $(y - x_1)$, which we denote by x. We obtain:

$$(p^5 + a_1 p^4 + a_2 p^3 + a_3 p^2 + a_4 p + a_5) x = (p^3 + b_1 p^2 + b_2 p + b_3) p^2 y , \quad (38.24)$$

where

$$\left. \begin{array}{l} a_1 = \dfrac{T_1 T_2 + T_1 T_3 + T_2 T_3}{T_1 T_2 T_3} = \dfrac{1}{T_1} + \dfrac{1}{T_2} + \dfrac{1}{T_3} , \\[3mm] a_2 = \dfrac{T_1 + T_2 + T_3 + k_1 k_2(k_3 + k_0 k_5 T_3)}{T_1 T_2 T_3} , \\[3mm] a_3 = \dfrac{1 + k_0 k_1 k_2(k_5 + T_3)}{T_1 T_2 T_3} , \\[3mm] a_4 = \dfrac{k_0 k_1 k_2(1 + k_6 T_3)}{T_1 T_2 T_3} , \quad a_5 = \dfrac{k_0 k_1 k_2 k_6}{T_1 T_2 T_3} , \\[3mm] b_1 = a_1 , \quad b_2 = \dfrac{T_1 + T_2 + T_3 + k_1 k_2 k_3}{T_1 T_2 T_3} , \quad b_3 = \dfrac{1}{T_1 T_2 T_3} . \end{array} \right\} \quad (38.25)$$

We see immediately from equation (38.24) that the static error in the given system (with constant magnitude y) and the stationary error with constant velocity py will be equal to zero*. Only accelerated variation of the input quantity with constant acceleration p^2y will cause a stationary error

$$x^0 = \frac{b_3}{a_5}\, p^2y = \frac{1}{k_0 k_1 k_2 k_6}\, p^2y \quad (p^2y = \text{const}) , \qquad (38.26)$$

i.e. a constant error quantity x_2^0 will be preserved in the steady-state with constant acceleration py (while in the steady-state of following with constant velocity there will be no error).

We now determine the system parameters T_3, k_3, k_5, k_6, starting from the required quality of the transient response and estimating it from the three roots closest to the imaginary axis. The characteristic equation

$$z^5 + a_1 z^4 + a_2 z^3 + a_3 z^2 + a_4 z + a_5 = 0$$

is represented in the form

$$(z^2 + c_1 z + c_2)(z^3 + \alpha_1 z^2 + \alpha_2 z + \alpha_3) = 0 .$$

We have the following relations among the coefficients:

$$\left.\begin{aligned}
a_1 &= c_1 + \alpha_1 , \\
a_2 &= c_2 + \alpha_2 + c_1 \alpha_1 , \\
a_3 &= \alpha_3 + c_1 \alpha_2 + c_2 \alpha_1 , \\
a_4 &= c_1 \alpha_3 + c_2 \alpha_2 , \\
a_5 &= c_2 \alpha_3 .
\end{aligned}\right\} \qquad (38.27)$$

The fundamental polynomial $(z^3 + \alpha_1 z^2 + \alpha_2 z + \alpha_3)$ is represented in the form

$$(z + \beta_3)(z^2 + \beta_1 z + \beta_2) ,$$

where

$$\alpha_1 = \beta_1 + \beta_3 , \qquad \alpha_2 = \beta_2 + \beta_3 \beta_1 , \qquad \alpha_3 = \beta_3 \beta_2 .$$

In accordance with (38.23) and (38.22) we obtain from the above

$$\beta_1 = \frac{2}{3}\alpha_1 , \qquad \beta_2 = \frac{\pi^2 + 4}{36}\alpha_1^2 ,$$

$$\alpha_2 = \left(\frac{\pi^2 + 4}{36} + \frac{2}{9}\right)\alpha_1^2 \approx 0 \cdot 61\alpha_1^2 ,$$

$$\alpha_3 = \frac{\pi^2 + 4}{108}\alpha_1^3 \approx 0 \cdot 128\alpha_1^3 .$$

From the magnitude of the permissible error x^0, taking into account the given $k_0 k_1 k_2$, we find the coefficient of the integrating unit

$$k_6 = \frac{p^2y}{k_0 k_1 k_2 x^0} \quad (p^2y = \text{const}) .$$

---

* Neglecting the load on the regulated object.

We then remark that

$$\frac{a_5}{a_4} = \frac{k_6}{1+k_6 T_3} = \frac{c_2 \alpha_3}{c_1 \alpha_3 + c_2 \alpha_2}.$$

Assuming $c_1 \ll c_2$ (this gives a higher frequency at the roots z_4 and z_5 and justifies the further numerical calculations), we have in the first approximation

$$\frac{a_5}{a_4} = \frac{k_6}{1+k_6 T_3} \approx \frac{\alpha_3}{\alpha_2} = \frac{1}{4 \cdot 76} \alpha_1.$$

Substituting here

$$\alpha_1 = \mu a_1 = \mu \left(\frac{1}{T_3} + k_T \right),$$

where μ is as yet an undetermined coefficient while k_T denotes the preassigned quantity

$$k_T = \frac{1}{T_1} + \frac{1}{T_2};$$

we obtain the quadratic equation with respect to T_3, from which

$$T_3 = -\frac{1}{2k_T} \left[1 + \frac{k_T}{k_6} - \frac{4 \cdot 76}{\mu} \pm \sqrt{\left(1 + \frac{k_T}{k_6} - \frac{4 \cdot 76}{\mu} \right)^2 - \frac{4k_T}{k_6}} \right].$$

Since T_3 should be real, we have

$$\mu < \frac{4 \cdot 76}{\left(1 - \sqrt{\frac{k_T}{k_6}} \right)^2}.$$

The two last formulae permit choosing the applicable values of T_3 and μ. After this a_1, b_1, b_3 become known, which means also a_5 from (38.26). We then calculate

$$\alpha_1 = \mu a_1, \qquad \alpha_2 = 0 \cdot 61 \alpha_1^2, \qquad \alpha_3 = 0 \cdot 128 \alpha_1^3,$$

$$c_1 = a_1 - \alpha_1, \qquad c_2 = \frac{a_5}{\alpha_3}$$

and a_2, a_3, a_4 from formulae (38.27).

Then from (38.25) we find k_5, k_3 and an improved value of k_6. Now, adopting these values for all the selected parameters, we may calculate the exact values of all the equation coefficients and their decomposition. After this all the roots of the characteristic equation

$$z_{1,2} = -\frac{\beta_1}{2} \pm \sqrt{\frac{\beta_1^2}{4} - \beta_2},$$

$$z_3 = -\beta_3,$$

$$z_{4,5} = -\frac{c_1}{2} \pm \sqrt{\frac{c_1^2}{4} - c_2},$$

are found and a knowledge of the roots gives the possibility of plotting the transient curve (see Part V). In this construction the right-hand part of the differential equation of the system (38.24) is taken fully into consideration, i.e. both the poles and the zeros of the transfer function of the closed system are taken completely into account, which eliminates the initial defect of considering the quality of the transient response only from the roots of the characteristic equation.

39. Calculation of the roots of equations and polynomials

The transient response in regulation depends very much on the pattern of distribution of all the roots of the characteristic equation in the complex plane, for example, if the roots are close together or if they are wide apart, etc. To a still greater degree the transient response depends on the mutual positions of the roots of the characteristic equation and the roots of the operational polynomial in the right-hand part of the differential equation of the closed system (poles and zeros of the transfer function of the closed system). The methods discussed here may be used to calculate the roots of this operational polynomial (zeros) and to compare them with the roots of the characteristic equation (poles).

In addition, calculation of the roots of various algebraic equations has already been required for various auxiliary purposes, for example in applying the frequency stability criterion (Section 30). Below we shall also sometimes find it useful to know the roots of the characteristic equation of the system (for example, in Part V) or certain auxiliary equations.

We shall consider several simple procedures for calculating the roots of the algebraic equation

$$a_0 z^n + a_1 z^{n-1} + \ldots + a_{n-1} z + a_n = 0 \qquad (39.1)$$

or, which is the same thing, the roots of the polynomial

$$f(z) = a_0 z^n + a_1 z^{n-1} + \ldots + a_{n-1} z + a_n . \qquad (39.2)$$

Simple case. If the left-hand part of the equation or the polynomial is expanded in factors

$$f(z) = (T_1 z + 1)(T_2^2 z^2 + T_3 z + 1)\ldots,$$

the roots are found by solution of the equations

$$T_1 z + 1 = 0 , \qquad T_2^2 z^2 + T_3 z + 1 = 0 , \ldots$$

In particular, if z^m may be factored out of the polynomial $f(z)$ this signifies that there is an m-fold zero root $(z = 0)$.

The characteristic equations of closed systems and polynomials $Q(z)$ and $R(z)$, figuring in the frequency stability criterion (Section 30) sometimes constitute such simple types of equations and polynomials.

Estimate of the moduli of all roots. Let there now exist equation (39.1) or a polynomial (39.2) not decomposed into factors. If all their coefficients are positive, the moduli of all roots $|z|$ satisfy the inequality *

$$m < |z| < M \,, \tag{39.3}$$

where m and M denote respectively the smallest and largest of the ratios

$$\frac{a_1}{a_0}, \ \frac{a_2}{a_1}, \ ..., \ \frac{a_{n-1}}{a_{n-2}}, \ \frac{a_n}{a_{n-1}} \,.$$

If in addition the stability condition is observed, then (39.3) signifies that all roots are located in the hatched region in Fig. 179, having a half-annular shape. If the polynomial (39.2) does not satisfy the stability conditions, the roots are located over the entire annulus.

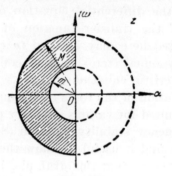

FIG. 179

On calculating the values of the polynomial. Below we shall require to calculate the values of a polynomial (39.2) for arbitrary real values of the number z. In direct substitution each value of z must be raised to a high power, which is a very laborious operation for "unrounded" values of z.

This necessity was also encountered in constructing Mikhailov curves and the amplitude-phase characteristics, as well as in calculations connected with the degree of stability. But there in the majority of cases "rounded" values were satisfactory.

To calculate the values of the polynomial tables constructed by K. P. Ivanov (Reference 31) may be used, where the problem is reduced only to the operations of addition and subtraction.

In addition, it is possible to speed up the calculations appreciably in comparison with the method of direct substitution of z, in the

* For proof see (Reference 35), p. 190.

following manner. Let it be required to calculate the value of a polynomial (39.2) for some $z = c$. We calculate a number of auxiliary numbers:

$$\left.\begin{aligned} b_1 &= ca_0 + a_1 , \\ b_2 &= cb_1 + a_2 , \\ &\cdots\cdots\cdots\cdots \\ b_{n-1} &= cb_{n-2} + a_{n-1} , \end{aligned}\right\} \qquad (39.4)$$

after which the required value of the polynomial (39.2) will be*:

$$f(c) = cb_{n-1} + a_n . \qquad (39.5)$$

With this method there are a total of n operations of multiplication, while with the ordinary substitution of z in the polynomial a minimum of $2n$ multiplications is required.

Finding the real roots. If among the roots of equation (39.1) are real ones, then (with positive coefficients of the equation) they are all located, from (39.3), within the segment

$$-M < z < -m . \qquad (39.6)$$

In the first approximation all the real roots may be found by plotting the curve

$$f(z) = a_0 z^n + a_1 z^{n-1} + \ldots + a_{n-1} z + a_n , \qquad (39.7)$$

where it is necessary to plot this curve only in the segment (39.6). In plotting the curve it is recommended for simplification to use

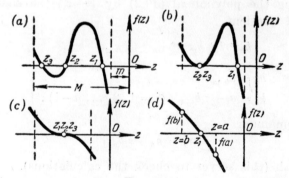

FIG. 180

the above method of calculating the values of $f(z)$. The points of intersection of the curve $f(z)$ with the z-axis give the approximate values of all real roots of the equation (39.1), for example the three simple roots z_1, z_2 and z_3 in Fig. 180a. If some real root is double, for example $z_2 = z_3$, the curve $f(z)$ will be tangent to the x-axis (Fig. 180b). If there is a triple real root, for example $z_1 = z_2 = z_3$, then in place

* Proof, see (Reference 35), p. 273.

of tangency with the x-axis the curve $f(z)$ will have a point of inflection (Fig. 180c). Analytically the criterion for multiple roots is the vanishing at the given point of the corresponding number of derivatives df/dz, d^2f/dz^2, etc.

If the precision of the graphical construction is insufficient, it is easily possible to find a more exact value of the root analytically. From the graph Fig. 180d it is reliably evident that the root z_1 lies between certain nearby values $z = a$ and $z = b$. Then, taking the curve $f(z)$ on the small segment ab as a straight line (Fig. 180d), we may calculate a more exact value of z_1 from the obvious (by similarity of triangles in Fig. 180d) formula

$$z_1 = \frac{bf(a) - af(b)}{f(a) - f(b)}, \qquad (39.8)$$

where $f(a)$ and $f(b)$ are the values of the polynomial $f(z)$ at $z = a$ and $z = b$, calculated by one of the above-described methods, where $f(a)$ and $f(b)$ should be substituted with their signs (in the given case they have opposing signs).

Finding complex roots. After all real roots of the equation have been found, for example z_1, z_2 and z_3, we divide our polynomial (39.2) in the following manner:

$$\frac{f(z)}{(z - z_1)(z - z_2)(z - z_3)} = \varphi(z). \qquad (39.9)$$

In dividing the polynomial (39.2) by $(z - z_1)$ the coefficients of the required quotient

$$b_0 z^{n-1} + b_1 z^{n-2} + \ldots + b_{n-2} z + b_{n-1}$$

will be

$$\left. \begin{array}{l} b_0 = a_0, \\ b_i = a_i + z_1 b_{i-1} \quad (i = 1, 2, \ldots, n-1). \end{array} \right\} \qquad (39.10)$$

Here the remainder

$$r_1 = a_n + z_1 b_{n-1}$$

should vanish (this serves to check the calculations).

Further, after division by $(z - z_2)$ we obtain the quotient

$$c_0 z^{n-2} + c_1 z^{n-3} + \ldots + c_{n-3} z + c_{n-2},$$

where

$$\left. \begin{array}{l} c_0 = b_0, \\ c_i = b_i + z_2 c_{i-1} \quad (i = 1, 2, \ldots, n-2) \end{array} \right\} \qquad (39.11)$$

and the remainder

$$r_2 = b_{n-1} + z_2 c_{n-2} = 0.$$

Division by $(z - z_3)$ is carried out similarly.

The polynomial $\varphi(z)$ (39.9) obtained in this way has a degree lower than the initial $f(z)$ by the number of previously found real roots. Since in this new polynomial $\varphi(z)$ there are no longer any real roots, it has necessarily an even degree.

In the simplest case when $\varphi(z)$ is a second-degree polynomial, its roots are calculated by simple solution of the quadratic equation

$$\varphi(z) = 0 .$$

The roots of this equation will be the required complex roots of equation (39.1).

If $\varphi(z)$ is a fourth-degree polynomial, to calculate its roots we may proceed in the following manner. Let $\varphi(z)$ have form

$$\varphi(z) = z^4 + az^3 + bz^2 + cz + d \qquad (39.12)$$

(if the coefficient of z^4 is not equal to unity it may be divided through the polynomial, which does not change the roots). To find its roots we first construct the auxiliary cubic equation

$$y^3 - by^2 - (ac - 4d)y - [(a^2 - 4b)d + c^2] = 0 . \qquad (39.13)$$

We then find any real root of this equation y_1 by the rule for finding the real roots described above. We then calculate the auxiliary quantities A and B from the formulae

$$
\left.
\begin{aligned}
A^2 &= \frac{a^2}{4} - b + y_1 , \\[1em]
B^2 &= \frac{y_1^2}{4} - d , \\[1em]
2AB &= \frac{ay}{2} - c .
\end{aligned}
\right\}
\qquad (39.14)
$$

If a minus sign is obtained in the last of these formulae, the numbers A and B must be given opposite signs, while if plus, the same signs (it is immaterial which).

Calculating A and B, we construct two quadratic equations:

$$
\left.
\begin{aligned}
z^2 + \left(\frac{a}{2} + A\right)z + \frac{y_1}{2} + B &= 0 , \\[1em]
z^2 + \left(\frac{a}{2} - A\right)z + \frac{y_1}{2} - B &= 0 ,
\end{aligned}
\right\}
\qquad (39.15)
$$

solving which, we find all the complex roots of the polynomial $\varphi(z)$ and therefore of the initial equation (39.1) or the polynomial (39.2).

For approximate calculation of the roots of the equation with pairs of complex roots far from each other, which occurs, for example, in the equation of motion of an aircraft, there is a special procedure described in the book of V. S. Vedrov (Reference 17). The numerical method developed by O. M. Kryzhanovskii is also of interest.

Simple numerical method of finding all roots of an algebraic equation (or polynomial). Let there be given an equation of arbitrary degree (39.1) or polynomial (39.2), i.e. the numerical values of all coefficients are given. It is required to find all their real and complex roots.

From the form of the last three members of the given polynomial, i.e.

$$a_{n-2}z^2 + a_{n-1}z + a_n ,$$

we estimate roughly if this corresponds to a quadratic equation with real or with complex roots. If the former, we begin by calculating one real root of the given polynomial while if the second, a pair of roots. All coefficients of the polynomial will be considered for concreteness positive, which is most important for the theory of automatic regulation.

The process of calculating the real root z_1 is as follows. Let us take the first approximation for it in the form

$$z_1' = - \frac{a_n}{a_{n-1}}$$

and divide* the polynomial (39.2) by $(z - z_1')$ until a binomial

$$b_{n-1}z + a_n ,$$

is obtained which is not divisible without remainder by $(z - z_1')$. Then as the second approximation for the required root we take the value

$$z_1'' = - \frac{a_n}{b_{n-1}}$$

and again divide the polynomial (39.2) by $(z - z_1'')$ until a remainder is obtained in the form

$$c_{n-1}z + a_n .$$

The third approximation of the root is

$$z_1''' = - \frac{a_n}{c_{n-1}}$$

with subsequent division of the polynomial (39.2) by $(z - z_1''')$. This process usually converges very rapidly to the required value of the root. In practice two divisions are sometimes satisfactory. But there are also cases where it diverges.

---

* This division may be carried out actually either by the method of elementary algebra or by formula (39.10).

To find the remaining roots of the same polynomial we proceed exactly in the same manner with the new polynomial of $(n-1)$st degree, obtained from the last division by $(z-z_1)$, where z_1 is the final stable value of the first real root.

The process of calculating a pair of roots is completely analogous to the above, where as the first approximation we assume that the required pair of roots corresponds to the trinomial

$$z^2 + \frac{a_{n-1}}{a_{n-2}}z + \frac{a_n}{a_{n-2}},$$

and the given polynomial (39.2) is divided by it until the trinomial

$$b_{n-2}z^2 + b_{n-1}z + a_n,$$

is obtained not divisible without remainder. We then take the second approximation in the form

$$z^2 + \frac{b_{n-1}}{b_{n-2}}z + \frac{a_n}{b_{n-2}}$$

and again divide the initial polynomial (39.2) by it to the remainder

$$c_{n-2}z^2 + c_{n-1}z + a_n.$$

The third approximation will be

$$z^2 + \frac{c_{n-1}}{c_{n-2}}z + \frac{a_n}{c_{n-2}},$$

by which (39.2) is again divided. This process also converges fairly rapidly. Obtaining a satisfactory approximation in the form of some trinomial

$$z^2 + bz + c, \tag{39.16}$$

we find the required pair of roots of the given polynomial (39.2) as the solution of the quadratic equation corresponding to the trinomial (39.16), i.e.

$$z_{1,2} = -\frac{b}{2} \pm \sqrt{\frac{b^2}{4} - c},$$

where the roots may be either complex or real.

To obtain the next roots we proceed in the same manner with the new polynomial of $(n-2)$nd-degree, obtained by division of (39.2) by the trinomial (39.16). This polynomial already exists as a result of the last division by the above-described process of calculation.

When all roots have been found it is useful to carry out an elementary check of the calculation based on the properties of the products and sums of all the roots of the equation, namely:

$$z_1 z_2 \dots z_n = (-1)^n \frac{a_n}{a_0},$$

$$z_1 + z_2 + \dots + z_n = -\frac{a_1}{a_0}.$$

Let us consider a numerical example to illustrate the above method for determining the real and complex roots. A sixth-degree equation is given:

$$z^6 + 25 \cdot 00z^5 + 292 \cdot 3z^4 + 337 \cdot 5z^3 + 338 \cdot 4z^2 + 175 \cdot 9z + 7 \cdot 360 = 0 \ .$$

We shall seek the values of the roots to three significant figures. We take the first approximation

$$z_1' = -\frac{7 \cdot 360}{175 \cdot 9} = -0 \cdot 04183 \ .$$

Dividing the left-hand side of the equation by $z + 0 \cdot 04183$, we obtain

$$z^5 + 24 \cdot 96z^4 + 291 \cdot 3z^3 + 325 \cdot 3z^2 + 324 \cdot 8z + \ldots$$

with the binomial remainder

$$162 \cdot 3z + 7 \cdot 360 \ .$$

We take the second approximation

$$z_1'' = -\frac{7 \cdot 360}{162 \cdot 3} = -0 \cdot 0453 \ .$$

Similarly dividing the left-hand side of the initial equation by $(z + 0 \cdot 0453)$ we obtain the new remainder

$$161 \cdot 3z + 7 \cdot 360 \ .$$

The third approximation is therefore

$$z_1''' = -\frac{7 \cdot 360}{161 \cdot 3} = -0 \cdot 0456 \ ,$$

which we take as the value of the required real root since the rapid convergence is here obvious and the fourth approximation will give practically the same value for z_1.

To determine the following roots we start from the polynomial obtained in the last division, which in this case has the form

$$z^5 + 24 \cdot 96z^4 + 291 \cdot 2z^3 + 324 \cdot 3z^2 + 323 \cdot 8z + 161 \cdot 3 \ .$$

The first approximation is

$$z_2' = -\frac{161 \cdot 3}{323 \cdot 8} = -0 \cdot 498 \ .$$

Division of the last polynomial by $(z + 0 \cdot 498)$ gives as the remainder

$$231 \cdot 5z + 161 \cdot 3 \ .$$

Therefore the second approximation will be

$$z_2'' = -\frac{161.3}{231.5} = -0.697 \ .$$

Dividing the same fifth-degree polynomial by $(z+0.697)$ we obtain the remainder

$$231.0z + 161.3 .$$

The third approximation

$$z_2''' = -\frac{161.3}{231.0} = -0.698 ,$$

which we take as the value of the second real root of the initial equation (a trial of the fourth approximation gives the same value, -0.698).

As a result of the last division the polynomial

$$z^4 + 24.26z^3 + 274.3z^2 + 132.8z + 231.0$$

is obtained. Here we note that the last three terms correspond to a quadratic equation with complex roots. Therefore as the first approximation we take the trinomial

$$z^2 + \frac{132.8}{274.3}z + \frac{231.0}{274.3} = z^2 + 0.484z + 0.842 .$$

We divide

$$
\begin{array}{ll}
z^4 + 24.26z^3\ \ + 274.3z^2\ \ + 132.8z + 231.0 & \underline{\ z^2 +\ \ 0.484z + 0.842\ } \\
\underline{z^4 +\ \ 0.484z^3 +\ \ \ 0.842z^2} & \ z^2 + 23.77z + ... \\
\ \ \ \ \ \ 23.77z^3\ \ + 273.4z^2\ \ \ + 132.8z & \\
\ \ \ \ \ \ \underline{23.77z^3 +\ \ \ 11.51z^2 +\ \ 20.02z} & \\
\ \ \ \ \ \ \ \ \ \ \ \ \ \ \ 261.9z^2\ \ + 112.8z + 231.0 . &
\end{array}
$$

We take the second approximation

$$z^2 + \frac{112.8}{261.9}z + \frac{231.0}{261.9} = z^2 + 0.431z + 0.881 .$$

We divide the fourth-degree polynomial by this, which gives the remainder

$$263.1z^2 + 111.8z + 231.0 .$$

The third approximation from this will be

$$z^2 + 0.425z + 0.877 . \tag{39.17}$$

This may already be taken as the required second-degree equation, since division by it gives a remainder close to the previous one (i.e. the process converges rapidly). As a result of this division the trinomial

$$z^2 + 23.83z + 263.3 \tag{39.18}$$

is obtained.

Consequently, the third and fourth roots of the sixth-degree initial equation are found by solving the quadratic equation corresponding to the trinomial (39.17), i.e.

$$z_{3,4} = -0.213 \pm i0.920 ,$$

and the last, fifth and sixth roots from the trinomial (39.18) are

$$z_{5,6} = -11 \cdot 92 \pm i 11 \cdot 01 \ .$$

All six roots of this sixth-degree equation have thus been calculated very simply. The sum and product of all roots gives

$$-0 \cdot 0456 - 0 \cdot 698 - 2 \cdot 0 \cdot 213 - 2 \cdot 11 \cdot 92 = -25 \cdot 01;$$
$$(-0 \cdot 0456)(-0 \cdot 698)(0 \cdot 213^2 + 0 \cdot 920^2)(11 \cdot 92^2 + 11 \cdot 01^2) = 7 \cdot 43;$$

and from the original sixth-degree equation they should be equal to $25 \cdot 00$ and $7 \cdot 36$ respectively. This result indicates that the method is sufficiently precise for our purposes.

We have already remarked that this method may sometimes be divergent, but even in these cases it is possible just the same to find the required roots.

Kh. L. Smolitskii proved the following theorems on the convergence of the given numerical method for finding the roots. Let there be calculated a real root z_1 of the polynomial $f(z)$. We put

$$b = \frac{a_n}{z_1}, \qquad q(z) = 1 - \frac{f(z)}{bz + a_n} \ .$$

If $|q(z_1)| < 1$, the calculation converges, if $|q(z)| > 1$, it diverges. When a pair of roots is calculated (including complex), we put

$$q(z) = 1 - \frac{f(z)}{bz^2 + cz + a_n},$$

where $bz^2 + cz + a_n$ is a trinomial corresponding to the two roots z_1 and z_2. If $|q(z_1)| < 1$ and $|q(z_2)| < 1$, the calculation converges while if $|q(z_1)| > 1$ or $|q(z_2)| > 1$ it diverges. Unfortunately both these theorems express the convergence condition in terms of the value of the required root.

D. A. Bashkirov gives the following recommendations to improve the convergence of calculation in those individual cases where it is poor or the calculation even diverges.

1. If in finding the real roots the sequence of values

$$z_1' = -\frac{a_n}{a_{n-1}}, \quad z_1'' = -\frac{a_n}{b_{n-1}}, \quad z_1''' = -\frac{a_n}{c_{n-1}}, \ \dots \qquad (39.19)$$

does not vary monotonically but "oscillates", a new approximate value of the root should be taken (for the next division) equal to the half-sum of the previous value and that which is obtained from the remainder, i.e. it is necessary to take

$$z_1''' = \frac{1}{2}\left(z_1'' - \frac{a_n}{c_{n-1}}\right), \ \dots$$

2. If in finding a real root the values (39.19), although monotonic, vary very slowly, as the next approximation it is necessary to take

$$z_1''' = \frac{z_1'' r' - z_1' r''}{r' - r''},$$

where r' and r'' are the remainders of the complete division of the polynomial by $z - z_1'$ and by $z - z_1''$ respectively.

3. If the calculation converges poorly or diverges in determination of complex roots, it is necessary to transform the given polynomial. In many cases it is sufficient in place of polynomial (39.2) to take the polynomial

$$a_0 + a_1 q + \ldots + a_{n-1} q^{n-1} + a_n q^n,$$

obtained by the substitution $z = 1/q$, and to calculate its roots $q_1, q_2, \ldots, q_n$. The roots of the original polynomial will be the inverse magnitudes. For example, for the polynomial

$$z^4 + 6z^3 + 31z^2 + 66z + 130$$

the calculation diverges. We write the new polynomial

$$130 q^4 + 66 q^3 + 31 q^2 + 6q + 1,$$

calculate its roots, and obtain

$$z_{1,2} = \frac{1}{q_{1,2}} = -1 \pm i3; \quad z_{3,4} = \frac{1}{q_{3,4}} = -2 \pm i3.$$

In other cases it is useful to transform the equation by shifting the imaginary axis in the root plane to the right. This is done according to formulae (37.6) and (37.7) where it is necessary to substitute $-\lambda$ by λ. It is also possible to employ other transformations, which provide a definite relation between the roots of the given and the new polynomial.

40. Choice of system parameters from the locations of all roots of the characteristic equation

We shall consider here two methods based on a knowledge of all roots of the characteristic equation.

Method of assignment of all roots. One of the possible methods of defining the parameters of the system from the locations of all roots of the characteristic equation was proposed by Z. Sh. Blokh (Reference 27). Recommendations concerning the assignment of the roots themselves were not considered in this method. We shall explain it by a single example, since this method has not been developed in general form.

Let there be given the structural diagram of the system shown in Fig. 181, where the element equations have the form

1) $(T_1 p + 1) x_1 = -k_1 x_5$,
2) $(T_2 p + 1) x_2 = k_2 (x_1 - x_6)$,
3) $(T_3 p + 1) x_3 = k_3 x_2$,
4) $(T_4 p + 1) x_4 = k_4 x_3$,
5) $T_5 p x_5 = x_4$,
6) $(T_6 p + 1) x_6 = k_6 p x_4$.

Since the open network is here a particular case of the circuit of Fig. 110a, where $m = 5$, $k = 1$, $1 = 4$, from (21.10) and (20.11)

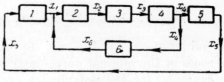

FIG. 181

we obtain the left-hand part $L(p)$ of the differential equation of the closed system in the form

$$L(p) = (T_1 p + 1) T_5 p [(T_2 p + 1)(T_3 p + 1)(T_4 p + 1)(T_6 p + 1) + \\ + k_2 k_3 k_4 k_6 p] + k_1 k_2 k_3 k_4 (T_6 p + 1) .$$

Consequently, the characteristic equation of the system (after division by $T_1 T_2 T_3 T_4 T_5 T_6$) will be

$$\left(z + \frac{1}{T_1}\right) z \left[\left(z + \frac{1}{T_2}\right)\left(z + \frac{1}{T_3}\right)\left(z + \frac{1}{T_4}\right)\left(z + \frac{1}{T_6}\right) + \frac{k_2 k_3 k_4 k_6}{T_2 T_3 T_4 T_6} z\right] + \\ + \frac{k_1 k_2 k_3 k_4}{T_1 T_2 T_3 T_4 T_5}\left(z + \frac{1}{T_6}\right) = 0 , \quad (40.1)$$

where all parameters $(k_i,\ T_i)$ are so far considered unknown.

This is a sixth-degree equation. Let all six roots $z_1, z_2, ..., z_6$, which the given system should have be given.

Then from well-known formulae expressing the relations between the roots and the coefficients of the equation

$$z^6 + a_1 z^5 + ... + a_5 z + a_6 = 0 , \quad (40.2)$$

we may calculate

$$\begin{aligned}
a_1 &= -(z_1 + z_2 + ... + z_6) , \\
a_2 &= z_1 z_2 + z_1 z_3 + ... + z_5 z_6 , \\
a_3 &= -(z_1 z_2 z_3 + z_1 z_2 z_4 + ... + z_4 z_5 z_6) , \\
&.............................. \\
a_6 &= z_1 z_2 ... z_6 .
\end{aligned} \quad (40.3)$$

We construct the function

$$H(z) = L(z) - \frac{k_1 k_2 k_3 k_4}{T_1 T_2 T_3 T_4 T_5}\left(z + \frac{1}{T_6}\right),$$

where $L(z)$ is the left-hand part of equation (40.2) in which all coefficients are calculated from formulae (40.3). Then in contrast to (40.2) the function $H(z)$ will have the form

$$H(z) = z^6 + a_1 z^5 + a_2 z^4 + a_3 z^3 + a_4 z^2 + a_5' z + a_6', \qquad (40.4)$$

where a_1, a_2, a_3, a_4 are as before and

$$a_5' = a_5 - \frac{k_1 k_2 k_3 k_4}{T_1 T_2 T_3 T_4 T_5}, \qquad a_6' = a_6 - \frac{k_1 k_2 k_3 k_4}{T_1 T_2 T_3 T_4 T_5 T_6}. \qquad (40.5)$$

Since (40.2) is a second expression for the same characteristic equation (40.1), the function $H(z)$ will correspond to the left-hand side of (40.1) without the last term.

Element 1 (Fig. 181) will be considered the regulated object and its parameters k_1 and T_1 given numbers.

Let us divide $H(z)$ by the first two factors of (40.1), i.e. by

$$\left(z + \frac{1}{T_1}\right) z .$$

We obtain the quotient

$$G(z) = z^4 + b_1 z^3 + b_2 z^2 + b_3 z + b_4 , \qquad (40.6)$$

where from (39.10) we have

$$b_i = a_i - \frac{1}{T_1} b_{i-1} \qquad (i = 1, 2, 3, 4, \ b_0 = 1)$$

and the remainder

$$r = \left(a_5' - \frac{1}{T_1} b_4\right) z + a_6' . \qquad (40.7)$$

Consequently

$$H(z) = \left(z + \frac{1}{T_1}\right) z G(z) + r .$$

In order for this expression for $H(z)$ actually to correspond, as is required above, to the left-hand side of equation (40.1) without the last term, the following equalities

$$G(z) = \left(z + \frac{1}{T_2}\right)\left(z + \frac{1}{T_3}\right)\left(z + \frac{1}{T_4}\right)\left(z + \frac{1}{T_6}\right) + \frac{k_2 k_3 k_4 k_6}{T_2 T_3 T_4 T_6} z , \qquad (40.8)$$

$$r = 0 . \qquad (40.9)$$

should be valid.

24

Since this should be satisfied for arbitrary z, from (40.7) we obtain two equations

$$a_6' = 0 \, ,$$

$$a_5' - \frac{1}{T_1} a_4 = 0 \, .$$

Substituting here (40.5) we solve these equations in the form

$$\frac{k_1 k_2 k_3 k_4}{T_1 T_2 T_3 T_4 T_5} = a_5 - \frac{1}{T_1} a_4 \, , \qquad (40.10)$$

$$T_6 = \frac{T_1 a_5 - a_4}{T_1 a_6} \, , \qquad (40.11)$$

where T_1, a_6, a_5, a_4 are known. Consequently, the time constant T_6 of the transient feedback 6 (Fig. 181) has been found.

We proceed further with the polynomial $G(z)$ (see formulae (40.6) and (40.8)) exactly in the same way as before with (40.2) and (40.1), namely, we calculate from (40.6) the quantity

$$\frac{k_2 k_3 k_4 k_6}{T_2 T_3 T_4 T_6} z \, ,$$

we divide the result by $(z + 1/T_6)$, employing formula (39.10). The remainder r is equated to zero. From it, assigning k_6, we find the quantity

$$\frac{k_2 k_3 k_4}{T_2 T_3 T_4} \, , \qquad (40.12)$$

and from it and (40.10) we calculate T_5. The quotient of this division, from (40.8), must be equated to the expression

$$\left(z + \frac{1}{T_2} \right) \left(z + \frac{1}{T_3} \right) \left(z + \frac{1}{T_4} \right) .$$

This signifies that having found the roots of the given quotient, of third degree, we should equate them to $(-1/T_2)$, $(-1/T_3)$, $(-1/T_4)$ from which we find T_2, T_3, T_4.

Further, since (40.12) is known, it is possible to define k_2, k_3, k_4 as well. Thus, all parameters of the system will be found.

It should be noted that this method cannot always give a good result since the majority of system parameters are rigorously defined here from a given distribution of roots. However in actual systems only a small number of parameters may be varied in wide limits. As a result of this, and even from the point of view of the quality of the response, there is hardly any practical significance in a rigid assignment of all roots of the characteristic equation of the system.

Numerical method. Application of the above method may lead to very complicated calculations. The main drawback consists in that rigid requirements are placed on the roots of the characteristic equation in this method, which cannot always be realised in practice. The problem is that, widely varying the parameters and structure of the regulator (with physical limits), we are still not able to vary the roots of the characteristic equation arbitrarily as a whole, since they also depend on the given dynamic properties of the regulated object.

This last circumstance may be the cause for repeating the calculations in the above method many times, with differing distributions of the roots. This may occur in a number of cases even when using the methods described in Section 38.

Therefore, considering the simple numerical method of finding all the roots of a polynomial of given degree, described in Section 39, it is expedient to abandon the preassignment of the roots and to apply the numerical method described below, taking into account in advance the limits of physical realisability of the parameters.

Let there be given a regulated object taking into account the requirements of system stability as a whole and satisfactorily small static and stationary errors of the system, and the structure of the regulator or several possible alternatives noted. For the description of the method to be more specific, we shall refer to the example of an aircraft with autopilot, the equations for which were presented in Section 25.

Let us assume that the parameters of the regulated object (in this example T_1, T_2, k_1, k_2) are given in numerical form and that certain parameters of the regulator (in this example T_3 and T_4) and its remaining parameters must be found (in this example the transfer factors of the autopilot k_ψ, $k_{\dot\psi}$, $k_{\ddot\psi}$, k_{fb}, which correspond to introduction into the regulation function of the first and second derivatives and the presence of an auxiliary stiff feedback). It is required to analyse if it is necessary to introduce all these factors and to select numerical values for the corresponding transfer factors.

In the solution of this problem we shall not start from a preassigned index of quality of root distribution, as before, but rather with the aim of achieving the most favorable values of these indices of those which may actually be obtained in the considered automatic regulation system in various alternative structures and in actually possible ranges of variation of the selected regulator parameters. These possible ranges of variation of the selected regulator parameters are defined from the design considerations and the requirement of sufficiently small static and stationary dynamic errors of the system; we shall assume them here as given.

Let us first consider the simplest alternative structure of the system with choice of a single regulator parameter—in this case, for example, the transfer factor k_ϑ at some numerically given average possible value of $k_{\dot\psi}$ and with $k_{\ddot\psi} = k_{fb} = 0$ (the circuits introducing the second derivative and auxiliary feedback into the system are disconnected). In other systems it is also possible to eliminate the first derivative, putting $k_{\dot\psi} = 0$, but here it should be introduced only because the nature of the equations of the regulated object in accordance with Section 33 make impossible satisfaction of the stability conditions of the system by a circuit with only $k_\vartheta^\cdot$.

Let us construct the characteristic equation of such a system.

$$a_0 z^n + a_1 z^{n-1} + \ldots + a_{n-1} z + a_n = 0 ,$$

where defined numbers and the magnitude of the selected parameter (k_ψ) in symbolic form enter into the coefficients. We take several numerical values of the required parameter (k_ψ) in the physically possible range. For each of them we find by a simple numerical method (Section 39) all the roots of the characteristic equation. As a result we obtain the entire pattern of variation of the roots with variation of the given parameter (k_ψ). This pattern may be illustrated by graphs of root variation.

From these graphs it is possible to select the value of k_ψ corresponding to the most favorable character of root distribution of all those possible for the given structure. At the same time, in dependence on specific technical requirements on the system it is possible to start from any concept of "favorable": the highest degree of stability with widely spaced roots; complexity or realness of the root nearest to the real axis; maximum approximation to the Popov condition (38.21), etc. The last co dition signifies that in the complex roots $z = \alpha \pm i\omega$ it is necessary to obtain the greatest value of the ratio $|\alpha|/\omega$ at the maximum value of $|\alpha|$.

Immediately after this, retaining the adopted optimum value of k_ψ, it is necessary to write the characteristic equation of the system so that the second of the selected parameters ($k_{\dot\psi}$) enter into it in symbolic form. Calculating in the same manner all the roots of the equation for several values of $k_{\dot\psi}$ and finding as a result the influence of this parameter on the root distribution, we take its optimum value (similarly to the above).

This process of choosing two optimum parameters of the regulator is, in essence, a process of successive approximation. In fact, assigning first the quantity $k_{\dot\psi}$ and varying k_ψ, we follow the character of variation of the roots along some straight line AB (Fig. 182a) inside the region of stability in the plane of these parameters. Let the optimum k_ψ correspond to the point C. Then, fixing the corresponding value k_{ψ_c} and varying the quantity $k_{\dot\psi}$, we traverse the line DE (Fig. 182a), establishing as a result a new optimum point F.

In addition to this it would be possible to make the solution more exact, again varying the parameter k_ψ at a new value of $k_{\dot\psi}$, i.e. moving along the line LM (Fig. 182a). This gives some new optimal point N. However in practice this is usually superfluous, firstly, in view of the approximateness of the system equations themselves and, secondly, as a result of the looseness of the concept of optimum root distribution of the characteristic equation.

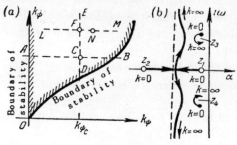

Fig. 182

In the given solution of the problem it is necessary also to take into account that the optimum point F should not be too close to the boundary of stability since from considerations presented in Section 31 it is always necessary to have some stability reserve.

If as a result of the above choice of one or two parameters of the regulator the root distribution at the optimal point $(k_\psi, k_{\dot\psi})$ is nevertheless not such as would be desirable in the investigated automatic regulation system, it is necessary to change the structure of the system (in our example to introduce either $k_{\ddot\psi}$, or k_{fb}).

It is necessary to construct the characteristic equation for the new structure where all the parameters in the coefficients are given numerically except the newly introduced one (for example, $k_{\ddot\psi}$). The values of the remaining regulator parameters $(k_\psi, k_{\dot\psi})$ are taken from the preceding calculation. For several values of the new parameter $(k_{\ddot\psi})$ all roots of the characteristic equation are determined by the simple numerical method (Section 39) and analogously to the above the optimal value of $k_{\ddot\psi}$ is chosen. From the character of the influence of this new parameter on the root distribution it will be evident whether its introduction into the structure has practical significance.

In this way testing the second alternative structure (for example, with introduction of k_{fb}), it is possible to choose the best, taking into account simultaneously the static error and other technical requirements on the system.

We note that when a system is made more complicated by the introduction of additional elements, in calculating the first simple structure it is recommended to choose the optimum values of its parameters, requiring real distributed roots. This provides wider possibilities in calculating the more complicated structures with additional elements. In the final alternative the last regulator parameter should be taken already on the basis of any arbitrary concept of optimal root distribution mentioned above, which it may be desired to have in the calculated system.

In all cases, when choosing the parameters according to the roots of the characteristic equation, it is useful to consider the trajectories traced out by the roots in the complex plane with variation of the system parameters.

Let us consider the following example, due to D. A. Bashkirov. Let there be given the characteristic equation

$$z^4 + 5 \cdot 87 z^3 + 23 \cdot 3 z^2 + 77 \cdot 6 z + 2 \cdot 69 + k(z^2 + 1 \cdot 254 z + 14 \cdot 5) = 0 \ .$$

It is required to determine the character of variation of the roots of this equation with variation of the parameter k in the limits from 0 to ∞. Assigning various numerical values to k, we calculate the roots by the numerical methods described in Section 39. The results of calculation are given in the table.

k	z_1	z_2	z_3	z_4
0	$-0 \cdot 035$	$-4 \cdot 50$	$-0 \cdot 670 \pm i4 \cdot 07$	
5	$-1 \cdot 44$	$-2 \cdot 98$	$-0 \cdot 727 \pm i4 \cdot 14$	
5·8	$-2 \cdot 20$	$i0 \cdot 30$	$-0 \cdot 740 \pm i4 \cdot 15$	
10	$-2 \cdot 10$	$i1 \cdot 93$	$-0 \cdot 832 \pm i4 \cdot 18$	
20	$-1 \cdot 54$	$i3 \cdot 47$	$-1 \cdot 397 \pm i4 \cdot 28$	
40	$-2 \cdot 11$	$i6 \cdot 19$	$-0 \cdot 821 \pm i3 \cdot 60$	
100	$-2 \cdot 26$	$i9 \cdot 89$	$-0 \cdot 675 \pm i3 \cdot 69$	
200	$-2 \cdot 29$	$i14 \cdot 1$	$-0 \cdot 645 \pm i3 \cdot 73$	
∞	$-2 \cdot 31$	$i\infty$	$-0 \cdot 627 \pm i3 \cdot 76$	

From the table it is evident that the system is stable with any positive value of k. The results presented in the table are represented in Fig. 182b from which the entire process of variation of the roots of the characteristic equation with variation of the parameter k from 0 to ∞ is clearly seen. With $k = 0$ the roots z_1 and z_2 are real while z_3 and z_4 are complex. With increase in the parameter k the real roots z_1 and z_2 approach each other; at some value k ($\sim 5 \cdot 7$) they merge; with further increase of k the roots z_1 and z_2 again diverge, but now as complex. The roots z_3 and z_4 in the entire range of variation of k $(0 \leqslant k \leqslant \infty)$ vary little and remain always complex.

Certain recommendations for choosing desirable root distributions of the characteristic equation as the initial material for selecting the system parameters are also presented in Section 43.

Knowing all roots of the characteristic equation, it is then necessary to plot the curves of the regulation process by any of the methods of part V for the optimal point, and perhaps for certain others. This permits a better founded choice of definite values of the regulator parameters and taking into account of the right-hand side of the differential equation of the closed system.

CHAPTER X

APPROXIMATE CRITERIA OF TRANSIENT QUALITY IN LINEAR SYSTEMS TAKING INTO ACCOUNT THE RIGHT-HAND SIDE OF THE EQUATION OF THE CLOSED SYSTEM

41. Integral criteria of transient quality

In the preceding chapter we have considered approximate criteria of the quality of the transient response based on the distribution of roots of the characteristic equation. These methods of analysis and synthesis of an automatic regulation system already yield very much. However at the start of calculation they do not take into account the form of the operational polynomial in the right-hand side of the differential equation of the closed system, which has a very substantial influence on the shape of the transient response; this right-hand side has been taken into account only at the end of the calculation in plotting the transient curve to verify the quality of the results obtained.

In the present chapter methods of investigation are considered which take into account not only the characteristic equation but the operational polynomial in the right-hand side of the differential equation of the closed system (i.e. the poles and the zeros of the transfer function) from the very beginning. Let us turn first of all to integral criteria of the transient quality, which have the purpose of relating two important aspects of the transient quality in a single criterion: the rate of attenuation and the magnitude of deviation of the regulated quantity during the transient (without giving one or the other individually). Such criteria in the theory of oscillation have been developed by L. I. Mandel'shtam, A. A. Kharkevich, N. D. Moiseev, B. V. Bulgakov, and others, and in the theory of regulation by V. S. Kulebakin, A. A. Krasovskii and A. A. Fel'dbaum.

For a monotonic process the area under the transient curve, termed the regulation area (Fig. 183a), could serve as the integral criterion of the quality. This area is the smaller, the smaller the maximum deviation x_{max} and the more intense the attenuation. The regulation area is expressed by the integral

$$\int_0^\infty x\,dt \qquad (x = x_r - x_r^0),\qquad\qquad (41.1)$$

where x is the deviation of the regulated quantity x_r from its value x_r^0 in the new steady-state. For stable linear systems $(x \to 0$ as $t \to \infty)$ this integral has a finite value. An index of system quality will be the minimum of the integral (41.1).

It is difficult, however, to determine in advance if the process is monotonic or not (see Section 37) and it is not always necessary to try for this, but for an oscillatory transient response the criterion (41.1) is not suitable since in this case the areas below the curve are added algebraically (Fig. 183b) and a minimum of the integral (41.1) may be obtained, for example, with the oscillatory process close to free harmonic oscillations, which is of course inadmissible, rather than for rapid attenuation.

A second integral criterion has therefore been proposed

$$\int_0^\infty |x|\,dt,\qquad\qquad (41.2)$$

i.e. the sum of absolute values of all areas under the transient response curve. But it has been found that its calculation from the equation coefficients is difficult.

Integral square criterion. In the light of the above it is expedient to go over to an integral square criterion, sometimes turned the "quadratic area" of regulation:

$$I = \int_0^\infty x^2\,dt \qquad (x = x_p - x_p^0),\qquad\qquad (41.3)$$

which is independent of the sign of the deviation and thus of the division of transient processes into monotonic and oscillatory.

Let in some automatic regulation system an external perturbation f (load or other) change discontinuously. In a static system a stepwise change of the steady-state value of the regulated quantity x_r (Fig. 42) will correspond to this. In an astatic system the steady-state value of the regulated quantity remains as before $(x_r^0 = x_r^{00})$.

Similarly with stepwise change of regulator adjustment y (input command in servomechanism) we will have the case of Fig. 42. The transient may have arbitrary form.

The quantity I (41.3) will be the smaller, the smaller is the sum of hatched areas in Fig. 42 or Fig. 183 (taken for the squares of the ordinates), i.e. the better the transient approximates to an ideal step of the regulated quantity immediately after the step in the load or the adjustment. Below we shall see that this estimate is not always the best, but meanwhile we shall consider it more closely.

We note that estimate (41.3) is also termed the quadratic dynamic error of the regulator. It may be written in dimensionless form:

$$I_0 = \frac{\int\limits_0^\infty x^2 dt}{h^2 \sqrt[n]{\dfrac{a_0}{a_n}}} = \frac{I}{h^2 \sqrt[n]{\dfrac{a_0}{a_n}}} , \qquad (41.4)$$

where $x = x(t)$ denotes the deviation of the regulated quantity in the transient from its value x_r^0 in the new steady-state (Fig. 42), h is

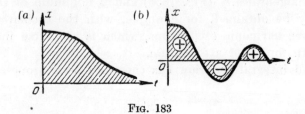

Fig. 183

some quantity having the dimensions of the regulated quantity (for example, the static deviation $x_r^0 - x_r^{00}$), a_0 and a_n are the first and last coefficients of the characteristic equation of the given system:

$$a_0 z^n + a_1 z^{n-1} + \ldots + a_{n-1}z + a_n = 0 , \qquad (41.5)$$

where the quantity $\sqrt{a_0/a_n}$ has the dimensions of time, as is evident from comparison of the dimensions of the corresponding terms of the differential equation of the system.

Let us consider one of the possible methods of calculating the quadratic integral estimate (41.3) with stepwise external force.

In general form the differential equation of an automatic regulation system (in symbolic operational notation), from (5.7), has the form

$$L(p)x_r = S(p)f(t) + N(p)y(t) , \qquad (41.6)$$

where x_r is the regulated quantity or its deviation, $f(t)$ is the external perturbation, for example in the form of a load variation, $y(t)$ is the external input force, for example adjustment of the regulator or servomechanism control point adjuster. The degrees of the polynomials $S(p)$ and $N(p)$ are always lower than $L(p)$ but their degrees may also be equal (for example, in formulae (20.21) and (24.39)).

Equation (41.6) when expanded has the form (5.6). Here, however, we shall not simultaneously vary f and y. Let the transient be caused by a unit step $1(t)$ (see Section 6) or a function f with $y = $ const, or a function y with $f = $ const. Then the equation of the closed system is written in the form

$$(a_0 p^n + a_1 p^{n-1} + \ldots + a_{n-1} p + a_n) x_p$$
$$= (b_0 p^m + b_1 p^{m-1} + \ldots + b_{m-1} p + b_m) 1(t) , \qquad (41.7)$$

where the operational polynomial in the right-hand side corresponds either to $S(p)$, or to $N(p)$. In the first case it is required of the system that it change the value of the regulated quantity as little as possible while in the second, that it follow as rapidly as possible the step $1(t)$ to a definite scale factor.

In this notation with $t < 0$, when $1(t) = 0$, we have $x_r = 0$, i.e. the quantity x_r here (in distinction to Fig. 42) is read from the level of the old steady-state x_r^{00}. In the new steady-state of the system, when $1(t) = 1$, we have for Fig. 42

$$x_r - x_r^{00} = \frac{b_m}{a_n} . \qquad (41.8)$$

For an astatic system when $1(t)$ corresponds to a step in the load $f(t)$, we have $b_m = 0$ and $x_r^0 = x_r^{00}$.

The deviation x of the regulated quantity from the new steady-state in an arbitrary transient response (hatched portion of Fig. 42), entering into formula (41.3), will be

$$x(t) = x_r(t) - \frac{b_m}{a_n} ,$$

where $x(t)$ is a solution of the equation (41.7).

Under the above conditions the formula for calculating the integral square error was obtained by A. A. Krasovskii in 1948; it is given here without proof:

$$I = \int_0^\infty x^2 dt = \frac{1}{2 a_n^2 \Delta} (B_m \Delta_m + B_{m-1} \Delta_{m-1} + \ldots + B_2 \Delta_2 + B_1 \Delta_1 +$$
$$+ B_0 \Delta_0) - \frac{b_m b_{m-1}}{a_n^2} , \qquad (41.9)$$

where Δ is the following nth-order determinant (equal to the older Hurwitz determinant, but written in a somewhat different form)

$$\Delta = \begin{vmatrix} a_n, & -a_{n-2}, & a_{n-4}, & -a_{n-6}, \ldots, \ldots \\ 0, & a_{n-1}, & -a_{n-3}, & a_{n-5}, \ldots, \ldots \\ 0, & -a_n, & a_{n-2}, & -a_{n-4}, \ldots, \ldots \\ 0, & 0, & -a_{n-1}, & a_{n-3}, \ldots, \ldots \\ \cdots\cdots\cdots\cdots\cdots\cdots\cdots\cdots\cdots \\ 0, & 0, & 0, & 0, \ldots, a_1 \end{vmatrix} , \qquad (41.10)$$

and $\Delta (k = m, m-1, ..., 2, 1, 0)$ in formula (41.9) denotes the determinant obtained from (41.10) by substitution in the $(m-k+1)$st column of the column

$$
\left.\begin{matrix} a_{n-1} \\ a_n \\ 0 \\ \ldots \\ 0 \end{matrix}\right| \tag{41.11}
$$

The coefficients $B_m, B_{m-1}, ...$ are calculated from the formulae

$$
\left.\begin{aligned}
B_m \quad &= b_m^2, \\
B_{m-1} &= b_{m-1}^2 - 2b_m b_{m-2}, \\
B_{m-2} &= b_{m-2}^2 - 2b_{m-1}b_{m-3} + 2b_m b_{m-4}, \\
&\cdots\cdots\cdots\cdots\cdots\cdots\cdots\cdots\cdots\cdots\cdots\cdots\cdots \\
B_k \quad &= b_k^2 - 2b_{k+1}b_{k-1} + 2b_{k+2}b_{k-2} + ... + 2(-1)^k b_m b_{2k-m}, \\
&\cdots\cdots\cdots\cdots\cdots\cdots\cdots\cdots\cdots\cdots\cdots\cdots\cdots \\
B_0 \quad &= b_0^2.
\end{aligned}\right\} \tag{41.12}
$$

In the determinant (41.10) all symbols with indices less than zero and greater than n are replaced by zeros while in (41.12) those less than zero and greater than m.

When $m = n$, (41.9) is replaced by the following:

$$
I = \int_0^\infty x^2 dt = \frac{1}{2a_n^2\Delta}(B_n'\Delta_n + B_{n-1}'\Delta_{n-1} + ... + B_2'\Delta_2 + B_1'\Delta_1) - \frac{b_n' b_{n-1}'}{a_n^2},
$$

where

$$
B_n' \quad = b_0^2\left(\frac{b_n}{b_0} - \frac{a_n}{a_0}\right)^2,
$$

$$
B_{n-1}' = b_0^2\left[\left(\frac{b_{n-1}}{b_0} - \frac{a_{n-1}}{a_0}\right)^2 - 2\left(\frac{b_n}{b_0} - \frac{a_n}{a_0}\right)\left(\frac{b_{n-2}}{b_0} - \frac{a_{n-2}}{a_0}\right)\right],
$$

$$
B_{n-2}' = b_0^2\left[\left(\frac{b_{n-2}}{b_0} - \frac{a_{n-2}}{a_0}\right)^2 - 2\left(\frac{b_{n-1}}{b_0} - \frac{a_{n-1}}{a_0}\right)\left(\frac{b_{n-3}}{b_0} - \frac{a_{n-3}}{a_0}\right) +
$$

$$
+ 2\left(\frac{b_n}{b_0} - \frac{a_n}{a_0}\right)\left(\frac{b_{n-4}}{b_0} - \frac{a_{n-4}}{a_0}\right),
$$

$$
\cdots\cdots\cdots\cdots\cdots\cdots\cdots\cdots\cdots\cdots\cdots\cdots
$$

$$
B_1' \quad = b_0^2\left(\frac{b_1}{b_0} - \frac{a_1}{a_0}\right)^2,
$$

$$
b_n' \quad = b_0\left(\frac{b_n}{b_0} - \frac{a_n}{a_0}\right),
$$

$$
b_{n-1}' = b_0\left(\frac{b_{n-1}}{b_0} - \frac{a_{n-1}}{a_0}\right).
$$

In addition, there exists an integral square criterion of the form (41.3) for a transient process caused by a unit impulse $1'(t)$. We denote this criterion by I'.

Its formula is given, for example, in the book of B. V. Bulgakov (Reference 16); it is written in the form

$$I' = \frac{(-1)^m G}{2a_0 \Delta_n} , \tag{41.13}$$

where

$$\Delta_n = \begin{vmatrix} a_1, & a_3, & a_5, & ..., & 0 \\ a_0, & a_2, & a_4, & ..., & 0 \\ 0, & a_1, & a_3, & ..., & 0 \\ \multicolumn{5}{c}{\dotfill} \\ 0, & 0, & 0, & ..., & a_n \end{vmatrix} , \tag{41.14}$$

$$G = \begin{vmatrix} g_0, & g_1, & g_2, & ..., & g_{n-1} \\ a_0, & a_2, & a_4, & ..., & 0 \\ 0, & a_1, & a_3, & ..., & 0 \\ \multicolumn{5}{c}{\dotfill} \\ 0, & 0, & 0, & ..., & a_n \end{vmatrix} , \tag{41.15}$$

and $a_0, a_1, ..., a_n$ denote the coefficients of the left-hand side of the equation of the given system (41.6) while $g_0, g_1, ..., g_m$ the coefficients of the expression

$$S(p)S(-p) = g_0 p^{2m} + g_1 p^{2(m-1)} + ... + g_{m-1} p^2 + g_m$$

or the expression

$$N(p)N(-p) = g_0 p^{2m} + g_1 p^{2(m-1)} + ... + g_{m-1} p^2 + g_m ,$$

depending on whether the transient follows a unit impulse of the load f or the adjustment y. Here, as before, m denotes the degree of the polynomial $S(p)$ or $N(p)$, respectively. From the determinant (41.15) it is evident that formula (41.13) is appropriate for the case when $m \leqslant n-1$. Here all values of g with indices greater than m are replaced by zeros. The determinant (41.14) is the older Hurwitz determinant.

The criterion for the unit impulse (41.13) is simpler than that for the unit step (41.9) but one of its properties should be remarked. For example, let there be the equation of an nth-order static system with an mth-degree polynomial in the right-hand side and the equation of an astatic system of the same order with an $(m+1)$st-degree polynomial in the right-hand side ($b_{m+1} = 0$). It is easily verified that that for both the systems the expression for the integral estimate (41.13) will be exactly the same. In other words, introduction of the factor p in the right-hand side of the equation of the system does not change the expression for the integral estimate (41.13), which cannot be justified from the point of view of the general requirements on the quality of a transient response or regulation. The criterion (41.9) takes on various expressions for both these systems.

The integral criteria I and I' (or the expressions for the dynamic square errors) are applied to the choice of structure and parameters of automatic regulation systems. The best parameters are those for which the magnitude of I or I' has the minimum value.

It is important that here, in contrast to the methods of Chapter IX, not only the characteristic equation of the system is considered but

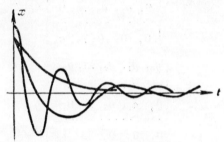

FIG. 184

also the operational polynomial in the right-hand side of the system equation and to some extent even the magnitude of the regulated quantity deviation is estimated simultaneously with the rate of attenuation in the form of the quadratic area under the transient curve.

In Section 44 we shall present one further formula for calculating the integral square criterion (41.3) from the given amplitude-phase characteristic of the closed system.

A defect of integral criteria is that there are no restrictions on the shape of the transient curve. It is found, for example, that three completely different responses as shown in Fig. 184 have the same value for the integral square criterion (41.3). It is frequently found that excessively strong oscillations exist for system parameters chosen for a minimum of this criterion, since the effort to approximate the process to an ideal step-function already noted causes a high velocity process in the transition to the steady-state value $x = 0$.

To improve the integral square criterion the expression has been proposed, where V is some (positive)-definite quadratic form of the quantity x and its derivatives $x^{(i)}$ with respect to time:

$$V(t) = \sum_{i,j=0}^{n-1} a_{ij} x^{(i)} x^{(j)}$$

$$(a_{ij} = a_{ji}),$$

which has been considered in connection with the theory of auto-matic regulation by A. A. Fel'dbaum.

Improved integral criterion. In many cases, to improve that integral square criterion of the transient quality, for a unit step of the ex-ternal force $f(t)$ or $y(t)$ (i.e. to reduce the oscillatory process by limiting the velocity and reducing the "scatter" of the possible forms of transient), it is usually sufficient to apply the following improved integral criterion:

$$I_k = \int_0^\infty (x^2 + T^2 \dot{x}^2)\,dt \,, \tag{41.16}$$

where x is the deviation of the regulated quantity from the new steady-state value and T is a preassigned time constant, the signific-ance of which is explained below.

While the minimum of the ordinary integral criterion (41.3) signifies approximation of the transient curve to an ideal step,

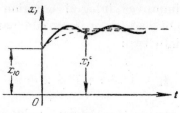

FIG. 185

the minimum of the improved integral estimate (41.16) as shown by A. A. Krasovskii corresponds to approximation of the response to an exponential. The actual response here may be also oscillatory (Fig. 185), but with small overshoot.

In essence, we transform expression (41.16)

$$I_k = \int_0^\infty (x^2 + T^2 \dot{x}^2)\,dt = \int_0^\infty (x + T\dot{x})^2\,dt - 2T \int_0^\infty x\dot{x}\,dt \,.$$

But taking into account Fig. 42 and (41.8) we have

$$2 \int_0^\infty x\dot{x}\,dt = x^2 \Big|_{t=0}^{t=\infty} = -(x_r^0 - x_r^{00})^2 = -\left(\frac{b_m}{a_n}\right)^2 .$$

Therefore

$$I_k = \int_0^\infty (x + T\dot{x})^2\,dt + T\left(\frac{b_m}{a_n}\right)^2 . \tag{41.17}$$

The lowest bound of the minimum I_k is consequently defined from the condition $x + T\dot{x} = 0$, from which

$$x = x_0 e^{-\frac{t}{T}} \quad \text{or} \quad x_r = x_r^0 - (x_r^0 - x_r^{00})e^{-\frac{t}{T}} ;$$

this corresponds to the broken-line curve in Fig. 185. In reality it is not possible in an arbitrary system to obtain zero value of integrand (41.17) and the transient curve will be somewhat different (for example, the full-line curve in Fig. 185).

It is now clear how the time constant T entering into (41.16) should be assigned. If speed is important and oscillations are admissible (or even necessary), the value of T is taken smaller. If monotonicity and smoothness of the process is important, it is taken greater.

In dimensionless form the improved criterion (41.16) may be represented, by analogy to (41.4), in the following manner:

$$I_{k0} = \frac{\int_0^\infty (x^2 + T^2 \dot{x}^2)\, dt}{h^2 \sqrt[n]{\frac{a_0}{a_n}}} = \frac{I_k}{h^2 \sqrt[n]{\frac{a_0}{a_n}}} . \tag{41.18}$$

To calculate the improved integral criterion I_k for a transient caused by a unit step of load $f(t)$ or input command $y(t)$, we separate the integral (41.16) into two:

$$I_k = \int_0^\infty x^2\, dt + T^2 \int_0^\infty \dot{x}^2\, dt .$$

The first of these represents the previous value of y, which is calculated according to formula (41.9). To calculate the second integral, it is necessary to write the differential equation for $\dot{x}$. Differentiating (41.7) and noting that $\dot{x} = \dot{x}$, we obtain

$$(a_0 p^n + a_1 p^{n-1} + \ldots + a_{n-1} p + a_n)\dot{x}$$
$$= (b_0 p^{m+1} + b_1 p^m + \ldots + b_{m-1} p^2 + b_m p)1(t) . \tag{41.19}$$

Therefore by analogy with (41.9) we find

$$\int_0^\infty \dot{x}^2 dt = \frac{1}{2a_n^2 \Delta}(B_m \Delta_{m-1} + B_{m-1}\Delta_{m-2} + \ldots + B_2 \Delta_1 + B_1 \Delta_0 + B_0 \Delta_{-1}) .$$

The final formula obtained (with $m \leqslant n-2$) is

$$I_k = \int_0^\infty (x^2 + T^2 \dot{x}^2)\, dt = \frac{1}{2a_n^2 \Delta}[B_m \Delta_m + (B_{m-1} + T^2 B_m)\Delta_{m-1} +$$
$$+ (B_{m-2} + T^2 B_{m-1})\Delta_{m-2} + \ldots + (B_1 + T^2 B_2)\Delta_1 +$$
$$+ (B_0 + T^2 B_1)\Delta_0 + T^2 B_0 \Delta_{-1}] - \frac{b_m b_{m-1}}{a_n^2} , \tag{41.20}$$

where we employ the previous notation (41.10), (41.11), (41.12). Only the determinant Δ_{-1} is new here, but it is constructed by the same rule as all the remaining, i.e. in the given case by replacement of the $(m+2)$nd column in the determinant (41.10) by the column (41.11).

But since the determinant (41.10) has a total of n columns, the last determinant in formula (41.20) has significance with the condition $m < n-1$, which in automatic regulation systems is frequently satisfied. In the case when $m = n-1$ it is necessary to apply the same form of the formula to the second integral in the expression I_k, according to (41.19), as for equation (41.7) in the case $m = n$. Consequently, with $m = n-1$ we obtain the formula

$$
I_k = \int_0^\infty (x^2 + T^2\dot{x}^2)\,dt = \frac{1}{2a_n^2\Delta}[(B_m + T^2B_n')\Delta_m +
$$
$$
+ (B_{m-1} + T^2B_{n-1}')\Delta_{m-1} + \ldots + (B_1 + T^2B_2')\Delta_1 +
$$
$$
+ (B_0 + T^2B_1')\Delta_0] - \frac{b_m b_{m-1}}{a_n^2} - T^2\frac{b_0^2 a_{n-1}}{a_0^2 a_n}, \qquad (41.21)
$$

where

$$
B_n' = -\frac{b_0^2 a_n^2}{a_0^2},
$$

$$
B_{n-1}' = b_0^2\left[\left(\frac{b_{n-1}}{b_0} - \frac{a_{n-1}}{a_n}\right)^2 - 2\left(-\frac{a_n}{a_0}\right)\left(\frac{b_{n-2}}{b_0} - \frac{a_{n-2}}{a_n}\right)\right],
$$

$$
B_{n-2} = b_0^2\left[\left(\frac{b_{n-2}}{b_0} - \frac{a_{n-2}}{a_n}\right)^2 - 2\left(\frac{b_{n-1}}{b_0} - \frac{a_{n-1}}{a_n}\right)\left(\frac{b_{n-3}}{b_0} - \frac{a_{n-3}}{a_n}\right) +
$$
$$
+ 2\left(-\frac{a_n}{a_0}\right)\left(\frac{b_{n-4}}{b_0} - \frac{a_{n-4}}{a_0}\right)\right],
$$

$$
\cdots\cdots\cdots\cdots\cdots\cdots\cdots\cdots
$$

$$
B_n' = b_0^2\left(\frac{b_1}{b_0} - \frac{a_1}{a_0}\right)^2.
$$

Similarly, applying formula (41.13), it would be possible as well to calculate the improved integral criterion (41.16) for the disturbance caused by an external unit impulse. Taking into account (41.15) and (41.19), where $1(t)$ must be substituted by $1'(t)$, from (41.13) we obtain

$$
I_k = \frac{(-1)^m G + T^2(-1)^{m+1}(-G)}{2a_0\Delta_n}
$$

or

$$
I_k' = (1 + T^2)I'. \qquad (41.22)
$$

Consequently, the integral criterion in the form (41.13) in essence here remains the same (since introduction of a common factor has no essential significance). This result may be explained by the fact that with impulse input the new steady-state regulated quantity is equal to the old and we are concerned here with the best approximation to the straight line $x = 0$, coinciding with the axis of abscissae, and not to a step as before.

The estimate (41.16) may also be calculated from the preassigned frequency characteristic of the system, for example in those cases where the equations of some elements of the system are unknown or when in general the entire calculation is carried out by frequency methods (see Section 44).

A defect of the above formulae for calculating either I or I_k is their expression in terms of determinants, which are difficult to expand in algebraic form when the characteristic equation is of high degree. In these cases it is possible to use existing special numerical procedures. The determinant Δ (41.10) itself, as the older Hurwitz determinant, in accordance with Section 29 has the form

$$\Delta = \Delta_n = a_3(a_1a_2 - a_0a_3) \quad \text{with} \quad n = 3 , \tag{41.23}$$

$$\Delta = \Delta_n = a_4[a_3(a_1a_2 - a_0a_3) - a_4a_1^2] \quad \text{with} \quad n = 4 , \tag{41.24}$$

$$\Delta = \Delta_n = a_5[(a_1a_2 - a_0a_3)(a_3a_4 - a_2a_5) - (a_1a_4 - a_0a_5)^2] \quad \text{with} \quad n = 5. \tag{41.25}$$

Only the determinant Δ_m is somewhat more complicated to calculate when the first column of Δ (41.10) with a single element a_n is replaced by the column (41.11) with two elements a_{n-1} and a_n and the determinant G with $m = n - 1$. All the remaining determinants are simpler.

Finding the minimum of the integral criterion. Let it be required, starting from the minimum of some integral criterion, to select two arbitrary parameters α an β in the given automatic system. These two parameters enter into the coefficients of the differential equation of the system. From the above formulae we find the expression of the corresponding integral estimate. This expression, if all parameters of the system are given except α and β, has the form

$$I = I(\alpha, \beta) .$$

To determine the values of α and β corresponding to the minimum of I, we calculate the partial derivatives with respect to α and β and equate them to zero. As a result we obtain two equations:

$$\frac{\partial I(\alpha, \beta)}{\partial \alpha} = 0 , \quad \frac{\partial I(\alpha, \beta)}{\partial \beta} = 0 \tag{41.26}$$

with two unknowns α and β. From these the required values of the parameters α and β are found. To verify that this is actually a minimum and not a maximum, it is possible to calculate the value of I for these values of α and β and then for some neighboring values. The value for the latter should be greater. It is possible to proceed similarly in the choice of several parameters with respect to the minimum integral criterion.

As we shall see below, the function $I(\alpha, \beta)$ will not always have a minimum with respect to these parameters. It is then necessary to choose them for the smallest value of the integral criterion I within a region indicated from other considerations.

It is also important to bear in mind that the expression for the integral criterion in terms of selected system parameters in algebraic form may be too complicated in a number of cases to test by formulae (41.26). In these cases it is possible to proceed otherwise: to assign several numerical values for one of the selected parameters (with all the remaining fixed) and to calculate for each of them the value I (or I_k). The result will make clear which values of the given parameter yield I_{min} (for clarity it is possible to plot the graph of I as a function of the selected parameter). It is necessary to proceed analogously also with the other selected parameters of the system.

In concrete calculations it is always necessary to take into account that simultaneously with this choice of parameters it is necessary, firstly, to ensure good static properties of the system and, secondly, to test whether the optimum point is not too close to the boundary of stability, since as shown in Section 31 it is always necessary to have some reserve of stability.

42. Examples of the choice of system parameters with respect to the minimum integral criterion

Let us consider certain examples of application of various forms of integral criteria for the transient quality.

To be able to have a clear opinion of the results obtained by choice of system parameters with respect to the minimum quadratic integral criterion, we take the Vyshnegradskii diagram for the third-order system and plot on it lines of equal values of the dimensionless integral square criterion I_0. We compare the results of the plot with the results of the previous methods for choice of parameters. We also compare the results of applying the integral square criteria, I' and I_k (see Section 41).

We consider three forms of differential equation for a closed third-order automatic system:

$$(a_0 p^3 + a_1 p^2 + a_2 p + a_3)x = b_0 \psi(t) , \qquad (42.1)$$

$$(a_0 p^3 + a_1 p^2 + a_2 p + a_3)x = (b_0 p^2 + b_1 p + b_2)\psi(t) , \qquad (42.2)$$

$$(a_0 p^3 + a_1 p^2 + a_2 p + a_3)x = (b_0 p^2 + b_1 p)\psi(t) , \qquad (42.3)$$

where by $\psi(t)$ is understood either the perturbation $f(t)$ or the input command $y(t)$. Equation (42.3) corresponds to an astatic system.

From the cases considered (42.2) and (42.3) it is possible, if necessary, to obtain in particular the estimate formulae for equations with first-degree polynomials in the right-hand part (with $b_0 = 0$).

Case (42.1). Let us calculate the quadratic integral criterion for the transient caused by a unit step of function $\psi(t)$ from formula (41.9). The determinant Δ will here be (41.23). In equation (42.1) $m = 0$. Therefore in formula (41.9) there will be in parentheses only a single term $B_0 \Delta_0$, not equal to zero, where on the basis of (41.11) we have:

$$\Delta_0 = \begin{vmatrix} a_2, & -a_1, & 0 \\ a_3, & a_2, & -a_0 \\ 0, & -a_3, & a_1 \end{vmatrix} = a_2(a_1 a_2 - a_0 a_3) + a_3 a_1^2 . \qquad (42.4)$$

As a result (41.9) gives

$$I = \frac{b_0^2}{2a_3^2} \left(\frac{a_2}{a_3} + \frac{a_1^2}{a_1 a_2 - a_0 a_3} \right) . \qquad (42.5)$$

This serves for choice of system parameters (entering into coefficients a_0, a_1, a_2, a_3) from the condition of minimum magnitude of the integral square criterion I.

Let us plot the criterion diagram in the Vyshnegradskii parameter plane A, B. From (29.9) we have

$$a_1 = A \sqrt[3]{a_0^2 a_3} , \qquad a_2 = B \sqrt[3]{a_0 a_3^2} .$$

Substituting this in expression (42.5), we obtain

$$I = \frac{b_0^2}{2a_3^2} \sqrt[3]{\frac{a_0}{a_3}} \left(B + \frac{A^2}{AB - 1} \right) . \qquad (42.6)$$

Let us find the dimensionless integral square criterion I_0, defined by formula (41.4), where in place of the quantity h we introduce the static deviation (41.8). Then

$$I_0 = \frac{I}{\dfrac{b_m^2}{a_n^2} \sqrt[n]{\dfrac{a_0}{a_n}}} . \qquad (42.7)$$

In this case ($m = 0, n = 3$) from (42.6) we obtain

$$I_0 = \frac{1}{2} \left(B + \frac{A^2}{AB - 1} \right) . \qquad (42.8)$$

With $I_0 = $ const. this gives in the plane (A, B) the curve

$$A^2 + (AB - 1)(B - 2I_0) = 0 .$$

The curves of constant values of integral square criterion I_0 plotted according to this equation are given in the diagram of Fig. 186 (from the work of A. A. Krasovskii, 1948). Broken lines show the curves taken from the Vyshnegradskii diagram (Fig. 169), indicating

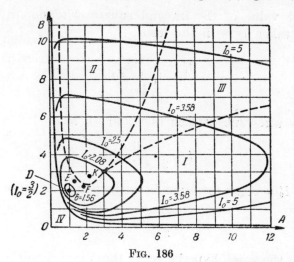

FIG. 186

the regions of monotonic (II, III) and oscillatory (I) responses. The minimum integral criterion is found from formulae (41.26), i.e.

$$\frac{\partial I_0}{\partial A} = 0, \quad \frac{\partial I_0}{\partial B} = 0,$$

which gives

$$AB - 2 = 0, \quad (AB - 1)^2 - A^3 = 0,$$

from which we find $A = 1, B = 2$. Consequently, the minimum integral square estimate $I_0 = 1 \cdot 5$ occurs at the point D (Fig. 186)*.

This point, however, lies too close to the stability boundary, which may not provide the necessary stability reserve (Section 31). Therefore it is better in practice not to take the system parameters exactly at the point D but somewhat to the right and above.

We now calculate for this case (42.1) the integral square criterion I' for the transient caused by the unit impulse $\psi(t)$ from formula (41.13). The determinant Δ_n has the form (41.23). The determinant G for equation (42.1), from (41.15), will be

$$G = \begin{vmatrix} b_0^2, & 0, & 0 \\ a_0, & a_2, & 0 \\ 0, & a_1, & a_3 \end{vmatrix} = b_0^2 a_2 a_3 .$$

---

* This result has significance, however, only in those cases where from (42.7) the quantities b_0, a_3, a_0 remain constant while the selected system parameters enter only into the coefficients a_1 and a_2 of equation (42.1).

Therefore from (41.13) we find

$$I' = \frac{b_0^2 a_2}{2a_0(a_1 a_2 - a_0 a_3)} = \frac{b_0^2}{2a_0^2} \sqrt[3]{\frac{a_0}{a_3}} \frac{B}{AB-1}. \tag{42.9}$$

The relative value of the integral square criterion, in distinction to (42.7) is taken here in the form

$$I_0' = \frac{I'}{\dfrac{b_0^2}{a_0^2} \sqrt[n]{\dfrac{a_0}{a_n}}}. \tag{42.10}$$

In this case after substitution of (42.9) we have

$$I_0' = \frac{B}{2(AB-1)}, \tag{42.11}$$

which with $I_0' = \text{const}$ corresponds in the plane (A, B) to the curves

$$\left(A - \frac{1}{2I_0'}\right)B = 1.$$

These are the same hyperbolae as the Vyshnegradskii hyperbola $AB = 1$, denoting the boundary of stability, but shifted to the

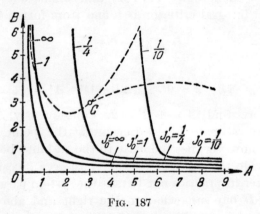

Fig. 187

right by the distance $1/2I'$ (Fig. 187). Consequently there does not exist a minimum of this criterion with finite values of the equation coefficients if the selected parameters of the system enter only into a_1 and a_2. The criterion decreases, i.e. becomes "better", with unlimited increase of parameter A or, which is the same, the coefficient a_1 of the system equation (42.1). From (42.10) this conclusion is invalid if the selected parameters of the system enter into the coefficients b_0, a_0 or a_3 of equation (42.1).

Case (42.2). Here $m = 2$. In (41.9) the determinant Δ_2, in accordance with (41.11), coincides with the determinant Δ_1 of the previous case. Therefore, taking into account (41.12) we have:

$$B_2 \Delta_2 = b_2^2 [a_2(a_1 a_2 - a_0 a_3) + a_3 a_1^2],$$

$$B_1 \Delta_1 = (b_1^2 - 2b_2 b_0) \begin{vmatrix} a_3, & a_2, & 0 \\ 0, & a_3, & -a_0 \\ 0, & 0, & a_1 \end{vmatrix} = (b_1^2 - 2b_2 b_0) a_1 a_3^2,$$

$$B_0 \Delta_0 = b_0^2 \begin{vmatrix} a_3, & -a_1, & a_2 \\ 0, & a_2, & a_3 \\ 0, & -a_3, & 0 \end{vmatrix} = b_0^2 a_3^2,$$

and (41.9) gives the following integral square criterion for the transient caused by a unit step function $\psi(t)$:

$$I = \frac{1}{2a_3^2} \left[\frac{b_2^2 a_2}{a_3} + \frac{b_2^2 a_1^2 + (b_1^2 - 2b_2 b_0) a_1 a_3 + b_0^2 a_3^2}{a_1 a_2 - a_0 a_3} - 2b_2 b_1 \right]. \quad (42.12)$$

In dimensionless form (42.7) we obtain from this

$$I_0 = \frac{1}{2} \left[B + \frac{A^2 + (\gamma_1^2 - \gamma_0) A + \gamma_0^2}{AB - 1} - 2\gamma_1 \right], \quad (42.13)$$

where A and B are the Vyshnegradskii parameters (29.9) and

$$\gamma_1 = \frac{b_1}{b_2} \sqrt[3]{\frac{a_3}{a_0}}, \qquad \gamma_0 = \frac{b_0}{b_2} \sqrt[3]{\frac{a_3^2}{a_0^2}}. \quad (42.14)$$

Let us find the point of minimum of this criterion with respect to the parameters A and B, From formulae (41.26) and (42.13) by calculation it is possible to obtain two equations:

$$B = \frac{1}{A} + F(A), \quad (42.15)$$

$$B = \frac{2A + \gamma_1^2 - \gamma_0}{F(A)}, \quad (42.16)$$

where

$$F(A) = \sqrt{A + \gamma_1^2 - \gamma + \frac{\gamma_0^2}{A}}. \quad (42.17)$$

The intersection of the two curves (42.15) and (42.16) in the plane (A, B) defines the minimum point of the integral criterion I_0 (42.13). To have an approximate idea of its position, we note that the difference between this criterion (42.13) and the criterion (42.8) for the previous case is

$$\frac{(\gamma_1^2 - \gamma_0) A + \gamma_2^0}{2(AB - 1)} - \gamma_1. \quad (42.18)$$

For given γ_1 and γ_2 it decreases with increase of parameters A and B (or, which is the same, a_1 and a_2). The point of minimum of the integral square estimate is thus here shifted from the previous point D (Fig. 186) in a direction opposite to the origin of coordinates, for example to the point F (with constant coefficients a_0, a_3, b_2 in equation (42.2)).

Finding the integral estimate (41.13) of the process with a unit-impulse perturbation for the same case (42.2), we see that there is no minimum with respect to the parameters a_1 and a_2.

The case (42.3). For an astatic system described by equation (42.3), putting $b_2 = 0$, from (42.12) we obtain the integral square criterion (for a step)

$$I = \frac{1}{2a_3^2} \frac{b_1^2 a_1 a_3 + b_0^2 a_3^2}{a_1 a_2 - a_0 a_3}. \qquad (42.19)$$

In place of (42.7) the dimensionless form of the criterion I_0 may be taken for the astatic system in the form

$$I_0 = \frac{I}{\dfrac{b_{m-1}^2}{a_n^2} \sqrt[n]{\dfrac{a_n}{a_0}}}. \qquad (42.20)$$

In this case ($m = 2$, $n = 3$) from (42.19) we have

$$I_0 = \frac{A + \gamma^2}{2(AB - 1)}, \qquad (42.21)$$

where

$$\gamma = \frac{b_0}{b_1} \sqrt[n]{\frac{a_3}{a_0}}. \qquad (42.22)$$

The integral square criterion for the impulse (41.13) will be here

$$I' = \frac{b_0^2 a_2 + b_1^2 a_0}{2a_0(a_1 a_2 - a_0 a_3)}, \qquad (42.23)$$

and in relative form (42.10) we obtain

$$I' = \frac{B + \dfrac{1}{\gamma^2}}{2(AB - 1)}. \qquad (42.24)$$

This criterion corresponds to the somewhat deformed hyperbola in Fig. 187. The criterion (42.21) for the astatic system also has a form analogous to a family of hyperbolae, but with decrease of I_0 they shift upwards. Consequently, there is no minimum for either criterion with respect to the parameters a_1 and a_2.

From the above calculations it is possible to conclude that in the given examples the integral square criterion (41.9) for the cases

(42.1) and (42.2) leads to definite recommendations for the choice of system parameters: the point D in Fig. 186 in the first case and the point F in the second. The point F apparently corresponds to a more favourable process, the point D lies too close to the oscillatory boundary of stability and gives a strongly oscillatory transient response.

From this point of view it may be considered that a system structure which leads to an equation of the form (42.2) is better than a system described by equation (42.1) since it gives a better response for the same form of criterion. For a final evaluation of the transient quality for given numerical values of the parameters it is necessary to consider the transient curve plotted for these values by any of the methods described in Part V.

The fact that a minimum criterion was not obtained in a number of cases above with respect to the parameters a_1 and a_2 does not in any way signify, of course, that these forms of criteria are of no use in the choice of specific physical parameters (k_i and T_i) entering into the coefficients of the differential equation of the system. We shall show this by an example.

Example. We shall select the transfer factor of the sensitive element k_2 in the automatic pressure regulation system (considered in Section 23) from the minimum integral square criterion, neglecting the mass of the moving parts of the sensitive element ($T_3 = 0$).

From (23.33) and (23.34) the differential equation of the system has the form

$$[(T_1 p + 1)(T_2 p + 1)(T_s p + 1) + k_1 k_2] \varphi = (T_2 p + 1)(T_s p + 1)\psi .$$

Here we have the case (42.2), where the coefficients will be

$$a_0 = T_1 T_2 T_s , \quad a_1 = T_1 T_2 + T_1 T_s + T_2 T_s , \quad a_2 = T_1 + T_2 + T_s ,$$
$$a_3 = 1 + k_1 k_2 , \quad b_0 = T_2 T_s , \quad b_1 = T_2 + T_s , \quad b_2 = 1 . \tag{42.25}$$

The integral estimate for a step (41.9) according to formula (42.12) takes the form in this case

$$I = \frac{1}{2(1 + k_1 k_2)^2}\left[\frac{a_2}{1 + k_1 k_2} + \frac{a_1^2 + a_1(b_1^2 - 2b_0)(1 + k_1 k_2) + b_0^2(1 + k_1 k_2)^2}{a_1 a_2 - a_0(1 + k_1 k_2)} - 2b_1\right],$$

where all quantities are given except k_2, which is to be selected from the condition of minimum I.

The integral criterion (41.13) (for impulse) takes in this case a more simpler form

$$I' = \frac{(b_0^2 a_2 + a_0 b_1^2 - 2a_0 b_0)(1 + k_1 k_2) + a_0 a_1}{2a_0(1 + k_1 k_2)[a_1 a_2 - a_0(1 + k_1 k_2)]} .$$

Let us find the parameter k_2 from the condition of minimum I'. After certain calculations we obtain

$$\frac{\partial I'}{\partial k_2} = \frac{(1+k_1k_2)^2 + 2c_1(1+k_1k_2) - c_2}{c_3(1+k_1k_2)^2[a_1a_2 - a_0(1+k_1k_2)]^2},\qquad (42.26)$$

where

$$\left.\begin{aligned}
c_1 &= \frac{a_0a_1}{b_0^2a_2 + a_0(b_1^2 - 2b_0)}, \\[2mm]
c_2 &= \frac{a_1^2a_2}{b^2a_2 + a_0(b_1^2 - 2b_0)}, \\[2mm]
c_3 &= \frac{2}{k_1[b_0^2a_2 + a_0(b_1^2 - 2b_0)]}.
\end{aligned}\right\}\qquad (42.27)$$

Equating (42.26) to zero, we obtain the quadratic equation with respect to $(1+k_1k_2)$. Noting that only one of its solutions will be positive, we obtain the required value of the parameter k_2 in the form

$$k_2 = \frac{1}{k_1}\left(\sqrt{c_1^2 + c_2 - c_1 - 1}\right),\qquad (42.28)$$

where c_1 and c_2 are calculated from formulae (42.27) in which all quantities are expressed by the prescribed system parameters using formulae (42.25).

Choice of system parameters for minimum of the improved integral criterion. For comparison with the previous results we consider the same case, but (from considerations discussed in Section 41) we limit ourselves only to consideration of the transient caused by a unit step function $\psi(t)$.

In the case (42.1), where $n = 3$ and $m = 0$, from formula (41.20) it is necessary to consider in addition to the above only the determinant

$$\Delta_{-1} = \begin{vmatrix} a_3, & a_2, & 0, \\ 0, & a_3, & -a_0, \\ 0, & 0, & a_1 \end{vmatrix} = a_3^2 a_1.$$

In the result formula (41.20) gives the following expression for the improved integral estimate:

$$I_k = \frac{b_0^2}{2a_3^3}\left(a_2 + \frac{a_3a_1^2 + T^2a_3^2a_1}{a_1a_2 - a_0a_3}\right).\qquad (42.29)$$

In dimensionless form (42.7) we have

$$I_{k_0} = \frac{1}{2}\left(B + \frac{A^2 + \tau^2 A}{AB - 1}\right),\qquad (42.30)$$

where A and B are the Vyshnegradskii parameters (29.9) and

$$\tau = T \sqrt[3]{\frac{a_3}{a_0}} \qquad (42.31)$$

is the dimensionless expression for the time constant of the exponential to which we desire to approximate the transient in the given regulation system.

From a comparison of the criterion obtained I_{k_0} (42.30) with the previous I_0 (42.8) we have

$$I_{k_0} = I_0 + \frac{\tau^2 A}{2(AB-1)} . \qquad (42.32)$$

The minimum estimate I_0 occurs at the point D (Fig. 186). From formula (42.32) it is evident that the additional term entering into the improved criterion I_{k_0} decreases both with increase of parameter A and, particularly, with increase of parameter B. However simultaneously with this the fundamental component I_0 increases.

As a result the minimum value of the improved estimate I_{k_0} shifts from the previous point D in the direction of increase of the coordinates A and B, for example, to the point E (Fig. 186). This shift will be the greater, the greater the prescribed value of the quantity τ. Simultaneously the entire curve of equal criterion values shifts in a corresponding manner, as plotted in the diagram (Fig. 186), so that it now encircles not the point D but the new point E.

The position of the point E for each given value of τ may be found from formulae (41.26), written for the parameters A and B on the basis of expression (42.30). As a result we obtain two equations

$$A^2 B - 2A - \tau^2 = 0 ,$$

$$(AB-1)^2 - A^2(A + \tau^2) = 0 .$$

Each of them individually gives

$$\left.\begin{array}{l} AB = 2 + \dfrac{\tau^2}{A} , \\[2mm] AB = 1 + A \sqrt{A + \tau^2} . \end{array}\right\} \qquad (42.33)$$

Plotting two curves from these equations with the coordinate axes $y = AB$, $x = A$ for given τ, we obtain at their point of intersection the values of A and AB (Fig. 188a). Dividing the latter by the former, we find also B. The values A and B obtained are the required coordinates of the point E (Fig. 186), where a minimum criterion I_{k_0} (42.30) occurs for given τ.

The position of the point E in the diagram (Fig. 186, see also the Vyshnegradskii diagram Fig. 169) shows that with use of the criterion I_{k_0} the best response obtained is smoother than with use of the criterion I_0. In Fig. 188b, c the approximate shapes of the transient curves for the points D and E are shown.

As we expect, the points D and E do not coincide with the point of maximum degree of stability C (see Fig. 173). The points C and D may be considered as extreme limits between which the best response is located.

The improved integral criterion of the transient quality I_{k_0} may be considered more successful, considering various requirements (by assigning T), which may be placed on the rate of attenuation and the smoothness of the transient process in various real systems.

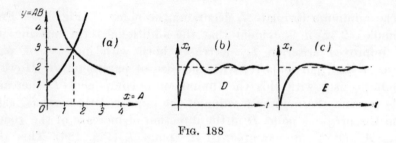

FIG. 188

An analogous calculation may be carried out for cases (42.2) and (42.3) from formula (41.21). In the case (42.2) we also obtain a shift of minimum integral criterion from the point E to some point K (Fig. 186) towards smoother processes. Here in the case of an astatic system the criterion I_{k_0} takes an expression which, in contrast to I_0 (42.21) also gives a definite minimum point in the Vyshnegradskii parameter plane (A, B).

43. Choice of system parameters with respect to the distribution of poles and zeros of the transfer function of the closed system

The differential equation of a closed automatic system has the form

$$L(p)x = S(p)f + N(p)y ,$$

where x is the deviation of the regulated quantity, f is the external perturbation on the regulated object, y is the external command input to the regulator, $L(p)$, $S(p)$, $N(p)$ are operational polynomials where the degrees of $S(p)$ and $N(p)$ are usually lower or at most equal to the degree of $L(p)$.

From Section 8 the transfer functions of a closed system with respect to the external force are denoted respectively:

$$W_f(p) = \frac{S(p)}{L(p)}, \qquad W_y(p) = \frac{N(p)}{L(p)} . \qquad (43.1)$$

The composition of the equations or, which is equivalent, the transfer functions for various closed systems is clear from Chapters V and VI.

The roots of the denominator $L(p)$ of the transfer function are termed the poles of the transfer function while the roots of the numerator $S(p)$ or $N(p)$ are the zeros of the transfer function. Both together are termed the singular points of the transfer function.

In Chapter IX we presented methods for selecting the system parameters from the distribution of roots of the characteristic equations $L(z) = 0$, i.e. the poles of the transfer function of the

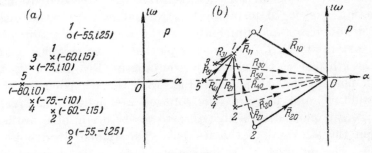

Fig. 189

closed system. But, as already mentioned previously in Section 36, the quality of the transient resulting from a change in the force f or y is not only defined by the denominator $L(p)$ but the entire transfer function $W_f(p)$ or $W_y(p)$ respectively. Therefore a more complete judgment of the transient quality may be obtained from an analysis of the relative positions of the poles and zeros of the transfer function of the closed system.

Here we shall consider certain recommendations for the most expedient distribution of the poles and zeros and on this basis a method for choosing the system parameters. From this it is possible to obtain also certain recommendations useful for solving problems by the methods of Chapter IX.

On the distribution of poles and zeros of the transfer function. The recommendations presented here were given by S. P. Strelkov in his work on the theory of linear amplifiers *.

Let us denote the poles of the transfer function of the closed system in the complex plane p by crosses and the zeros by circles (for example, Fig. 189a).

In the work by Strelkov an approximate formula is derived for determining the amplitude C_i and the phase δ_i of any of the components

$$C_i e^{\alpha_i t}\sin(\omega_i t + \delta_i)$$

in the solution of the differential equation describing the transient in the system with unit step of function f or y. It is written in complex form

$$C_i e^{i\delta_i} = -\frac{2 \prod\limits_{q=1}^{n-1} R_{q0} \prod\limits_{s=1}^{m} \bar{R}_{si}}{\prod\limits_{s=1}^{m} \bar{R}_{s0} \prod\limits_{q=1}^{n-1} R_{qi}} W_f(0) , \qquad (43.2)$$

where in place of $W_f(0)$ may be put $W_y(0)$ in accordance with formulae (43.1), depending on whether the transient is caused by a step of function f or y. In formula (43.2) n and m denote the degrees of the denominator and numerator of the transient function of the closed system (43.1), R_{q0} is a vector plotted in the complex plane p from the qth pole to the origin of coordinates (Fig. 189b), R_{qi} from the qth pole to the ith pole (in Fig. 189b the ith pole, for which the amplitude and phase of the solution are defined, is taken as pole 1), $\bar{R}_{s0}$ is plotted from the sth zero to the origin of coordinates, $\bar{R}_{si}$ from the sth zero to the ith pole. The symbol $\prod$ denotes the product. The product with respect to index q is conventionally written in the limits from 1 to $n-1$; but this should be understood such that the vector R_{n0} enters into the numerator of expression (43.2) while only the vector R_{i0} is absent (from the ith pole itself to the origin of coordinates, see Fig. 189b); in the numerator of expression (43.2) the vector R_{ii} is naturally absent, but the vector R_{ni} is included.

From formula (43.2) it follows that to reduce the amplitude of the ith component in the solution of the transient response equation it is necessary to consider how to distribute the poles and zeros of the function of the closed system so that the vectors plotted in Fig. 189b by full lines increase while the vectors plotted in broken line decrease. But, as is evident from (43.2), here it is not so much the magnitudes of the vectors which is important as their ratios. At the same time it is necessary to bear in mind that the poles cannot be brought too close to the imaginary axis since their distance from the imaginary axis (i.e. the real part) defines the rate of attenuation of the transient—the degree of stability of the system.

For example, for the distribution of poles and zeros shown in Fig. 189a, with $W_y(0) = 1$, we obtain the amplitudes of the individual components of the transient curve:

$$C_1 = 21 \cdot 6; \qquad C_2 = 140; \qquad C_3 = 194 .$$

Let us shift the poles, not changing the distances of the closest poles to the imaginary axis, in the following manner: the pole 1 from the point $(-60, i15)$ to the point $(-60, i25)$; the pole 3 from the point $(-75, i10)$ to the point $(-75, i25)$; the pole 5 from the point $(-80, i0)$ to the point $(-90, i0)$ and correspondingly the conjugate poles 2 and 4. We also shift the zero 1 from the point $(-55, i25)$ to the point $(-65, i30)$ and the conjugate zero 2. Now the amplitudes strongly decrease:

$$C_1 = 3 \cdot 5; \quad C_2 = 6 \cdot 2; \quad C_3 = 11 \cdot 6 \,.$$

A still greater difference is obtained if the poles remain in the same positions as is shown in Fig. 189*b* and only the zero 1 is shifted, from the point $(-55, i25)$ to the point $(-35, i15)$, and the conjugate zero 2. The amplitudes here strongly increase

$$C_1 = 123 \,, \quad C_2 = 524 \,, \quad C_3 = 920 \,.$$

These examples assume in all three cases $W_f(0) = 1$. But it is also necessary to take into account, firstly, that from (43.1) $W_f(0)$ is the ratio of constant terms of the operational polynomials $S(p)$ and $L(p)$ which also may vary with shift of poles and zeros. Secondly, from (20.11) the poles and zeros cannot change independently of each other.

In these examples the influence of the mutual positions of the poles and zeros of the transfer function of a closed system on the magnitude of deviation of the regulated quantity during the transient is very clearly seen. The intensity of damping of the transient is defined, as before, by the real parts of the poles, i.e. by the roots of the characteristic equation.

In this connection we note that it is exactly the mutual positions of poles and zeros of the transfer function, or in other words, the values of the coefficients of the operational polynomials in the left and right-hand sides of the differential equation of the system which define the initial conditions of the transient process (6.23) and, consequently, the arbitrary constants of the solution describing this process, which corresponds to the magnitude of deviation of the regulated quantity during the transient.

Varying the distribution of poles and zeros, taking into account formulae (20.11) in the interests of the quality of the transient response it is simultaneously necessary to verify, as always, the static and stationary dynamic errors of the system.

As a result of his analysis S. P. Strelkov makes the following recommendations:

(a) it is desirable to locate the zeros close to the region of pole distribution; zeros remote from the pole region lead to increase in amplitude of the oscillations in the transient responses;

(b) to decrease the deviations during the transient it is frequently expedient to separate the poles from each other while to increase the rate of damping of the transient, to remove them further from the imaginary axis;

(c) approach to each other for those poles remote from the imaginary axis presents little danger.

More concrete recommendations for each particular case of system may be obtained on the basis of applying formulae (43.2) and graphs similar to the graph of Fig. 189b, plotted for the given concrete system.

Choice of system parameters from the distribution of poles and zeros. Here we shall consider a numerical method. According to the general idea it is completely analogous to the numerical method for choosing the system parameters from the root distribution of the characteristic equation described in Section 40.

As was done there we shall not start from a preassigned pattern of pole and zero distribution of the transfer function of the closed system but we shall set the aim of achieving the most favourable (for example from the point of view of the above recommendations) distribution among those which may actually occur in the automatic regulation system under consideration in various alternative structures and in possible ranges of variation of the selected parameters of the regulator. These ranges may be considered given from design considerations and from the requirements of sufficiently small static and stationary dynamic errors.

Let us consider first the simplest type of structure, writing its differential equation according to the rules of Chapter VI with perturbation (or command) force in the right-hand side and correspondingly the transfer function of the closed system (43.1). Here the coefficients of the operational polynomials $L(p)$ and $S(p)$ (or $N(p)$) will consist of prescribed numbers and one or two selected parameters of the regulator (for example, k_ψ and $k_{\dot\psi}$, as in Section 40).

Assigning a certain average value of $k_{\dot\psi}$ and several values of k_ψ, for each of them we find by the simple numerical method (Section 39) all the roots of the polynomials $L(p)$ and $S(p)$. The former will be the poles and the latter the zeros of the transfer function. We shall thus find the variation of pole and zero distribution with variation of the parameter k_ψ (along some straight line AB inside the stability region, Fig. 182).

Choosing the value k_ψ for which the best pole and zero distribution is obtained (for example, from the above recommendations), we fix this value but vary the second parameter $k_{\dot\psi}$. Taking several numerical values in succession, for each of them we find all the poles and zeros in the same way. As a result the variation of pole and zero distribution of the transfer function along some straight line DE (Fig. 182) will be found, which permits determining the optimum point F with the best distribution.

Here it is again necessary to take care that this point satisfies also the requirements of static precision and other requirements and that it not be too close to the boundary of stability since, as always (Section 31), it is necessary to have some stability reserve.

If we do not succeed in these calculations in obtaining a satisfactory distribution of poles and zeros of the transient function of the closed system, we change its structure; for example, in addition to the previous we introduce k_{fb} or $k_{\psi}^{..}$, as in Section 40. Then, taking the previous values of k_{ψ} and $k_{\psi}^{.}$, we construct the transfer function in which the coefficients of the polynomials $L(p)$ and $S(p)$ include in algebraic form only the new parameter of the regulator k_{fb} (or $k_{\psi}^{..}$). Calculating all the poles and zeros of the transfer function for several values of k_{fb}, we find its optimum value.

This numerical method of choosing the system parameters, although at first glance too laborious in the amount of calculation, in many cases may prove less cumbersome with regard to calculation and rapid approach to the goal then the previous methods discussed in Sections 38–42. The main thing is that it apparently may be fairly effective in the sense of its flexibility and possibilities of "wringing out" of the given structure the best result in an arbitrary given most important part of its stability region.

This numerical method may employ various criteria of optimal pole and zero distribution of the transfer function of the closed system. One of them, following from the work of S. P. Strelkov, was discussed above. It is however necessary further to improve these criteria so that they would fully reflect the dynamic properties of the system not only in the transient process but in the presence of various perturbation and input forces in various classes of systems as well as the static properties (some considerations in this regard are given in the work of S. P. Strelkov).

After the above-described choice of system parameters it is easily possible to plot the transient curve (see Part V) both for the optimum point found in the calculation and for several others.

We remark that for a definite class of servomechanisms there exists the so-called method of standard coefficients. Its essence consists in that for definite combinations of coefficients in the numerator and denominator of the transfer function of the closed system of a given order transient curves are plotted in advance and those standard combinations of the coefficients are proposed which give the best result. Here the system parameters are to be chosen to provide the recommended values of the coefficients.

However, this standardisation is only possible for a narrow class of systems since, as discussed in Section 40, the given dynamic properties of the regulated object and various special requirements on the regulator and the system as a whole make it impossible to obtain rigorously prescribed relations for all the coefficients of the equation (or transfer function) and the concept of quality of regulation itself is different for different systems. The above-described numerical method permits taking into detailed account the specific properties of each concrete automatic system.

44. Approximate frequency criteria of transient quality

In those cases where the system is studied from the very beginning by frequency methods, i.e. the frequency stability criterion is applied (Section 30), the analysis of the transient quality is naturally

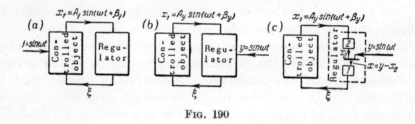

FIG. 190

also carried out from the frequency characteristics. In particular, this is absolutely necessary where we do not have equations (or, which is equivalent, transfer function expressions) for all the circuits of the system but some of the elements are described by experimentally recorded frequency characteristics.

Let us consider approximate transient quality criteria according to the frequency characteristics of the closed system.

Frequency characteristics of a closed system. The general concept of frequency characteristics of linear systems was given in Section 8. In the present case the frequency characteristics will define the properties of a closed automatic system in steady-state forced oscillations under the action either of a sinusoidal perturbation on the regulated object (Fig. 190a) or a sinusoidal variation of the command quantity on the regulator (Fig. 190b).

In the first case the amplitude A_f and the phase β_f of forced oscillations of the regulated quantity are defined as the modulus and argument of the amplitude-phase frequency characteristic of the closed system with respect to the perturbation:

$$A_f e^{i\beta_f} = W_f(i\omega), \tag{44.1}$$

and in the second case by the amplitude-phase frequency characteristic of the closed system with respect to the command quantity

$$A_y e^{i\beta_y} = W_y(i\omega) . \tag{44.2}$$

If the differential equation is known, and thus the corresponding
transfer functions of the closed system (43.1), the amplitude-phase
characteristics (44.1) and (44.2) are defined from Section 8 by simple
substitution of $p = i\omega$ in the expressions of the corresponding transfer
functions, i.e.

$$W_f(i\omega) = \frac{S(i\omega)}{L(i\omega)} , \qquad W_y(i\omega) = \frac{N(i\omega)}{L(i\omega)} . \tag{44.3}$$

Separating in these expressions the real and imaginary parts,
i.e. writing

$$W_f(i\omega) = U_f(\omega) + iV_f(\omega) , \qquad W_y(i\omega) = U_y(\omega) + iV_y(\omega) , \tag{44.4}$$

we obtain the so-called real $U(\omega)$ and imaginary $V(\omega)$ frequency
characteristics of the closed system.

If the equation of the closed system is unknown because some
of its elements are given by experimentally recorded frequency
characteristics, then by the methods described in Sections 20 and 21
we first determine the amplitude-phase characteristic of the corresponding open network $W(i\omega)$, which was used for studying the
stability of the closed system, and then we obtain the amplitude-
phase characteristics of the closed system $W_f(i\omega)$ and $W_y(i\omega)$.

We shall consider that the amplitude-phase characteristic $W(i\omega)$
for the open network of the given system is known (for example,
from the study of system stability). Then from (20.15) or (20.27)
the amplitude-phase characteristic of the closed system with respect
to perturbation will be

$$W_f(i\omega) = \frac{W'_1(i\omega)}{1 + W(i\omega)} , \tag{44.5}$$

where

$$W'_1(i\omega) = \frac{S_1(i\omega)}{Q_1(i\omega)} , \tag{44.6}$$

and $S_1(i\omega)$ and $Q_1(i\omega)$ are given by substitution of $p = i\omega$ in the
polynomials $S_1(p)$ and $Q_1(p)$ in the equation of the regulated object

$$Q_1(p)x_1 = R_1(p)x_m + S_1(p)f . \tag{44.7}$$

Formula (44.5) gives the amplitude and phase of forced oscillations
of the regulated quantity x_1.

The amplitude-phase characteristic of the closed system with
respect to the command input for the regulated quantity x_1, from

(20.28), will be

$$W_y(i\omega) = \frac{W(i\omega)}{W_2(i\omega)[1 + W(i\omega)]}, \qquad (44.8)$$

where $W_2(i\omega)$ is the amplitude-phase characteristic of the block of circuits 2 (Fig. 190c) between the point of measurement of the regulated quantity x_1 and the point of introduction of the input command y. For the regulation system block 2 usually represents the sensitive element of the regulator and for a servomechanism the basic feedback (see Fig. 3). Sometimes $W_2(i\omega) = 1$.

Formula (44.8) defines the amplitude and phase of forced oscillations of the regulated quantity x_1. For the error x (Fig. 190c) from (20.26) we have

$$W_y^x(i\omega) = \frac{1}{1 + W(i\omega)}, \qquad (44.9)$$

while for the quantity x_2 (Fig. 190c) from (22.29)

$$W_y^{x_2}(i\omega) = \frac{W(i\omega)}{1 + W(i\omega)}. \qquad (44.10)$$

Consequently, a knowledge of the amplitude-phase characteristic of the open network $W(i\omega)$ with small additions in the form $W_1^f(i\omega)$ and $W_2(i\omega)$ is sufficient to obtain the amplitude-phase characteristic of the closed system purely by calculations from the above formulae. We note that for cases (44.9) and (44.10) there are special Solodovnikov circle diagrams simplifying the calculations (Reference 11). These diagrams may be used also for the cases (44.5) and (44.8) with subsequent multiplication by $W_1^f(i\omega)$ and division by $W_2(i\omega)$ respectively.

These formulae are valid for systems of arbitrary structure with one regulated quantity. A more complicated case is considered at the end of Section 21.

We note that the amplitude-phase characteristics of the closed system are used directly to estimate the stationary errors of the automatic system in steady-state following and regulation both with oscillatory and arbitrary input functions *.

Example. We shall illustrate obtaining the frequency characteristics of the closed system by the example of the voltage regulation system considered in Section 24. The equations of the closed system according to (24.10), (24.20), (24.28) and (24.36) are:

$$\left. \begin{array}{c} (T_1 p + 1)\Delta V = -k_1 \Delta r - (b_0 p \pm b)f, \\ (T_2 p + 1)\Delta I_2 = k_2(\Delta V - \Gamma_2^0 p \Delta \alpha), \\ (T_4^2 p^2 + T_3 p + 1)\Delta \alpha = k_3 \Delta I_2, \quad \Delta r = k_4 \Delta \alpha, \end{array} \right\} \qquad (44.11)$$

---

* See end of Section 11.

where all coefficients were defined in Section 24. The perturbation from (24.12) is defined by variation of the load current and angular velocity. The regulator adjustment is assumed constant.

On the basis of these equations, from Section 20 and 21, we obtain the amplitude-phase characteristic of the open network:

$$W(i\omega) = \frac{k_1 k_2 k_3 k_4}{(T_1 i\omega + 1)[(T_2 i\omega + 1)(- T_4^2 \omega^2 + T_3 i\omega + 1) + k_2 k_3 \Gamma_2^0 i\omega]} \quad (44.12)$$

while from formula (44.5) the amplitude-phase characteristic of the closed system with respect to the perturbation

$$W_f(i\omega) = \frac{b_0 i\omega + b}{T_1 i\omega + 1} \cdot \frac{1}{1 + W(i\omega)}. \quad (44.13)$$

This expression gives the amplitude and phase of the forced voltage oscillations ΔU with input in the form of sinusoidal load current variation ΔI_1 and the angular velocity n with ΔI_1 and the angular velocity n. To obtain the amplitude-phase characteristics of the same closed system with respect to the command $W_y(i\omega)$, it is necessary to consider the load I_l and the angular velocity n constant, i.e. $f = 0$, but in constant, i.e. $f = 0$, but in place of this to vary the regulator adjustment by the rheostat R_s (Fig. 119), i.e. to introduce the variable command $\Delta R_s(t)$.

The quantity R_s enters into the equation of the electromagnet circuit of the sensitive element (24.18). Considering that it is multiplied by the variable I_2, i.e. enters in a non-linear manner, equation (24.18) is subject to linearisation. Denoting the left-hand side of this equation by F, we obtain

$$\left(\frac{\partial F}{\partial R_a}\right)^0 = I_2^0, \quad \left(\frac{\partial F}{\partial I_2}\right)^0 = R_2 + R_a^0, \quad \left(\frac{\partial F}{\partial \dot{I}_2}\right)^0 = L_2^0.$$

Therefore on the basis of the general formula for linearisation (18.5) we obtain in place of (24.18) the following electromagnet circuit equation

$$(T_2 p + 1)\Delta I_2 = k_2(\Delta V - \Gamma_2^2 p \Delta \alpha) - k_2' y,$$

where T_2 and k_2 are defined by the previous formulae (24.21), in which it is necessary to substitute R_s in place of R_s. In addition, we have

$$k_2' = \frac{I_0^2}{R_2 + R_a^0}, \quad y = \Delta R_a = R_a(t) - R_a^0,$$

where R_s^0 denotes the quantity R_s in the steady-state with constant regulator adjustment.

Now in place of (44.11) the system equations with $f = 0$ and $y = y(t)$ will have the form:

$$
\left.
\begin{aligned}
(T_1 p + 1)\Delta V &= -k_1 \Delta r\,, \\
(T_2 p + 1)\Delta I_2 &= k_2 (\Delta V - \Gamma_2^0 p \Delta \alpha) - k_2' y\,, \\
(T_4^2 p^2 + T_3 p + 1)\Delta \alpha &= k_4 \Delta I_2\,, \qquad \Delta r = k_4 \Delta \alpha\,.
\end{aligned}
\right\}
\qquad (44.14)
$$

As a result the amplitude-phase characteristic of the closed system with respect to command will be

$$
W_y(i\omega) = \frac{k_2'}{k_2} \cdot \frac{W(i\omega)}{1 + W(i\omega)}\,,
$$

where $W(i\omega)$ is the amplitude-phase characteristic of the open network (44.12). The expression $W_y(i\omega)$ gives the amplitude and phase for forced voltage oscillations ΔV with input in the form of sinusoidal variation of the adjustment rheostat resistance ΔR_s.

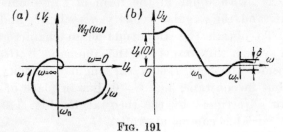

FIG. 191

The real frequency characteristic and its relation to the transient. Obtaining the amplitude-phase characteristic of the closed system $W_f(i\omega)$ or $W_y(i\omega)$, we find the corresponding real frequency characteristic $U_f(\omega)$ or $U_y(\omega)$ as the real part of expression (44.4) or as a function of U with respect to ω (Fig. 191b), defined from the graph of the amplitude-phase characteristic of the closed system (Fig. 191a) or analytically from (44.4).

We shall indicate the relation of the frequency characteristics of the system to the transient curve arising from a unit step of perturbation $f(t)$.

We employ the expression for the Fourier series (8.19), applying it to expansion of the rectangular periodic function $f(t)$ (Fig. 192a). In the present case we have

$$
f(t) = 1 \quad \text{with} \quad 0 < t < \frac{\pi}{\omega_0} \quad \text{and} \quad f(t) = 0 \quad \text{with} \quad \frac{\pi}{\omega_0} < t < \frac{2\pi}{\omega_0}\,.
$$

Therefore after integration formula (8.20) gives

$$
a_0 = \frac{1}{2}\,, \qquad a_k = 0\,, \qquad b_k = \frac{2}{k\pi}
$$

$$
(k = 1, 3, 5, \dots)\,.
$$

Substituting this in (8.19), we obtain the required expression

$$f(t) = \frac{1}{2} + \sum_{k=1}^{\infty} \frac{2}{k\pi} \sin k\omega_0 t \qquad (44.15)$$

$$(k = 1, 3, 5, \dots).$$

The step function $f(t) = 1(t)$ may be obtained from the rectangular periodic function if we let $T_0 = 2\pi/\omega_0 \to \infty$ (Fig. 192b). Here $\omega_0 \to 0$.

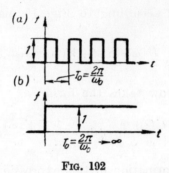

FIG. 192

We put $\Delta\omega = \omega_0$, $\omega = k\omega_0 = k\Delta\omega$ and, consequently, $k = \omega/\Delta\omega$. Then expression (44.15) is rewritten in the form

$$f(t) = \frac{1}{2} + \sum_{\frac{\omega}{\Delta\omega}=1}^{\infty} \frac{2\Delta\omega \sin \omega t}{\pi\omega} \quad \left(\frac{\omega}{\Delta\omega} = 1, 3, 5, \dots \right).$$

As $\Delta\omega \to 0$ this sum passes into the integral. As a result in place of the Fourier series for the periodic function (44.15) we obtain the Fourier integral for the non-periodic function

$$1(t) = \frac{1}{2} + \frac{1}{\pi} \int_0^{\infty} \frac{\sin \omega t}{\omega} d\omega. \qquad (44.16)$$

It is possible similarly to obtain the Fourier integral for any arbitrary non-periodic function $f(t)$.

This integral may be represented as an infinite sum of elementary input oscillations

$$\frac{d\omega}{\pi\omega} \sin \omega t.$$

From Section 8 each of these will correspond to an output oscillation in the form

$$\frac{d\omega}{\pi\omega} A(\omega) \sin[\omega t + \beta(\omega)].$$

As a result the overall response at the output of the system with input perturbation in the form of a unit step (44.16) will be

$$x(t) = \frac{A(0)}{2} + \frac{1}{\pi} \int\limits_0^\infty \frac{A(\omega)\sin[\omega t + \beta(\omega)]}{\omega} d\omega \quad \text{with} \quad t > 0 . \quad (44.17)$$

Further we have

$$A(\omega)\sin[\omega t + \beta(\omega)] = A(\omega)\cos\beta(\omega)\sin\omega t + A(\omega)\sin\beta(\omega)\cos\omega t .$$

This last expression according to Fig. 15 may be written in the form

$$U(\omega)\sin\omega t + V(\omega)\cos\omega t ,$$

where $A(0) = U(0)$.

Formula (44.17) now takes the form

$$x(t) = \frac{U(0)}{2} + \frac{1}{\pi} \int\limits_0^\infty \frac{U(\omega)}{\omega} \sin\omega t \, d\omega + \frac{1}{\pi} \int\limits_0^\infty \frac{V(\omega)}{\omega} \cos\omega t \, d\omega \quad (t > 0) .$$

For further transformation of this expression we employ the fact that with $t < 0$ the quantity x will be equal to zero (the deviation x is read from the old steady-state), i.e.

$$0 = \frac{U(0)}{2} + \frac{1}{\pi} \int\limits_0^\infty \frac{U(\omega)}{\omega} \sin\omega t \, d\omega + \frac{1}{\pi} \int\limits_0^\infty \frac{V(\omega)}{\omega} \cos\omega t \, d\omega \quad (t < 0) .$$

Substituting here t by $-t$ and subtracting from the above, we obtain finally

$$x(t) = \frac{2}{\pi} \int\limits_0^\infty \frac{U(\omega)}{\omega} \sin\omega t \, d\omega \quad (t > 0) ,$$

i.e. the curve of the transient process in the system $x(t)$ is defined by the real frequency characteristic of the closed system $U(\omega)$. We thus have

$$x(t) = \frac{2}{\pi} \int\limits_0^\infty \frac{U_f(\omega)}{\omega} \sin\omega t \, d\omega , \quad (44.18)$$

if the transient arises as a result of a unit step of perturbation f (load), and

$$x(t) = \frac{2}{\pi} \int\limits_0^\infty \frac{U_y(\omega)}{\omega} \sin\omega t \, d\omega \quad (44.19)$$

for a unit step of the command y (adjustment). Here x is read from the old steady-state existing before the step.

If the transient in the system is caused by a unit impulse in f or y, it is possible to employ the fact, according to Section 6, that the unit impulse is the time derivative of the unit step. Therefore the Fourier integral for the unit impulse is obtained by differentiating expression (44.16) with respect to t, namely

$$1'(t) = \frac{1}{\pi} \int_0^\infty \cos \omega t\, d\omega .$$

Consequently, formula (44.17) takes the form

$$x(t) = \frac{1}{\pi} \int_0^\infty A(\omega) \cos[\omega t + \beta(\omega)] d\omega \quad \text{with} \quad t > 0 .$$

From this it is evident that the final result for the transient curve with external perturbation on the system in the form of a unit impulse in f and y may also be obtained by differentiating formulae (44.18) and (44.19) with respect to t, which gives

$$x(t) = \frac{2}{\pi} \int_0^\infty U_f(\omega) \cos \omega t\, d\omega , \quad x(t) = \frac{2}{\pi} \int_0^\infty U_y(\omega) \cos \omega t\, d\omega . \quad (44.20)$$

respectively.

On the basis of these formulae it is possible to judge the transient quality in this system according to the real parts of the characteristics of the closed system $U_f(\omega)$ or $U_y(\omega)$ (considered in the present section), and to plot the transient curve (see Section 75).

Approximate criteria of transient quality. Here we present V. V. Solodovnikov's recommendations (Reference 11) for approximate criteria of transient quality from the form of the real frequency characteristic of a closed system, based on an analysis of the properties of integral (44.19), but not requiring its calculation. It is assumed that the transient is caused by a unit step* of the input command y.

The frequency interval $0 \leqslant \omega \leqslant \omega_p$ (Fig. 191b) in which $U_y(\omega) \geqslant 0$, is termed the positive interval. The interval of frequencies $0 \leqslant \omega \leqslant \omega_c$ is termed the interval of essential frequencies if at $\omega = \omega_c$ and further with $\omega > \omega_c$ the quantity $|U_y(\omega)|$ becomes and remains smaller than some given sufficiently small positive quantity δ. The influence of the remaining part of the real frequency characteristic (with $\omega \geqslant \omega_c$) on the transient quality may be neglected. If with $\omega > \omega_p$ it is found that $|U_y(\omega)| < 0.2\, U_y(0)$, then as the criterion of transient quality in the first approximation it is possible to take into consideration only the positive interval $0 \leqslant \omega \leqslant \omega_p$.

* Everywhere below we shall consider the unit step in y, but the same will be valid for f if we interchange $U_y(\omega)$ and $U_f(\omega)$.

We note that dropping the "tail" of the real frequency characteristic ($\omega > \omega_c$ or $\omega > \omega_p$) mainly influences the initial portion of the transient process which, consequently, will be estimated more roughly. The origin of the real frequency characteristic mainly defines the terminal part of the transient process.

On the basis of an analysis of integral (44.19) V. V. Solodovnikov has given the following criterion of the transient quality.

1. The static deviation x^0 of the regulated quantity obtained as a result of a unit step in external input is equal to the initial value of the real frequency characteristic $U(0)$. If we are concerned with

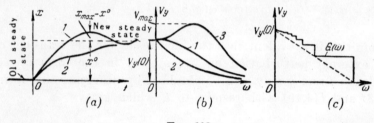

(a)   (b)   (c)

FIG. 193

a step of the input command, $U_y(0)$ should be equal as closely as possible either to 1, or to some k_0, if the system should reproduce the input command to a certain scale k_0 (for example, Section 26). If the step introduced is in the perturbation f, the value $U_f(0)$ should be as small as possible, where in an astatic system $U_f(0) = 0$.

2. For the overshoot $x_{\max} - x^0$ (curve 1 in Fig. 193a) not to exceed 18 per cent of the static deviation x^0, it is sufficient to have a positive non-increasing continuous characteristic $U_y(\omega)$ (curve 1 in Fig. 193b).

3. For a monotonic transient $x(t)$ (curve 2 in Fig. 193a) it is sufficient that the derivative $dU_y/d\omega$ be a negative continuous function of ω decreasing in modulus (curve 2 in Fig. 193b) with $U_y(\infty) = 0$.

4. The simplest criterion of non-monotonic transient is the presence of values $U_y(\omega) > U_y(0)$ (curve 3 in Fig. 193b). The transient will also be non-monotonic when the curve $U_y(\omega)$ for some ω passes above the stepwise curve $G(\omega)$ (Fig. 193c), where

$$G(\omega) = \cos \frac{\pi}{\left[\dfrac{\omega_p}{\omega}\right] + 1} \, ,$$

and $\left[\dfrac{\omega_p}{\omega}\right]$ denotes the next higher integral values; for example, if $\omega_p/\omega = 1\cdot25$ we take $\left[\dfrac{\omega_p}{\omega}\right] = 2$.

5. In the case where the real frequency characteristic $U_y(\omega)$ has the shape of Fig. 3 (Fig. 193*b*), which may be represented by the difference of two positive non-increasing continuous functions, the overshoot $x_{max} - x^0$ (Fig. 193*a*) will be less than $1\cdot18\,U_{max} - U_y(0)$.

6. For monotonic processes $x(t)$ the damping time t_1 to the value $x = 5$ per cent of the static deviation x^0 will be greater than $4\pi/\omega_p$.

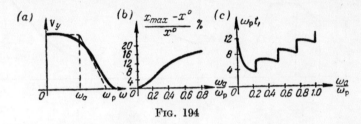

FIG. 194

In the general case $t_1 > \pi/\omega_p$ In general, with other conditions equal, the transient attenuates the more rapidly, the greater ω_p, i.e. the more drawn out is the region of positiveness of the real frequency characteristic $U_y(\omega)$ along the ω-axis.

7. If a given real frequency characteristic $U_y(\omega)$ may be approximately replaced by trapezoids (Fig. 194*a*), depending upon the ratio of lengths of the bases ω_a and ω_p of the trapezoids the magnitude of overshoot in per cent and the transient damping time in relative form $\omega_p t_1$ may be approximately estimated by graphs given in Fig. 194*b* and 194*c*, where the value of t_1 is included in the interval

$$\frac{\pi}{\omega_p} < t_1 < \frac{4\pi}{\omega_p}\,.$$

8. If the given frequency characteristic $U_y(\omega)$ may be approximately replaced by a polygon, shown in Fig. 195*a*, where

$$\frac{\omega_a}{\omega_b} \geqslant 0\cdot4; \qquad \frac{\omega_b}{\omega_p} \geqslant 0\cdot5; \qquad \frac{\omega_e}{\omega_p} \leqslant 0\cdot8\,,$$

the dependence of the maximum possible overshoot (in per cent) on the magnitude of the ratio $U_{max}/U_y(0)$ is defined by the curve in Fig. 195*b*. To a given upper bound of permissible values of transient damping time t_1 there corresponds a lower permissible bound on the magnitude of the positive interval ω_{pmin}, defined by the curve in Fig. 195*c*.

On the basis of the above simple criteria it is possible to estimate roughly the quality of the transient response of a closed automatic system from the form of its real frequency characteristic $U_y(\omega)$ and also from $U_f(\omega)$.

Following V. V. Solodovnikov, we present for illustration a number of transient curves $x_1(t), x_2(t), x_3(t), x_4(t)$ (Fig. 196*b*), which correspond to the real frequency characteristics of the closed system $U_1(\omega)$, $U_2(\omega)$, $U_3(\omega)$, $U_4(\omega)$, represented in Fig. 196a. The best transient $x_3(t)$ corresponds to the characteristic $U_3(\omega)$ while the poorest $x_1(t)$ to the characteristic $U_1(\omega)$, having the greatest peaks.

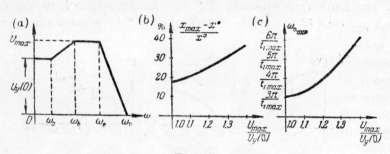

FIG. 195

Calculating the integral criterion of transient quality. For the choice of system parameters with respect to the minimum integral criteria of transient quality described in Sections 41 and 42 it is also possible to employ given frequency characteristics of the system (for example, in those cases where the equations of some circuits of the system are not known). The formulae for calculating the integral criteria are also derived from relation (44.17).

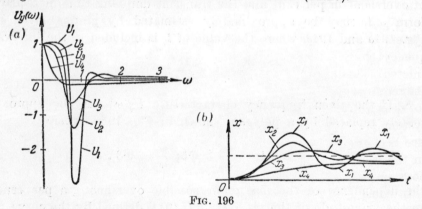

FIG. 196

As a result for the integral square criterion (41.3) the formula is obtained

$$I = \int_0^\infty x^2 dt = \frac{1}{\pi} \int_0^\infty \frac{1}{\omega^2} [A_f(\omega)]^2 d\omega , \qquad (44.21)$$

while for the improved integral criterion (41.16) we have

$$I_k = \int_0^\infty (x^2 + T^2 \dot{x}^2) dt = \frac{1}{\pi} \int_0^\infty \left(\frac{1}{\omega^2} + T^2\right)[A_f(\omega)]^2 d\omega , \qquad (44.22)$$

where $A_f(\omega)$ is the amplitude-frequency characteristic (resonance curve) of the closed system

$$A_f(\omega) = |W_f(i\omega)| .$$

In formulae (44.21) and (44.22) $A_y(\omega)$ may figure in place of $A_f(\omega)$.

The integral in both cases should be calculated graphically as the area bounded by the curve represented by the integrand as a function of ω. Calculating the value I or I_k for several numerical values of the selected system parameter, we find its optimum value corresponding to the minimum integral criterion. It is necessary to proceed similarly with the other selected system parameters.

Synthesis of correcting elements by frequency methods. This problem has recently been widely developed and applied due to the work of V. V. Solodovnikov and other scientists. Corrective networks are classed as series (connected in the basic network of elements with introduction of derivatives and integrals) and parallel (stiff and transient feedback). The synthesis (choice) of series corrective network consists in the following. The system is separated as in Section 34 into two blocks (Fig. 155), one of which (I) is the given part of the system while the second (II) the corrective network to be chosen. From the desired qualities of the system a real frequency characteristic of the overall system is chosen to be realised. The corresponding logarithmic frequency characteristic of the open system is calculated. From this latter the existing logarithmic frequency characteristic of the given portion of the system I is subtracted. The result is the logarithmic frequency characteristic of the required correcting system, which is designed from it. For a system so designed the new real frequency characteristic of the closed system is calculated and from it the transient response plotted (see Section 75), which verifies the quality of the entire calculation. In the case of synthesis of parallel correcting networks the calculations are somewhat more complicated.

In conclusion we note that choice of structure and optimal parameters of an automatic regulation system may be considered in certain respects as a problem analogous to the mathematical problem of the approximation of functions. This analogy has been systematically carried out in the work of V. A. Bodner (Reference 51), where applications of methods of interpolation, series expansion and successive approximations to the choice of optimum automatic regulation system parameters have been considered. All these methods are closely related to the integral criteria, various criteria based on the transfer functions, frequency characteristics, etc.

PART III

SPECIAL LINEAR AUTOMATIC REGULATION SYSTEMS

DERIVATION OF THE EQUATIONS OF SYSTEMS WITH DELAY AND WITH DISTRIBUTED PARAMETERS

45. Equations and frequency characteristics of linear systems with delay

Automatic systems which, having the same general structure as ordinary linear systems (Part II), differ from the latter in that one (or several) of their elements have the start of variation of the output quantity delayed (with respect to the start of input variation) by the magnitude τ, termed the time delay, are called linear systems with delay, where the delay time remains constant during the entire course of the process.

For example, if the ordinary linear element is described by the equation

$$T \frac{dx_2}{dt} + x_2 = kx_1 \qquad (45.1)$$

(aperiodic element), the equation of the corresponding linear element with delay will have the form

$$T \frac{dx_2(t)}{dt} + x_2(t) = kx_1(t-\tau) \qquad (45.2)$$

(aperiodic element with delay). This form of equation is termed equation with delayed argument or differential-difference equation.

Let us put $x_1^*(t) = x_1(t-\tau)$. Then equation (45.2) is written in ordinary form

$$T \frac{dx_2}{dt} + x_2 = kx_1^* . \qquad (45.3)$$

Thus, if the input quantity x_1 changes discontinuously from zero to unity (Fig. 197a) the variation of the quantity $x_1^* = x_1(t-\tau)$ in the right-side of the equation is represented graphically by Fig. 197b (step τ seconds later). Employing now the time characteristic of the ordinary aperiodic element (Fig. 95c) in application to equation (45.3), we obtain the change of output quantity x_2 in the form of the graph in Fig. 197c. This will be the time characteristic of the aperiodic element with delay (its aperiodic "inertial" property is defined by the time constant T and the delay by the quantity τ).

Linear element with delay. In the general case, as in (45.2), the equation of motion of an arbitrary linear element with delay may be separated into two equations

$$Q(p)x_2 = R(p)x_1^* \,, \quad \left.\vphantom{\begin{matrix}1\\1\end{matrix}}\right\}$$
$$x_1^*(t) = x_1(t-\tau) \,, \quad \left.\vphantom{\begin{matrix}1\\1\end{matrix}}\right\} \qquad (45.4)$$

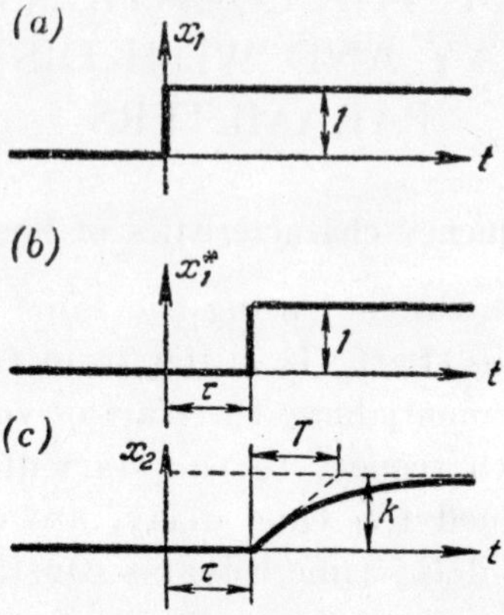

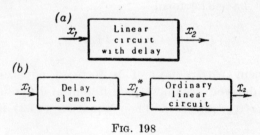

FIG. 197

which corresponds to the formal separation of the linear element with delay (Fig. 198a) into two elements: the ordinary linear element of the same order and with the same coefficients and a preceding delay element (Fig. 198b).

(a)

$$x_1 \longrightarrow \boxed{\begin{array}{c} \text{Linear} \\ \text{circuit} \\ \text{with delay} \end{array}} \longrightarrow x_2$$

(b)

$$x_1 \longrightarrow \boxed{\begin{array}{c} \text{Delay} \\ \text{element} \end{array}} \xrightarrow{x_1^*} \boxed{\begin{array}{c} \text{Ordinary} \\ \text{linear} \\ \text{circuit} \end{array}} \longrightarrow x_2$$

FIG. 198

The time characteristic of an arbitrary element with delay will thus be the same as for the corresponding ordinary circuit (Section 18) shifted in time to the right by a quantity τ. An example of a "pure" delay τ is an acoustic coupling line (propagation time of sound). Other examples may be automatic dosing systems for some material, moved by a transport belt (τ is the time of motion of the belt from over a defined section). In electronic instruments τ may denote the electron transit time.

In the first approximation a pipe line or long electric line entering into the system may be defined by the delay magnitude τ (for details see Section 46).

In addition, there may be in a real system a series of deviations from idealness which are difficult to describe mathematically and are therefore sometimes approximately considered by introduction into the equation of an appropriate delay magnitude τ (in reality their influence, of course, cannot correspond strictly to a constant magnitude τ). However it is necessary to bear in mind that each sharply expressed non-ideal characteristic in the form of dry friction or in the form of an insensitive zone, backlash, etc. should be considered as a non-linearity and not as a pure delay (see Part IV).

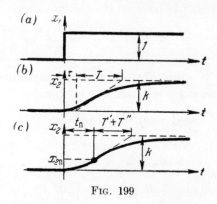

Fig. 199

The magnitude of delay τ in the system may be found experimentally by recording the time characteristics. For example, if in applying to the input of the circuit a step of a certain magnitude, taken as unity, the experimental curve is obtained for x_2 at the output shown in Fig. 199b, it may be approximately described as an aperiodic element with delay (45.2), taking the magnitudes τ T and k from the experimental curve (Fig. 199b).

We also remark that such an experimental curve, from the graph in Fig. 199c, may be treated as a time characteristic of an ordinary aperiodic second-order element with the equation

$$(T_2^2 p^2 + T_1 p + 1)x_2 = kx_1 \quad (T_1 > 2T_2), \tag{45.5}$$

where T_1, T_2 and k may be calculated by relations described in Section 19 for the given element, from certain measurements on the experimental curve (Fig. 199c), or by other methods.

Thus, from the point of view of the time characteristic of a real element, approximately described by a first-order equation with delayed argument (45.2), it may frequently be described to the same degree of approximation by an ordinary second-order differential equation * (45.5). To solve the question which of these equations better suits the given real element, it is possible to compare their amplitude-phase characteristics with the experimentally recorded amplitude-phase characteristic of the element, expressing its dynamic properties with forced oscillations. Plotting of the amplitude-phase characteristics of elements with delay will be discussed below.

For unified notation of the equations we represent the second of relations (45.4) for the delay element in operational form. Expanding the right-hand side in a Taylor series, we obtain

$$x_1(t-\tau) = x_1(t) + \frac{\dot{x}_1(t)}{1!}(-\tau) + \frac{\ddot{x}_1(t)}{2!}(-\tau)^2 + \dots + \frac{x_1^{(n)}(t)}{n!}(-\tau)^n + \dots$$

or in the previous symbolic operational notation

$$x_1(t-\tau) = \left[1 + \frac{-\tau p}{1!} + \frac{(-\tau p)^2}{2!} + \dots + \frac{(-\tau p)^n}{n!} + \dots \right] x_1 = e^{-\tau p} x_1 \,.$$

Consequently, the equation of an arbitrary linear element with delay (45.4) will now be written in the form

$$Q(p)x_2 = R(p)e^{-\tau p}x_1 \,. \tag{45.6}$$

The transfer function and amplitude-phase frequency characteristic of the linear element with delay will be respectively

$$W(p) = \frac{R(p)}{Q(p)} e^{-\tau p} = W_0(p)e^{-\tau p} \,, \tag{45.7}$$

$$W(i\omega) = \frac{R(i\omega)}{Q(i\omega)} e^{-i\tau\omega} = W_0(i\omega)e^{-i\tau\omega} \,, \tag{45.8}$$

where by $W_0(p)$ and $W_0(i\omega)$ are denoted the transfer function and amplitude-phase characteristic of the corresponding ordinary linear element without delay. Writing characteristic (45.8) in complex lorm (8.15), we obtain for the element with delay

$$W(i\omega) = A_0(\omega)e^{i-[\beta_0(\omega)-\tau\omega]} \,, \tag{45.9}$$

where $A_0(\omega)$ and $\beta_0(\omega)$ are the amplitude and phase for the corresponding ordinary linear element. From this we obtain the following rule.

To plot the amplitude-phase characteristic of an arbitrary linear element with delay it is necessary to take the characteristic of the corresponding ordinary linear element and shift each of its points

---

* If it is possible to get along with ordinary differential equations it is preferable since the methods of their investigation are in general simpler and substantially better developed, although, as will be shown in Section 70, the graphic plotting of the transient curve for equation (45.2) is simpler than for (45.5).

clockwise over a circle by the angle $\tau\omega$, where ω is the value of the frequency at the given point of the characteristic (Fig. 200a). Since at the origin the characteristic $\omega = 0$ while at the end $\omega = \alpha$, the initial point remains without change while the end of the characteristic is coiled up about the origin of coordinates (if the degree of the polynomial R is less than the polynomial Q).

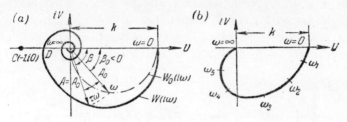

FIG. 200

Above it was mentioned that the real transient processes (time characteristics) of the form in Fig. 199b may frequently be described with the same degree of approximation by either equation (45.2) or (45.5). The amplitude-phase characteristics for equations (45.2) and (45.5) are shown in Fig. 200a and b respectively. The principal difference of the first curve is that it has a point D of intersection with the U-axis. In comparing both characteristics with each other and with the experimental amplitude-phase characteristic of the real element it is necessary to take into consideration not only the shape of the curve but the character of distribution of the frequencies along the curve.

Linear system with delay. Let any of the single-loop or multi-loop automatic systems considered in Sections 20 and 21, contain among its elements one circuit with delay. Then the equation of this element has the form (45.6). If there are several such elements, they may have various delay values $(\tau_1, \tau_2, ...)$. All general formulae introduced in Sections 20 and 21 for the equations and amplitude-phase characteristics of open networks and closed systems remain in all cases in force even for linear systems with delay, if we substitute in these formulae everywhere $R(p)e^{-\tau p}$ and $R(i\omega)e^{-i\omega\tau}$ in place of $R(p)$ and $R(i\omega)$ for the corresponding elements.

For example, for the open network with series connected elements, among which only one has delay τ, we obtain the equation

$$Q(p)x^{\text{out}} = R(p)e^{-\tau p}x_{\text{in}} , \qquad (45.10)$$

where $Q(p)$ and $R(p)$ are ordinary operational polynomials (20.3), and the amplitude-phase characteristic

$$W(i\omega) = \frac{R(i\omega)}{Q(i\omega)} e^{-i\tau\omega} = W_0(i\omega)e^{-i\tau\omega} . \qquad (45.11)$$

If two elements with delay τ_1 and τ_2 respectively are present in the open network, the network equation will obviously take the form

$$Q(p)x_{\text{out}} = R(p)e^{-(\tau_1+\tau_2)}p , \qquad (45.12)$$

which is equivalent to equation (45.10) with $\tau = \tau_1+\tau_2$. Thus, in studying the dynamics of an open network with series connected elements it is immaterial whether all the delay is concentrated in some single network or if it is distributed among various networks. This has practical importance for the theoretical analysis of cases where secondary non-ideal characteristics in the system are taken

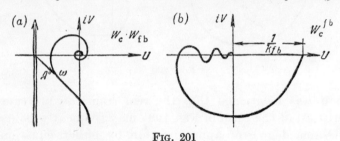

FIG. 201

into global approximate account, as was mentioned at the start of this section. For multi-loop networks more complicated relations are obtained.

If there is an element with feedback (Fig. 108) having delay τ i.e. if equations (21.1) take the form

$$\left.\begin{aligned}Q_c(p)x_{\text{out}} &= R_c(p)(x_{\text{in}} - x_{fb}) , \\ Q_{fb}(p)x_{fb} &= R_{fb}(p)e^{-\tau p}x_{\text{out}} , \end{aligned}\right\} \qquad (45.13)$$

then from (21.2) the element equation together with feedback will be:

$$[Q_c(p)Q_{fb}(p) + R_c(p)R_{fb}(p)e^{-\tau p}]x_{\text{out}} = R_c(p)Q_{fb}(p)x_{\text{in}} \qquad (45.14)$$

and the amplitude-phase characteristic

$$W_c^{fb}(i\omega) = \frac{W_c(i\omega)}{1 + W_c(i\omega)W_{fb}(i\omega)} , \qquad (45.15)$$

where

$$W_{fb}(i\omega) = \frac{R_{fb}(i\omega)}{Q_{fb}(i\omega)}e^{-i\tau\omega} . \qquad (45.16)$$

Let us take the same example as in Section 21, an oscillatory element with introduction of integral, included in feedback in the form of an aperiodic element, but we shall also introduce delay τ into the feedback and estimate its influence. In the curves plotted in Fig. 109 W_{fb} changes, taking the form of Fig. 200a. Therefore the product W_cW_{fb} and the amplitude-phase characteristic W_c^{fb} of the element together with feedback takes the form of Fig. 201a, b in place of Fig. 109c, d.

Example of system with delay. Let us take the engine velocity regulator considered in Section 22 (Fig. 74). We there derived the equations of all elements of the system taking into account their inertia. In addition to this we shall also take into account a delay τ in the effect of the regulating organ on the object. We shall represent this by introduction into the block diagram of the system of an

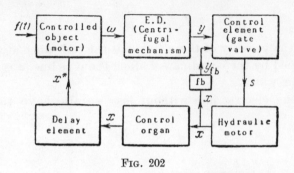

Fig. 202

additional delay element (Fig. 202). Let the object not have self-regulation and be fitted with a regulator with stiff feedback. The equations of such a system had the form (22.58).

Now they will be:

$$
\left.
\begin{aligned}
p\Delta\omega &= k_1'\Delta x^* - f(t) , \\
(T_4^2 p^2 + T_2 p + 1)\Delta y &= -k_2\Delta\omega , \\
(p + k_3 k_4 k_5)\Delta x &= k_3 k_4 \Delta y , \\
\Delta x^* &= e^{-\tau p}\Delta x .
\end{aligned}
\right\}
\tag{45.17}
$$

The equation of the closed system from (20.10) and (20.11) will be here:

$$
L(p)\Delta\omega = -S(p)f(t) ,
\tag{45.18}
$$

where

$$
\left.
\begin{aligned}
L(p) &= (T_4^2 p^2 + T_2 p + 1)(p + k_3 k_4 k_5)p + k_1' k_2 k_3 k_4 e^{-\tau p} , \\
S(p) &= (T_4^2 p^2 + T_2 p + 1)(p + k_3 k_4 k_5) .
\end{aligned}
\right\}
\tag{45.19}
$$

These equations will be used below in the analysis of system stability.

46. Equations of a linear system with distributed parameters

An automatic regulation system with distributed parameters is a system which has, aside from ordinary differential equations, also partial-differential equations. Physically this corresponds to taking into account wave phenomena or hydraulic shocks in pipes, wave processes in long electric lines in transmission from one circuit of the automatic regulation system to another or in the regulation of processes in the pipes or long lines themselves.

This question takes on practical importance most frequently in certain regulation systems including hydraulic, oil or gas pipe lines (either in the object or the regulator), more rarely in certain remote-control systems, etc.

It is well known, for example, that a hydroturbine water line is described, neglecting loss, by the equations

$$\frac{\partial v}{\partial t} = g\frac{\partial h}{\partial x}, \qquad \frac{\partial h}{\partial t} = \frac{a^2}{g}\frac{\partial v}{\partial x},$$

where v is the velocity of the water, h is the resistance at an arbitrary point, defined by the coordinate x along the pipe line, a is the velocity of sound in water.

For a long electric line without loss we also have the equations

$$-\frac{\partial u}{\partial x} = l\frac{\partial i}{\partial t}, \qquad -\frac{\partial i}{\partial x} = c\frac{\partial u}{\partial t},$$

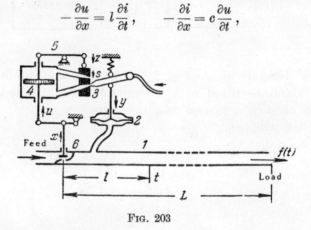

Fig. 203

where u is the voltage, i the current at an arbitrary point, defined by the coordinate x along the line, l and c are the inductance and capacitance per unit length.

After solution of these partial-differential equations taking into account the boundary conditions, defined by the adjacent elements of the automatic regulation system, we obtain for the system as a whole a differential-difference equation of the same type as for the system with delay in Section 45.

Let us derive the equations for the automatic gas pressure regulation system with pipe line shown schematically in Fig. 203. In this case the regulated object 1 (the pipe line) is an element with distributed parameters. For simplicity we shall consider it to be rectilinear while all loads are concentrated at the end of the pipe line.

The regulator consists of a sensitive element 2 (membrane pressure gauge), amplifiers 3 and 4 (jet tube and pneumatic engine), with stiff feedback 5 and feedback from the regulating organ 6 (valve). The perturbation $f(t)$ on the object is expressed by variation of some equivalent output cross section at the end of the pipe line according to arbitrary consumption (a similar system was studied by I. P. Kabakov in 1940 (Reference 21)).

Equation of the regulated object. The motion of the gas in the pipe line is subject to the equation

$$\frac{\partial w}{\partial t} + w \frac{\partial w}{\partial l} = -\frac{1}{\rho} \frac{\partial p}{\partial l}, \tag{46.1}$$

where the condition of conservation of mass

$$\frac{\partial \rho}{\partial t} + \rho \frac{\partial w}{\partial l} + w \frac{\partial \rho}{\partial l} = 0 \tag{46.2}$$

and the adiabatic equation of the gas state

$$\left(\frac{\rho}{\rho^0}\right)^k = \frac{p}{p^0}, \tag{46.3}$$

apply, where w, p, ρ are respectively the velocity, pressure and density of the gas in the running section of the pipe line with coordinate l at the instant t (the entire length of pipe line is denoted by L); k is the exponent in the equation of the adiabatic gas state; the upper indices 0 (p^0, ρ^0) denote that the given quantities relate to the steady-state of the system.

Differentiating (46.3), we have

$$k \left(\frac{\rho}{\rho^0}\right)^{k-1} \cdot \frac{1}{\rho^0} \frac{\partial \rho}{\partial t} = \frac{1}{p^0} \frac{\partial p}{\partial t},$$

from which

$$\frac{\partial \rho}{\partial t} = \frac{1}{a^2} \left(\frac{\rho^0}{\rho}\right)^{k-1} \frac{\partial p}{\partial t}, \tag{46.4}$$

where a is the velocity of sound in gas, defined by the formula

$$a = \sqrt{\frac{kp^0}{\rho^0}}. \tag{46.5}$$

Ordinarily the resistance to the motion of the gas in the pipe line is not taken into account, neglecting the relatively small terms $w \partial w / \partial l$ and $w \partial p / \partial l$. In addition, in view of the small magnitude of pressure deviation p in the regulation process from its steady-state value it is possible to consider that $p/p^0 \approx 1$ and, consequently, from (46.3) $\rho/\rho^0 \approx 1$. As a result we obtain from equations (46.1), (46.2) and (46.4)

$$\frac{\partial w}{\partial t} = -\frac{1}{\rho^0} \frac{\partial p}{\partial l}, \qquad \frac{\partial w}{\partial l} = -\frac{1}{\rho^0 a^2} \frac{\partial p}{\partial t}. \tag{46.6}$$

Let us introduce the relative deviation φ of the regulated quantity from its steady-state value and the relative coordinate λ along the pipe line:

$$\varphi = \frac{p - p^0}{p^0} = \frac{\Delta p}{p^0}, \qquad \lambda = \frac{l}{L} \quad (0 \leqslant \lambda \leqslant 1), \qquad (46.7)$$

and the relative deviation ψ of the gas velocity in the pipe line

$$\psi = k\,\frac{w - w^0}{w^0} = k\,\frac{\Delta w}{w^0}, \qquad (46.8)$$

where w^0 is the gas velocity in the pipe line in the steady-state process, k is the exponent in the adiabatic gas state equation (46.3).

Passing in equations (46.6) to these relative dimensionless variables, we obtain the reguired equation of the regulated object (pipe line) in the form

$$\gamma^2 T_0\,\frac{\partial \psi}{\partial t} = -\frac{\partial \varphi}{\partial \lambda}, \qquad T_0\,\frac{\partial \varphi}{\partial t} = -\frac{\partial \psi}{\partial \lambda}, \qquad (46.9)$$

where two constant parameters of the regulated object are introduced:

$$T_0 = \frac{L}{w^0}, \qquad \gamma = \frac{w^0}{a}. \qquad (46.10)$$

The first T_0 is obviously the time of passage of the gas over the given pipe line in the steady-state while the second γ is the ratio of steady-state velocity of the gas to the velocity of sound in it.

We note that equation (46.9) is equivalent to the so-called wave equation

$$\gamma^2 T_0^2\,\frac{\partial^2 \varphi}{\partial t^2} = \frac{\partial^2 \varphi}{\partial \lambda^2}, \qquad (46.11)$$

which is easily obtained if the first of equations (46.9) is differentiated with respect to λ and the second with respect to t and the results of differentiation equated.

To the system of partial differential equations (46.9) it is necessary to apply boundary conditions. For this we write the equation for the passage of the gas through the regulating valve at the start of the pipe line and the equation of gas consumption at its end.

We employ the expression for the gas velocity in terms of its consumption, namely

$$w = \frac{G}{g \rho F}, \qquad (46.12)$$

where G is the consumption of gas in weight per second, F is the cross-sectional area of the pipe, g is the acceleration of gravity.

We shall denote the values of all variables relating to the start and the end of pipe line by the indices 1 and 2 respectively. The gas consumption at the start of the pipe line G_1 will be considered a function of the regulating valve position x, i.e.

$$G_1 = G_1(x) \, . \tag{46.13}$$

This function is either given by analytical calculation or graphically from experiment (Fig. 204).

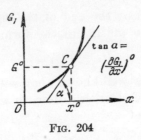

Fig. 204

On the basis of equations (46.12), (46.13), (46.3) and also Section 18 the small deviation Δw_1 of the velocity at the start of the pipe line w_1 from its steady-state value w^0 during the course of regulation will be:

$$w_1 - w^0 = \Delta w_1 = \left(\frac{\partial w_1}{\partial G_1}\right)^0 \Delta G_1 + \left(\frac{\partial w_1}{\partial \rho_1}\right)^0 \Delta \rho_1 = \frac{1}{g\rho^0 F}\Delta G_1 -$$

$$- \frac{G^0}{g(\rho^0)^2 F}\Delta \rho_1 = \frac{1}{g\rho^0 F}\left(\frac{\partial G_1}{\partial x}\right)^0 \Delta x - \frac{G^0}{g(\rho^0)^2 F}\left(\frac{\partial \rho_1}{\partial p_1}\right)\Delta p_1 \tag{46.14}$$

(steady-state values w^0, G^0, ρ^0 are written without the index 1, since they are identical along the entire pipe line). The quantity $\left(\frac{\partial G_1}{\partial x}\right)^0$ is the given slope at the point C (Fig. 204) corresponding to the steady-state process in the pipe line. On the basis of (46.3) and (46.5)

$$\left(\frac{\partial \rho_1}{\partial p_1}\right)^0 = \frac{1}{a^2} \, .$$

Let us introduce the dimensionless relative deviation of the regulating valve

$$\xi = \frac{x - x^0}{x_n} = \frac{\Delta x}{x_n} , \tag{46.15}$$

where x_n is a conventional nominal value, equal to

$$x_n = \frac{G^0}{k \cdot \left(\frac{\partial G_1}{\partial x}\right)^0} \, . \tag{46.16}$$

In addition, we note that from (46.12)

$$w^0 = \frac{G^0}{g\rho^0 F} \, . \tag{46.17}$$

Substituting these in (46.14), taking into account (46.8) and (46.7), we obtain the equation of gas transmission through the regulating valve at the start of the pipe line

$$\varphi_1 + \psi_1 = \xi, \tag{46.18}$$

which is the first boundary condition for the equations of the object (46.9).

The gas consumption at the end of the pipeline at the load may be written according to (46.12) in the form

$$G_2 = F g \rho_2 w_2. \tag{46.19}$$

On the other hand it is well known that with exit of the gas from the pipeline (in the case of critical flow, to which we limit ourselves for simplicity) we have

$$G_2 = Q \sqrt{2g \frac{p_2}{v_2}}, \tag{46.20}$$

where Q is the area of some equivalent output section at the end of the pipe line; this is a quantity which may vary arbitrarily according to the load; it therefore expresses the external perturbation on the given regulation system; p_2 is the pressure at the end of the pipeline before exit to the load; v_2 is the specific volume of the gas at the same point.

The deviation of consumption from its steady-state value during the regulation process on the basis of (46.19), (46.3), (46.17), (46.7) will be in linearised form:

$$\Delta G_2 = \left(\frac{\partial G_2}{\partial w_2}\right)^0 \Delta w_2 + \left(\frac{\partial G_2}{\partial \rho_2}\right)^0 \left(\frac{\partial \rho_2}{\partial p_2}\right) \Delta p_2$$

$$= F g \rho^0 \Delta w_2 + \frac{F g w^0}{a^2} \Delta p_2 = \frac{G^0}{k}(\psi_2 + \varphi_2). \tag{46.21}$$

Let us express ΔG_2 also from (46.20), i.e. through the variation of the output section at the load, considering for simplicity $v_2 = \text{const} = v^0$. We have:

$$\Delta G_2 = \left(\frac{\partial G_2}{\partial Q}\right)^2 \Delta Q + \left(\frac{\Delta G_2}{\partial p_2}\right)^0 \Delta p_2 = \sqrt{2g \frac{p^0}{v^0}} \Delta Q + Q^0 \sqrt{\frac{g}{2v^0 p^0}} \Delta p_2.$$

From this, considering that from (46.20)

$$G^0 = Q^0 \sqrt{2g \frac{p^0}{v^0}}, \tag{46.22}$$

and introducing the dimensionless variation of the output section, i.e. the external perturbation

$$f(t) = \frac{\Delta Q}{Q^0}, \tag{46.23}$$

and (46.7), we obtain

$$\Delta G_2 = G^0\left(f + \frac{1}{2}\varphi_2\right). \tag{46.24}$$

Comparison of expressions (46.21) and (46.24) gives the required equation of gas consumption at the end of the pipe line:

$$\psi_2 = kf(t) - \left(1 - \frac{k}{2}\right)\varphi_2, \tag{46.25}$$

which is the second boundary condition for the equation of the object (46.9). This equation of consumption (46.25) is valid for the general case of regulation with variable external perturb tion, expressed in variation of the relative magnitude of output section f at the load. In studying the transient process in the system, when after some perturbation the consumption has stabilised ($Q = $ const $= Q^0, f = 0$), equation (46.25) will be

$$\varphi_2 = -\left(1 - \frac{k}{2}\right)\varphi_2. \tag{46.26}$$

Regulator equation. Since the regulator here is the same as in Section 23, it is possible to employ equations (23.20), (23.25), (23.26) and (23.29).

In place of (23.20) the equation of the sensitive element here takes the form

$$T_1^2\ddot{\eta} + T_2\dot{\eta} + \eta = -k_1\varphi_1, \tag{46.27}$$

where we have introduced the time constants and transfer factors

$$T_1^2 = \frac{m}{c_1 - c_2 q_m}, \quad T_2 = \frac{c_3}{c_1 - c_2 q_m}, \\ k_1 = \frac{p^0 q_m}{(c_1 - c_2 q_m)y_n}. \left.\right\} \tag{46.28}$$

The variable φ in equation (46.27) is denoted by the index 1 to indicate that the sensitive element measures the gas pressure at the start of the pipeline. The notation in formulae (46.28) is as before.

The equation of the control element with jet tube from (23.25) will be

$$\sigma = \eta - \zeta. \tag{46.29}$$

The equation of the pneumatic drive from (23.26) is

$$T_s\dot{\xi} = \sigma, \tag{46.30}$$

where T_s is the time constant of the drive, defined by formula (23.27) in which in the given case x_n is taken from (46.16).

The equation of stiff feedback from (23.29) will be

$$\zeta = \xi . \tag{46.31}$$

The overall regulation system equation. For the given automatic regulation system we thus have the equation of the object (46.9) with boundary conditions (46.18) and (46.25) (or (46.26)) and the regulator equation (46.27), (46.29), (46.30) and (46.31).

The solution of the partial differential equations (46.9), as is well known, may be written in the form of the following sum of certain two functions in the arguments $(t - \gamma T_0 \lambda)$ and $(t + \gamma T_0 \lambda)$:

$$\left.\begin{aligned}
\varphi &= \Phi'(t - \gamma T_0 \lambda) + \Phi''(t + \gamma T_0 \lambda) , \\
\psi &= \frac{1}{\gamma}[\Phi'(t - \gamma T_0 \lambda) - \Phi''(t + \gamma T_0 \lambda)]
\end{aligned}\right\} \tag{46.32}$$

(it is easily verified that with these substitutions equations (46.9) are satisfied identically).

To find the functions Φ' and Φ'' we employ the boundary conditions. In investigating the transient process the gas consumption equation at the end of the pipeline (i.e. the second boundary condition) is taken in the form (46.26). This corresponds to the value $1 = L$, i.e. $\lambda = 1$. Therefore from condition (46.26) with substitution (46.32) we obtain

$$\Phi''(t + \gamma T_0) = \frac{1 + \gamma\left(1 - \dfrac{k}{2}\right)}{1 - \gamma\left(1 - \dfrac{k}{2}\right)} \, \Phi'(t - \gamma T_0) ,$$

from which

$$\Phi''(t) = b\Phi'(t - \tau) , \tag{46.33}$$

where we put

$$b = \frac{1 + \gamma\left(1 - \dfrac{k}{2}\right)}{1 - \gamma\left(1 - \dfrac{k}{2}\right)} , \qquad \tau = 2\gamma T_0 . \tag{46.34}$$

At the start of the pipe line, where $\lambda = 0$, we have from (46.32)

$$\left.\begin{aligned}
\varphi_1 &= \Phi'(t) + \Phi''(t) = \Phi'(t) + b\Phi'(t - \tau) , \\
\psi_1 &= \frac{1}{\gamma}[\Phi'(t) - \Phi''(t)] = \frac{1}{\gamma}[\Phi'(t) - b\Phi'(t - \tau)] .
\end{aligned}\right\} \tag{46.35}$$

To these equations it is necessary to add the first boundary condition (46.18) and the regulator equation.

Let us now write all these equations for the regulation system in symbolic operational form, noting first that from Section 45 equation (46.33) will have the operational form

$$\Phi'' = be^{-\tau p}\Phi . \tag{46.36}$$

As a result of all the above the regulation system equations will be:

$$
\left.\begin{array}{c}
\varphi_1 = (1 + be^{-\tau p})\Phi', \\[4pt]
\psi_1 = \dfrac{1}{\gamma}(1 - be^{-\tau p})\Phi', \\[4pt]
\varphi_1 + \psi_1 = \xi, \\[4pt]
(T_1^2 p^2 + T_2 p + 1)\eta = -k_1\varphi_1, \\[4pt]
\sigma = \eta - \zeta, \quad T_s p\xi = \sigma, \quad \zeta = \xi
\end{array}\right\} \quad (46.37)
$$

or, more concisely

$$
\left.\begin{array}{c}
\left[(1 + be^{-\tau p}) + \dfrac{1}{\gamma}(1 - be^{-\tau p})\right]\Phi' = \xi, \\[6pt]
(T_1^2 p^2 + T_2 p + 1)\eta = -k_1(1 + be^{-\tau p})\Phi', \\[6pt]
(T_s p + 1)\xi = \eta
\end{array}\right\} \quad (46.38)
$$

Eliminating from here the variables ξ and η, we arrive at a single differential equation for the given automatic regulation system

$$
\Big\{(T_1^2 p^2 + T_2 p + 1)(T_s p + 1)\left[(1 + be^{-\tau p}) + \dfrac{1}{\gamma}(1 - be^{-\tau p})\right] +
$$
$$
+ k_1(1 + be^{-\tau p})\Big\}\Phi' = 0, \quad (46.39)
$$

which may be transformed to

$$
\Big\{\left[(T_1^2 p^2 + T_2 p + 1)(T_s p + 1) + \dfrac{k_1\gamma}{\gamma+1}\right] +
$$
$$
+ b\,\dfrac{\gamma-1}{\gamma+1}\left[(T_1^2 p^2 + T_2 p + 1)(T_s p + 1) + \dfrac{k_1\gamma}{\gamma-1}\right]e^{-\tau p}\Big\}\Phi' = 0.
$$

This equation has basically the same form as the equation of a system with delay (for example, (45.18) and (45.19)). Here it defines the quantity Φ' through which we then find from the above relations the regulated quantity φ_1 and others. The parameter τ in this equation from (46.34) and (46.10) is calculated according to the formula

$$
\tau = 2\frac{L}{a}, \quad (46.40)
$$

i.e. τ is the double time of propagation of sound in the gas over the given pipeline.

Equation of the regulation system neglecting wave processes. It is interesting to compare the differential-difference equation (46.39) with that which would be obtained neglecting wave phenomena in the pipeline. We shall consider that the entire gas in the pipeline moves as a single mass with a single velocity and pressure; of course in this we take into account only the compressibility of the gas.

We shall consider that the input and output of gas per unit time will be in this case: $G_1 = G_1(x)$, $G_2 = G_2(p)$. The change in quantity of gas in the pipeline per unit time will be $G_1 - G_2$, but

$$G_1 - G_2 = (G_1 - G^0) - (G_2 - G^0) = \Delta G_1 - \Delta G_2 = \left(\frac{\partial G_1}{\partial x}\right)^0 \Delta x - \left(\frac{\partial G_2}{\partial p}\right)^0 \Delta p ,$$

or, employing (46.15), (46.16) and (46.7),

$$G_1 - G_2 = \frac{G^0}{k} \left[\xi - \frac{kp^0}{G^0} \left(\frac{\partial G_2}{\partial p}\right)^0 \varphi \right] . \qquad (46.41)$$

On the other hand, the quantity of gas (by weight) is equal to $g\rho FL$, since FL is the volume of the pipeline. Therefore the variation of quantity of gas per unit time, employing (46.4) and the relation $\rho^0/\rho \approx 1$ (small deviations) is written in the form

$$G_1 - G_2 = \frac{d}{dt}(g\rho FL) = \frac{gFL}{a^2}\frac{dp}{dt}$$

or with respect to (46.5), (46.7) and (46.17)

$$G_1 - G_2 = \frac{G^0 L}{kw^0} \dot{\varphi} . \qquad (46.42)$$

Comparing (46.41) and (46.42), we obtain the required equation of the regulated object (pipe line) neglecting wave processes:

$$T_0 \dot{\varphi} + \beta\varphi = \xi , \qquad (46.43)$$

where

$$T_0 = \frac{L}{w^0} , \qquad \beta = \frac{kp^0}{G^0}\left(\frac{\partial G_2}{\partial p}\right)^0 , \qquad (46.44)$$

there T_0 is the previous constant of the object (46.10) while β is a new constant parameter of the object where the value of the partial derivative is determined for the given object graphically, analogously to Fig. 204 or by calculation.

To this equation the object are added the previous regulator equations (46.27)–(46.31), where in place of φ_1 it is necessary to write φ. Consequently, in symbolic operational form the equations of the given pressure regulation system neglecting wave phenomena will be:

$$\left. \begin{array}{c} (T_0 p + \beta)\varphi = \xi , \\ (T_1^2 p^2 + T_2 p + 1)\eta = -k_1\varphi , \\ (T_s p + 1)\xi = \eta \end{array} \right\} \qquad (46.45)$$

$$[(T_0 p + \beta)(T_1^2 p^2 + T_2 p + 1)(T_s p + 1) + k_1]\varphi = 0 . \qquad (46.46)$$

Here we obtain an ordinary fourth-order differential equation in place of the third-order differential equation with delayed argument (46.39).

CHAPTER XII

INVESTIGATION OF STABILITY IN SYSTEMS WITH DELAY AND WITH DISTRIBUTED PARAMETERS

47. The Mikhailov stability criterion for linear systems with delay and with distributed parameters

In Section 45 the equations of linear systems with delay were given, which for the open network had the form

$$Q(p)x_{\text{out}} = R(p)e^{-\tau p}x_{\text{in}} , \tag{47.1}$$

and for the closed system

$$L(p)x = S(p)f , \tag{47.2}$$

where

$$\left. \begin{array}{l} L(p) = Q(p) + R(p)e^{-\tau p} , \\[2mm] S(p) = \dfrac{Q(p)S_1(p)}{Q_1(p)} . \end{array} \right\} \tag{47.3}$$

In Section 46 in deriving the equations for just a linear automatic regulation system with distributed parameters it was shown that it reduces to the same form in all those cases where the distributed circuit of the system is described by partial-differential wave equations (46.11) or (46.9).

From (47.3) the characteristic equation for such systems with distributed parameters and systems with delay has the transcendental form

$$Q(z) + R(z)e^{-\tau z} = 0 , \tag{47.4}$$

where $Q(z)$ and $R(z)$ are ordinary polynomials with the degree of $R(z)$ usually smaller or at most equal to the degree of $Q(z)$.

Equation (47.4) is sometimes written in other forms, for example

$$Q(z)e^{\tau z} + R(z)e^{-\tau z} = 0$$

or

$$Q(z)\cosh\tau z + R(z)\sinh\tau z = 0 .$$

But a more complicated form of equation may be met

$$Q(z) + R_1(z)e^{-\tau_1 z} + R_2(z)e^{-\tau_2 z} = 0 ,$$
$$Q(z)e^{\tau z} + R_1(z)e^{-\tau z} + R_2(z) = 0$$

etc.

Let us consider a characteristic equation of the form (47.4). It is well known that the solution of the differential-difference equations (47.2) may be written in the form of series and that for damping of the solution, i.e. for the stability of the system it is necessary and sufficient that all roots of the transcendental characteristic equation (47.4) have negative real parts. But in distinction to ordinary algebraic equations here, as a result of the presence of the factor $e^{-\tau z}$, the equation may have an infinite number of roots.

The Mikhailov stability criterion and the frequency stability criterion are applicable to these systems in their previous formulations (Sections 28 and 29). However as a result of the presence of the factor $e^{-i\tau\omega}$ there is a substantial change in the form of the Mikhailov curve for the closed system

$$L(i\omega) = Q(i\omega) + R(i\omega)e^{-i\tau\omega},\qquad(47.5)$$

as well as for the amplitude-phase characteristic of the open network

$$W(i\omega) = \frac{R(i\omega)}{Q(i\omega)}e^{-i\tau\omega}\qquad(47.6)$$

(for the definite rule of opening the network given below in Section 48).

Therefore such simple algebraic expressions as in Section 29 are not obtained for the Mikhailov curve. As a result for stability of first and second-order linear systems with delay positiveness of coefficients is insufficient and for third and higher order systems with delay the Vyshnegradskii, Routh and Hurwitz criteria are not applicable.

Algebraic criteria of stability for linear systems with delay were developed by the mathematicians L. S. Pontriagin and N. G. Chebotarev in 1942, who proved a whole series of very important theorems in this field. Regardless of certain examples of practical application, these criteria remain too complicated. A simpler algebraic criterion of stability for such systems was proposed by Yu. V. Vorob'ev in 1949 under the designation of the method of variable parameter (Reference 18) which was somewhat further perfected by V. G. Labazin.

Certain authors have simplified the problem by transforming the transcendental characteristic equation (47.4) to an ordinary algebraic equation by the substitution

$$e^{-\tau z} = 1 + \frac{-\tau z}{1!} + \frac{(-\tau z)^2}{2!} + \dots + \frac{(-\tau z)^n}{n!} + \dots$$

retaining only the first two or three terms of the expansion. Then any of the ordinary stability criteria (Vyshnegradskii, Routh, Hurwitz, etc.) is applied to the ordinary algebraic equation obtained through such substitution. However the simplified solution of the problem frequently leads to invalid results. It is therefore not recommended.

Mikhailov criterion. The possibility of extending the Mikhailov criterion to systems with distributed parameters (systems with delay) was shown by A. A. Sokolov in 1940 (Reference 9). This question was worked out in detail by N. N. Miasnikov in 1948. Following Miasnikov, let us consider individually two cases: 1) $R(z) = C$, 2) $R(z)$ is a polynomial in z.

The case where $R(z) = C$ in the characteristic equation (47.4). This case relates to a fairly broad class of problems. In particular, it is valid for the automatic velocity regulation system considered at the end of Section 45, where $C = k_1' k_2 k_3 k_4$.

When $R(z) = C$, dividing the entire equation (47.4) by C, we obtain the expression for the Mikhailov curve of the closed system with delay in the form

$$L(i\omega) = \frac{1}{C}Q(i\omega) + e^{-i\tau\omega} . \tag{47.7}$$

Consequently, the Mikhailov curve in this case may be obtained by geometric addition of two curves: an auxiliary ordinary Mikhailov curve $Q(i\omega)/C$ and the unit circle $e^{-i\tau\omega}$ (Fig. 205a). This addition is equivalent to motion of the rotating unit circle over the curve $Q(i\omega)/C$. The center of the circle beginning at the point $\omega = 0$ moves along the curve, while the radius rotates clockwise by the value $\tau\omega$ ($\tau = $ const), i.e. the angle of rotation of this radius is proportional to that value of ω corresponding to the position of the center of the circle on the curve $Q(i\omega)/C$. The resultant Mikhailov curve $L(i\omega)$ is generated by the tip of the radius D (Fig. 205b).

If the resultant curve $L(i\omega)$ satisfies the ordinary formulation of the Mikhailov stability criterion (Section 28) as, for example, in Fig. 205b with $n = 4$, the investigated system with delay is stable. The Mikhailov curve for the same system without delay will be $Q(i\omega)/C + 1$. It is clearly evident in Fig. 205 that the presence of delay τ may make a stable system unstable (Fig. 205c) and, vice versa, make an unstable system stable (Fig. 205d).

We shall show that for the determination of the stability of a system with delay it is not necessary to plot the resultant curve $L(i\omega)$ as such but only to plot the auxiliary Mikhailov curve $Q(i\omega)/C$ and the unit circle as in Fig. 205a.

In Fig. 206 are shown various cases of the relative positions of these curves. Aside from that, the point 0_1 and the auxiliary broken-line axes are shown, making it possible to judge the stability of the system without delay directly from the curve $Q(i\omega)/C$, without plotting $Q(i\omega)/C + 1$ separately. Thus, in cases *a, d, e, f* the system without delay is stable, while in cases *b, c, g* it is unstable.

Let us analyse in order all the cases shown in Fig. 206.

In case *a* the auxiliary Mikhailov curve $Q(i\omega)/C$ encloses the unit circle, without intersecting it or being tangent to it. The radius vector of the curve $Q(i\omega)/C$ is always (i.e. for arbitrary ω) greater than the radius vector of the unit circle. Therefore with addition of the latter in any way to the former along the entire curve $Q(i\omega)/C$, only a somewhat distorted shape of this curve is obtained, but the resultant Mikhailov curve will as before encircle the origin of coor-

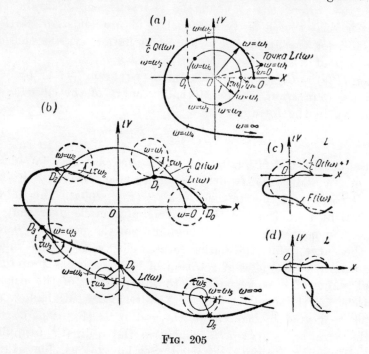

Fig. 205

dinates 0 and as before rotate by the same angle $n\pi/2$ about the origin of coordinates 0 as the initial curve $Q(i\omega)/C$. This case is illustrated, for example, by the curve *b* in Fig. 205.

Consequently, in this case the presence of delay does not disturb the system stability. Regardless of the value of delay τ the system remains stable. The stability reserve will of course vary with change of delay magnitude, as the resultant Mikhailov curve may be deformed towards the origin of coordinates in different ways for various τ.

Cases *b* and *c* (Fig. 206) relate to systems which are unstable without delay, where the auxiliary Mikhailov curve $Q(i\omega)/C$ does not intersect the unit circle. In these cases again the radius vector of the curve $Q(i\omega)/C$ is always greater than the radius vector of the unit circle. Therefore, with addition of the latter in any manner to the former, the resultant Mikhailov curve takes on a new shape but retains its location with respect to the origin of coordinates. As a result the system remains unstable for arbitrary delay value τ.

In cases d and e (Fig. 206) the system without delay is stable with the auxiliary Mikhailov curve $Q(i\omega)/C$ intersecting the unit circle once. In these cases, with the addition of the unit circle radius vector to that of the curve $Q(i\omega)/C$ it is possible that the resultant Mikhailov curve takes a different position with respect to the origin of coordinates than the initial curve.

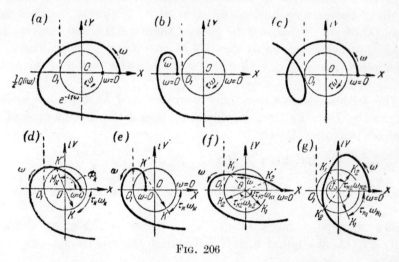

Fig. 206

Let us consider here the critical case where the resultant Mikhailov curve passes exactly through the origin of coordinates 0, which will correspond to the boundary of stability of the system with delay. It is obvious that we shall be incident on the origin of coordinates only if an equal and opposite radius vector of the unit circle is added to that of the curve $Q(i\omega)/C$.

For this, firstly, the radius vector of the curve $Q(i\omega)/C$ must be equal to unity. There is only one such point on the curve $Q(i\omega)/C$— the point of intersection K'. Secondly, it is necessary that the unit circle radius lie in the opposite direction OK exactly at the same value of ω as for the point K' on the curve $Q(i\omega)/C$. We denote this value of ω by ω_k.

Further, since the unit circle radius vector forms the angle $\tau\omega$ with the real X-axis, the given position of vectors OK' and OK is not possible for arbitrary delay τ but only for certain values $\tau = \tau_k$, termed critical, for which the product $\tau_k\omega_k$ gives the necessary $<KOX$ or $<KOX + 2\pi q$ $(q = 0, 1, 2, ...)$. From this the critical delay time for the given system will be:

$$\tau_k = \frac{<KOX + 2\pi q}{\omega_k} \qquad (q = 0, 1, 2, ...), \qquad (47.8)$$

where ω_k denotes the parameter ω for the auxiliary Mikhailov curve $Q(i\omega)/C$ at the point of intersection K', while $<KOX$ is the angle between the ray OK, opposite to the radius vector at the point of intersection K' and the real axis OX. Let us denote by τ_{kf} the fundamental critical value of delay, obtained from (47.8) with $q = 0$.

If the delay in the given system will be $\tau < \tau_{kf}$, the system will be stable since $<\tau\omega_k$ will be less than $<KOX$, as a result of which after vector addition the Mikhailov curve does not pass through the origin of coordinates but to the right of it. With $\tau > \tau_{kf}$ the system is unstable, since $<\tau\omega_k$ will be greater than $<KOX$ and the resultant Mikhailov curve passes to the left of the origin of coordinates. All remaining values of τ_k with $q \neq 0$ will lie in the region of instability of the system.

The critical value $\tau = \tau_k$ may be calculated analytically without a drawing. Here we find the modulus M and the argument Φ of the complex quantity $Q(i\omega)/C$:

$$M(\omega) = \sqrt{X^2 + Y^2}\,, \qquad \Phi(\omega) = \tan^{-1}\frac{Y}{X}\,, \tag{47.9}$$

where X and Y are the real and imaginary parts of the expression $Q(i\omega)/C$.

The required value $\omega = \omega_k$ (at the point K', Fig. 206d and e) and $<KOX$ are found analytically from the equations:

$$\left.\begin{array}{r} M(\omega_k) = 1\,, \\ <KOX = \pi - \Phi(\omega_k)\,. \end{array}\right\} \tag{47.10}$$

From ω_k thus found and $<KOX$ the required τ_k is calculated from formula (47.8).

Case f (Fig. 206) relates to a system which is stable without delay, where the auxiliary Mikhailov curve $Q(i\omega)/C$ intersects the unit circle twice (at the points K'_1 and K'_2).

By considerations analogous to the above we may here find first of all two fundamental critical delay values:

$$\tau_{k1} = \frac{<K_1OX}{\omega_{k1}}\,, \qquad \tau_{k2} = \frac{<K_2OX}{\omega_{k2}}\,, \tag{47.11}$$

where ω_{k1} and ω_{k2} are the values of the parameter ω for the curve $Q(i\omega)/C$ corresponding to the points of intersection K'_1 and K'_2 respectively.

It is further possible to write the following critical values:

$$\left.\begin{array}{ll} \tau_{k3} = \dfrac{<K_1OX + 2\pi}{\omega_{k1}}\,, & \tau_{k4} = \dfrac{<K_2OX + 2\pi}{\omega_{k2}}\,, \\[3mm] \tau_{k5} = \dfrac{<K_1OX + 4\pi}{\omega_{k1}}\,, & \tau_{k6} = \dfrac{<K_2OX + 4\pi}{\omega_{k2}} \end{array}\right\} \tag{47.12}$$

etc. Since in Fig. 206*f* $<K_1OX$ is less than $<K_2OX$, while the value $\omega_{k1} > \omega_{k2}$, we have

$$\tau_{k1} < \tau_{k2} \,. \tag{47.13}$$

In this case the behaviour of the point K_1' with increase of delay τ will be exactly the same as the behaviour of the point K' in the previous case. Therefore here with $\tau < \tau_{k1}$ the system with delay will be stable.

The behaviour of the point K_2' with increase of τ will be as follows.

With $\tau < \tau_{k2}$ the angle $<\tau\omega_{k2}$ will be less than $<K_2OX$, as a result of which the resultant Mikhailov curve passes below the origin of coordinates while with $\tau > \tau_{k2}$, above. Consequently, in distinction to the previous case here the system will not be unstable for all $\tau > \tau_{k1}$ but only for $\tau_{k1} < \tau < \tau_{k2}$.

With $\tau_{k2} < \tau < \tau_{k3}$ the system again becomes stable, with $\tau_{k3} < \tau < \tau_{k4}$ unstable, etc., with continuous alternation of the regions of stability and instability with increase of τ. This corresponds to the fact that since the Mikhailov curve in the presence of delay is "wavy" with increase of τ the waves deform in such a way that the points K_1' and the point K_2' are alternately incident on the origin of coordinates. Incidence of the point K_1' on the origin of coordinates always implies instability of the system while incidence of K_2' returns the system each time to the stable state. Usually only the first few stable regions are of practical importance.

Finally let us analyse case g (Fig. 206), where the system is unstable without delay and the auxiliary Mikhailov curve $Q(i\omega)/C$ intersects the unit circle at two points (K_1' and K_2'). Correspondingly we have two fundamental critical delays:

$$\tau_{k1} = \frac{<K_1OX}{\omega_{k1}}, \qquad \tau_{k2} = \frac{<K_2OXO_1}{\omega_{k2}}, \tag{47.14}$$

where addition of the symbol O_1 in the last expression denotes that we do not take the smaller angle but the obtuse angle ($> \pi$), as is clear from the drawing. In addition, it is possible to write the following critical times (47.12).

In this case the value ω_{k1} (at the point K_1' of the curve $Q(i\omega)/C$)) is less than ω_{k2} (at the point K_2'). The angle K_1OX is smaller than $<K_2OXO_1$. Two alternatives are therefore possible: either

$$\tau_{k1} < \tau_{k2} \tag{47.15}$$

or

$$\tau_{k2} < \tau_{k1} \,. \tag{47.16}$$

Let us consider the first case (the second case will be the same with substitution of τ_{k2} and τ_{k4} by τ_{k4} and τ_{k6}). Here, in distinction to the case d (Fig. 206) on the segment from $\omega = 0$ to the point K_1' the curve $Q(i\omega)/C$ passes above the unit circle. Therefore with the same addition of vectors the result here is reversed. The presence of the second point of intersection K_2' causes alternation of the regions of stability and instability as in the previous case, but with just the reverse result.

Thus, the system is unstable with $\tau < \tau_{k1}, \tau_{k2} < \tau < \tau_{k3}, \ldots$ and stable with $\tau_{k1} < \tau < \tau_{k2}, \tau_{k3} < \tau < \tau_{k4}, \ldots$ Here it is particularly interesting that a linear system unstable without delay becomes stable in the presence of a definite value of delay.

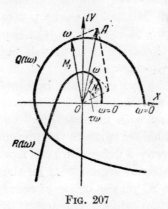

FIG. 207

General case. In the general case the characteristic equation of the system (47.4), when $R(z)$ is a polynomial, the plotting of the Mikhailov curve (47.5) will be as follows.

Let us denote by M_1 and Φ_1 the modulus and argument of the complex quantity $Q(i\omega)$ and by M_2 and Φ_2 the modulus and argument of $R(i\omega)$ (Fig. 207). Then the equation of the Mikhailov curve (47.5) may be represented in the form

$$L(i\omega) = M_1(\omega)e^{i\Phi_1(\omega)} + M_2(\omega)e^{i[\Phi_2(\omega)-\tau\omega]} . \qquad (47.17)$$

From this it is evident that the vector M_1 must be taken for some value ω and to it added geometrically the vector M_2 taken at the same value of ω but first rotated clockwise by the angle $\tau\omega$ (Fig. 207). The resultant is a single point A of the resultant Mikhailov curve corresponding to the given value of ω. Carrying this out for various values of ω, we obtain the entire resultant curve.

However in investigating the system stability it is not actually necessary to plot the resultant Mikhailov curve but to obtain two auxiliary Mikhailov curves: $Q(i\omega)$ and $R(i\omega)$. The first plays the same role as previously $Q(i\omega)/C$ and the second with rotation of its vectors by $\tau\omega$ the role of the previous unit circle. Ordinarily the degree of polynomial $R(z)$ is lower or at most equal to the degree of polynomial $Q(z)$, which will be taken as the basis for the following discussion.

If previously the principal role in the study of stability of the system was played by the ratio of moduli of the radius vectors of the curve $Q(i\omega)/C$ and the circle, and the distribution of their points of intersection, now the same role will be played by the ratio of moduli M_1 and M_2 of the two auxiliary Mikhailov curves and the locations of their points of intersection. In Fig. 208 are shown various alter-

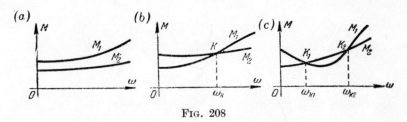

FIG. 208

native mutual locations of the curves $M_1(\omega)$ and $M_2(\omega)$. These curves are easily obtained either from the auxiliary Mikhailov curves (Fig. 207) or directly from the analytic expressions $Q(i\omega)$ and $R(i\omega)$ from formulae (47.9).

Without presenting considerations analogous to the preceding, we present here only the results (following Miasnikov).

In case a (Fig. 208) the system is stable for arbitrary τ if the first auxiliary curve $Q(i\omega)$ satisfies the Mikhailov stability criterion. In the contrary case with the same character of graph a (Fig. 208) we obtain an unstable system with arbitrary τ.

In case b (Fig. 208) there is a single critical delay τ where, if the system without delay is stable, it will be stable even in the presence of delay $\tau < \tau_k$ and unstable with delay $\tau > \tau_k$. Here the critical delay τ_k is defined in the following manner.

From the graph b (Fig. 208) the value of ω^k is taken at the point of intersection K. The value of ω corresponding to this point is found from the auxiliary Mikhailov curves $Q(i\omega)$ and $R(i\omega)$. For the resultant Mikhailov curve to be incident on the origin of coordinates (which defines the critical delay), it is necessary that the vectors M_1 and M_2 (after rotation of M_2) be oppositely directed, i.e. as in Fig. 209: $\tau_k \omega_k = \pi - \Phi_1 + \Phi_2$, from which the required critical delay will be:

$$\tau_k = \frac{\pi - \Phi_1 + \Phi_2}{\omega_k}. \qquad (47.18)$$

Finally, in case c (Fig. 208) we have two fundamental critical delay values τ_{k1} and τ_{k2}, defined in the same manner (47.18) for two values of the parameter ω, ω_{k1} and ω_{k2}, taken from the graph c

(Fig. 208) at the points of intersection K_1 and K_2 respectively. If the given regulation system without delay is stable it will be stable with delays $\tau < \tau_{k\min}$, where $\tau_{k\min}$ denotes the smaller of the above two values τ_{k1} and τ_{k2}. It is then possible to find the following critical values

$$\tau_k = \frac{\pi - \Phi_1 + \Phi_2 + 2\pi q}{\omega_k} \qquad (q = 1, 2, \dots)$$

and to establish the alternation of stability and instability regions as for the case e in Fig. 206.

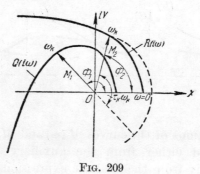

FIG. 209

48. Frequency stability criterion for linear systems with delay and with distributed parameters

The possibility of applying the frequency stability criterion to systems with distributed parameters (systems with delay) was described in 1941 by V. V. Solodovnikov. This question was developed in detail by Ia. Z. Tsypkin in 1946.

Opening of the system. If the linear element with delay enters into a block of the system for which the amplitude-phase characteristic is recorded experimentally, while the characteristics are given by equations only for the ordinary linear elements (without delay), the investigation of system stability differs in no way from the usual one (Section 30 and 35).

If the element with delay enters into a block of the system which is defined by equations (or transfer functions), the amplitude-phase characteristic $W(i\omega)$ of the open network with delay (47.6)

$$W(i\omega) = \frac{R(i\omega)}{Q(i\omega)} e^{-i\tau\omega} \qquad (48.1)$$

is obtained from the amplitude-phase characteristic

$$W_0(i\omega) = \frac{R(i\omega)}{Q(i\omega)} \qquad (48.2)$$

of the same network without delay (i.e. $\tau = 0$), by simple rotation of all vectors A of this characteristic clockwise by the appropriate angle $\tau\omega$ (Fig. 200a). The system should be opened in that line of the loop which includes the element with delay. Thus, if the delay element enters as shown in Fig. 202, the system may be opened in the usual manner (Fig. 210a), where the amplitude-phase characteristic of the open network, from (47.17) and (20.5), will be:

$$W(i\omega) = \frac{k_1'k_2k_3k_4}{i\omega(-T_4^2\omega^2 + T_2i\omega + 1)(i\omega + k_3k_4k_5)} e^{-i\tau\omega} . \qquad (48.3)$$

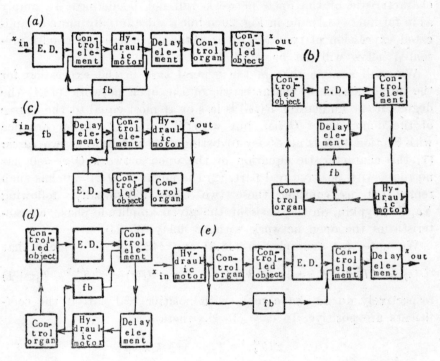

FIG. 210

If the element with delay enters into an auxiliary feedback (Fig. 210b), the system must be opened as shown in Fig. 210c, where from equations (22.57) with introduction of the factor $e^{-\tau p}$ in the right-hand side of the feedback equation, from formula (21.11) we obtain

$$W(i\omega) = \frac{k_5k_3k_4(-T_4^2\omega^2 + T_2i\omega + 1)}{-\omega^2(-T_4^2\omega^2 + T_2i\omega + 1) + k_3k_4k_1'k_2} e^{-i\tau\omega} . \qquad (48.4)$$

Finally, for the case where the delay enters into a part of the loop included in an auxiliary feedback (Fig. 210d), it is opened as shown in Fig. 210e (here in place of the feedback network we obtain a network with branching), where, from (22.57), with inclusion of the factor $e^{-\tau p}$ in the right-hand side of the slide-valve equation, and formula (21.29) we obtain:

$$W(i\omega) = \frac{k_3 k_4}{i\omega} \left[\frac{k_1' k_2}{i\omega(-T_4^2 \omega^2 + T_2 i\omega + 1)} + k_3 \right] e^{-i\tau\omega}, \qquad (48.5)$$

from which it is possible to obtain an expression of the form (47.6) after reduction to a common denominator.

When this rule of opening is not observed the amplitude-phase characteristic of the open network will not be defined as simply as in formula (48.1) and in Fig. 200a but a substantially more complicated expression of type (45.15) is obtained, where the results presented below will not be valid.

We shall assume that in the general case in the expression for the amplitude-phase characteristic of the open network (48.1) the degree of the numerator $R(i\omega)$ is less or at most equal to the degree of the denominator $Q(i\omega)$, but with $W_0(\infty) < 1^*$. In accordance with Section 30 it is necessary to distinguish the following two cases: (1) the characteristic equation of the open network $Q(z) = 0$ has no roots with positive real part, (2) the equation $Q(z) = 0$ has such roots. Let us consider these two cases individually, following Ya. Z. Tsypkin, on the basis of the given amplitude-phase characteristic of the open network without delay $W_0(i\omega)$.

We note, for example, in (48.3) and (48.5) it is evident that

$$Q(z) = z(T_4^2 z^2 + T_2 z + 1)(z + k_3 k_4 k_5) \quad \text{and} \quad Q(z) = z^2(T_2^4 z^2 + T_2 z + 1)$$

respectively do not have roots with positive real part if the coefficients are positive. In case (48.4), where

$$Q(z) = z^2(T_4^2 z^2 + T_2 z + 1) + k_1' k_2 k_3 k_4,$$

it is first necessary to calculate the roots or plot the auxiliary Mikhailov curve $Q(i\omega)$, which, from Section 27, indicates the number of roots with positive real part.

Case where the open network is stable or neutral. In this case, when the characteristic equation of the open network $Q(z) = 0$ has no roots with positive real part (but may have zero roots), for the closed system to be stable it is necessary that the amplitude-phase characteristic of the open network with delay (47.6) not enclose the point C with coordinates $(-1, i0)$.

Let us find the critical delay τ_k, i.e. such for which the system is incident on the boundary of stability (the amplitude-phase charac-

---

* In the contrary case the amplitude-phase characteristic of the open network with delay rotates clockwise an infinite number of times about the point $C(-1, i0)$, i.e. the closed system will be unstable for arbitrary delay τ.

teristic of the open network with delay passes through the point C without enclosing it), As is evident from Fig. 200a a point of the characteristic $\omega = \omega_k$ is incident on the point C when the condition

$$A(\omega_k) = 1\,, \\ \beta(\omega_k) - \tau_k\omega_k = -\pi \pm 2\pi q \quad (q = 0, 1, 2, \ldots)\,,\Bigg\} \quad (48.6)$$

is satisfied, where $\beta(\omega_k)$ is the phase of the open network without delay (48.2). For example, in Fig. 211a we have $\beta - \tau_k\omega_k = -\pi$,

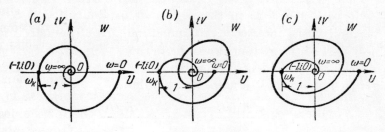

Fig. 211

in Fig. 211b $\beta - \tau_k\omega_k = -3\pi$; in Fig. 211$c$ also $\beta - \tau_k\omega_k = -3\pi$, but the latter does not correspond to the boundary of stability since the characteristic encloses the point C (the system is unstable).

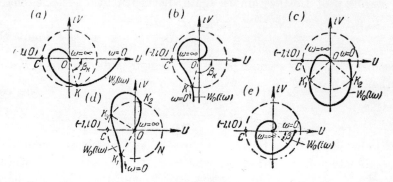

Fig. 212

From the two equations (48.6) the critical values τ_k and ω_k (frequency of free undamped oscillations at the boundary of stability) are determined. They are most simply found from the graph in the following manner.

We first analyse the case where the closed system without delay is stable. Let the amplitude-phase characteristic of the open network without delay (48.2) be known, shown in the form of graphs in Fig. 212a or b, where in Fig. 212a is shown a stable and in Fig. 212b a neutral open system. Let us plot about the origin of coordinates a unit circle (broken line in Fig. 212). We assume that a single point of intersection K is obtained. Then for satisfaction of condition

(48.6) it is necessary that $\tau_k \omega_k = <KOC + 2\pi q$, from which the required critical delay of the system will be

$$\tau_k = \frac{<KOC + 2\pi q}{\omega_k}, \qquad (q = 0, 1, 2, ...) \tag{48.7}$$

where ω_k is the frequency ω corresponding to the point K. The fundamental value τ_k with $q = 0$ is denoted by τ_{kf}.

It is obvious that with delay $\tau < \tau_{kf}$ the given system will be stable while with delay $\tau > \tau_{kf}$ unstable. All further values of τ_k (48.7) with $q \neq 0$ will lie in the region of instability.

If the unit circle intersects the amplitude-phase characteristic of the linear part of the system two or more times (Fig. 212c, d), several critical delays τ_k are possible. For example, in case c in Fig. 212 we obtain two fundamental critical delay values:

$$\tau_{k1} = \frac{<K_1 OC}{\omega_{k1}}, \qquad \tau_{k2} = \frac{<K_2 OC}{\omega_{k2}}, \tag{48.8}$$

where with delay $\tau < \tau_{k1}$ the system is stable, with delay $\tau_{k1} < \tau < \tau_{k2}$, unstable. With delay $\tau > \tau_{k2}$ the system is again stable, since the amplitude-phase characteristic of the open system with delay does not enclose the point C. However, with further increase of delay τ the stability of the system is again disturbed at

$$\tau_{k3} = \frac{<K_1 OC + 2\pi}{\omega_{k1}}. \tag{48.9}$$

Consequently, the second stability region will be $\tau_{k2} < \tau < \tau_{k3}$. Further with $\tau_{k3} < \tau < \tau_{k4}$, where

$$\tau_{k4} = \frac{<K_2 OC + 2\pi}{\omega_{k2}}, \tag{48.10}$$

there will again be a region of instability, which is replaced by the stable region $\tau_{k4} < \tau < \tau_{k5}$, where

$$\tau_{k5} = \frac{<K_1 OC + 4\pi}{\omega_{k1}}, \qquad \text{etc.} \tag{48.11}$$

Let us now turn to the case where the amplitude-phase characteristic of the linear part of the system has the form d (Fig. 212) and intersects the unit circle at three points: K_1, K_2 and K_3. In this case the fundamental critical delays will be:

$$\tau_{k1} = \frac{<K_1 OC}{\omega_{k1}}, \quad \tau_{k2} = \frac{<K_2 OCN}{\omega_{k2}}, \quad \tau_{k3} = \frac{<k_3 OCN}{\omega_{k3}} \tag{48.12}$$

(the letter N in these last expressions indicates that the angles should be taken "obtuse", i.e. including the arc N of Fig. 212d).

If we find from the calculations that $\tau_{k1} < \tau_{k2} < \tau_{k3}$, the system will be stable with delay $\tau < \tau_{k1}$ and unstable with delay $\tau > \tau_{k1}$.

In this case there is therefore only a single critical delay in the system (τ_{k1}), the remaining (τ_{k2} and τ_{k3}) are superfluous in the sense that for them the amplitude-phase characteristic of the open network with delay encloses the point C.

Let us consider a second possible case $\tau_{k2} < \tau_{k1} < \tau_{k3}$. Here the system is stable with $\tau < \tau_{k2}$ and unstable for $\tau > \tau_{k2}$.

If $\tau_{k2} < \tau_{k3} < \tau_{k1}$, the system will have two regions of stability $\tau < \tau_{k2}$ and $\tau_{k3} < \tau < \tau_{k1}$ and will be unstable for $\tau_{k2} < \tau < \tau_{k3}$ and $\tau > \tau_{k1}$.

The above is easily verified plotting the corresponding amplitude-phase characteristics of the open network with delay.

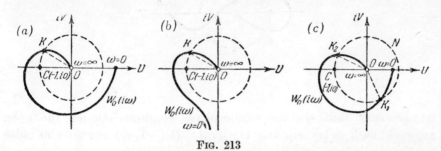

Fig. 213

We note, finally, that the closed system will be stable for arbitrary delay τ if the entire amplitude-phase characteristic of the open network without delay (for $\tau = 0$) is located inside the unit circle (Fig. 212e), i.e. when $A(\omega) < 1$ with $0 \leqslant \omega \leqslant \infty$. In this case no change of phase β through delay can bring the characteristic beyond the point C.

In those cases where the closed system without delay is unstable and there is a single point of intersection K between the characteristic (48.2) and the unit circle (Fig. 213a and b), it is obvious that with any rotation of the characteristic clockwise, i.e. for arbitrary delay τ, the system remains unstable.

If with an unstable closed system without delay there are two points of intersection K_1 and K_2 of the characteristic $W_0(i\omega)$ with the unit circle (Fig 213c), there will be two fundamental critical delays:

$$\tau_{k1} = \frac{< K_1 O C}{\omega_{k1}}, \qquad \tau_{k2} = \frac{< K_2 O C N}{\omega_{k2}}. \qquad (48.13)$$

From Fig. 213c it is obvious that if $\tau_{k1} < \tau_{k2}$, the system which is unstable without delay becomes stable in the presence of delay τ in the interval $\tau_{k1} < \tau < \tau_{k2}$. Here, if the following critical times

$$\tau_{k1} = \frac{< K_1 O C + 2\pi q}{\omega_{k1}}, \qquad \tau_{k2} = \frac{< K_2 O C N + 2\pi q}{\omega_{k2}}$$

alternate, then with $\tau_{k2} < \tau < \tau_{k1(q=1)}$ the system is unstable, with $\tau_{k1(q=1)} < \tau < \tau_{k2(q=1)}$ is again stable, etc.

If in formulae (48.13) $\tau_{k2} < \tau_{k1}$, the system will be unstable with arbitrary delay τ, as at $\tau = 0$.

The case where the open network is unstable. In this case, when the characteristic equation of the open network $Q(z) = 0$ has m roots with positive real part, for the closed system to be stable it

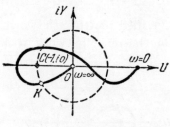

Fig. 214

is necessary that the amplitude-phase characteristic of the open network with delay encircle the point $C\ (-1, i0)$ counterclockwise by the angle $m\pi$.

If the closed system without delay is stable (for example, Fig. 214 with $m = 2$), we obtain the critical value

$$\tau_k = \frac{<KOC}{\omega_k}, \tag{48.14}$$

where with $0 < \tau < \tau_k$ the system is stable while with $\tau > \tau_k$ unstable. If the closed system without delay is unstable, it remains unstable with arbitrary τ.

49. Choice of structure and parameters of linear systems with delay and with distributed parameters from the condition of stability and the quality of the transient process

Let us describe here plotting of the stability region for linear systems with delay and systems with distributed parameters on the basis of the Mikhailov criterion, calculation of the roots and the frequency criteria of the transient quality.

Employment of the Mikhailov curve. As an example let us take the engine velocity regulation system (Fig. 74 and Fig. 202) with delay τ in the regulating organ. Let us examine the influence of the magnitude of delay τ on the choice of transfer factor k_2 of the centrifugal mechanism, for which we plot the stability region of the given system in the plane of the two parameters (k_2, τ). The differential equation of the system has the form (45.18). The characteristic equation will be:

$$(T_4^2 z^2 + T_2 z + 1)(z + k_3 k_4 k_5) z + k_1' k_2 k_3 k_4 e^{-\tau z} = 0 \, ,$$

or in expanded form after division by $k_1' k_3 k_4$:

$$a_0 z^4 + a_1 z^3 + a_2 z^2 + a_3 z + k_2 e^{-\tau z} = 0 \, , \qquad (49.1)$$

where

$$a_0 = \frac{T_4^2}{k_1' k_3 k_4} \, , \qquad a_1 = \frac{T_2}{k_1' k_3 k_4} + \frac{T_4^2 k_5}{k_1'} \, , \\[2mm] a_2 = \frac{1}{k_1' k_3 k_4} + \frac{T_2 k_5}{k_1'} \, , \qquad a_3 = \frac{k_5}{k_1'} \, . \qquad (49.2)$$

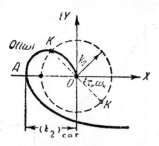

Fig. 215

These coefficients will be considered given. Let us plot the auxiliary Mikhailov curve (Fig. 215)

$$Q(i\omega) = X(\omega) + i Y(\omega) \, ,$$

where

$$X = -a_2 \omega^2 + a_0 \omega^4 \, , \qquad Y = a_3 \omega - a_1 \omega^3 \, . \qquad (49.3)$$

We shall also plot there (Fig. 215) a circle of radius k_2, representing the last term of the characteristic equation (49.1), i.e. $k_2 e^{-i\omega\tau}$. Assigning various values to k_2, we obtain different circles and in each find its critical delay τ_k. This defines individual points of the required boundary of stability (Fig. 216) in the coordinates (k_2, τ).

Let us assume for simplicity that the shape of the curve $Q(i\omega)$ is such that the radius vector continuously increases * along the curve with increase of ω (this is fully realisable). Then, as is evident from Fig. 215, a single point of intersection K' is obtained which, with increase of the radius of the circle k_2, will shift continuously counterclockwise along the curve $Q(i\omega)$. Therefore with increase of k_2 in the interval

$$0 \leqslant k_2 \leqslant \infty$$

* In the contrary case two points of intersection with the circle are possible, which may also be easily studied as in Fig. 206*f*.

the angle KOX (Fig. 215) will decrease continuously in the interval

$$+\pi \geqslant KOX \geqslant -\pi ,$$

where the value of ω_k at the point K varies in the interval

$$0 \leqslant \omega_k \leqslant +\infty .$$

From (47.8) the critical delay

$$\tau_k = \frac{<KOX}{\omega_k}$$

will vary in the following manner:

$$+\infty \geqslant \tau_k \geqslant 0 \quad \text{with} \quad +\pi \geqslant KOX \geqslant 0 ,$$
$$\tau_k < 0 \quad \text{with} \quad KOX < 0 .$$

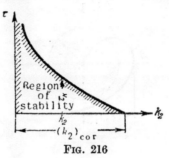

FIG. 216

We are interested only in positive delays τ (a negative τ corresponds to advance). The limiting case $\tau_k = 0$, when $<KOX = 0$ corresponds to incidence of the point K' on the point A (Fig. 215), i.e. the condition

$$(k_2)_{\text{lim}} = OA .$$

But $OA = -X_A$ with $Y_A = 0$. Therefore, finding from (49.3) the value $\omega_A^2 = a_3/a_1$ with $Y = 0$ and substituting it in X, we find

$$(k_2)_{\text{lim}} = \frac{a_3}{a_1^2}(a_1 a_2 - a_0 a_3) ,$$

where a_0, a_1, a_2, a_3 have the values (49.2).

Considering all the above, we obtain the boundary of stability represented in Fig. 216. The region of stability lies to the left of this curve, since the entire segment $0 < k_2 < (k_2)_{\text{lim}}$ with $\tau = 0$, as is evident from the Mikhailov curve, corresponds to a stable system, where the values $k_2 = 0$ and $(k_2)_{\text{lim}}$ correspond to the boundaries of stability.

Diagram of stability boundaries for a third-order system with delay. In Section 29 the boundary of stability for a third-order system was analysed (Fig. 143) in the Vyshnegradskii parameter plane A and B (29.9). Let us determine the influence of delay τ

in such a system on the shape of the stability boundary in the plane
of these dimensionless parameters A and B if the characteristic
equation of the system has the form

$$a_0 z^3 + a_1 z^2 + a_2 z + a_3 e^{-\tau z} = 0 . \qquad (49.4)$$

This question was studied in detail by N. N. Miasnikov by the above-
described application of the Mikhailov curve. We present only
certain results of his solution.

Introducing the new variable u (29.7), we reduce the equation
(49.4) similarly to (29.8) to the normalised form:

$$u^3 + A u^2 + B u + e^{-\tau_0 u} = 0 , \qquad (49.5)$$

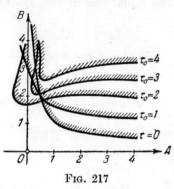

FIG. 217

where A and B are the previous Vyshnegradskii parameters (29.9)
and, in addition,

$$\tau_0 = \tau \sqrt[3]{\frac{a_3}{a_0}} , \qquad (49.6)$$

which we term the normalised delay (it is dimensionless, as are the
quantities A, B, u).

Plotting the boundaries of stability for the normalised equation
(49.5) by the method described in the above example yields the
diagram shown in Fig. 217. Here the curve $\tau = 0$ represents the
Vyshnegradskii hyperbola (Fig. 143), i.e. the boundary of stability
of the ordinary third-order linear system. The remaining curves
in Fig. 217 represent the boundaries of stability of the system for
various values of normalised delay ($\tau_0 = 1, 2, 3, 4$).

This diagram clearly shows the strong influence of delay τ in
the system on the shape of its stability boundary. Basically with
increase of τ the stability region narrows, but for certain values
of τ partially projects into the portion of the plane where the system
without delay is unstable. It is particularly important to take into
account the results obtained on the influence of delay in connection
with the conclusions evident from Chapters IX and X (see Fig. 169,

173, 186), the best values of parameters A and B from the point of view of transient quality are values located in the region of two or three units along both coordinate axes.

In studying real systems it is necessary to consider that the normalised value τ_0 figuring in the diagram (Fig. 217) is connected with a real delay time τ in the system by relation (49.6).

As an example let us take the direct acting automatic velocity regulation system (Fig. 13) where the equations of the object and sensitive element have the form (22.17) with $\beta = 0$ and (22.29), while the equation of transmission to the regulating organ $\xi = \eta$. We introduce, in addition, consideration of delay time as was done in Section 45. Then the equations of the system are written in the form

$$T_a p \varphi = \xi^* ,$$

$$(T_r^2 p^2 + T_k p + \delta)\eta = -\varphi ,$$

$$\xi = \eta , \quad \xi^* = \xi e^{-\tau p} .$$

The characteristic equation of the system will be

$$T_a T_r^2 z^3 + T_a T_k z^2 + \delta T_a z + e^{-\tau z} = 0 ,$$

and from (29.9) and (49.6) we have:

$$A = \frac{T_a T_k}{\sqrt[3]{T_a^2 T_r^4}} , \quad B = \frac{\delta T_a}{\sqrt[3]{T_a T_r^2}} , \quad \tau_0 = \tau \sqrt[3]{\frac{1}{T_a T_r^2}} .$$

If $T_a = 0{\cdot}24$ sec, $\delta = 0{\cdot}11$, $T_r^2 = 10^{-5}$ sec, $T_k = 2{\cdot}2 \cdot 10^{-3}$ sec, then $A = 3$, $B = 2$. As is evident from the diagram (Fig. 217), the system will be stable only for values $0 \leqslant \tau_0 \leqslant 2$, which corresponds to real time delays: $0 < \tau < 0{\cdot}028$ sec. For values $\tau > 0{\cdot}028$ sec the system is unstable.

Analytical expression for the stability boundaries. The boundaries of the stability region for systems with delay and systems with distributed parameters may be plotted as in Section 34 on the basis of the analytical expression for the Mikhailov curve. Thus, to plot the region of stability with respect to some arbitrary parameter α condition (28.6) is employed, expressing from it, as in Section 34, the parameter α in complex form and finding the points of intersection of the curve obtained with the real axis. If it is required to find the stability region in the plane of any two parameters α and β, the expression for the stability boundary from the Mikhailov criterion is used in the form (28.7), i.e. in the form of two equations:

$$X(\alpha, \beta, \omega) = 0 , \quad Y(\alpha, \beta, \omega) = 0 , \tag{49.7}$$

from which it is possible in principle to express:

$$\alpha = \alpha(\omega) , \quad \beta = \beta(\omega) . \tag{49.8}$$

Assigning various values $0 < \omega < +\infty$, in accordance with (49.8) we plot the curves point by point in the plane of parameters α, β and the singular lines $\omega = 0$ and $\omega = \infty$. The stability region is found from these curves as before (Section 34).

As an example let us consider the system aircraft-course autopilot, for which the equations in Section 25 were derived. Here the equation of the aircraft is written in the simplest form

$$T_1 \Delta\ddot{\psi} + \Delta\dot{\psi} = -k_1 \Delta\delta^* , \qquad (49.9)$$

and the autopilot equation (without feedback, but with introduction of two derivatives) in ideal form

$$\Delta\delta = k_\psi \Delta\psi + k_{\dot\psi}\Delta\dot\psi + k_{\ddot\psi}\Delta\ddot\psi . \qquad (49.10)$$

Non-idealness of the system is taken into account in the form of delay

$$\Delta\delta^*(t) = \Delta\delta(t-\tau) . \qquad (49.11)$$

The characteristic equation of such a system, from Section 45, will be:

$$(T_1 z + 1) z^2 + k_1 (k_\psi + k_{\dot\psi} z + k_{\ddot\psi} z^2) e^{-\tau z} = 0 . \qquad (49.12)$$

Let it be required to estimate the stability of the system for various values of delay τ by plotting the stability region in the parameter plane (k_ψ, τ). Factoring out k_ψ in (49.12) and putting

$$a = \frac{k_{\dot\psi}}{k_\psi} , \qquad b = \frac{k_{\ddot\psi}}{k_\psi} , \qquad (49.13)$$

we obtain the left-hand side of equation (49.12) in the form

$$L(z) = (T_1 z + 1) z^2 + k_\psi k_1 (1 + az + bz^2) e^{-\tau z} .$$

Letting $z = i\omega$, separating the real and imaginary parts by the formula $e^{-i\tau\omega} = \cos\tau\omega - i\sin\tau\omega$, and equating them separately to zero, we obtain equations (49.7) in the form

$$\left. \begin{array}{l} -\omega^2 + k_\psi k_1[(1-b\omega^2)\cos\tau\omega + a\omega\sin\tau\omega] = 0 , \\ -T_1\omega^3 + k_\psi k_1[a\omega\cos\tau\omega - (1-b\omega^2)\sin\tau\omega] = 0 . \end{array} \right\} \qquad (49.14)$$

Expressing from this k_ψ and τ, which play here the role of the parameters α and β, we find the equations (49.8)

$$\left. \begin{array}{l} k_\psi = \dfrac{\omega^2}{k_1} \sqrt{\dfrac{1 + T_1^2\omega^2}{a^2\omega^2 + (1-b\omega^2)^2}} , \\[12pt] \tau = \dfrac{1}{\omega}\left(\tan^{-1}\dfrac{a\omega}{1-b\omega^2} - \tan^{-1} T_1\omega + 2\pi q \right) \\[8pt] \qquad\qquad (q = 0, 1, 2, \ldots) . \end{array} \right\} \qquad (49.15)$$

All parameters except k_ψ and τ are given, with $T_1 > a$. Now, assigning various values to ω from 0 to $+\infty$, we shall calculate for each by formulae (49.15) the values of the parameters k_ψ and τ and plot point by point the corresponding curves in the plane k_ψ, τ, where we limit ourselves to positive values of k and τ.

To hatch the curves we find the sign of the determinant (34.12), taking on in the present case according to (49.14) (where the role of the parameters α and β is played by k_ψ and τ) the following form:

$$-\omega k_\psi k_1^2 \{[(1-b\omega^2)\cos\tau\omega + a\omega\sin\tau\omega]^2 +$$
$$+ [a\omega\cos\tau\omega - (1-b\omega^2)\sin\tau\omega]^2\}$$

or after expanding

$$-\omega k_\psi k_1^2 [(1-b\omega^2)^2 + a^2\omega^2] < 0 .$$

Therefore all the curves are hatched identically from the under side (Fig. 218). From this we conclude that only the lowest region may

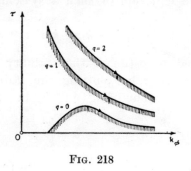

Fig. 218

be stable. For verification we write the characteristic equation of the given system (49.12) with respect to (49.13) in the absence of delay ($\tau = 0$):

$$T_1 z^3 + (1 + k_1 k_\psi b) z^2 + k_1 k_\psi a z + k_1 k_\psi = 0 ,$$

and apply the Vyshnegradskii stability criterion (29.3), which gives in the present case the following condition

$$k_\psi > \frac{T_1 - a}{k_1 b} .$$

Consequently the stability region denoted in Fig. 218 has been correctly found.

As a second example let us consider the automatic pressure regulation system in a pipe line, the equation of which has been derived in Section 46 taking into account wave phenomena. The characteristic equation of the system from (46.39) has the form

$$T_1^2 T_s z^3 + (T_1^2 + T_2 T_s) z^2 + (T_2 + T_s) z + 1 + \frac{k_1 \gamma}{\gamma + 1} +$$

$$+ b \frac{\gamma - 1}{\gamma + 1} \left[T_1^2 T_s z^3 + (T_1^2 + T_2 T_s) z^2 + \right.$$

$$\left. + (T_2 + T_s) z + 1 + \frac{k_1 \gamma}{\gamma - 1} \right] e^{-\tau z} = 0 . \quad (49.16)$$

Let us plot the stability region in the plane of the two regulator parameters (T_2, T_1^2), the significance of which is clear from (46.27) and (46.28). The plot of this stability region was carried out by the above method in 1940 by I. P. Kabakov (Reference 21) with reference to the development of this method by A. A. Sokolov (Reference 9) (I. P. Kabakov, as well as A. A. Sokolov, died in the Battle of Leningrad in 1941).

In the left-hand side of the characteristic equation (49.16) we substitute $z = i\omega$, separate the real and imaginary parts and equate them separately to zero. As a result we obtain two equations (49.7) in the form

$$P_1(\omega) + \frac{k_1 \gamma}{\gamma + 1} +$$

$$+ b \frac{\gamma - 1}{\gamma + 1} \left\{ \left[P_1(\omega) + \frac{k_1 \gamma}{\gamma - 1} \right] \cos \tau \omega + P_2(\omega) \sin \tau \omega \right\} = 0 , \quad \left. \right\} \quad (49.17)$$

$$P_2(\omega) + b \frac{\gamma - 1}{\gamma + 1} \left\{ P_2(\omega) \cos \tau \omega - \left[P_1(\omega) + \frac{k_1 \gamma}{\gamma - 1} \right] \sin \tau \omega \right\} = 0 ,$$

where

$$\left. \begin{array}{l} P_1(\omega) = 1 - (T_1^2 + T_2 T_s) \omega^2 , \\ P_2(\omega) = (T_2 + T_s) \omega - T_1^2 T_s \omega^3 . \end{array} \right\} \quad (49.18)$$

From (49.18) we find:

$$\left. \begin{array}{l} T_2 = \dfrac{P_2 - P_1 T_s \omega}{\omega (T_s^2 \omega^2 + 1)} , \\[3mm] T_1^2 = \dfrac{1}{\omega^2} \left(1 - \dfrac{P_1 + P_2 T_s \omega}{T_s^2 \omega^2 + 1} \right) , \end{array} \right\} \quad (49.19)$$

where we should substitute the values of P_1 and P_2 obtained from (49.17), i.e.

$$\left. \begin{array}{l} P_1 = - \dfrac{xz + k_1 \gamma (\gamma - 1) y^2}{x^2 + (\gamma - 1)^2 y^2} , \\[3mm] P_2 = \dfrac{k_1 \gamma x y - (\gamma - 1) y z}{x^2 + (\gamma - 1)^2 y^2} , \end{array} \right\} \quad (49.20)$$

where

$$\left. \begin{array}{l} x = 1 + b \dfrac{\gamma - 1}{\gamma + 1} \cos \tau \omega , \qquad y = \dfrac{b}{\gamma + 1} \sin \tau \omega , \\[3mm] z = \dfrac{k_1 \gamma}{\gamma + 1} (1 + b \cos \tau \omega) . \end{array} \right\} \quad (49.21)$$

Considering now all the system parameters except T_2 and T_1^2 given (including $\tau = 2L/a$), we shall give various values to ω, calculate for each ω first the quantities x, y, z (49.21), then P_1 and P_2 in accordance with (49.20) and, finally, T_2 and T_1^2 from formulae (49.19). The results of these calculations give us definite points in the plane (T_2, T_1^2), which are joined to give the required stability boundary (the continuous curve in Fig. 219) and the region of stability below and to the right of it.

For a more complete clarification of the effects of wave phenomena in pipelines on the stability of the system we plot also the

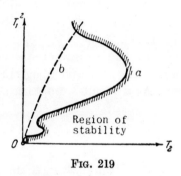

FIG. 219

stability boundary calculated without regard to wave phenomena, but taking into account compressibility of the gas, when the partial differential equation of the regulated object (46.9) is replaced by an ordinary differential equation (46.43). The characteristic equation of the system has in this case from (46.45) the form

$$T_1^2 T_s T_0 z^4 + (T_1^2 T_s \delta + T_1^2 T_0 + T_2 T_s T_0) z^3 + (T_1^2 \delta + T_2 T_s \delta + T_2 T_0 +$$
$$+ T_s T_0) z^2 + (T \delta_2 + T_0 + T_s \delta) z + \delta + k_1 = 0 .$$

Here it would be possible to employ the same method, but for illustration of different possibilities we turn to the Hurwitz criterion. From formula (29.19) we obtain the following equation of the stability boundary

$$(T_2 \delta + T_0 + T_s \delta)[(T_1^2 T_s \delta + T_1^2 T_0 + T_2 T_s T_0)(T_1^2 \delta + T_2 T_s \delta + T_2 T_0) +$$
$$+ T_s T_0) - T_1^2 T_s T_0 (T_2 \delta + T_0 + T_s \delta)] -$$
$$- (\delta + k_1)(T_1^2 T_s \delta + T_1^2 T_0 + T_2 T_s T_0)^2 = 0 .$$

Since all parameters except T_2 and T_1^2 are given, we have here the equation of a curve in coordinates (T_2, T_1^2), from which the stability boundary shown in broken line in Fig. 219 may be plotted point by point. Comparison of the continuous and broken-line boundaries (Fig. 219) gives us an idea of the effect of wave phenomena in the pipeline on the choice of regulator parameters in the given system with respect to the stability condition.

Degree of stability of linear systems with delay and with distributed parameters. It is obvious that the method described in Section 37 for determining the degree of stability and the choice of system parameters from it, based on the Mikhailov criterion, may also be applied to linear systems with delay and with distributed parameters.

The characteristic equation for these systems, from Section 47, has the form

$$Q(z) + R(z)e^{-\tau z} = 0 \ .$$

The shifted equation may be obtained by applying formula (37.7) to the polynomials $Q(z)$ and $R(z)$ and substituting $z = \zeta - \lambda$ in the expression $e^{-\tau z}$. Then, if

$$Q(z) = b_0 z^n + b_1 z^{n-1} + \dots + b_{n-1} z + b_n \ ,$$
$$R(z) = c_0 z^m + c_1 z^{m-1} + \dots + c_{m-1} z + c_m \ ,$$

the shifted equation will be:

$$Q_1(\zeta) + R_1(\zeta)e^{-\tau\zeta} = 0 \ , \qquad (49.22)$$

where

$$Q_1(\zeta) = b_0 \zeta^n + B_1 \zeta^{n-1} + \dots + B_{n-1}\zeta + B_n \ ,$$
$$R_1(\zeta) = c_0 \zeta^m + C_1 \zeta^{m-1} + \dots + C_{m-1}\zeta + C_m \ ,$$

and

$$B_k = \frac{Q^{(n-k)}(-\lambda)}{(n-k)!} \quad (k = 1, 2, \dots, n) \ ,$$

$$C_k = e^{\lambda\tau} \cdot \frac{R^{(m-k)}(-\lambda)}{(m-k)!} \quad (k = 1, 2, \dots, m) \ .$$

After constructing the shifted equation (49.22) the method of investigating stability described in the present paragraph is applied to it, in the same sense as in Section 37 the stability criterion of ordinary linear systems was applied to the problem of degree of stability.

Calculating the roots of simple transcendental equations. The characteristic equation for systems with delay as well as for a definite class of systems with distributed parameters, from Section 47, has the form

$$Q(z) + R(z)e^{-\tau z} = 0 \ . \qquad (49.23)$$

For equations with relatively low degrees of $Q(z)$ and $R(z)$ the following method of calculating the roots is applied. We substitute in equation (49.23) the values

$$z = \alpha + i\omega \ , \quad e^{-\tau z} = e^{-\tau a}(\cos\tau\omega - i\sin\tau\omega) \ .$$

We then separate the real and imaginary parts in the expression obtained. Each of them is equated to zero. The result is two equations with two unknowns α and ω. They may be solved graphically, plotting two curves in the plane (α, ω) from these equations. Their points of intersection (which, in general, will be infinitely many) give the required roots $z_i = \alpha_i + i\omega_i$ of the transcendental equation. Since the system is assumed stable, while complex roots are always conjugate, it is only necessary to plot these curves in the second quadrant of the plane (α, ω).

Frequency criteria of transient quality. It is possible to apply the approximate frequency criteria of transient quality considered in Section 44 to linear systems with delay if the frequency characteristic of the closed system is plotted taking into account the delay.

CHAPTER XIII

PULSE (DISCONTINUOUS) AUTOMATIC REGULATION SYSTEMS

50. Equations and frequency characteristics of linear pulse regulation systems

Pulse automatic regulation systems are one of the forms of discontinuous regulation systems (a second form of discontinuous regulation system is the relay system considered in Section 53). Certain general information on these systems has already been given in Section 4.

A linear pulse regulation system is an automatic regulation system which, in addition to elements described by ordinary linear differential equations, contains a pulse element, having at the input a continuous force and transforming it into pulses at equal time intervals proportional to the values of the input quantity at instants of time corresponding to the start of each pulse. This definition includes pulse elements of types *a* and *b* (Fig. 29 and 31) while the third type (*c*) will be non-linear since the magnitude of pulse is independent of the magnitude of input quantity and depends only on its sign, as in an ordinary non-linear relay-type element.

In addition, a key (and a chopper bar) which from some external cause closes a circuit in short impulses at equal time intervals may also be a pulse circuit. The difference between a key-type pulse circuit and a chopper bar is that the former "cuts out" defined sections from the continuously varying quantity (Fig. 220c), while the latter gives rectilinear pulses (Fig. 220a and b). Either pulse element may be realised by various electromechanical or electronic devices. We shall term them respectively pulse elements type *I*, type *II*, type *III* (Fig. 220a, b, c).

Here we shall consider special methods of studying linear pulse systems, but in a number of cases it will be necessary to bear in mind that these systems may be studied as ordinary linear systems (see the note at the end of Section 13).

Equations of pulse automatic regulation systems. As an example we take the pulse automatic regulation system for temperature θ, the schematic diagram of which is given in Fig. 30 and described in Section 4. Its block diagram is given in Fig. 221a. The regulated object may be, for example, a heat engine, the temperature in which θ should be maintained constant by varying the position ξ of the shutters (regulating organ), i.e. by varying the rate of cooling the engine.

In the general case there may be a number of continuous elements in an arbitrary linear pulse regulation system, described by ordinary

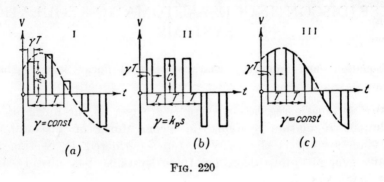

FIG. 220

linear differential equations and one discontinuous, pulse-element. It is therefore possible to represent the general structure of a pulse regulation system as shown in Fig. 221b where all the continuous elements are combined in a single block which is termed the ordinary

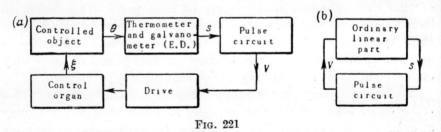

FIG. 221

linear part of the system. This may have any structure (arbitrary complexity, feedback, etc.). In the present example the linear part includes: the drive engine, regulating organ (shutters), regulated object and sensitive element (resistance thermometer with galvano-meter).

The equation of a regulated object of this type has already been derived in the form (9.15). Desiring to investigate only the transient process with steady-state conditions ($f_1 = 0$), we write the equation of the regulated object in the form

$$(T_1 p + 1)\theta = -k_1 \xi, \qquad (50.1)$$

where θ is the deviation of the regulated temperature, ξ is the position of the shutters. The time constant T_1 and the coefficient k_1 are defined by formulae (9.16) or experimentally.

The equation of the sensitive element is written in the form

$$(T_2 p + 1)s = k_2 \theta , \qquad (50.2)$$

where s is the position of the galvanometer pointer, read in the plane of the chopper bar (Figs. 30 and 31). The time constant T_2 defines the thermal inertia of the resistance thermometer and the galvanometer inertia (the latter is small).

The equations of drive and regulating organ are written in the form

$$J \frac{d^2\xi}{dt^2} = M_r - M_f , \qquad M_r = c_1 V , \qquad M_f = c_2 \frac{d\xi}{dt},$$

where J is the moment of inertia of the entire mass rotated by the engine (including the reduction gear and shutters), reduced to the axis of rotation of the shutters, ξ is the angle of rotation of the shutters, M_r and M_f are the rotary moment and the resistance moment reduced to the axis of the shutters, V is the voltage in the engine armature circuit (c_1, c_2 are proportionality factors). This equation is represented in the form

$$(T_3 p + 1)p\xi = k_3 V , \qquad T_3 = \frac{J}{c_2} , \qquad k_3 = \frac{c_1}{c_2} . \qquad (50.3)$$

From equations (50.1), (50.2), (50.3) it is possible to write the equation of the entire ordinary linear part of the system on the basis of (20.2) in the form

$$(T_1 p + 1)(T_2 p + 1)(T_3 p + 1)ps = -k_1 k_2 k_3 V . \qquad (50.4)$$

Finally, it is necessary to set up the pulse element equation. The pulse element is characterised by the following parameters (see Fig. 220): T is the pulse repetition period, γ is the pulse duty cycle (ratio of pulse duration to repetition period), k_p is the gain factor of the pulse element ratio of magnitude or duration of the pulse to the magnitude of the input force at the start of the pulse).

In the present example (Fig. 31) the pulse repetition period T will be the period of forced oscillations of the chopper bar 7. The pulse duration is defined by the time in which the galvanometer pointer 4 is pressed againts the rheostat 9. The pulse duty cycle γ will consequently be the ratio of this time interval to the period of oscillation of the bar (ordinarily $\gamma \ll 1$). The gain factor of the type I pulse element (Fig. 220) will be:

$$k_p = \left| \frac{V}{s} \right| = \left| \frac{V_{max}}{s_{max}} \right| ; \qquad (50.5)$$

it is defined by the rheostat and voltage source parameters. For a type *II* pulse element

$$k_p = \left| \frac{\gamma}{s} \right| = \left| \frac{\gamma_{\max}}{s_{\max}} \right|, \qquad (50.6)$$

which is defined by the design of the chopper bar.

We may now on the basis of the graph of Fig. 220*a* write the following equation for the type *I* pulse element:

$$\left. \begin{array}{ll} V = k_p s[n] & \text{with} \quad nT \leqslant t \leqslant (nT + \gamma T), \\ V = 0 & \text{with} \quad (nT + \gamma T) \leqslant t \leqslant (n+1)T, \end{array} \right\} \qquad (50.7)$$

where $n = 0, 1, 2, \ldots$ is the arbitrary ordinal number of the pulse period, where $\gamma = \text{const.}$ The notation $s[n]$ denotes the constant value s taken at the start of the nth pulse period.

The equation of the type *II* pulse element (Fig. 220*b*) will be:

$$\left. \begin{array}{ll} V = c \cdot \text{sign}\, s[n] & \text{with} \quad nT \leqslant t \leqslant (nT + \gamma T), \\ V = 0 & \text{with} \quad (nT + \gamma T) \leqslant t \leqslant (n+1)T, \end{array} \right\} \qquad (50.8)$$

where

$$\gamma = k_p \cdot |s[n]|$$

or, which is equivalent,

$$\gamma = k_p s[n] \cdot \text{sign}\, s[n] \qquad (50.9)$$

(both notations denote k_p, multiplied by the absolute value of s, which is necessary here since γ is always positive). The notation $V = c \cdot \text{sign}\, s[n]$ denotes that the voltage V remains constant, equal to some value c, but changes its sign with change in sign of s.

The equation of the type *III* pulse circuit (Fig. 220*c*) will be:

$$\left. \begin{array}{ll} V = k_p s & \text{with} \quad nT \leqslant t \leqslant (nT + \gamma), \\ V = 0 & \text{with} \quad (nT + \gamma T) \leqslant t \leqslant (n+1)T. \end{array} \right\} \qquad (50.10)$$

In the result we find that in the closed regulation system (Fig. 221) the pulse element gives pulses V at the input of the ordinary linear part (according to (50.7), (50.8) or (50.10)), which are transformed by the latter to the displacement S in accordance with equation (50.4); this displacement S is again applied to the input of the pulse element, where it is again transformed to pulses V, etc.

In the general case for the ordinary linear part of the system we will have the equation

$$Q(p)s = -R(p)V, \qquad (50.11)$$

where $Q(p)$ and $R(p)$ operational polynomials of arbitrary degree, the degree of the former usually being higher than the degree of the latter.

Below we shall consider two methods of studying linear pulse systems: using difference equations and a frequency method. We shall therefore first describe obtaining the difference equations and the frequency characteristics.

Obtaining the difference equations. Let there exist a pulse automatic temperature regulation system (Fig. 30) in which for simplicity we neglect the inertia of the regulator ($T_2 = T_3 = 0$). Let a pulse element type II be included in this system (the pulse duration is proportional to the input quantity). We shall illustrate obtaining the difference equations using this simple example*.

In studying the operation of any pulse system it is convenient to employ the relative time

$$\bar{t} = \frac{t}{T}, \tag{50.12}$$

i.e. in other words, it is convenient to measure the time by the number of periods T (pulse periods) rather than by seconds, as is usual. Then the equation of the pulse element (50.8) is written in the form

$$\begin{rcases} V = c \cdot \operatorname{sign} s[n] \quad \text{with} \quad n \leqslant \bar{t} \leqslant n+\gamma \,, \\ V = 0 \quad \text{with} \quad n+\gamma \leqslant \bar{t} \leqslant n+1 \,, \end{rcases} \tag{50.13}$$

where

$$\gamma = k_p \cdot s[n] \cdot \operatorname{sign} s[n] \,. \tag{50.14}$$

The equation of the regulated object (50.1) takes the form

$$\frac{T_1}{T} \frac{d\theta}{d\bar{t}} + \theta = -k_1 \xi \,, \tag{50.15}$$

the equation of the sensitive element (50.2) with $T_2 = 0$ will be:

$$s = k_2 \theta \,, \tag{50.16}$$

the equation of the drive with regulating organ (50.3) with $T_3 = 0$ will be:

$$\frac{1}{T} \frac{d\xi}{d\bar{t}} = k_3 V \,. \tag{50.17}$$

To determine the values of the variables at the initial instants of each pulse period we integrate the above equations over an arbitrary nth period. From (50.17) and (50.13) we obtain by integration:

$$\begin{rcases} \xi = \xi[n] + \alpha \cdot (\bar{t} - n) \cdot \operatorname{sign} s[n] \quad \text{with} \quad n \leqslant \bar{t} \leqslant n+\gamma \,, \\ \xi = \xi[n] + \alpha\gamma \cdot \operatorname{sign} s[n] \quad \text{with} \quad n+\gamma \leqslant \bar{t} \leqslant n+1 \,, \end{rcases} \tag{50.18}$$

---

* We present here an example considered by Ya. Z. Tsypkin in 1948.

where $\xi[n]$ is the value of ξ at the start of the nth pulse period. In (50.18) we put

$$\alpha = Tk_3c \,. \tag{50.19}$$

At the end of the nth and, consequently, the start of the $(n+1)$st pulse period from (50.18) and (50.14), considering that multiplication of the sign $s[n]$ by itself gives $+1$ we find

$$\xi[n+1] = \xi[n] + k_p\alpha s[n] \,. \tag{50.20}$$

The solution of equation (50.15), as is well known, will be

$$\theta = \theta[n]e^{-\beta(\bar{\imath}-n)} - k_1\beta e^{-\beta(\bar{\imath}-n)} \int_n^{\bar{\imath}} e^{-\beta(\bar{\imath}-n)}\xi d\bar{\imath} \,,$$

where $\theta[n]$ is the value of θ at the start of the nth pulse period and we employ the notation

$$\beta = \frac{T}{T_1} \quad (0 < \beta \ll 1) \,. \tag{50.21}$$

Taking into account (50.18) we integrate here separately for the two segments of variation of $\bar{\imath}$. Substituting then $\bar{\imath} = n+1$ (the end of the nth segment and the start of the $n+1$-st), we obtain

$$\theta[n+1] = \theta[n]e^{-\beta} - k_1(1-e^{-\beta})\xi[n] -$$
$$- \left\{ k_1 \frac{\alpha}{\beta} e^{-\beta}(1-e^{\beta\gamma}) + k_1\alpha\gamma \right\} \cdot \mathrm{sign}\, s[n] \,.$$

But from the smallness of $\gamma(\gamma \ll 1)$ we may assume

$$1 - e^{\beta\gamma} \approx -\beta\gamma \,.$$

Therefore, substituting (50.14) in the expression obtained for $\theta[n+1]$, we find

$$\theta[n+1] = \theta[n]e^{-\beta} - k_1(1-e^{-\beta})\xi[n] - k_1k_p\alpha(1-e^{-\beta})s[n] \,. \tag{50.22}$$

We have thus obtained the required difference equations (50.20) and (50.22) supplemented by relation (50.16), which together describe the transient process in the given pulse regulation system. These three equations may be reduced to a single one, eliminating two variables (ξ and s). Employing (50.16), from (50.20) and (50.22) we obtain two difference equations for the pulse regulation system

$$\left. \begin{aligned} \xi[n+1] - \xi[n] &= k_2k_p\alpha\theta[n] \,, \\ \theta[n+1] + \{k\alpha(1-e^{-\beta}) - e^{-\beta}\}\theta[n] &= -k_1(1-e^{-\beta})\xi[n] \,, \end{aligned} \right\} \tag{50.23}$$

where k denotes the overall gain factor

$$k = k_1k_2k_p \,.$$

We eliminate ξ from these two first-order difference equations. For this we rewrite the second of equations (50.23) for the $(n+1)$st interval (up to now it described the nth), namely

$$\theta[n+2] + \{k\alpha(1-e^{-\beta}) - e^{-\beta}\}\theta[n+1] = -k_1(1-e^{-\beta})\xi[n+1].$$

From this and from the second equation of (50.23) the values of $\xi[n]$ and $\xi[n+1]$ are substituted in the first equation of (50.23), previously multiplied by $k_1(1-e^{-\beta})$. The result is a single difference equation for the pulse regulation system

$$\theta[n+2] - \{1+e^{-\beta}-k\alpha(1-e^{-\beta})\}\theta[n+1] + e^{-\beta}\theta[n] = 0; \qquad (50.24)$$

this is a second-order homogeneous difference equation. It will be studied in Section 51.

Obtaining the frequency characteristics. Let us open the regulation system at the input to the pulse element. Then in place of the closed system (Fig. 221) we obtain the open network (Fig. 222). In place

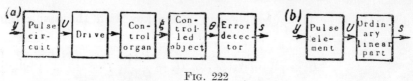

F<small>IG</small>. 222

of the displacement of the sensitive element s, as in the closed system, the input to the open network at the pulse element will now be an arbitrary external input quantity denoted in Fig. 222 by y. The displacement of the sensitive element s will be the output quantity of the open network.

For the ordinary linear portion of the system we have the input quantity V and the output s. In the general case this part may have a structure of arbitrary complexity (with feedback, etc.). Its equation, as discussed above, has the form (50.11) in the general case. The transfer function of the ordinary linear part will thus be:

$$W_0(p) = \frac{R(p)}{Q(p)} \qquad (50.25)$$

(in writing the transfer function of the open network, as has been done everywhere previously, the minus sign before $R(p)$ is omitted).

Similarly to the passage in the difference equations to the relative time (50.12), here in operational notation we pass to the relative operator

$$q = Tp, \qquad (50.26)$$

where T is the pulse repetition period. Then the transfer function in the general case will have the form

$$W_0(q) = \frac{R_0(q)}{Q_0(q)}, \qquad (50.27)$$

in place of (50.25), where $R_0(q)$ and $Q_0(q)$ are operational polynomials of the same degree as $R(p)$, $Q(p)$ but with somewhat changed coefficients as a result of the transformation (50.26) from p to q. We denote by $q_i (i = 1, 2, ..., n)$ the roots of the polynomial $Q_0(q)$ and by $Q_0'(q)$ the derivative of the polynomial $Q_0(q)$ with respect to q.

We present without derivation the expression in general form obtained by Ya. Z. Tsypkin (Reference 13) for the relative transfer function of the entire open network together with the pulse element

$$W^*(q) = k_p \left(H + \sum_{i=1}^{n} H_i \frac{e^{q_i}}{e^q - e^{q_i}} \right), \qquad (50.28)$$

where for the type I pulse element (Fig. 220a) we have

$$H = \lim_{q \to \infty} W_0(q), \qquad H_i = \frac{R_0(q_i)}{Q_0'(q_i)} \frac{1 - e^{-q_i \gamma}}{q_i}, \qquad (50.29)$$

and for the type III pulse element (i.e. a key with the assumption $\gamma \ll 1$, Fig. 220c):

$$H = \gamma \lim_{q \to \infty} q W_0(q), \qquad H_i = \frac{R_0(q_i)}{Q_0'(q_i)} \gamma. \qquad (50.30)$$

Formula (50.29) is valid when the polynomial $Q_0(q)$ has no multiple or zero roots. If $Q_0(q)$ has a single zero root, for example $q_1 = 0$, then the coefficient H_1 corresponding to it will be:

$$H_1 = \frac{R_0(0)}{Q_0'(0)} \gamma; \qquad (50.31)$$

this is obtained by a simple passage to the limit $q_i \to 0$ in formula (50.29).

The amplitude-phase frequency characteristic of the open pulse network is introduced in the form $W^*(i\omega^*)$, which is obtained by substitution of $q = i\omega^*$ in the expression for the transfer function of the open pulse network (50.28). This frequency characteristic, as an ordinary one (Section 8), may be represented in the form

$$W^*(i\omega^*) = U^*(\omega^*) + i V^*(\omega^*) \qquad (50.32)$$

or

$$W^*(i\omega^*) = A^*(\omega^*) e^{-i B^*(\omega^*)}, \qquad (50.33)$$

which corresponds to the graphic representation in the complex plane shown in Fig. 223, where only the following interval of frequency variation enters into consideration: $0 \leqslant \omega^* \leqslant \pi$. The relative frequency ω^* is related to the real frequency ω according to (50.26) by the relationship

$$\omega^* = T\omega. \qquad (50.34)$$

Let us consider the previous example of pulse system (with $T_2 = T_3 = 0$), but in distinction to it we take the pulse element type I, where the pulse duration γT will be constant while its amplitude will vary proportionally to the values of the input quantity at the start of the pulse, according to (50.7).

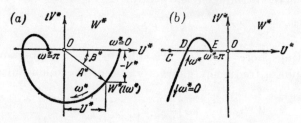

FIG. 223

According to the equation of the ordinary linear part of the system (50.4) we find the transfer function of this part (assuming $T_2 = T_3 = 0$):

$$W_0(p) = \frac{k_1 k_2 k_3}{(T_1 p + 1)p} .$$

Passing to the relative operator q (50.26), we obtain

$$W_0(q) = \frac{k_1 k_2 \beta \delta}{q(q + \beta)}, \tag{50.35}$$

where

$$\beta = \frac{T}{T_1}, \qquad \delta = T k_3 . \tag{50.36}$$

The operational polynomial $Q_0(q) = q(q + \beta)$ has the roots

$$q_1 = 0 , \qquad q_2 = -\beta .$$

Its derivative will be

$$Q_0'(q) = 2q + \beta .$$

The polynomial $R_0(q)$, as is evident from (50.35), degenerates here to a constant

$$R_1(q) = k_1 k_2 \beta \delta .$$

From formula (50.29) we find the result:

$$H = 0 , \qquad H_2 = \frac{k_1 k_2 \delta}{-\beta} \cdot (e^{\beta \gamma} - 1);$$

the quantity H_1, corresponding to the zero root $q_1 = 0$, is found separately from formula (50.31),

$$H_1 = k_1 k_2 \delta \gamma .$$

The transfer function of the overall open pulse network (50.28) will be

$$W^*(q) = k\delta \left[\frac{\gamma}{e^q - 1} - \frac{(e^{\beta\gamma} - 1)e^{-\beta}}{\beta(e^q - e^{-\beta})} \right], \qquad (50.37)$$

where we have introduced the overall gain factor

$$k = k_1 k_2 k_p . \qquad (50.38)$$

Substituting here $q = i\omega$, we obtain the expression for the amplitude-phase frequency characteristic of the open pulse network:

$$W^*(i\omega^*) = k\delta \left[\frac{\gamma}{e^{i\omega^*} - 1} - \frac{(e^{\beta\gamma} - 1)e^{-\beta}}{\beta(e^{i\omega^*} - e^{-\beta})} \right]. \qquad (50.39)$$

Employing the well known formula $e^{i\omega^*} = \cos\omega^* + i\sin\omega^*$ and introducing for conciseness

$$a = \frac{1}{\beta}(e^{\beta\gamma} - 1)e^{-\beta}, \qquad b = e^{-\beta}, \qquad (50.40)$$

we separate the real and imaginary parts in expression (50.39), which gives

$$W^*(i\omega^*) = U^*(\omega^*) + iV^*(\omega^*),$$

where

$$\left. \begin{aligned} U^*(\omega^*) &= -k\delta \left[\frac{\gamma}{2} + \frac{a(\cos\omega - b)}{1 + b^2 - 2b\cos\omega^*} \right], \\ V^*(\omega^*) &= -k\delta \sin\omega^* \left[\frac{\gamma}{2(1 - \cos\omega^*)} - \frac{a}{1 + b^2 - 2b\cos\omega^*} \right]. \end{aligned} \right\} \qquad (50.41)$$

Assigning various values to $\omega^*(0 \leqslant \omega^* \leqslant \pi)$, we plot the curve $W^*(i\omega^*)$ by points in the form of Fig. 223b.

51. Investigation of stability of pulse (discontinuous) linear regulation systems

The fundamental works on the investigation of pulse (discontinuous) regulation systems are those of A. I. Sidorov (1900), N. E. Zhukovskii (1909), Iu. G. Kornilov (1941) and most recently Ya. Z. Tsypkin and Yu. V. Dolgolenko.

Stability criterion for difference equations. In the general case, as is evident from Section 50, the system of difference equations describing the transient processes in a pulse regulation system reduces to a certain mth-order difference equation

$$a_0\theta[n+m] + a_1\theta[n+m-1] + ... + a_{m-1}\theta[n+1] + a_m\theta[n] = 0,$$

where θ is the deviation of the regulated quantity, $a_0, a_1, \ldots, a_m$ are constant coefficients expressed through the system parameters. Its general solution has the form

$$\theta[n] = C_1 z_1^n + C_2 z_1^n + \ldots + C_m z_m^n , \qquad (51.1)$$

where C_i are arbitrary constants, and z_i are the roots of the characteristic equation

$$a_0 z^m + a_1 z^{m-1} + \ldots + a_{m-1}z + a_m = 0 , \qquad (51.2)$$

if its roots are distinct.

The solution (51.1) expresses the course of the transient process in the pulse regulation system by a graph of the form of Fig. 224a, i.e. gives individual values of the regulated quantity at the start

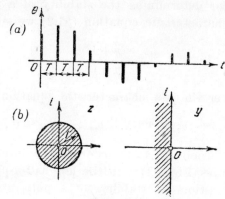

FIG. 224

of each pulse period. A pulse regulation system will be stable when these values tend to zero with unbounded increase in the number of pulses n.

Thus, for a pulse regulation system to be stable it is necessary and sufficient that all roots of the characteristic equation (51.2) be in modulus less than unity, since from (51.1) we have

$$\lim_{n \to \infty} \theta[n] = 0 \quad \text{for} \quad |z_j| < 1$$

$$(j = 1, 2, \ldots, m) .$$

Graphically, this corresponds to the interior of the unit circle in the complex root plane z (Fig. 224b).

Consequently, the first method of determining the stability is here calculation of the roots of the characteristic equation.

Thus, in the example considered above the characteristic equation of the pulse regulation system from (50.24) has the form

$$z^2 - \{1 - e^{-\beta} - k\alpha(1 - e^{-\beta})\}z + e^{-\beta} = 0 , \qquad (51.3)$$

and its roots will be

$$z_{1,2} = \frac{1 + e^{-\beta} - k\alpha(1 - e^{-\beta})}{2} \pm \sqrt{\frac{[1 + e^{-\beta} - k\alpha(1 - e^{-\beta})]^2}{4} - e^{-\beta}}.$$

With given system parameters it is easily verified if the stability condition $|z_{1,2}| < 1$ is satisfied or not, and the inverse problem may be solved, i.e. to choose the system parameters such that $|z_{1,2}| < 1$ (this method was applied by Yu. G. Kornilov).

In other problems, when the difference equations have higher than second order, the use of this method is difficult. It is necessary to find a stability criterion permitting avoiding calculation of the roots.

In this connection certain authors have proposed the following second method for determining the stability of a pulse regulation system. In the characteristic equation (51.2) we substitute

$$z = \frac{y + 1}{y - 1}. \tag{51.4}$$

The result is a certain new characteristic equation

$$b_0 y^m + b_1 y^{m-1} + \ldots + b_{m-1} y + b_m = 0, \tag{51.5}$$

where the substitution (51.4) transforms the interior of the unit circle in the z-plane (Fig. 224b) to the left half-y-plane (Fig. 224c). Therefore the question of stability of a pulse regulation system may be solved by applying any of the criteria known to us for the stability of ordinary linear systems (Chapter VII) to the transformed characteristic equation (51.5).

However this method is fairly cumbersome since it requires a preliminary transformation, as a result of which the coefficients (51.5) are expressed in a very complicated way through the system parameters.

A third method of determining the stability of a pulse regulation system is the application of a criterion proposed by Ya. Z. Tsypkin in 1948. This criterion is analogous in form to the Mikhailov criterion but is applied directly to the initial characteristic equation (51.2).

Let us derive this criterion by analogy with the derivation of the Mikhailov criterion (Sections 27 and 28). We consider the left-hand side of the characteristic equation (51.2)

$$F(z) = a_0 z^m + a_1 z^{m-1} + \ldots + a_{m-1} z + a_m.$$

This may be represented in the form

$$F(z) = a_0(z - z_1)(z - z_2) \ldots (z - z_m), \tag{51.6}$$

where $z_1, z_2, ..., z_m$ are the roots of the polynomial $F(z)$. For the system to be stable all roots z_1 should lie within the unit circle. The values

$$z = e^{i\omega}, \qquad (51.7)$$

correspond to all points of the perimeter of the unit circle (i.e. the boundary of stability), where the upper half of the contour (Fig. 225a) is traversed as ω varies in the interval $0 \leqslant \omega \leqslant +\pi$.

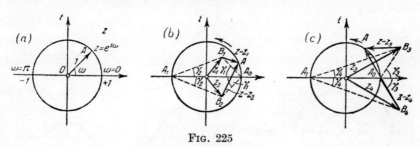

Fig. 225

Let the pair of complex roots $z_{1,2}$ be found inside the unit circle. Then with motion of the point A (Fig. 225b) over the upper semicircle from the position A_0 to A_1 the vector $B_1A = (z-z_1)$ rotates by the angle $\pi + \gamma_1 + \gamma_2$. The vector $B_2A = (z-z_2)$ rotates at the same time by the angle $\pi - \gamma_1 - \gamma_2$. The sum of rotations of these two vectors will be 2π. Consequently, the vector product $(z-z_1)(z-z_2)$ rotates by the angle 2π.

Let now the pair of complex roots $z_{3,4}$ lie outside the unit circle. Then with motion of the point A (Fig. 225c) over the upper semicircle from the position A_0 to A_1 the vector $B_3A = (z-z_3)$ rotates by the angle $-(\gamma_3 - \gamma_4)$, while the vector $B_4A = (z-z_4)$ by the angle $+(\gamma_3 - \gamma_4)$ The sum of these angles of rotation is equal to zero.

It is also easily verified that to each real root z_1 within the unit circle there will correspond an angle of rotation of the vector $(z-z_1)$ equal to π while to the real root lying outside the circle, zero.

As a result we find that with $z = e^{i\omega}$ and $0 \leqslant \omega \leqslant +\pi$ the vector $F(z)$, a product of the form (51.6), rotates by the total angle

$$\varphi = (m-l)\pi, \qquad (51.8)$$

where m is the degree of the polynomial $F(z)$, i.e. the number of all roots, while l is the number of its roots lying outside the unit circle.

But for the system to be stable it is necessary that all roots lie inside the unit circle ($l = 0$). From this we obtain the following formulation.

For a linear pulse regulation system to be stable it is necessary and sufficient that the vector $F(e^{i\omega})$ (Fig. 226a) with variation of ω from 0 to π rotate counterclockwise by the angle $m\pi$, where m is the degree of the characteristic equation (51.2) of the given system while $F(e^{i\omega})$ is the left-hand side of this equation in which in place of z we substitute $e^{i\omega}$. For example, the curve $F(e^{i\omega})$ in Fig. 226a corresponds to a third-order stable system.

The boundary of stability corresponds to passage of the curve $F(e^{i\omega})$ through the origin of coordinates.

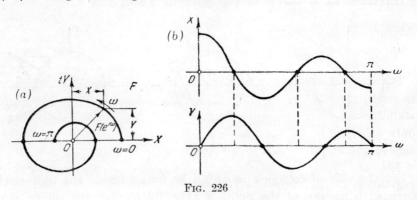

Fig. 226

The curve $F(e^{i\omega})$ is plotted in the following manner. In the left-hand part of the given characteristic equation of the system (51.2) we substitute $e^{i\omega}$ in place of z. The expression

$$F(e^{i\omega}) = a_0(e^{i\omega})^m + a_1(e^{i\omega})^{m-1} + \ldots + a_{m-1}e^{i\omega} + a_m .$$

is obtained.

The real and imaginary parts are separated using the well-known formula $e^{ik\omega} = \cos k\omega + i \sin k\omega$, which gives

$$F(e^{i\omega}) = X(\omega) + i Y(\omega) , \qquad (51.9)$$

where

$$\left. \begin{array}{l} X(\omega) = a_0 \cos m\omega + a_1 \cos(m-1)\omega + \ldots + a_{m-1}\cos \omega + a_m , \\ Y(\omega) = a_0 \sin m\omega + a_1 \sin(m-1)\omega + \ldots + a_{m-1}\sin \omega . \end{array} \right\} \qquad (51.10)$$

Then various values of ω from zero to π are assigned, calculating for each the values X and Y from these formulae and the entire curve $F(e^{i\omega})$ is plotted from these points in rectangular coordinates (Fig. 226a). In complete analogy to the ordinary Mikhailov criterion (Section 28), here, on the basis of the condition of intersection of the curve with the axes (Fig. 226a), a second formulation of the criterion is given: for a pulse regulation system to be stable it is necessary and sufficient that in the segment $0 \leqslant \omega \leqslant \pi$ each of the equations $X(\omega) = 0$ and $Y(\omega) = 0$ have m real roots and that all these roots alternate (Fig. 226b). Here for the function $Y(\omega) = 0$ the points $\omega = 0$ and $\omega = \pi$ are considered to be a single root.

From the shape of the curve $F(e^{i\omega})$ (Fig. 226a) it is easily seen that in the stable system the point $\omega = 0$ should lie to the right of the origin of coordinates while the point $\omega = \pi$ to the left for a system of odd order and to the right for a system of even order. But $e^{i0} = 1$ and $e^{i\pi} = -1$. Therefore a necessary condition for the stability of a pulse system of odd order is:

$$F(1) > 0 \quad \text{and} \quad F(-1) < 0 , \qquad (51.11)$$

while for a pulse system of even order

$$F(1) > 0 \quad \text{and} \quad F(-1) > 0 . \qquad (51.12)$$

Satisfaction of these necessary conditions of stability must always be verified before proceeding to a complete investigation of system stability. This verification is carried out very simply since it requires only substitution of the values $z = 1$ and $z = -1$ in the left-hand side of the characteristic equation (51.2) of the investigated system.

Let us apply this stability criterion to the pulse temperature regulation system considered in Section 50. Its characteristic equation has the form (51.3). Consequently,

$$F(z) = z^2 - (\{1 + e^{-\beta} - k\alpha(1 - e^{-\beta})\}z + e^{-\beta} . \qquad (51.13)$$

A necessary stability condition (51.12) for the given system will be;

$$F(1) = k\alpha(1 - e^{-\beta}) > 0 , \qquad (51.14)$$

$$F(-1) = 2(1 + e^{-\beta}) - k\alpha(1 - e^{-\beta}) > 0 . \qquad (51.15)$$

From the stability criterion the curve $F(e^{i\omega})$ should have in this case the form shown in Fig. 227a. To verify this, it is now sufficient to find the position of the point A of this curve and require that $X < 0$. For this we find from (51.13):

$$X(\omega) = \cos 2\omega - \{1 + e^{-\beta} - k\alpha(1 - e^{-\beta})\}\cos \omega + e^{-\beta} ,$$

$$Y(\omega) = \sin 2\omega - \{1 + e^{-\beta} - k\alpha(1 - e^{-\beta})\}\sin \omega ,$$

and from the condition $Y = 0$ at the point A we obtain

$$\cos \omega_A = \frac{1 + e^{-\beta} - k\alpha(1 - e^{-\beta})}{2} ,$$

and substituting this in the expression for $X(\omega)$, we come to the required condition

$$X_A = -1 + e^{-\beta} < 0 . \qquad (51.16)$$

Two conditions (51.14) and (51.16) are always satisfied with $k > 0$, $a > 0$ and $\beta > 0$, which corresponds to the physical significance of these quantities according to formulae (50.21), (50.19) and (50.23). From the third condition (51.15) we obtain

$$ka < 2\frac{1+e^{-\beta}}{1-e^{-\beta}} = 2\operatorname{cth}\frac{\beta}{2}. \qquad (51.17)$$

The system parameters should be chosen from this condition to make it stable. The graphical representation of the stability region (51.17) in the plane of parameters (β, $k\alpha$) is given in Fig. 227*b*.

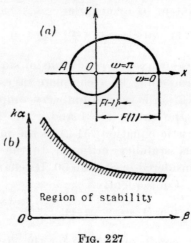

FIG. 227

Frequency stability criterion. In Section 50 we described obtaining the frequency characteristics for the open network with a pulse element, where the system is opened as shown in Fig. 222. The general formulation of the stability criterion according to Ya. Z. Tsypkin (Reference 13) is as follows.

If the ordinary linear part of the system (in open form) is stable or neutral, for the closed pulse regulation system to be stable it is necessary and sufficient that the frequency characteristic $W^*(i\omega^*)$ of the open network with a pulse element should not enclose the point $C(1, i0)$ with variation of ω^* from zero to π. In Fig. 223*a* and *b* are given the characteristics $W^*(i\omega^*)$ of the entire open network for the cases of stable and neutral ordinary linear parts of the system respectively.

Let us consider the same pulse temperature regulation system for which in Section 50 we obtained the frequency characteristic $W^*(i\omega^*) = U^*(\omega^*) + iV^*(\omega^*)$, defined by formulae (50.41). Its graph has the form of Fig. 223*b*. Therefore for the given closed pulse regulation system to be stable it is necessary that the points D and E lie to the right of the critical point C, i.e. that

$$U_D^* > -1 \quad \text{and} \quad U_E^* > -1. \qquad (51.18)$$

The coordinates U_D^* are calculated from the condition $V_D^* = 0$, which from (50.41) will be;

$$\frac{\gamma}{2(1-\cos \omega_D^*)} - \frac{a}{1+b^2-2b \cos \omega_D^*} = 0,$$

from which

$$\cos \omega_D^* = \frac{2a - \gamma(1+b^2)}{2(a-\gamma b)}.$$

Substituting this in the first of formulae (50.41) we obtain the required

$$U_D^* = k\delta \frac{a - \gamma b}{1 - b}.$$

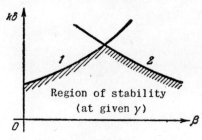

Region of stability
(at given y)

FIG. 228

The coordinate U_E^*, as is evident from Fig. 223b, is found by substituting $\omega = \pi$ in the first of formulae (50.41), namely;

$$U_E^* = -k\delta \left(\frac{\gamma}{2} - \frac{a}{1+b}\right).$$

Consequently, the stability conditions (51.18) take the form

$$k\delta \frac{a-\gamma b}{1-b} < 1 \quad \text{and} \quad k\delta\left(\frac{\gamma}{2} - \frac{a}{1+b}\right) < 1, \qquad (51.19)$$

where a and b are expressed through the parameters β and γ from formulae (50.40). These stability conditions are represented graphically in the form of the stability region in the plane of the two parameters $(\beta, k\delta)$, as shown in Fig. 228, where one part of the stability boundary (curve 1) is plotted from the equation

$$k\delta = \frac{(e^\beta - 1)\beta}{e^{\beta\gamma} - 1 - \beta\gamma},$$

following from the first condition (51.19), while the second part of the stability boundary (curve 2, Fig. 228) from the equation

$$k\delta = \frac{2(e^\beta + 1)\beta}{\beta\gamma(e^\beta + 1) - 2(e^{\beta\gamma} - 1)},$$

which follows from the second condition (51.19) with substitution of the inequality sign by the equality sign and the use of expressions (50.40).

PART IV

NON-LINEAR AUTOMATIC REGULATION SYSTEMS

CHAPTER XIV

DERIVATION OF THE EQUATIONS OF NON-LINEAR AUTOMATIC REGULATION SYSTEMS

52. General remarks

A non-linear automatic regulation system is one which contains at least one element described by a non-linear equation. In Section 5 the classification of non-linear types of elements was given, namely:

(1) a relay-type element, the possible shapes of characteristics of which were given in Fig. 24;

(2) element with piecewise-linear characteristic (having, for example, any of the forms shown in Fig. 34), as well as elements described by piecewise-linear differential equations;

(3) element with arbitrary curved characteristic;

(4) an element, the equation of which contains the product of variables or their derivatives and various other more complicated joint combinations;

(5) non-linear element with delay, where the delay is understood in the sense of Section 45 while the non-linearity may have any form;

(6) a non-linear pulse element.

Non-linear elements of the third and fourth types may be linearised in many cases as has been done in Chapter VI. Many real curved characteristics may be approximately substituted by polygonal, consisting of straight line segments, i.e. transferred to the first or second type of non-linear characteristics. However it is sometimes unavoidable to study curvilinear characteristics.

Considering this circumstance and the great practical importance of the two first types of non-linear elements, we shall give them major attention below. Methods will also be given convenient for the investigation of curved characteristics, and non-linear elements with delay are considered. Non-linear pulse elements will not be considered.

The general method of composing the equations for non-linear systems is as follows. Initially, according to the rules of Section 18, as was done in Chapter VI, the equations of all elements of the system for which it is possible are linearised, except one or two essentially non-linear elements (most frequently one). Then the equation is set-up for this last with all admissible simplifications of its characteristic.

The result is a system of ordinary linear equations to which are added one or two non-linear ones. According to this the generalised

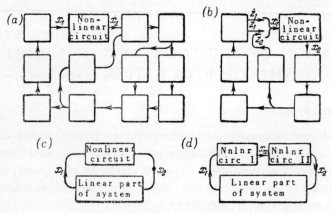

FIG. 229

block diagram of any non-linear automatic regulation system with a single non-linear element may be represented in the form of Fig. 229c, where the linear part may have a structure of any com-

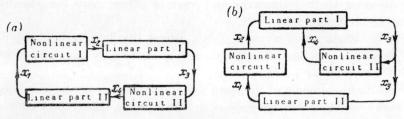

FIG. 230

plexity (with feedback, etc. as, for example, in Fig. 229a or 229b). With two non-linear elements there may be various combinations, depending on how they enter into the system (see, for example, Fig. 230).

Frequently in studying non-linear automatic regulation systems it is possible to separate the non-linear element in such a way that it is described directly by the dependence between the output and input quantities;

$$x_2 = F(x_1) , \qquad (52.1)$$

which may have any form (relay type, piecewise-linear or curved). But sometimes, as will be discussed in succeeding sections, this cannot be done and it is necessary to study the non-linear differential relations of the form

$$F(\dot{x}_2, x_2) = c_1 x_1 , \qquad F_1(\ddot{x}_2, \dot{x}_2) + F_2(x_2) = c_1 x_1 , \; \Big\}$$
$$x_2 = F(x_1, \dot{x}_1) , \qquad x_2 = F_1(x_1) + F_2(\dot{x}_1) . \qquad \Big\} \qquad (52.2)$$

More complicated cases are also encountered, where both quantities (output and input) enter separately into the non-linear function

$$F_2(\dot{x}_2, x_2) = F_1(x_1) , \qquad F_3(\dot{x}_2) + F_2(x_2) = F_1(x_1) , \qquad (52.3)$$

or together

$$F(\dot{x}_2, x_2, \dot{x}_1) = 0 , \qquad F_2(x_2) + F_1(x_2, x_1) = 0 \qquad (52.4)$$

etc.

According to this new criterion we divide all non-linear regulation systems and servomechanisms into three large classes;

(1) in the first class of non-linear systems are those in which the equation of the non-linear element reduces to any of the forms (52.1) and (52.2), i.e. when either only the output quantity (and its derivatives) or only the input quantity (and its derivatives) enter into the non-linear function. Here it is considered that the overall diagram of the system has the form of Fig. 229 with one non-linear element or with several, concentrated in a single place;

(2) the second class of non-linear systems includes such elements in which both quantities (input and output) enter into the non-linear function, for example in the form of (52.3) or (52.4), where the general system diagram has the form of Fig. 229 as before;

(3) in the third class of non-linear systems are all systems in which there are two or more non-linear elements, separated from each other by linear parts (Fig. 230).

We note that in all cases where any linear combination of different variables enters into the non-linear function, it should be denoted by a single symbol, and the given linear combination taken into account in deriving the overall equation of the linear part of the system. This occurs, for example, in those cases where derivatives are applied to the input of the non-linear element or it is included in feedback. Thus, if in Fig. 229*b* we have

$$x_2 = F(z_1 + k_1 \dot{z}_1 - k_2 z_2) ,$$

then we put

$$z_1 + k_1 \dot{z}_1 - k_2 z_2 = x_1 \qquad (52.5)$$

and reduce the equation of the non-linear element to the form (52.1).

The overall equation of the linear part of the system is composed of all the equations of the linear circuits and linear expressions of type (52.5) obtained with the non-linear isolated

$$Q_l(p) x_1 = - R_l(p) x_2 , \qquad (52.6)$$

where $Q_1(p)$ and $R_1(p)$ are operational polynomials, p denotes the derivative with respect to time.

Let us present examples of deriving the equations of various non-linear automatic regulation systems and servomechanisms.

53. Equations of systems with relay type non-linearity

Following the remarks made in Section 52, we present several examples of equations for relay type non-linear systems.

Automatic voltage regulation system. Let there exist a shunt dynamo (regulated object) with vibrator voltage regulator. The simplified schematic diagram of such a system is shown in Fig. 231.

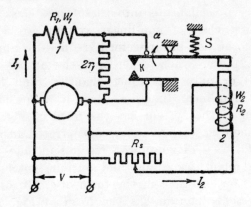

Fig. 231

When the contacts K close under the influence of the spring S the resistance denoted by $2r_1$ is cut out of the dynamo field circuit W_1. The system is calculated so that the voltage U at the dynamo terminals increases (with any actually possible load on the network fed by the given dynamo). As a result the current I_2 in the coil W_2 of the electromagnetic relay increases and the relay armature is attracted, which opens the contacts K. With contacts K open the resistance $2r_1$ is connected in the field circuit. This causes reduction of potential V, and thus reduction of the current I_2 and release of the relay, as a result of which the contacts K again close, cutting out the resistance $2r_1$ from the field circuit. Adjustment of the system to a desired nominal value of the regulated quantity V is carried out by setting the resistance R_s.

The regulated object (dynamo) is here the same as in Section 24. Therefore the equation of the regulated object will have as before the form (24.10), i.e.

$$(T_1 p + 1)\Delta V = -k_1 \Delta r + (b_0 p + b)f(t) , \qquad (53.1)$$

where the time constant T_1 and the coefficients k_1, b_0, b are defined by formulae (24.11). All values of variable quantities and parameters denoted by zero upper indices, including the operating point C of the dynamo characteristic (Fig. 120) entering here and below, will be related to the relative steady-state process which would occur if the resistance of the field winding was constant, equal to the mean value

$$R^0 = R_1 + r_1 . \tag{53.2}$$

Therefore we should assume in formulae (24.11)

$$r^0 = r_1 . \tag{53.3}$$

Intending to study the transient processes in the absence of external perturbations ($f(t) = 0$), in accordance with (53.1) we write the equation of the regulated object in the form

$$(T_1 p + 1)\Delta V = -k_1 \Delta r . \tag{53.4}$$

The equation of the sensitive element (winding of the electromagnet 2), as in Section 24, has the form (24.20). In this equation it is necessary to substitute the quantity $\Delta\alpha$ by ΔI_2, for which we employ the equation of motion of the armature (24.28) in which we neglect the moment of inertia of the armature ($T_4 = 0$) and friction ($T_3 = 0$) as small quantities. In the result, we obtain from (24.20) and (24.28) the equation of the sensitive element in the form

$$(T_2'' p + 1)\Delta I_2 = k_2 \Delta V , \tag{53.5}$$

where

$$T_2'' = T_2 + k_2 k_3 \Gamma_2^0 , \tag{53.6}$$

and the parameters T_2, k_2, k_3 and Γ_2^0 are defined from formulae (24.21), (24.29) and (24.17). The origin for reading the magnitude of deviation ΔI_2 in equation (53.5) will be defined below.

The regulating organ (contacts K cutting the resistance $2r_1$ in and out discontinuously) is a non-linear relay type circuit. Its output quantity—the resistance r of the field circuit—varies discontinuously with operation and release of the relay, i.e. depending on the magnitude of the current I_2 in the coil 2 of the electromagnetic relay. This is represented in Fig. 232a, where I_c and I_o are the currents of the completely closed and open relay respectively. To derive the equation of such a non-linear circuit it is convenient to introduce the deviations ΔI_2 and Δr from certain constant values I_2^0 and R^0. As shown in Fig. 232a and in formula (53.2), we assume:

$$I_2^0 = \frac{I_o + I_c}{2} = I_o + i_1 , \qquad R^0 = R_1 + r_1 . \tag{53.7}$$

Then the characteristic of the given non-linear circuit in deviations takes the form of Fig. 232b, symmetrical with respect to the origin

470   *The Dynamics of Automatic Control Systems*

of coordinates. It corresponds to the form 7 in Fig. 24 (relay characteristic with hysteresis loop).

In this connection the equation of the non-linear circuit (Fig. 232*b*) will be:

$$\Delta r = r_1 \cdot \text{sign} (\Delta I_2 - i_1) \quad \text{with} \quad \frac{d\Delta I_2}{dt} > 0 , \qquad (53.8)$$

$$\Delta r = r_1 \cdot \text{sign} (\Delta I_2 + i_1) \quad \text{with} \quad \frac{d\Delta I_2}{dt} < 0 , \qquad (53.9)$$

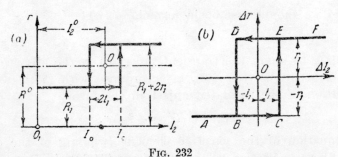

FIG. 232

where the expression "$\text{sign} (\Delta I_2 - i_1)$" denotes the sign of the quantity $(\Delta I_2 - i_1)$. If formulae (53.8) and (53.9) are expanded in greater detail, we obtain (Fig. 232*b*):

$$\begin{array}{ll}
\Delta r = -r_1 , & \text{when} \quad \Delta I_2 - i_1 < 0 \ (\text{segment } ABC) , \\
\Delta r = +r_1 , & \text{when} \quad \Delta I_2 - i_1 > 0 \ (\text{segment } EF)
\end{array}$$
with $\frac{dI_2}{dt} > 0$ (motion to the right);

$$\begin{array}{ll}
\Delta r = +r_1 , & \text{when} \quad \Delta I_2 + i_1 > 0 \ (\text{segment } FED) , \\
\Delta r = -r_1 , & \text{when} \quad \Delta I_2 + i_1 < 0 \ (\text{segment } BA)
\end{array}$$
with $\frac{dI_2}{dt} < 0$ (motion to the left) ,

where at the points C and D the relay state changes (jumps to points E and B respectively).

Thus, we have obtained the equations of the non-linear circuit (53.8)—(53.9) and the equations of the linear part of the system (53.4) and (53.5) which, according to (20.2), are combined in a single equation:

$$(T_1 p + 1)(T_2'' p + 1)\Delta I_2 = -k_1 k_2 \Delta r . \qquad (53.10)$$

The constant values from which the deviations are read are defined by (24.3), (24.19) and (53.7) from the algebraic equations of the relative steady-state of the system:

$$V^0 = (R_1 + r_1) I_1^0 ,$$
$$(R_2 + R_s) I_2^0 = V^0 , \qquad I_2^0 = \frac{I_o + I_c}{2} , \qquad (53.11)$$

using the dynamo characteristics (Fig. 120). It is also possible to carry out matching of the fundamental system parameters from these formulae.

Automatic temperature regulation system. Let us consider the system whose schematic diagram is shown in Fig. 81 and which was described in Section 13. The equation of the regulated object, derived in Section 9 for the transient process in the absence of perturbations ($f = 0$) has the form (9.15), namely:

$$(T_1 p + 1)\theta = -k_1\xi , \tag{53.12}$$

where θ is the deviation of the regulated temperature, ξ is the displacement of the regulating organ (shutters), while the time constant T_1 and the coefficient k_1 are defined by formulae (9.12) or experimentally.

The equation of the sensitive element (bimetallic plate 2, Fig. 81) is written in the form

$$(T_2 p + 1)x = k_2\theta , \tag{53.13}$$

where x is the displacement of the end of the plate 2, sliding over the contact plates 7; T_2 is the time constant defined basically by the thermal inertia of the sensitive element.

The contact block 7 is moved by means of stiff mechanical feedback from the regulating organ drive. Consequently, the equation of the (stiff) feedback will be:

$$x_{fb} = k_{fb}\xi . \tag{53.14}$$

The equation of the drive and the regulating organ, as in (50.3), will here be:

$$(T_3 p + 1)p\xi = k_3 V , \tag{53.15}$$

where T_3 is the mechanical time constant of the electric motor with reduction gear and damper.

These four elements exhaust the linear part of the system. The electromagnetic relay controlling the regulating organ drive is a non-linear relay type element. The input quantity of this element is the relative displacement of the bimetallic plate 2 and the shoe 7, equal to $x - x_{fb}$, while the output quantity is the voltage V across the field circuit of the motor (Fig. 81). We put

$$s = x - x_{fb} . \tag{53.16}$$

Noting that the linear part of the system in this case (Fig. 233) is an open network with branching, on the basis of formulae (21.27) and (21.28) we obtain the equation of the linear part of the system in the form *

$$Q(p)s = R(p)V , \qquad (53.17)$$

where

$$\left.\begin{array}{l} Q(p) = (T_1 p + 1)(T_2 p + 1)(T_3 p + 1)p , \\ R(p) = -k_3[k_1 k_2 + k_{fb}(T_1 p + 1)(T_2 p + 1)] . \end{array}\right\} \qquad (53.18)$$

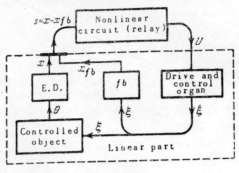

FIG. 233

We now derive the equation of the non-linear element (relay). Let us take the voltage V applied to one of the windings of the motor field 4 (Fig. 81) as positive and the other as negative. The voltage is constant in magnitude and equal to some value c. In the ideal case the relay will switch instantaneously with passage of the quantity s through the zero position (Fig. 234a).

In reality we have here two basic non-ideal factors. Firstly, about the zero position the quantity s has some zone of insensitivity $\pm s^*$ (Fig. 234b). Secondly, when the end of the bimetallic plate 2 (Fig. 81) is incident on the contact plate, the current I in the control circuit of relay 3 increases exponentially (Fig. 234c):

$$I = \frac{c}{R}(1 - e^{-\frac{t}{T}}) , \qquad T = \frac{L}{R}, \qquad (53.19)$$

where L and R are the inductance and resistance of the control circuit. Therefore even with $s = s^*$ the relay does not operate instantaneously but after a time delay τ_1 during which the quantity s increases by some value Δs_1 (Fig. 234b), where from (53.19) we have

$$\tau_1 = T \ln \frac{c}{c - RI_c}, \qquad (53.20)$$

---

* In the present case blocks 1 and 2 of Fig. 111 correspond to the drive and regulating organ of Fig. 233, block II is the regulated object and sensitive element, block III is the feedback, while in place of the equation of block IV it is necessary to take equation (53.16), taking into account the minus sign existing there with application of formulae (21.28).

and I_c is the current of the completely closed relay 3. With decrease in s the relay also does not open instantaneously at $s = s^*$ but after a delay τ_2 during which the quantity s reduces by some value Δs_2 (Fig. 234b). Now the current I in the control circuit of the relay decreases exponentially (Fig. 234d):

$$I = \frac{c}{R} e^{-\frac{t}{T}},$$ (53.21)

from which we obtain

$$\tau_2 = T \ln \frac{c}{I_0 R},$$ (53.22)

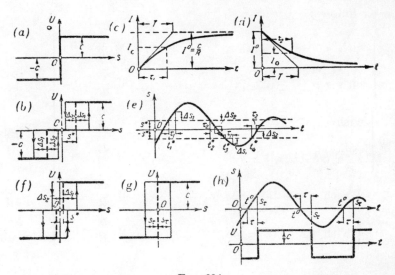

Fig. 234

where I_o is the current of the open relay. We note that

$$
\left.
\begin{aligned}
\tau_2 &= \tau_1 && \text{with} && I_c + I_o = \frac{c}{R}. \\
\tau_2 &> \tau_1 && \text{with} && I_c + I_o < \frac{c}{R}, \\
\tau_2 &< \tau_1 && \text{with} && I_c + I_o > \frac{c}{R}.
\end{aligned}
\right\}
$$ (53.23)

Thus the magnitudes of delay with relay operation τ_1 and τ_2 are completely defined and constant during the operation of the given system while the quantities Δs_1 and Δs_2 (Fig. 234b) obviously depend on the rate of change of s, i.e. the rate of change of the regulation process, and during the transient process they will be variable. Thus, in Fig. 234e in the second swing of the oscillation with the same τ_1 and τ_2 the quantities Δs_1 and Δs_2 will be smaller than in the first.

This is the principal difference between the given non-linear element and that of the previous example, where the instant of switching is not defined by time but only by the value of the input quantity (there this role was played by the quantity ΔI_2).

A non-linear (in the present case relay) element of this type is termed a non-linear element with delay (in the present case of relay type). Its characteristic has the form of Fig. 234b, where Δs_1 and Δs_2 are unknown and defined by the overall variation of $s(t)$ in the regulation process with given delays τ_1 and τ_2 (Fig. 234e). In Fig. 234b it is assumed that $|\Delta s_2| < s^*$.

The equations of the non-linear element are written in complete form as follows:

$$V = c \begin{cases} \text{with } s > (s^* + |\Delta s_1|) \,, & \text{if } \dfrac{ds}{dt} > 0 \,, \\[2em] \text{with } s > (s^* - |\Delta s_2|) \,, & \text{if } \dfrac{ds}{dt} < 0 \,, \end{cases}$$

$$V = 0 \begin{cases} \text{with } -(s^* - |\Delta s_2|) < s < (s^* + |\Delta s_1|) \,, & \text{if } \dfrac{ds}{dt} > 0 \,, \\[2em] \text{with } (s^* - |\Delta s_2|) > s > -(s^* + |\Delta s_1|) \,, & \text{if } \dfrac{ds}{dt} < 0 \,, \end{cases} \qquad (53.24)$$

$$V = -c \begin{cases} \text{with } s < -(s^* - |\Delta s_2|) \,, & \text{if } \dfrac{ds}{dt} > 0 \,, \\[2em] \text{with } s < -(s^* + |\Delta s_1|) \,, & \text{if } \dfrac{ds}{dt} < 0 \,, \end{cases}$$

where

$$\begin{aligned} \Delta s_1 &= s(t^* + \tau_1) - s^* \quad \text{with} \quad \left(s \cdot \dfrac{ds}{dt}\right) > 0 \,, \\[1em] \Delta s_2 &= s(t^* + \tau_2) - s^* \quad \text{with} \quad \left(s \cdot \dfrac{ds}{dt}\right) < 0 \,. \end{aligned} \qquad (53.25)$$

In the ideal case (Fig. 234a) they reduce to the simpler form

$$V = c \cdot \operatorname{sign} s \,. \qquad (53.26)$$

If the zone of insensitivity s^* is sufficiently small, while the operation time of the relay is large, its characteristic may take the form of Fig. 234f.

The idealised case taking into account delay is represented in Fig. 234g; to this there corresponds the equation

$$\begin{aligned} V &= c \cdot \operatorname{sign}(s - |s_\tau|) \quad \text{with} \quad \dfrac{ds}{dt} > 0 \,, \\[1em] V &= c \cdot \operatorname{sign}(s + |s_\tau|) \quad \text{with} \quad \dfrac{ds}{dt} < 0 \,, \end{aligned} \qquad (53.27)$$

where

$$s_\tau = s(t^0 + \tau),\tag{53.28}$$

if τ denotes the given total magnitude of delay in the non-linear element (as a whole), while t^0 is the time of passage of the quantity s through zero (Fig. 234h).

In the first rough approximation such a system (but without feedback) was considered in Sections 9 and 10 as a relay system with hysteresis loop, where operation was defined not by time but by a given value of input quantity. We note further that in the presence of feedback, according to Section 13 it may be studied roughly as an ordinary linear system. Below (in the examples of Chapter XVI) this system will be considered in detail as non-linear.

Automatic torpedo course regulation system. Let us take the simple element described in Section 4 (Fig. 26). The equation of rotation of the torpedo about the vertical axis (yaw) as the regulated object will be written approximately in the form

$$J\ddot{\psi} + c_1\dot{\psi} = -c_2\delta,\tag{53.29}$$

where $J\ddot{\psi} + c_1\dot{\psi} = -c_2\delta$ is the angle of deviation of the torpedo from the given direction, J is its moment of inertia with respect to the vertical axis, $c_1\dot{\psi}$ is the resistive moment of the medium (water), $c_2\delta$ is the rudder moment, δ is the angle of rudder rotation. Dividing this by c_1, we obtain the equation of the regulated object in the form

$$(T_1 p + 1)p\psi = -k_1\delta,\tag{53.30}$$

where

$$T_1 = \frac{J}{c_1}, \qquad k_1 = \frac{c_2}{c_1}.$$

The sensitive element is a three-stage gyroscope, rotating the gate valve arm feed of the pneumatic rudder drive by an angle equal to the angle of deviation of the torpedo. Consequently, the equation of the sensitive element will be:

$$s = k_2\psi,\tag{53.31}$$

where s is the magnitude of gate valve displacement from the neutral position.

We shall consider that the piston of the rudder drive 3 (Fig. 26) with open gate valve, rapidly taking on full velocity, instantaneously* shifts the rudder from one extreme position to the other.

---

* More exactly, in such a small time that the torpedo has not appreciably turned, i.e. a time much smaller than the possible period of oscillation of the torpedo.

In this approximate representation the linear part of the system is limited to equations (53.30) and (53.31). The single equation of the linear part of the system will therefore be:

$$(T_1 p + 1)ps = -k_1 k_2 \delta .\qquad(53.32)$$

The rudder drive together with the rudder (drive and regulating organ) constitute a non-linear element, the equation of which form the above may be represented either in the simplest form (Fig. 235a)

$$\delta = c \cdot \mathrm{sign}\, s;\qquad(53.33)$$

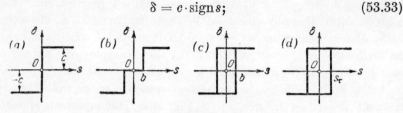

Fig. 235

or, if there is an appreciable zone of insensitivity (Fig. 235b), in the form

$$\left.\begin{array}{l}\delta = 0 \quad \text{with} \quad -b < s < +b , \\ \delta = c \cdot \mathrm{sign}\, s \quad \text{with} \quad |s| > b;\end{array}\right\}\qquad(53.34)$$

or, if the hysteresis loop has an appreciable value (Fig. 235c),

$$\left.\begin{array}{l}\delta = c \cdot \mathrm{sign}\,(s - b) \quad \text{with} \quad \dfrac{ds}{dt} > 0 , \\[2mm] \delta = c \cdot \mathrm{sign}\,(s + b) \quad \text{with} \quad \dfrac{ds}{dt} < 0 ;\end{array}\right\}\qquad(53.35)$$

or, finally, in the idealised case with delay (Fig. 235d)

$$\left.\begin{array}{l}\delta = c \cdot \mathrm{sign}\,(s - |s_\tau|) \quad \text{with} \quad \dfrac{ds}{dt} > 0 , \\[2mm] \delta = c \cdot \mathrm{sign}\,(s + |s_\tau|) \quad \text{with} \quad \dfrac{ds}{dt} < 0 ,\end{array}\right\}\qquad(53.36)$$

where

$$s_\tau = s(t^0 + \tau) .\qquad(53.37)$$

In studying the system as a whole one of these four alternatives may be taken depending upon which of them will best correspond to the properties of the given relay system.

54. Equations of systems with non-linearity in the form of dry friction and backlash

We present examples of the equations for non-linear systems with dry friction or backlash in mechanical transmission.

Servomechanism with linear and dry friction. In Section 26 we derived equations of a servomechanism in linear form. Let us now consider the case where to the linear friction moment M_{lf} is added a dry friction moment M_{df}, having a constant magnitude equal to some value c, and changing its direction (sign) with change of sign of angular velocity of the object $\dot\beta$ (Fig. 236). Consequently, the equation of the controlled object (26.1) taking into account (26.3) now takes the form

$$J\ddot\beta = M_r - M_{lf} - M_{df}, \qquad M_r = c_1 I_4, \qquad M_{lf} = c_2\dot\beta, \qquad (54.1)$$

where

$$\left.\begin{array}{ll} M_{df} = c\cdot\operatorname{sign}\dot\beta & \text{with} \quad \dot\beta \neq 0, \\ -c \leqslant M_{df} \leqslant +c & \text{with} \quad \dot\beta = 0. \end{array}\right\} \qquad (54.2)$$

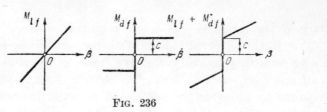

FIG. 236

An important property of the dry friction consists in that (in distinction to relay characteristics) it does not always signify instantaneous switching of the quantity M_{df} at $\dot\beta = 0$. Here two alternatives are possible:

$$\left.\begin{array}{llll} 1) & \dot\beta = 0 & \text{and} & |M_r| > c, \\ 2) & \dot\beta = 0 & \text{and} & |M_r| < c. \end{array}\right\} \qquad (54.3)$$

In the first case the velocity of the object $\dot\beta$ passes through zero and its motion will continue without stopping according to (54.1). In the second case the controlled object stops, during which the quantity M_{df} does not switch but changes slowly in the interval $-c \leqslant M_{df} \leqslant +c$ (or the reverse), where M_{df} has always defined values

$$M_{df} = M_r \qquad (\dot\beta = 0, |M_r| < c). \qquad (54.4)$$

In this case the motion is renewed only when the rotary moment reaches the value $|M_r| = c$ and exceeds it.

If there remains $|M_r| < c$, the system will be stationary. Therefore the equilibrium position of the controlled object is indeterminate within a certain segment, namely, with any value $|M_r| < c$, i.e. in accordance with (54.1) with any value of armature current in the interval $|I_4| < c/c_1$. This corresponds in turn, as is evident from (26.17), to any value $|I_3| < c/c_1 k_5$ and further, according to (26.10), (26.11) and (26.14), to any value of error

$$|\gamma| < \frac{c}{c_1 k_2 k_3 k_4 k_5}. \qquad (54.5)$$

This expression defines the dead zone of the system. It is expressed, as is evident from (26.9), (26.8) and (26.23), in that on the one hand, the system will not move with variation of the adjuster angle in the interval

$$\alpha = \frac{1}{k_0}\left(\beta \pm \frac{c}{c_1 k}\right) \qquad (\beta = \text{const}) \qquad (54.6)$$

and, on the other hand, that the system will have an error due to dry friction, namely, in the equilibrium position we have:

$$k_0\alpha - \frac{c}{c_1 k} \leqslant \beta \leqslant k_0\alpha + \frac{c}{c_1 k} \qquad (54.7)$$

in place of the required $\beta = k_0\alpha$ as required, where β may take on any value in the interval (54.7). With motion of the system to one side with arbitrary velocity the dry friction introduces a constant error of one sign, such as with $f^0 = ck_1/c_1$ in formula (26.28), which corresponds to an effective additional external load $M_1^0 = c$.

Thus, the equation of the controlled object as a non-linear element of the system from (54.1) and (54.2), taking into account (54.3), will have the form

$$\left.\begin{array}{c} J\ddot{\beta} + c_2\dot{\beta} + c \cdot \text{sign}\,\dot{\beta} = c_1 I_4 \text{ with } \dot{\beta} \neq 0 \text{ or } \dot{\beta} = 0 \text{ and } |I_4| > \dfrac{c}{c_1}, \\[2mm] \beta = \text{const with } \dot{\beta} = 0 \text{ and } |I_4| < \dfrac{c}{c_1}. \end{array}\right\} \qquad (54.8)$$

The equations of all the remaining elements of the given servomechanism, i.e. (26.8), (26.9), (26.10), (26.11), (26.14) and (26.17), remain without change in the linear form. Taken together they form the linear part of the system, with the single equation

$$(T_2 p + 1)(T_3 p + 1)(T_4 p + 1)I_4$$
$$= k_0(k + k'p)\alpha - [(T_2 p + 1)(T_3 p + 1)k_6 p + k + k'p]\beta , \qquad (54.9)$$

where we employ the notation (26.23). This equation may be substantially simplified if we neglect (as small) the inductance of the motor armature (i.e. $T_4 = 0$) and eliminate the differentiating element (i.e. put $k' = 0$ and $T_2 = 0$)

$$(T_3 p + 1)I_4 = k_0 k\alpha - [(T_3 p + 1)k_6 p + k]\beta , \qquad (54.10)$$

where now $k = k_2 k_4 k_5 : k_0$.

Servomechanism with backlash. Let us now assume that in the same servomechanism the non-linearity does not consist in dry friction but in the presence of backlash in the mechanical power transmission between the motor M (Fig. 128) and the controlled object. All the backlash is combined in a single resultant backlash and it is represented conventionally in the form of a yoke with free play $\pm b$. Thus, between the drive and the controlled object is now a new non-linear element represented in Fig. 237a, the input quantity of which is denoted by β_1.

The characteristic of this non-linear element is represented in Fig. 237b. Its significance is as follows. If there were no backlash, β would be equal to β_1 and the characteristic would be a straight line at an angle of 45°, represented in Fig. 237b by the broken line.

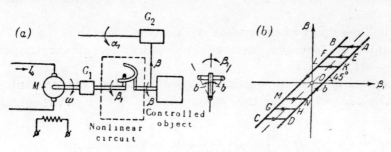

FIG. 237

As a result of the backlash, with motion towards increase in angle β this line shifts to the right by the quantity b (the pin presses against the right side of the yoke). With change of direction of motion the pin will first be displaced inside the gap, without moving the yoke ($\beta = \text{const}$). In the characteristic this corresponds to the horizontal segment of length $2b$ (*AB* or *EF* or *KL*, etc., in dependence on the actual value of β at this instant). The yoke then begins to move, which corresponds to the straight line *BC*, shifted to the left from the origin of coordinates by the value b.

In equilibrium of the system the pin and yoke may take on any relative position within the backlash, with causes the backlash error of the system, equal to $\pm b$. With motion of the system to one side there will be a constant lag of the object due to the backlash by the magnitude b, not taking into account the lag caused by the load (26.28).

The previous equation of the controlled object (26.6), including the drive, is now separated into two non-linear equations. The first non-linear equation of the controlled object with drive will be:

$$\left.\begin{array}{ll}(T_1 p + 1)p\beta_1 = k_1 I_4 & \text{with} \quad \dot{\beta} \neq 0 \,, \\ (T_1' p + 1)p\beta_1 = k_1 I_4 & \text{with} \quad \dot{\beta} = 0 \end{array}\right\} \qquad (54.11)$$

(with pin pressed against the yoke, and with pin moving freely inside the gap, respectively), where T_1 and k_1 have the previous values (26.7), while T_1' is smaller than T_1 by the magnitude $J_1 : c_2$, J_1 is the moment of inertia of the controlled object. In addition, it is neces-

480   *The Dynamics of Automatic Control Systems*

sary to write a second equation of the non-linear element with backlash, corresponding to the characteristic of Fig. 237b:

$$\left.\begin{array}{lll} \beta = \beta_1 - b & \text{with} & \dot\beta_1 > 0 , \\ \beta = \beta_1 + b & \text{with} & \dot\beta_1 < 0 , \\ \beta = \text{const} & \text{with} & |\beta_1 - \beta| < b . \end{array}\right\} \qquad (54.12)$$

Consequently, the controlled object will lag in its oscillations, corresponding to the segments *AB*, *CD*, etc. of the characteristic of Fig. 237b.

The linear part of the system remains the same as in the previous example. Its equation has the form (54.9) or, in the simplified case—(54.10).

Automatic pressure regulation system (taking into account dry friction). Let us consider the system (Fig. 117) for which the equations

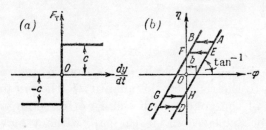

FIG. 238

in linear form were obtained in Section 23. In the sensitive element 2, 3, 4 the mass is negligible but dry friction may have an appreciable value. Therefore the equation of motion of the membrane coupling rod (23.14) is written in the form

$$P - F_m - F_f - F_s = 0 , \qquad (54.13)$$

where F_f is the dry friction force having the constant value c, varying direction with change of sign of the velocity $\dot y$ (Fig. 238a) and taking on various values during the time of stopping, i.e.

$$\left.\begin{array}{lll} F_T = c \cdot \text{sign}\,\dot y & \text{with} & \dot y \neq 0 , \\ -c \leqslant F_T \leqslant +c & \text{with} & \dot y = 0 ; \end{array}\right\} \qquad (54.14)$$

the remaining notation in formula (54.13) is the same as in Section 23.

As a result after transition to dimensionless relative deviations (23.9) and (23.17) we obtain in place of (23.18) the following equation of the sensitive element as a non-linear element:

$$\left.\begin{array}{l} b \cdot \text{sign}\,\dot\eta + \delta\eta = -\varphi \ \text{with} \ \dot\eta \neq 0 \ \text{or} \ \dot\eta = 0 \ \text{and} \ |\varphi + \delta\eta| = b , \\ \eta = \text{const with} \ |\varphi + \delta\eta| < b , \end{array}\right\} \qquad (54.15)$$

where the coefficient δ is defined by formula (23.19) and

$$b = \frac{c}{q_m p_n}. \tag{54.16}$$

Let us plot the characteristic of this non-linear element with dry friction in the coordinates $(-\varphi, \eta)$. It is easily seen that the first of equations (54.15) corresponds to the straight lines DA and BC with $\dot{\eta} > 0$ and $\dot{\eta} < 0$, while the second equation $(\eta = \text{const})$ to the segments AB, CD, EF, GH, etc. From comparison of Fig. 238*b* and Fig. 237*b* it is evident that dry friction in this non-linear circuit (without mass) is equivalent to backlash, half of which is equal to b (54.16), which cannot at all be said about the dry friction in the servomechanism, where the mass (moment of inertia) was taken into account.

All the remaining elements of the system (Fig. 117) form the linear part, which is described by equations (23.12), (23.25), (23.26) and (23.29). The single equation of the linear part from this will be:

$$(T_1 p + 1)(T_s p + 1)\varphi = k_1 \eta \tag{54.17}$$

(with $f = 0$).

55. Equations of systems with other types of non-linearity

Let us consider several examples of deriving the equations of automatic systems with other types of non-linearities than those in Section 54 and 53.

Automatic aircraft course regulation system with limited-linear rudder characteristic. Let us take the aircraft with course autopilot,

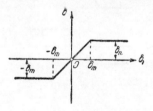

FIG. 239

described in Section 25 (Fig. 125) the rudder direction cannot deviate without limit, it has stops in the extreme positions, corresponding to certain values $\delta = \pm \delta_m$.

The equation of the aircraft (25.8) or (25.10) and the equation of the course autopilot (25.26) or (25.28) is left in its previous linear form, but, firstly, we shall consider the free motion of the system about the zero steady-state $(\psi^0 = 0, \delta^0 = 0, f_1 = f_2 = 0)$ and, secondly, at the output of the autopilot the quantity δ will be replaced by the relative δ_1, adding to this the corresponding non-linear rudder characteristic of Fig. 239, termed limited-linear characteristic.

Then the rudder equation as a non-linear element will be:

$$\left.\begin{array}{lll} \delta = \delta_1 & \text{with} & -\delta_m \leqslant \delta_1 \leqslant +\delta_m, \\ \delta = \delta_m \cdot \operatorname{sign}\delta_1 & \text{with} & \delta_1 \leqslant -\delta_m \quad \text{and} \quad \delta_1 \geqslant +\delta_m. \end{array}\right\} \quad (55.1)$$

The equation of the linear part from the above will consist of the aircraft equation in the form

$$[(T_1 p + 1)(T_2 p + 1) + k_2 T_2] p\psi = -k_1(T_2 p + 1)\delta \qquad (55.2)$$

or, in a roughly simplified form,

$$(T_1 p + 1) p\psi = -k_1 \delta \qquad (55.3)$$

and of the autopilot equation

$$[(T_3 p + 1)(T_4 p + 1) p + k_{fb}]\delta_1 = (k_\psi + k_{\dot{\psi}} p + k_{\ddot{\psi}} p^2)\psi \qquad (55.4)$$

(with stiff feedback) or

$$(T_3 p + 1)(T_4 p + 1) p\delta_1 = (k_\psi + k_{\dot{\psi}} p + k_{\ddot{\psi}} p^2)\psi \qquad (55.5)$$

(without feedback), where all the notation are as before (Section 25).

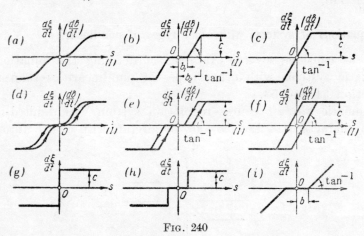

FIG. 240

Automatic regulation system with non-linear drive characteristic of the regulating organ. The regulating organ drive, regardless of type (electrical, Fig. 77, 125, 128; hydraulic, Fig. 78; pneumatic, Fig. 82, 117), always has, firstly, a certain zone of insensitivity at the origin of coordinates (Fig. 240a) and, secondly, a zone of "saturation" at the edges. In addition, there may also be present hysteresis (Fig. 240d). These two curvilinear characteristics may be approximately replaced by piecewise-linear (Fig. 240b, e or c, f, i). Finally, there exist drives with constant velocity (Fig. 240g, h), relating to non-linear relay type elements.

The zone of insensitivity b_1 is expressed in that the electric motor has a definite minimum starting current $(I = b_1)$, below which the motor shaft will be stationary $(\xi = 0$ or $\delta = 0)$. In a hydraulic motor the slide valve has a so-called zone of overlap (its pistons are somewhat wider than the openings covered by them), as a result of which they admit the working fluid to the motor cylinder only after moving by a certain magnitude $s = b_1$.

The pneumatic drive is similar, where the role of the slide valve is played by the gate valve. The zone of saturation occurs when with increase of current above a certain value $I = b_2$ the velocity of the regulating organ remains constant $(\xi = c$ or $\delta = c)$; the same occurs for the hydraulic motor with $s \geqslant b_2$ when the gate valve openings are completely open.

The terms "saturation" and "hysteresis" are applied here in a generalised sense to denote non-linearities of a definite type; they do not necessarily correspond to the physical phenomena of saturation and hysteresis.

The equation of the regulating organ drive taking into account the above circumstances, in place of the previous linear form has a non-linear form

$$p\xi = F(s) , \qquad (55.6)$$

where $F(s)$ is a non-linear function given graphically (Fig. 240a or d). In other notations we have:

$$p\xi = F(I) \quad \text{or} \quad p\delta = F(I) . \qquad (55.7)$$

In the approximate form (Fig. 240b) equation (55.6) may be expanded in the following manner:

$$
\left.
\begin{aligned}
p\xi &= 0 & \text{with} && -b_1 \leqslant s \leqslant +b_1 , \\
p\xi &= k_c(s - b_1) & \text{with} && +b_1 \leqslant s \leqslant +b_2 , \\
p\xi &= k_c(s + b_1) & \text{with} && -b_1 \geqslant s \geqslant -b_2 , \\
p\xi &= c \cdot \operatorname{sign} s & \text{with} && |s| \geqslant b_2 .
\end{aligned}
\right\} \qquad (55.8)
$$

In the presence of hysteresis (Fig. 240d) it is necessary to write two columns of such expressions with different values b_1 and b_2, one for motion to the right $(\dot{s} > 0)$ and the other for motion to the left $(\dot{s} < 0)$. The equations of the relay characteristics (Fig. 240g, h) have been considered in Section 53.

This defines the equation of the regulating organ drive as a non-linear element. The equation of the linear part is set up in the usual manner in dependence on the specific automatic system in which the drive is applied.

Servomechanism with linear and quadratic friction. In Section 54 we considered a servomechanism with linear and dry friction, and in Section 26 with linear friction. Let now the controlled object in the same servomechanism (Fig. 128) have in addition to linear also quadratic friction, i.e. the equation of the object has the form

$$J\ddot{\beta} = M_r - M_f, \qquad M_r = c_1 I_4, \tag{55.9}$$

where

$$M_f = c_2\dot{\beta} + c_3\dot{\beta}^2 \cdot \operatorname{sign}\dot{\beta} \tag{55.10}$$

(Fig. 241). Then the equation of the controlled object as a non-linear element will be

$$J\ddot{\beta} + c_2\dot{\beta} + c_3\dot{\beta}^2 \cdot \operatorname{sign}\dot{\beta} = c_1 I_4. \tag{55.11}$$

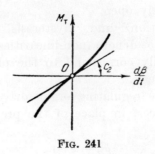

Fig. 241

The equation of the linear part of the system in complete form will be (54.9) as before, or more simply (neglecting the inductance of the motor armature and without the differentiating element), (54.10).

Automatic regulation system with variable gain factor. In a number of cases, to increase the quality of the regulation process, it is desirable that the input to the regulating organ not be proportional to the deviation of the regulated quantity but be amplified or attenuated with increase of this deviation (as compared with the linear function). Examples of such inputs with variable gain factors may be the characteristics with limited linearity (Fig. 239) and with saturation (Fig. 240a). However they give decrease of gain factor with increase of deviation. We now consider two examples of characteristics with variable gain factor on the side of its increase.

Let the winding of the rheostat 3 in the indirect-acting voltage regulation system (Fig. 19) be constructed so that its resistance does not vary proportionally to the displacement s of the slide, as a result of which its output voltage to the motor armature varies non-linearly according to the function shown by the graph of Fig. 242a or Fig. 242b. The voltage is not plotted along the axis of ordinates in these graphs but the velocity $\dot{\xi}$ directly, which we consider proportional to the voltage.

Consequently, the equation of the regulating organ drive as a non-linear element will be in the case of the characteristic of Fig. 242a:

$$\Delta\dot{\xi} = k_4 s \qquad \text{with} \quad |s| < b \,,$$
$$\Delta\dot{\xi} = k_4 b + k_4'(s-b) \qquad \text{with} \quad s > b \,, \qquad (55.12)$$
$$\Delta\dot{\xi} = -k_4 b + k_4'(s+b) \qquad \text{with} \quad s < -b \,,$$

and in the case of the characteristic (Fig. 242b)

$$\Delta\dot{\xi} = F(s) \qquad (55.13)$$

in place of the usual linear dependency (Fig. 242c)

$$\Delta\dot{\xi} = k_4'' s \,. \qquad (55.14)$$

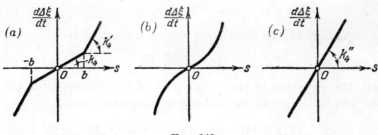

Fig. 242

The linear part of the system (Fig. 19) consists of a *dc* shunt dynamo (regulated object), the electromagnet 2 with spring (sensitive element) and the rheostat 5 (regulating organ).

The equation of such a regulated object was obtained in Section 24 in the form (24.10) or (24.13)

$$(T_1 p + 1)\Delta V = -k_1\Delta r \,, \qquad (55.15)$$

where T_1, k_1 are calculated from formulae (24.11).

The equation of the sensitive element (electromagnet 2) in accordance with (24.20), neglecting the quantity Γ_2, is written in the form

$$(T_2 p + 1)\Delta I_2 = k_2\Delta V \,, \qquad (55.16)$$

where T_2 and k_2 are defined from (24.21). To this it is necessary to add the equation of motion of the electromagnet armature 3 (Fig. 19)

$$m\ddot{s} = F_2 - F_s - F_r$$

where F_2, F_s and F_r are the forces of electromagnet, spring and damping resistance, and

$$F_2 = c_2 I_2^2 \,, \quad F_s = F_1 + c_1 s \,, \quad F_r = c_3\dot{s} \,.$$

From this after transformation to deviations according to the rules of Section 18 we obtain

$$m\ddot{s} = 2c_2 I_2^0 \Delta I_2 - c_1 s - c_3 \dot{s} \, ,$$

where I_2^0 is the steady state value of current from which the deviation ΔI_2 is read. As a result we arrive at the equation

$$(T_4^2 p^2 + T_3 p + 1)s = k_3 \Delta I_2 \, , \qquad (55.17)$$

where

$$T_4^2 = \frac{m}{c_1}, \qquad T_3 = \frac{c_3}{c_1}, \qquad k_3 = \frac{2c_2 I_2^0}{c_1} \, . \qquad (55.18)$$

In simplified form, without mass and damper, this equation will be

$$s = k_3 \Delta I_2 \, . \qquad (55.19)$$

The equation of the regulating organ (rheostat 5)

$$\Delta r = k_5 \Delta \xi \, . \qquad (55.20)$$

Thus, the equation of the linear part of the system from (55.15), (55.16), (55.19) and (55.20) will be in simplified form

$$(T_1 p + 1)(T_2 p + 1)s = -k_1 k_2 k_3 k_5 \Delta \xi \, . \qquad (55.21)$$

With this we conclude consideration of examples of deriving the equations of various non-linear automatic regulation systems. All these examples illustrate cases where the overall layout of the system has the form of Fig. 229c with non-linearities of the first class (except the dry friction in the servomechanism in the presence of stops). Combinations of these non-linearities may lead to non-linearities of the second and third classes (see Section 52).

CHAPTER XV

STUDY OF STABILITY AND SELF-OSCILLATIONS IN NON-LINEAR AUTOMATIC REGULATION SYSTEMS

56. Phase trajectories and the Andronov point transformation method

In Sections 9 and 10 we have discussed the essential properties of processes in non-linear systems which make the question of the system stability more complex. Aside from the system structure and the values of its parameters, here, in contrast to linear systems, the initial conditions also have significance for the stability of one or another steady-state process. A new type of steady-state process is possible—self-oscillations, i.e. stable self-oscillations with constant amplitude in the absence of external oscillatory forces. When self-oscillations arise in the system, the steady-state corresponding to a constant value of regulated quantity is frequently impossible.

Consequently, in place of two types of regions in the plane of the system parameters (stable and unstable), as in linear systems, there may be: (1) a region of stability of an equilibrium state with constant value of the regulated quantity; (2) a region of stable self-oscillations; (3) a region of instability of the system; (4) many other more complex cases. Self-oscillations are not possible in all non-linear systems. The region of stability may be such that the system is stable for arbitrary initial conditions, i.e. both with small and large initial deviations and velocities (to which the equations studied are valid), as was the case in linear systems. But there may occur new phenomena, when the region of stability is such that the system is only small-signal stable, i.e. for sufficiently small initial deviations and velocities (up to a certain limit), and large-signal unstable, i.e. for sufficiently large initial deviations. There may be present simultaneously certain possible stable states, for example a small-signal stable equilibrium state and a large-signal stable oscillation.

Up to now we have studied the stability of linear systems. However these linear systems were obtained from real ones by linearisation under the assumption of smallness of the deviations of all variables from certain steady-state values. With increase of deviations the linearised system will be in many cases non-linear. Where instability was obtained in the linear solution, with increase of deviations stable self-oscillations may arise in the system as a result of essential non-linearity of some circuit (for example, in systems with saturation non-linearity). And, on the contrary, where a system in the linear solution was stable, with increase of deviations it may become unstable as a result of non-linearities; for example, it is obvious that if an aircraft with autopilot is stable in altitude in the linear solution, with sufficiently great angular deviations in the vertical plane as a result of non-linearities of the aerodynamic characteristics it may fall on its tail or pass into a nose dive, i.e. the flight altitude regulation system which is small-signal stable may be large-signal unstable.

In this section we shall illustrate certain of these properties by the construction of phase trajectories for simple second-order systems. In this investigation the mutual variation of coordinates and velocities in transient and oscillatory processes will be determined, but the duration of the process and the magnitude of the period (frequency) of oscillation remain unknown. To determine these factors, it is necessary to solve in addition the differential equation with respect to time.

Example 1. Let us take an automatic regulation system with object without self-regulation and with the regulating organ drive having constant velocity. From Sections 22 and 23 the equation of a regulated object without self-regulation will be:

$$T_a \dot{\varphi} = \xi; \tag{56.1}$$

for a regulator without mass and damper, with stiff feedback, i.e. $\delta \eta = -\varphi$, $\sigma = \eta - \zeta$, $\zeta = \xi$, we obtain

$$\sigma = -\frac{1}{\delta}\varphi - \xi. \tag{56.2}$$

The regulating organ drive can have two forms of constant velocity: (1) with instantaneous switching (Fig. 240*g*) in passage of the control element (gate valve, jet tube) through the neutral position ($\sigma = 0$); (2) with zone of insensitivity (Fig. 240*h*) as a result of the presence of "overlap" of the gate valve or the jet tube. In the first case the regulating organ drive equation will be

$$\xi = c \cdot \text{sign}\,\sigma, \tag{56.3}$$

and in the second

$$\begin{aligned}\xi &= 0 && \text{with} \quad |\sigma| < b, \\ \xi &= c \cdot \text{sign}\,\sigma && \text{with} \quad |\sigma| > b.\end{aligned} \tag{56.4}$$

Let us take the phase plane (x, y), putting

$$x = \varphi, \quad y = \dot{\varphi}, \tag{56.5}$$

i.e. along the x-axis we plot the deviation of the regulated quantity φ and along the y-axis the rate of change of this deviation $\dot{\varphi}$. From equations (56.1), (56.2) and (56.5) we have:

$$\xi = T_a y, \qquad \sigma = -\frac{1}{\delta}x - T_a y.$$ (56.6)

Consequently, switching of the drive in the first alternative ($\sigma = 0$) will occur at

$$x = -\delta T_a y,$$ (56.7)

which corresponds to the straight line AB (Fig. 243a) in the phase plane, where from (56.6) the values $\sigma > 0$ correspond to the portion to the left of the straight line AB, while $\sigma < 0$, to the right.

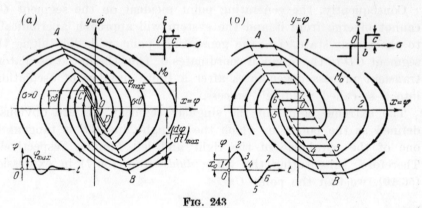

FIG. 243

On the basis of the first of relations (56.6) and (56.3) with $\sigma < 0$ we obtain

$$\frac{dy}{dt} = -\frac{c}{T_a},$$ (56.8)

and from (56.5),

$$\frac{dx}{dt} = y,$$ (56.9)

from which we find the equation of the phase trajectories:

$$\frac{dy}{dx} = -\frac{c}{T_a y}$$ (56.10)

or after integration

$$x = -\frac{T_a}{2c}y^2 + C_1.$$

This is a family of parabolae, shown in Fig. 243a to the right of the line AB (they are symmetrical with respect to the X-axis). Since (56.8) and (56.9) are the projections of the velocity v of the generating point M on the x and y-axes, we have $v_y < 0$ and the sign of v_x agrees with the sign of y. In accordance with this in Fig. 243a we indicate the direction of motion of the generating point M over the phase trajectories by arrows. By similar means we easily plot the parabolae to the left of the line AB.

As a result, as is evident from the general disposition of phase trajectories (Fig. 243a), a stable system is obtained with a damped oscillatory transient process. The number of oscillations will be finite. In fact, there is a singular segment CD in which all the phase trajectories merge. To find the behaviour of the system on this segment, we recall that for it, from (56.7) and (56.5)

$$\delta T_a \dot{\varphi} + \varphi = 0 \quad \text{or} \quad \varphi = C_2 e^{-\frac{t}{\delta T_a}}.$$

Consequently, the generating point incident on the segment CD cannot emerge from it and the system will approach aperiodically to the steady-state, i.e. the generating point will slide along the segment CD to the origin of coordinates 0. Thus the initial oscillatory transient process degenerates after a finite number of oscillations into a so-called "sliding" process.

The extreme points of the singular segment CD are obviously defined as the points in which the straight line AB is tangent to one of the parabolae of the right and left families respectively. Therefore, substituting the value dy/dx from (56.7) in expression (56.10), we find the point C:

$$y_c = c\delta.$$

From the pattern of phase trajectories the transient response curve $\varphi(t)$ may be found qualitatively for arbitrary initial conditions. The initial conditions define the initial position of the generating point M and by this define the phase trajectory illustrating the course of the process. It indicates (Fig. 243a) the maximum deviation of the regulated quantity φ_{max}, the maximum velocity $\dot{\varphi}_{max}$ as well as all succeeding deviations, the number of oscillations etc.

We shall now consider the same system, but taking into account the zone of insensitivity. In this case switching of the drive (at $\sigma = -b$ and $\sigma = +b$) corresponds in the phase plane according to (56.6), to two inclined straight lines (Fig. 243b):

$$x = -\delta T_a y + b\delta \quad \text{and} \quad x = -\delta T_a y - b\delta.$$

Between these lines $|\sigma| < b$, to the right of them $\sigma < -b$, to the left $\sigma > b$ (with $b > 0$).

With $|\sigma| < b$ we obtain from (56.4), (56.6) and (56.5)

$$\frac{dy}{dt} = 0, \quad \frac{dx}{dt} = y,$$

from which (with $y \neq 0$)

$$\frac{dy}{dx} = 0 \quad \text{or} \quad y = C_3$$

(straight lines parallel to the x-axis in the strip AB in Fig. 243b).

With $|\sigma| > b$ we obtain the previous parabolae. As a result the system is again stable and has an oscillatory transient, but in place of the singular point 0 we obtain a singular segment ($y = 0$, $-b\delta < x < b\delta$), i.e. the steady-state is not uniquely defined. This corresponds to the fact that the regulator may be in equilibrium at any point within the zone of insensitivity. Here exactly the same "sliding" process is possible as in the case of Fig. 243a.

In the present example the system is stable with arbitrary values of the parameters and with arbitrary initial conditions. However we have carried out here a very rough idealisation of the regulator equations (neglecting mass and damping), in Chapter XVI we shall see that taking the inertia of the regulator into account may strongly change the entire pattern of the process in this system.

Example 2. Let now in an analogous automatic regulation system (Section 22 or 23) the equation of the regulated object have the form

$$T_a \dot{\phi} + \beta \phi = \xi . \tag{56.11}$$

(object with self-regulation).

The regulator, as in example 1, will be assumed without mass and damping, but with stiff feedback, i.e.

$$\sigma = -\frac{1}{\delta} \phi - \xi , \tag{56.12}$$

while the regulating organ drive is taken in two forms: (1) with constant velocity and zone of insensitivity (Fig. 240h), i.e.

$$\left. \begin{array}{llll} \dot{\xi} = 0 & \text{with} & |\sigma| < b , \\ \dot{\xi} = c \cdot \operatorname{sign} \sigma & \text{with} & |\sigma| > b , \end{array} \right\} \tag{56.13}$$

and (2) with variable velocity and a zone of insensitivity (Fig. 240i with $k_c = 1/T_s$):

$$\left. \begin{array}{llll} \dot{\xi} = 0 & \text{with} & |\sigma| < b , \\ T_s \dot{\xi} = \sigma - b \cdot \operatorname{sign} \sigma & \text{with} & |\sigma| > b . \end{array} \right\} \tag{56.14}$$

The coordinates of the phase plane are taken as before in the form (56.5). Then from (56.11) and (56.12) we obtain

$$\sigma = -\frac{1}{\delta} \phi - (T_a \dot{\phi} + \beta \phi) = -\left(\frac{1}{\delta} + \beta\right) x - T_a y . \tag{56.15}$$

The instants of switching the drive $\sigma = \pm b$ therefore correspond to the straight lines

$$y = -\frac{1}{T_a}\left(\frac{1}{\delta} + \beta\right)x \mp \frac{b}{T_a}. \tag{56.16}$$

The strip AB (Fig. 244a) between these lines corresponds to values $|\sigma| < b$. To the right of the strip $\sigma < -b$, to the left $\sigma > b$. Differentiating (56.11) with regard to (56.5) we obtain

$$\frac{dx}{dt} = y, \qquad \frac{dy}{dt} = -\frac{\beta}{T_a}y + \frac{\xi}{T_a}, \tag{56.17}$$

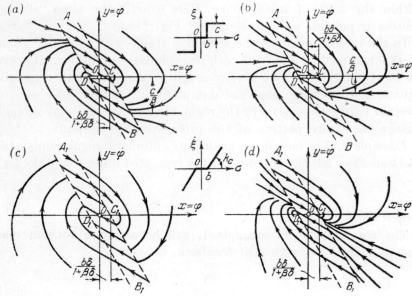

FIG. 244

from which we find for the region inside the strip AB, i.e. for $|\sigma| < b$, from (56.13) the equation of the phase trajectories in the form of straight line segments:

$$\frac{dy}{dx} = -\frac{\beta}{T_a} \qquad \text{or} \qquad y = -\frac{\beta}{T_a}x + C_1,$$

where, since $v_x = dx/dt = y$, above the x-axis we have $v_x > 0$ while below $v_x < 0$ (these define the directions of the arrows in Fig. 244).

For the region to the right of the strip AB, i.e. with $\sigma < -b$, from (56.17) and (56.13) we obtain

$$\frac{dy}{dx} = -\frac{\beta}{T_a} - \frac{c}{T_a y}. \tag{56.18}$$

This coincides with equation (10.22) in the example of Section 10, differing from it only in the notation of the constants. Therefore here to the right of the strip AB the curves should be plotted which were plotted to the right of the line $EFGH$ in Fig. 64, as shown in Fig. 244a and b. A similar pattern will apply to the left of the strip AB, i.e. the given regulation system is stable. The transient response is oscillatory for large values of c/β (Fig. 244a) and aperiodic for small c/β, i.e. with a large self-regulation factor of the regulated object β (Fig. 244b).

The steady-state operation of the system may correspond to any point of the singular segment CD, which corresponds to the insensitive zone of the regulating organ drive. At which point of the singular segment CD the system will arrive depends upon which phase trajectory it traverses, i.e. the initial conditions.

We shall now investigate the same regulation system but with the other regulating organ drive characteristic (56.14).

With $|\sigma| < b$ we obtain in the phase plane $(x = \varphi, y = \dot{\varphi})$ the same strip $A_1 B_1$ (Fig. 244c, d), as in the preceding case.

To the right of the strip $A_1 B_1$, where $\sigma < -b$, from (56.11), (56.12) and (56.14) we have:

$$(T_a p + \beta)\varphi = \xi ,$$

$$(T_s p + 1)\xi = -\frac{1}{\delta}\varphi + b ,$$

from which we obtain the system equation

$$\ddot{\varphi} + \frac{T_a + \beta T_s}{T_a T_s}\dot{\varphi} + \frac{1 + \beta\delta}{T_a T_s \delta}\varphi = \frac{b}{T_a T_s} . \tag{56.19}$$

This equation coincides with equation (10.6), if we put $x = \varphi - b\delta/(1 + \beta\delta)$. Since here all coefficients are positive, the pattern of phase trajectories is obtained either in the form of Fig. 58c or in the form of Fig. 60b, depending upon on whether the roots of the characteristic equation

$$z^2 + \frac{T_a + \beta T_s}{T_a T_s}z + \frac{1 + \beta\delta}{T_a T_s \delta} = 0 .$$

are complex or real. The corresponding two patterns are shown in Fig. 244c and d. Here the abscissa of the singular point, from the above, will be

$$x^0 = -\frac{b\delta}{1 + \beta\delta} ,$$

i.e. it concides with the point D_1 (Fig. 244c and d).

The system is stable in both cases (neglecting the regulator inertia), where, in the case of Fig. 244c the transient process is oscillatory and in the case of Fig. 244d aperiodic. The singular segment $C_1 D_1$

as before corresponds to the region of possible steady-states depending upon the initial conditions.

Example 3. The equation of the automatic course regulator of a marine torpedo in simplified form has the linear part (53.30) and (53.31), i.e.

$$T_1\ddot{\psi} + \dot{\psi} = -k_1\delta , \qquad s = k_2\psi , \qquad (56.20)$$

and the non-linear element (we take first a single case—Fig. 235c),

$$\begin{cases} \delta = c\cdot\text{sign}(s-b) & \text{with} \quad \dot{s} > 0 , \\ \delta = c\cdot\text{sign}(s+b) & \text{with} \quad \dot{s} < 0 . \end{cases} \qquad (56.21)$$

We shall show that here the steady-state equilibrium of the system with constant value $\psi = 0$ is unstable, but a stable oscillatory process * will occur.

Let us take the phase plane (x, y) with coordinates $x = \psi, y = \dot{\psi}$ (angle of deviation and angular rate of change deviation of the torpedo axis from the prescribed course). Equations (56.20) and (56.21) are rewritten in the form

$$\frac{dx}{dt} = y , \qquad \frac{dy}{dt} = -\frac{y}{T_1} - \frac{k_1}{T_1}\delta ,$$

$$\delta = c\cdot\text{sign}\left(x - \frac{b}{k_2}\right) \quad \text{with} \quad y > 0 , \qquad (56.22)$$

$$\delta = c\cdot\text{sign}\left(x + \frac{b}{k_2}\right) \quad \text{with} \quad y < 0 .$$

From a comparison of these equations with the simplified equations of the temperature regulation system at the end of Section 10 their complete agreement is evident. Therefore here, as in Fig. 64, the steady-state torpedo motion will be oscillatory where the pattern of phase trajectories will have the form shown in Fig. 245a.

Here the curve AB is the limiting cycle, corresponding to the oscillatory process defined by equation (10.23) with such a value of the arbitrary constant C_1 as satisfies the condition

$$y_A = -y_B , \quad \text{i.e.} \quad (y)_{x=\frac{b}{k_2}} = -(y)_{x=-\frac{b}{k_2}} , \qquad (56.23)$$

since just in this case the closed limiting cycle ABD (Fig. 245a) is obtained. Finding in this way C_1 we find the amplitude of oscillation a as the value of x with $y = 0$, i.e. from (10.23),

$$a = k_1 c T_1 \ln k_1 c + C_1 .$$

---

* If we had studied here the two other cases (Fig. 235a, b), analogously to the previous examples we would obtain stability with respect to the equilibrium state $\psi = 0$.

The values of (56.23) give the amplitude q of the oscillations in velocity y. It is also possible to determine all these graphically directly from the drawing (Fig 245a). The period of oscillations remains unknown. We now introduce into the characteristic of the non-linear element (rudder drive) a zone of insensitivity as shown

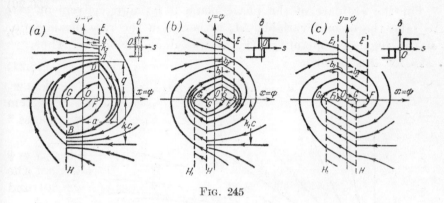

Fig. 245

in Fig. 245b, c. Thus, on the segment $b_1 b_2$ of the characteristic $\delta = f(s)$ (Fig. 245b) we have $\delta = 0$ and from (56.22)

$$y = -\frac{x}{T_1} + C_2 ,$$

which corresponds to the inclined straight lines within the strip $EFF_1 E_1$ in the phase plane (Fig. 245b) There is an analogous strip $HGG_1 H_1$ in the lower part of the plane. The remainder is filled by the same curves as in Fig. 245a. As a result, with increase of the zone of insensitivity $b_1 b_2$ the dimensions of the limiting cycle, and thus of the amplitude of oscillation, decrease. With $b_1 = 0$ the limiting cycle degenerates to the point 0.

With further increase of the zone of insensitivity the characteristic of the non-linear element and the pattern of phase trajectories take the forms shown in Fig. 245c. Here oscillations are absent and a steady-state process with constant value of ψ occurs. The previous unstable singular segment $F_1 G$ has now become stable. Further increase of the zone of insensitivity leads to widening of the segment $F_1 G$, i.e. to increase of the steady-state error of the system due to an excessively broad region of equilibrium.

Example 4. Let us consider the vibrator voltage regulator, the equations of which were derived in Section 53. We shall employ equations (53.4) and (53.5), namely:

$$\left.\begin{array}{l} (T_1 p + 1)\Delta V = -k_1 \Delta r , \\ (T_2'' p + 1)\Delta I_2 = k_2 \Delta V , \end{array}\right\} \tag{56.24}$$

496   *The Dynamics of Automatic Control Systems*

where the equation of the non-linear element (regulating organ) from (53.8) and (53.9) will be:

$$\Delta r = r_1 \cdot \mathrm{sign}\,(\Delta I_2 - i_1) \quad \text{with} \quad \dot{\Delta I_2} > 0 \,, \\ \Delta r = r_1 \cdot \mathrm{sign}\,(\Delta I_2 + i_1) \quad \text{with} \quad \dot{\Delta I_2} < 0 \,. \tag{56.25}$$

For the ordinate of the phase plane it is more convenient here to take the second variable ΔI_2 rather than the rate of deviation of the regulated quantity $\Delta \dot{V}$, as was done previously. Thus, we take for this problem

$$x = \Delta V \,, \quad y = \Delta I_2 \,. \tag{56.26}$$

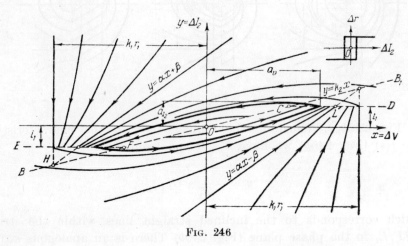

Fig. 246

Then the equations (56.24) are transformed to the form

$$\frac{dx}{dt} = -\frac{1}{T_1}(x + k_1 \Delta r) \,, \tag{56.27}$$

$$\frac{dy}{dt} = -\frac{1}{T_2''}(y - k_2 x) \,, \tag{56.28}$$

where from (56.25), (56.26) and (56.28) we have

$$\Delta r = r_1 \cdot \mathrm{sign}\,(y - i_1) \quad \text{with} \quad y < k_2 x \,, \\ \Delta r = r_1 \cdot \mathrm{sign}\,(y + i_1) \quad \text{with} \quad y > k_2 x; \tag{56.29}$$

the first of these conditions is therefore valid below the straight line BB_1 (Fig. 246) and the second above it. For the former the relay switches at $y = i_1$, i.e. on the line CD (Fig. 246), while for the latter at $y = -i_1$, i.e. on the line EF. The drawing is made under the assumption that $k_1 k_2 r_1 > i$.

As a result we find that above the line $EFCD$ we have

$$\Delta r = r_1 \,, \tag{56.30}$$

and below the line *EFCD*,

$$\Delta r = -r_1 . \tag{56.31}$$

Let us first consider the upper region. For it, dividing (56.28) by (56.27) and considering (56.30) we obtain the equation of the phase trajectories

$$\frac{dy}{dx} = \frac{T_1}{T_2''} \frac{y - k_2 x}{x + k_1 r_1} \tag{56.32}$$

which may be represented in the form

$$\frac{dy}{dx} = \frac{T_1}{T_2''} \frac{y + k_1 k_2 r_1 - k_2(x + k_1 r_1)}{x + k_1 r_1}$$

and integrate, applying the auxiliary substitution

$$y + k_1 k_2 r_1 = z(x + k_1 r_1) ,$$

where z is a new variable in place of y. As a result we find the following equation of the phase trajectories (with $T_1 > T_2''$),

$$y = \alpha x + \beta + C_1(x + k_1 r_1)^\gamma \qquad (\gamma > 1) , \tag{56.33}$$

where C_1 is an arbitrary constant,

$$\alpha = \frac{k_2 T_1}{T_1 - T_2''}, \qquad \beta = \frac{k_1 k_2 r_1 T_2''}{T_1 - T_2''}, \qquad \gamma = \frac{T_1}{T_2''} > 1 \tag{56.34}$$

(with $\gamma = 1$ the solution will have another form, while with $\gamma < 1$ we have $\alpha = 0$ and $\beta < 0$, which we shall not investigate).

To represent the entire set of phase trajectories, the straight line

$$y_1 = \alpha x + \beta \tag{56.35}$$

may be plotted in the phase plane, and to all the ordinates of this line we add

$$y_2 = C_1(x + k_1 r_1)^\gamma , \tag{56.36}$$

giving C_1 arbitrary values (to each value of C_1 we obtain a given phase trajectory). These will be parabolae of degree γ with the axis

$$x = -k_1 r_1 \tag{56.37}$$

and with a common origin at the point H (Fig. 246), having the coordinates

$$x = -k_1 r_1 , \qquad y = -k_1 k_2 r_1 .$$

All the branches of these parabolae lying above the line *EFCD* (since the above calculations are valid only there) are shown in Fig. 246. The directions of the arrows on the phase trajectories obtained are defined by the projections of the generating point velocity $v_x = dx/dt$ which from (56.27), will be negative to the right of the straight line (56.37) and positive to the left; the projection of $v_y = dy/dt$, from (56.28), will be negative above the line $y = k_2 x$ and positive below (at all points of the straight line $y = k_2 x$ the tangents to the phase trajectories are horizontal).

We plot similarly all the phase trajectories below the line *EFCD*, since their differential equation differs from (56.32) only by the substitution $-r_1$ for $+r_1$ according to (56.31).

As a result we see from Fig. 246 that all phase trajectories emerging from the singular segment *FOC* diverge, while all trajectories arriving from the edges of the drawing converge. Both sets approach asymptotically to the steady-state limiting cycle, denoted in the drawing by the heavy closed curve (lens-shaped). This corresponds to an oscillatory steady-state process in the system, where the dimensions of the limiting cycle a_V and a_{I_2} represent the amplitudes of oscillations of the regulated voltage ΔV and the current in the electromagnetic relay winding ΔI_2 respectively.

The phase trajectory forming this limiting cycle may be defined as a curve (56.33) for which

$$(x)_{y=i_1} = -(x)_{y=-i_1}, \qquad (56.38)$$

which defines the value of the arbitrary constant C_1. The value of x (56.38) for this curve gives the required amplitude a_V. The amplitude a_{I_2} is defined as the ordinate of intersection of the curve of the limiting cycle with the straight line $y = k_2 x$ (since, as we have seen above, the tangents to the phase trajectories on the points of this line are horizontal).

It is evident from the drawing (Fig. 246) that the limiting cycle lies to the left of the point *L* and encloses the point *C*. Therefore we have $x_C < a_V < x_L$, i.e. the amplitude of oscillation of the regulated voltage is included in the interval

$$\frac{i_1}{k_2} < a_V < \frac{i_1 + \beta}{\alpha},$$

where α and β are defined by formulae (56.34). The amplitude of a_{I_2} will be somewhat greater than i_1. The period of oscillation is not defined.

Example 5. Let us consider a servomechanism with dry friction in the controlled object, for which the equations were written in Section 54. The equation of the regulated object (54.8) as a non-linear element in the absence of linear friction ($c_2 = 0$) has the form

$$\left. \begin{array}{l} J\ddot{\beta} + c \cdot \operatorname{sign}\dot{\beta} = c_1 I_4 \quad \text{with} \quad \dot{\beta} \neq 0 \quad \text{on} \quad \dot{\beta} = 0 \quad \text{and} \quad |I_4| > \dfrac{c}{c_1}, \\[4mm] \dot{\beta} = \text{const} \quad \text{with} \quad \dot{\beta} = 0 \quad \text{and} \quad |I_4| < \dfrac{c}{c_1}. \end{array} \right\} \qquad (56.39)$$

In writing the equations of all the remaining (linear) elements of the system we neglect their time constants (in order to be able to consider the equation of the entire system as a second-order equation) and we assume that the input device of the servomechanism is set to zero $(\alpha = 0)$. Introduction of the derivative into the regulation function is retained.

As a result we obtain from (54.9) for the linear part of the system

$$I_4 = -(k_6 + k')\dot{\beta} - k\beta .$$

Substituting this in the equation of the object (56.39) and putting

$$a_1 = \frac{c_1}{J}(k_6 + k') , \qquad a_2 = \frac{c_1 k}{J} , \qquad b_1 = \frac{c}{J} , \qquad (56.40)$$

we obtain the equation of the entire servomechanism;

$$\left. \begin{array}{c} \ddot{\beta} + a_1 \dot{\beta} + a_2 \beta = -b_1 \cdot \operatorname{sign} \beta \quad \text{with} \quad \dot{\beta} \neq 0 \quad \text{or} \\[2mm] \text{with} \quad \dot{\beta} = 0 \quad \text{and} \quad |\beta| > \dfrac{c}{c_1 k} , \end{array} \right\} \qquad (56.41)$$

$$\beta = \text{const} \quad \text{with} \quad \dot{\beta} = 0 \quad \text{and} \quad |\beta| < \frac{c}{c_1 k} \qquad (56.42)$$

For the coordinates of the phase plane we take, as usual, $x = \beta$, $y = \dot{\beta}$. The condition $y = 0$ and $|x| < c/c_1 k$ for which, from (56.42), $\beta = \text{const}$, i.e. the system is in equilibrium, is represented in the phase plane by the segment AB (Fig. 247)

Outside this segment, from (56.41), it is necessary to consider individually two cases $y = \dot{\beta} \geqslant 0$ and $y = \dot{\beta} \leqslant 0$, i.e. the upper and lower halves of the phase plane. With $y \leqslant 0$ we have from (56.41)

$$\ddot{x} + a_1 \dot{x} + a_2 x = b_1 .$$

This equation coincides with equation (10.6) with a shift by the magnitude $x = b_1/a_2$. Consequently, below the x-axis it is necessary to plot the same curves as in Fig. 58c (if $a_1^2 < 4a_2$) or as in Fig. 60b (if $a_1^2 > 4a_2$), but with shift of the origin of coordinates to the point A, as in Fig. 247a and b respectively.

Similar curves are plotted above the x-axis, but with shift of the origin of coordinates to the point B (Fig. 247), since from (56.41) with $y > 0$ we have the equation

$$\ddot{x} + a_1 \dot{x} + a_2 x = -b_1 .$$

In both cases (Fig. 247a and b) the system is stable, where in the first case the transient consists of a finite number of damped oscillations of the controlled object while in the second case we have an aperiodic motion. The position of equilibrium of the object is

33

not defined uniquely, the object may stop at any point of the singular segment AB (Fig. 247), as occured previously in the presence of a zone of insensitivity (see Example 1). The singular segment AB is defined by the relationships $|M_r| = |c_1 I_4| < c$, where c is the absolute value of the dry friction moment with motion of the controlled object.

We note that the simplification of the system equations carried out here has permitted their exact solution but this solution, giving

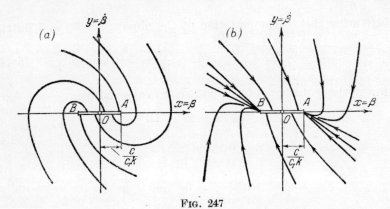

FIG. 247

stability of the system for arbitrary numerical values of the system parameters, does not fully reflect the actual pattern of phenomena in the given non-linear system.

Example 6. Let us now consider the contact servomechanism with dry friction (for example, Fig. 6a), differing from the preceding in that the rotary moment will now be constant in magnitude and changes only sign. Consequently, there will be two non-linearities in the system simultaneously: the relay characteristic of the rotary moment and the dry friction. The system equations in simplest form will be:

$$
\begin{aligned}
J\ddot{\beta} + M_{df} &= M_r\,, \\
M_{df} &= c \cdot \text{sign}\,\dot{\beta}\,, \\
M_r &= -c_1 \cdot \text{sign}\,(\beta - b) \quad \text{with} \quad \dot{\beta} > 0\,, \\
M_r &= -c_1 \cdot \text{sign}\,(\beta + b) \quad \text{with} \quad \dot{\beta} < 0\,,
\end{aligned}
\qquad (56.43)
$$

if the characteristics of the non-linear elements are such as shown in Fig. 248a to the right. Here, since $c_1 > c$, stopping as in (56.42) cannot occur here.

Switching of the relay will take place at $x = +b$ if $y > 0$ and at $x = -b$ if $y < 0$, which corresponds to the line $ABDE$ in the phase plane (Fig. 248a). It is therefore necessary to consider the four quadrants separately:

1) EDx,   where $M_r = -c_1$, $M_{df} = c$,

2) ABx,   where $M_r = -c_1$, $M_{df} = -c$,

3) ABF,   where $M_r = c_1$, $M_{df} = -c$,

4) EDF,   where $M_r = c_1$, $M_{df} = c$.

For the first of these, from (56.43) the system equation reduce to the form

$$J\ddot{\beta} = -(c_1 + c),$$

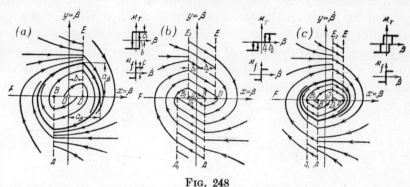

Fig. 248

while since $\beta = x$ and $\dot{\beta} = y$, we have

$$\frac{dx}{dt} = y, \qquad \frac{dy}{dt} = -\frac{c_1 + c}{J},$$

from which the phase trajectory equation will be:

$$\frac{dy}{dx} = -\frac{c_1 + c}{Jy} \quad \text{or} \quad y^2 = -2\frac{c_1 + c}{J}x + C_1. \tag{56.44}$$

The corresponding parabolae are plotted in the quadrant EDx (Fig. 248a).

In the quadrant ABx the equation of the system (56.43) will be:

$$J\ddot{\beta} = -c_1 + c,$$

which corresponds to the phase trajectories

$$y^2 = -2\frac{c_1 - c}{J}x + C_2. \tag{56.45}$$

Analogously in the quadrants ABF and EDF we obtain the parabolae:

$$y^2 = 2\frac{c_1 + c}{J}x + C_3, \tag{56.46}$$

$$y^2 = 2\frac{c_1 - c}{J}x + C_4. \tag{56.47}$$

respectively.

As we see, the singular segment BD is unstable since the phase trajectories emerge from it. It is possible that in the present case the phase trajectories will converge from within and without to a limiting cycle as shown in Fig. 248a. Then there will exist a steady-state oscillatory process (stable). The amplitudes a_β and $a_{\dot\beta}$ of the oscillations of angle β and angular velocity $\dot\beta$ of the controlled object are shown in Fig. 248a.

Let us verify if stable oscillations will actually exist in this case. In Fig. 248a it is evident that for the presence of a closed limiting cycle it is necessary that one of the parabolae in the quadrants EDx, expressed by equation (56.44), have the ordinate y with $x = b$ equal to that for one of the parabolae in the quadrant EDF (equation (56.47)), where the abscissae of these parabolae with $y = 0$ should be equal in absolute value and opposite in sign. We obtain on this basis the following equalities:

$$a_{\dot\beta}^2 = -2\frac{c_1+c}{J}b + C_1 = 2\frac{c_1-c}{J}b + C_3 \,,$$

$$0 = -2\frac{c_1+c}{J}a_\beta + C_1 = 2\frac{c_1-c}{J}(-a_\beta) + C_3 \,.$$

From this, by subtracting the second expression from the first, we find:

$$a_{\dot\beta}^2 = 2\frac{c_1+c}{J}(a_\beta - b) = 2\frac{c_1-c}{J}(a_\beta + b) \,,$$

which gives the following amplitude of oscillation

$$a_\beta = \frac{c_1}{c}b \,, \qquad a_{\dot\beta} = \sqrt{2\frac{c_1^2-c^2}{cJ}\,b} \,. \tag{56.48}$$

This result shows that actually everywhere where $c_1 > c$ there will exist the limiting cycle shown in Fig. 248a, corresponding to steady-state oscillations of the system. In addition, from formulae (56.48) it is evident that the amplitude of oscillation is proportional to the width of the loop $2b$ of the relay characteristic and that in the absence of the loop ($b = 0$) oscillations will be absent.

Let us now turn to the case where in the same contact servo-mechanism the sign of the rotary moment varies according to the relay characteristic shown in Fig. 248b at the right, where there exists an insensitive zone within which $M_r = 0$, specifically:

$$M_r = 0 \begin{cases} \text{with} \quad -b_1 < \beta < b_2 \quad \text{and} \quad \dot\beta > 0 \,, \\ \text{with} \quad -b_2 < \beta < b_1 \quad \text{and} \quad \dot\beta < 0 \,, \end{cases}$$

$$M_r = -c_1 \begin{cases} \text{with} \quad \beta > b_2 \quad \text{and} \quad \dot\beta > 0 \,, \\ \text{with} \quad \beta > b_1 \quad \text{and} \quad \dot\beta < 0 \,, \end{cases}$$

$$M_r = c_1 \begin{cases} \text{with} \quad \beta < -b_1 \quad \text{and} \quad \dot\beta > 0 \,, \\ \text{with} \quad \beta < -b_2 \quad \text{and} \quad \dot\beta < 0 \,. \end{cases}$$

Here the equation of the controlled object

$$J\ddot{\beta} + M_{df} = M_r , \}$$
$$M_{df} = c \cdot \text{sign}\,\dot{\beta} . \}$$

(56.49)

remains in force.

It is obvious that the results of the previous solution in the quadrants EDx, ABx, A_1B_1F and E_1D_1F (Fig. 248b) will be valid here. Between these quadrants there appears a new strip, bounded by the lines $EDBA$ and $E_1D_1B_1A_1$, which corresponds to the insensitive zone ($M_r = 0$). For this strip the system equation will be from (56.49)

$$\ddot{\beta} = -\frac{c}{J} \quad \text{with} \quad \dot{\beta} > 0 ,$$

$$\ddot{\beta} = \frac{c}{J} \quad \text{with} \quad \dot{\beta} < 0 .$$

This gives the parabolae

$$y^2 = -\frac{2c}{J}x + C_5 \quad \text{with} \quad y > 0 ,$$

$$y^2 = \frac{2c}{J}x + C_6 \quad \text{with} \quad y < 0 ,$$

respectively, the segments of which are plotted inside the strip in Fig. 248b. Here we already obtain damped transient oscillations with passage to a stable equilibrium corresponding to some point of the singular segment B_1D.

The case of the characteristics in the form of Fig. 248c are studied similarly, where again self-oscillations appear.

Example 7. Let us consider the automatic pressure regulation system with dry friction in the sensitive element. From (54.15) we have for the non-linear sensitive element the equation

$$\delta\eta = -\varphi - b\,\text{sign}\,\dot{\eta} \quad \text{with} \quad \dot{\eta} \neq 0 \quad \text{or} \quad \dot{\eta} = 0 \quad \text{and} \quad |\delta\eta + \varphi| = b ,$$
$$\eta = \text{const} \quad \text{with} \quad |\delta\eta + \varphi| < b ,$$

(56.50)

where δ and b are coefficients (Fig. 238b).

The equation of the linear part of the system from (54.17) will be

$$\ddot{\varphi} + \left(\frac{1}{T_1} + \frac{1}{T_s}\right)\dot{\varphi} + \frac{1}{T_1 T_s}\varphi = \frac{k_1 \eta}{T_1 T_s} .$$

(56.51)

Here within each period of oscillation in the regulation process it is necessary to distinguish the following four stages (Fig. 249a).

(1) The motion of the generating point over the straight line EA, where $\dot{\varphi} > 0, \dot{\eta} < 0$ and equation (56.50) has the form

$$\delta\eta = -\varphi + b \quad (\dot{\varphi} > 0 , \ \varphi_E < \varphi < \varphi_{max});$$

This motion occurs until φ reaches its maximum value, when $\dot{\varphi} = 0$, $\dot{\eta} = 0$ (the point A, Fig. 249a).

(2) The motion of the generating point over the straight line AB, when $\dot{\varphi} < 0$, $\dot{\eta} = 0$ and equation (56.50) has the form

$$\eta = \text{const} = \eta_{AB} \qquad (\dot{\varphi} < 0 \ , \ \varphi_{max} > \varphi > \varphi_B);$$

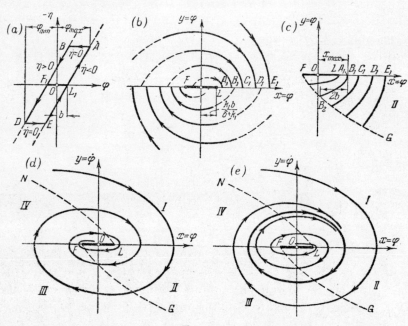

FIG. 249

which is valid up to emergence of the generating point onto the straight line BD, and consequently,

$$\varphi_B = \varphi_{max} - 2b \ , \qquad \eta_{AB} = -\frac{1}{\delta}(\varphi_{max} - b) \ .$$

(3) Motion of the generating point over the straight line BD, where $\dot{\varphi} < 0$, $\dot{\eta} > 0$, and equation (56.50) is written in the form

$$\delta\eta = -\varphi - b \qquad (\dot{\varphi} < 0 \ , \ \varphi_B > \varphi > \varphi_{min});$$

this stage terminates at the point $\varphi = \varphi_{min}$, when $\dot{\varphi} = 0$, $\dot{\eta} = 0$ (the point D in Fig. 249a).

(4) Motion of the generating point over the straight line DE, where $\dot{\varphi} > 0$, $\dot{\eta} = 0$. From (56.50) we have

$$\eta = \text{const} = \eta_{DE} \qquad (\dot{\varphi} > 0 \ , \ \varphi_{min} < \varphi < \varphi_E) \ ,$$

where

$$\varphi_E = \varphi_{min} + 2b \ , \qquad \eta_{DE} = \frac{1}{\delta}(|\varphi_{min}| - b) \ .$$

After this the generating point again passes onto the straight line *EA* and the stages of motion repeat, beginning with the first, with the difference that in each new cycle the straight lines *AB* and *DE* may be higher or lower than those in the preceding cycles.

The equation of the overall regulation system in the first stage, from (56.51) and the equation $\delta\eta = -\varphi + b$, will be:

$$\ddot{\varphi} + a_1\dot{\varphi} + a_2\varphi = b_1 \quad (\dot{\varphi} > 0 ,\ \varphi_{min} + 2b < \varphi < \varphi_{max}) , \quad (56.52)$$

where we put

$$a_1 = \frac{1}{T_1} + \frac{1}{T_s} , \qquad a_2 = \frac{\delta + k_1}{T_1 T_s \delta} , \qquad b_1 = \frac{k_1 b}{T_1 T_s \delta} .$$

Analogously, for the second stage, employing the formulae of (2) above, we obtain:

$$\ddot{\varphi} + a_1\dot{\varphi} + a_3\varphi = -b_2 \quad (\dot{\varphi} < 0 ,\ \varphi_{max} > \varphi > \varphi_{max} - 2b) , \quad (56.53)$$

where

$$a_3 = \frac{1}{T_1 T_s} , \qquad b_2 = \frac{k_1(\varphi_{max} - b)}{T_1 T_s \delta} .$$

For the third stage

$$\ddot{\varphi} + a_1\dot{\varphi} + a_2\varphi = -b_1 \quad (\dot{\varphi} < 0 ,\ \varphi_{max} - 2b < \varphi < \varphi_{min}) . \quad (56.54)$$

Finally, for the fourth stage the equation of the system will be

$$\ddot{\varphi} + a_1\dot{\varphi} + a_3\varphi = b_3 \quad (\dot{\varphi} > 0 ,\ \varphi_{min} < \varphi < \varphi_{min} + 2b) , \quad (56.55)$$

where

$$b_3 = \frac{k_1(|\varphi_{min}| - b)}{T_1 T_s \delta} .$$

Let us put $x = \varphi$ and $y = \dot{\varphi}$. Then the equation of the first stage (56.52) agrees with equation (10.6) except for a shift of magnitude $x = b_1/a_2$. As a result, in the first stage we obtain the same phase trajectories as in Fig. 58c (if $a_1^2 < 4a_2$), but with shift of origin of coordinates to the point *L* (Fig. 249b), where

$$x_L = \frac{b_1}{a_2} = \frac{k_1 b}{\delta + k_1} .$$

The first stage, according to (56.52) and (56.55), extends to the entire upper half of the phase plane. But since the left-hand boundary ($\varphi = \varphi_{min} + 2b$) is still unknown (it becomes known in the fourth stage), while the right-hand boundary ($\varphi = \varphi_{max}$) corresponds to the value $\dot{\varphi} = 0$, i.e. the x-axis, we provisionally plot the above curves over the entire upper half of the phase velocity plane (Fig. 249b).

Similarly for the third stage, as yet not knowing the left-hand boundary ($\varphi = \varphi_{max} - 2b$), we provisionally plot over the entire lower half of the phase plane (Fig. 249b) curves as in Fig. 58c, but, in accordance with equation (56.54), with a shift of the origin of coordinates to the point F, where

$$x_F = -\frac{b_1}{a_2} = -\frac{k_1 b}{\delta + k_1}.$$

Let us now plot the phase trajectories individually for the second stage. Let us take the points A_1, B_1, C_1, D_1, E_1 at the ends of the phase trajectories of the first stage (Fig. 249b). The abscissae of each of these is the corresponding value $x_{max} = \varphi_{max}$, which must be used to plot the phase trajectories of the second stage according to equation (56.53). We take, for example, the point B_1 (Fig. 249c). The phase trajectory corresponding to this in the second stage will be, from (56.53), that curve taken from Fig. 58c (if $a_1^2 < 4a_3$), for which we have at $y = 0$

$$x = x_{B1} + \frac{b_2}{a_3} = x_{B1} + \frac{k_1}{\delta}(x_{B1} - b) = \left(1 + \frac{k_1}{\delta}\right)x_{B1} - \frac{b}{\delta}k_1, \quad (56.56)$$

where x_{B1} is taken from Fig. 249b and the quantity b from Fig. 249a. This curve is plotted from the point B_1 below the axis of abscissae as shown in Fig. 249c. The end of this curve, as shown by formula (56.53) should correspond to the value $\varphi = \varphi_{max} - 2b$ or, in the present case, $x = x_{B1} - 2b$. Therefore, measuring off the distance $2b$ as shown in Fig. 249c, we find the terminal point B_2 on this curve.

Proceeding in exactly the same way for all remaining points (A_1, C_1, B_1, E_1), we plot all the phase trajectories represented in Fig. 249c. The locus of their terminal points automatically gives us the boundary of the second stage of the motion (broken-line $FB_2 G$).

From (56.55) in the fourth stage the pattern of phase trajectories will be symmetrical to the above with respect to the origin of coordinates 0, where in place of the quantity x_{max} we will have $|x_{min}|$, which does not alter the situation.

It now remains to plot all the curves obtained in a single drawing. For this we plot the boundaries FG and LN of the second and fourth stages (Fig. 249d). In regions II and IV we plot the curves shown in Fig. 249c and those symmetrical to them with respect to the origin of coordinates. In regions I and III we plot the curves of Fig. 249b.

In Fig. 249d and e are represented two possible forms of joining the phase trajectories in all four regions. The first gives a stable system with transient in the form of damped oscillations and a singular segment FL including the steady-state region (corresponding to the segment F_1L_1 of the non-linear characteristic of Fig. 249a). In the second form (Fig. 249e) divergent oscillations are obtained close to the singular segment FL, as a result of which the system tends to a steady-state oscillation with bounded amplitude (the stable limiting cycle, marked in Fig. 249e by a heavy line, corresponds to the latter).

It is similarly possible to join the phase trajectories in most cases where $a_1^2 > 4a_3$ or $a_1^2 > 4a_2$, employing in place of Fig. 58c the corresponding curves of Fig. 60b. As a result for certain conditions there may be obtained regulation with aperiodic attenuated transient.

The Andronov point-transformation method. Let us illustrate the basis of the method by the last example 7 and then in a somewhat more general form.

We take the initial position of the generating point M_0 somewhere in the strip Ox (Fig. 250a). One stage of motion of the system (denoted in Fig. 249 by the region II) consists in passage of the gener-

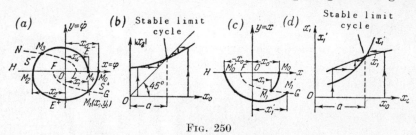

FIG. 250

ating point over the line FG, bounding this stage, to a certain position M_1 (Fig. 250a). The next stage (III in Fig. 249) transfers the generating point to the position M_2 in the strip OH (Fig. 250a), then to the position M_3 on the curve LN and, finally, M_4 on the initial semi-axis Ox.

To each position $M_0(x_0, 0)$ on the semi-axis Ox there corresponds a definite position of the point $M_1(x_1, y_1)$ on the curve FG. This is termed the point transformation of the semi-axis Ox to the curve FG; in Fig. 249c it is shown how this transformation takes place. For briefness we shall term it, for example, the transformation S^+ (but for our purposes this is not essential). Further (Fig. 250a) the point transformation of the curve FG to the semi-axis OH, termed E takes place, then the point transformation S^- of the half-axis OH to the curve LN and the transformation E^- of the curve LN to the initial semi-axis Ox.

All these as a whole (or, so to speak, the transformation $S^+ E^+ S^- E^-$) is termed the point transformation of the semi-axis Ox into itself. In the present case this transformation is written in the form

$$x_4 = f(x_0) ,$$

where x_4 and x_0 denote the abscissae of the points M_4 and M_0 (Fig. 250a). If with arbitrary x_0 we find $x_4 < x_0$, there will be an attenuated process in the system while if $x_4 > x_0$, a divergent process. If the equality $x_4 = x_0$ is possible, we obtain in the phase plane a limiting cycle which, as we know, may represent either stable oscillations or the limit of small-signal stability, or may correspond to a singular case of bifurcation (see below).

In those cases where the general pattern of phase trajectories divides into two symmetrical parts, it is sufficient to study only half of the entire point transformation.

In the above example the upper half-plane (Fig. 249) is symmetrical with the lower with respect to the origin of coordinates. It is therefore sufficient to consider only the first half of the transformation $(S^+ E^+)$, i.e. the point transformation of Ox to the semi-axis OH (Fig. 258), and to express it in the form

$$|x_2| = f(x_0) \quad (x_2 < 0), \tag{56.57}$$

where the condition for the presence of a limiting cycle in the phase plane will be $|x_2| = x_0$ with $x_2 < 0$.

Let, for example, the function (56.57) have the form of the curve shown in Fig. 250b. We plot in this graph further the straight line from the origin of coordinates at an angle of 45° to the coordinate axes. If it intersects the curve, then at the point of intersection we obtain $|x_2| = x_0$. To determine what type of limiting cycle this represents, it is necessary to take the initial point x_0 on the axis of abscissae at first to the left and then to the right of the point of intersection and to follow the course of the point transformation as shown by arrows in Fig. 250b. In this case the process converges from both sides to the point of intersection. Consequently, we have here a stable limiting cycle corresponding to an oscillatory process in the system. In this example the abscissa of the point of intersection (Fig. 250b) gives the amplitude of oscillation. It is easily verified that this corresponds to the pattern of phase trajectories represented in Fig. 249d.

It is possible to proceed in a different way. Let us assume that the transformation S^+ from the point M_0 to M_1 is carried out fairly simply, but it is found that from the point M_1 thus found the corresponding point M is more difficult to find than to determine M_2 from a given position of M_2. We then pass to the curve FG from two sides, taking simultaneously the point $M_0(x_0)$ on the semi-axis Ox and the point $M_0'(-x_0)$ on the semi-axis OH and finding the corresponding points M_1 and M_1' (Fig. 250c). As a result we obtain the point transformations of the semi-axes Ox and OH to the curve FG expressed by certain functions

$$x_1 = f_1(x_0) \quad \text{and} \quad x_1' = f_2(x_0).$$

Representing this in the form of two curves (Fig. 250*d*), we analyse them in the same manner as the curve and straight line in Fig. 250*b*.

Thus, these graphs (termed the point transformation diagrams) correspond to stable limiting cycles, i.e. the presence of steady-state oscillations in the system. Other possible forms of point transformation diagrams are shown in Fig. 251. Here Fig. 251*a* corresponds to an unstable limiting cycle; it bounds the region of initial conditions (x_0, y_0) for which the system is stable with respect to the steady-state with constant value of the regulated quantity

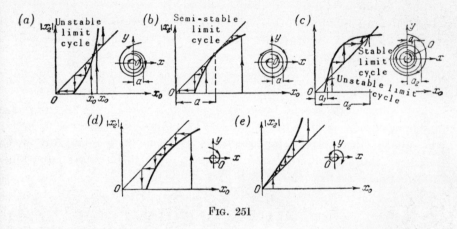

FIG. 251

$(x = 0)$. With initial conditions x_0, y_0 outside the contour of this limiting cycle, the system is unstable (the system is small-signal stable and large-signal unstable).

Fig. 251*c* corresponds to two limiting cycles, of which the smaller is unstable and the larger stable. Consequently, with initial conditions x_0, y_0 inside the first limiting cycle, the system is stable as in the previous case; for all other initial conditions it tends to steady-state oscillations defined by the second limiting cycle.

This case may degenerate to that shown in Fig. 251*b*, where both limiting cycles merge in a single semi-stable cycle. This type of singular case is termed bifurcation.

Finally, in Fig. 251*d* and *e* are shown cases where in the diagram of the point transformation the curve $|x_2| = f(x_0)$ does not intersect the line plotted at 45° to the axes. This denotes stability (*d*) and instability (*e*) respectively, for arbitrary initial conditions within which the equations of the system are valid.

We note that the above considerations are only qualitative since the time t is absent from them. The course of the process in time and the period (frequency) of oscillation remain unknown. To obtain a complete solution of the problem it is necessary in addition to these considerations to solve the differential equations in individual sections with respect to time (as in the method of matching solutions, p. 541). Therefore the corresponding time parameter is introduced into the point transformation which we shall not consider here.

For systems of higher than second order, in place of the phase plane we deal with the phase space and with the point transformations of surfaces rather than lines. New properties of the processes arise there. However in view of the excessive complexity of such constructions we shall not consider them.

Method of isoclines. Above we have considered examples of second-order non-linear systems for which the phase trajectories were easily found by integration of the equations over sections. In those cases where integration is difficult, the shape of the phase trajectories, if only qualitatively, may be studied by the use of the so-called method of isoclines without integrating the equations. Quantitatively this method has relatively low precision. Its application is as yet limited to second-order systems.

An isocline is a line for which at all points of intersection with the phase trajectories, the latter are inclined at a single defined angle to the axis of abscissae x. Thus, if the differential equation of the phase trajectories

$$\frac{dy}{dx} = f(x, y) , \qquad (56.58)$$

is known, to obtain the isoclines it is necessary to put

$$\frac{dy}{dx} = c .$$

The equation of the isocline is thus

$$f(x, y) = c , \qquad (56.59)$$

where c denotes the slope of the phase trajectories. To each given value c there corresponds a single isocline.

For example, the frequently encountered non-linear equation (Reference 7)

$$\ddot{x} - k(1 - x^2)\dot{x} + x = 0;$$

may be written in the form

$$y = \frac{dx}{dt} , \quad \frac{dy}{dt} = k(1 - x^2)y - x ,$$

from which the differential equation of the phase trajectories will be

$$\frac{dy}{dx} = k(1 - x^2) - \frac{x}{y} ,$$

while the equation of the isoclines

$$k(1 - x^2) - \frac{x}{y} = c .$$

Assuming various values for c (with given k), we plot for each of them the curve in the phase plane according to this equation — the isocline (full-line curves in Fig. 252). Then along each curve we mark arrows at angles $\alpha = \operatorname{arctg} c$ to the axis of abscissae (in Fig. 252

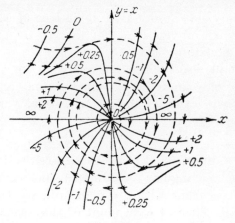

FIG. 252

the values of c are marked on each curve). From these arrows the required phase trajectories are derived; some of them are shown in Fig. 252 by broken line. In this case a stable limiting cycle is obtained, which corresponds to self-oscillations in the system *.

57. Theorems of Liapunov's direct method and their applications

We make the preliminary observation that in describing Lia-punov's direct method, also called Liapunov's second method, we shall employ the differential equations of the automatic system in the form (10.1), assuming that they are written for the transient process in deviations in all variables from their steady-state values, with the new constant values of the perturbation and command forces, $f = f^0$ and $y = y^0$ respectively. Consequently, these equations for the non-linear nth-order system take the form:

$$
\left.
\begin{aligned}
\frac{dx_1}{dt} &= X_1(x_1, x_2, \ldots, x_n) \,, \\
\frac{dx_2}{dt} &= X_2(x_1, x_2, \ldots, x_n) \,, \\
&\cdots\cdots\cdots\cdots\cdots\cdots \\
\frac{dx_n}{dt} &= X_n(x_1, x_2, \ldots, x_n) \,,
\end{aligned}
\right\}
\tag{57.1}
$$

* For application of the method of isoclines see, for example, V. A. Bodner, Avtokolebaniia v sisteme soderzhashchei kompressor (Self-oscillations in a system containing a compressor), "Inzhenernyi sbornik" (technical symposium), vol. VI, 1950.

where the functions X_1, X_2, ..., X_n are arbitrary and contain arbitrary forms of non-linearity, but satisfy always the condition

$$X_1 = X_2 = ... = X_n = 0 \quad \text{with} \quad x_1 = x_2 = ... = x_n = 0 \; , \quad (57.2)$$

since in the steady-state process all deviations of the variables and their derivatives are obviously equal to zero by the definition of the concept of deviation.

Further we shall also require the following concepts.

The concepts of sign-definite, sign-constant and sign-variable functions. Let there exist a function of several variables

$$V = V(x_1, x_2, ..., x_n) \; .$$

We consider an n-dimensional phase space (see Section 10), in which $x_1, x_2, ..., x_n$ are rectangular coordinates (in particular this can represent the phase plane with $n = 2$ or ordinary three-dimensional space with $n = 3$). Then at each point of this space the function V will have a certain definite value. We shall require below functions $V(x_1, x_2, ..., x_n)$ which vanish at the origin of coordinates (i.e. with $x_1 = x_2 = ... = x_n = 0$) and are continuous in some region about it.

The function V is termed sign-definite in some region if at all points of this region about the origin of coordinates it retains a given sign and nowhere vanishes except at the origin of coordinates itself.

The function V is termed sign-constant if it retains the same sign but may vanish not only at the origin of coordinates but at other points of the given region.

The function V is termed sign-variable if in the given region about the origin of coordinates it may have both signs.

Let us present examples of all three types of function V. Let $n = 2$ and $V = x_1^2 + x_2^2$. This is a sign-definite (positive) function, since $V = 0$ only when $x_1 = 0$ and $x_2 = 0$ simultaneously and $V > 0$ for all real values of x_1 and x_2. Analogously for any n the function $V = x_1^2 + x_2^2 + ... + x_n^2$ will be positive-definite while $V = -(x_1^2 + x_2^2 + ... + x_n^2)$ is negative-definite.

If we take the function $V = x_1^2 + x_2^2$ with $n = 3$, it will not be sign-definite since, while it remains positive for arbitrary x_1, x_2 and x_3, it may vanish not only with $x_1 = x_2 = x_3 = 0$ but also for any value of x_3, if $x_1 = x_2 = 0$ (i.e. along the entire x_3-axis, Fig. 253a). Consequently, this will be a sign-constant (positive) function.

Finally, the function $V = x_1 + x_2$ will be sign-variable since it is positive for all points of the plane to the right of the line $x_1 = -x_2$ (Fig. 253b) and negative to the left of this line.

We note that in certain problems we require a function V which does not vanish only at the origin of coordinates but on a given finite segment AB (Fig. 253c). Then the sign-definiteness of the function V will denote its constant sign and non-vanishing in some region about this segment.

The Liapunov function and its derivative with respect to time. An arbitrary function

$$V = V(x_1, x_2, ..., x_n), \qquad (57.3)$$

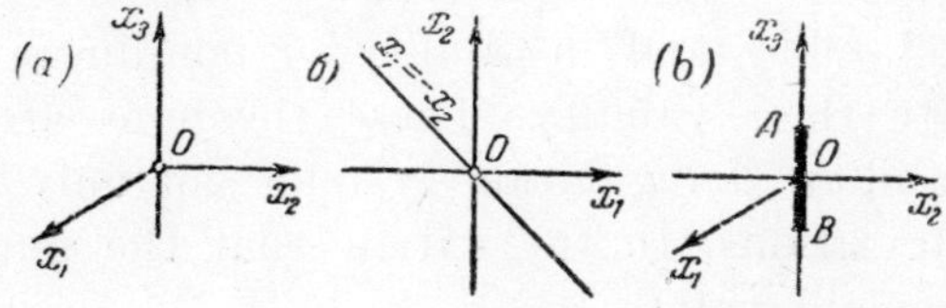

FIG. 253

vanishing identically with $x_1 = x_2 = ... = x_n = 0$, will be called a Liapunov function if for the quantities $x_1, x_2, ..., x_n$ we take those deviations of the variables of the regulation system in the transient

$$x_1 = x_1(t), \quad x_2 = x_2(t), ..., x_n = x_n(t),$$

in which equations (57.1) are written for this system.

The time derivative on the Liapunov function (57.3) will be:

$$\frac{dV}{dt} = \frac{\partial V}{\partial x_1} \cdot \frac{dx_1}{dt} + \frac{\partial V}{\partial x_2} \cdot \frac{dx_2}{dt} + ... + \frac{\partial V}{\partial x_n} \frac{dx_n}{dt} .$$

Substituting here the values $dx_1/dt, ..., dx_n/dt$ from the prescribed equations of the regulation system in the general case (57.1), we obtain the derivative of the Liapunov function with respect to time in the form

$$\frac{dV}{dt} = \frac{\partial V}{\partial x_1} X_1 + \frac{\partial V}{\partial x_2} X_2 + ... + \frac{\partial V}{\partial x_n} X_n, \qquad (57.4)$$

where $X_1, X_2, ..., X_n$ are the right-hand sides of equations (57.1) of the automatic regulation system, constituting prescribed functions of the deviations $x_1, x_2, ..., x_n$.

Consequently, the time derivative of the Liapunov function, just as V, is a certain function of the deviations i.e.

$$\frac{dV}{dt} = W(x_1, x_2, ..., x_n), \qquad (57.5)$$

where from the properties of (57.2) this function W, as V, vanishes identically with $x_1 = x_2 = ... = x_n = 0$. Therefore we may apply to the same degree all the concepts of sign-definiteness, sign-constancy and sign-variability in a certain region about the origin of coordinates that were discussed above with respect to the function V.

Here we have been concerned only with non-linear equations in which the time t does not enter explicitly, since we shall limit ourselves to this case below. In general the Liapunov method may be applied as well in the presence of the time t in explicit form, in particular, for equations with variable coefficients (linear and non-linear).

Basing ourselves on these preliminary considerations, we shall give the general formulation of Liapunov's theorems (References 3, 19, 25, 37) on stability and instability of non-linear systems and shall demonstrate their validity. These theorems are suitable for studying the stability of regulation systems not only for small but also for large deviations, to the extent that the initial equations of the system remain valid.

Liapunov's theorem on the stability of non-linear systems. The formulation of the theorem is as follows: if the equations of an nth-order system are given in the form (57.1) it is possible to choose such a sign-definite Liapunov function $V(x_1, x_2, ..., x_n)$, that its time derivative $W(x_1, x_2, ..., x_n)$ will also be sign-definite (or sign-constant), but have the opposite sign to V, then the given system is stable. With the function W sign-definite, asymptotic stability will occur.

Let us illustrate the validity of this theorem geometrically. For simplicity we take a third-order system ($n = 3$). Equations (57.1) for it will be in general form:

$$\left.\begin{array}{l} \dfrac{dx_1}{dt} = X_1(x_1,\, x_2,\, x_3)\,, \\[2mm] \dfrac{dx_2}{dt} = X_2(x_1,\, x_2,\, x_3)\,, \\[2mm] \dfrac{dx_3}{dt} = X_3(x_1,\, x_2,\, x_3)\,. \end{array}\right\} \qquad (57.6)$$

Let us take the positive-definite Liapunov function in the form

$$V = a^2x^2 + b^2x_2^2 + c^2x^2\,, \qquad (57.7)$$

where a, b, c are arbitrarily given real numbers. We shall assign to the quantity V increasing constant values $V = 0, C_1, C_2, C_3, ...$, which signifies:

$$a^2x_1^2 + b^2x_2^2 + c^2x_3^2 = 0\,,$$
$$a^2x_1^2 + b^2x_2^2 + c^2x_3^2 = C_1\,,$$
$$a^2x_1^2 + b^2x_2^2 + c^2x_3^2 = C_2\,,$$

The first of these expressions corresponds to a single point $x_1 = x_2 = x_3 = 0$ (origin of coordinates in the phase space), while the remaining are ellipsoidal surfaces in the phase space, where each successive ellipsoid contains the previous one completely within itself (Fig. 254).

Let us now take the derivative of the Liapunov function with respect to time. From (57.4) and (57.7)

$$\frac{dV}{dt} = 2a^2x_1 \cdot X_1(x_1, x_2, x_3) + 2b^2x_2 \cdot X_2(x_1, x_2, x_3) +$$
$$+ 2c^2x_3 \cdot X_3(x_1, x_2, x_3) = W(x_1, x_2, x_3),$$

where the functions X_1, X_2, X_3 are taken from the prescribed equations of the regulation system (57.6).

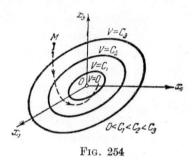

F‍IG. 254

If the function $W(x_1, x_2, x_3)$ thus obtained is negative-definite i.e. if

$$\frac{dV}{dt} < 0 \qquad (57.8)$$

at all points of the given phase space, except the origin of coordinates, where

$$\frac{dV}{dt} = 0 \quad \text{(with } x_1 = x_2 = x_3 = 0\text{)},$$

then for arbitrary initial conditions as a result of (57.8) the generating point M (Fig. 254) will move towards decreasing values of V, i.e. will intersect the ellipsoids represented in Fig. 254 from without. As a result in the course of time M will tend to the origin of coordinates 0 of the phase space and cannot emerge from those ellipsoids into which it has penetrated.

But this signifies attenuation with time of all deviations x_1, x_2, x_3 in the transient, i.e. stability of the given regulation system. We have thus illustrated the validity of the theorem for a third-order system (with sign-definite function W).

From this there follows the validity of the theorem in the general case. The considerations remain analogous, only in place of three equations (57.6) there will be n equations (57.1). As before, for an arbitrary positive-definite Liapunov function $V(x_1, x_2, ..., x_n) = C$ we obtain certain closed surfaces enclosing the origin of coordinates

(Fig. 254), but now in place of ordinary three-dimensional space, in the n-dimensional phase space (sometimes termed hyper-surfaces). Therefore if the derivative $dV/dt = W(x_1, x_2, ..., x_n)$ is negative-definite, the trajectories of the generating point M in n-dimensional space for arbitrary initial conditions will in the course of time intersect these surfaces only from without, which indicates the stability of the system.

If the function W is not sign-definite but sign-constant, it is obvious that the trajectories of the generating point M will not always intersect the surface $V = c$ and may be tangent to them at those points where W vanishes (aside from the origin of coordinates). But since at all other points of phase space the function W has the same sign, as a result of which the generating point may only pass the surface $V = c$ from without, in solving the problem it is only necessary to check whether the generating point does not "stick" at the point where $W = 0$ (see example below).

Note on the Liapunov stability theorem. In connection with the formulation of the Liapunov stability theorem it is necessary to make the following two important remarks.

(1) The theorem concerns the choice of Liapunov function $V(x_1, x_2, ..., x_n)$. With regulation system equations given in the form (57.1) it may be possible to select several different forms of the function V, since it is only required to obtain sign-definiteness of it and its derivative. Different forms of the function V, satisfying the theorem, may give differing forms of the stability condition for a given regulation system. Some of these will be broader, others narrower; the latter may enter into the former as particular cases, etc.

Therefore, in general, the given Liapunov theorem ensures obtaining sufficient conditions for stability, which will not always be necessary, i.e. in satisfying the conditions of the theorem the system will certainly be stable, but these conditions may not include the entire region of stability of the system with respect to the parameters. In fact, choosing the function V satisfying the theorem we are not certain that a second form of the function V cannot be found which would more fully include the stability region of the given system.

Geometrically this signifies that, having obtained a defined family of surfaces $V = C$ (Fig. 254) and verifying that the trajectories of the generating point M approach the origin of coordinates, intersecting these surfaces from without, we are not certain that there do not exist other forms of trajectories of the generating point M which at individual points may intersect the given surface from inside, but nevertheless in the course of time approach without limit the origin of coordinates. These trajectories will correspond to a second family of surfaces $V = C$, i.e. to a different choice of the Liapunov function.

In a number of engineering problems it is possible to satisfy these sufficient stability conditions completely. The degree of closeness of these sufficient stability conditions to be necessary and sufficient will depend on the degree of success in choosing the Liapunov function V, i.e. this will determine how completely the entire stability region of the given system is included. There exist, of course, functions $V(x_1, x_2, ..., x_n)$ which satisfy the entire stability region.

(2) To the above formulation of the Liapunov theorem it is necessary to add that the Liapunov stability concept admits that with sign-definite function V its derivative W need not necessarily be sign-definite or sign-constant, but may vanish identically over the entire phase space involved. In this case, by considerations analogous to the above, it is easily verified that the generating point M (Fig. 254) will remain for all time on some one of the surfaces $V = \text{const}$, where it has been placed by the initial conditions. As a result the system, although it will not approach asymptotically to some steady-state, will remain for all time sufficiently close to it if the initial deviations were small. However such a case does not as yet present any practical interest and we exclude it from consideration.

The Liapunov theorem on the instability of non-linear systems. Since the previous Liapunov theorem gives in general only sufficient conditions for stability and since, aside from the stability region, a non-linear system may have a number of singular regions (see the start of Section 56), there may arise the need for the separate determination of the regions of instability by use of the following Liapunov theorem which gives sufficient conditions for instability of the system.

The theorem is formulated as follows: if with the equations of an nth-order system given in the form (57.1) the derivative $W(x_1, x_2, ..., x_n)_3$ of any Liapunov function $V(x_1, x_2, ..., x_n)$ is sign-definite, where the function V in some region adjacent to the origin of coordinates has sign identical to the sign of the derivative W, the given system is unstable.

We shall illustrate the correctness of this theorem geometrically as follows. For some given second-order system ($n = 2$) let there be found such a sign-variable function $V(x_1, x_2)$ for which the derivative

$$\frac{dV}{dt} = \frac{\partial V}{\partial x_1} X_1(x_1, x_2) + \frac{\partial V}{\partial x_2} X_2(x_1, x_2) = W(x_1, x_2)$$

is positive-definite. Let the loci $V(x_1, x_2)$ be distributed in the phase plane as shown in Fig. 255, where the loci AB and CD correspond to values $V = 0$ and separate the regions within which $V > 0$ and $V < 0$.

Let us take the generating point M as shown in Fig. 255. Since there $V < 0$ and everywhere

$$W = \frac{dV}{dt} > 0 \,,$$

the generating point M will move in the course of time and intersect the loci $V = C$, passing from smaller values of C to larger. In this it may temporarily approach the origin of coordinates but will

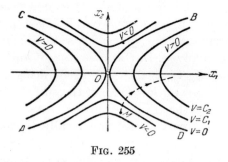

FIG. 255

finally diverge without limit from the origin of coordinates. This corresponds to a divergent process, i.e. instability of the system. The validity of the theorem for systems of any order n may be shown by similar considerations in n-dimensional phase space.

Let us present two examples of application of these Liapunov theorems to the study of non-linear automatic regulation systems.

Example taking into account the non-linearity of the regulating organ drive. An example of this type with respect to the system aircraft with course autopilot (in simplified form) was considered in the work of A. I. Lur'e and V. N. Postnikov in 1944, on the basis of the work of B. V. Bulgakov, solving this problem by a different method (see below, Section 66). The block diagram of the given automatic regulation system is shown in Fig. 256a.

Let all the elements of the system be linear, except for the electric motor (with reduction gear), for which we shall consider its real characteristic (Fig. 256b). It may have an arbitrary curved form with a dead zone (with $|V| < b_1$) and a zone of saturation (with $|V| > b_2$). The slope of the characteristic and its curvature may be arbitrary, except that the conditions

$$\frac{dF}{dV} \geqslant 0 \,, \quad F > 0 \quad \text{with} \quad V > b_1 \quad \text{and} \quad F < 0 \quad \text{with} \quad V < -b_1 \,, \quad (57.9)$$

should be observed. It is required to find the stability conditions of the given automatic regulation system.

The equation of the aircraft as a regulated object in a rough approximation according to Section 25 will be

$$T_1\ddot{\psi} + \dot{\psi} = -k_1\delta , \qquad (57.10)$$

where ψ is the deviation of the course angle of the aircraft, δ is the rudder deviation.

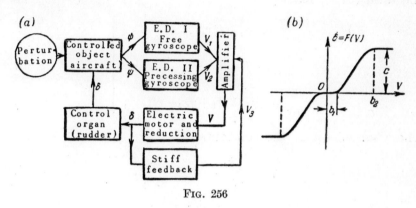

FIG. 256

The equations of the sensitive elements (gyroscopes with potentiometers)

$$V_1 = k_2\psi , \qquad V_2 = k_3\dot{\psi} . \qquad (57.11)$$

The feedback equation

$$V_3 = k_4\delta . \qquad (57.12)$$

The amplifier equation

$$V = k_5V_1 + k_6V_2 - k_7V_3 . \qquad (57.13)$$

The equation of the electric motor with gear reduction and rudder

$$\delta = F(V) , \qquad (57.14)$$

where $F(V)$ is given by the graph of Fig. 256*b*.

Equations (57.11), (57.12) and (57.13) may be reduced to a single one:

$$V = k_\psi\psi + k_{\dot\psi}\dot{\psi} - k_{fb}\delta , \qquad (57.15)$$

where

$$k_\psi = k_2k_5 , \qquad k_{\dot\psi} = k_3k_6 , \qquad k_{fb} = k_4k_7 .$$

To pass to equations of type (57.1) we substitute the new variables

$$\left. \begin{array}{l} x_1 = \dfrac{1}{T_1k_1}\psi + \dfrac{1}{T_1}\delta , \qquad x_2 = -\dfrac{1}{T_1}\delta , \\[3mm] x_3 = \dfrac{1}{T_1k_1k_{\dot\psi}}V = \dfrac{k_\psi}{T_1k_1k_{\dot\psi}}\psi + \dfrac{1}{T_1k_1}\dot{\psi} - \dfrac{k_{fb}}{T_1k_1k_{\dot\psi}}\delta \end{array} \right\} \qquad (57.16)$$

and the dimensionless time

$$\tau = \frac{t}{T_1}. \tag{57.17}$$

With introduction of these variables the differential equations of the entire system (57.10), (57.14), (57.15) are transformed to the form (57.1), namely:

$$\left.\begin{array}{l} \dfrac{dx_1}{d\tau} = -x_1 + f(x_3)\,, \\[2mm] \dfrac{dx_2}{d\tau} = -f(x_3)\,, \\[2mm] \dfrac{dx_3}{d\tau} = (\gamma-1)x_1 + \gamma x_2 - rf(x_3)\,, \end{array}\right\} \tag{57.18}$$

where we substitute the constants

$$\gamma = \frac{T_1 k_\psi}{k_{\dot\psi}}\,, \qquad r = \frac{k_\psi}{k_1 k_{\dot\psi}}\,, \tag{57.19}$$

and

$$f(x_3) = F(T_1 k_1 k_{\dot\psi} x_3)\,,$$

i.e. the function $f(x_3)$ has the same properties as the given function $F(V)$ (Fig. 256b), and differs only in scale along the axis of abscissae because of the substitution of the variable V by x_3 according to the third of equalities (57.16).

Steady-state flight with this system from (57.10), (57.14), (57.15) and the graph of Fig. 256b will occur with

$$\delta = 0\,, \qquad \dot\psi = 0\,, \qquad |\psi| < \frac{b_1}{k_{\dot\psi}}\,, \tag{57.20}$$

i.e. the presence of the dead zone of the motor permits the course angle in the steady-state process to have any constant value in the limits (57.20).

In the new variables (57.16) the steady-state flight is defined by the values

$$x_1 = 0\,, \qquad x_3 = 0\,, \qquad |x_3| < \frac{b_1}{T_1 k_1 k_{\dot\psi}}\,, \tag{57.21}$$

to which there corresponds an arbitrary point of the segment AB in the phase space (Fig. 257a).

In finding the stability conditions we consider two cases: $\gamma > 1$ and $0 < \gamma < 1$.

Case $\gamma > 1$. Let us take the Liapunov function in the form

$$V = \frac{\gamma-1}{2}x_1^2 + \frac{\gamma}{2}x_2^2 + \int\limits_0^{x_3} f(x_3)\,dx_3\,. \tag{57.22}$$

Here the integral will always be positive since the function $f(x_3)$ is odd (see condition (57.9)). Therefore V is a positive-definite function if $\gamma > 1$ vanishes on the steady-state segment AB (Fig. 257). The surfaces $V(x_1, x_2, x_3) = C$ enclose this segment (Fig. 257b), converging to it with decrease of C.

Let us compose the derivative of the Liapunov function:

$$W = \frac{dV}{d\tau} = \frac{\partial V}{\partial x_1}\frac{dx_1}{d\tau} + \frac{\partial V}{\partial x_2}\frac{dx_2}{d\tau} + \frac{\partial V}{\partial x_3}\frac{dx_3}{d\tau} ,$$

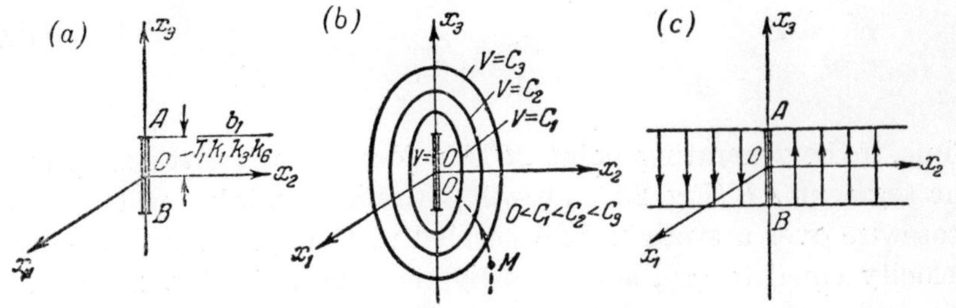

FIG. 257

where the partial derivatives are taken from (57.22), while the derivatives with respect to dimensionless time, from the system equations (57.18). Then

$$W = -(\gamma-1)x_1^2 + (\gamma-1)x_1 f(x_3) - \gamma x_2 f(x_3) + \\ + f(x_3)[(\gamma-1)x_1 + \gamma x_2 - rf(x_3)] .$$

We represent this in the form

$$W = -(\gamma-1)[f(x_3) - x_1]^2 - (r - \gamma + 1)[f(x_3)]^2 . \qquad (57.23)$$

This function W is sign-constant, since it does not include the coordinate x_2 and therefore vanishes not only on the segment of the steady-state AB but in an entire strip of width AB in the plane x_2x_3 (Fig. 257c). But outside this strip, from (57.23), it will be everywhere negative with

$$r > \gamma - 1, \quad \text{if} \quad \gamma > 1 . \qquad (57.24)$$

Therefore according to the Liapunov stability theorem expression (57.24) is a sufficient condition for stability of the given non-linear system aircraft-with-course-autopilot (with arbitrary curvature and arbitrary slope of the drive characteristic, having the form of Fig. 256b).

The trajectories of the generating point M will intersect the surfaces $V = C$ from without, where $W = dV/d\tau < 0$. It is only necessary to verify whether the generating point M "sticks" at a point where W vanishes (outside the steady-state segment AB). In the present case we are concerned with whether the generating point remains in the strip (shown in Fig. 257c) where $W = 0$ if it should accidentally be incident on it.

To answer this question we find the projections of the generating point M velocity $dx_1/d\tau$, $dx_2/d\tau$, $dx_3/d\tau$, when the point is at an arbitrary location in the strip. Since there

$$x_1 = 0 , \qquad |x_2| < \frac{b_1}{T_1 k_1 k_{\dot\psi}} , \qquad f(x_3) = 0 ,$$

the required velocity projections from (57.18) will be

$$\frac{dx_1}{d\tau} = 0 , \qquad \frac{dx_2}{d\tau} = 0 , \qquad \frac{dx_3}{d\tau} = \gamma x_2 .$$

Thus, if the generating point M is incident on the given strip outside the segment AB (Fig. 257c), it will not remain in it but will pass over it crosswise over a straight line parallel to the x_3-axis with a constant velocity equal to γx_2, as shown by the arrows in Fig. 257c. Passing the strip, the generating point will again intersect the surfaces $V = C$ from without, i.e. the given regulation system will be stable.

The case $0 < \gamma < 1$. For this case we take the Liapunov function in the form

$$V = \frac{1-\gamma}{2} x_1^2 + \frac{\gamma}{2} x_2^2 + \int_0^{x_3} f(x_3) \, dx_3 .$$

Its derivative will be

$$W = \frac{dV}{d\tau} = - (1 - \gamma) x_1^2 - r [f(x_3)]^2 .$$

From this analogously to the above we come to the sufficient condition for stability of the system in the form

$$r > 0 , \qquad \text{if} \quad 0 < \gamma < 1 . \tag{57.25}$$

General conclusion. The sufficient conditions for stability (57.24) and (57.25) obtained in the problem after substitution of the expressions for γ and r in terms of the system parameters (57.19) take the forms

$$k_{fb} > (T_1 k_\psi - k_{\dot\psi}) k_1 , \qquad \text{if} \quad k_{\dot\psi} < T_1 k_\psi;$$

$$k_{fb} > 0 , \qquad \text{if} \quad k_{\dot\psi} > T_1 k_\psi ,$$

respectively.

The first of these stability conditions indicates that the transfer factor of the feedback must be made sufficiently large if the derivative $\dot\psi$ is not sufficiently intensely introduced into the regulation function. From the second of the stability conditions it follows that the system will be stable with arbitrary feedback if the transfer factor with respect to the derivative is sufficiently large.

The fact that these stability conditions are sufficient but not necessary is clearly seen from the fact that they are independent of the motor characteristics (Fig. 256*b*), i.e. they are the same for any curvature, any slope and any dead zone (including a single-valued relay motor characteristic with constant velocity as well as linear characteristic). At the same time the true stability conditions (necessary and sufficient) should depend on the shape of the motor

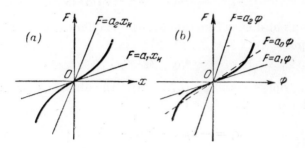

FIG. 258

characteristic. These stability conditions guarantee that with their satisfaction the system will be safely stable. But, in general, it may be stable even in some region outside the limits of these stability conditions.

Example taking into account non-linearity of the regulated quantity gauge. On the basis of the above Liapunov theorems, M. A. Aizerman proved in 1946 that if the system equation contains non-linearity:

$$
\begin{aligned}
\frac{dx_1}{dt} &= a_{11}x_1 + a_{12}x_2 + \ldots + a_{1n}x_n + F(v_k) , \\
\frac{dx_2}{dt} &= a_{21}x_1 + a_{22}x_2 + \ldots + a_{2n}x_n , \\
&\qquad \ldots \ldots \ldots \ldots \ldots \ldots \ldots \ldots \ldots \ldots \\
\frac{dx_n}{dt} &= a_{n1}x_1 + a_{n2}x_2 + \ldots + a_{nn}x_n ,
\end{aligned}
\qquad (57.26)
$$

where $F(x_k)$ is a single-valued non-linear function, vanishing at $x_k = 0$, while k is an arbitrary whole number $1, 2, \ldots, n$, for the system to be stable it is sufficient if for the linearised system (57.26), with substitution $F(x_k) = ax_k$, the Liapunov function V may be constructed with derivative W a negative-definite function for any value a in the interval $a_1 < a < a_2$, if the curve $F(x_k)$ lies between the straight lines $F = a_1 x_k$ and $F = a_2 x_k$, as shown, for example, in Fig. 258*a*.

In the previous system of aircraft with course autopilot (Fig 256a), for example, let the equation of the regulated object have the form (57.10), the rudder drive have the linear characteristic $\delta = k_8 V$, but the rheostat with sensitive element 1 (gauge of regulated quantity ψ) have a non-linear characteristic, as a result of which the non-linear autopilot equation

$$\delta = F(\psi) + k_{\dot\psi}\dot\psi - k_{fb}\delta , \qquad (57.27)$$

is obtained, where

$$k_{\dot\psi} = k_3 k_6 k_8 , \qquad k_{fb} = k_4 k_7 k_8 ,$$

and $F(\psi)$ is a non-linear function of the form, for example, of Fig. 258b.
Let us put

$$x_1 = -\delta , \qquad x_2 = \psi , \qquad x_3 = \dot\psi .$$

Then the autopilot equation (57.27) and the aircraft equation (57.10) take the form (57.26), specifically:

$$\left.\begin{array}{l} \dot x_1 = -k_{fb}x_1 - k_{\dot\psi}x_3 - F(x_2) , \\ \dot x_2 = x_3 , \\ \dot x_3 = \dfrac{k_1}{T_1}x_1 - \dfrac{1}{T_1}x_3 . \end{array}\right\} \qquad (57.28)$$

Let us assign the function V in the form

$$V = \frac{1}{2}b_1 x_1^2 + \frac{1}{2}b_2 x_2^2 + \frac{1}{2}b_3 x_3^2 + b_{12}x_1 x_2 + b_{13}x_1 x_2 + b_{23}x_2 x_3 ,$$

where all six coefficients b are unknown. We require that the function

$$W = \frac{\partial V}{\partial x_1}\dot x_1 + \frac{\partial V}{\partial x_2}\dot x_2 + \frac{\partial V}{\partial x_3}\dot x_3 \qquad (57.29)$$

with fixed value of $F(x_2) = a_0 x_2$ in equations (57.28) have the form

$$W_0 = -(x_1^2 + x_2^2 + x_3^2) . \qquad (57.30)$$

Then by equating corresponding coefficients of expressions (57.29) and (57.30) it is possible to find all six quantities b from the system of six algebraic equations. Below we present the solutions for only three coefficients which are required further, namely:

$$b_1 = \frac{D_1}{aD} , \qquad b_{12} = \frac{1}{a_0} , \qquad b_{12} = \frac{D_{13}}{a_0 D} , \qquad (57.31)$$

where

$$\left.\begin{array}{l} D = (T_1 k_{fb}+1)(k_{fb}+k_{\dot\psi}k_1) - a_0 k_1 T_1 , \\ D_1 = a_0 k_1(T_1 k_{\dot\psi}+k_1) + (T_1 k_{fb}+1)(a_0+k_1) , \\ D_{13} = T_1[a_0(T_1 a_0 + k_{fb}k_1 - k_{\dot\psi}) + k_{fb}(T_1 k_{fb}+1)] . \end{array}\right\} \qquad (57.32)$$

Example. Let it be required to write the canonical equations for the automatic motor velocity regulation system considered in Section 22 when the hydraulic drive has a non-linear characteristic. Let the regulated object not have self-regulation while the regulator is fitted with stiff feedback. Then on the basis of Section 22 the regulation system equations have the form

$$\left.\begin{array}{l} T_a\dot{\varphi} = \xi\,, \\ T_r^2\ddot{\eta} + T_k\dot{\eta} + \delta\eta = -\varphi\,, \\ \sigma = \eta - \zeta\,, \quad \zeta = \xi\,, \\ \dot{\xi} = f(\sigma)\,. \end{array}\right\} \qquad (58.18)$$

The last equation is the non-linear equation of the hydraulic drive, where $f(\sigma)$ may have any of the forms represented in Fig. 259.

Introducing the notation

$$\eta_1 = \varphi\,, \quad \eta_2 = \dot{\eta}\,, \quad \eta_3 = \eta\,,$$

we rewrite the system equations (58.18) in the form

$$\dot{\eta}_1 = \frac{\xi}{T_a}\,,$$

$$\dot{\eta}_2 = -\frac{\eta_1}{T_r^2} - \frac{T_k}{T_r^2}\eta_2 - \frac{\delta}{T_r^2}\eta_3\,,$$

$$\dot{\eta}_3 = \eta_2\,, \quad \sigma = \eta_3 - \xi\,,$$

$$\dot{\xi} = f(\sigma)\,.$$

In this case we have equations of type (58.1), in which

$$n = 4\,, \quad b_1 = \frac{1}{T_a}\,, \quad c_3 = 1\,, \quad r = 1\,,$$

$$a_{21} = -\frac{1}{T_r^2}\,, \quad a_{22} = -\frac{T_k}{T_r^2}\,, \quad a_{23} = -\frac{\delta}{T_r^2}\,, \quad a_{32} = 1\,,$$

while all remaining coefficients are equal to zero. The determinant (58.3) is here:

$$D(\lambda) = \begin{vmatrix} -\lambda\,, & 0\,, & 0 \\ -\dfrac{1}{T_r^2}\,, & -\dfrac{T_k}{T_r^2} - \lambda\,, & -\dfrac{\delta}{T_r^2} \\ 0\,, & 1\,, & -\lambda \end{vmatrix} = -\lambda\left(\lambda^2 + \frac{T_k}{T_r^2}\lambda + \frac{\delta}{T_r^2}\right). \qquad (58.19)$$

Its roots have the values

$$\lambda_{1,2} = \frac{-T_k \pm \sqrt{T_k^2 - 4T_r^2\delta}}{2T_r^2}\,.$$

The required canonical equations are therefore written in the form (58.9) where the coefficients β_1, β_2 and β_3 are to be calculated according to formula (58.7) since among the coefficients c_1, c_2, c_3 only c_3 is non-vanishing, we must determine only $N_3(\lambda)$ and $D'(\lambda)$. From (58.19) we have in this example:

$$N_3(\lambda) = \frac{1}{T_a} \begin{vmatrix} -\dfrac{1}{T_r^2}, & -\dfrac{T_k}{T_r^2} - \lambda \\ 0, & 1 \end{vmatrix} = -\frac{1}{T_a T_r^2},$$

$$D'(\lambda) = -3\lambda^2 - 2\frac{T_k}{T_r^2}\lambda + \frac{\delta}{T_r^2}.$$

Consequently, we obtain from (58.7):

$$\beta_1 = -\frac{c_3 N_3}{D'(\lambda_1)} = \frac{1}{T_a(-3T_r^2\lambda_1 - 2T_k\lambda_1 + \delta)},$$

$$\beta_2 = -\frac{c_3 N_3}{D'(\lambda_2)} = \frac{1}{T_a(-3T_r^2\lambda_2 - 2T_k\lambda_2 + \delta)},$$

$$\beta_3 = -\frac{c_3 N_3}{D'(0)} = \frac{1}{T_a \delta}.$$

The canonical equations will therefore be:

$$\dot{x}_1 = \lambda_1 x_1 + f(\sigma), \quad \dot{x}_2 = \lambda_2 x_2 + f(\sigma), \quad \dot{x}_3 = f(\sigma),$$
$$\dot{\sigma} = \beta_1 x_1 + \beta_2 x_2 + \beta_3 x_3 - f(\sigma).$$

The equations for the old variables in terms of the new variables, are found on the basis of formulae (58.11), for which we need to know, in addition to the preceding, the values

$$N_1(\lambda) = \frac{1}{T_a} \begin{vmatrix} -\dfrac{T_k}{T_r^2} - \lambda, & -\dfrac{\delta}{T_r^2} \\ 1, & -\lambda \end{vmatrix} = \frac{1}{T_a}\left(\lambda^2 + \frac{T_k}{T_r^2}\lambda + \frac{\delta}{T_r^2}\right),$$

$$N_2(\lambda) = -\frac{1}{T_a} \begin{vmatrix} -\dfrac{1}{T_r^2}, & -\dfrac{\delta}{T_r^2} \\ 0, & -\lambda \end{vmatrix} = -\frac{\lambda}{T_a T_r^2}.$$

The canonic equations for various concrete non-linear systems are written similarly, if their equations relate to one of the three above classes. For equations of higher degrees it is necessary to have numerically given coefficients of the equations and to calculate the roots λ by the methods presented in Section 39.

On the choice of the Liapunov functions. We present here recommendations for the choice of Liapunov functions after reduction of the non-linear automatic regulation system equations to the canonic form. We limit ourselves here only to the case where the linear part of the system is stable, i.e. all roots λ of the polynomial $D(\rho)$ (or $D(\lambda)$) have negative real parts, where one of them may be zero.

Let the system be described by the canonic equations (58.9) (or, which is equivalent, (58.15) or (58.17)). Among the $n-1$ roots λ let there be s real roots $(\lambda_1, \lambda_2, \ldots, \lambda_s)$ and the remaining complex $(\lambda_{s+1}, \lambda_{s+2}, \ldots, \lambda_{n-1})$. We shall first assume that the characteristic of the non-linear branch $f(\sigma)$ has no dead zone and has the form b, d or f in Fig. 259 (we shall take the dead zone into account later), i.e. $f(\sigma) > 0$ with $\sigma > 0$ and $f(\sigma) < 0$ with $\sigma < 0$, so that everywhere for arbitrary σ we have:

$$\sigma f(\sigma) > 0 \quad \text{and} \quad \int_0^\sigma f(\sigma)\,d\sigma > 0 \quad (\sigma \neq 0), \qquad (58.20)$$

with these quantities vanishing only for $\sigma = 0$.

It is recommended to take the Liapunov function (Reference 20) in the form of the following negative-definite function:

$$V = -\int_0^\sigma f(\sigma)\,d\sigma + \Phi(x_1, x_2, \ldots, x_{n-1}) + F(a_1 x_1, a_2 x_2, \ldots, a_{n-1} x_{n-1}), \quad (58.21)$$

where

$$\left.\begin{aligned}
\Phi(x_1, x_2, \ldots, x_{n-1}) &= -\frac{1}{2}(A_1 x_1^2 + A_2 x_2^2 + \ldots + A_s x_s^2) - \\
&\quad - (c_1 x_{s+1} x_{s+2} + c_3 x_{s+3} x_{s+4} + \ldots + c_{n-s+2} x_{n-2} x_{n-1}), \\
F(a_1 x_1, a_2 x_2, \ldots, a_{n-1} x_{n-1}) &= \sum_{\alpha=1}^{n-1} \sum_{\beta=1}^{n-1} \frac{a_\alpha x_\alpha a_\beta x_\beta}{\lambda_\alpha + \lambda_\beta},
\end{aligned}\right\} \quad (58.22)$$

and $A_1, A_2, \ldots, A_s, c_1, c_3, \ldots, c_{n-s+2}$ are arbitrary small positive coefficients. Here it is important that $x_1, x_2, \ldots, x_s$ are real quantities while $x_{s+1}, x_{s+2}, \ldots, x_{n-1}$ are complex conjugate, pairwise as a result of which $x_{s+1}, x_{s+2} = |x_{s+1}|^2$ (the sum of squares of the real and imaginary parts). The numbers $a_1, \ldots, a_s$ are real, $a_{s+1}, \ldots, a_{n-1}$ are complex conjugate, pairwise as yet unknown.

It is found (Reference 20) that with this choice of the Liapunov function $V(x_1, x_2, \ldots, x_{n-1}, \sigma)$ its derivative with respect to time $dV/dt = W(x_1, x_2, \ldots, x_{n-1}, \sigma)$ will be sign-definite if the following auxiliary system of quadratic equations

$$\left.\begin{aligned}
2a_1 \sqrt{r} - 2a_1 \sum_{\alpha=1}^{n-1} \frac{a_\alpha}{\lambda_1 + \lambda_\alpha} + \beta_1 &= 0, \\
2a_2 \sqrt{r} - 2a_2 \sum_{\alpha=1}^{n-1} \frac{a_\alpha}{\lambda_2 + \lambda_\alpha} + \beta_2 &= 0, \\
\cdots\cdots\cdots\cdots\cdots\cdots\cdots\cdots\cdots\cdots\cdots \\
2a_{n-1} \sqrt{r} - 2a_{n-1} \sum_{\alpha=1}^{n-1} \frac{a_\alpha}{\lambda_{n-1} + \lambda_\alpha} + \beta_{n-1} &= 0,
\end{aligned}\right\} \quad (58.23)$$

has at least one set of solutions with respect to the unknowns $a_1, a_2, ..., a_{n-1}$, where $a_1, ..., a_s$ are real, $a_{s+1}, ..., a_{n-1}$ are complex conjugate pairwise.

As a result finding the stability of the non-linear system reduces here to determining the conditions for which the quadratic equations (58.23) have a solution of the given form.

With the presence among the roots $\lambda_1, ..., \lambda_{n-1}$ of a single zero root, for example $\lambda_{n-1} = 0$, the Liapunov function (58.21) is written in the form

$$V = -\int_0^\sigma f(\sigma)\,d\sigma + \Phi(x_1, ..., x_{n-2}) + F(a_1x_1, a_2x_2, ..., a_{n-2}x_{n-2}) +$$
$$+ \tfrac{1}{2}\beta_{n-1}x_{n-1}^2 ,$$

where it is required that $\beta_{n-1} < 0$. Equations (58.23) here preserve the previous form with substitution of $(n-1)$ by $(n-2)$.

When the canonical equations of the regulation system have the form (58.14), the Liapunov function is taken in the form

$$V = \Phi(x_1, x_2, ..., x_n) + F(a_1x_1, a_2x_2, ..., a_n, x_n)$$

and equations (58.23) are substituted by the following:

$$\left.\begin{array}{c} -2a_1 \displaystyle\sum_{\alpha=1}^{n} \frac{a_\alpha}{\lambda_1 + \lambda_\alpha} + \gamma_1 = 0 , \\[2mm] -2a_2 \displaystyle\sum_{\alpha=1}^{n} \frac{a_\alpha}{\lambda_2 + \lambda_\alpha} + \gamma_2 = 0 , \\[2mm] \dots\dots\dots\dots\dots\dots\dots\dots \\[2mm] -2a_n \displaystyle\sum_{\alpha=1}^{n} \frac{a_\alpha}{\lambda_n + \lambda_\alpha} + \gamma_n = 0 . \end{array}\right\} \qquad (58.24)$$

Below it will be shown how to solve equations (58.23) for non-linear automatic regulation systems of third, fourth and in part fifth orders. For systems of higher order their solution becomes very difficult. Therefore for high order non-linear systems a simplified procedure for finding the stability conditions may be applied, which naturally gives narrower sufficient conditions, but reduces the number of equations. This method consists in the following.

Let one of the real roots λ in the canonical equations of the regulation system (58.9) (or (58.15) or (58.17)) correspond to the negative constant β, say λ_1 and β_1. Then the Liapunov function is taken in the form

$$V = -\int_0^\sigma f(\sigma)\,d\sigma + \tfrac{1}{2}\beta_1 x_1^2 + \Phi(x_2, ..., x_{n-1}) + F(a_2x_2, ..., a_{n-1}x_{n-1}) ,$$

while from equations (58.23) the first drops out completely and in the remaining summation with respect to the index α goes from 2 to $(n-1)$. There is thus one quadratic equation less and one unknown a_1 drops out.

Finally we note that taking into account the dead zone σ_0 of the non-linear circuit (Fig. 259c, e, g) does not cause any additional difficulties. All calculations remain as before. The entire difference consists in that the Liapunov function V will be zero not at the point $\sigma = 0, x_1 = 0, ..., x_{n-1} = 0$, as before, but on the segment $\sigma \leqslant |\sigma_0|, x_1 = 0, ..., x_{n-1} = 0$, which now corresponds to a set of possible steady-states of the regulation system. The surfaces $V = C$ will in this case encircle the given segment, as in Fig. 257b.

Cases where study of stability reduces to analysis of two quadratic equations. The investigation of stability of the following non-linear automatic regulation systems reduces to analysis of two quadratic equations of the type (58.23):

(a) third-order regulation systems, the equations of which are reduced to canonical form (58.9), (58.15) or (58.17);

(b) fourth-order regulation systems, the equations of which have the same form (58.9) or (58.17), but in the presence of a zero root of the polynomial $D(p)$ or $D(\lambda)$;

(c) fourth-order regulation systems with equations of the same type as in case a), without a zero root, but with the simplified procedure mentioned above.

The quadratic equations of type (58.23) in these cases take the form

$$2a_1 \sqrt{r} - \frac{a_1^2}{\lambda_1} - \frac{2a_1 a_2}{\lambda_1 + \lambda_2} + \beta_1 = 0 ,$$

$$2a_2 \sqrt{r} - \frac{2a_2 a_1}{\lambda_2 + \lambda_1} - \frac{a_2^2}{\lambda_2} + \beta_2 = 0 .$$

Here the sufficient stability conditions of the system are found as the conditions that the solutions of these equations a_1 and a_2 are real with real λ_1 and λ_2 (and therefore, real β_1 and β_2 as well) or that the solutions a_1 and a_2 are complex conjugate with complex λ_1 and λ_2 (and β_1 and β_2).

It is shown (References 20) that with the substitutions

$$\left.\begin{array}{l} \Gamma^2 = \dfrac{\beta_1}{\lambda_1} + \dfrac{\beta_2}{\lambda_2} + r , \\[2mm] \vartheta = \dfrac{r(\lambda_1 - \lambda_2)^2 + (\beta_1 - \beta_2)(\lambda_1 - \lambda_2)}{4\lambda_1\lambda_2} , \end{array}\right\} \tag{58.25}$$

the required sufficient stability conditions of the system will be:

$$\Gamma > 0 \quad \text{for} \quad \vartheta > -\frac{r}{4} \tag{58.26}$$

and

$$\Gamma > 2 \sqrt{-\vartheta} - \sqrt{r} \quad \text{for} \quad \vartheta < -\frac{r}{4}. \tag{58.27}$$

These conditions are represented graphically in Fig. 260a and b for two different values ($r = 1$ and $r = 0$).

These stability conditions are sufficient with any single-valued non-linear characteristic $f(\sigma)$ of the type Fig. 259 and are independent of its specific shape.

Example. Let us find the sufficient stability conditions for the non-linear automatic engine velocity regulation system for which

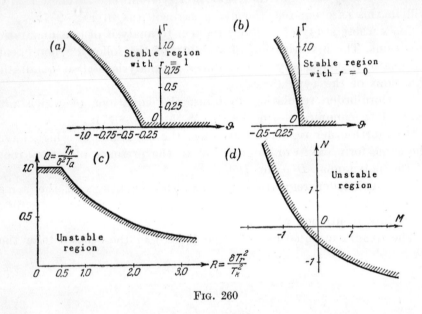

Fig. 260

we have obtained the canonic equations above. This is a fourth-order system but with a zero root λ_3. From formulae (58.25) we obtain for it:

$$\left. \begin{aligned} \Gamma^2 &= 1 - \frac{T_k}{\delta^2 T_\alpha}, \\ \vartheta &= -\frac{1}{4}\left(4 - \frac{T_k}{\delta^2 T_\alpha} - \frac{T_k^2}{\delta T_r^2}\right). \end{aligned} \right\} \tag{58.28}$$

Substituting the quantities Γ^2 and ϑ from these formulae, we may employ the graph of Fig. 260a directly to determine the system stability. However it is better to plot the stability region in the plane of parameters

$$Q = \frac{T_k}{\delta^2 T_\alpha}, \qquad R = \frac{\delta T_r^2}{T_k^2}. \tag{58.29}$$

For this expression (58.28) must be substituted in the stability conditions (58.26) and (58.27) which gives, taking into account the notation (58.29),

$$
\left.
\begin{aligned}
Q < 1 \quad &\text{for} \quad R < \frac{1}{2}\,, \\[2mm]
Q < \frac{1}{R} - \frac{1}{4R^2} \quad &\text{for} \quad R > \frac{1}{2}\,.
\end{aligned}
\right\}
\tag{58.30}
$$

The corresponding stability region of the system is represented in Fig 260c.

Cases where the investigation of stability reduces to the analysis of three quadratic equations. The investigation of the stability of non-linear automatic regulation systems reduces to the analysis of three quadratic equations of type (58.23) in the same three cases (a, b, c) as above, but with the order of the system equations higher by unity, i.e. systems of fourth and fifth orders respectively.

In this case the sufficient condition for stability of the system is expressed in the form (Reference 20)

$$
M^3 + N^3 - M^2 N^2 - \frac{9}{8} MN + \frac{27}{256} > 0\,,
\tag{58.31}
$$

where

$$
M = \frac{1}{4}\left(r\Gamma g_3^{-2/3}[B_1 + r(g_1^2 - 2g_2)] \right)\,,
$$

$$
N = -\frac{1}{4\Gamma}(r\Gamma g_3)^{-1/3}\left(\frac{2g_1 g_3 - g_2^2}{g_3}\Gamma^2 + g_3 B_2 \right)\,,
$$

and we substitute

$$
\Gamma^2 = r + \frac{\beta_1}{\lambda_1} + \frac{\beta_2}{\lambda_2} + \frac{\beta_3}{\lambda_3}\,,
$$

$$
B_1 = \beta_1 \lambda_1 + \beta_2 \lambda_2 + \beta_3 \lambda_3\,,
$$

$$
B_2 = \frac{\beta_1}{\lambda_1^3} + \frac{\beta_2}{\lambda_2^3} + \frac{\beta_3}{\lambda_3^3}\,,
$$

with g_1, g_2, g_3 being the coefficients of the characteristic equation of the linear part of the system, figuring in the derivation of the canonic equations. In the present case (after extracting the zero root, if it is present) we have

$$
\lambda^3 + g_1 \lambda^2 + g_2 \lambda + g_3 = 0\,.
$$

As before, the stability conditions (58.31) are only sufficient and do not depend on the shape of the non-linear characteristic $f(\sigma)$ of the types in Fig. 259. Graphic representation of the condition is given in Fig. 260d.

Supplement. Here we have discussed cases where the non-linear system is described by equations of type (58.9), (58.15) or (58.17).

The number of quadratic equations to which the investigation was reduced was less than the order of the system. If the equations of the non-linear regulation system reduce to the form (58.14), the number of quadratic equations will be equal to the order n of the system. But the equations will have in this a somewhat simpler form (58.24) in view of the absence of the quantity r.

Comparing equations (58.24) with the preceding (58.23), we conclude that for a second-order non-linear system (58.14) all the above is valid for the case of two quadratic equations if we put $r = 0$ (Fig. 260b) and in formulae (58.25) we substitute β_1 and β_2 by γ_1 and γ_2.

For a third-order non-linear system (58.14) it is possible to apply the above case of three quadratic equations, putting $r = 0$ and substituting β_1, β_2, β_3 by γ_1, γ_2, γ_3.

Finally, for the fourth-order non-linear system (58.14) the sufficient stability conditions are obtained (Reference 20) in the same form as inequality (58.31) with the additional conditions:

$$\gamma_1\lambda_1 + \gamma_2\lambda_2 + \gamma_3\lambda_3 + \gamma_4\lambda_4 > 0\,,$$

$$\frac{\gamma_1}{\lambda_1} + \frac{\gamma_2}{\lambda_2} + \frac{\gamma_3}{\lambda_3} + \frac{\gamma_4}{\lambda_4} > 0\,,$$

where in inequality (58.31) the quantities M and N have the following values:

$$M = \frac{1}{4}(C_1^2 C_2 g_4^2)^{-1/3}[C_1(g_1^2 - 2g_2) - C_3]\,,$$

$$N = -\frac{1}{4}(C_1 C_2^2 g_4^2)^{-1/3}[C_2(2g_2g_4 - g_3^2) + C_4 g_4^2]\,,$$

where

$$C_1 = \gamma_1\lambda_1 + \gamma_2\lambda_2 + \gamma_3\lambda_3 + \gamma_4\lambda_4\,,$$

$$C_2 = \frac{\gamma_1}{\lambda_1} + \frac{\gamma_2}{\lambda_2} + \frac{\gamma_3}{\lambda_3} + \frac{\gamma_4}{\lambda_4}\,,$$

$$C_3 = \gamma_1\lambda_1^3 + \gamma_2\lambda_2^3 + \gamma_3\lambda_3^3 + \gamma_4\lambda_4^3\,,$$

$$C_4 = \frac{\gamma_1}{\lambda_1^3} + \frac{\gamma_2}{\lambda_2^3} + \frac{\gamma_3}{\lambda_3^3} + \frac{\gamma_4}{\lambda_4^3}\,,$$

and the quantities g_1, g_2, g_3, g_4 are the coefficients of the characteristic equation of the linear part of the system $D(\lambda) = 0$, which in this case has the form

$$\lambda^4 + g_1\lambda^3 + g_2\lambda^2 + g_3\lambda + g_4 = 0\,.$$

In the last two sections we have presented only the basic ideas of the methods of studying stability of non-linear systems using the Liapunov theorems and only the simplest results, having the form of final calculational formulae of a more or less general character and which may be of practical interest in the study of stability of certain non-linear automatic regulation systems.

In general the Liapunov theory gives the most general methods for studying the stability of non-linear systems, including the stability of periodic processes, which requires special study. It will without doubt find further widely varying applications in the future. In this question there are as yet many difficulties. An important field of application of this theory is the investigation of the stability of linear systems with time-variable parameters.

59. Determination of self-oscillation in relay systems by the method of matching solutions

Above, in Section 56, using the phase plane we have demonstrated self-oscillations of certain second-order non-linear systems. Earlier, at the end of Section 9, we have studied oscillations in a second-order relay system by the method of matching solutions. However for relay systems of arbitrary order an exact analytic solution also exists (but not for other non-linear systems), since the relay characteristics are simpler than other non-linear characteristics in that the output quantity takes on only defined constant values $\pm c$ (and in the presence of a zone of insensitivity also the value zero).

We present here the solution of A. I. Lur'e for a relay system or arbitrary order by the method of matching solutions, in the simplified presentation of A. M. Kats, assuming that the equations of the automatic regulation system have the initial form (58.1) and have already been reduced to the special canonic form (58.9) as shown in Section 58, i.e. to the form

$$
\left.
\begin{aligned}
\dot{x}_1 &= \lambda_1 x_1 + f(\sigma) , \\
\dot{x}_2 &= \lambda_2 x_2 + f(\sigma) , \\
&\cdots\cdots\cdots\cdots\cdots\cdots \\
\dot{x}_{n-1} &= \lambda_{n-1} x_{n-1} + f(\sigma) , \\
\dot{\sigma} &= \beta_1 x_1 + \beta_2 x_2 + \ldots + \beta_{n-1} x_{n-1} - rf(\sigma) ,
\end{aligned}
\right\}
\qquad (59.1)
$$

where $f(\sigma)$ denotes the given relay characteristic. For example this is the form taken by the equations of an automatic regulation system with a constant velocity regulating organ drive (an electric or pneumatic relay turns on the drive to full velocity immediately on one or the other side).

Let us consider the case where the relay characteristic has a hysteresis loop without insensitive zone (Fig. 261). In the particular case $b = 0$ this will be an ideal relay characteristic. The required oscillations are assumed symmetrical, i.e. the second half of the oscillation period repeats the first with reversed sign (unsymmetrical oscillations may be encountered only in rare cases).

Let us denote the half-period of oscillation by T. In the course of one-half period, when $\sigma > 0$ and, from Fig. 261, $f(\sigma) = c$, equations (59.1) have the form

$$\dot{x}_j = -\lambda_j x_j + c \qquad (j = 1, 2, \ldots, n-1),$$

$$\dot{\sigma} = \sum_{j=1}^{n-1} \beta_j x_j - rc .$$

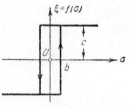

Fɪɢ. 161

If the roots λ_j do not vanish, the general solution of these equations will be:

$$x_j = -\frac{c}{\lambda_j} + C_j e^{\lambda_j t} \qquad (j = 1, 2, \ldots, n-1),$$

$$\sigma = -c\left(\sum_{j=1}^{n-1} \frac{\beta_j}{\lambda_j} + r\right) t + \sum_{j=1}^{n-1} \frac{C_j \beta_j}{\lambda_j} e^{\lambda_j t} + C_n ,$$

where $C_1, C_2, \ldots, C_n$ are arbitrary constants of integration. They are defined from the conditions of periodicity, expressing the fact that at the end of the half-period of oscillation each variable should be equal to its value at the start of the period with opposite sign, namely:

$$x_j(T) = -x_j(0) \qquad (j = 1, 2, \ldots, n-1),$$
$$\sigma(T) = -\sigma(0),$$

if the time t is read from the origin of the given half-period of oscillations. As a result we obtain:

$$C_j = \frac{2c}{\lambda_j(1 + e^{\lambda_j T})} \qquad (j = 1, 2, \ldots, n-1),$$

$$C_n = \frac{c}{2}\left(\sum_{j=1}^{n-1} \frac{\beta_j}{\lambda_j} + r\right) T - \sum_{j=1}^{n-1} \frac{C_j \beta_j(1 + e^{\lambda_j T})}{2\lambda_j} .$$

Consequently the above solution takes the form

$$\left. \begin{aligned} x_j &= -\frac{c}{\lambda_j}\left(1 - \frac{2e^{\lambda_j t}}{1 + e^{\lambda_j T}}\right) \qquad (j = 1, 2, \ldots, n-1), \\ \sigma &= -c\left[\left(\sum_{j=1}^{n-1} \frac{\beta_j}{\lambda_j} + r\right)\left(t - \frac{T}{2}\right) + \sum_{j=1}^{n-1} \frac{\beta_j}{\lambda_j^2}\left(1 - \frac{2e^{\lambda_j t}}{1 + e^{\lambda_j T}}\right)\right]. \end{aligned} \right\} \qquad (59.2)$$

in the time interval $0 < t < T$.

At the start of the half-period (at the moment of switching the relay) we have from Fig. 261 $\sigma = b$. Substituting this in (59.2) we obtain the equation for finding the half-period of oscillation T:

$$\left(\sum_{j=1}^{n-1} \frac{\beta_j}{\lambda_j} + r\right) \frac{T}{2} - \sum_{j=1}^{n-1} \frac{\beta_j}{\lambda_j^2} \tanh \frac{\lambda_j T}{2} = \frac{b}{c} . \qquad (59.3)$$

The period of oscillation will be $2T$. Consequently, the oscillation frequency

$$\omega = \frac{2\pi}{2T} = \frac{\pi}{T} .$$

It must be noted that for relay switching to occur, it is necessary, according to Fig. 261, for the quantity σ at $\sigma = b$ to be increasing, i.e. it is necessary that $\dot\sigma > 0$ at this instant. From this we find that it is necessary to satisfy the following switching condition:

$$r + \sum_{j=1}^{n-1} \frac{\beta_j}{\lambda_j} \tanh \frac{\lambda_j T}{2} < 0 . \qquad (59.4)$$

In addition, reverse switching of the relay should not occur within a half-period, i.e. we require $\sigma > -b$ with $0 < t < T$. This may be verified, plotting the curve $\sigma(t)$ according to the last of formulae (59.2). The amplitude of oscillation is found for any of the variables as its maximum value within the half-period $(0 < t < T)$ on the basis of formulae (59.2). The latter also give the entire curve of oscillation in the segment $0 < t < T$ (in the second half-period it repeats with reversed sign, then with the original sign, etc.).

If one of the roots λ_j is equal to zero, for example $\lambda_{n-1} = 0$, formulae (59.2), (59.3) and (59.4) are substituted by

$$\left.\begin{array}{l}
x_j = -\dfrac{c}{\lambda_j}\left(1 - \dfrac{2}{1+e^{\lambda_j T}} e^{\lambda_j t}\right) \quad (j = 1, 2, \ldots, n-2) , \\[2mm]
x_{n-1} = c\left(t - \dfrac{T}{2}\right) , \\[2mm]
\sigma = -c\left[\left(\displaystyle\sum_{j=1}^{n-2} \frac{\beta_j}{\lambda_j} + r\right)\left(t - \frac{T}{2}\right) + \right.\\[4mm]
\left. + \displaystyle\sum_{j=1}^{n-2} \frac{\beta_j}{\lambda_j^2}\left(1 - \frac{2}{1+e^{\lambda_j T}} e^{\lambda_j t}\right) + \frac{\beta_{n-1}}{2}(T-t)\right] ,
\end{array}\right\} \qquad (59.5)$$

$$\left(\sum_{j=1}^{n-2} \frac{\beta_j}{\lambda_j} + r\right) \frac{T}{2} - \sum_{j=1}^{n-2} \frac{\beta_j}{\lambda_j^2} \tanh \frac{\lambda_j T}{2} = \frac{b}{c} , \qquad (59.6)$$

$$r + \sum_{j=1}^{n-2} \frac{\beta_j}{\lambda_j} \tanh \frac{\lambda_j T}{2} + \frac{\beta_{n-1} T}{2} < 0 . \qquad (59.7)$$

respectively.

The stability of oscillation is defined on the basis of the equations of the given system in small deviations from the given oscillatory process. These equations are linear equations with periodically varying coefficients. According to the Liapunov theory (presented without derivation) the necessary and sufficient condition for stability of oscillation is the negativeness of the real parts of all roots of the following characteristic equation:

$$\sum_{j=1}^{n-1} \frac{\beta_j}{\lambda_j}\tanh\frac{\lambda_j T}{2} \cdot \frac{z-\tanh\dfrac{\lambda_j T}{2}}{1-z\tanh\dfrac{\lambda_j T}{2}} = r \,, \tag{59.8}$$

while if $\lambda_{n-1} = 0$, then

$$\sum_{j=1}^{n-2} \frac{\beta_j}{\lambda_j}\tanh\frac{\lambda_j T}{2} \cdot \frac{z-\tanh\dfrac{\lambda_j T}{2}}{1-z\tanh\dfrac{\lambda_j T}{2}} + \frac{\beta_{n-1}T}{2}z = r \,, \tag{59.9}$$

where by z, as everywhere above, we denote the variable of the characteristic equation.

Example. Let us consider the system aircraft with course-autopilot (in simplified form) which was considered in Section 57, except that the characteristic of the rudder drive will be taken in the relay form of Fig. 261. In Section 57 we obtained the condition of system stability on the basis of the Liapunov theorems (system stability with respect to the steady-state with constant value of course angle). Here we shall seek the self-oscillations and the conditions under which they occur.

The equations of the aircraft and autopilot, from (57.10), (57.15) and (57.14) will be written here in the form

$$\begin{aligned}
T_1\ddot{\psi}+\dot{\psi} &= -k_1\xi \,, \\
\sigma &= k_\psi\psi+k_{\dot\psi}\dot{\psi}-k_{fb}\xi \,, \\
\xi &= f(\sigma) \,,
\end{aligned} \right\} \tag{59.10}$$

where ψ is the deviation of the aircraft from the prescribed course, ξ is the rudder deviation, σ is the control force on the rudder drive (the derivative is introduced into the regulation function and feedback is present). Let the last of equations (59.10) be represented by the graph of Fig. 261 (the rudder drive has constant velocity).
Putting

$$\dot{\psi} = \eta_1 \,, \quad \psi = \eta_2 \,, \tag{59.11}$$

we bring equations (59.10) to the form (58.1), namely:

$$\dot{\eta}_1 = -\frac{1}{T_1}\eta_1 - \frac{k_1}{T_1}\xi\,,$$

$$\dot{\eta}_2 = \eta_1\,,$$

$$\sigma = k_{\dot{\psi}}\eta_1 + k_\psi \eta_2 - k_{fb}\xi\,,$$

$$\dot{\xi} = f(\sigma)\,.$$

Consequently, in equations (58.1) in this case we have:

$$a_{11} = -\frac{1}{T_1}\,, \qquad a_{12} = 0\,, \qquad b_1 = -\frac{k_1}{T_1}\,,$$

$$a_{21} = 1\,, \qquad a_{22} = 0\,, \qquad b_2 = 0\,,$$

$$c_1 = k_{\dot{\psi}}\,, \qquad c_2 = k_\psi\,, \qquad r = k_{fb}\,.$$

The determinant (58.3) is here

$$D(p) = \begin{vmatrix} -\dfrac{1}{T_1}-p\,, & 0 \\ 1\,, & -p \end{vmatrix} = \left(\frac{1}{T_1}+p\right)p\,,$$

and its roots

$$\lambda_1 = -\frac{1}{T_1}\,, \qquad \lambda_2 = 0\,.$$

Calculating $N_1(p)$ and $N_2(p)$ according to the discussion of formula (58.3) and the derivative $D'(p)$ and the coefficients β_1, β_2, h_1, h_2 from formulae (58.7) and (58.12), we obtain

$$N_1(p) = \frac{k_1}{T_1}p\,, \qquad N_2(p) = \frac{k_1}{T_1}\,, \qquad D'(p) = \frac{1}{T_1}+2p\,,$$

$$\beta_1 = k_1\left(k_\psi - \frac{k_{\dot{\psi}}}{T_1}\right)\,, \qquad \beta_2 = -k_1 k_\psi\,, \qquad h_1 = k_1\,, \qquad h_2 = -k_1 T_1\,.$$

As a result the canonical equations (58.9) will be:

$$\left.\begin{aligned} \dot{x}_1 &= -\frac{1}{T_1}x_1 + f(\sigma)\,, \\ \dot{x}_2 &= f(\sigma)\,, \\ \dot{\sigma} &= k_1\left(k_\psi - \frac{k_{\dot{\psi}}}{T_1}\right)x_1 - k_1 k_\psi x_2 - k_{fb}f(\sigma)\,, \end{aligned}\right\} \qquad (59.12)$$

while the expressions (58.11) for the previous variables η_1, η_2, ξ in terms of the canonical variables x_1 and x_2 have the form

$$\eta_1 = k_1 x_1 - k_1 x_2\,,$$

$$\eta_2 = -k_1 T_1 x_1 + k_1 T_1 x_2 - k_1 y_2\,,$$

$$-k_1 k_\psi y_2 = k_1 T_1\left(k_\psi - \frac{k_{\dot{\psi}}}{T_1}\right)x_1 + (k_1 k_{\dot{\psi}} - k_1 T_1 k_\psi + k_{fb})x_2 + \sigma\,.$$

Substituting y_2 from the last equation in the second and employing (59.11), we obtain the following expression for the initial variables in terms of the canonical variables:

$$\left.\begin{aligned} \dot{\psi} &= k_1(x_1 - x_2)\,, \qquad \xi = x_2\,, \\ \psi &= \frac{1}{k_\psi}[-k_1 k_\psi x_1 + (k_1 k_{\dot\psi} + k_{fb})x_2 + \sigma]\,. \end{aligned}\right\}$$ (59.13)

Further, from (59.6) we write the equation for finding the half-period of oscillation:

$$\left[-k_1 T_1\left(k_\psi - \frac{k_{\dot\psi}}{T_1}\right) + k_{fb}\right]\frac{T}{2} + k_1 T_1^2\left(k_\psi - \frac{k_{\dot\psi}}{T_1}\right)\tanh\frac{T}{2T_1} = \frac{b}{c}$$

or

$$(1-\alpha)\frac{T}{2T_1} - \frac{b\alpha}{ck_{fb}T_1} = \tanh\frac{T}{2T_1}\,,$$ (59.14)

where we put

$$\alpha = \frac{k_{fb}}{k_1(T_1 k_\psi - k_{\dot\psi})}\,.$$ (59.15)

The left-hand side of equality (59.14) is represented by the straight line AB (Fig. 262a) and the right-hand side by the curve OD. The point of intersection is the solution of equation (59.14). From the graph of Fig. 262a it is evident that equation (59.14) has a solution only under the condition

$$-\infty < \alpha < 1\,,$$ (59.16)

where we have

$$0 < T < \infty\,.$$

With $\alpha > 1$ the straight line AB does not intersect the curve OD, which signifies the absence of oscillation for these values of α.

But aside from equality (59.14) it is also necessary to satisfy the switching condition (59.7), which in this case will be:

$$k_{fb} + k_1 T_1\left(k_\psi - \frac{k_{\dot\psi}}{T_1}\right)\tanh\frac{T}{2T_1} - \frac{k_1 k_\psi T}{2} < 0$$

or

$$\alpha + \tanh\frac{T}{2T_1} - \frac{k_1 k_\psi T}{k_{fb}}\alpha < 0\,.$$ (59.17)

Consequently, if the value of α lies in the interval (59.16), but condition (59.17) is not satisfied, there will be no oscillation in the system.

To study the stability of oscillation we write the characteristic equation (59.9). It takes here the form

$$k_1 T_1 \left(k_\psi - \frac{k_{\dot{\psi}}}{T_1} \right) \tanh \frac{T}{2T_1} \cdot \frac{z + \tanh \dfrac{T}{2T_1}}{1 + z \tanh \dfrac{T}{2T_1}} - \frac{k_1 k_\psi T}{2} z = k_{fb} .$$

The case $1 + z\tanh(T/2T_1) = 0$, when the denominator vanishes, is not real. Therefore, considering $1 + z\tanh(T/2T_1) \neq 0$, we reduce

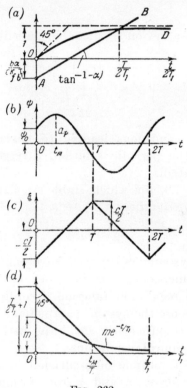

Fig. 262

this equation to a common denominator, employing the notation of (59.15), which gives:

$$\frac{k_1 k_\psi T}{2k_{fb}} z^2 + \left(1 - \frac{1}{\alpha} \right) z + \left[\left(\frac{k_1 k_\psi T}{2k_{fb}} + 1 \right) \coth \frac{T}{2T_1} - \frac{1}{\alpha} \tanh \frac{T}{2T_1} \right] = 0 .$$

Since this characteristic equation is of second degree, for stability of the investigated oscillations it is necessary and sufficient that all its coefficients be positive. The coefficient of z^2 is positive. The coefficient of z, from (59.16) is also positive. Therefore the condition for stability of oscillation reduces to positiveness of the constant term of this equation, i.e.

$$\left(\frac{k_1 k_\psi T}{2k_{fb}} + 1\right)\coth\frac{T}{2T_1} - \frac{1}{\alpha}\tanh\frac{T}{2T_1} > 0 .$$

From this, considering (59.16), we conclude that these are two regions of stable oscillations

$$-\infty < \alpha < 0 \quad \text{and} \quad \frac{\left(\tanh\dfrac{T}{2T_1}\right)^2}{\dfrac{k_1 k_\psi T}{2k_{fb}} + 1} < \alpha < 1 . \qquad (59.18)$$

Between them is a region of unstable periodic solutions

$$0 < \alpha < \frac{\left(\tanh\dfrac{T}{2T_1}\right)^2}{\dfrac{k_1 k_\psi T}{2k_{fb}} + 1} , \qquad (59.19)$$

where, with initial conditions leading to deviations greater than the amplitude of the periodic solution, divergent oscillations are obtained in the system.

The condition $\alpha < 0$, for which stable oscillations always occur, according to (59.15) signifies

$$k_{\dot\psi} > T_1 k_\psi , \qquad (59.20)$$

i.e. the unstable system (59.19) may be brought to a stable oscillatory system by increasing the intensity of introduction of the derivative into the regulation function according to (59.20). Here it is necessary to choose the system parameters such that the amplitude of oscillation is sufficiently small and its frequency acceptable (with respect to technical conditions).

To calculate the amplitude of oscillation it is first necessary to write the solutions for x_1, x_2 and σ from formulae (59.5), namely:

$$x_1 = cT_1\left(1 - \frac{2}{1 + e^{-\frac{T_1}{T_1}}}e^{-\frac{t}{T_1}}\right),$$

$$x_2 = c\left(t - \frac{T}{2}\right),$$

$$\sigma = -c\left\{\left[-k_1 T_1\left(k_\psi - \frac{k_{\dot\psi}}{T_1}\right) + k_{fb}\right]\left(t - \frac{T}{2}\right) + \right.$$

$$\left. + k_1 T_1^2\left(1 - \frac{2}{1 + e^{-\frac{T}{T_1}}}e^{-\frac{t}{T_1}}\right) - \frac{k_1 k_\psi}{2}t(T - t)\right\} .$$

Then, from the last of formulae (59.13) it is necessary to write the solution for the angle of yaw $\psi(t)$ of the aircraft and the angle of rudder deviation $\xi = x_2$, which gives:

$$\left. \begin{aligned} \psi &= ck_1 T_1 \left[\frac{t}{2T_1}(T-1) + t - \frac{T}{2} - \frac{k_{\dot\psi} + T_1}{k_\psi}\left(1 - \frac{2}{1 + e^{-\frac{T}{T_1}}} e^{-\frac{t}{T_1}}\right) \right], \\ \xi &= c\left(t - \frac{T}{2}\right) \quad (0 \leqslant t \leqslant T). \end{aligned} \right\} \qquad (59.21)$$

From these equations we may plot the graph of aircraft oscillation (Fig. 262b) and rudder oscillation (Fig. 262c), where

$$\psi_0 = ck_1 T_1 \left[\frac{k_{\dot\psi} + T_1}{k_\psi}\left(\frac{2}{1 + e^{-\frac{T}{T_1}}} - 1\right) - \frac{T}{2} \right].$$

The amplitude of rudder oscillation, as is evident from Fig. 262c, will be

$$a_\xi = \frac{cT}{2},$$

where c is the velocity of rudder motion according to the characteristic of Fig. 261.

The amplitude of aircraft oscillation (with respect to the yaw angle) a_ψ is found as the maximum of the function $\psi(t)$ in the segment $0 < t < T$. Taking the derivative of ψ (59.21) with respect to t and equating it to zero, we obtain the following equation for the time t_m, corresponding to the maximum ψ:

$$\frac{T}{2T_1} + 1 - \frac{t}{T_1} = me^{-\frac{T}{T_1}},$$

where

$$m = \frac{2(k_{\dot\psi} + T_1)}{k_\psi T_1(1 + e^{-\frac{T}{T_1}})}.$$

This equation is solved graphically as shown in Fig. 262d. The quantity t_m thus found is substituted in the first of formulae (59.21) which gives the required amplitude of aircraft oscillation

$$a_\psi = \psi(t_m).$$

The frequency of oscillation is defined in terms of the half-period T, found graphically (Fig. 262a) on the basis of equation (59.14).

We note that the solution of this example, in the interests of simplicity, was carried out only for the simplified equations of motion of the aircraft with respect to course (the first of equations (59.10)) and under the assumption of a rigorously constant velocity of the rudder drive.

CHAPTER XVI

THE APPROXIMATE DETERMINATION OF OSCILLATIONS AND STABILITY OF NON-LINEAR SYSTEMS

60. The approximate method of Krylov and Bogoliubov for second-order non-linear systems

As is evident from the previous chapter, the exact determination of oscillations and the study of stability of non-linear systems is in general a difficult problem. Plotting of processes in the phase plane is exact only in integrable cases and is convenient only for the study of second-order systems. For systems of higher order only certain simple particular cases are solved exactly. The study of stability by means of the Liapunov theorems is in principle universal, but in practice limited.

As a result of this, approximate methods of determining oscillations and stability of non-linear systems are widely used in regulation theory at present, and we shall now consider them.

The basis of the majority of approximate methods of studying non-linear automatic regulation systems is the work of N. M. Krylov and N. N. Bogoliubov (References 5, 6). The entire present chapter will be devoted to various methods developed on this basis.

N. M. Krylov and N. N. Bogoliubov established the method of "equivalent linearisation" of non-linearity (termed here harmonic linearisation), the method of harmonic balance with application of symbolic frequency methods and the method of energy balance (see Reference 6).

The first work of Krylov and Bogoliubov in this field was the study of hunting in synchronous machines, published in 1932. They then developed the above methods for systems of various types from mechanical to electronic.

The Krylov-Bogoliubov method of harmonic balance was applied to particular problems in the theory of automatic regulation in 1941 by V. A. Kotel'nikov and later by L. S. Gol'dfarb and others.

Aside from these methods the same results may be obtained by the well-known variational principle of Galerkin, as shown by

A. I. Lur'e and A. I. Chekmarev in 1938 in problems in the theory of oscillations and by V. A. Bodner in 1946 in problems of regulation theory.

Further development of asymptotic approximate methods of studying non-linear systems was carried out by N. N. Bogoliubov (Reference 50) in 1945 and 1949 and by Yu. A. Mitropolskii.

In Chapter 8 of the book by S. P. Strelkov (Reference 23) other approximate methods (Mandel'shtam, Andronov, Teodorchik) are presented, giving similar results in the first approximation.

In the present section we describe one of the approximate methods now termed the method of slowly varying functions, applicable to non-linear second-order systems, permitting not only finding the periodic solutions (limiting cycles) but studying approximately the course of the transient process for various initial conditions (Krylov and Bogoliubov have also studied processes in non-linear systems of higher than second order, processes in the presence of external periodic forces, including cases of resonance, as well as the construction of higher-order approximations).

Transient equation. Let the non-linear second-order equation for the transient process in the closed automatic system have the form

$$\ddot{x} + F(x, \dot{x}) = 0 , \tag{60.1}$$

where x is the deviation of the regulated quantity while $F(x, \dot{x})$ is a non-linear function which may also include linear terms in x and $\ddot{x}$, if they are present in the equation.

To derive the formulae of the approximate solution we represent the non-linear function $F(x, \dot{x})$ in the form

$$F(x, \dot{x}) = \omega_0^2 x + \varepsilon f(x, \dot{x}) , \tag{60.2}$$

so that equation (60.1) takes the form

$$\ddot{x} + \omega_0^2 x + \varepsilon f(x, \dot{x}) = 0 , \tag{60.3}$$

where the letter ε is introduced only to be able to note below the relatively small order of the quantity $\varepsilon f(x, \dot{x})$.

For example, equation (60.1) for the simple automatic temperature regulation system considered in Section 9, from (9.15) and Fig. 53a has the form

$$T_1 \ddot{\theta} + \dot{\theta} + k_1 \xi(\theta) = 0 , \tag{60.4}$$

where the function $\xi(\theta)$ is represented by the full lines in Fig. 263a and is described analytically by formulae (9.17) and (9.18). We plot in Fig. 263a some "average" straight line (broken line in Fig. 263a). Then the non-linear function $\xi(\theta)$ may be written in the form

$$\dot{\xi} = k_2 \theta + f_1(\theta) ,$$

where k_1 is the tangent of the slope angle of the "mean" straight line (Fig. 263a), while $f_1(\theta)$ is represented in Fig. 263b. The linear term $k_2\theta$ represents the principal part of the function ξ while $f_1(\theta)$ is some non-linear increment.

As a result the system equation (60.4) will be:

$$\ddot{\theta} + \omega_0^2\theta + \varepsilon f(\theta, \dot{\theta}) = 0 ,$$

where

$$\omega_0^2 = \frac{k_1 k_2}{T_1} , \qquad \varepsilon f(\theta, \dot{\theta}) = \frac{k_1}{T_1} f_1(\theta) + \frac{\dot{\theta}}{T_1} .$$

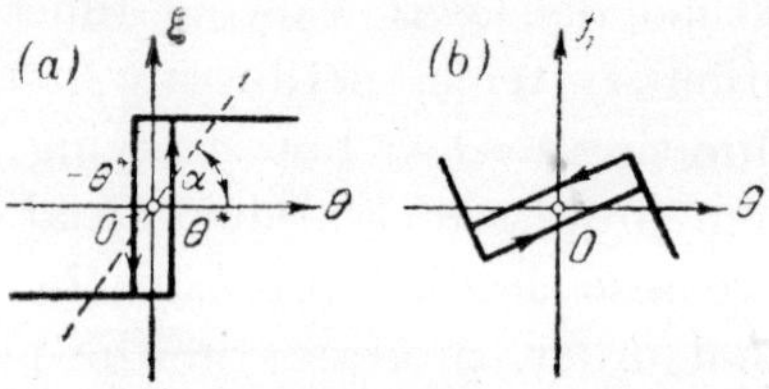

FIG. 263

These operations as a whole are used only for the general derivation of the formula for the approximate solution while in the solution of specific problems by this method, as will be clear from the following, it is necessary only to find the quantity ω_0; the function $\varepsilon f(\theta, \dot{\theta})$ need not be found.

We thus have a non-linear system equation in the form (60.3). We shall seek its solution in the form

$$\left.\begin{array}{l} x = a\sin(\omega_0 t + \varphi) , \\ \dot{x} = a\omega_0\cos(\omega_0 t + \varphi), \end{array}\right\} \tag{60.5}$$

where a and φ are unknown functions of time

$$a = a(t) , \qquad \varphi = \varphi(t) . \tag{60.6}$$

We note that if $\varepsilon = 0$, equation (60.3) corresponds to a solution in the form of simple harmonic oscillations (60.5) with constant values of a and φ. If in equation (60.3) $\varepsilon \neq 0$, then, roughly speaking, the greater ε, the more strongly the solution (60.5) will differ from simple harmonic oscillations. Here $a(t)$ denotes the variable amplitude of oscillation while $\varphi(t)$ is the variable phase which actually is a correction to the assumed approximate frequency of oscillation ω_0. Thus, the solution (60.5) and (60.6) fully describes the transient in the non-linear system with equation (60.3). The true value of the variable frequency of oscillation at an arbitrary instant will obviously be:

$$\omega = \omega_0 + \frac{d\varphi}{dt} . \tag{60.7}$$

The solution has not as yet become approximate, if we assume that we know how to find the function (60.6), exactly corresponding to the given equation (60.3) and the adopted form of solution (60.5). The entire problem thus consists in finding the functions (60.6), i.e. the functions $a(t)$ and $\varphi(t)$.

To find them, we first differentiate the first of equations (60.5) with respect to time

$$\dot{x} = \frac{da}{dt} \sin(\omega_0 t + \varphi) + a \frac{d\varphi}{dt} \cos(\omega_0 t + \varphi) + a\omega_0 \cos(\omega_0 t + \varphi),$$

from which, considering the second formula in (60.5), we obtain:

$$\frac{da}{dt} \sin(\omega_0 t + \varphi) + a \frac{d\varphi}{dt} \cos(\omega_0 t + \varphi). \qquad (60.8)$$

Differentiating now the second of equations (60.5)

$$\ddot{x} = \frac{da}{dt} \omega_0 \cos(\omega_0 t + \varphi) - a\omega_0^2 \sin(\omega_0 t + \varphi) - a\omega_0 \frac{d\varphi}{dt} \sin(\omega_0 t + \varphi);$$

substituting this and (60.5) in the given equation (60.3), we come to the expression

$$\frac{da}{dt} \omega_0 \cos(\omega_0 t + \varphi) - a\omega_0 \frac{d\varphi}{dt} \sin(\omega_0 t + \varphi) = -\varepsilon f(a\sin u, \ a\omega_0 \cos u), \quad (60.9)$$

where for conciseness we put $u = \omega_0 t + \varphi$.

As a result, from the two equations (60.8) and (60.9) simutaneously we find the following expressions for the derivatives of a and φ:

$$\left. \begin{aligned} \frac{da}{dt} &= -\frac{1}{\omega_0} \varepsilon f(a\sin u, \ a\omega_0 \cos u)\cos u, \\ \frac{d\varphi}{dt} &= \frac{1}{a\omega_0} \varepsilon f(a\sin u, \ a\omega_0 \cos u)\sin u, \end{aligned} \right\} \qquad (60.10)$$

where

$$u = \omega_0 t + \varphi, \qquad (60.11)$$

Equations (60.10) define the required functions $a(t)$ and $\varphi(t)$, as yet without approximation. However it is not possible to solve them exactly. We shall find approximate formulae.

If in the prescribed system equation (60.3) ε is sufficiently small, then from (60.10) the derivatives da/dt and $d\varphi/dt$ will be sufficiently small, infinitesimals of the same order. Then $a(t)$ and $\varphi(t)$ will be sufficiently slowly varying functions of time. We shall consider them to be such that within each individual period of oscillation we may put $a = $ const, but change it in passage from one period of oscillation to the neighboring, etc.

Then the right-hand sides of equations (60.10) may be replaced within each period by the average values, taken as usual, in the form

$$\frac{1}{2\pi} \int_0^{12\pi} \cdot$$

As a result the "averaged" equations (60.10) will take the form:

$$\left.\begin{aligned}
\frac{da}{dt} &= -\frac{1}{2\pi\omega_0} \int_0^{2\pi} \varepsilon f(a\sin u,\ a\omega_0\cos u)\cos u\, du\,, \\[2mm]
\frac{d\varphi}{dt} &= \frac{1}{2\pi\omega_0 a} \int_0^{2\pi} \varepsilon f(a\sin u,\ a\omega_0\cos u)\sin u\, du\,,
\end{aligned}\right\} \tag{60.12}$$

where in the integrands we assume $a = $ const. and they are therefore in many cases very simply integrated. Thus, the problem of determining $a(t)$ and $\varphi(t)$ is solved approximately.

It is still necessary to eliminate the preliminary decomposition of the non-linear function $F(x, \dot{x})$ in the equation of the automatic system (60.1) into two components (60.2). For this we introduce into the integrand in equation (60.12) in place of the function εf the initial function F in accordance with the relation (60.2), while the second of expressions (60.12) is substituted in formula (60.7) and squared, where we neglect the term containing ε^2 as a second order infinitesimal. As a result of all this formulae (60.12) take the final form

$$\left.\begin{aligned}
\frac{da}{dt} &= -\frac{1}{2\pi\omega_0} \int_0^{2\pi} F(a\sin u,\ a\omega_0\cos u)\cos u\, du\,, \\[2mm]
\omega^2 &= \frac{1}{\pi a} \int_0^{2\pi} F(a\sin u,\ a\omega_0\cos u)\sin u\, du\,.
\end{aligned}\right\} \tag{60.13}$$

Thus the transient in the non-linear system described by a differential equation of the form (60.1) is defined by the solution

$$x = a(t)\sin u(t)\,, \tag{60.14}$$

where the functions $a(t)$ and $u(t)$ are found approximately from the equations

$$\frac{da}{dt} = -\frac{a}{2\omega_0} q_1(a, \omega_0)\,, \qquad \left(\frac{du}{dt}\right)^2 = \omega^2 = q(a, \omega_0)\,, \tag{60.15}$$

where

$$\left.\begin{aligned}
q_1(a, \omega_0) &= \frac{1}{\pi a} \int_0^{2\pi} F(a\sin u,\ a\omega_0\cos u)\cos u\, du\,, \\[2mm]
q(a, \omega_0) &= \frac{1}{\pi a} \int_0^{2\pi} F(a\sin u,\ a\omega_0\cos u)\sin u\, du\,.
\end{aligned}\right\} \tag{60.16}$$

In this solution a and ω are approximate values of the variable amplitude and frequency of oscillation of the deviation from the regulated quantity x in the transient. In solving the problem the final formulae for the values of q_1 and q for certain non-linear functions given below in Section 61 may be used.

If the differential equation of the non-linear system is given in the form (60.3) the transient is described by the solution

$$x = a(t)\sin[\omega_0 t + \varphi(t)] \, .$$

The functions $a(t)$ and $\varphi(t)$ are defined from equations (60.12), where the integrands are always functions only of a. The variable frequency of oscillation $\omega = \omega_0 + d\varphi/dt$.

All these formulae give only the first approximation. In the works of Krylov and Bogoliubov (Reference 6) improved solutions with successive aproximations are also worked out. We shall not however present them here.

Example. Let us take the automatic temperature regulation system considered in Section 9 where the non-linear regulator has the hysteresis relay characteristic $\xi(\theta)$ shown in Fig. 263a. The equation of the closed system, as already noted, has here the form (60.4) or

$$\ddot{\theta} + F(\theta, \dot{\theta}) = 0 \, , \quad \text{where} \quad F(\theta, \dot{\theta}) = \frac{k_1}{T_1}\xi(\theta) + \frac{\dot{\theta}}{T_1} \, .$$

From (60.14) the transient response curve will be

$$\theta = a(t)\sin u(t) \, ,$$

where to determine $a(t)$ and $u(t)$ we have on the basis of (60.13) the following equations

$$\frac{da}{dt} = -\frac{1}{2\pi\omega_0}\int_0^{2\pi}\left[\frac{k_1}{T_1}\xi(a\sin u) + \frac{1}{T_1}a\omega_0\cos u\right]\cos u\, du \, ,$$

$$\left(\frac{du}{dt}\right)^2 = \omega^2 = \frac{1}{\pi a}\int_0^{2\pi}\left[\frac{k_1}{T_1}\xi(a\sin u) + \frac{1}{T_1}a\omega_0\cos u\right]\sin u\, du$$

or

$$\frac{da}{dt} = -\frac{ak_1}{2\omega_0 T_1}\cdot\frac{1}{\pi a}\int_0^{2\pi}\xi(a\sin u)\cos u\, du - \frac{a}{2T_1} \, ,$$

$$\left(\frac{du}{dt}\right)^2 = \omega^2 = \frac{k_1}{T_1}\cdot\frac{1}{\pi a}\int_0^{2\pi}\xi(a\sin u)\sin u\, du$$

where in the remaining integrals ξ is the non-linear function represented in Fig. 263a. These integrals are consequently the values of $q_1(a)$ and $q(a)$ for the relay characteristic of the type in Fig. 267e which are calculated below in the form (61.37). Taking these values and considering also the value of ω_0 found for this example at the beginning of the section, we obtain:

$$\frac{da}{dt} = -\frac{ak_1}{2\omega_0 T_1}\cdot\left(-\frac{4cb}{\pi a^2}\right)\frac{a}{2T_1} = \frac{2cb}{\pi a}\sqrt{\frac{k_1}{T_1 k_2}} - \frac{a}{2T_1}, \qquad (60.17)$$

$$\left(\frac{du}{dt}\right)^2 = \omega^2 = \frac{4ck_1}{\pi a T_1}\sqrt{1 - \frac{b^2}{a^2}}. \qquad (60.18)$$

From the first equation we find

$$\frac{2a\,da}{b_1^2 - a^2} = \frac{dt}{T_1},$$

where we put

$$b_1^2 = \frac{4cb}{\pi}\sqrt{\frac{k_1 T_1}{k_2}}. \qquad (60.19)$$

Integrating this with the initial conditions: $a = a_0$ at $t = 0$, we obtain:

$$a^2 = [b_1^2 + (a_0^2 - b_1^2)]e^{-\frac{t}{T_2}}. \qquad (60.20)$$

From equation (60.17) it is evident that with the initial amplitude

$$a_0 > 2\sqrt{\frac{cb}{\pi}\sqrt{\frac{k_1 T_1}{k_2}}} = b_1$$

we have $da/dt < 0$, i.e. the transient oscillations are damped, while with the initial amplitude

$$a_0 < 2\sqrt{\frac{cb}{\pi}\sqrt{\frac{k_1 T_1}{k_2}}} = b_1$$

we obtain $da/dt > 0$, which corresponds to divergent oscillations.

Knowing coefficients (60.19), for each initial value of a_0 we may, from equation (60.20), plot the curves of amplitude variation $a(t)$ of the oscillations in temperature deviation θ during the transient (Fig. 264a). This construction is easily carried out if various values are taken for a and the corresponding values of t found from formula (60.20).

The oscillation frequency ω will be variable in time and is defined by formula (60.18) or its graph Fig. 264b in dependence on the amplitude of oscillation a, found above. The dependence of the frequency of free oscillations on the amplitude is a characteristic property of non-linear systems.

The graphs of Fig. 264a show that in this example the system is unstable with respect to the steady-state with constant value of regulated quantity ($a = 0$), but has a stable steady-state oscillation with amplitude

$$a_l = b_1 = 2 \sqrt{\frac{cb}{\pi}} \sqrt{\frac{k_1 T_1}{k_2}} , \qquad (60.21)$$

to which the amplitude of oscillation tends in the transient processes for arbitrary initial conditions.

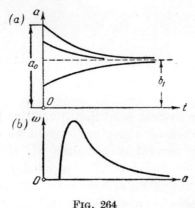

Fig. 264

All the results of the approximate solution in the present example agree qualitatively with the exact solution presented in Section 9, but this approximate solution is simpler and has the same form for the entire transient.

Finding the periodic solutions (limiting cycles) and self-oscillations. The limiting cycle, as we know (Sections 10 and 56), corresponds to self-oscillations in the system if it is stable. An unstable limiting cycle in the simplest case defines the limits of initial conditions to which the system is small-signal stable (but other, more complicated cases are possible). The limiting cycle (periodic solution) is characterised by a constant amplitude of oscillation. In the general case it is therefore found, according to the first equation of (60.13), from the condition

$$\int_0^{2\pi} F(a_l \sin u , \ a_l \omega_0 \cos u) \cos u \, du = 0 . \qquad (60.22)$$

From this its amplitude a_l is found, after which from the second of formulae (60.13) its frequency $\omega = \omega_l$ is calculated. It is assumed that the oscillation has approximately the form

$$x = a_l \sin \omega_l t ,$$

although in reality the form of oscillation is non-sinusoidal or is not exactly sinusoidal (non-linear).

We note, however, that the quantity ω_0 enters into formulae (60.22) and (60.13), but, as is evident from the start of this section, is not always strictly defined. In such cases in finding the limiting cycle it is natural to take the required frequency of the limiting cycle for ω_0. Then the limiting cycle will be defined simultaneously by two conditions:

$$
\left.
\begin{aligned}
\int_0^{2\pi} F(a_l\sin u ,\ a_l\omega_l\cos u)\cos u\, du = 0 , \\[2mm]
\pi a_l\omega_l^2 = \int_0^{2\pi} F(a_l\sin u ,\ a_l\omega_l\cos u)\sin u\, du ,
\end{aligned}
\right\}
\qquad (60.23)
$$

where a_1 and ω_1 are the required constants.

If for some given system condition (60.22) or (60.23) gives a real positive value a_1, then for the given system we obtain the limiting cycle. If there are several such values a_1, there will be several limiting cycles. If condition (60.22) or (60.23) does not have real positive solutions, the given system does not have limiting cycles, i.e. it is either stable or unstable for arbitrary initial conditions or there is a more complex pattern of phase trajectories without limiting cycles.

After obtaining the limiting cycle it is always necessary to test its stability. If a solution is found for the transient (as in Fig. 264), it is evident from it whether the limiting cycle is stable or unstable. We shall now explain how to proceed when we are interested only in the limiting cycle and do not require the transient response.

We introduce the notation

$$
G(a) = \frac{1}{2\pi}\int_0^{2\pi} F(a\sin u ,\ a\omega_0\cos u)\cos u\, du . \qquad (60.24)
$$

Now the first of formulae (60.13) takes the form

$$
\frac{da}{dt} = -\frac{1}{\omega_0} G(a) , \qquad (60.25)
$$

while the condition of the limiting cycle (60.22) will be

$$
G(a_l) = 0 . \qquad (60.26)
$$

To investigate the stability of the limiting cycle let us consider the variation of the amplitude a in the transient with small deviation a from the amplitude a_1 of the limiting cycle. Let $a = a_1 + \Delta a$.

Writing equation (60.25) with respect to the deviation Δa in linearised form according to the rules of Section 18, we obtain

$$\frac{d\,\Delta a}{dt} = -\frac{1}{\omega_0}\left(\frac{\partial G}{\partial a}\right)_{a=a_l}\cdot \Delta a \ .$$

From this it is evident that with

$$\left(\frac{\partial G}{\partial a}\right)_{a=a_l} > 0 \qquad\qquad (60.27)$$

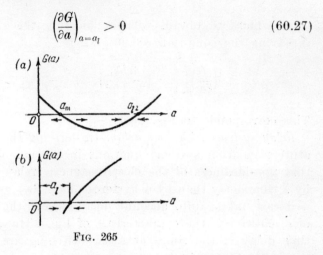

FIG. 265

the derivative $\Delta\dot{a}$ will be negative with $\Delta a > 0$ and positive with $\Delta a < 0$. Consequently, in both cases $\Delta a \to 0$, i.e. the limiting cycle is stable *.

If

$$\left(\frac{\partial G}{\partial a}\right)_{a=a} < 0 \ , \qquad\qquad (60.28)$$

the deviation $|\Delta a|$ increases, i.e. the limiting cycle is unstable.

According to condition (60.26) the limiting cycles are found easily by graphical methods as the points of intersection of the curve $G(a)$, plotted according to equation (60.24), with the axis of abscissae a (Fig. 265). The stability and instability of the limiting cycles are defined according to (60.27) and (60.28) by the sign of the slope of the curve $G(a)$ at these points. If, for example, the curve $G(a)$ has the form shown in Fig. 265a, the limiting cycle with amplitude a_{l1} will be unstable while the limiting cycle with amplitude a_{l2} will be stable. The arrows in Fig. 265a denote that the transient oscillation amplitude diverges from the value a_{l1} and approaches either to zero or to the value a_{l2}. In this case, consequently, the system will be small-signal stable up to such initial deviations for which

---

* This stability condition, strictly speaking, is not sufficient since the frequency is not varied here. But in practice in many particular cases it is found sufficient. Krylov and Bogoliubov (Reference 5) give conditions with variation of frequency.

the amplitude of oscillation does not exceed a_{l_1} and has a stable oscillation with amplitude a_{l_2}.

In the temperature regulation example according to (60.17) we have

$$G(a) = -\frac{4cbk_1 - \pi a_l}{2\pi T_1 a_l} \, ,$$

from which we obtain without plotting the single value (60.21) satisfying the condition (60.26), where

$$\left(\frac{\partial G}{\partial a}\right)_{a=a_l} = \left(\frac{4cbk_1}{2\pi T_1 a^2}\right)_{a=a_l} = \frac{\pi}{8T_1 cbk_1} > 0 \, .$$

This corresponds to Fig. 265b.

Relay systems with time delay. In deriving the automatic temperature regulation system equations in Section 53 it was explained that non-idealness of the electromagnetic relay is better described by a time delay than by a hysteresis loop. Let us consider the idealised case taking into account delay, where the relay has no zone of insensitivity (the characteristic of Fig. 234a) and has a constant time delay τ; the times of relay switching are illustrated by the graphs of Fig. 234g, h and equation (53.27). In the linear part of the system we neglect the time constants of the sensitive element T_2 and the drive T_2. Then the system equation is the same as in the above example:

$$T_1\ddot{\theta} + \dot{\theta} + kF_\tau(\theta) = 0 \, , \tag{60.29}$$

where $F_\tau(\theta)$ is defined by a graph of the form of Fig. 234a with an additional time delay τ.

Let us employ the solution applied by G. S. Pospelov for an equation of this type. We shall seek the solution in the form

$$\theta = a\sin(\omega t - \varphi) \quad [a = a(t) \, , \ \varphi = \varphi(t)] \, .$$

To obtain the approximate equation of the transient we substitute this solution in (60.29) and neglect terms containing d^2a/dt^2, $d^2\varphi/dt^2$ and $(da/dt)(d\varphi/dt)$ as a result of the assumption on slow variation of the functions a and φ in time. As a result we obtain the equation

$$2\frac{da}{dt}\,\omega T_1\cos(\omega t - \varphi) + 2a\omega T_1\frac{d\varphi}{dt}\sin(\omega t - \varphi) - a\omega^2 T_1\sin(\omega t - \varphi) +$$

$$+ a\omega\cos(\omega t - \varphi) + kF_\tau[a\sin(\omega t - \varphi)] = 0 \, , \tag{60.30}$$

where the function $F_\tau[a\sin(\omega t - \varphi)]$ has the form shown in Fig. 234h below. If we expand this in a Fourier series and limit ourselves only to the first harmonic, we obtain

$$F_\tau[a\sin(\omega t-\varphi)]\approx\frac{4c}{\pi}\sin[\omega(t-\tau)\varphi]$$

$$=\frac{4c}{\pi}\cos\omega\tau\sin(\omega t-\varphi)-\frac{4c}{\pi}\sin\omega\tau\cos(\omega t-\varphi).\qquad(60.31)$$

Substituting this in (60.30), collecting all coefficients of the sine and cosine and equating them separately to zero, we obtain the required equations

$$\left.\begin{aligned}\frac{da}{dt}&=\frac{1}{2\omega T_1}\left(-a\omega+\frac{4ck}{\pi}\sin\omega\tau\right),\\\frac{d\varphi}{dt}&=\frac{1}{2a\omega T_1}\left(a\omega^2 T_1-\frac{4ck}{\pi}\cos\omega\tau\right),\end{aligned}\right\}\qquad(60.32)$$

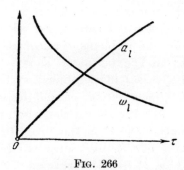

Fɪɢ. 266

defining the variation of amplitude and frequency of the transient oscillation.

To find the periodic solution (self-oscillation), it is necessary to put $a=\text{const}=a_l$, $\omega=\omega_l$, $\varphi=\text{const}$. Substituting this in equation (60.32), we obtain

$$\frac{4ck}{\pi}\sin\omega_l\tau=a_l\omega_l,\qquad\frac{4ck}{\pi}\cos\omega_l\tau=a_l\omega_l^2 T_1,$$

from which we find the following equations to determine the frequency ω and the amplitude a_l of oscillations:

$$\left.\begin{aligned}T_1\omega_l\tan\omega_l\tau&=1,\\a_l&=\frac{4ck}{\pi\omega_l\sqrt{1+T_1^2\omega_l^2}}.\end{aligned}\right\}\qquad(60.33)$$

The character of variation of the frequency and amplitude of oscillations defined by these formulae, in dependence on the magnitude of time delay τ, is shown in Fig. 266.

Comparison of these approximate results with the exact solution (method of matching solutions as in Section 9) shows their excellent agreement.

61. Krylov-Bogoliubov harmonic linearisation of non-linearity

We now describe the approximate method of determining the periodic solutions (in particular, oscillatory) of non-linear systems of arbitrary order*, also based on the work of Krylov and Bogoliubov, 1934 (Reference 5) and 1937 (Reference 6). Krylov and Bogoliubov have termed this the method of equivalent linearisation or the method of harmonic balance, proving that the method of energy balance also reduces to this.

This approximate method is a very powerful means of studying non-linear systems (in particular, oscillatory) because of its simplicity and of the universality of its apparatus in application to the most varied non-linearities. It is necessary however to bear in mind that it solves the problem approximately. There are definite limitations to its applicability, which will be discussed below. These limitations are usually well satisfied in problems of automatic regulation theory. Practical calculations and experiment show the applicability of this method to many classes of non-linear systems.

Basis of harmonic linearisation of non-linearity. Krylov and Bogoliubov (Reference 6) have shown that the approximate solution of the non-linear equation (60.1) in the form (60.14)–(60.16) corresponds (to a magnitude of the order of ε^2) to representation of the non-linear function $F(x, \dot{x})$ in the form

$$F(x, \dot{x}) \approx q(a, \omega)x + q_1(a, \omega)\dot{x} . \qquad (61.1)$$

On this basis they recommend even for more complicated high-order systems than (60.1) separating the non-linear element and the corresponding non-linear expression and replacing it approximately by an expression of type (61.1), which is similar to a linear one, but differs substantially from the latter in that its coefficients are functions of the amplitude and frequency of the required oscillations in the system. We shall follow this recommendation below, terming the approximate substitution of non-linearity harmonic linearisation and further introducing special approximate equations for the non-linear elements.

The approximate expression (61.1) may be obtained directly (without reference to the preceding section) in the following manner. Let there be given some non-linear expression of the form

$$y = F(x, \dot{x}) \qquad (61.2)$$

---

* The method presented in Sections 61, 62, 63, 68 was proposed by the author at the II All-Union Conference on the Theory of Regulation in November 1953. This method is further developed in Sections 64 and 67.

and given $x = a \sin \omega t$. Then

$$y = F(a \sin \omega t, \ a\omega \cos \omega t). \tag{61.3}$$

Putting

$$u = \omega t, \tag{61.4}$$

we expand the function in the right-hand part of equation (61.3) in a Fourier series. We obtain

$$y = \frac{1}{2\pi} \int_0^{2\pi} F(a \sin u, \ a\omega \cos u) \, du +$$

$$+ \left[\frac{1}{\pi} \int_0^{2\pi} F(a \sin u, \ a\omega \cos u) \sin u \, du \right] \sin \omega t +$$

$$+ \left[\frac{1}{\pi} \int_0^{2\pi} F(a \sin u, \ a\omega \cos u) \cos u \, du \right] \cos \omega t +$$

$$+ \text{higher harmonics} \tag{61.5}$$

The first integral in this expansion is a certain constant quantity. Let us put

$$\int_0^{2\pi} F(a \sin u, \ a\omega \cos u) \, du = 0, \tag{61.6}$$

which signifies the absence of a constant component in the given expansion. In the present chapter we shall everywhere assume satisfaction of the condition of absence of a constant component (61.6). Below (Section 67) we shall give a method for investigating oscillations in the presence of a constant component, i.e. when condition (61.6) is not satisfied.

If we neglect higher harmonics and take into consideration that

$$\sin \omega t = \frac{x}{a} \quad \text{and} \quad \cos \omega t = \frac{\dot{x}}{a\omega},$$

formula (61.5) with condition (61.6) may be written in the form

$$y \approx q(a, \omega) x + \frac{q_1(a, \omega)}{\omega} \dot{x}, \tag{61.7}$$

where

$$q(a, \omega) = \frac{1}{\pi a} \int_0^{2\pi} F(a \sin u, \ a\omega \cos u) \sin u \, du,$$

$$q_1(a, \omega) = \frac{1}{\pi a} \int_0^{2\pi} F(a \sin u, \ a\omega \cos u) \cos u \, du. \tag{61.8}$$

Thus the non-linear expression (61.2) with $x = a \sin \omega t$ to within higher harmonics is replaced by a quasi-linear expression (61.7).

37

Its coefficients are constant with constant values of a and ω, i.e. when we are concerned with the periodic solution. During the transient oscillations with variation of a and ω they also vary. For various amplitudes and frequencies of the periodic solutions the coefficients and expressions (61.7) will be different in magnitude. This circumstance, very important below, is the essential property distinguishing the expression (61.7) obtained as a result of harmonic linearisation from the ordinary method of linearisation (Section 18), leading to purely linear expressions with which we have been concerned in the previous parts of the book. This permits analysing approximately the fundamental properties of the non-linear oscillations which we could not obtain with ordinary linearisation, applying to expression (61.7) linear methods of investigation.

Approximate equations of the non-linear elements of the first class. The first class (Section 52) contains all non-linear elements described by equations of type (52.1) and (52.2) with arbitrary non-linearity. Let there exist a non-linear automatic regulation system (Fig. 229a), the linear part of which, having arbitrary structure, is described by an ordinary linear differential equation of arbitrary order (52.6), while the non-linear element, say, has the equation

$$x_2 = F(x_1, \dot{x}_1) . \tag{61.9}$$

For the approximate determination of the periodic solution (in particular, oscillatory) in the absence of a constant component we put

$$x_1 = a \sin \omega t , \tag{61.10}$$

and, employing formulae (61.2) and (61.7), we replace this non-linear differential equation by the following approximate equation (for oscillation):

$$x_2 = \left[q(a, \omega) + \frac{q_1(a, \omega)}{\omega} p \right] x_1 , \tag{61.11}$$

where $q(a, \omega)$ and $q_1(a, \omega)$ are defined by formulae (61.8), where a and ω denote the amplitude and frequency of the input oscillation to the non-linear circuit x_1.

The approximation of such harmonic linearisation of the non-linear equation (61.9) consists, firstly, in that the non-linear oscillation of x_1 in the closed system (Fig. 229) is assumed sinusoidal (61.10), and, secondly, higher harmonics of x_2 at the output of the non-linear element are neglected (according to (61.5)), i.e. writing equation (61.11) we automatically consider the oscillation of x_2 to be sinusoidal.

Both of these assumptions will be justified with arbitrary non-linearity if the neglected harmonics pass through the linear part of the system with much greater attenuation than the fundamental component. The linear parts of the majority of automatic regulation systems and servomechanisms have just this property, since their amplitude-phase characteristics (in the open state) have small radius-vectors at high frequencies. This property of the system may be quantitatively estimated from the amplitude-frequency characteristic of the linear part of the system.

Therefore harmonic linearisation of the equations of non-linear elements, which will be widely applied below in studying oscillatory processes in non-linear systems, is admissible in practice for the majority of regulation systems and servomechanisms with arbitrary character of non-linearity (for a more exact solution see Section 64).

If the equation of the non-linear element has, instead of (61.9), the form

$$F(\dot{x}_2, x_2) = c_1 x_1 ,\qquad (61.12)$$

where x_2, as before, is the output quantity of the non-linear element, in place of (61.10) we put

$$x_2 = a \sin \omega t ,\qquad (61.13)$$

and as a result of harmonic linearisation we obtain the approximate equation of the element in the form

$$\left[\frac{q_1(a,\,\omega)}{\omega}\, p + q(a,\,\omega)\right] x_2 = c_1 x_1 ,\qquad (61.14)$$

where $q_1(a,\,\omega)$ and $q(a,\,\omega)$ are defined by (61.8), except that here a and ω, in contrast to the preceding, denote the amplitude and frequency of oscillation of the output quantity of the non-linear element x_2. Expressions (61.13) and (61.14), as the above, denote the oscillations at the input and output of the non-linear element in sinusoidal form. It is necessary to consider that the formula of harmonic linearisation (61.14) is connected in the present case with an additional restriction: it is assumed that the combination terms entering into the first harmonic of the non-linear function in higher harmonics of the argument x_2 are negligible. In the contrary case there should be introduced additional terms in the coefficients q_1 and q (see Section 64).

We also present formulae of harmonic linearisation for the equation of a non-linear element of simpler type (52.1). Here two alternatives are possible: (1) the curve $F(x_1)$ has a hysteresis loop (for example, Fig. 235c, Fig. 240d and e) and (2) the curve $F(x_1)$ does not have a hysteresis loop.

In the presence of the hysteresis loop, when a dependence on the sign of the derivative is actually observed, the non-linear equation

$$x_2 = F(x_1) ,\qquad (61.15)$$

after harmonic linearisation is replaced by the following approximate equation (with $x_1 = a \sin \omega t$):

$$x_2 = \left[q(a) + \frac{q_1(a)}{\omega} p \right] x_1 , \qquad (61.16)$$

where

$$q(a) = \frac{1}{\pi a} \int_0^{2\pi} F(a \sin u) \sin u \, du , \qquad \left.\right\}$$

$$q_1(a) = \frac{1}{\pi a} \int_0^{2\pi} F(a \sin u) \cos u \, du , \qquad (61.17)$$

and with the absence of the constant component

$$\int_0^{2\pi} F(a \sin u) \, du = 0 . \qquad (61.18)$$

If the curve $F(x_1)$ does not have a hysteresis loop, we obtain $q_1(a) = 0$, since with $x = a \sin u$ we have

$$q_1(a) = \frac{1}{\pi a} \int_0^{2\pi} F(a \sin u) \cos u \, du = \frac{1}{\pi a^2} \int_0^0 F(x_1) \, dx_1 = 0$$

(with a hysteresis loop this integral does not vanish as a result of the difference in shape of the curve $F(x_1)$ with increasing and decreasing x_1).

Consequently, in the absence of the hysteresis loop the non-linear equation (61.15) is replaced by a simpler approximate equation

$$x_2 = q(a) x_1 , \qquad (61.19)$$

i.e. the curved or polygonal characteristic $x_2 = F(x_1)$ is replaced by a rectilinear one, the slope of which $q(a)$ depends on the magnitude of oscillation. In other words, the non-linear element is compared to a "linear" one with transfer factor (gain factor), dependent on the amplitude a of the input oscillation x_1. The hysteresis loop also introduces, according to (61.16), the derivative, giving a phase delay, since $q_1(a) < 0$. Thus, non-linear delay in coordinate in the form of a hysteresis loop is transformed in harmonic linearisation to an equivalent linear phase delay.

In cases where the non-linear element is described by a complicated equation including the sum of various linear and non-linear expressions, each of the non-linear terms is subjected separately to harmonic linearisation. Here we may encounter a different character of non-linear function.

For example, in harmonic linearisation of the second of equations (52.2) we are concerned with the function $F(\ddot{x}, \dot{x})$ with $x = a\sin\omega t$. In the first case we obtain

$$F(\ddot{x}, \dot{x}) \approx \left[\frac{q_2(a, \omega)}{-\omega^2} p^2 + \frac{q_1(a, \omega)}{\omega} p \right] x , \qquad (61.20)$$

where

$$\left. \begin{aligned} q_2(a, \omega) &= \frac{1}{\pi a} \int_0^{2\pi} F(-a\omega^2\sin u , \; a\omega\cos u)\sin u\,du , \\[2ex] q_1(a, \omega) &= \frac{1}{\pi a} \int_0^{2\pi} F(-a\omega^2\sin u , \; a\omega\cos u)\cos u\,du , \end{aligned} \right\} \qquad (61.21)$$

under the condition

$$\int_0^{2\pi} F(-a\omega^2\sin u , \; a\omega\cos u)\,du = 0 . \qquad (61.22)$$

If the function $F(\ddot{x}, \dot{x})$ or the function $F(\dot{x})$ is the only non-linear function in the equation of the non-linear element, with harmonic linearisation we may put

$$\dot{x} = a\sin\omega t$$

and thus reduce the problem to the previous formulae. But now the quantity a in all calculations will be the magnitude of oscillations in velocity $\dot{x}$ and not the coordinate x. The latter will then have the amplitude

$$a_x = \frac{a}{\omega} .$$

Approximate equations of non-linear elements of the second class. The second class includes all non-linear elements described by equations of type (52.3) and (52.4) with arbitrary non-linearity and with the same general structure as before (Fig. 229). The essential difference of the elements of this class is that both variables (x_1 and x_2) are included in the non-linear function. Therefore in harmonic linearisation it is necessary to introduce into the equation two unknown amplitudes, putting

$$x_2 = a_2\sin\omega t , \qquad x_1 = a_1\sin(\omega t + \beta) . \qquad (61.23)$$

For equations of type (52.3), where x_1 and x_2 enter separately into the non-linear functions, the harmonic linearisation of non-linearity is carried out individually for each. Thus, for the equation

$$F_2(\dot{x}_2, x_2) = F_1(x_1) \qquad (61.24)$$

we have in the left-hand side, according to (61.12) and (61.14) *

$$\left[\frac{q_3(a_2,\,\omega)}{\omega}\,p + q_2(a_2,\,\omega)\right] x_2\,,$$

where

$$q_3(a_2,\,\omega) = \frac{1}{\pi a_2}\int_0^{2\pi} F_2(a_2\sin u\,,\ a_2\omega\cos u)\sin u\,du\,,$$

$$q_2(a_2,\,\omega) = \frac{1}{\pi a_2}\int_0^{2\pi} F_2(a_2\sin u\,,\ a_2\omega\cos u)\cos u\,du\,.$$
(61.25)

In linearising the right-hand side of equation (61.24), in accordance with (61.23) we put $u = \omega t + \beta$ and then from (61.15) and (61.16) we obtain

$$\left[q(a_1) + \frac{q_1(a_1)}{\omega}\,p\right] x_1\,,$$

where

$$q(a_1) = \frac{1}{\pi a_1}\int_0^{2\pi} F(a_1\sin u)\sin u\,du\,,$$

$$q_1(a_1) = \frac{1}{\pi a_1}\int_0^{2\pi} F(a_1\sin u)\cos u\,du\,.$$
(61.26)

Thus, the non-linear equation (61.24) is replaced by the following approximate equation:

$$\left[\frac{q_3(a_2,\,\omega)}{\omega}p + q_2(a_2,\,\omega)\right] x_2 = \left[q(a_1) + \frac{q_1(a_1)}{\omega}p\right] x_1\,,$$
(61.27)

where the coefficients are defined by formulae (61.25) and (61.26), and in the absence of a hysteresis loop we have in the right hand side (61.24)

$$q_1(a_1) = 0\,.$$

The two amplitudes a_l and a_2 introduced here are not mutually independent. They are related by the amplitude-phase characteristic of the linear part of the system since for the linear part (Fig. 229), a_2 is the amplitude of input oscillations and a_l of output. If the equation of the linear part has the form (52.6), the ratio of amplitudes defined as the modulus of the amplitude-phase characteristic of the linear part of the system will be:

$$\frac{a_1}{a_2} = A = \left|\frac{R_l(i\omega)}{Q_l(i\omega)}\right|\,.$$
(61.28)

* Here, as in formula (61.14), we introduce the additional assumption on the negligibility of combination terms. For a more exact solution see Section 64.

This relation must be taken into account in investigating equation (61.27). It is convenient to have its graphic representation (Fig. 51a).

The phase shift β indicated in formulae (61.23) and in Fig. 51b will be

$$\beta = \arg \frac{R_i(i\omega)}{Q_i(i\omega)} \qquad (61.29)$$

(it has no influence on the process of harmonic linearisation).

Harmonic linearisation is carried out somewhat differently in those cases where the variables x_1 and x_2 are not separable in the non-linear expression of type (52.4). In these cases we represent the second of expressions (61.23) in the form

$$x_1 = A a_2(\cos\beta \sin \omega t + \sin\beta \cos \omega t) ,$$

where A and β are as before. Considering the first of expressions (61.23), we obtain

$$x_1 = \xi(\omega)x_2 + \frac{\xi_1(\omega)}{\omega}\dot{x}_2 , \qquad (61.30)$$

where we put

$$\xi(\omega) = A(\omega)\cos\beta(\omega) , \qquad \xi_1(\omega) = A(\omega)\sin\beta(\omega) . \qquad (61.31)$$

Expression (61.30) is substituted in equation (52.4) which is to be subjected to harmonic linearisation. As a result only the variable x_2 and its derivative $\dot{x}_2$ remain in the non-linear function. After this harmonic linearisation is carried out as usual for an element of the first class. The complication consists here in that more complicated functions of the oscillation frequency (61.31) will enter into the coefficients of the equation; they are given either analytically according to (61.28) and (61.29) or graphically on the basis of Fig. 51a and b.

We proceed similarly with harmonic linearisation of the third class of non-linearity (Fig. 230), taking into account the amplitude-phase characteristics of the two or more individual linear parts of the system.

Calculation of the coefficients of the approximate equations of non-linear elements. In calculating the coefficients of the approximate equations of non-linear elements according to formulae (61.8), (61.21), (61.25) and, in particular, from formulae (61.17), (61.26) it is necessary to bear in mind that with symmetrical non-linear characteristics the integral $(0, 2\pi)$ may be obtained by the double integral $(0, \pi)$, i.e.

$$\int_0^{2\pi} = 2 \int_0^{\pi} , \qquad (61.32)$$

while for symmetry with respect to the origin of coordinates of a hysteresisless characteristic $x_2 = F(x_1)$ we may write:

$$\int\limits_{\iota}^{2\pi} = 4 \int\limits^{\frac{\pi}{2}} .$$ (61.33)

Let us calculate the coefficients for certain simple non-linear elements. We may then use them directly in solving various specific problems.

Coefficients of the approximate equations of relay circuits. Let us find the coefficients $q(a)$ and $q_1(a)$ of the approximate equations of the most typical relay circuits according to formulae (61.17).

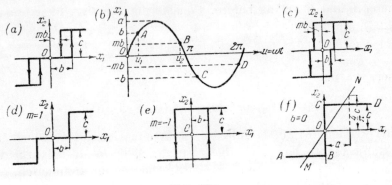

FIG. 267

Let us take the general form of the characteristic of the relay circuit $x_2 = F(x_1)$ shown in the graph of Fig. 267a, where m is an arbitrary fraction in the interval $-1 \leqslant m \leqslant 1$. As particular cases we shall obtain the equations of two types of relay circuits.

If the oscillations of the input quantity $x_1 = a \sin \omega t$ have an amplitude $a < b$, then from Fig. 267a there will be no motion in the system. If the amplitude $a > b$, switching of the relay takes place at the points A, B, C, D (Fig. 267b) at which we have:

$$u_1 = \sin^{-1}\frac{b}{a}, \qquad u_2 = \pi - \sin^{-1}\frac{mb}{a} .$$ (61.34)

Consequently, after using the properties (61.32) each of the integrals in (61.17) separates into three components

$$\int\limits_{0}^{\pi} = \int\limits_{0}^{u_1} + \int\limits_{u_1}^{u_2} + \int\limits_{u_2}^{\pi} ,$$

where the first and third vanish according to Fig. 267a and b. Therefore expressions (61.17) take the form

$$q(a) = \frac{2}{\pi a} \int\limits_{u_1}^{u_2} c \sin u \, du \,, \qquad q_1(a) = \frac{2}{\pi a} \int\limits_{u_1}^{u_2} c \cos u \, du \,,$$

from which

$$\left.\begin{aligned} q(a) &= \frac{2c}{\pi a}\left(\cos u_1 - \cos u_2\right) = \frac{2c}{\pi a}\left(\sqrt{1 - \frac{b^2}{a^2}} + \sqrt{1 - \frac{m^2 b^2}{a^2}}\right), \\ q_1(a) &= -\frac{2c}{\pi a}\left(\sin u_1 - \sin u_2\right) = -\frac{2cb}{\pi a^2}(1-m) \quad (a > b)\,, \end{aligned}\right\} \quad (61.35)$$

and the approximate equation of the relay circuit with characteristic in the form of Fig. 267a will have the form (61.16) with the values $q(a)$ and $q_1(a)$ obtained here.

Let us consider particular cases.

For the relay circuit without hysteresis loop, but with a zone of insensitivity b (Fig. 267d), putting $m = 1$, from the above formulae we obtain

$$q(a) = \frac{4c}{\pi a}\cos u_1 = \frac{4c}{\pi a}\sqrt{1 - \frac{b^2}{a^2}}\,, \qquad q_1(a) = 0 \quad (a > b)\,. \qquad (61.36)$$

For the relay characteristic with hysteresis loop of type Fig. 267d, putting $m = -1$, we have:

$$\left.\begin{aligned} q(a) &= \frac{4c}{\pi a}\cos u_1 = \frac{4c}{\pi a}\sqrt{1 - \frac{b^2}{a^2}}\,, \\ q_1(a) &= -\frac{4c}{\pi a}\sin u_1 = -\frac{4cb}{\pi a^2} \quad (a > b)\,. \end{aligned}\right\} \qquad (61.37)$$

Finally, for the ideal relay circuit (Fig. 267f), putting $b = 0$, we find:

$$q(a) = \frac{4c}{\pi a}\,, \qquad q_1(a) = 0\,. \qquad (61.38)$$

The significance of harmonic linearisation of the relay characteristic is easily seen of from the last example. The expression $q(a)$ denotes the substitution of the polygonal characteristic $ABCD$ by the straight line MN (Fig. 267f) with slope such that this line MN approximately replaces that segment of the polygon $ABCD$ which includes the given amplitude a. This makes clear the inversely proportional dependence of q on a, given by formula (61.38), since the greater the amplitude a of the input quantity oscillation x_1, the lower the slope of the line MN, approximately replacing the polygon $ABCD$.

Similar considerations relate to the relay characteristic in Fig. 267d for which the slope of the straight line substituting it is given by formula (61.36). Consequently, each hysterisisless relay circuit with oscillation is equivalent to such a "linear" element, the transfer factor (gain factor) $q(a)$ of which decreases with increase in amplitude of oscillation of the input quantity.

Concerning the relay circuit with hysteresis loop, from (61.16) and (61.37) it is replaced by a linear element with a similar gain factor to the preceding $q(a)$, but, in addition, with introduction of the negative derivative in the right-hand side of the equation.

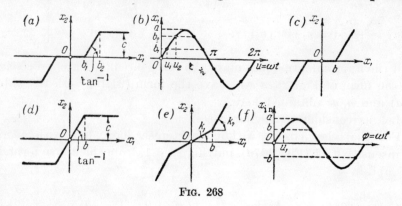

FIG. 268

The introduction of the negative derivative, in contrast to the positive, (see Section 15) introduces a phase delay in the response of the element to the input force. This is the "linear equivalent" replacing the effect of the non-linearity in the form of a hysteresis loop. Here the coefficient $q(a)$ for the derivative, according to (61.37), also decreases with increase in amplitude a of the input quantity oscillation x_1, which is understandable since the effect of the hysteresis loop on the oscillation in the relay circuit should be smaller, the greater the amplitude of oscillation in comparison with the width of hysteresis loop.

Coefficients of the approximate equations of other simple non-linear elements. Let us consider a non-linear element with insensitive zone and with saturation (Fig. 268a). From Fig. 268b, here

$$u_1 = \sin^{-1}\frac{b_1}{a}, \quad u_2 = \sin^{-1}\frac{b_2}{a} = \sin^{-1}\frac{c + b_1 k}{ak}, \quad (61.39)$$

the integral (61.17) on the segment $(0, \pi)$ separates into five components, where the first two vanish. Therefore

$$q(a) = \frac{2}{\pi a} \int_{u_1}^{u_2} k(a\sin u - b_1)\sin u\,du + \frac{2}{\pi a} \int_{u_2}^{\pi - u_2} c\sin u\,du +$$

$$+ \frac{2}{\pi a} \int_{\pi - u_2}^{\pi - u_1} k(a\sin u - b_1)\sin u\,du\,,$$

from which with the substitution $c = (b_2 - b_1)k$ and $b_1 = a \sin u_1$, $b_2 = a \sin u_2$ we obtain

$$q(a) = \frac{2k}{\pi}\left(u_2 - u_1 + \frac{1}{2}\sin 2u_2 - \frac{1}{2}\sin 2u_1\right) \quad (a > b_2), \quad (61.40)$$

where u_1 and u_2 are defined by formulae (61.39). In view of the absence of hysteresis loop here $q_i(a) = 0$.

Thus, the approximate equation of the non-linear element with characteristic in the form of Fig. 268a will be (61.19) where $q(a)$ has the expression (61.40).

As a particular case, the value of $q(a)$ for an element with insensitive zone without saturation (Fig. 268c) follows from this. For this we put in the preceding solution $a < b_2$, and, consequently, $u_2 = \pi/2$. Then

$$q(a) = k - \frac{2k}{\pi}\left(\sin^{-1}\frac{b}{a} + \frac{b}{a}\sqrt{1 - \frac{b^2}{a^2}}\right) \quad (a > b). \quad (61.41)$$

As we see, an element with insensitive zone is similar to a linear element with reduction of gain factor. This reduction of gain factor is appreciable at low amplitudes and small at large, where $0 \leqslant q(a) \leqslant k$ with $b \leqslant a \leqslant \infty$.

For the second particular case, an element with saturation without insensitive zone (Fig 268d), putting $b_1 = 0$, i. e $u_1 = 0$, from (61.40) and (61.39) we obtain

$$q(a) = \frac{2k}{\pi}\left(\sin^{-1}\frac{c}{ak} + \frac{c}{ak}\sqrt{1 - \frac{c^2}{a^2k^2}}\right) \quad \left(a > \frac{c}{k}\right), \quad (61.42)$$

where with $a < c/k$ we have $q(a) = k$ (linear characteristic). At input oscillations including the saturation zone, the given element is equivalent to a linear element with the gain factor $q(a)$ decreasing with increase in amplitude (in contradiction to the preceding).

For the element with variable gain factor according to Fig. 268e and f, from formula (61.17), taking into account (61.32) we obtain

$$q(a) = \frac{2}{\pi a}\int_0^\pi k_1 a \sin u \sin u \, du +$$

$$+ \frac{2}{\pi a}\int_{u_1}^{\pi - u_1} [k_2(a \sin u - b) + k_1 b]\sin u \, du +$$

$$+ \frac{2}{\pi a}\int_{\pi - u_1}^\pi k_1 a \sin u \sin u \, du,$$

which with the substitution $\sin u_1 = b$ gives

$$q(a) = k_2 - \frac{2}{\pi}(k_2 - k_1)\left(\sin\frac{b}{a} + \frac{b}{a}\sqrt{1 - \frac{b^2}{a^2}}\right) \quad (a > b). \quad (61.43)$$

Here the polygonal characteristic (Fig. 268e) is replaced by a single straight line with slope $q(a)$ between k_1 and k_2, where the slope varies in the interval $k_1 \leqslant q(a) \leqslant k_2$ with increase of amplitude $b \leqslant a \leqslant \infty$. For amplitudes $a < b$ we have a linear characteristic with slope k.

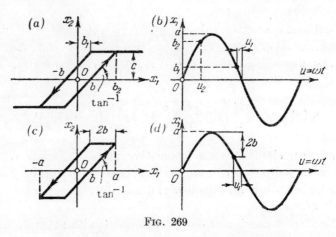

FIG. 269

For the non-linear element with saturation and with hysteresis loop (Fig. 269a) the approximate equation takes the form (61.16) where according to Fig. 269b and formulae (61.17) we have

$$q(a) = \frac{2}{\pi a}\int_0^{u_2} k(a\sin u - b)\sin u\,du + \frac{2}{\pi a}\int_{u_2}^{\pi - u_1} c\sin u\,du +$$

$$+ \frac{2}{\pi a}\int_{\pi - u_1}^{\pi} k(a\sin u + b)\sin u\,du;$$

and similarly $q_1(a)$ From this

$$q(a) = \frac{k}{\pi}\left(u_2 + \frac{1}{2}\sin 2u_2 + u_1 + \frac{1}{2}\sin 2u_1\right),$$
$$q_1(a) = -\frac{k}{\pi}(\sin^2 u_2 - \sin u_1) \quad (a > b_2), \quad (61.44)$$

where

$$u_2 = \sin^{-1}\frac{b_2}{a} = \sin^{-1}\frac{c+bk}{ak}, \quad u_1 = \sin^{-1}\frac{b_1}{a} = \sin^{-1}\frac{c-bk}{ak}. \quad (61.45)$$

If in this non-linear element the amplitude of oscillation of the input quantity x_1 will be $a < b_2$, the oscillation will not include the saturation zone and a purely hysteresis characteristic (Fig. 269c) is obtained. In this case

$$u_2 = \frac{\pi}{2}, \qquad u_1 = \sin^{-1}\left(1 - \frac{2b}{a}\right). \tag{61.46}$$

The approximate equation of the element with hysteresis characteristic of the type of Fig. 269c will therefore have the form (61.16), where from (61.44)

$$
\left.
\begin{aligned}
q(a) &= \frac{k}{\pi}\left(\frac{\pi}{2} + u_1 + \frac{1}{2}\sin 2u_1\right), \\
q_1(a) &= -\frac{k}{\pi}\cos^2 u_1 = -\frac{4kb}{\pi a}\left(1 - \frac{b}{a}\right) \quad (a > b),
\end{aligned}
\right\} \tag{61.47}
$$

where u_1 is calculated from formula (61.46).

The same type of characteristic (Fig. 269c) was obtained for a sensitive element with dry friction in the pressure regulation system considered in Section 54 (see Fig. 238b), where we neglected the mass. Consequently, for a non-linear element with dry friction the same formulae (61.47) will be valid substituting

$$k = \frac{1}{\delta}, \tag{61.48}$$

while equation (54.15) for the oscillatory process in approximate form (61.16) will be

$$\eta = \left[q(a) + \frac{q_1(a)}{\omega}\, p\right]\varphi. \tag{61.49}$$

This type of characteristic (Fig. 269c) occurred also for the non-linear element with backlash in a servomechanism (Fig. 237b), where we had $k = 1$. Consequently, equation (54.12) of the given non-linear element is approximately (for an oscillatory process) written in the form

$$\beta = \left[q(a) + \frac{q_1(a)}{\omega}\right]\beta_1, \tag{61.50}$$

where $q(a)$ and $q_1(a)$ are defined from formulae (61.47), in which it is necessary to put $k = 1$.

62. Approximate determination of oscillations and their stability using the Mikhailov criterion and algebraic criteria

Basing ourselves on the above harmonic linearisation of non-linearity, let us derive the approximate equation of the entire closed non-linear automatic system (Fig. 229a). Let the differential equation of the linear part of the system be known,

$$Q_l(p)x_1 = -R_l(p)x_2, \tag{62.1}$$

where the linear part may have a structure of any complexity (and an equation of any order).

The approximate equation of the non-linear element in the oscillation, obtained by harmonic linearisation (Section 61) is written in the form

$$Q_n(p)x_2 = R_n(p)x_1 , \qquad (62.2)$$

where for the various non-linearities considered in Section 61 the operational polynomials $Q_n(p)$ and $R_n(p)$ will have differing expressions. For example, for the non-linear equation (61.9), according to (61.11) we have

$$Q_n(p) = 1 , \qquad R_n(p) = q(a, \omega) + \frac{q_1(a, \omega)}{\omega} p ,$$

for the non-linear characteristic (61.15) without hysteresis loop,

$$Q_n(p) = 1 , \qquad R_n(p) = q(a) ,$$

and for the non-linear equation (61.24), according to (61.27) we obtain

$$Q_n(p) = \frac{q_3(a_2, \omega)}{\omega} p + q_2(a_2, \omega) , \qquad R_n(p) = q(a_1) + \frac{q_1(a_1)}{\omega} p ,$$

where a_1 and a_2 are related by (61.28) or the corresponding graph of Fig. 51a.

As we see, the amplitude a and the frequency ω of the required oscillatory process enter into the coefficients of equation (62.2).

On the basis of equations (62.1) and (62.2) it is possible to write the conventional characteristic equation of the closed nonlinear system in the form

$$Q_l(z)Q_n(z) + R_l(z)R_n(z) = 0 \qquad (62.3)$$

with the same properties of the coefficients.

When there arise in the closed system free, undamped oscillations of constant amplitude $a = a_l$ and constant frequency $\omega = \omega_l$ (self-oscillation), the coefficients of equation (62.2) and thus the coefficients of the characteristic equation (62.3) become constant. At the same time it is known from linear theory that the appearance of these oscillations in a system with constant coefficients corresponds to the presence of a pair of purely imaginary roots in the characteristic equation of the system.

It is thus possible to determine the appearance in a closed non-linear system of undamped free oscillations of the form $x \approx a_l \sin \omega_l t$ ($a_l = $ const, $\omega_l = $ const), substituting in the characteristic equation (62.3) of the system $z = i\omega_l$. If this substitution $z = i\omega_l$ corresponds to some real positive values $a = a_l$ and $\omega = \omega_l$ with given parameters of the system, these oscillations are possible. But the substitution $z = i\omega_l$ in the characteristic equation with constant coefficients is equivalent to finding the boundary of stability of the linear system. Consequently, the appearance of undamped free oscillations in a non-linear system may be found by applying to the characteristic equation (62.3) any of the methods for determining the boundary of stability of a linear system described in Chapters VII and VIII.

In the present section we shall use for this purpose the Mikhailov stability criterion, developed for linear systems.

Let us term the Mikhailov curve for the closed non-linear system the graph of the function

$$L(i\tilde\omega) = Q_l(i\tilde\omega)Q_n(i\tilde\omega) + R_l(i\tilde\omega)R_n(i\tilde\omega) , \qquad (62.4)$$

which corresponds (with $z = i\tilde\omega$) to the left-hand side of the conventional characteristic equation (62.3) of the non-linear system with arbitrary given values of amplitude a and frequency ω in the coefficients of expressions $Q_n(i\tilde\omega)$ and $R_n(i\tilde\omega)$. To distinguish the frequency of oscillation in the system ω from the parameter $\tilde\omega$, varying along the Mikhailov curve, we mark the latter by the tilde $\sim$. The Mikhailov curve will have the usual form for linear systems.

We note that if the equation of the non-linear element has the form $x_2 = F(x_1)$, in the presence of the hysteresis loop the expression for the Mikhailov curve (62.4), according to (61.16) will be

$$L(i\tilde\omega) = Q_l(i\tilde\omega) + R_l(i\tilde\omega)\left[q(a) + \frac{q_1(a)}{\omega}i\tilde\omega\right] ,$$

and in the absence of the hysteresis loop

$$L(i\tilde\omega) = Q(i\tilde\omega) + R(i\tilde\omega)q(a) .$$

The latter case is characterised by the fact that the frequency ω of the required oscillations does not enter into the coefficients for the Mikhailov curve expression, but only the amplitude a.

For the characteristic equation to have purely imaginary roots $z = i\omega_l$, the Mikhailov curve, as is well known, should pass through the origin of coordinates (as, for example, in Fig. 270). Here the value of $\tilde\omega$ at the origin of coordinates gives the frequency of required oscillations $\tilde\omega = \omega_l$. Therefore the quantity ω entering into the coefficients of the characteristic equation should be equated to this value $\tilde\omega_l$. The magnitude a in these coefficients gives the required amplitude of oscillations a_l.

Basic method of determining the periodic solutions. Let us separate the real and the imaginary parts in the Mikhailov curve expression (62.4),

$$L(i\tilde\omega) = X(\tilde\omega) + iY(\tilde\omega) . \qquad (62.5)$$

From the condition of passage of the Mikhailov curve through the origin of coordinates we require that with $\tilde{\omega} = \omega = \omega_l$ and $a = a_l$, $X(\tilde{\omega}) = 0$ and $Y(\tilde{\omega}) = 0$ simultaneously. This gives us two equations:

$$\left.\begin{array}{l} X(\omega_l,\ a_l) = 0\ , \\ Y(\omega_l,\ a_l) = 0; \end{array}\right\} \tag{62.6}$$

from which the unknown frequency ω_l and amplitude a_l of the required oscillations in the given non-linear system are defined. As we see, this method represents a combination of the Krylov-Bogoliubov method of harmonic balance with the method of plotting the stability region from the linear Mikhailov criterion.

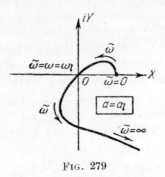

Fig. 279

We recall that self-oscillations correspond to a stable periodic solution. Therefore, after ω_l and a_l are determined from equations (62.6), it is necessary to investigate the stability of the corresponding periodic solution. If it is found unstable, this will not be oscillatory but the limit for initial conditions which may separate a damped transient (small-signal) from a divergent transient (large-signal) or may correspond to still more complicated patterns.

If equation (62.6) does not have real positive solutions for a_l and ω_l, the periodic solutions in general (including oscillatory) are not possible in the given non-linear system.

The study of stability of the periodic solution is given below separately.

Using equations (62.6) it is not only possible to determine the frequency ω_l and amplitude a_l of self-oscillations with given system parameters, but to plot the graphs of ω_l and a_l as functions of any parameter of the system, for example the gain factor k. For this it is necessary in equations (62.6) to assume the parameter k to be variable and to write this equation in the form

$$\left.\begin{array}{l} X(\omega_l,\ a_l,\ k) = 0\ , \\ Y(\omega_l,\ a_l,\ k) = 0\ , \end{array}\right\} \tag{62.7}$$

From this it is possible to find the dependence

$$a_l = a_l(k) , \qquad \omega_l = \omega_l(k) ,$$

for example in the form of the graph of Fig. 271. On the basis of these graphs it will be possible to select the parameter k such that the amplitude of oscillation be sufficiently small, that its frequency be not dangerous for the given system or, finally, that oscillations be completely absent $(k < k_b)$.

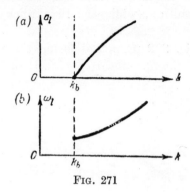

FIG. 271

In addition, using the same equations (62.6) it is possible to plot the loci of equal values of amplitude and frequency in the plane of any two parameters of the system, for example k_1 and k_2. For this we write equations (62.6) in the form

$$\left. \begin{aligned} X(\omega_l, \ a_l, \ k_1, \ k_2) &= 0 , \\ Y(\omega_l, \ a_l, \ k_1, \ k_2) &= 0 . \end{aligned} \right\} \qquad (62.8)$$

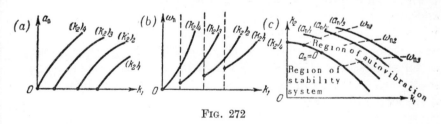

FIG. 272

Then, giving the parameter k_2 various numerical values, we plot as before for each of them the values

$$a_l = a_l(k_1) , \qquad \omega_l = \omega_l(k_1) ,$$

for example in the form of Fig. 272a and b. On the basis of these two graphs it is easy to plot the curves of equal values of a_l (full-line) and ω_l (broken-line), represented in Fig. 272c.

The curves of Fig. 272c may be plotted directly, taking various numerical values of amplitude a_l and obtaining for each of them

38

from equations (62.8) the values

$$k_1 = k_1(\omega_l) \quad \text{and} \quad k_2 = k_2(\omega_l) \,,$$

After this, varying ω_l, it is possible to plot by points the corresponding curves $a_l = \text{const}$ in the coordinates (k_1, k_2), as shown by the full lines in Fig. 272c. On these curves frequency markers ω_l are obtained, which may also be joined (broken-line curves).

The second procedure is the more convenient when there is only a single periodic solution, while the first when there may be two or more.

The graphs of Fig. 272 permit choosing the values of two parameters (k_1 and k_2) of the non-linear system. If such graphs are plotted

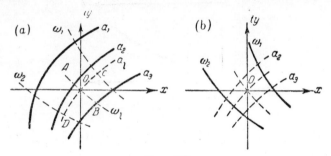

Fig. 273

for various possible system structures, it will also be possible to select the most suitable structure for the proposed closed automatic system taking into account non-linearity.

Graphical illustration. Since at the point where the Mikhailov curve passes through the origin of coordinates (Fig. 270) the current value of $\tilde{\omega}$ should coincide with the value ω_l, entering into the coefficients for the Mikhailov curve expression (62.4), for convenience of solution we first identify the values of $\tilde{\omega}$ and ω in the expression (62.4). Then the required frequency ω_l and amplitude a_l of self-oscillation are found from the condition

$$Q_l(i\omega)Q_n(i\omega) + R_l(i\omega)R_n(i\omega) = 0 \,, \tag{62.9}$$

where ω and a enter into the coefficients. Assigning various numerical values to a, we plot for each of them in the complex plane the curve

$$f(\omega) = Q_l(i\omega)Q_n(i\omega) + R_l(i\omega)R_n(i\omega) \,. \tag{62.10}$$

To satisfy condition (62.9) it is necessary to take that value of a for which the curve passes through the origin of coordinates.

If, for example, for three different values of a the curves $f(\omega)$ lie as shown in Fig. 273a, the required values $a = a_l$ and $\omega = \omega_l$

may be found by the following interpolation (as in Section 38 in determining the degree of stability):

$$a_l = a_2 + \frac{AO}{AB}(a_3 - a_2) \, , \qquad (62.11)$$

$$\omega_l = \omega_1 + \frac{CO}{CD}(\omega_2 - \omega_1) \, . \qquad (62.12)$$

We note that the curves $f(\omega)$ will not in general be Mikhailov curves since we have not only varied the running value of $\tilde{\omega}$ of the Mikhailov curve in plotting them but also ω, entering into the coefficients. However these curves $f(\omega)$ are Mikhailov curves in those cases where the quantity ω does not enter into the coefficients of expression (62.4). This occurs, for example, everywhere in non-linear elements with hysteresisless characteristics $x_2 = F(x_1)$ of arbitrary form (but the method of determining a_l and ω_l itself remains, of course, valid even when these are not Mikhailov curves, i.e. for arbitrary non-linearities).

It is possible to represent this method in a changed form, namely, to assign constants to the values of ω rather than a, and to plot the curves

$$\varphi(a) = Q_l(i\omega)Q_n(i\omega) + R_l(i\omega)R_n(i\omega) \qquad (62.13)$$

for constant values of ω and varying a (full-line curves in Fig. 272b). The interpolation remains the same, (62.11), (62.12).

This method is presented here only as a graphical illustration. Below we shall everywhere apply the above fundamental method based on the analytic expression for the Mikhailov curve.

Application of algebraic criteria. To determine the presence of a pair of purely imaginary roots in the characteristic equation (62.3) it is also possible to apply the algebraic criteria of Vyshnegradskii and Hurwitz. Thus, if equation (62.3) is of third degree in z, it may be written in the form

$$a_0 z^3 + a_1 z^2 + a_2 z + a_3 = 0 \, , \qquad (62.14)$$

where its coefficients will contain the required values of frequency ω_l and amplitude a_l of self-oscillation.

The condition for the presence of a pair of purely imaginary roots from the Vyshnegradskii criterion according to (29.4) will be

$$a_1 a_2 = a_0 a_3 \, , \qquad (62.15)$$

but here we obtain only a single equation with two unknowns a_l and ω_l. To find the second, we represent equation (62.14) in the presence of imaginary roots $z = \pm i\omega_l$ in the form

$$(z^2 + \omega_l^2)(a_0 z + b) = 0 \, .$$

Expanding and equating the coefficients of this equation to the corresponding coefficients of (62.14) we find

$$a_0 \omega_l^2 = a_2 . \tag{62.16}$$

From the two equations (62.15) and (62.16) the unknown amplitude a_l and frequency ω_l entering into the above coefficients are found. Just as in the first method of using the Mikhailov criterion, here on the basis of equations (62.15) and (62.16) it is possible to plot graphs of a_l and ω_l in dependence on a single parameter of the system or in a plane of two parameters for the purpose of their selection.

If equation (62.3) is of fourth degree in z:

$$a_0 z^4 + a_1 z^3 + a_2 z^2 + a_3 z + a_4 = 0 , \tag{62.17}$$

the condition for the presence of a pair of purely imaginary roots from (29.19) will be:

$$a_3(a_1 a_2 - a_0 a_3) - a_4 a_1^2 = 0 . \tag{62.18}$$

In addition, writing equation (62.17) in the form

$$(z^2 + \omega_l^2)(a_0 z^2 + b_1 z + b_2) = 0 ,$$

expanding and equating the coefficients obtained to the corresponding coefficients of (62.17), we find

$$a_1 \omega_l^2 = a_3 . \tag{62.19}$$

Using the two equations (62.18) and (62.19) the entire problem for the fourth-order non-linear system is solved.

We note that for systems with non-linearity of the type $x_2 = F(x_1)$ without hysteresis loop the frequency ω does not enter into the coefficients of the characteristic equation. Therefore from equations (62.15) or (62.18) the amplitude a_l is determined directly and then from (62.16) or (62.19) the frequency ω_l. For systems with more complex non-linearities two equations are obtained with two unknowns.

Taking into account time delay in a non-linear system. A constant delay τ may exist in a non-linear system (here understood in the same sense as in Section 45). An example of the derivation of the equations for such a system was considered in Section 53. At the end of Section 60 we investigated such a second-order system. We shall now consider a non-linear system of arbitrary order with delay and arbitrary character of non-linearity.

If there exists a delay τ in the linear part of the system, then from Section 45 the equation of the linear part (62.1) takes the form

$$Q_l(p)x_1 = -R_l(p)e^{-\tau p}x_2$$

(the factor $e^{-\tau p}$ may, in general, enter into this otherwise). The expression for the Mikhailov curve (32.4) will be:

$$L(i\tilde{\omega}) = Q_l(i\tilde{\omega})Q_n(i\tilde{\omega}) + R_l(i\tilde{\omega})(\cos\tau\tilde{\omega} - i\sin\tau\tilde{\omega})R_n(i\tilde{\omega}). \quad (62.20)$$

After this the basic method of finding self-oscillations described above is applied, i.e. the real and imaginary parts are separated in the form (62.5) and equations (62.6) are written, defining the frequency ω_l and the amplitude a_l of the required self-oscillation.

If the delay τ exists in the non linear element itself, we proceed as follows. We first carry out harmonic linearisation of the non-linear element without regard to the delay, according to the rules of Section 61. We then shift the output quantity by the delay time τ, i.e. the approximate equation of the non-linear element, instead of (62.2), is now written in the form

$$Q_n(p)x_2 = R_n(p)e^{-\tau p}x_1. \quad (62.21)$$

As a result, considering the equation of the linear part (62.1), we come to the same expression for the Mikhailov curve (62.20) and to the previous method for solving the problem (see example 6 in Section 63).

Stability of periodic solutions. It has been stated above that not every periodic solution of the equations of motion of a non-linear system will correspond to self-oscillations, but only the stable solutions. In concrete problems it is frequently immediately evident from physical considerations if self-oscillations occur or not. It is therefore sometimes not necessary to investigate the stability of the periodic solution mathematically. However, in many cases it is still necessary to study this question.

The problem of studying the stability of a periodic solution reduces, in general, to analysis of the linear equation with periodically varying coefficients. A. M. Liapunov (Reference 3) developed the corresponding methods. But in many cases their use still presents great difficulty. Therefore here we abandon the rigorous investigation of the stability of the periodic solutions and present the simplest rough methods.

We shall describe two approximate methods of studying the stability of a periodic solution: (1) averaging coefficients and (2) use of the Mikhailov curve. Strictly, they do not give sufficient conditions for stability. But practically in the majority of cases the use of one of these is found sufficient to judge the stability of the periodic solution found.

Averaging periodic coefficients in the study of stability. Let us write the differential equation of the closed system in small deviations Δx from the investigated periodic solution $x = a_l \sin \omega_l t$. For the linear part of the system on the basis of equation (62.1) we obtain

$$Q_l(p)\Delta x_1 = -R_l(p)\Delta x_2 \,. \tag{62.22}$$

The equation of the non-linear element, for example (61.9) for small deviations takes the form

$$\Delta x_2 = \left(\frac{\partial F}{\partial x_1}\right)_l \Delta x_1 + \left(\frac{\partial F}{\partial \dot x_1}\right)_l \Delta \dot x_1 \tag{62.23}$$

(and analogously for other types of non-linear equations), where the index l signifies that in the partial derivatives it is necessary to substitute $x = a_l \sin \omega_l t$ and $\dot x = a_l \omega_l \cos \omega_l t$. As a result these partial derivatives are periodically varying coefficients. In problems of the theory of regulation they may vary either continuously or discontinuously (see examples in Section 63). We average the periodic coefficients obtained, after which in place of (62.23) we shall have a linear equation with constant coefficients

$$\Delta x_2 = [\varkappa(a_l,\ \omega_l) + \varkappa_1(a_l,\ \omega_l)p]\Delta x_1 \,, \tag{62.24}$$

where

$$\varkappa(a_l,\ \omega_l) = \frac{1}{2\pi}\int_0^{2\pi} \left(\frac{\partial F}{\partial x_1}\right)_l du \,, \quad \varkappa_1(a_l,\ \omega_l) = \frac{1}{2\pi}\int_0^{2\pi} \left(\frac{\partial F}{\partial \dot x_1}\right)_l du \,, \tag{62.25}$$

and $u = \omega_l t$.

The characteristic equation of the system, defining the stability of the periodic solution, from (62.22) and (62.24) will be

$$Q_l(p) + R_l(p)[\varkappa(a_l,\ \omega_l) + \varkappa_1(a_l,\ \omega_l)p] = 0 \,. \tag{62.26}$$

If this satisfies the stability criterion (Mikhailov, Vyshnegradskii, Hurwitz or other), the investigated periodic solution is stable and, consequently, self-oscillation occurs in the system. In the contrary case the periodic solution is unstable, which as we know corresponds either to small-signal stability and large-signal instability of the system or a more complicated pattern of processes.

In cases where the non-linear element has an equation of the form (61.15) (with or without hysteresis loop), the averaged characteristic equation for studying the stability of the periodic solution will be

$$Q_l(p) + R_l(p)\varkappa(a_l) = 0 \,, \tag{62.27}$$

where

$$\varkappa(a_l) = \frac{1}{2\pi}\int_0^{2\pi} \left(\frac{\partial F}{\partial x_1}\right) du \,, \quad u = \omega_l t \,. \tag{62.28}$$

For the second class of non-linear element with equation (61.24) we obtain the characteristic equation for studying the stability of the periodic solution in the form

$$Q_l(p)[\varkappa_2(a_2, \omega_l)p + \varkappa_1(a_2, \omega_l)] + R_l(p)\varkappa(a_1\mathbf{Q} = 0 , \qquad (62.29)$$

where

$$\varkappa_2(a_2, \omega_l) = \frac{1}{2\pi}\int_0^{2\pi}\left(\frac{\partial F_2}{\partial \dot{x}_2}\right)du, \quad \varkappa_1(a_2, \omega_l) = \frac{1}{2\pi}\int_0^{2\pi}\left(\frac{\partial F_2}{\partial x_2}\right)_l du,$$

$$\varkappa(a_1) = \frac{1}{2\pi}\int_0^{2\pi}\left(\frac{\partial F_1}{\partial x_1}\right)_l du , \qquad\qquad (62.30)$$

and the amplitudes a_1 and a_2 are related by (61.28).

Use of the Mikhailov curve, defining the periodic solution. To each concrete value of a there will correspond a definite Mikhailov

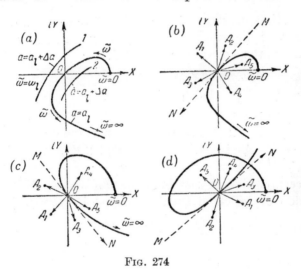

Fig. 274

curve. With $a = a_l$ it passes through the origin of coordinates (Fig. 274a).

To investigate the stability of the periodic solution with amplitude $a = a_l$ we assign a small increment of amplitude Δa. Then with $a = a_l + \Delta a$ the Mikhailov curve takes either the position 1 or the position 2 (Fig. 274a). Then, as is well known from linear theory (Section 28), the curve 1 enclosing the origin of coordinates corresponds to damped oscillations of the transient while the curve 2 to divergent oscillations.

Therefore, if with $\Delta a > 0$ the Mikhailov curve takes the position 1, while with $\Delta a < 0$ the position 2, the transient in the system will be such that oscillations with amplitude greater then a_l attenuate while oscillations with amplitude smaller than a_l diverge. Consequently, the transient process converges from both sides to the investigated periodic process with amplitude a_l. This signifies that the latter is stable (self-oscillations). If, with $\Delta a > 0$ we obtain the curve 2, while with $\Delta a < 0$ the curve 1, the transient process diverges on both sides, i.e. the investigated periodic solution is unstable.

For this investigation there is no necessity of plotting the Mikhailov curves. The entire investigation may be carried out analytically. In fact, to determine if the Mikhailov curve with $\Delta a > 0$ takes the position 1 (Fig. 274a) it is sufficient to determine where the point of Mikhailov curve ($\tilde{\omega} = \omega_l$), which at $a = a_l$ coincided with the origin of coordinates, will shift with increase of a. If it shifts in the directions OA_1, OA_2 or OA_3 (Fig. 274b), the periodic process with amplitude $a = a_l$ is stable, while if in the directions OA_4 or OA_5, unstable.

This direction of shift of the point $\tilde{\omega} = \omega_l$ from the origin of coordinates with increase in a is obviously defined by the following projections on the coordinate axes (X, Y):

$$\left(\frac{\partial X}{\partial a}\right)_l \quad \text{and} \quad \left(\frac{\partial Y}{\partial a}\right)_l, \tag{62.31}$$

where X and Y denote the real and imaginary parts of the Mikhailov curve expression (62.5) while the index l denotes the substitution $a = a_l$, $\tilde{\omega} = \omega_l$. As is evident from Fig. 274b, for stability of this periodic solution the vector defined by the prejections (62.31) should lie on a certain side of the tangent MN to the Mikhailov curve, the direction of which in turn is defined by the projections

$$\left(\frac{\partial X}{\partial \tilde{\omega}}\right)_l \quad \text{and} \quad \left(\frac{\partial Y}{\partial \tilde{\omega}}\right)_l. \tag{62.32}$$

From the positions of the vector with projections (62.31) relative to the vector with projections (63.32) it is immediately evident whether the given periodic solution with amplitude a_l is stable or unstable.

In Fig. 274c and d are shown the same vectors as in Fig. 274b but for other forms of the Mikhailov curve. It is evident that in all cases for the investigated periodic solution to be stable it is necessary that the vector with projections (62.31) lie to the right of the tangent MN if we look along the Mikhailov curve towards increasing $\tilde{\omega}$, where the direction of the tangent MN is defined by the vector with projections (62.32). This geometric stability condition for the periodic solution may be written in the following analytic form:

$$\left(\frac{\partial X}{\partial a}\right)_l\left(\frac{\partial Y}{\partial \tilde{\omega}}\right)_l - \left(\frac{\partial X}{\partial \tilde{\omega}}\right)_l\left(\frac{\partial Y}{\partial a}\right)_l > 0. \tag{62.33}$$

Satisfaction of this stability condition for the periodic solution may be verified analytically in each specific problem without any curve plotting for equations of not higher than fourth degree with positive coefficients, while for equations of higher than fourth degree additional conditions are introduced.

Estimating the stability of the system in the absence of periodic solutions. The approximate equations of a non-linear system derived in Section 61 and at the start of the present section are convenient only for oscillatory processes defined by periodic solutions and for oscillatory transients in the immediate vicinity of these periodic

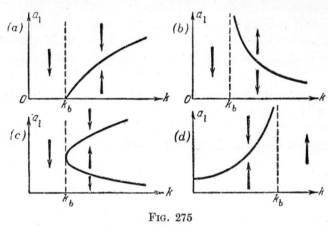

Fig. 275

solutions. Therefore, strictly speaking, using these approximate equations we may analyse only periodic solutions and their stability or instability for small deviations from this oscillatory regime, which has been carried out above.

In practice from an analysis of the approximate equations obtained for the non-linear system it is frequently possible to draw substantially wider conclusions. In particular, in certain cases it is possible to estimate the system stability in those regions of its parameters in which a periodic solution is completely absent.

For example, finding the amplitude of periodic solutions as shown in Fig. 271a, we then determine that the given periodic solution is stable, i.e. corresponds to self-oscillation. Let us denote the stability of the periodic solution on the graph by vertical arrows, converging to the given periodic solution (Fig. 275a). This notation illustrates that the periodic processes converge from both sides (i.e. with initial amplitudes greater than a_l and smaller than a_l) to the self-oscillatory process with amplitude a_l. Let k in the given case denote the gain factor of the regulator. The graph of Fig. 275a shows that oscillations arise in the system with $k > k_b$. It is natural to draw the conclusion that in the region $0 < k < k_b$ (where a periodic solution does not exist) the given regulation system will be stable, as shown in Fig. 275a by the vertical arrow.

A similar conclusion for the region $0 \leqslant k \leqslant k_b$ may be made in the case of the unstable periodic solution in Fig. 275b and in the presence of two periodic solutions in Fig. 275c, one of which is stable, the other unstable. If self-oscillation is observed in the region $0 \leqslant k \leqslant k_b$, as shown in Fig. 275d, it is natural to assume that the region $k > k_b$ will be a region of instability of the given linear system.

Finally, if no periodic solutions are obtained for the given non-linear system for any values of its parameters in the simplest case when the system contains a non-linear circuit without hysteresis with characteristic $x_2 = F(x_1)$, from the geometric illustration of finding self-oscillation (see above) we find that the Mikhailov curve will either enclose the origin of coordinates for each value of a or will not enclose it for any value of a. From this it is frequently possible to conclude that in the first case the given non-linear system is stable while in the second unstable.

All these estimates must, of course be critically thought out each time, or, if possible, the Liapunov theorems should be used. A reliable test will also be plotting of the transient response curve (see Chapter XVIII).

63. Examples

Let us consider several examples of applying the method described in the preceding section.

Example 1. Let us find the influence of a limited linear motor characteristic on the processes in a servomechanism. Let the servo-

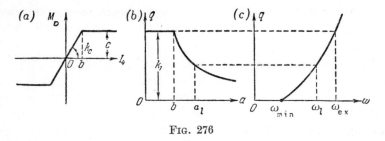

FIG. 276

mechanism be constructed according to the diagram of Fig. 128 but without the differentiating device. The motor characteristic has a saturated type non-linearity (Fig. 276a). The remaining elements of the system are linear. Then the equation of the controlled object with motor for free motion of the system $f(t) = 0$ in place of (26.6) takes the form

$$(T_1 p + 1) p \beta = c' F(I_4),$$

where $F(I_4)$ is defined by the graph of Fig. 276a. Applying to the right-hand side of this equation the formula for harmonic linearisation (61.42) with the substitution $c = bk_c$, we obtain the approximate equation of the controlled object with motor in the form

$$(T_1 p + 1) p\beta = q(a) I_4 , \qquad (63.1)$$

where

$$q(a) = k_1 = c'k_c \quad \text{for} \quad a \leqslant b ,$$
$$q(a) = \frac{2}{\pi} k_1 \left(\sin^{-1} \frac{b}{a} + \frac{b}{a} \sqrt{1 - \frac{b^2}{a^2}} \right) \quad \text{for} \quad a > b , \Bigg\} \qquad (63.2)$$

as shown graphically in Fig. 276d. Here a denotes the amplitude of oscillations of the quantity I_4.

The general equation of the remaining part of the servomechanism (without the differentiating device), neglecting the inductance of the motor armature, from (54.10) will be

$$(T_3 p + 1) I_4 = -[k + (T_3 p + 1) k_6 p]\beta , \qquad (63.3)$$

where

$$k = \frac{k_2 k_4 k_5}{k_0} .$$

In (54.10) we take $\alpha = 0$, since we are investigating here free motion of the system. On the basis of (63.1) and (63.3) we obtain the characteristic equation

$$(T_1 z + 1)(T_3 z + 1) z + q(a)[k + (T_3 z + 1) k_6 z] = 0 . \qquad (63.4)$$

After reducing the left-hand side to the form $a_0 z^3 + a_1 z^2 + a_2 z + a_3$ and substituting $z = i\omega$ we obtain the expression for the M.khailov curve $L(i\tilde{\omega}) = X(\tilde{\omega}) + iY(\tilde{\omega})$, where

$$X(\tilde{\omega}) = kq(a) - [T_1 + T_3 + T_3 + T_3 k_6 q(a)]\tilde{\omega}^2 , \Bigg\}$$
$$Y(\tilde{\omega}) = [1 + k_6 q(a)]\tilde{\omega} - T_1 T_3 \tilde{\omega}^3 . \qquad (63.5)$$

We shall now explain the influence of the parameter k (the overall gain factor) on oscillations in the system.

Equating, according to (62.6), expressions (63.5) to zero (putting $\tilde{\omega} = \omega_l$, $a = a_l$), we find from the second equation

$$q(a_l) = \frac{T_1 T_3 \omega_l^2 - 1}{k_6} , \qquad (63.6)$$

and from the first

$$k = \left[\frac{T_1 + T_3}{q(a_l)} + T_3 k_6 \right] \omega_l^2 . \qquad (63.7)$$

Formula (63.6) gives the graph shown in Fig. 276c, where

$$\omega_{\min} = \frac{1}{\sqrt{T_1 T_3}}, \qquad \omega_w = \sqrt{\frac{1 + k_1 k_6}{T_1 T_3}}. \tag{63.8}$$

The graphs in Fig. 276b and c define the relation between the amplitude a_l and the frequency ω_l of the periodic solution in the given system.

Let us find the dependence of a_l on the magnitude of k. For this, taking various ω_l, we take from the graph of Fig. 276 corresponding values of a_l and from formula (63.7) we calculate k. The result is

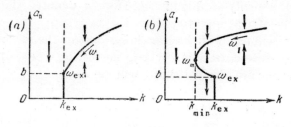

Fig. 277

the graph $a_l(k)$ of the type of Fig. 277a or 277b. To determine in which cases they occur, we find $k_{\min}$. Differentiating (63.7) with respect to ω_l, taking into account (63.6) and equating the result to zero, we obtain the corresponding value of ω_m in the form

$$\omega_m^2 = \frac{1}{T_1 T_3}\left(1 + \sqrt{1 + \frac{T_1}{T_3}}\right), \tag{63.9}$$

where $k_{\min}$ is found by substituting ω_m in (63.6) and (63.7).

It is obvious that if $\omega_m > \omega_B$, then $k_{\min}$ does not exist and the first case in Fig. 277 occurs while with $\omega_m < \omega_B$, the second. Comparing (63.9) and (63.8), we conclude that for a system in which the parameters satisfy the condition

$$k_1 k_6 \leqslant \sqrt{1 + \frac{T_1}{T_3}}, \tag{63.10}$$

the graph in Fig. 277a applies while for a system with parameters

$$k_1 k_6 > \sqrt{1 + \frac{T_1}{T_3}} \tag{63.11}$$

Let us investigate the stability of the periodic solution according to criterion (62.33). For this we first find from (63.5) the expressions

$$\left.\left(\frac{\partial X}{\partial \tilde{\omega}}\right)\right|_l = 1 + k_6 q(a_l) - 3T_1 T_3 \omega_l^2$$

$$= -2T_1 T_2 \omega_l^2 < 0 \; ,$$

$$\left.\left(\frac{\partial Y}{\partial \tilde{\omega}}\right)\right|_l = -2[T_1 + T_2 k q(a_l)] \omega_l$$

$$= -2T_1 \omega_l (1 + T_2^2 \omega_l^2) > 0 \; ,$$

$$\left(\frac{\partial X}{\partial a}\right) = (k - T_3 k_6 \omega_l^2)\left(\frac{dq}{da}\right)_l$$

$$= \frac{(T_1 + T_3)\,\omega_l^2}{q(a_l)}\left(\frac{dq}{da}\right)_l < 0 \; ,$$

$$\left(\frac{\partial Y}{\partial a}\right)_l = k_6 \omega_l \left(\frac{dq}{da}\right)_l < 0 \; ,$$

$$(63.12)$$

since from the graph of Fig. 276*b* the derivative dq/da is negative.

It is easily verified that with $\omega > \omega_m$, where ω_m is defined by formula (63.9), criterion (62.33) is satisfied while with $\omega < \omega_m$ it is not satisfied. From this we conclude that all periodic solutions in Fig. 277*a* are stable (i.e. correspond to self-oscillations). The vertical arrows in Fig. 277*a* show that the transient solutions with larger and smaller amplitudes converge to the given periodic solution. In Fig. 277*b* only the upper branch of the curve (above the point ω_m) corresponds to stable periodic solutions, i.e. self-oscillations, while the lower branch $(\omega_m - \omega_B)$ is unstable.

As already remarked, a_l here denotes the amplitude of oscillations of the quantity I_4. To find the amplitude a_β of oscillations in the regulated quantity β, it is necessary to employ equation (63.1), from which

$$a_\beta = \frac{q(a_l)}{\omega_l \sqrt{T_1^2 \omega_l^2 + 1}}\, a_l = \frac{T_1 T_3 \omega_l^2 - 1}{k_6 \omega_l \sqrt{T_1^2 \omega_l^2 + 1}}\, a_l \; , \qquad (63.13)$$

as the modulus of the corresponding transfer function with $p = i\omega_l$. Here the quantities a_l and ω_l are defined by the graph of Fig. 277*a* or *b*.

Considering that $q(a) = k_1$ with $a = b$ (Fig. 276*b*) we find from formula (63.7) with the substitution $\omega_l = \omega_B$ from (63.8) the value k_B marked in Fig. 277

$$k_B = \left(\frac{T_1 + T_3}{k_1} + T_3 k_6\right)\frac{1 + k_1 k_6}{T_1 T_3} \; .$$

Exactly the same value k is the boundary of stability for a linear system when in place of (63.1) the equation of the controlled object with motor has the linear form $(T_1 p + 1) p\beta = k_1 I_4$. From this it may be concluded that in the case (63.10), to which the graph of

Fig. 277a applies, the given non-linear system remains stable in the same region as the linear system, but has in addition a steady-state oscillatory regime there where the linear system is unstable. Consequently, limitation of the linear characteristic in the form of saturation in the motor (Fig. 276a) limits the oscillation of the system occuring with $k > k_B$ in the linear system. This is also observed in practice.

In the case (63.11), for which the graph defining the oscillations has the form of Fig. 277b, self-oscillation may appear with $k < k_B$ (but $> k_m$), i.e. before reaching the boundary of stability of the linear system. But in this case, as is evident from Fig. 277b, with small initial amplitudes of the transient (below the curve $\omega_m \omega_B$) the equilibrium state remains stable. Here in the region of parameters $k_m < k < k_B$ (Fig. 277b) we have as it were two limiting cycles (Fig. 63c) and in the region $k_B < k < \infty$, one.

The case represented in Fig. 277b is termed "stiff excitation" of self-oscillation. This excitation of oscillation before reaching the boundary of stability is possible, as is evident from (63.11), only with fairly high factor k_6, which, in essence, is the coefficient of transient feedback. In the absence of such coupling this phenomenon cannot occur.

In Fig. 278a and b graphs are given for the oscillation frequency ω_l as a function of the parameter k for the cases represented in Fig. 277a and b respectively.

Example 2. In the same servomechanism we take into account, in addition to the preceding, a zone of insensitivity, concentrating both non-linearities conventionally in the motor characteristic (Fig. 279a). Analogously to the above we obtain the equation of the controlled object with motor in the form

$$(T_1 p + 1) p\beta = q(a) I_4, \tag{63.14}$$

where from formulae (61.41), (61.40), (61.39) we have:

$$
\left.
\begin{aligned}
& q(a) = k_1 \left[1 - \frac{2}{\pi} \left(\sin^{-1}\frac{b_1}{a} + 2\frac{b_1}{a}\sqrt{1 - \frac{b_1^2}{a^2}} \right) \right] \\
& \qquad \text{with} \quad b_1 \leqslant a \leqslant b_2, \\
& q(a) = k_1 \frac{2}{\pi}(u_2 - u_1 + \sin 2u_2 - \sin 2u_1) \\
& \qquad \text{with} \quad a \geqslant b_2, \\
& u_1 = \sin^{-1}\frac{b_1}{a}, \quad u_2 = \sin^{-1}\frac{b_2}{a};
\end{aligned}
\right\} \tag{63.15}
$$

these formulae are represented graphically in Fig. 279b. The amplitude of oscillation of the quantity I_4 is, as before, denoted by a.

The characteristic equation has the previous form (63.4), just as expression (63.5) and the relations (63.6) and (63.7) following from them, from which

$$q(a_l) = \frac{T_1 T_3 \omega_l^2 - 1}{k_6} ,$$

(63.16)

$$k = \frac{T_1 + T_1 T_3^2 \omega_l^2}{T_1 T_3^2 \omega_l^2 - 1} k_6 \omega_l^2 .$$

(63.17)

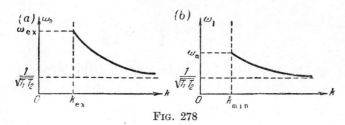

FIG. 278

We shall assign various values to ω_l. To each value of ω_l, from formula (63.16) and the graph (Fig. 279b) there correspond two values of amplitude a_l, one in the interval $b_1 < a_l < b_2$ and the other $a_l > b_2$. Then, since in the graph $0 \leqslant q \leqslant q_{max}$, from (63.16)

$$(\omega_l)_{min} \leqslant \omega_l \leqslant (\omega_l)_{max} ,$$

(63.18)

where

$$(\omega_l)_{min}^2 = \frac{1}{T_1 T_3} , \qquad (\omega_l)_{max}^2 = \frac{1 + k_6 q_{max}}{T_1 T_3} ,$$

(63.19)

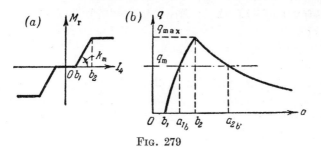

FIG. 279

and q_{max} is the value of $q(a)$ at $a = b_2$; it is taken from the graph (Fig. 279b) or calculated from (63.15) according to the formula

$$q_{max} = k_1 \left[1 - \frac{2}{\pi} \left(\sin^{-1} \frac{b_1}{b_2} + 2 \frac{b_1}{b_2} \sqrt{1 - \frac{b_1^2}{b_2^2}} \right) \right] ,$$

(63.20)

(for the significance of b_1 and b_2 see Fig. 279b).

Substituting now various values of ω_l (in the interval (63.18)) in the expression for k (63.17), we see that with $\omega_l = (\omega_l)_{min}$ we obtain $k = \infty$, while with increase of ω the value of k decreases.

Let us determine if it decreases monotonically or if an intermediate minimum in the value of k is possible. Testing expression (63.17) for a minimum (by equating the derivative $dk/d\omega_l$ to zero) gives the result that a minimum is possible with

$$(\omega_l)_m^2 = \frac{1}{T_1 T_3}\left(\sqrt{1+\frac{T_1}{T_3}}\right), \qquad (63.21)$$

where from (63.17) we obtain

$$k_{min} = \frac{k_6}{T_1}\left(1+\sqrt{1+\frac{T_1}{T_3}}\right)^2 . \qquad (63.22)$$

Substituting the value (63.21) in formula (63.16) gives

$$q_m = \frac{1}{k_6}\sqrt{1+\frac{T_1}{T_3}} . \qquad (63.23)$$

Further it is necessary to distinguish two cases:

(1) the system parameters are such that the value q_m calculated from formula (63.23) is greater than q_{max} on the graph (Fig. 279b);

(2) the parameters of the system are such that the given value q_m is less than q_{max}.

In the first case (when $q_m > q_{max}$) from the graph (Fig. 279b) the value q_m does not correspond to any real amplitude of oscillation. Consequently, the minimum k does not exist and there is a monotonic k with increase of ω_l. Assigning arbitrary values to ω_l, we calculate for each of them from formula (63.17) the value of k (abscissa of the graph in Fig. 280a) from formula (63.16) the quantity q, for which we take from the graph of Fig. 279b two values of amplitude $a_l(b_1 < a_l < b_2$ and $a_l > b_2)$. We obtain as a result two curves in the graph of Fig. 280a, representing the dependence of amplitude and frequency of the periodic solutions on the coefficient k. Here from (63.17) with the substitution ω_{max} (63.19) we have for Fig. 280:

$$k_b = \frac{1+k_6 q_{max}}{q_{max}}\left[\frac{1}{T_3}+\frac{1}{T_1}(1+k_6 q_{max})\right] . \qquad (63.24)$$

In the second case (when $q_m < q_{max}$) a minimum k exists, where according to Fig. 279b two values of amplitude a_{1b} and a_{2b} correspond to it. The corresponding points a_{1b} and a_{2b} are also shown in the graph of Fig. 280b. The magnitude of k_b is defined from formula (63.22), i.e. for Fig. 280b we have

$$k_b = k_{min} = \frac{k_6}{T_1}\left(1+\sqrt{1+\frac{T_1}{T_3}}\right)^2 . \qquad (63.25)$$

Assigning values to ω_l and calculating the coefficient k from formula (63.17) we obtain the curves $Aa_{1b}C$ and $Ba_{2b}C$, where the amplitude a_b is defined from formula (63.16) and from the graph in Fig. 279b. At the point C, where $\omega_l = (\omega_l)_{max}$, from (63.19) and (63.17) we have:

$$k_n = \frac{1 + k_6 q_{max}}{q_{max}} \left[\frac{1}{T_3} + \frac{1}{T_1} (1 + k_6 q_{max}) \right]. \qquad (63.26)$$

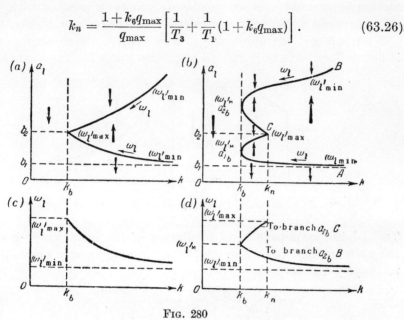

Fig. 280

Let us investigate the stability of all the periodic solutions found. The expressions for the partial derivatives figuring in (62.33) will have the form (63.12), but their signs will differ. Thus, on the basis of (63.12) and the graph of Fig. 279b we have:

$$\left(\frac{\partial X}{\partial a} \right)_l > 0 \quad \text{and} \quad \left(\frac{\partial Y}{\partial a} \right) > 0 \quad \text{with} \quad b_1 < a < b_2, \qquad (63.27)$$

$$\left(\frac{\partial X}{\partial a} \right)_l < 0 \quad \text{and} \quad \left(\frac{\partial Y}{\partial a} \right)_l < 0 \quad \text{with} \quad a > b_2. \qquad (63.28)$$

This leads to the following results. The lower curve in Fig. 280a corresponds to unstable periodic solutions, the upper, to stable. The same relates to the curves $a_{1b}A$ and $a_{2b}B$ in Fig. 280b. But in this case there are also two additional curves $a_{1b}C$ and $a_{2b}C$, where the lower of these two additional curves corresponds to stable periodic solutions while the upper to unstable. All these relations are indicated by vertical arrows in Fig. 280.

In the result, as is evident from Fig. 280, the given servomechanism with non-linear drive has a region of stable equilibrium: $k < k_b$. Outside this region with $k > k_b$ it has small-signal stability for initial amplitudes of oscillation located below the lower curve in Fig. 280. If the initial amplitudes of oscillation are above this lower curve, self-oscillation is established in the system, with amplitude and frequency defined by the upper curve in Fig. 280. In addition, for certain relations among the parameters of the system the formation of an additional self-oscillatory process is possible with lower amplitude and higher frequency, defined by the curve $a_{1b}C$ (Fig. 280b).

We recall that the amplitude of oscillation in the present example is not defined for the regulated quantity β but for the quantity I_4.

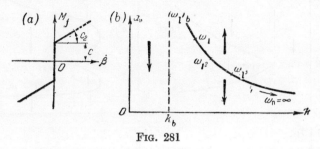

FIG. 281

To find the amplitude a_β of oscillation of the quantity β, knowing the values a_l and ω_l in Fig. 280, it is necessary according to (63.14) to employ the formula

$$a_\beta = \frac{a_l q(a_l)}{|(T_1 p + 1)p|_{p=i\omega}} = \frac{a_l q(a_l)}{\omega_l \sqrt{T_1^2 \omega_l^2 + 1}}. \tag{63.29}$$

Similarly it is possible to define the amplitude of the first harmonic of oscillation of other variables in other elements of the system.

In Fig. 280c and d are shown graphs for the value of the oscillation frequency ω_l for the cases shown in Fig. 280a and b respectively.

Example 3. Let us now consider a servomechanism with linear motor characteristic but we shall take into account dry friction simultaneously with linear (Fig. 281a). The equation of the controlled object with motor now has the form (54.8). Here two cases are possible: (1) oscillation without stopping, when the conditions of the first of equations (54.8) are realised; (2) oscillations with stopping, when the two equations (54.8) apply alternately. Let us consider the first case and define the conditions of its realisation.

Thus, we write the first of equations (54.8), dividing it by c_2, in the form

$$T_1 \ddot{\beta} + \dot{\beta} + k_7 \cdot \operatorname{sign} \dot{\beta} = k_1 I_4 , \quad k_7 = \frac{c}{c_2} , \quad k_1 = \frac{c_1}{c_2} , \quad T_1 = \frac{J}{c_2} , \tag{63.30}$$

with the condition that

$$|I_4| > \frac{k_7}{k_1} \quad \text{with} \quad \dot{\beta} = 0 . \tag{63.31}$$

Let us put $x = \dot{\beta}$. Then this equation will be:

$$(T_1 p + 1)x + F(x) = k_1 I_4, \qquad x = p\beta, \tag{63.32}$$

where

$$F(x) = k_7 \cdot \operatorname{sign} x. \tag{63.33}$$

Since motion is assumed without stopping, the non-linear function (63.33) is subjected to harmonic linearisation as a relay characteristic and on the basis of formula (61.38), putting

$$x = a \sin \omega t,$$

we obtain

$$F(x) \approx \frac{4k_7}{\pi a} x, \tag{63.34}$$

where a is the amplitude of velocity oscillations $x = p\beta$. The amplitude of oscillation of the angle β will be:

$$a_\beta = \frac{a}{\omega} \left(\beta = -\frac{a}{\omega} \cos \omega t \right).$$

(63.34) represents the well-known formula for linearisation of dry friction (see Section 13). Let us find the conditions for which it is here valid. According to (63.31) and (63.32) we have

$$|I_4|_{\dot{\beta}=0} = \left| \frac{T_1 \dot{x}}{k_1} \right|_{x=0} = \left| \frac{T_1 a\omega \cos \omega t}{k_1} \right|_{\sin \omega t = 0} = \frac{T_1 a\omega}{k_1} > \frac{k_7}{k_1},$$

from which

$$a\omega > \frac{k_7}{T_1} \quad \text{or} \quad a_\beta \omega^2 > \frac{k_7}{T_1}, \tag{63.35}$$

which is the condition under which the further solution is valid.

The characteristic equation of the entire closed system from (63.32), (63.34) and (54.10) takes the form

$$(T_3 z + 1)\frac{4k_7}{\pi a} z + k_1(T_3 z + 1)k_6 z + k_1 k + (T_1 z + 1)(T_3 z + 1)z = 0.$$

In the expression for the Mikhailov curve $L(i\tilde{\omega}) = X(\omega) + iY(\omega)$ we have in the present case:

$$\left. \begin{aligned}
X(\tilde{\omega}) &= k_1 k - \left(\frac{4k_7}{\pi a} T_3 + k_1 k_6 T_3 + T_3 + T_1 \right) \tilde{\omega}^2, \\
Y(\tilde{\omega}) &= \left(\frac{4k_7}{\pi a} + k_1 k_6 + 1 \right) \tilde{\omega} - T_1 T_3 \tilde{\omega}^3.
\end{aligned} \right\} \tag{63.36}$$

Equating them to zero, we obtain two equations for finding periodic solutions. To investigate the influence of the coefficient k

on the system dynamics, we express the quantities k and a_l in terms of ω_l from these two equations:

$$k = \frac{T_1 \omega_l^2}{k_1}(T_3^2 \omega_l^2 + 1), \qquad a_l = \frac{4 k_7}{\pi(T_1 T_3 \omega_l^2 - 1 - k_1 k_6)}. \qquad (63.37)$$

We note that $a_l = \infty$ with

$$(\omega_l)_b^2 = \frac{1 + k_1 k_6}{T_1 T_3}, \qquad k_b = \frac{1 + k_1 k_6}{k_1}\left(\frac{1 + k_1 k_6}{T_1} + \frac{1}{T_3}\right). \qquad (63.38)$$

Varying ω_l in the interval $(\omega_l)_b \leqslant \omega_l \leqslant +\infty$, we plot the graph $a_l = f(k)$ according to formulae (63.37), as shown in Fig. 281b. The condition for which this solution is valid was expressed by inequality (63.35). Substituting in it the values $a = a_l$ and $\omega = \omega_l$ from (63.37), we bring it to the form

$$\frac{4\sqrt{2 T_1 b}}{\pi[b - 2 T_3(1 + k_1 k_6)]} > 1, \qquad (63.39)$$

where

$$b = \sqrt{T_1^2 + 4 k_1 k T_1 T_3^2} - T_1.$$

To study the stability of this periodic solution we find from (63.36):

$$\left(\frac{\partial X}{\partial a}\right)_l > 0, \qquad \left(\frac{\partial Y}{\partial a}\right)_l < 0, \qquad \left(\frac{\partial X}{\partial \tilde{\omega}}\right)_l < 0, \qquad \left(\frac{\partial V}{\partial \tilde{\omega}}\right)_l < 0.$$

Criterion (62.33) is not satisfied, which signifies that the given periodic solution is unstable. This is shown by the conventional vertical arrows in Fig. 281b.

It is easy to verify that the value k_b (63.38) coincides with the boundary of stability of a linear system without dry friction. Consequently, the addition of dry friction somewhat broadens the region of stability of the system but in a very peculiar way, namely: instability of the periodic solution found signifies that with $k > k_b$ and satisfaction of condition (63.39) the system may be small-signal stable (with initial conditions which give initial amplitudes of transient oscillation in the system lying below the curve in Fig. 281b). However the system is large-signal unstable (with initial amplitudes of oscillation above this curve). This may be explained physically by the fact that at large amplitudes and, consequently, at high velocities the damping effect of dry friction, which has the same magnitude at any velocity, becomes negligible, as a result of which the system is unstable in the same way as it was in the absence of dry friction.

When (63.39) is not satisfied, investigation of both equations (54.8) simultaneously is necessary (this corresponds to non-linearity of the second class, since it involves both quantities: input I_4 and output β). Here the oscillations of angle β will take place with stopping. This is a more complicated problem.

Example 4. Let there act in the same system not dry friction but resistance to motion of object proportional to the square of the velocity (simultaneously with linear), as in Fig. 282a. The

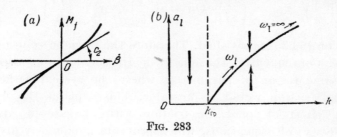

FIG. 283

equation of the controlled object with motor has in this case the form (55.11). Let us rewrite here in a different way by analogy to the preceding example:

$$(T_1 p + 1)x + F(x) = k_1 I_4 , \qquad x = p\beta , \qquad (63.40)$$

where

$$T_1 = \frac{J}{c_2} , \qquad k_1 = \frac{c_1}{c_2} , \qquad F(x) = k_8 x^2 \cdot \operatorname{sign} x , \qquad k_8 = \frac{c_3}{c_2} .$$

Putting $x = a \sin \omega t$, from the formulae of harmonic linearisation (61.17) we obtain:

$$q(a) = \frac{1}{\pi a} \int_0^{2\pi} k_8 a^2 \sin^2 u (\operatorname{sign} \sin u) \sin u \, du$$

$$= \frac{1}{\pi a} \int_0^{\pi} k_8 a^2 \sin^3 u \, du - \frac{1}{\pi a} \int_0^{2\pi} k_8 a^2 \sin^3 u \, du = \frac{8 k_8 a}{3\pi} .$$

Consequently

$$F(x) \approx \frac{8 k_8 a}{3\pi} x .$$

Setting up the characteristic equation as before, we come to the expression

$$\left. \begin{aligned} X(\tilde{\omega}) &= k_1 k - \left(T_1 + T_3 + k_1 k_6 T_3 + \frac{8 k_8 a}{3\pi} T_3 \right) \tilde{\omega}^2 , \\ Y(\tilde{\omega}) &= \left(1 + k_1 k_6 + \frac{8 k_8 a}{3\pi} \right) \tilde{\omega} - T_1 T_3 \tilde{\omega}^3 . \end{aligned} \right\} \qquad (63.41)$$

Equating them to zero, we find

$$k = \frac{T_1 \omega_l^2}{k_1} (T_3^2 \omega_l^2 + 1) , \qquad a_l = \frac{3\pi}{8 k_8} (T_1 T_3 \omega_l^2 - 1 - k_1 k_6) . \qquad (63.42)$$

The limiting values of ω_l and k coincide here with the above (63.38) but they no longer correspond to $a_l = \infty$ but to $a_l = 0$. As a result we obtain the graph for determining the amplitude and frequency of the periodic solution, represented in Fig. 282b.

From (63.41) we have

$$\left(\frac{\partial X}{\partial a}\right)_l < 0 \, , \quad \left(\frac{\partial Y}{\partial a}\right)_l > 0 \, , \quad \left(\frac{\partial X}{\partial \tilde{\omega}}\right)_l < 0 \, , \quad \left(\frac{\partial Y}{\partial \tilde{\omega}}\right)_l < 0 \, .$$

Criterion (62.33) is satisfied. Therefore the periodic solution found is stable. Consequently, the quadratic friction leads to oscillations in the same region of parameters where the system without this additional friction would be unstable. This explains the increased damping effect of quadratic friction with increase in amplitude (and velocity) of oscillations, which prevents unbounded divergence of the system. We note that passage of the form of resistance to the motion of the object at high velocities from linear to quadratic is fully realistic.

The amplitude and frequency of oscillations are here defined by the graph (Fig. 282b) or formulae (63.42), where the amplitude of oscillation of the angle β will be $a_\beta = a_l/\omega_l$.

Example 5. In the same servomechanism let it be required to take into account the effect of backlash in the mechanical transmission between the motor and the controlled object (shown schematically in Fig. 237) with linear motor characteristic and linear friction. In the oscillatory processes which interest us here the dependence between the angles of rotation β (after the backlash) and β_1 (before the backlash) will have the non-linear form shown in Fig. 237b, where b is the half-width of the backlash. Aside from this non-linear dependence a second non-linearity is present (54.11). Assuming that the moment of inertia of the controlled object J_1 is large in comparison with the reduced moment of inertia of the motor, we shall put in equation (54.11) $T_1' = 0$.

The first non-linearity (Fig. 237b) after harmonic linearisation with $\beta_1 = a \sin \omega t$, from formula (61.50) takes the form

$$\beta = \left[q(a) - \frac{q_1(a)}{\omega} p \right] \beta_1 , \tag{63.43}$$

where $q(a)$ and $q_1(a)$ are defined from formulae (61.47) in which it is necessary to take $k = 1$ (since the characteristic of Fig. 237b has a slope of 45°), namely:

$$q(a) = \frac{1}{\pi} \left(\frac{\pi}{2} + u_1 + \frac{1}{2} \sin 2u_1 \right) , \\ q_1(a) = \frac{1}{\pi} \cos^2 u_1 = \frac{4b}{a}\left(1 - \frac{b}{a} \right) , \tag{63.44}$$

where

$$u_1 = \sin^{-1}\left(1 - \frac{2b}{a}\right). \qquad (63.45)$$

The second non-linearity (54.11) is written in the form $F(\ddot{\beta}_1, \dot{\beta}_1)$ $= k_1 I_4$. It is subject to harmonic linearisation according to formulae (61.20) and (61.21) also with $\beta_1 = a\sin\omega t$. The relation between

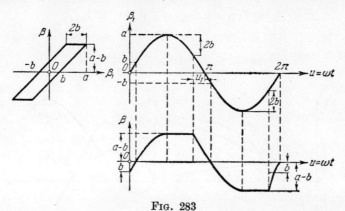

FIG. 283

the angles β_1 and β is shown in Fig. 283. From the lower graph in Fig. 283 and formula (54.11) it is evident that

$$F(\ddot{\beta}_1, \dot{\beta}_1) = T_1\ddot{\beta}_1 + \dot{\beta}_1$$

with

$$0 < u < \frac{\pi}{2}, \quad \pi - u_1 < u < \frac{3\pi}{2}, \quad 2\pi - u_1 < u < 2\pi$$

and further (assuming that $T_1' = 0$)

$$F(\ddot{\beta}_1, \dot{\beta}_1) = \dot{\beta}_1$$

with

$$\frac{\pi}{2} < u < \pi - u_1, \quad \frac{3\pi}{2} < u < 2\pi - u_1.$$

The condition of absence of the constant component (61.22) is here satisfied, while the second of formulae (61.21) takes the form

$$q_1(a, \omega) = \frac{1}{\pi a}\left[\int_0^{2\pi} (a\omega\cos u)\cos u\, du + \right.$$

$$+ \int_0^{\pi/2} T_1(-a\omega^2\sin u)\cos u\, du + \int_{\pi - u_1}^{3\pi/2} T_1(-a\omega^2\sin u)\cos u\, du +$$

$$\left. + \int_{2\pi - u_1}^{2\pi} T_1(-a\omega^2\sin u)\cos u\, du\right];$$

$q_2(a, \omega)$ is defined similarly. Integrating and equating the results to the expressions (63.44) we obtain

$$q_1(a, \omega) = \omega - q_1(a)\, T_1 \omega^2 ,$$

where $q_1(a)$ is the same as in formulae (63.44). As a result in place of the non-linear equation (54.11) with $T_1' = 0$ we have

$$[q_2(a)\, T_1 p + 1 - q_1(a)\, T_1 \omega]\, p \beta_1 = k_1 I_4 , \qquad (63.46)$$

where

$$q_2(a) = \frac{1}{\pi}\left(\frac{\pi}{2} + u_1 - \frac{1}{2}\sin 2u_1\right), \qquad (63.47)$$

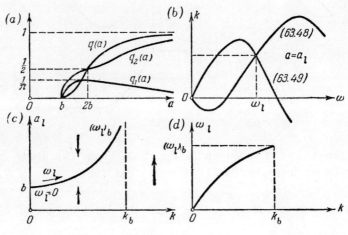

FIG. 284

and $q_1(a)$, u_1 are the same as in (63.44) and (63.45). In Fig. 284a are shown graphs for the magnitudes of the coefficients $q(a)$, $q_1(a)$, $q_2(a)$.

On the basis of (63.43), (63.46) and the linear part (54.10) we come to the characteristic equation

$$(T_3 z + 1)[q_2(a)\, T_1 z + 1 - q_1(a)\, T_1 \omega]z +$$
$$+ k_1[(T_3 z + 1)k_6 z + k]\left[q(a) - \frac{q_1(a)}{\omega}z\right] = 0 .$$

Consequently, in the Mikhailov curve expression we have

$$X(\tilde{\omega}) = k_1 k q(a) - [T_3 - T_3 T_1 \omega q_1(a) + T_1 q_2(a) + k_1 k_6 T_3 q(a)]\tilde{\omega}^2 ,$$

$$Y(\tilde{\omega}) = \left[1 - T_1 q_1(a)\,\omega + k_1 k_6 q(a) - k_1 k \frac{q_1(a)}{\omega}\right]\tilde{\omega} -$$
$$- \left[T_1 T_3 q_2(a) - k_1 k_6 T_3 \frac{q_1(a)}{\omega}\right]\tilde{\omega}^3 .$$

To investigate the influence of the parameter k on the free oscillations of the system we equate this expression to zero, substituting $\tilde{\omega} = \omega$ and we express the quantity k in each of them individually:

$$k = \frac{k_6 q_1(a)}{q(a)} \omega + \left[\frac{T_1 q_2(a)}{k_1 q(a)} + T_3 k_6 + \frac{T_3}{k_1 q(a)}\right] \omega^2 - $$
$$- \frac{T_1 T_3 q_1(a)}{k_1 q(a)} \omega^2, \qquad (63.48)$$

$$k = \left[\frac{k_6 q(a)}{q_1(a)} + \frac{1}{k_1 q_1(a)}\right] \omega - \left(\frac{T_1}{k_1} - T_3 k_6\right) \omega^2 - \frac{T_1 T_3 q_2(a)}{k_1 q_1(a)} \omega^3. \qquad (63.49)$$

Assigning various values $a = a_l$, for each value we plot from these equations two curves $k(\omega)$ (Fig. 284b). Their point of intersection gives the corresponding values ω_l and k. As a result it is possible to plot the graphs (Fig. 284c and d) of the amplitude a_l and frequency ω_l of the periodic solution in dependence on the parameter k (each pair of curves as in Fig. 284b gives a single point on each of the graphs of Fig. 284c and d).

At $a = \infty$, as is evident from Fig. 284a, we have $q(a) = q_2(a) = 1$ and $q_1(a) = 0$. Therefore we find from the expressions $X(\omega_l) = 0$ and $Y(\omega_l) = 0$:

$$(\omega_l)_b^2 = \frac{1 + k_1 k_6}{T_1 T_3}, \qquad k_b = \frac{(1 + k_1 k_6)(T_1 + T_3 k_1 k_6)}{x_1 T_1 T_3}, \qquad (63.50)$$

where along the curve in Fig. 284c the frequency ω_l varies in the interval $0 \leqslant \omega_l \leqslant (\omega_l)_b$.

To investigate the stability of the periodic solution here, in contrast to the preceding examples, we employ the method of averaging the periodic coefficients discussed in Section 62. The linear part of the system from (54.10) corresponds to an equation in deviations

$$(T_3 p + 1) \Delta I_4 = -[(T_3 p + 1) k_6 p + k] \Delta \beta. \qquad (63.51)$$

The first non-linearity (Fig. 283) gives an equation in deviations

$$\Delta \beta = \varkappa(a) \Delta \beta_1, \qquad (63.52)$$

where in accordance with formula (62.28) the coefficient $\varkappa(a)$ is defined as the average value over a period $\partial \beta / \partial \beta_1$. The quantity $\partial \beta / \partial \beta_1 = 1$ with motion of the system, when $\beta = \beta_1 + b$ and $\partial \beta / \partial \beta_1 = 0$ when the system is stationary, as shown in Fig. 285c (with $\beta_1 = a \sin \omega t$). On this basis we obtain

$$\varkappa(a) = \frac{\pi + 2u_1}{2\pi} = \frac{1}{2} + \frac{u_1}{\pi}, \qquad (63.53)$$

The second non-linearity (54.11) with $T'_i = 0$ corresponds to an equation in deviations

$$[\varkappa_1(a)p + 1]p\Delta\beta_1 = k_1\Delta I_4 \,, \tag{63.54}$$

where the coefficient $\varkappa_1(a)$ as the average value of the derivative $\partial F/\partial\dot\beta_1$ (where F denotes the left-hand side of the non-linear equation (54.11)) according to Fig. 285d, will be

$$\varkappa_1(a) = T_1 \frac{\varkappa + 2u_1}{2\pi} = T_1\varkappa(a) \,. \tag{63.55}$$

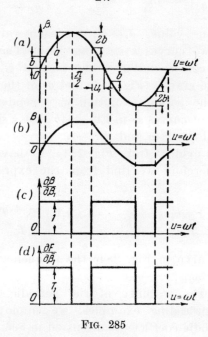

FIG. 285

On the basis of equations (63.51), (63.52), (63.54) we obtain the characteristic equation

$$T_1 T_3\varkappa(a)p^3 + [T_1\varkappa(a) + T_3 + k_1k_6T_3\varkappa(a)]p^2 +$$
$$+ [1 + k_1k_6\varkappa(a)]p + k_1k\varkappa(a) = 0 \,.$$

The condition of stability of the periodic solution from this, applying the Vyshnegradskii criterion (29.3), may be written in the form

$$k < \frac{\left[T_1 + \dfrac{T_3}{\varkappa(a)} + k_1k_6T_3\right]\left[\dfrac{1}{\varkappa(a)} + k_1k_6\right]}{k_1T_1T_3} \,. \tag{63.56}$$

It is everywhere satisfied since from (63.53) and (63.45) we have $0 \leqslant \varkappa(a) \leqslant 1$, as a result of which the right-hand side of inequality

(63.56) is greater than the quantity k_b (63.50) while the value k in Fig. 284c is limited by the condition $k < k_b$.

In addition, it is easily seen that the quantity k_b (63.50) coincides with the boundary of stability of the linear system (without backlash). Consequently, from the graph of Fig. 284c the backlash in the given servomechanism establishes self-oscillation in that region where the system without backlash was stable; the region of instability of the system remains without change.

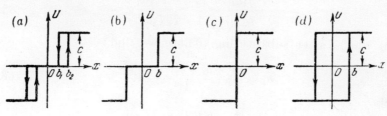

FIG. 286

Example 6. Let there exist a relay temperature regulation system (Fig. 27), described according to Section 53 by the equations (without feedback and neglecting the constant T_2)

$$
\begin{aligned}
(T_1 p + 1)\theta &= -k_1\xi, & x &= k_2\theta, \\
(T_3 p + 1)p\xi &= k_3 V, & V &= F(x),
\end{aligned}
\right\} \tag{63.57}
$$

where $F(x)$ is the relay characteristic shown in Fig. 286a. At the end of this example we shall also take into account time delay in the relay, instead of hysteresis delay.

The harmonic linearisation of the relay characteristic Fig. 286a according to formulae (61.16) and (61.35) gives

$$
V = \left[q(a) - \frac{q_1(a)}{\omega} p \right] x, \tag{63.58}
$$

where

$$
\begin{aligned}
q(a) &= \frac{2c}{\pi a^2}\left(\sqrt{a^2 - b_1^2} + \sqrt{a^2 - b_2^2}\right), \\
q_1(a) &= \frac{2c(b_2 - b_1)}{\pi a^2}.
\end{aligned}
\right\} \tag{63.59}
$$

From equations (63.57) and (63.58) we obtain the following characteristic equation for the closed system:

$$
(T_1 z + 1)(T_3 z + 1)z + k_1 k\left[q(a) - \frac{q_1(a)}{\omega} z \right] = 0,
$$

where

$$
k = k_2 k_3.
$$

From this we obtain the expression for the Mikhailov curve

$$\left.\begin{aligned} X(\tilde{\omega}) &= k_1 k q(a) - (T_1 + T_3)\,\tilde{\omega}^2 , \\ Y(\tilde{\omega}) &= \left[1 - k_1 k\,\frac{q_1(a)}{\omega}\right]\tilde{\omega} - T_1 T_3 \tilde{\omega}^3 . \end{aligned}\right\} \qquad (63.60)$$

Let us investigate the influence of parameter k on the stability and self-oscillations in the given system. Equating (63.60) to zero, with $a = a_l,\ \omega = \tilde{\omega} = \omega_l$, we have:

$$\frac{q(a_l)}{q_1(a_l)} = \frac{(T_1 + T_3)\,\omega_l}{1 - T_1 T_3 \omega_l^2} , \qquad (63.61)$$

from which, after substituting (63.59) we find

$$a_l = \frac{(v^2 + b_1^2 + b_2^2)^2 - 4 b_1^2 b_2^2}{4 z^2} , \qquad (63.62)$$

where

$$v = \frac{(b_2 - b_1)(T_1 + T_3)\,\omega_l}{1 - T_1 T_3 \omega_l^2} .$$

Then from the second equation (63.60) taking into account (63.59) we obtain

$$k = \frac{\pi(1 - T_1 T_3 \omega_l^2)\,\omega_l}{2 c k_1 (b_2 - b_1)}\cdot a_l^2 . \qquad (63.63)$$

From (63.62) and (63.63) it is possible to plot graphs for the amplitude a_l as a function of the parameter k by points corresponding to individual values of frequency ω_l, as was done in the previous examples. At the same time, since k is positive, from (63.63) it is necessary to assign values of ω_l in the interval

$$0 \leqslant \omega_l^2 \leqslant \frac{1}{T_1 T_3} . \qquad (63.64)$$

Let us consider particular cases.

Let the relay have the characteristic of Fig. 286b, where $b_1 = b_2 = b$. For this case we obtain from (63.59)

$$q(a) = \frac{4c}{\pi a^2}\sqrt{a^2 - b^2} , \qquad q_1(a) = 0 . \qquad (63.65)$$

Therefore the second of equations (63.60) gives the constant value of frequency of the periodic solution

$$\omega_l^2 = \frac{1}{T_1 T_3} . \qquad (63.66)$$

Substituting this in the first equation (63.60), taking into account (63.65) we find

$$k = \frac{\pi(T_1 + T_3)\,a_l^2}{4 c k_1 T_1 T_3 \sqrt{a_l^2 - b^2}}\,(b \leqslant a_l \leqslant \infty) . \qquad (63.67)$$

Here $k = \infty$ in two cases: $a_b = b$ and $a_b = \infty$. Let us find $k_{\min}$ from the condition of vanishing of the derivative of k with respect to a_l. We obtain

$$k_{\min} = \frac{\pi b (T_1 + T_3)}{2 c k_1 T_1 T_3} \quad \text{with} \quad a_l = b \sqrt{2}. \tag{63.68}$$

The corresponding graph of a_l as a function of the parameter k is shown in Fig. 287a. For this particular relay characteristic

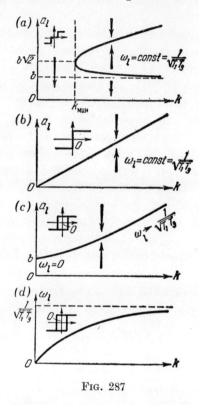

F$_{\text{IG}}$. 287

(Fig. 286b) to investigate the stability we employ criterion (62.33) for which we first find from (63.60) and (63.65)

$$\left(\frac{\partial X}{\partial a}\right)_l = \frac{4 c k_1 k}{\pi a \sqrt{a^2 - b^2}} \left(\frac{2b^2}{a^2} - 1\right)$$

$$\begin{cases} > 0 & \text{for} \quad a < b \sqrt{2} \\ < 0 & \text{for} \quad a > b \sqrt{2} \end{cases}$$

$$\left(\frac{\partial Y}{\partial a}\right)_l = 0 , \quad \left(\frac{\partial y}{\partial \tilde{\omega}}\right)_l < 0 .$$

Consequently, the lower branch of the curve in Fig. 287a corresponds to an unstable periodic solution and the upper to a stable (oscillatory).

In a second particular case let the relay characteristic be ideal (Fig. 286c), i.e. $b_1 = b_2 = b = 0$. Here we obtain the previous constant value ω_l (63.66) and from (63.67) the linear dependence

$$a_l = \frac{4ck_1 T_1 T_3}{\pi(T_1 + T_3)}\, k \,, \tag{63.69}$$

shown in Fig. 287b. Here only self-oscillation is possible: the region of stability of the equilibrium state existing in Fig. 287a here drops out.

As we see, the zone of insensitivity has a stabilising significance for a relay automatic regulation system, where the width of the stability region $(0 \leqslant k \leqslant k_{min})$ from (63.68) is proportional to the width of zone of insensitivity $2b$. Comparison of the given solution, taking into account the inertia of the regulator T_3 with a solution neglecting T_3 shows the importance of taking into account this factor. For example, for a characteristic of the form Fig. 286c neglecting T_3 we find only stability ($a_l = 0$) for arbitrary numerical values of the parameters (which does not actually occur), while taking into account T_3 only self-oscillations (Fig. 287b). For a characteristic of the form of Fig. 286b in place of an unlimited region of stability (neglecting T_3) a strictly limited region of stability is obtained and further a region of self-oscillation with large amplitude with simultaneous existence of small-signal stability (Fig. 287a).

Further, in the third particular case when the relay has a purely hysteresis characteristic (Fig. 286b), i.e. $b_1 = -b_2 = -b$, from (63.59) we have

$$q(a) = \frac{4c}{\pi a^2} \sqrt{a^2 - b^2} \,, \qquad q_1(a) = \frac{4cb}{\pi a^2} \,. \tag{63.70}$$

Then from (63.62) we find

$$a_l^2 = \frac{(1 + T_1^2 \omega_l^2)(1 + T_3^2 \omega_l^2)}{(1 - T_1 T_3 \omega_l^2)^2}\, b^2 \,, \tag{63.71}$$

while from (63.63)

$$k = \frac{\pi b \omega_l (1 + T_1^2 \omega_l^2)(1 + T_3^2 \omega_l^2)}{4ck_1(1 - T_1 T_3 \omega_l^2)} \,. \tag{63.72}$$

The curves in Fig. 287c and d plotted from these formulae define the amplitude and frequency of the periodic solution as functions of the magnitude of the parameter k. We shall here determine the stability of the periodic solution by the method of averaging the periodic coefficients. To calculate the coefficient $\varkappa(a)$ from (62.28) it is necessary to know the derivative of U with respect to x, which, however, becomes infinite at $x = b$, when $\dot{x} > 0$ and at $x = -b$, when $\dot{x} < 0$. To avoid this, we replace the given characteristic

(Fig. 286*d*) by a new one (Fig. 288*a*), from which the given characteristic is obtained by the limiting process $h \to 0$. (For a second method using the delta function, see example 1 in Section 64). For the characteristic in Fig. 288*a* with variation of x according to the function $x = a \sin \omega t$ (Fig. 288*b*) the derivative $\partial U / \partial x$ takes on the value shown in Fig. 288*c*, where

$$u_1 = \sin^{-1} \frac{b}{a}, \qquad u_2 = \sin^{-1} \frac{b+h}{a}. \qquad (63.73)$$

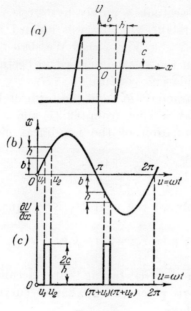

FIG. 288

Averaging its value (62.28) according to Fig. 288*c* with limiting passage to the given characteristic $(h \to 0)$ we have:

$$\varkappa(a) = \lim_{h \to 0} \frac{2 \cdot \dfrac{2c}{h}(u_2 - u_1)}{2\pi} = \lim_{u_2 \to u_1} \frac{2c(u_2 - u_1)}{\pi a (\sin u_2 - \sin u_1)},$$

since $h = a \sin u_2 - a \sin u_1$.

Putting $u_2 = u_1 + \Delta u$ and taking the derivatives of the numerator and denominator with respect to Δu, we obtain:

$$\varkappa(a) = \lim_{\Delta u \to 0} \frac{2c}{\pi a \cos(u_1 + \Delta u)} = \frac{2c}{\pi \sqrt{a^2 - b^2}}. \qquad (63.74)$$

Thus, from (63.57) and (63.74) we obtain the following characteristic equation:

$$T_1 T_3 z^3 + (T_1 + T_3) z^2 + z + k_1 k \varkappa(a) = 0. \qquad (63.75)$$

Then the condition for stability of the periodic solution according to the Vyshnegradskii criterion (29.3) will be

$$(T_1 + T_3) > T_1 T_3 k_1 k \varkappa (a) .$$

Substituting here $\varkappa(a)$ from (63.74) and the values a_l^2 and k from (63.71) and (63.72), we verify that they are satisfied. Consequently there will be stable self-oscillation in the system $x = a_l \sin \omega_l t$, with amplitude and frequency defined by the graphs of Fig. 287c and d or formulae (63.71), (63.72).

In the last case we took a purely hysteresis relay characteristic, when the delay in relay switching was defined by a definite value of input coordinate $x = b$ (Fig. 286d). We shall now consider a case with time delay τ in the relay described in Section 53 (see example of temperature regulation system).

Let the relay characteristic have the form of Fig. 286c, but with a constant time delay τ. Then from (62.21) and (63.70), where $b = 0$, the approximate equation of the non-linear element in place of (63.58) will be

$$V = \frac{4c}{\pi a} e^{-\tau p} x .$$

As a result we obtain the characteristic equation of the system

$$(T_1 z + 1)(T_3 z + 1) z + k_1 k \frac{4c}{\pi a} e^{-\tau z} = 0 .$$

The substitution $z = i\omega$ taking into account the expression $e^{-i\tau\omega} = \cos\tau\omega - i\sin\tau\omega$ gives the Mikhailov curve expression $L(i\tilde{\omega}) = X(\tilde{\omega}) + iY(\tilde{\omega})$, where

$$X(\tilde{\omega}) = \frac{4ck_1 k}{\pi a} \cos\tau\tilde{\omega} - (T_1 + T_3)\tilde{\omega}^2 ,$$

$$Y(\tilde{\omega}) = -\frac{4ck_1 k}{\pi a} \sin\tau\tilde{\omega} + \tilde{\omega} - T_1 T_3 \tilde{\omega}^3 .$$

Equating them to zero according to (62.6), we obtain two equations from which we find

$$(T_1 + T_3)\omega_l \tan\tau\omega_l = 1 - T_1 T_3 \omega_l^2 ,$$

$$a_l = \frac{4ck_1 k}{\pi \omega_l \sqrt{1 + (T_1^2 + T_3^2)\omega_l^2 + T_1^2 T_3^2 \omega_l^4}} .$$

The first defines the frequency and the second the amplitude of oscillation in dependence on the regulator gain factor k and on the other parameters of the system. From comparison of the formulae obtained with (60.33) it is possible to see the character of the effect of the regulator time constant T_3 on the oscillations in the system.

We note that in all relay systems considered in the present example, a_l denoted the amplitude of oscillations of the quantity x. The amplitude of oscillations a_θ of the regulated quantity θ (temperature) according to the second of equations (63.57) will be

$$a_\theta = \frac{a_l}{k_2}.$$

Example 7. Let us consider an automatic regulation system with regulating organ drive in the form of a two-phase motor. The charac-

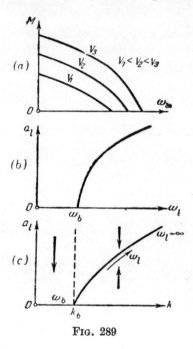

Fig. 289

teristic of this motor for various values of the control voltage V has the form shown in Fig. 289a.

Linearising the characteristic, it is usually assumed

$$M = c_1 V - c_2 \omega_m . \tag{63.76}$$

But this is valid in the first approximation only for the left-hand segment of the characteristic. If a larger portion of the characteristic is employed it is necessary to take into account its non-linearity. Considering that in Fig. 289a with increase of ω_m the coefficient c_1 decreases while the coefficient c_2 increases, we adopt for a description of this characteristic in place of (63.76) the following non-linear expression:

$$M = \frac{c_1}{1 + c_3 \cdot |\omega_m|} V - (c_2 + c_4 \cdot |\omega_m|) \omega_m \tag{63.77}$$

40

(the absolute values ω_m are employed in the coefficients since ω_m reverses while the coefficients should remain positive numbers). Similarly it is possible to take some other more suitable arbitrary non-linear function to describe the motor characteristic.

Let us make the substitution

$$x = \omega_m . \qquad (63.78)$$

Then the differential equation of the motor will be

$$J\frac{dx}{dt} = \frac{c_1}{1 + c_3 |x|} V - c_2 x - c_4 |x| x ,$$

where J is the moment of inertia of the entire mass rotating with the motor, reduced to the motor shaft. Reducing to a common denominator, we obtain

$$J\frac{dx}{dt} + J c_3 |x| \frac{dx}{dt} + c_2 x + (c_2 c_3 + c_4)|x|x + c_3 c_4 x^3 = c_1 V . \qquad (63.79)$$

Here we have three non-linear functions

$$F_1 = |x|\frac{dx}{dt} , \qquad F_2 = |x|x , \qquad F_3 = x^2 .$$

Their harmonic linearisation according to the rules of Section 61 gives

$$F_1 \approx \frac{4a}{3\pi}\frac{dx}{dt} , \qquad F_2 \approx \frac{8a}{3\pi} x , \qquad F_3 = \frac{3a^2}{4} x .$$

Substituting this in (63.79) we obtain the following approximate equation of the two-phase motor (for oscillation):

$$[T_3(1 + b_1 a)p + (1 + b_2 a + b_3 a^2)]x = k_3 V \qquad (63.80)$$

in place of the ordinary linear equation $(T_3 p + 1)x = k_3 V$, where

$$\left.\begin{array}{c} T_3 = \dfrac{J}{c_2} , \qquad k_3 = \dfrac{c_1}{c_2} , \\[2mm] b_1 = \dfrac{4c_3}{3\pi} , \qquad b_2 = 2b_1 + \dfrac{8c_4}{3\pi c_2} , \qquad b_3 = \dfrac{3c_3 c_4}{4c_2} . \end{array}\right\} \qquad (63.81)$$

Here a denotes the amplitude of oscillation of the angular velocity of the motor $x = \omega_m$.

Further, the velocity of the regulating organ $p\xi$ taking into account the transfer factor of the gear reduction and using the notation (63.78) will be

$$p\xi = k_4 x . \qquad (63.82)$$

The equations of the regulated object and the sensitive element of the regulated will be taken in the forms

$$(T_1 p + 1)\varphi = -k_1\xi , \qquad V = k_2\varphi , \qquad (63.83)$$

respectively, where φ is the deviation of the regulated quantity.

The characteristic equation of the overall closed system according to (63.80), (63.82) and (63.83) will be

$$[T_1(1+b_1a)z+(1+b_2a+b_3a^2)](T_1z+1)z+k_1k = 0 , \qquad (63.84)$$

where

$$k = k_2k_3k_4 .$$

In the Mikhailov curve expression we have here, consequently,

$$\left.\begin{aligned} X(\tilde{\omega}) &= k_1k-[T_3(1+b_1a)+T_1(1+b_2a+b_3a^2)]\,\tilde{\omega}^2 , \\ Y(\tilde{\omega}) &= (1+b_2a+b_3a^2)\,\tilde{\omega}-T_3T_1(1+b_1a)\,\tilde{\omega}^3 . \end{aligned}\right\} \qquad (63.85)$$

To find the periodic solutions we equate (63.85) to zero. Let us now consider the influence of the parameter k (the overall gain factor of the regulator). Equating the second of expressions (63.85) to zero and assuming $\omega = \tilde{\omega} = \omega_l$ and $a = a_l$, we obtain the equation

$$b_3a_l^2 - (b_1T_3T_1\omega_l^2 - b_2)\,a_l - (T_3T_1\omega_l^2 - 1) = 0 ,$$

from which

$$a_l = \frac{b_1T_3T_1\omega_l^2 - b_2 + \sqrt{(b_1T_3T_1\omega_l^2 - b_2)^2 + 4b_3(T_3T_1\omega_l^2 - 1)}}{2b_3} . \qquad (63.86)$$

From (63.81) it is evident that $b_2 > b_1$. Therefore (63.86) gives the dependence of amplitude a_l on frequency ω_l of the required periodic solution in graphical form as shown in Fig. 289b, where

$$\omega_b = \frac{1}{\sqrt{T_3T_1}} . \qquad (63.87)$$

Further, equating the first of expressions (63.85) to zero with $\tilde{\omega} = \omega = \omega_l$ and $a = a_l$ and using the second, we obtain the formula for the parameter k, the influence of which is of interest:

$$k = \frac{T_3}{k_1}(1 + b_1a_l)(1 + T_1^2\omega_l^2)\,\omega_l^2 . \qquad (63.88)$$

From this formula, using the previous results, we obtain the graph of the self-oscillation amplitude a_l as a function of the magnitude of k, shown in Fig. 289c.

Let us investigate the stability of this periodic solution. For this we derive the equation of the system in deviations from the periodic solution. The equation of the linear part in deviations from (63.82) and (63.83) will be:

$$(T_1p + 1)p\Delta V = -k_1k_2k_4\Delta x .$$

For the equation of the non-linear element (63.79), having the form

$$F(\dot{x}, x) = c_1V ,$$

we find

$$\frac{\partial F}{\partial \dot{x}} = J + J c_3 |x| \, ,$$

$$\frac{\partial F}{\partial z} = J c_3 \frac{dx}{dt} \cdot \operatorname{sign} x + c_2 + 2 \left(c_2 c_3 + c_4 \right) |x| + 3 c_3 c_4 x^2 \, .$$

From (62.25) we obtain

$$\varkappa_1 = J + J \frac{2 c_3 a_l}{\pi}, \qquad \varkappa = c_2 + \frac{4}{\pi} \left(c_2 c_3 + c_4 \right) a + \frac{3}{2} c_3 c_4 a^2 \, .$$

Therefore the approximate equation in deviations for the non-linear element (63.79), from (62.24) and (63.81) will be:

$$\left[T_3 \left(1 + \frac{3}{2} b_1 a_l \right) p + \left(1 + \frac{3}{2} b_2 a_l + 2 b_3 a_l^2 \right) \right] \Delta x = k_3 \Delta V \, ,$$

while the characteristic equation for investigating the stability of the periodic solution takes the form

$$\left[T_3 \left(1 + \frac{3}{2} b_1 a_l \right) z + \left(1 + \frac{3}{2} b_2 a_l + 2 b_3 a_l^2 \right) \right] (T_1 z + 1) z + k_1 k = 0 \, .$$

From this the condition of stability (from the Vyshnegradskii criterion

$$\left[T_3 \left(1 + \frac{3}{2} b_1 a_l \right) + T_1 \left(1 + \frac{3}{2} b_2 a_l + 2 b_3 a_l^2 \right) \right] \times$$

$$\times \left(1 + \frac{3}{2} b_2 a_l + 2 b_3 a_l^2 \right) - T_3 T_1 k_1 k \left(1 + \frac{3}{2} b_1 a_l \right) > 0 \, ,$$

while the existence of the periodic solution in accordance with the previous characteristic equation (63.84) corresponds to the following equality:

$$[T_3 (1 + b_1 a_l) + T_1 (1 + b_2 a_l + b_3 a_l^2)] (1 + b_2 a_l + b_3 a_l^2) - T_3 T_1 k_1 k (1 + b_1 a_l) = 0 \, .$$

From a comparison of the two last expressions we see that for stability of the periodic solution the inequality

$$\left(T_3 + T_1 \frac{1 + \frac{3}{2} b_2 a_l + 2 b_3 a_l^2}{1 + \frac{3}{2} b_1 a_l} \right) \left(1 + \frac{3}{2} b_2 a_l + 2 b_3 a_l^2 \right)$$

$$> \left(T_3 + T_1 \frac{1 + b_2 a_l + b_3 a_l^2}{1 + b_1 a_l \omega_l} \right) 1 + b_2 a_l + b_3 a_l^2) \, ,$$

must be satisfied.

For large amplitudes a_l its satisfaction is obvious. From this it follows that it is satisfied over the entire single-valued curve in Fig. 289c. Consequently, the periodic solution found is stable; it corresponds to oscillations in the given system with amplitude and frequency defined by the graphs in Fig. 289b and c or the corresponding formulae given above. The amplitude of oscillations for the regulated quantity β from (63.82) will be

$$a_\beta = \frac{k_4}{\omega_l} a_l .$$

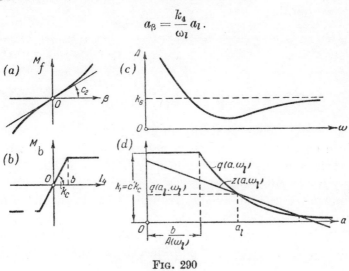

FIG. 290

Substituting the value of ω_b (63.87) in the expression (63.88) and putting $a_b = 0$, we find the limiting value of the parameter k in the form

$$k_b = \frac{T_1 + T_3}{k_1 T_1 T_3} .$$

For values of the gain factor $k < k_b$ the given system is stable with respect to the equilibrium state while with $k > k_b$ self-oscillation arises in it.

Example 8. Above we have considered the influence of drive non-linearity and then the influence of quadratic friction individually. We now consider the simultaneous effects of drive non-linearity and quadratic (plus linear) friction. The friction moment is described by the non-linear equation (55.10) or, which is equivalent, the graph in Fig. 290a. Let the non-linear drive have a saturation type characteristic (Fig. 290b).

Then the equation of the motor and controlled object in place of (63.40) takes the form

$$(T_1 p + 1)x + F(x) = c' F_1(I_4) , \qquad x = p\beta , \qquad (63.89)$$

where $F(I_4)$ is defined by the graph (Fig. 290b).

In the present case we have a non-linearity of the second class. According to Section 61 we assume

$$x = a \sin \omega t , \quad I_4 = Aa \sin (\omega t + B) , \qquad (63.90)$$

where $A(\omega)$ and $B(\omega)$ are the modulus and argument of the amplitude-phase characteristic of the linear part, where it is necessary to multiply the equation (63.89), according to (63.89), by p. As a result we obtain

$$W_\pi(i\omega) = k_6 + \frac{k}{(T_3 i\omega + 1) i\omega} = k_6 - \frac{kT_3}{1 + T_3^2 \omega^2} - i \frac{k}{(1 + T_3^2 \omega^2) \omega} .$$

From this

$$A = \sqrt{ k_6^2 + \frac{k^2 - 2kk_6 T_3 \omega^2}{(1 + T_3^2 \omega^2) \omega^2} } , \qquad (63.91)$$

which is represented graphically in Fig. 290c.

Since in equation (63.89) the variables $x = p\beta$ and I_4 enter separately, their harmonic linearisation may be carried out individually. We apply to the non-linearity in the left-hand side of equation (63.89) the formulae from the previous Example 4 (with quadratic friction) while to the non-linearity in the right-hand side formulae (63.1) and (63.2) in which in place of a we substitute Aa in accordance with (63.90). As a result the non-linear equation (63.89) takes the form

$$\left(T_1 p + 1 + \frac{8k_8 a}{3\pi} \right) p\beta = q(a, \omega) I_4 , \qquad (63.92)$$

where

$$\left. \begin{array}{l} q(a, \omega) = k_1 = c'k_c \quad \text{with} \quad a \leqslant b , \\[2mm] q(a, \omega) = \dfrac{2k_1}{\pi} \left(\sin^{-1} \dfrac{b}{aA(\omega)} + \dfrac{b}{aA(\omega)} \sqrt{ 1 - \left[\dfrac{b}{aA(\omega)} \right]^2 } \right) \\[4mm] \hspace{5cm} \text{with } a > b \end{array} \right\} \quad (63.93)$$

and $A(\omega)$ is defined by formula (63.91) or the graph (Fig. 290c).

From equations (63.92) and (54.10) we obtain the characteristic equation of the closed system in the form

$$(T_3 z + 1) \left(T_1 z + 1 + \frac{8k_8 a}{3\pi} \right) z + [(T_3 z + 1) k_6 z + k] q(a, \omega) = 0 .$$

The Mikhailov curve expression is thus

$$L(i\widetilde{\omega}) = X(\widetilde{\omega}) + i Y(\widetilde{\omega}) ,$$

where

$$K(\widetilde{\omega}) = kq(a, \omega) - \left[T_1 + T_3 + k_6 T_3 q(a, \omega) + \frac{8k_8 a}{3\pi} T_3 \right] \widetilde{\omega}^2 ,$$

$$Y(\widetilde{\omega}) = \left[1 + k_6 q(a, \omega) + \frac{8k_8 a}{3\pi} \right] \widetilde{\omega} - T_1 T_3 \widetilde{\omega}^3 .$$

Equating them to zero, we obtain

$$q(a_l, \omega_l) = \frac{1}{k_6}\left(T_1 T_3 \omega^2 - 1 - \frac{8k_8 a}{3\pi}\right),$$

$$k = \frac{T_1 \omega^2 (1 + T_3^2 \omega^2)}{q(a_l, \omega_l)}. \tag{63.94}$$

From the first equation we find easily all possible values of amplitude a_l and frequency ω_l as follows.

We assign some value to ω_l. From the graph in Fig. 290c we find the corresponding $A(\omega_l)$. From formula (63.93) we plot the curve $q(a, \omega_l)$, shown in Fig. 290d.

We call right-hand side of the first of equations (63.94) z

$$z(a, \omega) \equiv \frac{1}{k_6}\left(T_1 T_3 \omega^2 - 1 - \frac{8k_8 a}{3\pi}\right),$$

and plot the straight line $z(a, \omega_l)$ according to this formula in the same Fig. 290d. At the points of intersection we obtain the required values of a_l as well as the values of $q(a_l, \omega_l)$. After this we calculate the value of the parameter k from the second of formulae (63.94).

Carrying out the same operation for various values of ω_l and obtaining for each the corresponding a and k, we can thus obtain graphs similar to those which were obtained in the previous examples. The amplitude of oscillation of the angle β will be $\alpha_\beta = a_l/\omega_l$. Then according to (63.94) from the condition of positiveness of the quantity $q(a_l, \omega_l)$ we should have $\omega_l > 1/T_1 T_3$.

Example 9. For simplicity in all examples above we have limited ourselves to third-order equations. The method is unchanged for arbitrary order of equation of the non-linear system. Let us take, for example, the automatic course regulator of the aircraft with non-linear rudder drive. The aircraft equation (with respect to course) taking into account the angle of slip, according to (25.8) will be

$$[(T_1 p + 1)(T_2 p + 1) + k_2 T_2] p \psi = -k_1 (T_2 p + 1)\delta$$

(in the transient without external perturbations). The autopilot with feedback and with introduction of two derivatives is characterised by the equations: (a) the linear equation of the sensitive elements and the magnetic amplifier according to (25.11), (25.19) and (25.24)

$$(T_3 p + 1)I = (k_3 k_4 + k_3' k_5 p + k_3'' k_6 p^2)\psi - k_7 k_9 \delta$$

and (b) the rudder drive non-linear equation

$$p\delta = F(I),$$

where $F(I)$ may have any of the forms shown in Fig. 240.

For example, in the presence of hysteresis and saturation (Fig. 240*f*) the equation of this non-linear element will be

$$p\delta = \left[q(a) + \frac{q_1(a)}{\omega} p\right] I,$$

where $q(a)$ and $q_1(a)$ are defined by formulae (61.44) with $q_1(a) < 0$. With a zone of insensitivity and saturation (Fig. 240*b*) without a hysteresis loop, the equation will be

$$p\delta = q(a) I,$$

where $q(a)$ is given by (61.40) and, in particular cases, by (61.41) or (61.42).

According to the above the characteristic equation of the system will be

$$[(T_1z+1)(T_2z+1)+k_2T_2]z + \left\{(T_3z+1)z+k_7k_9\left[q(a)+\frac{q_1(a)}{\omega}z\right]\right\} +$$

$$+ k_1(T_2z+1)(k_3k_4+k_3'k_5z+k_3''k_6z^2)\left[q(a)+\frac{q_1(a)}{\omega}z\right] = 0,$$

where $q_1(a) < 0$ in the presence of hysteresis and $q_1(a) = 0$ without it.

It is possible to consider somewhat simplified types of systems. If the autopilot does not have feedback ($k_9 = 0$) and the second derivative is not introduced ($k_3'' = 0$), then taking into account the angle of slip of the aircraft ($T_2 \neq 0$) and the inertia of the autopilot ($T_3 \neq 0$) the characteristic equation of the system takes the form

$$[(T_1z+1)(T_2z+1)+k_2T_2](T_3z+1)z^2 +$$

$$+ k_1(T_2z+1)(k_3k_4+k_3'k_5z)\left[q(a)+\frac{q_1(a)}{\omega}z\right] = 0. \qquad (63.95)$$

Putting here $z = i\omega$, we obtain the corresponding expression for the Mikhailov curve

$$L(i\widetilde{\omega}) = X(\widetilde{\omega}) + iY(\widetilde{\omega}), \qquad (63.96)$$

and, as in the previous examples, equating $X(\widetilde{\omega})$ and $Y(\widetilde{\omega})$ to zero, we can plot the dependence of a_l on the parameters k_3 and k_3'. From these graphs we may draw conclusions as to the possibility of self-oscillation and the region of stability of the given system with respect to these parameters. If the drive characteristic has no hysteresis loop, the system will be stable for those values of the parameters for which the Mikhailov curve (63.96) satisfies the linear stability criterion for arbitrary constant value a in the interval $0 \leqslant a \leqslant \infty$.

Considering various alternatives, it is possible to examine the effects of introduction of derivatives, feedback, individual time constants and transfer factors on the system with non-linear rudder drive.

Example 10. In all above examples we have started from the Mikhailov curve expression for the non-linear system. But, as shown in Section 62, algebraic criteria may be used for the same purpose. Let us illustrate this.

Let us consider, for example, the automatic relay regulation system considered above in Example 6. There we obtained the characteristic equation for determining self-oscillation in the form

$$(T_1z+1)(T_3z+1)z + k_1k\left[q(a) - \frac{q_1(a)}{\omega}z\right] = 0$$

or

$$T_1T_3z^3 + (T_1+T_3)z^2 + \left[1 - k_1k\frac{q_1(a)}{\omega}\right]z + k_1kq(a) = 0 .$$

This is a third-degree equation. Therefore we use conditions (62.15) and (62.16) which in this case take the form

$$(T_1+T_3)\left[1 - k_1k\frac{q_1(a_l)}{\omega_l}\right] = T_1T_3k_1kq(a_l) ,$$

$$T_1T_3\omega_l^2 = 1 - k_1k\frac{q_1(a_l)}{\omega_l} .$$

Substituting the second in the first, we may write

$$(T_1+T_3)\,\omega_l^2 = k_1kq(a_l) .$$

From the last two equations we easily obtain the previous relations (63.61) and (63.63) and from them all the previous results of Example 6.

The matter is completely analogous for all the other examples analysed above, where a third-degree characteristic equation was obtained.

As a second example let us take the characteristic equation of the aircraft with non-linear autopilot (63.95), assuming for simplicity $T_3 = 0$ and $q_1(a) = 0$ (absence of hysteresis loop). It is written in the form

$$T_1T_2z^4 + (T_1+T_2)z^3 + [1 + k_2T_2 + k_1T_2k_3'k_5q(a)]z^2 + $$
$$+ k_1(T_2k_3k_4 + k_3'k_5)q(a)z + k_1k_3k_4q(a) = 0 .$$

To determine the periodic solutions we employ conditions (62.18) and (62.19) which here take the form

$$(T_2k_3k_4 + k_3'k_5)\{(T_1+T_2)[1 + k_2T_2 + k_1T_2k_3'k_5q(a_l)] - $$
$$- T_1T_2k_1(T_2k_3k_4 + k_3'k_5)q(a_l)\} - k_3k_4(T_1+T_2)^2q(a) = 0 ,$$

$$(T_1+T_2)\,\omega_l^2 = k_1(T_2k_3k_4 + k_3'k_5)q(a_l) .$$

From the first equation it is possible to express $q(a_l)$, and thus determine the amplitude a_l as a function of the system parameters. After this, from the second equation we define the frequency ω_l. In more complicated cases the frequency ω_l enters into the first equation as well (for example, taking into account a hysteresis loop). Then these two equations are solved simultaneously.

64. Improved first approximation in determining self-oscillation

The method considered above for determining self-oscillation is a first approximation to a solution of the problem when only the fundamental component of non-linear oscillation is considered. In this the fundamental component of the non-linear function was calculated only from the fundamental component of the argument. We have limited ourselves above to this first approximation in studying non-linear automatic regulation systems, firstly, because in the majority of problems of regulation theory it gives sufficient precision for practical purposes, and, secondly, because the construction of higher-order approximations is in general very difficult (we have fully succeeded in taking into account higher harmonics only for the relay system, Section 69, for which there also exists the exact solution described in Section 59).

In a number of cases it is possible to check the qualitative and quantitative correctness of the result by a consideration of the amplitude-frequency characteristic of the linear part of the system, which shows to what extent the higher harmonics, neglected in the calculation, are actually attenuated in passage through the linear part. In addition, after definite system parameters are selected on the basis of the given approximate study, it is possible to plot for them the curve of the regulation process (see Chapter XVIII), which serves as an estimate of the degree of correctness of the calculation. Finally, experimental results may serve as a criterion.

Along with this, it is possible to propose the following improved solution of the problem in comparison with the first approximation considered above based on recommendations of N. N. Bogoliubov for cases where it is necessary to take into account at least some of the higher harmonics of the argument of the non-linear function.

Let us consider a non-linear system of the form in Fig. 229, where the equation of the linear part is

$$Q_l(p)x_1 = -R_l(p)x_2 , \tag{64.1}$$

while the equation of the non-linear element, for example

$$x_2 = F(x_1, \dot{x}_1) . \tag{64.2}$$

Previously we have sought a solution in the form $x_1 = a \sin \omega t$, assuming that practically no higher harmonics pass through the linear part. We now take these higher harmonics into account and write:

$$x_1 = a \sin \omega t + x_{1h}, \qquad \dot{x}_1 = a\omega \cos \omega t + \dot{x}_{1h}, \qquad (64.3)$$

where x_{1h} are higher harmonics,

$$x_{1h} = a_2 \sin(2\omega t + \varphi_2) + a_3 \sin(3\omega t + \varphi_3) + \ldots + a_n \sin(n\omega t + \varphi_n) \qquad (64.4)$$

(only a limited number n o' harmonics can have substantial value). The presence of given multiple frequencies in the higher harmonics is defined by the expansion of the given function (64.2) in a Fourier series with $x_1 = a \sin \omega t$, while the amplitudes and phases of these harmonics depend also on the linear part. For example, for single-valued odd (symmetrical) non-linear functions $F(x)$ there will be present in the expansion only odd harmonics where frequently it is sufficient to take into account only the third harmonic. Then

$$x_{1h} = a_3 \sin(3\omega t + \varphi_3), \qquad (64.5)$$

where a_3 and φ_3 are as yet unknown.

Let us expand the non-linear function (64.2) in a Taylor series taking into account (64.3). Assuming that the first harmonic predominates, we limit ourselves to the first terms of the expansion. In the result, putting $u = \omega t$, we obtain

$$F(x_1, \dot{x}_1) = F(a \sin u, a\omega \cos u) + F'_{x1}(a \sin u, a\omega \cos u) x_{1h} +$$
$$+ F'_{\dot{x}_1}(a \sin u, a\omega \cos u) \dot{x}_{1h}, \qquad (64.6)$$

where F'_{x1} and $F'_{\dot{x}1}$ denote the partial derivatives of the given function $F(x_1, \dot{x}_1)$ with respect to x_1 and $\dot{x}_1$. Previously we took the first harmonic of the function $F(a \sin u, a\omega \cos u)$. Now we join to this function, according to (64.6), corrections taking into account the presence of higher harmonics in the argument x_1 of the non-linear function. Substituting the expression for x_{1h} in (64.6), we shall now calculate according to the previous rules for harmonic linearisation the fundamental components of all three terms of expression (64.6).

It is obvious that as a result of this improvement the approximate equation for the non-linear element (64.2), in place of (61.11), takes the following form:

$$x_2 = \left(q + q' + \frac{q_1 + q'_1}{\omega} p \right) x_{1l} + x_{2h}. \qquad (64.7)$$

where $x_{1l} = a \sin \omega t$ is the fundamental component of the variable x_1 while x_{2h} are the higher harmonics of the variable x_2. Here q and q_1 are defined as before by formulae (61.8) while the quantities q' and q'_1 represent corrections to these coefficients taking into account higher harmonics and are defined by the formulae

$$
q' = \frac{1}{\pi a} \int\limits_{0}^{2\pi} [F'_{x_1}(a\sin u,\, a\omega\cos u)x_{1h} +
$$

$$
+ F'_{\dot{x}1}(a\sin u,\, a\omega\cos u)\dot{x}_{1h}]\sin u\, du \,,
$$

$$
q'_1 = \frac{1}{\pi a} \int\limits_{0}^{2\pi} [F'_{x1}(a\sin u,\, a\omega\cos u)x_{1h} +
$$

$$
+ F'_{\dot{x}1}(a\sin u,\, a\omega\cos u)\dot{x}_{1h}]\cos u\, du \,.
$$

(64.8)

Among the higher harmonics x_{2h} of the non-linear function $x_2 = F(x_1, \dot{x}_1)$ it is necessary also to determine those which are of the same harmonic order as were taken into account in the argument x_1 (64.4). In determining the higher harmonics introduced to improve the first approximation, it is natural to limit ourselves to the expression $F(x_1, \dot{x}_1) = F(a\sin u, a\omega\cos u)$. This agrees with the fact that expression (64.6) was adopted as the improved fundamental component. As a result, applying the formulae for the Fourier series coefficients, taking into account (64.4), we obtain:

$$
x_{2h} = \frac{1}{\pi a_2}\left(r_2\cos\varphi_2 + s_2\sin\varphi_2 + \frac{s_2\cos\varphi_2 - r_2\sin\varphi_2}{2\omega}\,p \right)x_{12} +
$$

$$
+ \frac{1}{\pi a_3}\left(r_3\cos\varphi_3 + s_3\sin\varphi_3 + \frac{s_3\cos\varphi_3 - r_3\sin\varphi_3}{3\omega}\,p \right)x_{13} +
$$

$$
\ldots + \frac{1}{\pi a_n}\left(r_n\cos\varphi_n + s_n\sin\varphi_n + \frac{s_n\cos\varphi_n - r_n\sin\varphi_n}{n\omega}\,p \right)x_{1n} \,,
$$

(64.9)

where

$$
r_2 = \int\limits_{0}^{2\pi} F(a\sin u,\, a\omega\cos u)\sin 2u\, du \,,
$$

$$
s_2 = \int\limits_{0}^{2\pi} F(a\sin u,\, a\omega\cos u)\cos 2u\, du \,,
$$

$$
r_3 = \int\limits_{0}^{2\pi} F(a\sin u,\, a\omega\cos u)\sin 3u\, du \,,
$$

$$
s_3 = \int\limits_{0}^{2\pi} F(a\sin u,\, a\omega\cos u)\cos 3u\, du \,,
$$

$$
\cdots\cdots\cdots\cdots\cdots\cdots\cdots\cdots
$$

$$
r_n = \int\limits_{0}^{2\pi} F(a\sin u,\, a\omega\cos u)\sin nu\, du \,,
$$

$$
s_n = \int\limits_{0}^{2\pi} F(a\sin u,\, a\omega\cos u)\cos nu\, du \,,
$$

(64.10)

and the higher harmonics of the argument x_1 figuring in (64.4) are here denoted by

$$x_{12} = a_2 \sin(2\omega t + \varphi_2) \,, \quad x_{13} = a_3 \sin(3\omega t + \varphi_3), \, \dots, \, x_{1n} = a_n \sin(n\omega t + \varphi_n) \,.$$

Substituting (64.7) and (64.9) in the equation of the linear part (64.1), we divide it into n equations. To determine the fundamental component of the oscillation $x_{1l} = a \sin \omega t$ we obtain the characteristic equation

$$Q_l(z) + \left(q + q' + \frac{q_1 + q_1'}{\omega} z\right) R_l(z) = 0 \,, \tag{64.11}$$

and to determine the higher harmonics $x_{12}, x_{13}, \dots, x_{1n}$ we obtain the characteristic equations

$$\left.\begin{aligned}
Q_l(z) + \frac{1}{\pi a_2}\left(r_2 \cos\varphi_2 + s_2 \sin\varphi_2 + \frac{s_2 \cos\varphi_2 - r_2 \sin\varphi_2}{2\omega} z\right) R_l(z) = 0 \,, \\
Q_l(z) + \frac{1}{\pi a_3}\left(r_3 \cos\varphi_3 + s_3 \sin\varphi_3 + \frac{s_3 \cos\varphi_3 - r_3 \sin\varphi_3}{3\omega} z\right) R_l(z) = 0 \,, \\
\dots\dots\dots\dots\dots\dots\dots\dots\dots\dots\dots\dots\dots\dots\dots\dots\dots\dots \\
Q_l(z) + \frac{1}{\pi a_n}\left(r_n \cos\varphi_n + s_n \sin\varphi_n + \frac{s_n \cos\varphi_n - r_n \sin\varphi_n}{n\omega} z\right) R_l(z) = 0 \,,
\end{aligned}\right\} \tag{64.12}$$

respectively, where the quantities $r_2, s_2, r_3, s_3, \dots, r_n, s_n$ are functions of the amplitude a and frequency ω of the fundamental component. Consequently, each of equations (64.12) individually defines the amplitude a_j and phase φ_j corresponding to the jth harmonic as functions of a and ω.

Let us now demonstrate the proposed method for determining this dependence, for example, for the nth harmonic. Substituting in the last equation of (64.12) $z = in\omega$, we come to the expression

$$Q_l(in\omega) + \frac{1}{\pi a_n} (r_n + is_n)(\cos\varphi_n - i\sin\varphi_n) R_l(in\omega) = 0 \,,$$

from which we obtain

$$\pi a_n e^{i\varphi_n} = \Phi_n(a, \omega) \,, \tag{64.13}$$

where

$$\Phi_n(a, \omega) = -\frac{(r_n + is_n) R_l(in\omega)}{Q(in\omega)} \,. \tag{64.14}$$

From the last formula it is possible to plot the series of curves $\Phi(\omega)$ in the complex plane for various values of a (Fig. 291a). Plotting a circle of arbitrary radius πa_n in the same graph, we obtain at the points of intersection a, b, c of this circle with the curves $\Phi(a, \omega)$, according (64.13), values of the phase φ_n for various values of a (as the angular coordinates of the points). We plot the result in the plane of the coordinates a_n, φ_n (Fig. 291b) in the form of points A_1, B_1, C_1. At these points we write the values of ω which occur at the points A, B, C. Plotting in Fig. 291a a series of circles of various radii πa_n, we find new points in the plane (a_n, φ_n), which joined by a smooth curve give the required dependence of a_n and φ_n on a and ω in the form the graph of Fig. 291b *.

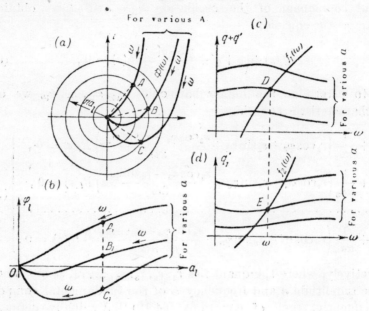

FIG. 291

All remaining equations (64.12) are individually solved by analogous means.

All these relations must be used to find the fundamental component from equation (64.11), where the coefficients q' and q_1' depend on all a_j and φ_j. Therefore, applying to equation (64.11) the previous method of finding the periodic solution (Section 62), we obtain two equations

$$\left.\begin{array}{l} X(a, \omega, a_2, \varphi_2, a_3, \varphi_3, \ldots, a_n, \varphi_n) = 0 , \\ Y(a, \omega, a_2, \varphi_2, a_3, \varphi_3, \ldots, a_n, \varphi_n) = 0 . \end{array}\right\} \qquad (64.15)$$

Thus, the periodic solution (64.3)–(64.4) will be fully defined in a more exact form than the first approximation.

In particular, if the equation of the non-linear element has the form of an odd single-valued function $x_2 = F(x_1)$ and only the third

---

* It is not necessary to plot the graphs of Fig. 291a and b, in place of which we calculate $a_n = |\Phi_n(a, \omega)|/\pi$ and $\varphi_n = \arg\Phi_n(a, \omega)$.

harmonic (64.5) is taken into account, formulae (64.8) take the form

$$
\left.
\begin{aligned}
q' &= \frac{a_3 \cos \varphi_3}{\pi a} \int_0^{2\pi} F'_{x1}(a \sin u) \sin 3u \sin u \, du \, , \\[2ex]
q'_1 &= \frac{a_3 \sin \varphi_3}{\pi a} \int_0^{2\pi} F'_{x1}(a \sin u) \cos 3u \cos u \, du \, ,
\end{aligned}
\right\}
\tag{64.16}
$$

While formula (64.9) will be:

$$
x_{2h} = \frac{1}{\pi a_3} \left(r_3 \cos \varphi_3 - \frac{r_3 \sin \varphi_3}{3\omega} p \right) x_{1h} \, , \qquad x_{1h} = a_3 \sin(3\omega t + \varphi_3) \, , \tag{64.17}
$$

where, from (64.10)

$$
r_3 = \int_0^{2\pi} F(a \sin u) \sin 3u \, du \, . \tag{64.18}
$$

Formula (64.14) takes the form

$$
\Phi_3(a, \, \omega) = - \frac{r_3(a) \, R_l(i3\omega)}{Q_l(i3\omega)} \, , \tag{64.19}
$$

as a result of which the plotting of curves $\Phi(a, \omega)$ in Fig. 291a or the equivalent calculations are substantially simplified.

Equation (64.15), defining the fundamental component of the required periodic solution, is also simplified, taking the form

$$
X(a, \, \omega, \, a_3, \, \varphi_3) = 0 \, , \qquad Y(a, \, \omega, \, a_3, \, \varphi_3) = 0 \, . \tag{64.20}
$$

Here we have carried out calculations for the non-linear element with equation $x_2 = F(x, \dot{x}_1)$, and $x_2 = F(x_1)$. The same method of improving the solution remains valid for the other forms of non-linear elements considered in the previous paragraphs. In particular, for a non-linear element described by the equation

$$
F(x_2, \, \dot{x}_2) = c_1 x_1 \, , \tag{64.21}
$$

all previous formulae (64.3)–(64.10) remain in force, if we substitute in them x_1 by x_2 and x_2 by $c_1 x_1$. In formulae (64.11)–(64.14) it is necessary to interchange Q_1 and R_1. The final equation in improved form will have the same general structure as (64.15).

Example 1. Let us improve the first approximation in determining self-oscillation for the non-linear servomechanism considered in Example 1 of Section 63. We shall take into account only the third harmonic, i.e. we shall seek the periodic solution in the form

$$
I_4 = I_{4l} + I_{4h} \, , \qquad I_{4l} = a \sin \omega t \, , \qquad I_{4h} = a_3 \sin(3\omega t + \varphi_3) \, . \tag{64.22}
$$

The derivative $F'(I_4)$ from the graph of Fig. 276a will be:

$$F'(I_4) = k_c \quad \text{with} \quad -b \leqslant I_4 \leqslant +b\,,$$
$$F'(I_4) = 0 \quad \text{with} \quad I_4 < -b \quad \text{and} \quad I_4 > +b\,.$$

Therefore, putting

$$u_1 = \sin^{-1} \frac{b}{a}\,,$$

from formulae (64.16), introducing in them $c'F$ in place of F and taking into account the previously introduced $c'k_c = k_1$, we obtain:

$$q' = \frac{k_1 a_3 \cos\varphi_3}{\pi a} \left(\int\limits_{-u_1}^{u_1} \sin 3u \sin u\, du + \int\limits_{\pi-u_1}^{\pi+u_1} \sin 3u \sin u\, du \,,\right)$$

$$q_1' = \frac{k_1 a_3 \sin\varphi_3}{\pi a} \left(\int\limits_{-u_1}^{u_1} \cos 3u \cos u\, du + \int\limits_{\pi-u_1}^{\pi+u_1} \cos 3u \cos u\, du \,,\right)$$

from which we find $q' = q_1' = 0$ with $a \leqslant b$ and

$$\left. \begin{aligned} q' &= \frac{4k_1 b^3}{\pi a^3} \sqrt{1 - \frac{b^2}{a^2}}\, \frac{a_3}{a} \cos\varphi_3\,, \\ q_1' &= \frac{4k_1 b}{\pi a} \left(1 - \frac{b^2}{a^2}\right)^{3/2} \frac{a_3}{a} \sin\varphi_3 \end{aligned} \right\} \quad \text{for} \quad a > b\,. \quad (64.23)$$

From formulae (64.18), also with substitution of F by $c'F$ and $c'k_c = k_1$ we obtain $r_3 = 0$ with $a \leqslant b$ and

$$r_3 = \frac{4k_1 b}{3} \left(1 - \frac{b^2}{a^2}\right)^{3/2} \quad \text{for} \quad a > b\,. \quad (64.24)$$

As a result, according to (64.7) and (64.17) the equation of the non-linear element (controlled object with drive) will, in place of the preceding (63.1), be:

$$(T_1 p + 1)p\beta = \left[q(a) + q'(a, a_3, \varphi_3) + \frac{q_1'(a, a_3, \varphi_3)}{\omega} p \right] I_{4l} +$$
$$+ \frac{1}{\pi a_3} \left[r_\varepsilon(a) \cos\varphi_3 - \frac{r_3(a) \sin\varphi_3}{3\omega} p \right] I_{4h}\,, \quad (64.25)$$

where $q(a)$ has the previous value (63.2).

The periodic solution (64.22) will be sought separately for each of the two components in the right-hand side of this equation. Joining the equation for the remaining part of the system (63.3), we obtain the characteristic equation for the first harmonic equation

$$(T_1 z + 1)(T_3 z + 1)z + \left(q + q' + \frac{q_1'}{\omega} p \right) [k + (T_3 p + 1) k_6 p] = 0\,, \quad (64.26)$$

while the third harmonic is defined graphically (Fig. 291a) employing, from (64.19) and (64.26), the expression

$$\Phi_3(a,\,\omega) = -\frac{r_3(a)[k + (T_3 3i\omega + 1)k_6 3i\omega]}{(T_1 3i\omega + 1)\,(T_3 3i\omega + 1)3i\omega}\,, \qquad (64.27)$$

as a result of which we obtain a graph of the form in Fig. 291b for a_3 and φ_3 in dependence on a and ω.

From equation (64.26) after substituting $z = i\omega$ and separating the real and imaginary parts we obtain two equations (64.20) in the form

$$X = (q + q')k - q_1'k_6\omega) - (q + q')\,T_3 k_6\omega^2 - (T_1 + T_3)\,\omega^2 = 0\,,$$
$$Y = q_1'k + \omega + (q + q')k_6\omega - q_1'T_3 k_6\omega^2 - T_1 T_3\omega^3 = 0\,.$$

From this we easily find the functions

$$q + q' = f_1(\omega)\,, \qquad q_1' = f_2(\omega)\,. \qquad (64.28)$$

In addition, let us plot further the curves $q + q'$ against ω and q_1' against ω for various values of a (Fig. 291c and d). These curves are plotted as follows. We take an arbitrary value for the amplitude of the fundamental component a. This corresponds to a definite curve in Fig. 291b from which we take values of the quantities a_3 and φ_3 in dependence on ω, after which from formulae (64.23) and (63.2) we calculate q', q_1', and q and plot a series of curves (Fig. 291c and d). Finally, on the same graphs we plot the curves $f_1(\omega)$ and $f_2(\omega)$ from formulae (64.28). The solution of the entire problem will be that value of ω for which in Fig. 291c and d the curves $f_1(\omega)$ and $f_2(\omega)$ intersect the curves corresponding to one single value of a (for example, points D and E).

This defines the corrected values of amplitude a and frequency ω of the fundamental component in the periodic solution. Knowing them, from the graph of Fig. 291b we can then take the values of a_3 and φ_3. As a result the required periodic solution will be completely defined:

$$I_4 = a\sin\omega t + a_3\sin(3\omega t + \varphi_3)\,.$$

To find the form of the periodic solution for the regulated quantity β in the given system

$$\beta = a_\beta\sin(\omega t + \varphi_\beta) + a_{33}\sin(3\omega t + \varphi_{3\beta})\,,$$

it is necessary to employ equation (64.25), from which we find a_β, φ_β, $a_{3\beta}$, $\varphi_{3\beta}$ with the use of equalities

$$a_\beta e^{i\varphi_\beta} = a\,\frac{q + q' + iq_1'}{(T_1 i\omega + 1)i\omega}\,, \qquad a_{3\beta}e^{i\varphi_{3\beta}} = \frac{r_3(a)}{\pi(3T_1 i\omega + 1)3i\omega}\,,$$

where we substitute the values of ω, a, $q+q'$ and q_1' taken at the points D and E (Fig. 291), defining the periodic solution for the variable I_4.

Example 2. Let us consider the relay system examined in example 6 of Section 63. Let the characteristic of the relay circuit have the form of Fig. 286b (with a zone of insensitivity). We shall seek the periodic solution in the form

$$x = a\sin\omega t + a_3\sin(3\omega t + \varphi_3) . \tag{64.29}$$

Calculation of the coefficients q' and q_1' (64.16) here has the following feature. The characteristic $F(x)$ (Fig. 286b) has discontinuities at $x = b$ and $x = -b$ of the magnitude c, and at all remaining x it is constant. The derivative of the discontinuity, according to Section 6, is an impulse (delta-function). Therefore the quantity $F_x'(x)$ entering into (64.16) will be zero for all x except $x = b$ and $x = -b$ where it will be an impulse of area c. Taking into account that $x = a\sin u$ enters into F_x' in formula (64.16) and employing relation (61.33) we rewrite this formula in the form

$$q' = \frac{4a_3\cos\varphi_3}{\pi a} \int\limits_0^{\frac{\pi}{2}} F_x'(a\sin u)\sin 3u \sin u \frac{du}{dx}\, dx$$

$$= \frac{4a_3\cos\varphi_3}{\pi a^2} \int\limits_0^{a} F_x'(x)\sin 3u\, \mathrm{tg}\, u\, dx .$$

But in the interval $0 \leqslant x \leqslant a$ the quantity $F_x'(x)$ is not equal to zero only at a single point $x = b$ where at this point we have $u = u_1 = \sin - I(b/a)$. Therefore the above integral will be the area of the impulse c, multiplied by the quantities $\sin 3u_1 \tan u_1$. As a result, taking into consideration that

$$\sin u_1 = \frac{b}{a} ,$$

we obtain

$$q' = \frac{4cb^2 a_3\cos\varphi_3}{\pi a^3\sqrt{a^2 - b^2}} \left(3 - 4\frac{b^2}{a^2}\right) ,$$

$$q_1' = \frac{4ca_3\sin\varphi_3}{\pi a^2} \left(1 - 4\frac{b^2}{a^2}\right) \sqrt{1 - \frac{b^2}{a^2}} . \tag{64.30}$$

From formula (64.18) we find

$$r_3 = 4 \int\limits_0^{\frac{\pi}{2}} c\sin 3u\, du = \frac{4c}{3}\left(1 - 4\frac{b^2}{a^2}\right) \sqrt{1 - \frac{b^2}{a^2}} . \tag{64.31}$$

Consequently, the equation of the non-linear element, from (64.17) here takes the form

$$V_2 = \left(q + q' + \frac{q_1'}{\omega}p\right)x_l + \frac{1}{\pi a_3}\left(r_3\cos\varphi_3 - \frac{r_3\sin\varphi_3}{3\omega}p\right)x_h ,$$

where $x_l = a\sin\omega t$, $x_h = a_3\sin(3\omega t + \varphi_3)$.

Joining to this the equations for the linear part (63.57) we obtain the characteristic equation for the fundamental component in the from

$$(T_1z + 1)(T_3z + 1)z + kk_1\left(q + q' + \frac{q_1'}{\omega}z\right) = 0 , \qquad (64.32)$$

where q has the previous value (63.65). To determine the third harmonic we find from (64.19)

$$\Phi_3(a, \omega) = -\frac{r_3(a)kk_1}{(3T_1i\omega + 1)(3T_3i\omega + 1)3i\omega} . \qquad (64.33)$$

This permits us to find graphically (Fig. 291a) a_3 and φ_3 as functions of a and ω (Fig. 291b).

Then, substituting in (64.32) $z = i\omega$, we write equations (64.20) in the form

$$X = kk_1(q + q') - (T_1 + T_3)\omega^2 = 0 ,$$
$$Y = kk_1q_1' + \omega - T_1T_3\omega^3 = 0 .$$

From this we find

$$q + q' = f_1(\omega) = \frac{(T_1 + T_3)\omega^2}{kk_1} ,$$

$$q = f_2(\omega) = \frac{T_1T_3\omega^3 - \omega}{kk_1} .$$

After this the problem is solved by the same method as in Example 1.

65. Approximate frequency method for determining self-oscillation

On the basis of the work of N. M. Krylov and N. N. Bogoliubov (Reference 5, 6) L. S. Gol'dfarb developed the application of frequency stability criteria to determine self-oscillations in non-linear systems for non-linearities of the type $x_2 = F(x_1)$ and $x_2 = F(x_1, \dot{x}_1)$. We shall here be concerned only with non-linearities $x_2 = F(x_1)$ since in the other cases more complicated graphical constructions are encountered.

Frequency characteristic. As usual, let the non-linear element be segregated in the automatic regulation system (Fig. 229c). We open the system in the manner shown in Fig. 292a where the equation of the non-linear element has the form

$$x_2 = F(x_1) \,, \tag{65.1}$$

while the equation of the linear part of the system will be

$$Q_l(p)x_3 = R_l(p)x_2 \,. \tag{65.2}$$

Closing the system corresponds to the substitution

$$x_3 = -x_1 \,. \tag{65.3}$$

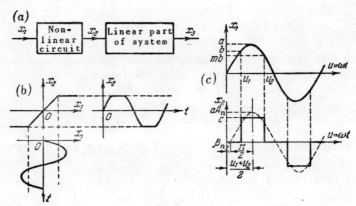

FIG. 292

We apply sinusoidal oscillations to the input of the non-linear element (Fig. 292a)

$$x_1 = a\sin \omega t \,. \tag{65.4}$$

At the output of the non-linear element we obtain forced oscillations according to (65.1)

$$x_2 = F(a\sin \omega t) \,, \tag{65.5}$$

which may be found, for example, as shown in Fig. 292b.

We expand (65.5) in a Fourier series and retain only the fundamental component, dropping all higher harmonics. It is obvious that this approximate representation of the forced oscillation is equivalent to harmonic linearisation of the non-linearity considered in Section 61. On this basis, to determine the fundamental harmonic of forced oscillations of the quantity x_2 we may employ the same method as applied in Section 8 for linear systems, as follows.

From (61.16) the approximate transfer function of the non-linear element with equation $x_2 = F(x_1)$ will be

$$W_n = q(a) + \frac{q_1(a)}{\omega}p$$

and

$$W_n = q(a)$$

in the presence of a hysteresis loop and in its absence respectively. Here expressions $q(a)$ and $q_1(a)$ are defined by formulae (61.17) and satisfaction of condition (61.18) is required.

The approximate complex gain factor or approximate amplitude-phase characteristic of the non-linear element with equation $x_2 = F(x_1)$ in the presence of the hysteresis loop will thus be

$$W_n(a) = q(a) + iq_1(a) \tag{65.6}$$

and without the hysteresis loop

$$W_n(a) = q(a) . \tag{65.7}$$

This approximate amplitude-phase characteristic defines the amplitude and phase of the fundamental component at the output of the non-linear element (if a sinusoidal signal is applied to the input), namely, expression (65.6) may be represented in the form

$$W_n(a) = A_n(a) e^{i\beta_n(a)} ,$$

where

$$A_n(a) = \sqrt{[q(a)]^2 + [q_1(a)]^2} , \qquad \beta_n(a) = \tan^{-1} \frac{q_1(a)}{q(a)} . \tag{65.8}$$

Consequently, the fundamental amplitude at the output will be $a_2 = aA_n(a)$ while the phase shift $\beta_n(a)$, where a is the amplitude at the input to the non-linear element. As a result we have the following forced oscillations at the output of the non-linear element (fundamental component):

$$x_2 \approx aA_n(a) \sin[\omega t + \beta_n(a)] .$$

For example, the output quantity x_2 of the relay circuit with characteristic of Fig. 267a varies during the forced oscillations as shown by the continuous polygonal line in Fig. 292c. The broken line shows the fundamental sinusoid of component, where from (65.8) and (61.35) we have

$$a_2 = aA_n = \frac{4c}{\pi} \sin \frac{u_2 - u_1}{2} = \frac{2c\sqrt{2}}{\pi} \sqrt{1 - \frac{mb^2}{a^2} + \sqrt{\left(1 - \frac{b^2}{a^2}\right)\left(1 - \frac{m^2 b^2}{a^2}\right)}} ,$$

$$\beta_n = -\left(\frac{u_1 + u_2}{2} - \frac{\pi}{2}\right) = -\tan^{-1} \frac{b(1-m)}{\sqrt{a^2 - b^2} + \sqrt{a^2 - m^2 b^2}} .$$

The actual stepwise curve is replaced in this case by a sinusoid (fundamental component), the peak of which coincides with the axis of symmetry of the actual rectangul r waveform (Fig. 292c).

For non-linear elements with equations the form $x_2 = F(x_1)$ without hysteresis loop, as we know from Section 61, $q_1(a) = 0$. Consequently, for such elements $A_n = q(a)$ and $\beta_n = 0$, i.e. the forced oscillations do not have a phase shift at the output.

One of the principal differences in the character of forced oscillations in non-linear systems from those in linear is their essential dependence not only on the frequency but on the amplitude of the input oscillation. This principal property is registered by the approximate expression for the amplitude-phase characteristic written here for the non-linear element. In formulae (65.6)–(65.8) we

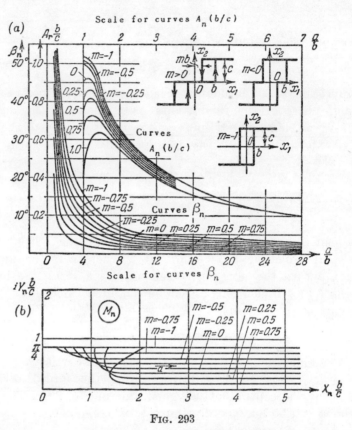

Fig. 293

obtained a dependence only on amplitude *a*, since consideration was limited only to non-linearities of the type $x_2 = F(x_1)$. For more complicated non-linear elements the frequency ω also enters into the amplitude-phase characteristic. In addition, as we shall see below, a dependence on frequency will always enter through the linear part of the system.

In Section 61 we presented expressions $q(a)$ and $q_1(a)$ for the most typical relay and other simple non-linear elements. On this basis we plot approximate amplitude and phase characteristics, calculating according to formulae (65.8). The results for the simplest cases are presented in Figs. 293 and 294 (the graphs are taken from the work by L. S. Gol'dfarb, 1947). They also present the inverse amplitude-phase characteristics

$$M_n(a) = \frac{1}{W_n(a)} = X_n(a) + iY_n(a) . \qquad (65.9)$$

The graphs indicate all necessary notation and the types of non-linear element characteristics. It is possible similarly to plot graphs for other specific non-linear elements.

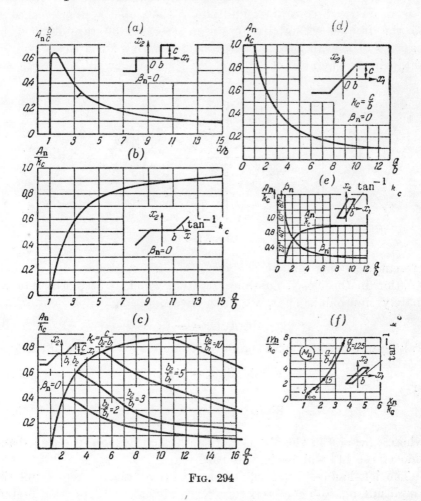

Fig. 294

The amplitude-phase characteristic of the linear part of the system will have, according to (65.2), the form

$$W_l(i\omega) = \frac{R_l(i\omega)}{Q_l(i\omega)} . \qquad (65.10)$$

The overall approximate amplitude-phase characteristic of the closed network with non-linear element will be

$$W(a, \omega) = W_n(a) W_l(i\omega) = [q(a) + iq_1(a)] W_l(i\omega) . \qquad (65.11)$$

Consequently, the amplitude and phase of the fundamental component of the output quantity x_3, defined by the formulae

$$a_3 = |W(a, \omega)|a \quad \text{and} \quad \beta_3 = \arg W(a, \omega), \qquad (65.12)$$

depend here not on the frequency ω as in linear systems, but also on the input amplitude a.

Finding self-oscillations in closed systems. Undamped sinusoidal oscillations with constant amplitude in the closed system, according to the frequency stability criterion (Section 30) are defined by passage of the amplitude-phase characteristic of the closed system through the point $(-1, i0)$, i.e. by the equality $W = -1$. In the

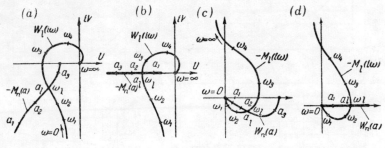

Fig. 295

present case this will be the condition for existence of a periodic solution in the closed non-linear system which is assumed approximately sinusoidal. Thus, we have the condition

$$W(a, \omega) = -1 .$$

Taking into account (65.11) and (65.9) we may write this in the form

$$W_l(i\omega) = -M_n(a) \qquad (65.13)$$

or

$$W_l(i\omega) = -\frac{1}{q(a)+iq_1(a)} , \qquad (65.14)$$

where $q_1(a) = 0$ in the absence of the hysteresis loop (the right-hand side of (65.14) will be in this case real).

The left-hand side of equation (65.14) or (65.13) represents the amplitude-phase characteristic of the linear part of the system while the right-hand side, the amplitude-phase characteristic of the non-linear element (fundamental component), taken with opposite sign. This equation may be solved graphically as the point of intersection of the two characteristics (Fig. 295a and b). At the point of intersection we take from the curve $W_l(i\omega)$ the value of the frequency ω_l while from the curve $M_n(a)$ we take the amplitude a_l of the required periodic solution. Fig. 295a corresponds to a system with non-linear element having a hysteresis loop, when, from (65.6) and (65.9), the characteristic $M_n(a)$ is complex. In the absence of the hysteresis loop when $M_n(a)$ is real, we obtain the graph of Fig. 295b.

In place of (65.13) it is possible to employ also the expression

$$-\frac{1}{W_l(i\omega)} = W_n(a) , \tag{65.15}$$

i.e. to seek a solution as the point of intersection of the amplitude-phase characteristic of the non-linear element with the inverse amplitude-phase characteristic of the linear part of the system taken with reversed sign (Fig. 295c and d).

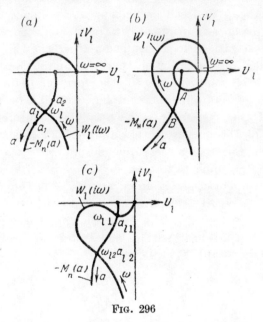

Fig. 296

The stability of the periodic solution is roughly estimated as follows (this method is not rigorous, but in many cases its application is sufficient). We give a small increment of amplitude $a = a_l + \Delta a$. Then with positive Δa we obtain on the curve $- M_n(a)$, for example, the point a_1 (Fig. 296a), while with negative Δa, the point a_2. For the periodic solution to be stable it is obviously necessary that with positive Δa the oscillations are damped while with negative Δa they diverge. From the frequency criterion (Section 30) for a stable or neutral closed system it is necessary that the resultant amplitude-phase characteristic $W(a, \omega)$ in the first case should not enclose the point $(-1, i0)$ and in the second should enclose it. But the overall characteristic $W(a, \omega)$ is not plotted in this method. Therefore the above conclusion must be extended to the properties of the curves $W_l(i\omega)$ and $- M_n(a)$.

From this we find that for the periodic solution to be stable (if the linear part of the system in the open state is stable or neutral) it is necessary that the amplitude-phase characteristic of the linear part $W_l(i\omega)$ not enclose the point a_1 corresponding to positive Δa and enclose the point a_2 corresponding to negative Δa. From this criterion the graphs of Fig. 296a and Fig. 296b (at the point B) give a stable periodic solution which corresponds to self-oscillations in the closed system at frequency ω_l and amplitude a_l.

In the graph of Fig. 296c the values ω_{l_1} and a_{l_1} correspond to unstable while the values ω_{l_2}, a_{l_2} to stable periodic solutions. In the simplest case this may signify small-signal stability of the system (up to amplitude a_{l_1}) and self oscillations at frequency ω_{l_2} and amplitude a_{l_2} if the initial amplitude of the transient exceeds the value a_{l_1}.

In such investigations it is assumed, either that all system parameters be given numerically, or that the amplitude-phase characteristics of the elements appear in the form of definite graphs. If it is required to determine the influence of one or two arbitrary parameters of the system it is necessary to consider all possible combinations of the curves $W_l(i\omega)$ and $-M_n(a)$ for various values of these parameters using the same methods.

Let us consider some examples.

Automatic temperature regulation system. The equations of the automatic temperature regulation system with a relay element were derived in Section 53. The expression for the amplitude-phase characteristic of the linear part of the system according to (53.18), neglecting the constant T_2, will be

$$W_l(i\omega) = \frac{k_3}{(T_3 i\omega + 1)i\omega} \left[\frac{k_1 k_2}{T_1 i\omega + 1} + k_{fb} \right]. \qquad (65.16)$$

In this case it is obvious that the common denominator of the transfer function of the linear part of the system

$$Q_l(p) = (T_1 p + 1)(T_3 p + 1)p \qquad (65.17)$$

has no roots with positive real part while the zero root indicates that the linear part of the system is neutral.

The expression in square brackets in (65.16) with $k_{fb} = 0$ (system without feedback) corresponds to an aperiodic element (regulated object and sensitive element). It is represented in Fig. 297a. In the presence of stiff feedback in the system ($k_{fb} \neq 0$) this graph shifts to the right by the quantity k_{fb} (Fig. 297b).

The coefficient outside the square brackets in (65.16) corresponds to an aperiodic integrating element (drive with regulating organ). It is represented in Fig. 297c.

Multiplying these characteristics (by the rules of Section 20) we obtain the amplitude-phase characteristics $W_l(i\omega)$ of the linear part of the system (in the open state) in the absence of feedback (Fig. 297d) and in the presence of stiff feedback (Fig. 297e). We plot on the same graph the curve inverse in magnitude and opposite in sign to the amplitude-phase characteristic $-M_n(a)$ of the non-linear element (in this case a relay). Here this curve is represented

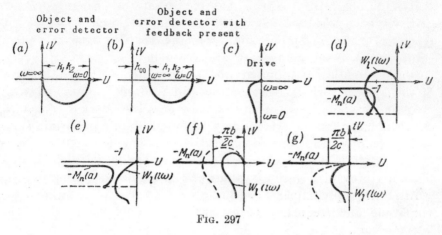

Fɪɢ. 297

in accordance with Fig. 293b for the case where the relay is characterised by the graph of Fig. 234b, with the quantities Δs_1 and Δs_2 given as constants.

As is evident from Fig. 297d, self-oscillation is possible in the closed regulation system without feedback since the curves $W_1(i\omega)$ and $-M_n(a)$ intersect while introduction of the feedback may eliminate these oscillations (Fig. 297e). It is also obvious that with choice of parameters for the linear part of the system (i.e. deformation of the curve W_l in Fig. 297d) it would be possible to eliminate oscillation of the closed non-linear system even without feedback. On the contrary, an unsuccessful choice of parameters may lead to oscillations of the system even in the presence of stiff feedback if in Fig. 297e the curves intersect. The smaller the hysteresis loop, i.e. the smaller the quantities Δs_1 and Δs_2 (Fig. 234b) the greater will be m (Fig. 293) and the easier, as is evident in Fig. 293b and Fig. 297d, e will it be to make the closed system stable.

When the relay has a purely hysteresis characteristic (Fig. 234g, where the quantity s_τ is given as constant), the curve $-M_n(a)$ degenerates according to Fig. 293b ($m = -1$) into a straight line (broken line in Fig. 297e), where in this case it is not possible to achieve elimination of oscillation, but its amplitude may be decreased.

If in the graph of Fig. 234b for our relay with zone of insensitivity there is no hysteresis loop ($\Delta s_1 = \Delta s_2 = 0$), then from Fig. 294$a$

and formula (65.9) the inverse amplitude-phase characteristic of the non-linear element $-M_n(a)$ will be real, as shown in Fig 297f and g. Here the closed system without feedback may be oscillatory if $W_l(i\omega)$ has the form shown by the broken line (Fig 297f). Introduction of stiff feedback, as is evident from Fig 297g, completely eliminates oscillation

From this preliminary examination we may conclude, firstly, that additional stiff feedback has important stabilising properties in the system and, secondly, that the zone of insensitivity of the relay has stabilising properties. From the point of view of system stabilising it is advantageous to increase both of these. However, these possibilities are limited due to increase of the static error of the system with increase of the stiff feedback factor and with increase of zone of insensitivity of the relay. The latter is connected with the fact that the system may be found in an equilibrium state at any point of the zone of insensitivity; a uniquely defined equilibrium state is not obtained but an entire region of possible equilibrium states with various values of the regulated quantity.

After these preliminary conclusions we proceed to determine the amplitude and frequency of oscillation in those cases where the latter occurs.

For an ideal relay characteristic in accordance with (65.7) and (61.38) we have

$$-M_n(a) = -\frac{1}{W_n(a)} = -\frac{\pi}{4c}a \qquad (0 \leqslant a \leqslant \infty) \qquad (65.18)$$

(the entire negative real axis is filled, Fig 298a). Therefore $W_1(i\omega)$ in the absence of stiff feedback (continuous curve) intersects it and the presence of stiff feedback does not intersect it (broken line curve). In the first case we obtain the point of intersection D, defining the periodic solution (a_l, ω_l). It will be stable (i.e. correspond to self-oscillation), since the curve $W_l(i\omega)$ encloses the segment of the straight line $-M_n(a)$ with smaller amplitudes (the linear part is neutral according to (63.17), as a result of which this criterion may be applied). In the second case curve $W_l(i\omega)$ intersects the straight line $-M_n(a)$ only at the point where $a = 0$, $\omega = \infty$, i.e. oscillations are absent (a small amplitude would be obtained here if we did not neglect the constant T_2).

The amplitude of oscillation a_l is defined in the first case by the distance 1 (Fig. 298a) along the line $-M_n(a)$ to the point of intersection, where, taking into account (65.18), we obtain

$$a_l = \frac{4c}{\pi l}, \qquad (65.19)$$

where l is taken from the graph or calculated according to

$$l = - U_l(\omega_l) ,$$

and the oscillation frequency ω_l is found from the condition

$$V_l(\omega_l) = 0 ,$$

if $U_1(\omega_l)$ and $V_1(\omega_l)$ denote the real and imaginary parts of the expression $W_l(i\omega)$ which, from (65.16) with $k_{fb} = 0$, has the form

$$W_l(i\omega) = \frac{k_1 k_2 k_3}{(T_1 i\omega + 1)(T_3 i\omega + 1) i\omega} . \qquad (65.20)$$

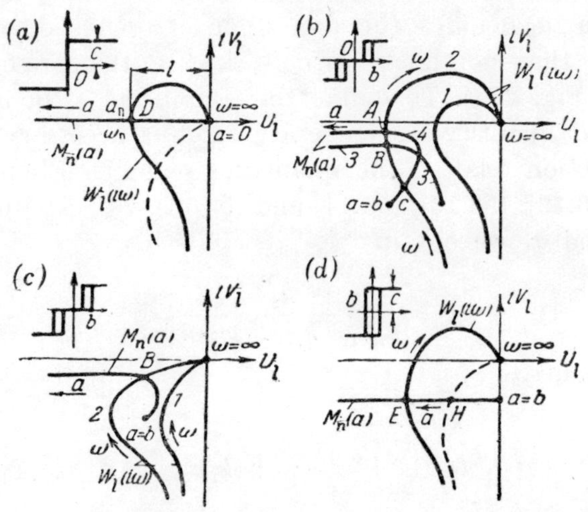

Fig. 298

From this it is evident, for example, that with increase of transfer factor of the regulator $k_2 k_3$ the amplitude of oscillation increases.

For the relay characteristic in the form of Fig. 234b (with given Δs_1 and Δs_2) the behaviour of the system without stiff feedback is found from Fig. 298b. Here self-oscillation may be absent (curve 1 of Fig. 298b), a single periodic solution is possible (curves 2 and 3, intersecting at the point B) or two periodic solutions (curves 2 and 4, intersecting at the points A and C). Here the curve 3 corresponds to smaller while the curve 4 to larger values of m in the relay characteristic (Fig. 293). The points B and A correspond to stable oscillations. The point C corresponds to an unstable periodic process which may signify small-signal stability of the system (with $a < a_C$) and a tendency to oscillation with amplitude $a = a_A$ for large signals. The amplitude and frequency of oscillation are defined from the same curves at the points of intersection.

In the present case the effect of the regulator transfer factor $k_2 k_3$ (without stiff feedback) consists in that increasing $k_2 k_3$, we pass, according to (65.20), from the curve 1 to the curve 2 (Fig. 298b), i. e. oscillations appear in the system only when the transfer factor $k_2 k_3$ exceeds a certain limiting value defined by the instant of tangency of curve 1 to curve 3 or 4.

Oscillations in the presence of stiff feedback are defined analogously, as shown in Fig. 298c.

Finally, with a purely hysteresis relay characteristic we obtain only an oscillatory process (Fig. 298d), with amplitude and frequency in the absence of stiff feedback defined by the point E and in its presence by the point H.

In all the above cases, as in general in the frequency method under consideration, a_l denotes the amplitude of oscillation of the input quantity to the non-linear circuit, i.e. in the present case the quantity s (Fig. 233). To define the amplitude a_θ of oscillation of the regulated quantity θ (temperature), it is necessary to find the transfer function relating the quantities s and θ. Eliminating from equations (53.12), (53.16), (53.14) and (53.13) with $T_2 = 0$ the quantities ξ, x_{fb} and x, we obtain

$$\theta = \frac{k_1}{k_1 k_2 + k_{fb}(T_1 p + 1)} s \, ,$$

and consequently,

$$a_\theta = \frac{k_1 a_l}{|k_1 k_2 + k_{fb}(T_1 i \omega_l + 1)|} = \frac{k_1 a_l}{\sqrt{(k_1 k_2 + k_{fb})^2 + k_{fb}^2 T_1^2 \omega_l^2}} \, . \quad (65.21)$$

For a system without feedback ($k_{fb} = 0$) we have

$$a_\theta = \frac{a_l}{k_2} \, . \quad (65.22)$$

It is similarly possible to determine the amplitude of the fundamental component of oscillation for other variables in the system.

Taking account of time delay in the relay. Analysing the above example of an automatic temperature regulation system we assumed that in the relay characteristic Fig. 234 the quantities Δs_1, Δs_2, s_τ were given as constants, i.e. the relay characteristic had an ordinary hysteresis form with opening and closing of the relay given by the input coordinate. In deriving the temperature regulation system equations in Section 53 it was found that the relay in this system is a non-linear element with delay, i.e. the corresponding time delays τ_1, τ_2, τ were given while the quantities Δs_1, Δs_2, s_τ are unknown and defined by the course of the process itself.

In investigating such a non-linear system with delay we assume for simplicity that $\tau_1 = \tau_2 = \tau$, i.e. that the delays in operating and releasing of the relay are the same. Such a non-linear element with delay may be separated into two parts: (1) an ordinary non-linear element characterised by the graph of Fig. 299*b*, or *c*, and (2) a delay element described by the equation (Section 45)

$$x_2^* = x_2 e^{-\tau p} .$$

It will then be possible to write the expression for the amplitude-phase characteristic of the linear part of the system together with the delay element in the form

$$W_{l3}(i\omega) = W_l(i\omega) e^{-i\tau\omega} = \frac{R(i\omega)}{Q(i\omega)} e^{-i\tau\omega} . \tag{65.23}$$

The rule for plotting such a characteristic is described in Section 45.

Let the relay be characterised by the curve in Fig. 234*b* while

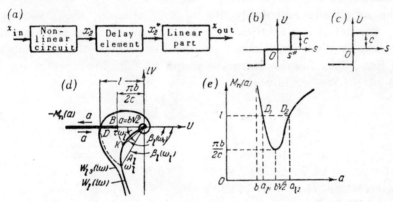

Fig. 299

after separation of the delay element by Fig. 299*b*. In this case for a system with stiff feedback we obtain the curves $W_l(i\omega)$ and $W_{l3}(i\omega)$ shown in Fig. 299*d* and the straight line $M_n(a)$ on the basis of formula (65.9) and Fig. 294*a*. If the curves $W_{l3}(i\omega)$ and $-M_n(a)$ intersect, oscillations will occur. But, as is evident from Fig. 299*d*, with sufficiently small delays τ these curves need not intersect, i.e. oscillations will be absent.

Here, as in linear systems, a critical time delay may be defined up to which oscillations are absent, which may be found without plotting the curve $W_{l3}(i\omega)$, only from the curves $W_l(i\omega)$ and $-M_n(a)$. In fact, in the critical case some point of the curve $W_{l3}(i\omega)$ is incident on the extreme point B (Fig. 299*d*). This, as is evident from the drawing, corresponds to a point K on the curve $W_l(i\omega)$ at which

$$\left. \begin{aligned} A_l(\omega_k) &= \frac{\pi b}{2c}, \\ \beta_l(\omega_k) - \tau_k \omega_k &= -\pi \quad (\beta_l < 0) . \end{aligned} \right\} \tag{65.24}$$

From the first condition we find the magnitude of ω_k and from the second the critical time delay

$$\tau_k = \frac{1}{\omega_k}[\pi + \beta_l(\omega_k)] \qquad (\beta_l < 0) . \qquad (65.25)$$

This solution may be found directly from the graph $W_l(i\omega)$ or analytically, employing expression (65.16).

If the relay has no zone of insensitivity, i.e. $b = 0$, then the point B is incident on the origin of coordinates in Fig. 299d and oscillations will occur for any value of time delay in relay operation ($\tau_k = 0$). It is therefore expedient that the time delay in the relay considered here be relatively small while the zone of insensitivity have a large value (but not exceed permissible values from static calculation of the precision of regulation).

The amplitude and frequency of oscillation in the presence of delay are defined as follows. The point of intersection D (Fig. 299d) gives two periodic solutions since the line $-M_n(a)$ has two values of a here. This follows from the graph of Fig. 294a, where on the basis of (61.36) we have

$$M_n(a) = \frac{1}{W_n(a)} = \frac{\pi a^2}{4c\sqrt{b^2 - a^2}} , \qquad (65.26)$$

which is represented by the graph of Fig. 299e. Two points D_1 and D_2 on the graph of Fig. 299e correspond to the distance 1 of the point of intersection D in Fig. 299d, giving two values of amplitude a_{l_1} and a_{l_2}. The frequency ω_l of the two periodic solutions is the same and is defined by the point D on the curve $W_{l_3}(i\omega)$.

Here the periodic solution with smaller amplitude a_{l_1} will be unstable and with larger amplitude a_{l_2} stable, since in the first case the point with positive increment Δa on the line $-M_n(a)$ is enclosed by the curve $W_{l_3}(i\omega)$ while in the second case is not enclosed. Consequently the system may be small-signal stable (to amplitude a_{l_1}) and large-signal oscillatory, with the amplitude to which the system tends with initial transient amplitudes exceeding the value a_{l_1}.

We note that the point of intersection D of the curve $W_{l_3}(i\omega)$ with the line $-M_n(a)$ may be found without plotting the curve $W_{l_3}(i\omega)$ directly from the amplitude-phase characteristic $W_l(i\omega)$ of the linear part of the system without the delay element. For this it is necessary to find a point ω_l on the curve $W_l(i\omega)$ (Fig. 299d) which with rotation of the vector A_1 by the angle ω_l would be incident on the line $-M_n(a)$, which gives us the point D (magnitude of delay τ given, ω_l unknown). The condition for finding ω_l in the present case will be:

$$\tau\omega_l + |\beta_l| = \pi;$$

after this we find the value $l = A_l$ and then the amplitude of oscillation a_{l_2} from the graph of Fig. 299e.

After this we calculate the amplitude a_θ of the oscillation in the regulated quantity θ from (65.21) or (65.22).

Aircraft course automatic regulation system with limited-linear rudder characteristic. The equations of such a system were presented in Section 55. The characteristic of the non-linear element (Fig. 239) relates to the form $x_2 = F(x_1)$, as a result of which it is possible here to apply the above-described frequency method. The amplitude-phase characteristics of the linear part of the system consists of the aircraft characteristic which, from (55.2), has the form

$$W_c(i\omega) = \frac{k_1(T_2 i\omega + 1)}{[(T_1 i\omega + 1)(T_2 i\omega + 1) + k_2 T_2]i\omega} , \qquad (65.27)$$

and the autopilot characteristics from (55.4)

$$W_a(i\omega) = \frac{x_\psi k_{\dot\psi} + ki\omega - k_{\ddot\psi}\omega^2}{(T_3 i\omega + 1)(T_4 i\omega + 1)i\omega + k_{fb}} ; \qquad (65.28)$$

the result is

$$W_l(i\omega) = W_c(i\omega) \cdot W_a(i\omega) . \qquad (65.29)$$

The common denominator of the transfer function of the linear part will thus be

$$Q(p) = p[(T_1 p + 1)(T_2 p + 1) + k_2 T_2][(T_3 p + 1)(T_4 p + 1)p + k_{fb}] .$$

Since for a quadratic trinomial (in the first square brackets) the absence of roots with positive real parts ensures positiveness of all coefficients, for such roots to be absent from the entire polynomial $Q(p)$ it is necessary and sufficient that they not be present in the polynomial

$$Q_a(p) = [(T_3 p + 1)(T_4 p + 1)p + k_{fb}] ,$$

i.e. that the auxiliary Mikhailov curve $Q_a(i\omega)$ have the form shown in Fig. 300a or that the Vyshnegradskii criterion (29.2) and (29.3) for $Q_a(p)$ to be satisfied. The Mikhailov curve $Q_a(i\omega)$ in Fig. 300b corresponds to a single root while in Fig. 300c to a pair of roots of the polynomial $Q_a(p)$ with positive real part.

Thus, if the condition of Fig. 300a is satisfied (or the Vyshnegradskii criterion) and in the expression

$$Q_c(p) = p[(T_1 p + 1)(T_2 p + 1) + k_2 T_2]$$

all coefficients are positive, we may apply the previously described formulation of the stability of the periodic solution.

If the autopilot has no feedback ($k_{fb} = 0$), then

$$Q(p) = p^2[(T_1 p + 1)(T_2 p + 1) + k_2 T_2](T_3 p + 1)(T_4 p + 1) ,$$

and to have possibility of applying the above formulation it is sufficient only to have all coefficients of $Q(p)$ positive.

Let us consider here an autopilot without feedback und without introduction of the second derivative ($k_{fb} = k_{\ddot{v}} = 0$). The amplitude-phase characteristics (65.27), (65.28), (65.29) for this case are shown in Fig. 301a, b, c, respectively.

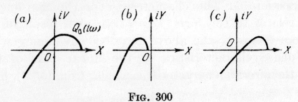

FIG. 300

The approximate amplitude-phase characteristic of the non-linear element $W(a) = q(a)$ from Fig. 239 is defined by formula (61.42) in which it is necessary to put $c = \delta_m$ and $k = 1$. Graphically it is represented in Fig. 294d. Therefore the amplitude-phase charac-

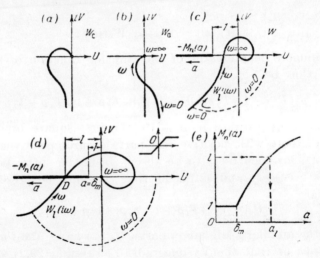

FIG. 301

teristic inverse in magnitude and opposite in sign $- M_n(a)$ is located on the negative part of the real axis (Fig. 301) to the left of the point $(-1, i0)$. With this relative disposition of characteristics, as in Fig. 301c, oscillations will be absent from the closed system "aircraft–course–autopilot".

It is interesting to note that in the case of a linear system, when in the equations of Section 55 we have $\delta_1 = \delta$, then $W(i\omega) = W_l(i\omega)$. Therefore the condition obtained for absence of oscillation (not enclosing the point $(-1, i0)$ of the characteristic $W_l(i\omega)$ in Fig. 301c) coincides with the condition for stability of the linear system (without limiting the rudder travel). But the behaviour of linear systems and systems with limited-linear rudder characteristics will be substantially different when the characteristic $W_l(i\omega)$ encloses the point $(-1, i0)$. In particular, the linear system will be unstable while the non-linear (with bounded rudder travel) takes on, as evident from Fig. 301*d*, stable oscillations defined by the point of intersection *D*. The oscillation frequency is taken from the point *D* on the curve $W_l(i\omega)$, while to find the amplitude of oscillation a_l the distance *l* is taken from the drawing Fig. 301*d* and from it we find a_l, using the graph of Fig. 301*e*. This graph is plotted according to (65.7) and (61.42) with $k = 1$ and $c = \delta_m$, from the formula

$$M_n(a) = \frac{1}{W_n(a)} = \frac{\pi}{2} : \left(\sin^{-1}\frac{\delta_m}{a} + \frac{\delta_m}{a} \sqrt{1 - \frac{\delta_m^2}{a^2}} \right).$$

Here it is necessary to consider that a_l denotes the amplitude of oscillation of the input quantity to the non-linear element, i.e. the artificially introduced quantity δ_1. To determine the amplitude of fundamental component a_ψ of aircraft oscillation over the course, it is necessary to employ according to equation (55.5) the amplitude characteristic of the autopilot, namely

$$\frac{a_l}{a_\psi} = |W_a(i\omega_l)|,$$

from which

$$a_\psi = \frac{a_l}{|W_a(i\omega_l)|}, \tag{65.30}$$

where $W_a(i\omega)$ is defined by formula (65.28) or the graph of Fig. 301*b*. It is similarly possible to determine the amplitude of the fundamental components of oscillations in other variables of the given regulation system.

Thus, the bounded linear characteristic shown in Fig. 301*d* (analogous to a characteristic with saturation) leads to the presence of a stable oscillation beyond the limits of the boundary of stability in place of divergent oscillations, where the amplitude of stable oscillations increases with distance from the stability region. Practical limits are connected here with the admissible magnitude of oscillation a_l. In addition, it is important to recall that this entire theory is valid only for such deviations for which the given automatic system equations are valid—in the present case, to the extent that the linearised aircraft equations remain valid.

66. Bulgakov's approximate methods

B. V. Bulgakov in articles published in 1942 and 1946 developed in parallel two alternatives to the approximate method of the small parameter for studying non-linear automatic regulation systems of arbitrary order. They derive, on the one hand, from the well-known methods of Liapunov and Poincaré, and on the other hand, they are a development of the Krylov-Bogoliubov ideas, with which we have become partially acquainted in Section 60 *et seq.* We present here only the applied aspect of these methods in a form enabling them to be employed for investigating specific non-linear automatic regulation systems.

Later, for a certain class of equations, A. I. Lur'e developed an analogous method which is presented below as a third method.

These methods are as approximate as those in the previous sections.

First Bulgakov method. Let the automatic regulation system be described by several differential equations in which there are non-linear terms. Each non-linear term, as in Section 60, is represented

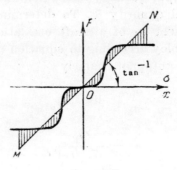

Fig. 302

in the form of a sum of a principal linear component and a "small" non-linear increment. For example, if there is a non-linear term $F(x)$, the graph of which is shown in Fig. 302, we write it in the form

$$F(x) = hx + \varepsilon f(x), \qquad (66.1)$$

where h is the slope of the substituted straight line MN, plotted as yet arbitrarily, while $\varepsilon f(x)$ is a "small" non-linear increment, the graph of which is represented by the ordinates hatched in Fig. 302.

All the differential equations of the transient in the non-linear automatic system will be written so that the left-hand sides are linear (including the linear components hx (66.1) of the non-linear terms), while the right-hand sides have only "small" non-linear increments $\varepsilon f(x)$. Let the equations of the transient process in the regulation system (in symbolic operational form) take the form

$$
\left.
\begin{aligned}
\Phi_{11}(p)x_1 + \Phi_{12}(p)x_2 + \ldots + \Phi_{1m}(p)x_m &= \varepsilon f_1(x_1, \ldots, x_m) , \\
\Phi_{21}(p)x_1 + \Phi_{22}(p)x_2 + \ldots + \Phi_{2m}(p)x_m &= \varepsilon f_2(x_1, \ldots, x_m) , \\
&\cdots\cdots\cdots\cdots\cdots\cdots\cdots\cdots \\
\Phi_{m1}(p)x_1 + \Phi_{m2}(p)x_2 + \ldots + \Phi_{mm}(p)x_m &= \varepsilon f_m(x_1, \ldots, x_m) ,
\end{aligned}
\right\}
\tag{66.2}
$$

where by $\Phi_{ji}(p)$ we denote operational polynomials. This is a very general form for the equations. Ordinarily, in concrete automatic regulation systems only two or three variables will be present in each equation, i.e. many of the operators Φ_{ji} will vanish while the remaining will have low degrees. Many of the right-hand sides (66.2) will also vanish and only in certain right-hand sides will non-linear increments εf_j in one or two variables be present (and possibly their derivatives). For example, the system element equations will have such a form; then the number of variables m will correspond to the number of elements in the system (n will denote below, as always, the order of the overall equation of the system).

The linear system obtained from (66.2) by dropping all right-hand sides is termed the simplified system.

The characteristic equation of the simplified system will be denoted by

$$
D(z) = 0 , \tag{66.3}
$$

where all its coefficients will be assumed positive.

To determine the periodic solutions of the non-linear system (66.2) we assume that in the characteristic equation (66.3) of the simplified system there is a pair of purely imaginary roots $z = \pm i\omega_0$. In this case the left-hand side of equation (66.3) may be written in the form

$$
D(z) = (z^2 + \omega_0^2)D_1(z) , \tag{66.4}
$$

where the polynomial $D_1(z)$ has a degree lower than the degree of $D(z)$ by two. The quantity ω_0 and all coefficients of the polynomial $D_1(z)$ are found by equating expressions (66.4) and (66.3).

For example, in the case of a fourth-order system, when the characteristic equation of the simplified system (66.3) has the form

$$
a_0 z^4 + a_1 z^3 + a_2 z^2 + a_3 z + a_4 = 0 , \tag{66.5}
$$

equation (66.4) is written in the form

$$
(z^2 + \omega_0^2)(b_0 z^2 + b_1 z + b_2) = 0 ,
$$

where $\omega_0^2, b_0, b_1, b_2$ are unknown. Eliminating parentheses

$$
b_0 z^4 + b_1 z^3 + (b_2 + b_0 \omega_0^2)z^2 + b_1 \omega_0^2 z + b_2 \omega_0^2 = 0
$$

and equating the coefficients of this equation with the coefficients of (66.5), we find, firstly, from the average coefficients

$$b_2 + b_0 \omega_0^2 = a_2 \tag{66.6}$$

and, secondly, from all remaining coefficients

$$b_0 = a_0 , \quad b_1 = a_1 , \quad \omega_0^2 = \frac{a_3}{b_1} = \frac{a_3}{a_1}, \quad b_2 = \frac{a_4}{\omega_0^2} = \frac{a_4 a_1}{a_3}, \tag{66.7}$$

where the third relation is particularly important, defining the quantity ω_0. Substituting from here the values ω_0^2, b_0, b_2 in formula (66.6), we obtain

$$a_3(a_1 a_2 - a_0 a_3) - a_4 a_1^2 = 0 . \tag{66.8}$$

From (29.19) this is the condition that the simplified (linear) system be found on the boundary of stability (with purely imaginary roots in the characteristic equation), if all coefficients a_0, a_1, a_2, a_3, a_4 are positive.

Thus, in comparing coefficients of expressions (66.4) and the given equation (66.3) all coefficients of the polynomial $D_1(z)$ and the quantity ω_0 are defined and the conditions for finding the simplified system on the boundary of stability are identically satisfied, taking the form in the present case, according to (29.24),

$$\Delta_{n-1} = 0 , \tag{66.9}$$

where Δ_{n-1} is the penultimate Hurwitz determinant for the characteristic equation of the simplified system (66.3). Here all previous Hurwitz determinants and the coefficient a_1 should be positive.

The periodic solution of the simplified system ((66.2) with $\varepsilon = 0$) will now have the form

$$x_j^* = A_0(L_j \sin \omega_0 t + M_j \cos \omega_0 t) . \tag{66.10}$$

where A_0 is a coefficient to be determined below while L_j and M_j are defined as the real and imaginary parts of the following expression:

$$L_j + i M_j = \frac{F_{lj}(i\omega_0)}{F_{lg}(i\omega_0)}, \tag{66.11}$$

where $F_{lj}(i\omega_0)$ is the algebraic complement (minor) of the element $\Phi_{lj}(p)$ in the operational determinant

$$\left. \begin{array}{cccc} \Phi_{11}(p) & \Phi_{12}(p) & \dots & \Phi_{1m}(p) \\ \Phi_{21}(p) & \Phi_{22}(p) & \dots & \Phi_{2m}(p) \\ \dots & \dots & \dots & \dots \\ \Phi_{m1}(p) & \Phi_{m2}(p) & \dots & \Phi_{mm}(p) \end{array} \right\} \quad \text{with} \quad p = i\omega_0 , \tag{66.12}$$

derived on the basis of the given equations of the regulation system (66.2). We note that the left-hand side of the characteristic equation (66.3) is the same determinant, in which the letter p is substituted by the letter z.

For the quantity $F_{lg}(i\omega_0)$ in formula (66.11) we select at will one of the non-zero algebraic complements $F_{lj}(i\omega)$.

The periodic solution for the non-linear system (66.2) with $\varepsilon \neq 0$ is constructed as follows. In place of t we introduce the new independent variable

$$\tau = (1+\alpha)t, \tag{66.13}$$

where $\alpha \neq 0$ with $\varepsilon \neq 0$ and $\alpha = 0$ with $\varepsilon = 0$ (it becomes defined below). Here the previous differential operator $p = d/dt$ substituted by the new $p' = d/d\tau$. It is obvious that

$$p = (1+\alpha)p'. \tag{66.14}$$

In the required periodic solution we limit ourselves to the first approximation in the form

$$x_j \approx x_j^* + \left(\frac{\partial x_j}{\partial \varepsilon}\right)_{\varepsilon=0} \varepsilon \quad (j = 1, 2, ..., m), \tag{66.15}$$

where x_j^* is defined by formula (66.10), i.e. this is the solution with $\varepsilon = 0$. To find the additional term of the solution (66.15) we differentiate the given equations of the regulation system (66.2) with respect to ε, taking into account (66.14). We then apply the Fourier series expansion and write the condition for a periodic solution. As a result of this and further auxiliary transformations we come to the following relationship:

$$A_0\left[\frac{\partial D(z)}{\partial z} z\alpha\right]_{z=i\omega_0} = \frac{i}{\pi} \sum_{l=1}^{m} F_{lg}(i\omega_0) \int_0^{2\pi} \varepsilon f_l(x_1^*, x_2^*, ..., x_m^*) e^{-iu} du, \tag{66.16}$$

where $D(z)$ is the left-hand side of the characteristic equation (66.3), $u = \omega_0 t$, $F_{lg}(i\omega_0)$ are the algebraic complements analogous to those entering into (66.11). The integrands in (66.16) contain the non-linear (right-hand) sides of the regulation system equations (66.2) where we have substituted in them the expressions $x_1^*, x_2^*, ..., x_m^*$, defined by formula (66.10). These integrals have the same significance of average over the period as in the Krylov-Bogoliubov method (Section 60).

Separating the real and imaginary parts in (66.16) we obtain two equations to determine two unknowns A and α.

The required periodic solution is written in the form

$$x_j = A_0(L_j \sin \omega_l t + M_j \cos \omega_l t), \tag{66.17}$$

where L_j and M_j are as before, $\omega_l = (1+\alpha)\,\omega_0$. The solution obtained (66.17), as is well known, may be written also in the form

$$x_j = A_j \sin(\omega_l t + \delta) \qquad (j = 1, 2, ..., m), \qquad (66.18)$$

where A_j, ω_l, δ are the amplitude, frequency and initial phase of the periodic solution for the variable x_j, characterising the states of various elements of the regulation system according to the given differential equations (66.2). Here

$$\left. \begin{aligned} A_j &= A_0 \sqrt{L_j^2 + M_j^2}, \qquad \delta = \tan^{-1} \frac{L_j}{M_j}, \\ \omega_l &= (1+\alpha)\,\omega_0, \end{aligned} \right\} \qquad (66.19)$$

where L_j and M_j are defined from (66.11) and A_0 and α from (66.16). The quantity A_0 is a coefficient defining the amplitude of the periodic solution, α is the so-called incremental frequency.

Finding in this way the periodic solution, we must investigate its stability. If this solution is stable it will correspond to a real steady-state oscillatory process in the regulation system. If the solution is unstable, in the simplest case it may correspond to an unstable limiting cycle, indicating the boundary for the initial conditions to which the system is small-signal stable. But in this case there may occur in general other patterns of processes.

The stability of oscillations is determined by constructing and analysing the equations in small deviations from the given oscillatory process. The conditions for formation of oscillations in the system are defined on the basis of (66.9) and the following relations. The solution of both these questions is discussed below in specific examples.

The second Bulgakov method. The second Bulgakov method permits writing the approximate equations for the transient response of a system of arbitrary order in a form analogous to equations (60.12) and is based on the transformation of the automatic regulation system equations to equations in normal coordinates.

The differential equations of a non-linear automatic system are given in the form (66.2). Let the characteristic equation (66.3) of the simplified system have n_1 real roots z_k and a further n_2 pairs of complex roots $z_k = \beta_k \pm i\omega_k$, with no multiple roots. As the normal coordinates we take the amplitudes a_k $(k = 1, 2, ..., n_1 + n_2)$ of the individual components $a_k \sin u_k$ of the general solution and the angular variables or phases u_k $(k = n_1 + 1, ..., n_1 + n_2)$. There will obviously be $n = n_1 + 2n_2$ normal coordinates in all (equal to the order of the system). Here a_k and u_k are the required functions of time (exactly the same as a and u in Section 60).

After transformation of the given equations (66.2) to normal coordinates and after "averaging" them (the significance of this is the same as in Section 60) we obtain the following approximate differential equations for determining the amplitudes a_k and phases u_k:

$$
\left.
\begin{aligned}
\frac{da_k}{dt} &= z_k a_k + \frac{1}{(2\pi)^{n_2} D'(z_k)} \sum_{s=1}^{m} B_{sk} \int_0^{2\pi} \cdots \\
&\quad \cdots \int_0^{2\pi} \varepsilon f_s du_{n_1+1} \cdots du_{n_1+n_2} \qquad (k = 1, 2, \ldots, n_1), \\
\frac{da_k}{dt} &= \beta_k a_k + \frac{2}{(2\pi)^{n_2}} \operatorname{Re}\left[\frac{1}{D'(\beta_k + i\omega_k)} \sum_{s=1}^{m} B_{sk} \int_0^{2\pi} \cdots \right. \\
&\quad \left. \cdots \int_0^{2\pi} \varepsilon f_s e^{-iu_k} du_{n_1+1} \cdots du_{n_1+n_2} \right] \\
&\qquad\qquad (k = n_1 + 1. \ldots, n_1 + n_2), \\
\frac{du_k}{dt} &= \omega_k + \frac{2}{(2\pi)^{n_2} a_k} \operatorname{Im}\left[\frac{1}{D'(\beta_k + i\omega_k)} \sum_{s=1}^{m} B_{sk} \int_0^{2\pi} \cdots \right. \\
&\quad \left. \cdots \int_0^{2\pi} \varepsilon f_s e^{-iu_k} du_{n_1+1} \cdots du_{n_1+n_2} \right] \\
&\qquad\qquad (k = n_1 + 1, \ldots, n_1 + n_2),
\end{aligned}
\right\} \qquad (66.20)
$$

where D' is the derivative of the left-hand side of $D(z)$ of the characteristic equation (66.3) with respect to z. The functions εf_s in the integrands are the non-linear (right-hand) parts of the given regulation system equations (66.2), where in place of $x_1, x_2, \ldots, x_m$ in these functions we should substitute their expressions in terms of the normal coordinates:

$$
\left.
\begin{aligned}
x_1 &= \sum_{k=1}^{n_1} K_{1k} a_k + \sum_{k=n_1+1}^{n_1+n_2} N_{1k} a_k \sin(u_k + \delta_{1k}), \\
x_2 &= \sum_{k=1}^{n_1} K_{2k} a_k + \sum_{k=n_1+1}^{n_1+n_2} N_{2k} a_k \sin(u_k + \delta_{2k}), \\
&\cdots\cdots\cdots\cdots\cdots\cdots\cdots\cdots\cdots\cdots\cdots \\
x_m &= \sum_{k=1}^{n_1} K_{mk} a_k + \sum_{k=n_1+1}^{n_1+n_2} N_{mk} a_k \sin(u_k + \delta_{mk}),
\end{aligned}
\right\} \qquad (66.21)
$$

where

$$
\left.
\begin{aligned}
K_{sk} &= \frac{F_{ls}(z_k)}{F_{lg}(z_k)}, \\
N_{sk} e^{i\delta_{sk}} &= \frac{F_{ls}(\beta_k + i\omega_k)}{F_{lg}(\beta_k + i\omega_k)},
\end{aligned}
\right\} \qquad (66.22)
$$

$$
\left.
\begin{aligned}
B_{sk} &= F_{sg}(z_k) && \text{for} \quad k = 1, 2, \ldots, n_1, \\
B_{sk} &= F_{sg}(\beta_k + i\omega_k) && \text{for} \quad k = n_1 + 1, \ldots, n_1 + n_2,
\end{aligned}
\right\} \qquad (66.23)
$$

and F denotes the corresponding algebraic complements, just as in formula (66.11).

Thus the solution for the transient in the system is written in the form (66.21), where the amplitudes $a_k(t)$ and phases $u_k(t)$ are defined from the differential equations (66.20) The transient response in the non-linear automatic regulation system can thus be found to a rough approximation (better methods are given in Part V). We note that if there were no non-linear terms in the system equations (66.2) from (66.20) we would have $a_k = C_k e^{\beta_k t}$ and $u_k = \omega_k t + \vartheta_k$ and the solution (66.21) would take on the usual form for linear systems.

To find the periodic solutions it is necessary to put in equations (66.20)

$$a_k = \text{const}\,, \qquad u_k = (1+\alpha_k)\,\omega_k t\,, \qquad (66.24)$$

and then equation (66.20) serves to define the amplitudes a_k and the corrections α_k to the frequencies of the periodic solution.

Investigating the stability of this periodic solution we see whether it corresponds to steady-state oscillations in the system or if it will be unstable (see Example 1 below).

Third method (Lur'e method). In his monograph (Reference 20) A. I. Lur'e proposes an approximate method for finding self-oscillation in a non-linear automatic regulation system for the two most frequent forms of differential equations already discussed above in Section 58, based on the same theoretical foundations. Let us consider these two cases separately without going into details, which can be found in the cited monograph.

1. Let the equations of the non-linear regulation system have the form

$$\begin{aligned}
\dot{x}_1 &= a_{11}x_1 + a_{12}x_2 + \ldots + a_{1n}x_n + b_1 F(\sigma)\,, \\
\dot{x}_2 &= a_{21}x_1 + a_{22}x_2 + \ldots + a_{2n}x_n + b_2 F(\sigma)\,, \\
&\cdots\cdots\cdots\cdots\cdots\cdots\cdots\cdots\cdots\cdots\cdots\cdots \\
\dot{x}_n &= a_{n1}x_1 + a_{n2}x_2 + \ldots + a_{nn}x_n + b_n F(\sigma)\,, \\
\sigma &= c_1 x_1 + c_2 x_2 + \ldots + c_n x_n\,,
\end{aligned} \qquad (66.25)$$

where, in particular cases, many coefficients may be zero.

We introduce, as in the Bulgakov method, the simplified system (replacing the given non-linear characteristic by a linear one, Fig. 302)

$$\begin{aligned}
\dot{x}_1 &= a_{11}x_1 + a_{12}x_2 + \ldots + a_{1n}x_n + b_1 h\sigma\,, \\
\dot{x}_2 &= a_{21}x_1 + a_{22}x_2 + \ldots + a_{2n}x_n + b_2 h\sigma\,, \\
&\cdots\cdots\cdots\cdots\cdots\cdots\cdots\cdots\cdots\cdots\cdots\cdots \\
\dot{x}_n &= a_{n1}x_1 + a_{n2}x_2 + \ldots + a_{nn}x_n + b_n h\sigma\,, \\
\sigma &= c_1 x_1 + c_2 x_2 + \ldots + c_n x_n\,.
\end{aligned} \qquad (66.26)$$

The characteristic equation of the simplified system is written in the form

$$D(z) - hE(z) = 0 \, , \qquad (66.27)$$

where $hE(z)$ is a polynomial including all the terms of the equation which contain the factor h. The magnitude of h, as before, is taken such that the characteristic equation of the linearised system (66.27) has a pair of purely imaginary roots $\pm i\omega$ (the condition for the presence of a periodic solution) and negative real parts for all remaining roots. Consequently, from (66.27) we have

$$h = \frac{D(i\omega_0)}{E(i\omega_0)} \, . \qquad (66.28)$$

But, since h is real, the imaginary part of this expression should be zero, from which we find the value ω_0, specifically: if we separate the real and imaginary parts in the numerator and denominator of (66.28) in the form

$$D(i\omega_0) = D_1(\omega_0) + iD_2(\omega_0) \, ,$$

$$E(i\omega_0) = E_1(\omega_0) + iE_2(\omega_0) \, ,$$

then

$$\frac{D(i\omega_0)}{E(i\omega_0)} = \frac{D_1 E_1 + D_2 E_2}{E_1^2 + E_2^2} + i \frac{D_2 E_1 - D_1 E_2}{E_1^2 + E_2^2} \, .$$

From this the equation for determining ω_0 takes the form

$$D_2(\omega_0) E_1(\omega_0) - D_1(\omega_0) E_2(\omega_0) = 0 \, , \qquad (66.29)$$

after which the quantity h is found from the formula

$$h = \frac{D_1(\omega_0) E_1(\omega_0) + D_2(\omega_0) E_2(\omega_0)}{[E_1(\omega_0)]^2 + [E_2(\omega_0)]^2} \, . \qquad (66.30)$$

After this we calculate the amplitude a_l of the periodic solution for the quantity σ and the correction to the frequency $\Delta\omega_l$ according to the equation

$$D(i\omega_0) - \vartheta(a_l) E(i\omega_0) = -i[D'(i\omega_0) - hE'(i\omega_0)]\Delta\omega_l \, , \qquad (66.31)$$

where

$$\vartheta(a_l) = \frac{i}{\pi a_l} \int_0^{2\pi} F(a_l \sin u) e^{-iu} du \qquad (66.32)$$

or, which is equivalent,

$$\vartheta(a) = q(a) + iq_1(a) \, , \qquad (66.33)$$

where $q(a)$ and $q_1(a)$ are the same as in the Krylov-Bogoliubov method and are defined by formulae (61.17) from the given non-linear function. The expression $D'(i\omega_0) - hE'(i\omega_0)$ in equation (66.31) denotes the derivative of the left-hand side of the characteristic equation (66.27) with respect to z with subsequent substitution of $i\omega_0$ in place of z.

The expressions $q(a)$ and $q_1(a)$ were calculated in Section 61 for various forms of non-linear characteristics.

Separating the real and imaginary parts in equation (66.31), we obtain two equations with two unknowns: a_l (amplitude) and $\Delta\omega_l$ (correction for frequency). Consequently, the frequency of the periodic solution will be:

$$\omega_l = \omega_0 + \Delta\omega_l, \tag{66.34}$$

where ω_0 was found previously from (66.29). In the first approximation the periodic solution itself is written in the form

$$\left.\begin{aligned}
\sigma &= C(A\cos\omega_l t + B\sin\omega_l t)\,, \\
x_j &= -C(A_j\cos\omega_l t + B_j\sin\omega_l t) \quad (j = 1, 2, ..., n)\,,
\end{aligned}\right\} \tag{66.35}$$

where

$$C = \frac{a_l}{\sqrt{A^2 + B^2}}, \tag{66.36}$$

and A, B, A_j, B_j are defined by the following equalities:

$$\left.\begin{aligned}
A - iB &= \frac{2E(i\omega_0)}{D'(i\omega_0) - hE'(i\omega_0)}, \\
A_j - iB_j &= \frac{2N_j(i\omega_0)}{D'(i\omega_0) - hE'(i\omega_0)} \quad (j = 1, 2, ..., n)\,,
\end{aligned}\right\} \tag{66.37}$$

where N_j are defined as in Section 58.

The condition for existence of the periodic solution is the presence of at least one real solution of equation (66.31) for the amplitude a_l.

The condition of stability of the periodic solution has the form

$$\mathrm{Re}\left[\frac{E(i\omega_0)}{D'(i\omega_0) - hE'(i\omega_0)}\frac{d\vartheta(a)}{da}\right] < 0; \tag{66.38}$$

it has been derived previously by application of the Liapunov theorems. If the periodic solution is stable, it corresponds to a steady-state oscillatory process in the system.

In conclusion we note particularly the case where the non-linear function $f(\sigma)$ does not have a hysteresis loop. The equation for determining the amplitude (66.31) takes a simpler form

$$D(i\omega_0) - q(a_l)E(i\omega_0) = 0 \tag{66.39}$$

and the frequency correction $\Delta\omega_l = 0$. The condition of stability of the periodic solution will now be:

$$\frac{dq(a)}{da}\mathrm{Re}\frac{E(i\omega_0)}{D(i\omega_0) - hE(i\omega_0)} < 0\,. \tag{66.40}$$

In place of a system of two equations for a_l and $\Delta\omega_l$ we obtain here a single equation (66.39) with a single unknown a_l.

2. Let us now consider a second form of the differential equations of a non-linear system:

$$
\left.
\begin{aligned}
\dot{x}_1 &= a_{11}x_1 + a_{12}x_2 + \dots + a_{1,n-1}x_{n-1} + b_1\xi\,, \\
\dot{x}_2 &= a_{21}x_1 + a_{22}x_2 + \dots + a_{2,n-1}x_{n-1} + b_2\xi\,, \\
&\cdots\cdots\cdots\cdots\cdots\cdots\cdots\cdots\cdots\cdots\cdots \\
\dot{x}_{n-1} &= a_{n-1,1}x_1 + a_{n-1,2}x_2 + \dots + a_{n-1,n-1}x_{n-1} + b_{n-1}\xi\,, \\
\xi &= F(\sigma)\,, \\
\sigma &= c_1 x_1 + c_2 x_2 + \dots + c_{n-1}x_{n-1} - r\dot{\xi}\,.
\end{aligned}
\right\} \quad (66.41)
$$

The simplified system is obtained by the substitution of $\xi = F(\sigma)$ by $\xi = h\sigma$. The characteristic equation of the simplified system is written in the form

$$(z + rh)\,D(z) - hE(z) = 0\,. \tag{66.42}$$

The quantities ω_0 and h are defined by separating the real and imaginary parts in the equation

$$(i\omega_0 + rh)\,D(i\omega_0) - hE(i\omega_0) = 0\,. \tag{66.43}$$

After this the equation for determining the amplitude a_l and the correction to the frequency $\Delta\omega_l$ is set up in the form

$$
\begin{aligned}
[i\omega_0 + r\vartheta(a_l)]\,&D(i\omega_0) - \vartheta(a_l)\,E(i\omega_0) \\
&= -i[D(i\omega_0) + (i\omega_0 + rh)\,D'(i\omega_0) - hE'(i\omega_0)]\,\Delta\omega_l\,,
\end{aligned} \tag{66.44}
$$

where $\vartheta(a_l)$ is defined by the given non-linear function $F(\sigma)$ through formula (66.32) or (66.33). Separating the real and imaginary parts, we find the amplitude a_l of the periodic solution for the quantity σ and the correction to the frequency $\Delta\omega_l$ (the frequency of the periodic solution will be $\omega_l = \omega + \Delta\omega_l$).

The periodic solution in the first approximation is written in the form

$$\sigma = \frac{\omega_0}{h}\,C(A\sin\omega_l t - B\cos\omega_l t)\,,$$

$$\xi = -C(A\cos\omega_l t + B\sin\omega_l t)\,,$$

$$x_j = C(A_j\cos\omega_l t + B_j\sin\omega_l t)\,,$$

$$(j = 1, 2, \dots, n-1)\,,$$

where

$$C = \frac{ah}{\omega_0\sqrt{A^2 + B^2}}\,,$$

and the quantities A, B, A_j, B_j are defined from the equalities

$$A - iB = \frac{-2D(i\omega_0)}{D(i\omega_0) + (i\omega_0 + rh)\,D'(i\omega_0) - hE'(i\omega_0)}\,,$$

$$A_j - iB_j = \frac{-2N_j(i\omega_0)}{D(i\omega_0) + (i\omega_0 + rh)\,D'(i\omega_0) - hE'(i\omega_0)}\,,$$

where the expressions N_j are found from the determinant

$$\begin{vmatrix} a_{11} - z & a_{12} & \cdots & a_{1,n-1} \\ a_{21} & a_{22} - z & \cdots & a_{2,n-1} \\ \cdots\cdots\cdots\cdots\cdots\cdots\cdots\cdots \\ a_{n-1,1} & a_{n-1,2} & \cdots & a_{n-1,n-1} - z \end{vmatrix}$$

by substitution of the jth column by the column $b_1, b_2, \ldots, b_{n-1}$ (here all coefficients are taken from the differential equations of the system (66.41)).

The condition for stability of the periodic solution has the form

$$\frac{\omega_0}{h}\,\mathrm{Im}\left[-\frac{D(i\omega_0)}{D(i\omega_0) + (i\omega_0 + rh)\,D'(i\omega_0) - hE'(i\omega_0)}\,\frac{d\vartheta(a)}{da}\right] < 0\,.$$

Similarly to the preceding all formulae are simplified when the non-linear characteristic $F(\sigma)$ has no hysteresis loop, where the expression $\vartheta(a)$ (66.33) is substituted by $q(a)$.

An estimate of the precision of each such approximate methods of solution in general form is difficult. It has been carried out for simple particular cases, for which there exists an exact solution of the problem, by comparing the results of solution.

We present two examples of the application of the Bulgakov approximate methods described above, in general form, to concrete non-linear automatic regulation problems.

Example 1. B. V. Bulgakov has illustrated his second method in the following example (Reference 15) (presented here in somewhat simplified form). Let the differential equations of the regulated object and regulator be given in the form

$$T_b^2 \ddot{\varphi} + T_a \dot{\varphi} + \beta\varphi = -\xi\,, \tag{66.45}$$

$$\left.\begin{aligned} T_q^2 \ddot{\xi} + T_s \dot{\xi} &= F(\sigma)\,, \\ \sigma &= k_1\varphi + k_2\dot{\varphi} + k_3\ddot{\varphi} - k_4\xi\,, \end{aligned}\right\} \tag{66.46}$$

respectively, where $F(\sigma)$ is the non-linear characteristic of the regulating organ drive, given graphically in the form of Fig. 303a. We employ here a notation in which φ is the deviation of the regulated quantity, ξ is the deviation of the regulating organ, β, T_a, T_b^2 are constant parameters of the object, $k_1, k_2, k_3, k_4, T_s, T_q^2$ are constant regulator parameters. Let us consider the case where the constant T_q^2 characterising the inertia of the regulating organ drive may by neglected, i.e. we shall assume $T_q^2 = 0$.

As we see, the regulated object is here described by a second order equation and has self-regulation if $\beta > 0$; it is unstable if

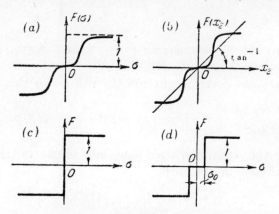

FIG. 303

$\beta < 0$; it is neutral if $\beta = 0$. The regulator has stiff feedback $(-k_4\xi)$, while the first and second derivatives ($\dot{\varphi}$ and $\ddot{\varphi}$) are introduced into the regulation function.

It is required to find the region of stability of the system and to determine possible oscillations in the system.

Eliminating ξ from expression (66.46) using equation (66.45), we obtain (with $T_q^2 = 0$):

$$\left.\begin{aligned}
&T_s T_b^2 \dddot{\varphi} + T_s T_a \ddot{\varphi} + T_s \beta \dot{\varphi} + F(\sigma) = 0 , \\
&\sigma = (k_1 + k_4\beta)\varphi + (k_2 + k_4 T_a)\dot{\varphi} + (k_3 + k_4 T_b^2)\ddot{\varphi} .
\end{aligned}\right\} \quad (66.47)$$

Let us introduce the new variables

$$x_1 = (k_1 + k_4\beta)\varphi , \qquad x_2 = \sigma , \qquad (66.48)$$

as well as the relative time and the differential operator

$$\bar{t} = \sqrt{\frac{k_1 + k_4\beta}{k_3 + k_4 T_b^2}} , \qquad p = \frac{d}{d\bar{t}} . \qquad (66.49)$$

In addition, we also introduce the quantity h corresponding to the approximate substitution of the non-linear drive characteristic by a linear one (Fig. 303b). Then equations (66.47) in symbolic operational form will be:

$$\left.\begin{aligned}
&(p^3 + c_1 p^2 + c_2 p)x_1 + \gamma h x_2 = \gamma[hx_2 - F(x_2)] , \\
&-(p^2 + c_3 p + 1)x_1 + x_2 = 0 ,
\end{aligned}\right\} \quad (66.50)$$

where

$$c_1 = \frac{T_a}{T_b^2}\sqrt{\frac{k_3 + k_4 T_b^2}{k_1 + k_4 \beta}}, \qquad c_2 = \frac{\beta(k_3 + k_4 T_b^2)}{T_b^2(k_1 + k_4 \beta)}, \\[2mm] c_3 = \frac{k_2 + k_4 T_a}{\sqrt{(k_1 + k_4 \beta)(k_3 + k_4 T_b^2)}}, \qquad \gamma = \frac{k_3 + k_4 T_b^2}{T_b^2 T_s}\sqrt{\frac{k_3 + k_4 T_b^2}{k_1 + k_4 \beta}}. \quad \Bigg\} \quad (66.51)$$

Expressions (66.50) correspond to the general form of writing the automatic system equations (66.2).

The operational determinant (66.12) will be in this case

$$\begin{vmatrix} p^3 + c_1 p^2 + c_2 p\,, & \gamma h \\ -(p^2 + c_3 p + 1)\,, & 1 \end{vmatrix} = p^3 + (c_1 + \gamma h)p^2 + (c_2 + c_3 \gamma h)p + \gamma h\,. \quad (66.52)$$

Therefore the characteristic equation (66.3) of the simplified system is written in the form

$$z^3 + (c_1 + \gamma h)z^2 + (c_2 + c_3 \gamma h)z + \gamma h = 0\,. \quad (66.53)$$

To find possible oscillations in the system according to (66.4) it must be represented in the form

$$(z^2 + \omega_0^2)(z + b) = 0\,. \quad (66.54)$$

Expanding and equating with the coefficients of (66.53), we obtain, firstly,

$$\omega_0^2 = c_2 + c_3 \gamma h\,, \qquad b = c_1 + \gamma h \quad (66.55)$$

and, secondly, the condition for formation of oscillations

$$(c_1 + \gamma h)(c_2 + c_3 \gamma h) = \gamma h\,,$$

which of course coincides with the condition for finding the linearised system at the boundary of stability, in the given case (29.4), following from the Vyshnegradskii stability criterion. Let us write this condition in the form

$$c_3 \gamma^2 h^2 + \gamma(c_1 c_3 + c_2 - 1)h + c_1 c_2 = 0\,,$$

The roots of this equation will be

$$h_{1,2} = \frac{-(c_1 c_3 + c_2 - 1) \mp \sqrt{(c_1 c_3 + c_2 - 1)^2 - 4c_1 c_2 c_3}}{2c_3 \gamma}\,. \quad (66.56)$$

In this connection we obtain two values for ω_0^2 and b (66.55):

$$(\omega_0^2)_{1,2} = \frac{1}{2}\left[c_2 - c_1 c_3 + 1 \mp \sqrt{(c_1 c_3 + c_2 - 1)^2 - 4c_1 c_2 c_3}\right], \\[2mm] b_{1,2} = \frac{1}{2c_3}\left[c_1 c_3 - c_2 + 1 \mp \sqrt{(c_1 c_3 + c_2 - 1)^2 - 4c_1 c_2 c_3}\right]. \quad \Bigg\} \quad (66.57)$$

If the quantity (66.56) is positive, then ω_0 is real. Let us assume that this occurs. Then the characteristic equation (66.53), according to (66.54), will have the roots

$$z_1 = -b, \quad z_{2,3} = \pm i\omega_0, \tag{66.58}$$

where in place of b and ω_0 it is necessary to substitute either b_1, ω_{01}, or b_2, ω_{02} form (66.57).

Consequently, for the general formulae of the second Bulgakov method in this case we have $n_1 = 1$, $n_2 = 1$, $m = 2$, $n = 3$, $\beta_2 = 0$, $\omega_2 = \omega_0$. Let us find the values F_{11} and F_{12}, necessary for formulae (66.22) and (66.23) as the algebraic complements of the elements in the first row of the operational determinant (66.52):

$$F_{11} = 1, \quad F_{12} = p^2 + c_3 p + 1 .$$

Therefore from formulae (66.22), assuming $l = 1$, $q = 2$, we obtain

$$K_{11} = \frac{F_{11}(z_1)}{F_{12}(z_1)} = \frac{1}{b^2 - c_3 b + 1}, \quad K_{21} = \frac{F_{12}(z_1)}{F_{12}(z_1)} = 1 ,$$

$$N_{11} e^{i\delta_{11}} = \frac{F_{11}(i\omega_0)}{F_{12}(i\omega_0)} = \frac{1}{1 - \omega_0^2 + c_3 i\omega_0}, \quad N_{21} e^{i\delta_{21}} = 1 .$$

The solutions of (66.21) for the transient in the system will therefore be:

$$\begin{aligned} x_1 &= K_{11} a_1 + N_{11} a_2 \sin(u + \delta_{11}) , \\ x_2 &= a_1 + a_2 \sin u . \end{aligned} \tag{66.59}$$

To determine the functions $a_1(t)$, $a_2(t)$, $u(t)$ entering here, it is necessary to employ formulae (66.20). Since in equations (66.50) we have $\varepsilon f_2 = 0$, formulae (66.20) for the given case are written in the form

$$\begin{aligned} \frac{da_1}{dt} &= -ba_1 + \frac{B_{11}}{2\pi D'(z_1)} \int_0^{2\pi} \varepsilon f_1(a_1 + a_2 \sin u) \, du , \\ \frac{da_2}{dt} &= \frac{1}{\pi} \operatorname{Re}\left[\frac{B_{12}}{D'(i\omega_0)} \int_0^{2\pi} \varepsilon f_1(a_1 + a_2 \sin u) e^{-iu} du \right] , \\ \frac{du}{dt} &= \omega_0 + \frac{1}{\pi a_2} \operatorname{Im}\left[\frac{B_{12}}{D'(i\omega_0)} \int_0^{2\pi} \varepsilon f_1(a_1 + a_2 \sin u) e^{iu} du \right] . \end{aligned} \tag{66.60}$$

From (66.23) we find the quantities

$$B_{11} = F_{12}(z_1) = b^2 - c_3 b + 1 ,$$
$$B_{12} = F_{12}(i\omega_0) = 1 - \omega_0^2 + c_3 i\omega_0 .$$

From (66.50) we have

$$\varepsilon f_1(x_2) = \gamma[hx_2 - F(x_2)] ,$$

while from (66.54) we obtain:

$$D'(z) = 2z(z+b) + z^2 + \omega_0^2 \,,$$

$$D'(z_1) = b^2 + \omega_0^2 \,, \qquad D'(i\omega_0) = 2\omega_0(-\omega_0 + ib) \,.$$

Substituting this in (60.60), we obtain the following approximate equations for determining the amplitudes a_1, a_2 and the phases u (which figure in the solution (66.59)):

$$
\left.
\begin{aligned}
\frac{da_1}{d\bar{t}} &= -ba_1 + \gamma \frac{b^2 - c_3 b + 1}{b^2 + \omega_0^2} \left[ha_1 - \frac{1}{2\pi} \int_0^{2\pi} F(a_1 + a_2 \sin u)\, du \right], \\[2mm]
\frac{da_2}{d\bar{t}} &= \gamma \frac{\omega_0^2 - 1 + c_3 b}{2(b^2 + \omega_0^2)} \left[ha_2 - \frac{1}{\pi} \int_0^{2\pi} F(a_1 + a_2 \sin u)\sin u\, du \right], \\[2mm]
\frac{du}{d\bar{t}} &= \omega_0 + \gamma \frac{b(\omega_0^2 - 1) - c_3 \omega_0^2}{2a_2 \omega_0 (b^2 + \omega_0^2)} \left[ha_2 - \frac{1}{\pi} \int_0^{2\pi} F(a_1 + a_2 \sin u)\sin u\, du \right].
\end{aligned}
\right\} \quad (66.61)
$$

The time variables a_1 and a_2 define the transient. To find the periodic solution ($a_1 = \text{const}$, $a_2 = \text{const}$), it is necessary to put

$$\frac{da_1}{d\bar{t}} = 0 \quad \text{and} \quad \frac{da_2}{d\bar{t}} = 0 \,. \qquad (66.62)$$

In addition, recalling that previously there was no rigid basis for choosing the quantity h in Fig. 303b, we shall now define it such that the integral in the first of formulae (66.60) vanishes, since it represents the mean error over a period, substituting the non-linear characteristic $F(x_2)$ by the linear $h = x_2$. This signifies vanishing of the expression in square brackets in the first of equations (66.61). But taking into account the first condition (66.62) we obtain

$$a_1 = 0 \,.$$

The second condition (66.62) according to the second equation of (66.61) gives

$$ha_l = \frac{1}{\pi} \int_0^{2\pi} F(a_l \sin u)\sin u\, du \,, \qquad (66.63)$$

where by a_l we express the value of the amplitude a_2 for the required periodic process. To determine a_l we may have recourse to the graphic solution of equation (66.63). Let us put

$$J(a_l) = \frac{1}{\pi} \int_0^{2\pi} F(a_l \sin u)\sin u\, du \qquad (66.64)$$

and from calculations using this formula we plot the curve $J(a_l)$. It takes the form of the graph of Fig. 304a, differing little in shape from the given non-linear characteristic $F(x_2)$ Fig. 303b). In the same graph we plot the inclined straight lines $h_1 h_l$ and $h_2 h_l$, where h_1 and h_2 are taken from (66.56). The four points of intersection define according to (66.63) four possible values of a_l in the required periodic solution.

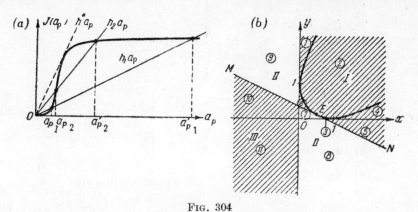

Fɪɢ. 304

Periodic solutions are not possible if $h_{1,2}$ (66.56) are not positive or if $h_{1,2} > h^*$ (Fig. 304a), i.e. when the straight lines do not intersect the curve $J(a_l)$. In place of four, two periodic solutions are possible if only one of the straight lines $h_{1,2}a_l$ intersects the curve $J(a_l)$.

Let us take the parameter plane (66.51):

$$x = c_2 = \frac{\beta(k_3 + k_4 T_b^2)}{T_b^2(k_1 + k_4\beta)}, \quad y = c_1 c_3 = \frac{T_a(k_2 + k_4 T_a)}{T_b^2(k_1 + k_4\beta)}, \qquad (66.65)$$

and, using (66.56), we divide it into regions (Fig. 304b) within which there will be either a stable equilibrium state, self-oscillation, or an unstable system (see below).

Vanishing of the radicand (66.56) corresponds to the parabola

$$(-x+y)^2 - 2\left(x+y-\frac{1}{2}\right) = 0,$$

the axis of which is the bisectrix of the coordinates. It is tangent to the coordinate axes at the points $(0, 1)$ and $(1, 0)$ (Fig. 304b). In addition, it is necessary to find the extreme cases of intersection when one of the straight lines $h_{1,2} a_l$ takes up a tangential position $h^* a_l$ (Fig. 304a). Substituting this value of h^* in the quadratic equation from which we have found $h_{1,2}$ (66.56), we obtain a straight line tangent to the parabola at the point E with coordinates

$$x = \left(\frac{\gamma h^*}{\gamma h^* + c_1}\right)^2, \quad y = \left(\frac{c_1}{\gamma h^* + c_1}\right)^2; \qquad (66.66)$$

rather, this will be a family of straight lines if we assign various values of c_1 and γ. One of them is represented in Fig. 304b.

From expressions (66.61) and from comparing them with the quantity h^* the following result is obtained for various sections of the plane numbered in Fig. 304b:

$$
\left.
\begin{array}{llll}
1) & h_1 < 0, & h_2 < 0, \\
2) & h_{1,2} \text{ complex}, \\
3) & h_1 > h^*, & h_2 > h^*, \\
4) & h_1 < 0, & h_2 < 0, \\
5) & h_1 > h^*, & h_2 < 0,
\end{array}
\right\} \text{ damped oscillations}
$$

$$
\left.
\begin{array}{llll}
6) & 0 < h_1 < h^*, & 0 < h_2 < h^*, \\
7) & 0 < h_1 < h^*, & h^* < h_2, \\
8) & 0 < h_1 < h^*, & h_2 < 0, \\
9) & h_1 < 0, & 0 < h_2 < h^*,
\end{array}
\right\} \text{ self oscillations}
$$

$$
\left.
\begin{array}{llll}
10) & h_1 < 0, & h^* < h_2, \\
11) & h_1 < 0, & h_2 < 0
\end{array}
\right\} \text{ divergent oscillations.}
$$

We note that these conclusions cannot be considered rigorously proved. They are as approximate as all the previous sections of this chapter.

Let us consider these results. Only damped or only divergent oscillations may occur in the system when neither straight line $h_{1,2} = a_l$ intersects the curve $J(a_l)$ (Fig. 304a), i.e. either $h_i < 0$, or $h_i > h^*$, or they are complex. Oscillations are possible if at least one of the straight lines $h_{1,2} = a_l$ intersects the curve $J(a_l)$. But here either two or four periodic solutions are obtained (according to the number of points of intersection in Fig. 304a). It is necessary to investigate which of these is stable. We take the first two equations (66.61):

$$\frac{da_1}{dt} = G(a_1, a_2), \qquad \frac{da_2}{dt} = G_2(a_1, a_2), \qquad (66.67)$$

where $G_1(a_1, a_2)$ and $G_2(a_1, a_2)$ are abbreviated notation for the right-hand sides of the first two equations (66.61).

In the periodic solution we had $a_1 = 0$, $a_2 = a_l$. Let us investigate the periodic process in small deviations from the given periodic solution. For this we linearise equation (66.67) according to the rules of Section 18, which gives

$$\frac{d\Delta a_1}{dt} = \left(\frac{\partial G_1}{\partial a_1}\right)^0 \Delta a_1 + \left(\frac{\partial G_1}{\partial a_2}\right)^0 \Delta a_2, \qquad \frac{d\Delta a_2}{dt} = \left(\frac{\partial G_2}{\partial a_1}\right)^0 \Delta a_1 + \left(\frac{\partial G_2}{\partial a_2}\right)^0 \Delta a_2,$$

where the zero upper index denotes the substitution $a_1 = 0$, $a_2 = a_l$ in the partial derivatives.

Carrying out the calculations, we find that the condition of stability of the periodic solution reduces to:

$$\left(\frac{\partial G_1}{\partial a_1}\right)^0 \left(\frac{\partial G_2}{\partial a_2}\right)^0 > 0 \tag{66.68}$$

(compare with condition (60.27) for a second-order system).

In the section of the plane 9 (Fig. 304b) according to the above table there are two periodic solutions with amplitudes a_{l_2} and a'_{l_2}. Of these a_{l_2} is stable, a'_{l_2} unstable. Consequently, there will be stable oscillations in the system with small amplitude a_{l_2} (Fig. 304a), but it is only small-signal stable since with initial conditions outside the limiting cycle defined by the amplitude a'_{l_2}, the system has divergent oscillations.

In the sections of the plane 7 and 8 there are also two periodic solutions but with amplitudes a_{l_1} and a'_{l_1}. Of these a'_{l_1} is stable. Therefore the system will have a stable oscillation of large amplitude a'_{l_1}. In addition, it will be small-signal stable with respect to the steady-state with constant value of the regulated quantity ($a_l = 0$), when the initial conditions are within the small limiting cycle a_{l_1}. However the latter is rarely possible in practice.

Finally, in the section of the plane 6 there are all four periodic solutions with amplitudes a_{l_1}, a_{l_2}, a'_{l_2}, a'_{l_1}. Of these a_{l_2} and a'_{l_1} are stable. With initial conditions lying inside the unstable limiting cycle a'_{l_2} oscillations of small amplitude a_{l_2} are established while outside it oscillations of large amplitude a'_{l_1}.

Thus as a result we obtain in the parameter plane three principle regions (Fig. 304b): *I*, the system is stable with respect to the steady-state with constant value of the regulated quantity; *II*, the system has a steady-state oscillatory regime (discussed in detail above); *III*, the system is unstable. It is important to take into account that the straight line *MN* changes its position in dependence on the values of γ and c_1 (66.51), always tangent to the parabola at the point (66.66).

In this example we again emphasise the singular properties of non-linear automatic systems. While in linear systems there are always only two possibilities, either stability or instability, here we find intermediate regions of self-oscillation, as broad as the first two.

In Section 72, we will plot the curve of the transient for this example.

Example 2. As an illustration of the first Bulgakov method we present the solution of A. M. Letov for a system in which the regulated object and regulator are described by equations

$$T_b^2 \ddot{\varphi} + T_a \dot{\varphi} + \beta\varphi = -\xi \,, \qquad (66.69)$$

$$\left.\begin{array}{l} \xi = F(\sigma) \,, \\ \sigma = k_1\varphi + k_2\dot{\varphi} + k_3 \int \varphi\,dt - k_4\xi \,, \end{array}\right\} \qquad (66.70)$$

respectively, where the notation is the same as in Example 1 with $T_q^2 = 0$. This system is characterised by the presence in the regulation function of the first derivative and integral instead of the first and second derivatives as before. The integral was introduced to eliminate the static error of the system arising from the presence of stiff feedback (see Section 14).

Let us introduce the new variables

$$x_1 = \sqrt{\frac{k_4(k_1 + k_4\beta)}{T_b^2}} \int \varphi\,dt \,, \qquad x_2 = \frac{k_4}{k_1 + k_4\beta}\sigma \,, \qquad (66.71)$$

and the relative time and differential operator

$$\bar{t} = \sqrt{\frac{k_1 + k_4\beta}{T_b^2 k_4}}\, t \,, \qquad p = \frac{d}{d\bar{t}} \,. \qquad (66.72)$$

Eliminating, as before, the variable ξ from equations (66.70), using (66.69), introducing the new variables (66.71) and the constants

$$\left.\begin{array}{ll} c_0 = T_a \sqrt{\dfrac{T_b^2 k_4}{k_1 + k_4\beta}} \,, & c_1 = \dfrac{k_4\beta}{k_1 + k_4\beta} \,, \\[3mm] c_2 = \dfrac{k_3}{k_1 + k_4\beta}\sqrt{\dfrac{T_b^2 k_4}{k_1 + k_4\beta}} \,, & c_3 = \dfrac{k_2 + k_4 T_a}{\sqrt{(k_1 + k_4\beta)\, T_b^2 k_4}} \end{array}\right\} \qquad (66.73)$$

we obtain two equations:

$$\left.\begin{array}{l} [(c_3 - c_0)p^3 + (1 - c_1)p^2 + c_2 p]x_1 - (p + h)x_2 = \varepsilon f_1(x_2) \,, \\ \qquad -(p^3 + c_3 p^2 + p + c\,)x_1 + x_2 = 0 \,, \end{array}\right\} \qquad (66.74)$$

where

$$\varepsilon f_1(x_2) = F_1(x_2) - hx_2 \,, \qquad F_1(x_2) = \frac{k_4^2}{k_1 + k_4\beta}\sqrt{\frac{k_4 T_b^2}{k_1 + k_4\beta}} \cdot F\left(\frac{k_4\sigma}{k_1 + k_4\beta}\right);$$

consequently, the graph $F_1(x_2)$ (Fig. 305b) has the same form as the graph $F(\sigma)$ (Fig. 305a) except for a change of scale along both coordinate axes in accordance with the last formula.

The operational determinant (66.12) in the present case has the form

$$\begin{vmatrix} (c_3 - c_0)p^3 + (1 - c_1)p^2 + c_2 p \,, & -(p + h) \\ -(p^3 + c_3 p^2 + p + c_2) \,, & 1 \end{vmatrix}$$
$$= p^4 + (c_0 + h)p^3 + (c_1 + c_3 h)p^2 + hp + c_2 h \,. \qquad (66.75)$$

The characteristic equation (66.3) of the simplified system will then be

$$D(z) = z^4 + (c_0 + h)z^3 + (c_1 + c_3 h)z^2 + hz + c_2 h = 0 . \qquad (66.76)$$

To obtain the periodic solutions we represent it from (66.4) in the form

$$D(z) = (z^2 + \omega_0^2)(z^2 + b_1 z + b_2) = 0 . \qquad (66.77)$$

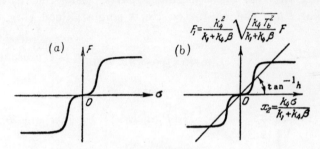

(a)

(b)

$$F_1 = \frac{k_4^2}{k_1 + k_4 \beta} \sqrt{\frac{k_4 T_6^2}{k_1 + k_4 \beta}} F$$

$$\tan^{-1} h$$

$$x_2 = \frac{k_4 \sigma}{k_1 + k_4 \beta}$$

FIG. 305

Equating coefficients of both equations (it is here possible to employ the final formulae (66.7) and (66.8), derived previously for the fourth-degree equation) we obtain

$$\omega_0^2 = \frac{h}{c_0 h} , \qquad b_1 = c_0 + h , \qquad b_2 = c_2(c_0 + h) , \qquad (66.78)$$

$$(c_3 - c_2)h^2 + (c_1 + c_0 c_3 - 2c_0 c_2 - 1)h + c_0(c_1 - c_0 c_2) = 0 , \qquad (66.79)$$

where the last corresponds to the condition of the boundary of stability (29.19) of the simplified system.

For further calculations in accordance with (66.12) and (66.75) it is necessary to find (assuming $l = 1, q = 2$)

$$F_{11}(i\omega_0) = 1 , \qquad F_{12}(i\omega_0) = (c_2 - c_3 \omega_0^2) - i\omega_0(\omega_0^2 - 1) .$$

Then formula (66.11) gives

$$L_1 + iM_1 = \frac{1}{(c_2 - c_3 \omega_0^2) - i\omega_0(\omega_0^2 - 1)} , \qquad L_2 + iM_2 = 1 .$$

Therefore the periodic solution (66.10) of the simplified system will be

$$x_1^* = A_0(L_1 \sin \omega_0 t + M_1 \cos \omega_0 t) , \qquad x_2^* = A_0 \sin \omega_0 t . \qquad (66.80)$$

We now find the frequency correction α. We calculate from (66.77)

$$\frac{\partial D(z)}{\partial (z)} = 2z(z^2 + b_1 z + b_2) + (z^2 + \omega_0^2)(2z + b_1 + b_2) .$$

Then from formula (66.16), taking into account the second solution (66.80), denoting the amplitude A_0 of the periodic solution for the coordinate x_2 as before, by a_l, we obtain (taking $q = 1$):

$$a_l[-2\omega_0^2(-\omega_0^2 + b_1 i\omega_0 + b_2)\alpha] = \frac{i}{\pi} \int_0^{2\pi} \varepsilon f_l(a_l \sin u)\,e^{-iu}du \ .$$

Separating the real and imaginary parts, using (66.75) and considering that since the characteristic is single valued (Fig. 305) we have

$$\int_0^{2\pi} \varepsilon f_1(a_l \sin u)\cos u\,du = 0 \ ,$$

we obtain

$$-2a_l\omega_0^2\alpha(b_2 - \omega_0^2) = \frac{1}{\pi}\int_0^{2\pi} [F_1(a_l \sin u) - ha_l \sin u]\sin u\,du \ ,$$

$$-2a_l\omega_0^3\alpha b_1 = 0 \ .$$

The last equation gives the frequency correction $\alpha = 0$. Then from the first we have:

$$ha_l = J(a_l) \ , \tag{66.81}$$

where

$$J(a_l) = \frac{1}{\pi}\int_0^{\pi} F_1(a_l \sin u)\sin u\,du \ . \tag{66.82}$$

Comparing this with (66.63) and (66.64), we obtain here in principle exactly the same graphic solution as in Fig. 304a and the same pattern of dividing the parameter plane into regions (Fig. 304b) if as the coordinates (x, y) of the plane we take

$$x = c_1 - c_0 c_2 \ , \qquad y = c_0(c_3 - c_2) \ . \tag{66.83}$$

This agreement is obtained since here, as in Example 1, we have a quadratic equation for determining h (66.79). The significance of each region is the same as in Example 1. We mention only the method of investigating the stability of the periodic solution in the present example.

Let us write the differential equations of the transient (66.74) in deviations from the investigated periodic solution x_1^*, x_2^*, putting $x_1 = x_1^* + \Delta x_1$, $x_2 = x_2^* + \Delta x_2$. We obtain

$$\left.\begin{array}{l} [(c_3 - c_0)p^3 + (1 - c_1)p^2 + c_2 p]\Delta x_1 - (p + \bar{h})\Delta x_2 = 0 \ , \\ -(p^3 + c_3 p^2 + p + c_2)\Delta x_1 + \Delta x_2 = 0 \ , \end{array}\right\} \tag{66.84}$$

where $\bar{h}$ is the new value for h, obtained in accordance with Section 18 as the coefficient of the linear term of the Taylor series expansion of the function $F_1(x_2)$ about the steady-state process $x_2^* = a_l \sin \omega_0 t$. But since this last is oscillatory, $\bar{h}$ is also a periodic function of t. In accordance with the general approximate character of the method the constant value averaged over the period

$$\bar{h} = \frac{1}{2\pi} \int\limits_0^{2\pi} F_1'(a_l \sin u)\, du = \frac{1}{2}\left[\frac{dJ(a_l)}{da_l} + \frac{J(a_l)}{a_l}\right], \qquad (66.85)$$

is taken, where $J(a_l)$ is expression (66.82).

Then stability of the periodic solution is defined by the Hurwitz criterion applied to the linear equation in deviations (66.84). The characteristic equation will here have the form (66.76) substituting h by $\bar{h}$. We require the coefficients to be positive:

$$c_0 + \bar{h} > 0, \quad c_1 + c_3\bar{h} > 0, \quad \bar{h} > 0, \quad c_2\bar{h} > 0$$

and inequality (29.18), to be satisfied, specifically:

$$(c_3 - c_2)\bar{h}^2 + (c_1 + c_0 c_3 - 2c_0 c_2 - 1)\bar{h} + c_0(c_1 - c_0 c_2) > 0,$$

where $\bar{h}$ has the value (66.85). All this leads to the results described at the end of Example 1.

CHAPTER XVII

SELF-OSCILLATIONS IN THE PRESENCE OF AN EXTERNAL FORCE AND FORCED OSCILLATIONS OF NON-LINEAR SYSTEMS

67. Approximate determination of self-oscillations with slowly varying external force and in the presence of constant components

In the preceding chapter we have studied the oscillations of non-linear systems about an equilibrium state under the assumption of absence of a constant component. The condition of absence of a constant component (61.6) may be violated either when the characteristic of the non-linear circuit is unsymmetrical or when there is a slowly varying external force of arbitrary form. In the former the constant component may be present even in the absence of the external force, but we shall consider this question as a special case of determining oscillations in the presence of a slowly varying external force.

Let us assume that at an arbitrary point in the system an external force is introduced (perturbation or command) $f(t)$ (Fig. 306), where the equation of the linear part of the system has the form

$$Q_l(p)x_1 = -R_l(p)x_2 + S(p)f(t) . \qquad (67.1)$$

Let us assume that the external force on the system $f(t)$ varies fairly slowly in comparison with the period of self-oscillation of the given system. This occurs very frequently in oscillatory servomechanisms (and program-control systems), when $f(t)$ denotes the command function at the input to the system, as well as in integrators and other computing systems operating in the oscillatory regime, where $f(t)$ denotes the integrand or other input function. The same may occur in ordinary control systems where $f(t)$ denotes an external perturbation (change of load, etc.).

In the general case we shall consider that $f(t)$ itself and all its derivatives entering into the given equation (67.1) vary so slowly that in determining self-oscillations they may be considered constant during a period of oscillation. If $f(t)$ itself has an oscillatory character, its frequency of variation is assumed many times smaller than the frequency of self-oscillation in the given system. In particular cases the external force $f(t)$ may be a constant quantity

$$f(t) = \text{const} \qquad (67.2)$$

or may vary with constant velocity

$$f(t) = c_1 t + c_2 . \qquad (67.3)$$

The non-linear element of the system may belong to the first or second class, i.e. it may be described by any of equations (52.1), (52.2), (52.3), (52.4). The same method extends to non-linear systems

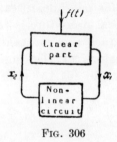

FIG. 306

of the third class (with several non-linear elements separated by linear parts). The equations of the non-linear elements may contain various dissymmetries, leading to the presence of a constant component.

In the present section we shall employ harmonic linearisation for the solution of these problems and the fundamental method of determining self-oscillations described in Section 62.

Harmonic linearisation of non-linearity. For the harmonic line-arisation of, for example, the non-linear function

$$y = F(x, \dot{x}) \qquad (67.4)$$

it is now necessary to put:

$$x = x^0 + x^p , \quad \text{where} \quad x^p = a \sin u , \quad \omega = \frac{du}{dt}. \qquad (67.5)$$

We have here three known functions: "the constant" component x^0, the amplitude a and the frequency ω of the periodic solution x^p (self-oscillations). All three quantities vary slowly with variation of $f(t)$.

Substituting (67.5), expanding the non-linear function (67.4) in a Fourier series and limiting ourselves to the fundamental component, we obtain in place of (61.7) the approximate expression

$$y = q^0(a, \omega, x^0) + q(a, \omega, x^0) x^p + \frac{q_1(a, \omega, x^0)}{\omega} \dot{x}^p , \qquad (67.6)$$

where

$$q^0(a, \omega, x^0) = \frac{1}{2\pi} \int\limits_0^{2\pi} F(x^0 + a\sin u, \ a\omega\cos u)\,du\ ,$$

$$q(a, \omega, x^0) = \frac{1}{\pi a} \int\limits_0^{2\pi} F(x^0 + a\sin u, \ a\omega\cos u)\sin u\,du\ , \qquad (67.7)$$

$$q_1(a, \omega, x^0) = \frac{1}{\pi a} \int\limits_0^{2\pi} F(x^0 + a\sin u, \ a\omega\cos u)\cos u\,du\ .$$

Harmonic linearisation for non-linearities of other types is carried out analogously. The general procedure is the same as in Section 61 but everywhere we introduce the constant components x^0 and q^0.

The approximate equations of the non-linear elements of the first class (61.11), (61.12) and (61.15) take the forms

$$x_2^0 + x_2^p = q^0(a, \omega, x_1^0) + \left[q(a, \omega, x_1^0) + \frac{q_1(a, \omega, x_1^0)}{\omega}p\right]x_1\ , \qquad (67.8)$$

$$\left[\frac{q_1(a, \omega, x_2^0)}{\omega}p + q(a, \omega, x_2^0)\right]x_2^p + q^0(a, \omega, x_2^0) = c_1(x_1^0 + x_1^p)\ , \qquad (67.9)$$

$$x_2^0 + x_2^p = q^0(a, x_1^0) + \left[q(a, x_1^0) + \frac{q_1(a, x_1^0)}{\omega}p\right]x_1^p\ , \qquad (67.10)$$

respectively, where q^0, q, q_1, are calculated from formulae (67.7) in which for the third case $a\omega\cos u$ is omitted.

For a non-linear element of the second class (61.24) we obtain the approximate equation

$$\left[\frac{q_3(a_2, \omega, x_2^0)}{\omega}p + q_2(a_2, \omega, x_2^0)\right]x_2^p + q_2^0(a_2, \omega, x_2^0)$$
$$= \left[q(a_1, x_1^0) + \frac{q_1(a_1, x_1^0)}{\omega}p\right]x_1^p + q^0(a_1, x_1^0)\ , \qquad (67.11)$$

for the same harmonic linearisation formulae (67.7), but with the addition of a relation among the amplitude (61.28). The approximate equations taking into account the constant components are analogous for other types of elements.

Approximate equations of the non-linear system. Thus, the approximate equation of the non-linear element may be represented in the form

$$Q_n(p)x_2^p + Q^0 = R_n(p)x_1^p + R^0\ , \qquad (67.12)$$

where, for example, in the case (67.10) we have $Q^0 = x_2^0$, $R^0 = q^0(a, x_1^0)$, for the case (67.9) we have $Q^0 = q^0(a, \omega, x_2^0)$, $R^0 = c_1x_1^0$, while in the case (67.11) we obtain $Q^0 = q_2^0(a_2, \omega, x_2)$, $R^0 = q^0(a_1, x_1^0)$.

The equation of the linear part of the system (67.1) with substitution of $x_1 = x_1^0 + x_1^p$ and $x_2 = x_2^0 + x_2^p$ is written in the form

$$Q_l(p)x_1^p + Q_l(p)x_1^0 = -R_l(p)x_2^p - R_l(p)x_2^0 + S(p)f(t) . \quad (67.13)$$

From the system of equations (67.12), (67.13) we separate the equations for the "constant" components:

$$Q^0 = R^0 , \qquad Q_l(p)x_1^0 + R_l(p)x_2^0 = S(p)f(t) , \quad\quad (67.14)$$

and the equations for the periodic components:

$$\left. \begin{aligned} Q_n(p)x_2^p &= R_n(p)x_1^p , \\ Q_l(p)x_1^p &= -R_l(p)x_2^p . \end{aligned} \right\} \quad\quad\quad (67.15)$$

For the latter two equations we may write the characteristic equation

$$Q_l(z)Q_n(z) + R_l(z)R_n(z) = 0 \quad\quad\quad (67.16)$$

and the expression for the Mikhailov curve

$$L(i\tilde{\omega}) = Q_l(i\tilde{\omega})Q_n(i\tilde{\omega}) + R_l(i\tilde{\omega})R_n(i\tilde{\omega}) , \quad\quad\quad (67.17)$$

where the four unknown quantities $(a, \omega, x_1^0, x_2^0)$ enter into the coefficients.

Determination of self-oscillation in the presence of constant components and with slowly varying external force. We apply here the basic method (Section 62). For the equations of the periodic components (67.15) we compose the characteristic equation (67.16) and the expression for the Mikhailov curve (67.17), in which we separate the real and imaginary parts: $F(i\omega) = X(\omega) + iY(\omega)$. From this we obtain the following two equations:

$$\left. \begin{aligned} X(\omega_l, a_l, x_1^0, x_2^0) &= 0 , \\ Y(\omega_l, a_l, x_1^0, x_2^0) &= 0 , \end{aligned} \right\} \quad\quad\quad (67.18)$$

to which we join the equations for the constant components (67 14) namely:

$$Q^0 = R^0 , \qquad Q_l(p)x_1^0 + R_l(p)x_2^0 = S(p)f(t) \quad\quad (67.19)$$

As a result of this the four unknowns are determined: $\omega_1, a_1, x_1^0, x_2^0$. Most frequently either x_2^0 will not enter into expressions X^2 and Y, as, for example, in cases (67.8) and (67.10), or x_1^0, as in the case (67.9)· Then equality $Q^0 = R^0$ separates off while the remaining three will define three unknowns.

These equations are used similarly to those in Sections 62 and 63 to determine the dependence of the quantities $\omega_1, a_1, x_1^0, x_2^0$ on the system parameters. In addition these equations show the dependence of these quantities on the slowly varying external force. This circumstance is very important, as in practice in many oscillatory systems and computer systems a very substantial influence of the slowly varying external force on the frequency and amplitude of oscillations in the system is observed.

If the external force has a constant magnitude (67.2), all calculations are substantially simplified.

Example. Let the servomechanism considered in Example 1, Section 63 have an input force $\alpha(t)$, which we shall consider slowly varying with constant velocity $\dot{\alpha} = \text{const}$, $\alpha = \dot{\alpha}t$. We shall consider the values of α to be constant within a period of oscillation.

The equation of the linear part of the system according to (54.10), in place of the previous (63.3) will be:

$$(T_3 p + 1)I_4 = -[k + (T_3 p + 1)k_6 p]\beta + k_0 k \alpha . \qquad (67.20)$$

The equations of the non-linear element (drive and controlled object) will be as before:

$$(T_1 p + 1)p\beta = c'F(I_4) , \qquad (67.21)$$

where $F(I_4)$ is defined by the graph in Fig. 276a. We put

$$\beta = \beta^0 + \beta^p , \quad p\beta = \dot{\beta}^0 + p\beta^p , \quad I_4 = I_4^0 + I_4^p , \quad I_4^p = a\sin u , \quad \omega = \frac{du}{dt},$$

where β^0 is a slowly varying value of the angle β, which is considered constant within a period of oscillation (the self-oscillation β^p is superimposed on it).

Harmonic linearisation of the equation for the non-linear element (67.21) according to formulae (67.6) and (67.7) gives:

$$(T_1 p + 1)p\beta^p + \dot{\beta}^0 = q^0(a, I_4^0) + q(a, I_4^0)I_4^p , \qquad (67.22)$$

where with $a > b + I_4^0$ we have:

$$
\left.
\begin{aligned}
q^0(a, I_4^0) &= \frac{k_1 a}{\pi}\left[\left(\frac{\pi}{2} - u_1\right)\sin u_1 - \cos u_1 + \right.\\
&\qquad\qquad \left. + \left(\frac{\pi}{2} + u_2\right)\sin u_2 + \cos u_2\right],\\
q(a, I_4) &= \frac{k_1}{\pi}\left(u_2 + u_1 + \frac{1}{2}\sin 2u_2 + \frac{1}{2}\sin 2u_1\right),\\
u_1 &= \sin^{-1}\frac{b - I_4^0}{a}, \quad u = \sin^{-1}\frac{b + I_4^0}{a};
\end{aligned}
\right\} \qquad (67.23)
$$

with $b - I_4^0 < a < b + I_4^0$ we obtain:

$$q^0(a, I_4^0) = \frac{k_1 a}{\pi}\left[\left(\frac{\pi}{2} - u_1\right)\sin u_1 - \cos u_1\right] + k_1 I_4^0,$$

$$q(a, I_4^0) = \frac{k_1}{\pi}\left(\frac{\pi}{2} + u_1 + \frac{1}{2}\sin 2u_1\right), \qquad (67.24)$$

$$u_1 = \sin^{-1}\frac{b - I_4^0}{a},$$

while with $0 < a < b - I_4^0$ the given element becomes linear, with

$$q^0(a, I_4^0) = k_1 I_4^0, \qquad q(a, I_4^0) = k_1; \qquad (67.25)$$

it is assumed in all cases that $|I_4^0| \leqslant b$ (the quantity b is defined in Fig. 276a).

Differentiating equation (67.20) with respect to time, with constant velocity $p\beta = \beta^0$ we obtain:

$$\beta^0 = k_0\dot{\alpha}. \qquad (67.26)$$

Therefore the equations for the constant components (67.14) are written here in the form

$$k_0\dot{\alpha} = q^0(a, I_4^0), \qquad I_4^0 = -(k\beta^0 + k_6 k_0\dot{\alpha}) + k_0 k\alpha. \qquad (67.27)$$

The equations for the periodic component (67.15) will be here:

$$(T_1 p + 1)p\beta^p = q(a, I_4^0)I_4^p,$$
$$(T_3 p + 1)I_4^p = -[k + (T_3 p + 1)k_6 p]\beta^p. \qquad (67.28)$$

Writing for them the characteristic equation and the expression for the Mikhailov curve, we obtain, as in Example 1 of Section 63, the expressions

$$q(a_l, I_4^0) = \frac{T_1 T_3 \omega_l^2 - 1}{k_6},$$

$$k = \left[\frac{T_1 + T_3}{q(a_l, I_4^0)} + T_3 k_6\right]\omega_l^2. \qquad (67.29)$$

Combining them with the first equations (67.27), we find three quantities: ω_1, a_1, I_4 in dependence on the parameter k and on the given velocity α. After this from the second equation of (67.27) we determine the quantity β^0, and consequently, the error $\beta^0 - k_0\alpha^0$ which is a slowly varying part of the total stationary dynamic error; the second part of the total error is the self-oscillation: $\beta^p = a_\beta\sin\omega_l t$, where α_β is defined as in Example 1 of Section 63 by the formula

$$a_\beta = \frac{T_1 T_3 \omega_l^2 - 1}{k_6 \omega_l \sqrt{T_1^2 \omega_l^2 + 1}}a_l.$$

In a similar manner we may consider the influence of slowly varying external forces in other systems, in particular in relay systems. The greatest practical interest occurs where the self-oscillatory regime is the basic operating anode of the system.

Oscillations in non-linear systems containing unsymmetrical non-linearities, without external forces, are considered in the same manner.

68. Approximate determination of forced oscillations in vibrational linearisation of non-linear systems

The approximate methods employed in the preceding chapter for determining self-oscillation may be applied as well for the approximate study of forced oscillations in non-linear systems with sinusoidal external force. Different sides of this question have been studied in the works of N. M. Krylov and N. N. Bogoliubov, A. A. Andronov, N. V. Butenin, G. S. Pospelov, M. A. Aizerman, V. V. Petrov and G. M. Ulanov and others.

Forced oscillations of non-linear systems display a number of completely new interesting properties, depending substantially on the character of the non-linearity and on the relationships among the system parameters and the frequency and amplitude of the external force.

In the present section we describe a method of studying only the question, important for the theory of regulation, of determining forced oscillations of a non-linear system at the frequency of an external periodic force. This may have differing practical meanings, but the most important of this type is the following.

Let there be a non-linear system which operates in the self-oscillatory regime. In practice it is known that self-oscillations may be suppressed if at some point of the system from outside oscillations are introduced with constant amplitude and frequency exceeding the natural frequency of the system. As a result under certain conditions there occurs "interruption" of the self-oscillation and the system begins to carry out forced oscillations at the frequency of the external force (capture phenomenon). The relationships of the parameters may be so chosen that the forced oscillations of the system will have such a small amplitude that they may be practically neglected. Thus, a non-linear self-oscillatory system takes on as it were the properties of a continuous linear system and in many calculations may be practically considered as a whole as a linear system. This phenomenon is termed vibrational linearisation, or sometimes induced stabilisation, of the non-linear systems and is an important technical means of improving regulation processes.

It has been discussed partially in Section 13, where we found the transfer factor (gain factor) which the non-linear element obtains after such vibrational linearisation.

The problem now consists, therefore, in knowing how to determine the conditions for which the non-linear self oscillatory system will carry out forced oscillations at the frequency of the external periodic force and to determine the amplitude of these forced oscillations.

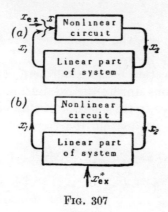

Fig. 307

Second-order relay system with delay. First we present the approximate solution of this problem for a second-order relay system, obtained by G. S. Pospelov.

Let there be a closed system consisting, as before, of a certain linear part and a non-linear element (in the given case, relay), where an additional external periodic force x_{ex} is applied to the input of the latter (Fig. 307a). Let us take

$$x_{ex} = c_{ex}\sin\omega_{ex}. \tag{68.1}$$

Let the equation of the linear part be:

$$(T_1 p + 1)px_1 = -kx_2, \tag{68.2}$$

while the relay has the characteristic

$$x_2 = F_\tau(x), \qquad x = x_1 + x_{ex}, \tag{68.3}$$

and $F_\tau(x)$ has the simple form of Fig. 286c with the addition of a constant time delay τ. An example of this type of system is the automatic temperature control considered at the end of Section 60 (in simplified form).

Substituting (68.3) in (68.2) and putting $x_1 = x - x_{ex}$, we obtain

$$(T_1 p + 1)px + kF_\tau(x) = (T_1 p + 1)px_{ex},$$

while substitution of expression (68.1) here leads to the equation

$$T_1\ddot{x} + \dot{x} + kF_\tau(x) = -A\sin(\omega_{ex}t - \alpha), \tag{68.4}$$

where

$$A = c_{ex}\omega_{ex}\sqrt{1+T_1^2\omega_{ex}^2}, \qquad \alpha = \tan^{-1}\frac{1}{T_1\omega_{ex}}. \tag{68.5}$$

According to the above, we shall seek a periodic solution of the non-linear equation (68.4) with given frequency ω_{ex} and the conditions of existence for such a solution, i.e. the conditions for capture. We will write the required solution approximately in the form

$$x = a\sin(\omega_{ex}t-\varphi),$$

where the unknowns are the amplitude of forced oscillations $a(t)$ and the phase shift $\varphi(t)$.

By analogy with Section 60 we shall here consider a and φ to be slowly varying functions during the establishment of the oscillations and constant in the steady-state forced oscillations. After substitution of the expression for x equation (68.4) will be:

$$2\frac{da}{dt}\omega_{ex}T_1\cos(\omega_{ex}t-\varphi)+2a\omega_{ex}T_1\frac{d\varphi}{dt}\sin(\omega_{ex}t-\varphi)-$$
$$-a\omega_{ex}^2T_1\sin(\omega_{ex}t-\varphi)+a\omega_{ex}\cos(\omega_{ex}t-\varphi)+kF_\tau[a\sin(\omega_{ex}t-\varphi)]$$
$$= -A\sin(\omega_{ex}t-\alpha).$$

Let us employ previous approximate formula (60.31) and further substitute here

$$A\sin(\omega_{ex}t-\alpha) = A\cos(\varphi-\alpha)\sin(\omega_{ex}t-\varphi)+A\sin(\varphi-\alpha)\cos(\omega_{ex}t-\varphi).$$

Then, collecting all terms with sines and cosines and equating coefficients for them individually to zero, we obtain the following two equations for determining the amplitude a and the phase shift φ during the transient forced oscillations:

$$\left.\begin{array}{l}\dfrac{da}{dt} = \dfrac{1}{2\omega_{ex}T_1}\left[-a\omega_{ex}+\dfrac{4ck}{\pi}\sin\omega_{ex}\tau-A\sin(\varphi-\alpha)\right],\\[3mm]\dfrac{d\varphi}{dt} = \dfrac{1}{2\omega_{ex}aT_1}\left[a\omega_{ex}^2T_1-\dfrac{4ck}{\pi}\cos\omega_{ex}\tau-A\cos(\varphi-a)\right].\end{array}\right\} \tag{68.6}$$

In the steady-state forced oscillations we have $a=\text{const}=a_{ex}$ and $\varphi=\text{const}=\varphi_{ex}$, i.e.

$$x = a_{ex}\sin(\omega_{ex}t-\varphi_{ex}), \tag{68.7}$$

where the amplitude a_{ex} and the phase shift φ_{ex} of forced oscillations are found by equating to zero the right-hand sides of equations (68,6) from which

$$\left.\begin{array}{l}a_{ex} = \left[\dfrac{4ck}{\pi A}\cos(\omega_{ex}\tau-\alpha)\pm\sqrt{1-\left(\dfrac{4ck}{\pi A}\right)^2\sin^2(\omega_{ex}\tau-\alpha)}\right]c_{ex},\\[4mm]\sin\varphi_{ex} = \dfrac{4ck}{\pi A}\sin(\omega_{ex}\tau-\alpha),\end{array}\right\} \tag{68.8}$$

where the quantities A and α are calculated from formulae (68.5).

From these expressions it follows that these forced oscillations may exist only when

$$\frac{4ck}{\pi A}\left|\sin\left(\omega_{ex}\tau - \alpha\right)\right| \leqslant 1$$

(otherwise the amplitude a_{ex} is imaginary while $\sin\varphi_{ex}$ is greater than unity). Substituting here the values of A and α from (68.5), we obtain the condition for the amplitude c_{ex} of the external periodic force:

$$c_{ex} \geqslant \frac{4ck}{\pi\omega_{ex}\sqrt{1 + T_1^2\omega_{ex}^2}}\left|\sin\left(\omega_{ex}\tau - \tan^{-1}\frac{1}{T_1\omega_{ex}}\right)\right|. \qquad (68.9)$$

In addition, it is necessary to investigate the stability of the periodic solution found, the more so because formula (68.8) gives two values for the amplitude. For this we employ the equations of transient oscillations (68.6). Giving the amplitude and phase small deviations $a = a_{ex} + \Delta a$, $\varphi = \varphi_{ex} + \Delta\varphi$ and linearising equations (68.6) according to the rules of Section 18, we obtain

$$\frac{d(\Delta a)}{dt} = \left(\frac{\partial F_1}{\partial a}\right)_{ex}\Delta a + \left(\frac{\partial F_1}{\partial\varphi}\right)_{ex}\Delta\varphi,$$

$$\frac{d(\Delta\varphi)}{dt} = \left(\frac{\partial F_2}{\partial a}\right)_{ex}\Delta a + \left(\frac{\partial F_2}{\partial\varphi}\right)_{ex}\Delta\varphi,$$

where F_1 and F_2 denote the right-hand sides of equations (68.6), while the index ex denotes substitution of the values $a = a_{ex}$ and $\varphi = \varphi_{ex}$ in the partial derivatives.

The characteristic equation will here be

$$z^2 - \left[\left(\frac{\partial F_1}{\partial a}\right)_{ex} + \left(\frac{\partial F_2}{\partial\varphi}\right)_{ex}\right]z + \left(\frac{\partial F_1}{\partial a}\right)_{ex}\left(\frac{\partial F_2}{\partial\varphi}\right)_{ex} - \left(\frac{\partial F_1}{\partial\varphi}\right)_{ex}\left(\frac{\partial F_2}{\partial a}\right)_{ex} = 0.$$

Since this is of second degree, from Section 27 for the variables Δa and $\Delta\varphi$ to be attenuated (and therefore, for stability of the periodic solution) it is necessary and sufficient that the coefficients of the equation be positive, i.e.

$$\left(\frac{\partial F_1}{\partial a}\right)_{ex} + \left(\frac{\partial F_2}{\partial\varphi}\right)_{ex} < 0,$$

$$\left(\frac{\partial F_1}{\partial a}\right)_{ex}\left(\frac{\partial F_2}{\partial\varphi}\right)_{ex} - \left(\frac{\partial F_1}{\partial\varphi}\right)_{ex}\left(\frac{\partial F_2}{\partial a}\right)_{ex} > 0.$$

Substituting here the values of the partial derivatives from the right-hand sides of equations (68.6), we obtain the following inequalities:

$$a_{ex} > \frac{2kc}{\pi\omega_{ex}}\sin\omega_{ex}\tau,$$

$$a_{ex} > \frac{4kc\cos\left(\omega_{ex}\tau - \alpha\right)}{\pi\omega_{ex}\sqrt{1 + T_1^2\omega_{ex}^2}}.$$

The second is always satisfied while the first, after substitution of (68.8) and (68.5), gives:

$$c_{ex} > \left[\frac{2kc\sin\omega_{ex}\tau}{\pi\omega_{ex}} - \frac{4kc\cos(\omega_{ex}\tau - \alpha)}{\pi\omega_{ex}\sqrt{1 + T_1^2\omega_{ex}^2}} \right]^2$$
$$+ \left[\frac{4\sin(\omega_{ex}\tau - \alpha)}{\pi\omega_{ex}\sqrt{1 + T_1^2\omega_{ex}^2}} \right]^2. \qquad (68.10)$$

As a result we obtain the following: if the frequency ω_{ex} of the external periodic force is such that the inequality

$$\frac{2\cos(\omega_{ex}\tau - \alpha)}{\sqrt{1 + T_1^2\omega_{ex}^2}} \geqslant \sin\omega_{ex}\tau, \qquad (68.11)$$

is satisfied, the amplitude c_{ex} of this force should satisfy condition (68.9). If inequality (68.11) is not satisfied, the amplitude c_{ex} should satisfy condition (68.10). As we see, in both cases the amplitude of

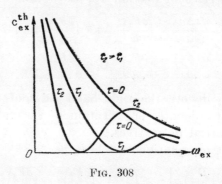

Fig. 308

external periodic force applied to the system should be greater than a certain so-called threshold value in order that the self-oscillations be interrupted and the system carry out only forced oscillations at the frequency of the external force ω_{ex}.

This threshold amplitude c_{ex} is determined by replacing the inequality sign by the equality sign in formulae (68.9) and (68.10). Fig. 308 shows the dependence of threshold value of amplitude c_{ex} of the external periodic force on its frequency ω_{ex} for various values of delay time in the relay τ. The curves are tangent to the axis of abscissae at points corresponding to the natural frequencies of oscillation of the system with the given delays.

Thus, to interrupt self-oscillation and force the system to oscillate at the frequency of the external periodic force, it is necessary to take the amplitude of the latter c_{ex} above the corresponding curve of Fig. 308. If a smaller amplitude is taken, self-oscillation is not interrupted and the system carries out a complex resultant process.

The frequency ω_{ex} of the external periodic force should be so chosen that vibrational linearisation will be achieved ("suppression" of self-oscillation), i.e. that the amplitude a_{ex} of forced oscillations in the system be fairly small. This amplitude is defined by formula (68.8). If for rough orientation we drop the radical in this formula, substitute A from (68.5) and take the cosine equal to unity, we obtain

$$a_{ex} \approx \frac{4ck}{\pi\omega_{ex}\sqrt{1 + T_1^2\omega_{ex}^2}}.$$

This expression shows that the amplitude of forced oscillations decreases with increase of frequency. In addition, the expression coincides with (60.33), i.e. the amplitude of forced oscillations is equal to the amplitude of self-oscillation at the same frequency. Consequently, to obtain a smaller amplitude it is necessary to take the frequency ω_{ex} of the external periodic force in every case greater than the frequency ω_1 of self-oscillation in the given system. In the graph of Fig. 308 this will be to the right of the point of tangency of the corresponding curve with the axis of abscissae.

For a substantial reduction of amplitude it is necessary to go far to the right (to take $\omega_{ex} \gg \omega_1$). However it is not possible to increase the external frequency without limit, since at too high a frequency the system will not react at all. For this reason the frequency ω_{ex} should be limited to the value $\omega_{ex} < \pi/\tau$, at which the delay time τ in the relay does not exceed a half-period of forced oscillations. Thus, for vibrational linearisation of the given relay system the frequency ω_{ex} should be taken in the interval

$$\omega_l \ll \omega_{ex} < \frac{\pi}{\tau},$$

and the amplitude c_{ex} above the corresponding curve in Fig. 308.

The exact determination of threshhold values for the amplitude of the external periodic force, carried out by G. S. Pospelov, showed good agreement between the given approximate result with the exact one for this problem.

Non-linear system of arbitrary order. Now, in the same general system (Fig. 307), let the linear part have an arbitrary structure and be described by an equation of arbitrary order:

$$Q_l(p)x_1 = -R_l(p)x_2. \tag{68.12}$$

The non-linear element is also arbitrary, where after harmonic linearisation (Section 61) we obtain for it the approximate equation

$$Q_n(p)x_2 = R_n(p)x, \qquad x = x_1 + x_{ex}, \tag{68.13}$$

where the external periodic force

$$x_{\text{ex}} = c_{\text{ex}}\sin\omega_{\text{ex}}t ,\qquad (68.14)$$

is given, while the forced oscillations are sought approximately in the form

$$x = a\sin(\omega_{\text{ex}}t - \varphi)\qquad (68.15)$$

with unknown a and φ. In the transient process they vary with time while in the steady-state forced oscillations they take on certain constant values $a = a_{\text{ex}}$ and $\varphi = \varphi_{\text{ex}}$. If it is necessary to take into account the delay τ in the non-linear element in place of (68.13) it is necessary to write

$$Q_n(p)x_2 = R_n(p)e^{-\tau p}x .\qquad (68.16)$$

Above we have started from the external periodic force x_{ex} applied directly to the input of the non-linear element (Fig. 307*a*). If it is applied to some other point of the system (Fig. 307*b*), we shall denote this in the following manner:

$$x_{\text{ex}}^{*} = c_{\text{ex}}^{*}\sin(\omega_{\text{ex}}t + \varphi^{*}) .\qquad (68.17)$$

In this case we have the following equation for the linear part:

$$Q_l(p)x = -R_l(p)x_2 + S_l(p)x_{\text{ex}}^{*} .\qquad (68.18)$$

The output quantity x of the linear part may be represented here in the form

$$x = x_1 + x_{\text{ex}} ,$$

where x_1 and x_{ex} are individually defined by the equations

$$Q_l(p)x_1 = -R_l(p)x_2 ,$$

$$Q_l(p)x_{\text{ex}} = S_l(p)x_{\text{ex}}^{*} ,$$

and the quantity x_{ex} is represented in the form (68.14). We then obtain

$$c_{\text{ex}} = \left|\frac{S_l(i\omega_{\text{ex}})}{Q_l(i\omega_{\text{ex}})}\right| c_{\text{ex}}^{*} ,\qquad \varphi^{*} = -\arg\frac{S_l(i\omega_{\text{ex}})}{Q_l(i\omega_{\text{ex}})} .\qquad (68.19)$$

From this it is evident that in an arbitrary concrete problem the structure of Fig. 307*b* may be reduced to the structure of Fig. 307*a*, employing formula (68.19). We shall therefore further consider only the structure of Fig. 307*a*.

Let us write expression (68.14) in the form

$$x_{\text{ex}} = c_{\text{ex}}\sin(\omega_{\text{ex}}t - \varphi + \varphi) = c_{\text{ex}}\cos\varphi\sin(\omega_{\text{ex}}t - \varphi) + c_{\text{ex}}\sin\varphi\cos(\omega_{\text{ex}}t - \varphi) .$$

Considering (68.15), this may be represented in the form

$$x_{\text{ex}} = \left(\frac{c_{\text{ex}}\cos\varphi}{a} + \frac{c_{\text{ex}}\sin\varphi}{a\omega_{\text{ex}}}p\right)x .\qquad (68.20)$$

Substituting (68.13) and (68.20) in equation (68.12), we obtain

$$\left[Q_l(p)\,Q_n(p)\left(1 - \frac{c_{\mathrm{ex}}\cos\varphi}{a} - \frac{c_{\mathrm{ex}}\sin\varphi}{a\omega_{\mathrm{ex}}}\,p\right) + R_l(p)\,R_n(p)\right]x = 0\ . \qquad (68.21)$$

This expression may be considered as a homogeneous linear differential equation, where the given frequency of oscillation ω_{ex} enters into the coefficients along with the unknown quantities the amplitude a and the phase shift φ of the forced oscillations to be found. The problem of determining the forced oscillations of a non-linear system thus reduces to finding the sinusoidal periodic solution of the special homogeneous equation (68.21). Its characteristic equation will be

$$Q_l(z)\,Q_n(z)\left(1 - \frac{c_{\mathrm{ex}}\cos\varphi}{a} - \frac{c_{\mathrm{ex}}\sin\varphi}{a\omega_{\mathrm{ex}}}\,z\right) + R_l(z)\,R_n(z) = 0\ . \qquad (68.22)$$

This differs from the characteristic equation (62.3), defining self-oscillation, only in that the first component contains a new factor, including the required phase shift of forced oscillations.

As a result, for the approximate determination of forced oscillations in the non-linear system we may now apply the same fundamental method which was employed in Section 62 to find self-oscillation. The difference here will be, firstly, a certain change in the characteristic equation (68.22) in place of (62.3) and, secondly, in that we are not seeking a and ω as before, but a and φ for given $\omega = \omega_{\mathrm{ex}}$.

If there is a constant time delay τ, then from (62.21) it is necessary in place of $R_n(z)$ to write $R_n(z)\,e^{-\tau z}$ in the characteristic equation (68.22).

By our basic method discussed in Section 62, we seek an expression for the Mikhailov curve for equation (68.22), i.e. we substitute $z = i\tilde{\omega}$ and separate the real and imaginary parts $X(\tilde{\omega})$ and $Y(\tilde{\omega})$. They should vanish with $\tilde{\omega} = \omega_{\mathrm{ex}}$, $a = a_{\mathrm{ex}}$, $\varphi = \varphi_{\mathrm{ex}}$ where ω_{ex} is the given frequency, while a_{ex} and φ_{ex} are the required amplitude and phase of forced oscillations, i.e.

$$\left.\begin{aligned} X(\omega_{\mathrm{ex}},\,a_{\mathrm{ex}},\,\varphi_{\mathrm{ex}}) &= 0\ , \\ Y(\omega_{\mathrm{ex}},\,a_{\mathrm{ex}},\,\varphi_{\mathrm{ex}}) &= 0 \end{aligned}\right\} \qquad (68.23)$$

constitute two equations with two unknowns a_{ex} and φ_{ex} for given ω_{ex}. These equations may be employed to determine the dependence of these quantities on the system parameters and to determine the threshold values of amplitude c_{ex} of the external periodic force (as the condition for existence of real values a_{ex} and φ_{ex} in equations (68.23)).

The stability of the periodic solution (for forced oscillations) may be roughly estimated by the same method of determining the coefficients as in Section 62. The stability conditions must be employed since in a real regulation system only stable oscillations may be established.

In addition to the above method of determining the quantities a_{ex} and φ_{ex}, based on setting up and solving equations (68.23), we may employ also the following graphic method. Substituting $z = i\omega_{ex}$ in the characteristic equation (68.22), we obtain the expression

$$a\left[1 + \frac{R_l(i\omega_{ex})R_n(\omega_{ex}, a)}{Q_l(i\omega_{ex})Q_n(\omega_{ex}, a)}\right] = c_{ex}(\cos\varphi + i\sin\varphi),\qquad (68.24)$$

where for given ω_{ex} the left-hand side is a function of only of a while the right-hand side of φ, i.e. we have the equation

$$\Phi(a) = c_{ex}(\cos\varphi + i\sin\varphi),\qquad (68.25)$$

where

$$\Phi(a) = a\left[1 + \frac{R_l(i\omega_{ex})R_n(\omega_{ex}, a)}{Q_l(i\omega_{ex})Q_n(\omega_{ex}, a)}\right].\qquad (68.26)$$

For each given value of ω_{ex} the function $\Phi(a)$ may be plotted point by point in the complex plane, taking a as the running para-

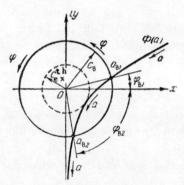

Fig. 309

meter along the curve (Fig. 309). The right-hand side of equation (68.25) gives a circle of radius c_{ex} in the complex plane with the values of φ varying along the circumference. Consequently, the points of intersection of the curve $\Phi(a)$ with the circle of radius c_{ex} will be solutions of equation (68.25) and give us the required values of amplitude a_{ex} and phase φ_{ex} of the forced oscillations at the given frequency ω_{ex}. In Fig. 309 two solutions are obtained. The stability of each of them may be approximately determined in the above manner.

Plotting in Fig. 309 a series of curves $\Phi(a)$ for various values of ω_{ex}, we find the values of a_{ex} and φ_{ex} at various forced oscillation frequencies.

The minimum radius of circle which touches the curve $\Phi(a)$ is the threshold value of c_{ex} of the external periodic force, below which forced oscillations at frequency ω_{ex} are not possible in a pure form; it is also not possible for them to suppress the self-oscillation of the system (a complex resultant process is obtained in the system).

If there is a delay τ in the non-linear element, then in expression (68.26) it is necessary to introduce the factor $e^{-\tau\omega_{ex}} = \cos\tau\omega_{ex} - i\sin\tau\omega_{ex}$, specifically:

$$\Phi(a) = a\left[1 + \frac{R_l(i\omega_{ex})R_n(\omega_{ex}, a)}{Q_l(i\omega_{ex})Q_n(\omega_{ex}, a)}\left(\cos\tau\omega_{ex} - i\sin\tau\omega_{ex}\right)\right], \quad (68.27)$$

and the method of solving the problem remains as before.

Let us consider an example of an automatic temperature regulation relay system (taking into account inertia of the regulating organ drive), described by equations (63.57). The relay characteristic $V = F(x)$ is taken in two alternatives: 1) the hysteresis characteristic (Fig. 286d) and 2) hysteresisless (Fig. 286c), but with delay τ.

From (63.57) the equation of the linear part of the system will be

$$(T_1 p + 1)(T_3 p + 1) p x = -k_1 k V, \quad (68.28)$$

where $k = k_2 k_3$.

The approximate equation of the relay in the first case (Fig. 286d), according to (63.58) and (63.70) has the form

$$\begin{aligned} V &= \left[q(a) - \frac{q_1(a)}{\omega}p\right]x, \\ q(a) &= \frac{4c}{\pi a^2}\sqrt{a^2 - b^2}, \qquad q_1(a) = \frac{4cb}{\pi a^2}, \end{aligned} \right\} \quad (68.29)$$

while in the second case (Fig. 286c with delay)

$$V = \frac{4c}{\pi a} e^{-\tau p}. \quad (68.30)$$

The characteristic equation (68.22) for determining the forced oscillations under the action of an external periodic force $x_{ex} = c_{ex}\sin\omega_{ex}t$ applied to the input of the relay will be

$$(T_1 z + 1)(T_3 z + 1)z\left(1 - \frac{c_{ex}\cos\varphi}{a} - \frac{c_{ex}\sin\varphi}{a\omega_{ex}}z\right) +$$
$$+ k_1 k R_n(a, z) = 0, \quad (68.31)$$

where for the first case

$$R_n(a, z) = \left[q(a) - \frac{q_1(a)}{\omega}z\right],$$

and for the second

$$R_n(a, z) = \frac{4c}{\pi a} e^{-\tau z}.$$

We shall first illustrate the first method of solving the problem. Substituting in the above characteristic equation $z = i\tilde{\omega}$ and separating the real and imaginary parts, we obtain:

$$X(\tilde{\omega}) = -(T_1 + T_3)\,\tilde{\omega}^2 \left(1 - \frac{c_{ex}\cos\varphi}{a}\right) +$$
$$+ (-T_1 T_3 \tilde{\omega}^3 + \tilde{\omega})\frac{c_{ex}\sin\varphi}{a\omega_{ex}}\,\tilde{\omega} + X_n(\tilde{\omega})\,,$$

$$Y(\tilde{\omega}) = (-T_1 T_3 \tilde{\omega}^3 + \tilde{\omega})\left(1 - \frac{c_{ex}\cos\varphi}{a}\right) +$$
$$+ (T_1 + T_3)\,\tilde{\omega}^2 \frac{c_{ex}\sin\varphi}{a\omega_{ex}}\,\tilde{\omega} + Y_n(\omega)\,,$$

where for the first case

$$X_n(\tilde{\omega}) = k_1 k q(a)\,, \qquad Y_n(\tilde{\omega}) = -k_1 k \frac{q_1(a)}{\omega}\,\tilde{\omega}\,,$$

and the second

$$X_n(\tilde{\omega}) = k_1 k \frac{4c}{\pi a}\cos\tau\tilde{\omega}\,, \qquad Y_n(\tilde{\omega}) = -k_1 k \frac{4c}{\pi a}\sin\tau\tilde{\omega}\,.$$

Equating X and Y to zero according to (68.23) we obtain the following equations for determining the amplitude a_{ex} and the phase φ_{ex} of forced oscillations:

$$-\omega_{ex}^2(T_1 + T_3)(a_{ex} - c_{ex}\cos\varphi_{ex}) + \omega_{ex}(1 - T_1 T_3 \omega_{ex}^2)c_{ex}\sin\varphi_{ex} + f_1 = 0\,,$$

$$\omega_{ex}(1 - T_1 T_3 \omega_{ex}^2)(a_{ex} - c_{ex}\cos\varphi_{ex}) - \omega_{ex}^2(T_1 + T_3)c_{ex}\sin\varphi_{ex} + f_2 = 0\,,$$

where for the first case

$$f_1 = k_1 k a_{ex} q(a_{ex})\,, \qquad f_2 = k_1 k a_{ex} q_1(a_{ex})\,,$$

and the second

$$f_1 = k_1 k \frac{4c}{\pi}\cos\tau\omega_{ex}\,, \qquad f_2 = -k_1 k \frac{4c}{\pi}\sin\tau\omega_{ex}\,.$$

The second case is simpler to study in that the quantities f_1 and f_2 are given constants (not dependent on the required a_{ex} and φ_{ex}).

Let us now illustrate the second (graphic) method of solving the problem. On the basis of the given system equations (68.28)–(68.30) we may immediately write the function $\Phi(a)$ from formula (68.26) or (68.27). For the first case (Fig. 286d) we have:

$$\Phi(a) = a\left[1 + \frac{k_1 k[q(a) - iq_1(a)]}{(T_1 i\omega_{ex} + 1)(T_3 i\omega_{ex} + 1)i\omega_{ex}}\right],$$

and for the second case (286c with delay)

$$\Phi(a) = a + \frac{k_1 k \dfrac{4c}{\pi}(\cos\tau\omega_{ex} - i\sin\tau\omega_{ex})}{(T_1 i\omega_{ex} + 1)(T_3 i\omega_{ex} + 1)i\omega_{ex}}.$$

Assigning various values to the variable a, we plot the curve $\Phi(a)$ by points in the complex plane and find the points of intersection with the circle of radius c_{ex}, as was shown in Fig. 309.

Approximate frequency method of determining forced oscillations. Let us describe this method, following L. S. Gol'dfarb. Let the non-linear element in the system of Fig. 307 be defined by the equation

$$x_2 = F(x_1) . \tag{68.32}$$

Let us find for it the approximate amplitude-phase characteristic $W_n(a)$ according to formulae (65.6) and (65.7). We consider two cases.

First case. The transfer function x_1/x_{ex}^* of the closed system (Fig. 307) is such that

$$\frac{x_1}{x_{ex}^*} = \frac{1}{1 + W_l(i\omega)\,W_n(a)} = \frac{M_l(i\omega)}{M_l(i\omega) + W_n(a)} , \tag{68.33}$$

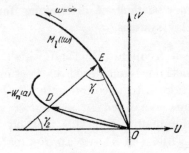

FIG. 310

where $M_l(i\omega) = 1/W_l(i\omega)$ is the inverse amplitude-phase characteristic of the linear part. Let us represent the characteristics $M_l(i\omega)$ and $-W_n(a)$ in the complex plane (Fig. 310). The amplitude a_{ex} of forced oscillations of the quantity x_1 defines the point D while the frequency ω_{ex} the point E. From formula (68.33) and the drawing (Fig. 310) we find

$$\frac{a_{ex}}{c_{ex}} = \frac{|M_l(i\omega_{ex})|}{|M_l(i\omega_{ex}) + W_n(a)|} = \frac{OE}{DE} ,$$

from which the amplitude c_{ex} of the external periodic force x_{ex}^* takes the values

$$c_{ex} = \frac{DE}{OE}\, a_{ex} . \tag{68.34}$$

Shifting the point D along the curve $W_n(a)$, we may thus find the dependence of a_{ex} on c_{ex} at the given frequency ω_{ex}, while shifting the point E, the dependence of these quantities on the frequency ω_{ex}.

Second case. The transfer function x_1/x_{ex}^* of the closed system (Fig. 307) is such that

$$\frac{x_1}{x_{ex}^*} = \frac{W_l(i\omega)}{1 + W_l(i\omega) W_n(a)} = \frac{1}{M_l(i\omega) + W_n(a)}. \qquad (68.35)$$

Then on the basis of this formula and the drawing (Fig. 310) we obtain:

$$\frac{a_{ex}}{c_{ex}} = \frac{1}{|M_l(i\omega) + W_n(a)|} = \frac{1}{DE},$$

from which

$$c_{ex} = DE \cdot a_{ex}. \qquad (68.36)$$

In other cases, when the transfer function does not come under the particular forms (68.33) and (68.35) the construction is more complicated.

69. Improved frequency method of determining forced oscillations and self-oscillations in relay systems

We describe here a frequency method which is more exact than the approximate methods considered in Section 68 and in Chapter XVI, since we take into account here all the harmonics of the non-linear oscillations expanded in a Fourier series and not only the fundamental component. But this method is convenient only for relay systems, while the above approximate methods may be used for almost any non-linear systems. However it is very useful, since relay systems are the most important type of non-linear systems (in Section 59 an exact method was considered for determining self-oscillations in such systems). The frequency method presented here was proposed by Ya. Z. Tsypkin. His idea was also partially developed by Yu. V. Dolgolenko. Certain initial considerations on self-oscillations were published previously by G. N. Nikol'skii. Here we shall follow the presentation of Ya. Z. Tsypkin.

Let there exist a relay system with structure shown in Fig. 307*a* (in Section 68 on p. 675 it was shown how the configuration of Fig. 307*b* reduces to this), where the linear part is described by differential equation (68.12), i.e. there is a defined transfer function

$$W_l(p) = \frac{R_l(p)}{Q_l(p)} \qquad (69.1)$$

(the minus sign, as usual, is omitted), while the non-linear element has the relay characteristic shown in Fig. 311*a*, denoted further by

$$x_2 = F(x), \qquad x = x_1 + x_{ex}, \qquad (69.2)$$

where x_1 is the output quantity of the linear part while x_{ex} is the external periodic force

$$x_{ex} = c_{ex}\sin(\omega_{ex}t - \varphi); \qquad (69.3)$$

here in contrast to Section 68 the phase shift φ is introduced into the expression for the external force so that the required forced oscillations of the system may be written with zero initial phase (which does not affect the essence of the matter).

Let T be the half-period of forced oscillations, i.e.

$$x(0) = b, \qquad x(T) = -b; \qquad (69.4)$$

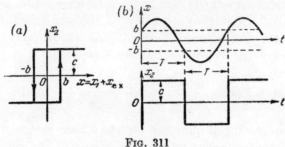

Fig. 311

In the steady-state forced oscillations at the given frequency ω_{ex} the output quantity of the relay element x_2 is a sequence of rectangular pulses of given duration T, amplitude c and with alternating sign (Fig. 311b).

As in Section 59 for self-oscillations, here for the steady-state forced oscillations we write the following conditions. Firstly, switching of the relay occurs at

$$T = \frac{\pi}{\omega_{ex}}.$$

Secondly, the conditions for switching are

$$\dot{x}(0) > 0, \qquad \dot{x}(T) < 0;$$

thirdly, switching within a half-period should be absent

$$x(t) > -b \qquad \text{with} \qquad 0 < t < T.$$

Considering that $x = x_1 + x_{ex}$ and employing (69.3) and (69.4), we write these conditions in the forms

$$x_1(T) - c_{ex}\sin\varphi = -b, \qquad (69.5)$$

$$\dot{x}_1(T) - \frac{\pi}{T}c_{ex}\cos\varphi < 0, \qquad (69.6)$$

$$x_1(t) + c_{ex}\sin\left(\frac{\pi}{T}t - \varphi\right) > -b \qquad \text{with} \qquad 0 < t < T. \qquad (69.7)$$

respectively. These conditions for the existence of forced oscillations of the system at the frequency of the external periodic force will be used below to find the forced oscillations.

We note in passing that to find the self-oscillations of the system in the absence of the external periodic force ($x_{ex} = 0$), we employ the analogous conditions

$$T = \frac{\pi}{\omega_{ex}}, \tag{69.8}$$

$$\dot{x}_1(t) < 0 , \tag{69.9}$$

$$x_1(t) > -b \quad \text{with} \quad 0 < t < T . \tag{69.10}$$

In approximate methods we have substituted the actual curve of oscillation of the output quantity of the non-linear element by its fundamental component. Now for the curve $x_2(t)$ (Fig. 311b) we shall employ the complete Fourier series

$$x_2 = F(x) = \frac{4c}{\pi} \sum_{m=1}^{\infty} \frac{1}{2m-1} \sin (2m-1)\, \omega_{ex}(t); \tag{69.11}$$

this constitutes the input quantity for the linear part of the system.

Now the output quantity of the linear part of the system x_1 may be obtained on the basis of the amplitude-phase characteristic of the linear part

$$W_l(i\omega) = \frac{R_l(i\omega)}{Q_l(i\omega)} = A(\omega) e^{i\beta}(\omega) , \tag{69.12}$$

where $A(\omega)$ and $\beta(\omega)$ denote, as before, the modulus and argument of the amplitude-phase characteristic. As already discussed in Section 8, to determine the output quantity x_1 when the input is given in the form (69.11), it is necessary to multiply each harmonic individually by the corresponding values of $W_1(i\omega)$, where $\omega = (2m-1)\,\omega_{ex}$ and $m = 1, 2, ..., \infty$, and then add. In addition, if we determine the quantity x_1 in the closed system (Fig. 307a), then from (68.12) it is necessary to introduce the common minus sign. As a result we obtain

$$x_1 = -\frac{4c}{\pi} \sum_{m=1}^{\infty} \frac{A\left((2m-1)\,\omega_{ex}\right)}{2m-1} \sin \left[(2m-1)\,\omega_{ex} + \beta\left((2m-1)\,\omega_{ex}\right)\right]$$
$$(0 < t < T) . \tag{69.13}$$

In particular, with $t = T$, taking into account (69.4), we have:

$$x_1(T) = \frac{4c}{\pi} \sum_{m=1}^{\infty} \frac{A\left((2m-1)\,\omega_{ex}\right)}{2m-1} \sin \beta\left((2m-1)\,\omega_{ex}\right) ,$$

$$\dot{x}_1(T) = \frac{4c}{\pi}\, \omega_{ex} \sum_{m=1}^{\infty} A\left((2m-1)\,\omega_{ex}\right) \cos \beta\left((2m-1)\,\omega_{ex}\right) . \tag{69.14}$$

But the quantities $A \cos \beta$ and $A \sin \beta$ from Fig. 50 are the real and imaginary parts of the amplitude-phase characteristics of the linear part $W_1(i\omega) = U_1(\omega) + iV_1(\omega)$. Therefore expressions (69.14), considering also (69.4), may be rewritten in the form

$$
\left.
\begin{aligned}
x_1(T) &= \frac{4c}{\pi} \sum_{m=1}^{\infty} \frac{V_l\big((2m-1)\,\omega_{\text{ex}}\big)}{2m-1}, \\
\frac{T}{\pi}\dot{x}_1(T) &= \frac{4c}{\pi} \sum_{m=1}^{\infty} U\big((2m-1)\,\omega_{\text{ex}}\big).
\end{aligned}
\right\}
\tag{69.15}
$$

For convenience in further investigations we introduce the condition for the frequency characteristic of the relay system

$$
W_r(\omega) = U_r(\omega) + iV_r(\omega),
\tag{69.16}
$$

with

$$
\left.
\begin{aligned}
U_r(\omega) &= \frac{T}{\pi}\dot{x}_1(T) = \frac{4c}{\pi} \sum_{m=1}^{\infty} U_l\big((2m-1)\,\omega_{\text{ex}}\big), \\
V_r(\omega) &= x_1(T) = \frac{4c}{\pi} \sum_{m=1}^{\infty} \frac{V_l\big((2m-1)\,\omega_{\text{ex}}\big)}{2m-1}.
\end{aligned}
\right\}
\tag{69.17}
$$

We shall construct this characteristic in the following manner. On the given amplitude-phase characteristic of the linear part of the system (69.12), shown in Fig. 312a, we mark off the points

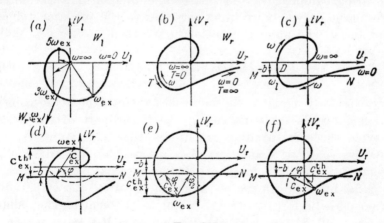

Fig. 312

$\omega_{\text{ex}}, 3\omega_{\text{ex}}, 5\omega_{\text{ex}}, ..., (2m-1)\,\omega_{\text{ex}}, ...$, and then reduce their ordinates by $1, 3, 5, ..., 2m-1, ...$, times respectively and to the points thus obtained we plot the radius vectors (Fig. 312a). The geometric sum of these vectors, multiplied by $4c/\pi$, according to (69.17) and (69.16) gives the vector of the characteristic $W_r(\omega_{\text{ex}})$. This will be one point of the required curve. Carrying out the same operation for various values of ω_{ex}, we obtain the complete curve of the relay system frequency characteristic $W_r(\omega)$ (Fig. 312b).

If in the given relay system (in its linear part or in the relay itself) there is a constant time delay τ, then only the initial amplitude-phase characteristic of the linear part is changed, which in place of (69.12) should be taken in the form

$$W_l(i\omega) = \frac{R_l(i\omega)}{Q_l(i\omega)}\, e^{-i\tau\omega} = A(\omega)\, e^{i\beta(\omega)},$$

and all the remaining, as well as the further calculations considered below, remain as before (except the investigation of stability).

Determining self-oscillations. Let us plot on the graph $W_r(\omega)$ the straight line MN, at a distance $-b$ from the U_r-axis and parallel to it (Fig. 312c). At the point D of intersection of this line with the curve W_r we have $V_r = -b$, $U_r < 0$. According to (69.17) this denotes $x_1(T) = -b$, $\dot{x}_1(T) < 0$, which coincides with the conditions for the existence of self-oscillations (69.8) and (69.9). Consequently the point D (Fig. 312c) defines the frequency of self-oscillation ω_1 in the given relay system.

The waveform of self-oscillations of the quantity x_1 is determined by formula (69.13), in which ω_{ex} is substituted by ω_1. Consequently, to determine the amplitude of self-oscillation a_1 it is here necessary to carry out a fairly cumbersome summation of individual harmonics with various amplitudes and phases and to find the maximum of the resultant curve. If we limit ourselves to the fundamental component (as in the approximate methods), then

$$a_l \approx \frac{4c}{\pi} A(\omega_l) = \frac{4c}{\pi} |W_l(i\omega_l)|. \tag{69.18}$$

It is similarly possible to find the waveform of self-oscillations of other intermediate variables in the linear part of the system, employing the corresponding amplitude-phase characteristics.

Determining forced oscillations. Let us mark on the curve $W_r(\omega)$ the point for the given frequency of the external periodic force ω_{ex} (Fig. 312d) and plot an arc of radius c_{ex} (equal to the amplitude of external periodic force) with this point as the centre. The point of intersection of this arc with the straight line MN lying to the left of the iV_r-axis defines the phase shift φ of the unknown forced oscillations of the quantity x_1 at the given frequency ω_{ex}, since the conditions (see Fig. 312d)

$$V_r(\omega_{ex}) - c_{ex}\sin\varphi = -b,$$
$$U_r(\omega_{ex}) - c_{ex}\cos\varphi < 0,$$

which from (69.17) are equivalent to conditions (69.5) and (69.6) for the existence of these forced oscillations, are satisfied.

In Fig. 312d there is a single point, while in Fig. 312e two (two periodic solutions), in Fig. 312e again a single point.

From these graphs it is evident that forced oscillations of the system at the given frequency ω_{ex} do not arise for all amplitudes c_{ex} of the external periodic force. There exists a minimum value, which as we have seen in Section 68, is termed the threshold value c_{ex}^{th} of the amplitude of the external force. For points ω_{ex} lying to the left of the iV_r—axis, the threshold value of c_{ex} is equal to the shorter distance from the point ω_{ex} to the line MN (Fig. 312d and e). For points ω_{ex} to the right of the iV_r—axis the threshhold c_{ex} is equal to the distance from the point ω_{ex} to the point of intersection of the straight line MN with the iV_r—axis (Fig. 312f), since in the latter case for smaller c_{ex} condition (69.6) is violated.

It is still necessary to determine the amplitude a_{ex} of forced oscillations of the quantity x_1 or other variable in the linear part of the system. This is particularly important where the external periodic forced is applied for vibrational linearisation of the relay system, since in these cases it is necessary to take the frequency ω_{ex} such that the amplitude a_{ex} is sufficiently small (much smaller than the amplitude of self-oscillation a_1). The forced-oscillation amplitude is determined after detailed plotting of the oscillation curve from formula (69.13) or, as in approximate methods, from the fundamental component

$$a_{ex} \approx \frac{4c}{\pi} A(\omega_{ex}) = \frac{4c}{\pi} |W_l(i\omega_{ex})|, \qquad (69.19)$$

which may be used for preliminary calculations.

For more exact plotting of the regulation curves both in the oscillatory regimes and in others, it is recommended to use the numerical-graphical method of Bashkirov, described below in Chapter XVIII.

Stability of oscillations. According to the Liapunov theory, for stability of forced oscillations, it is required that all roots of the characteristic equation

$$\frac{c_{ex}\omega_{ex}}{2c}\cos\varphi + (1-z)\sum_{j=1}^{n}\frac{C_j p_j e^{p_j T}}{1+e^{p_j T}}\cdot\frac{1}{z+e^{p_j T}} = 0 \qquad (69.20)$$

have modulus less than unity: $|z_k| < 1$ $(k = 1, 2, ..., n)$. Here we employ the notation: p_j are the roots of the denominator $Q_1(p)$ of the transfer function $W_1(p)$ of the linear part of the system, $T = \pi/\omega_{ex}$,

$$C_j = \lim_{p\to p_j}(p-p_j)W_l(p).$$

45

To investigate the stability of self-oscillations in place of (69.20) we take the characteristic equation

$$\sum_{j=1}^{n} \frac{C_j e^{p_j T}}{1 + e^{p_j T}} \cdot \frac{1}{z + e^{p_j T}} = 0, \qquad (69.21)$$

where $T = \pi/\omega_1$, and again we require $|z_k| < 1$ $(k = 1, 2, ..., n)$.

Both equations are valid only in the absence of multiple and zero roots of $Q_1(p)$.

In the presence of a zero root of $Q_1(p)$, which is frequently the case, the left-hand sides of the characteristic equations are more complicated.

Let us transform equations (69.20), substituting

$$z = e^{pT}. \qquad (69.22)$$

Then the second term of the equation will resemble the transfer function of a pulse regulation system (Chapter XIII). Therefore here we employ similar calculations, reducing the left-hand side of equation (69.20) finally to the form

$$q = W^*(p), \qquad (69.23)$$

where

$$q = \frac{\pi}{2c} [c_{ex} \cos\varphi - U_r(\omega_{ex})], \qquad (69.24)$$

$$W^*(p) = \sum_{m=-\infty}^{\infty} W_l (p + i(2m-1)\omega_{ex}). \qquad (69.25)$$

The left-hand side of equation (69.21) is reduced to the form

$$\frac{1}{1 - c^{pT}} [q + W^*(p)], \qquad (69.26)$$

where

$$T = \frac{\pi}{\omega_l}, \qquad q = -\frac{\pi}{2c} U_r(\omega_l), \qquad (69.27)$$

while $W^*(p)$ has expression (69.25) with substitution of ω_{ex} by ω_1. We plot the curve

$$W^*(i\omega) = U^*(\omega) + iV^*(\omega) \quad \text{with} \quad 0 < \omega < \omega_{ex} \qquad (69.28)$$

according to formula (69.25), substituting in it $p = i\omega$. If the real and imaginary parts are separated, we obtain

$$\left.\begin{array}{l} U^*(\omega) = - \sum_{m=-\infty}^{\infty} U_l (\omega + (2m-1)\omega_{ex}), \\[2mm] V^*(\omega) = - \sum_{m=-\infty}^{\infty} V_l (\omega + (2m-1)\omega_{ex}). \end{array}\right\} \qquad (69.29)$$

Consequently it is necessary to start from the given amplitude-phase characteristic of the linear part of the system. Let it have the form of Fig. 312a. We plot the curves $U_1(\omega)$ and $V_1(\omega)$ (Fig. 313a and b); for positive ω they are taken from Fig. 312a and then symmetrically extended towards negative ω. After this each of the

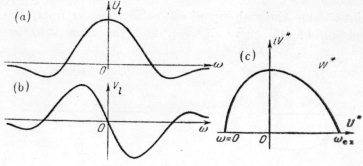

FIG. 313

curves is repeated many times shifted along the ω-axis by the quantity $(2m-1)\omega_{ex}$, where $m = 0, 1, 2, ...,$ and $-1, -2, ...$ The ordinates of all curves are summed on the segment $0 < \omega < \omega_{ex}$, which from (69.29) gives the values of $U^*(\omega)$ and $V^*(\omega)$, and thus the required curve $W^*(\omega)$ with $0 < \omega < \omega_{ex}$ (Fig. 313c).

We note the positions of the extreme points of the curve:

$$W^*(0) = \frac{\pi}{2c}\, U_r(\omega_{ex}), \qquad W^*(\omega_{ex}) = 2\sum_{m=0}^{\infty} U_l(2m\omega_{ex}).$$

Analysing all the above relationships, Ya. Z. Tsypkin came to the following result.

Forced oscillations at the frequency ω_{ex} will be stable if the difference between the numbers of positive and negative passages of the curve $W^*(i\omega)$ through the real axis on the segment $(-\infty, -q)$ with increasing ω from 0 to ω_{ex} is equal to zero (when the linear part is stable or neutral). If the denominator of the transfer function of the linear part of the system $Q_1(p)$ has s roots with positive real part, the above difference should be equal to s.

In this formulation a positive transition is downwards (points A and C in Fig. 314a), while negative is upwards (point B), where the distance q is calculated from formula (69.24). If the value of $W^*(i\omega)$ at $\omega = 0$ or at $\omega = \omega_{ex}$ is itself on the segment $(-\infty, -q)$, we consider that the curve $W^*(i\omega)$ carries out here a half transition.

If the curve $W^*(i\omega)$ does not intersect the segment $(-\infty, -q)$ at all (Fig. 314b and c), with stable or neutral linear part the forced oscillations will be stable (with neutral linear part the curve passes to infinity as in Fig. 314c). If the leftmost point $\omega = 0$ of the curve $W^*(i\omega)$ does not intersect the real axis, the stability condition for forced oscillations will be $U^*(0) > -q$, i.e. $\cos\varphi > 0$. Then of two periodic solutions possible in Fig. 312e that one will be stable for which $|\varphi| < 90°$ (the left point of intersection of the arc with the straight line MN).

To investigate the stability of self-oscillations we apply the same construction of the curve $W^*(i\omega)$, and the same criterion with

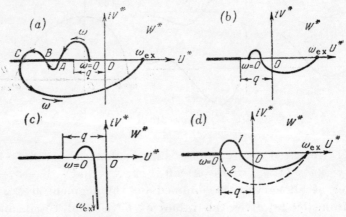

FIG. 314

substitution of ω_{ex} by ω_1. In this it is found that the origin of the curve $W^*(i\omega)$ at $\omega = 0$ is located at the point $(-q, i0)$, as shown in Fig. 314d, with a vertical tangent. In this case we should consider that curve 1 (Fig. 314d) has no passage at the point $\omega = 0$ while curve 2 has a half passage. The curve 1 (in the absence of passages at other points and with stable linear part of the system) corresponds to a stable self-oscillation while curve 2 to an unstable periodic solution.

Example. Let us consider the same automatic regulation relay system considered in the example on p. 719. The transfer function of the linear part of the system, from (68.28), will be

$$W_l(p) = \frac{k_1 k}{(T_1 p + 1)(T_3 p + 1)p}. \tag{69.30}$$

The corresponding amplitude-phase characteristic of the linear part $W_1(i\omega)$ is shown in Fig. 315a. According to it by the above-described method of summing vectors (Fig. 312a) we plot the individual points W_r and obtain the frequency characteristic of the relay system $W_r(\omega)$ in the form of Fig. 315b. Its point of intersection with the line MN defines the frequency of self-oscillation in the given relay system. From the graph it is evident that the frequency of self-oscillation will be the greater, the smaller the width of hysteresis loop b (Fig. 311a).

The amplitude of self-oscillation is difficult to determine here. As a rough estimate we may take the amplitude of the fundamental component (69.18), where $A(\omega_1)$ is the radius-vector of the curve $W_1(i\omega)$ at the point $\omega = \omega_1$ in Fig. 315a.

To find the conditions of interruption of self-oscillations [using forced oscillations at various frequencies ω_{ex}, from Fig. 312b it is necessary to take on the characteristic W_r of the given system

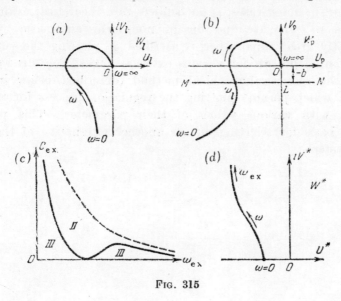

Fig. 315

(Fig. 315b) various points ω_{ex} and to determine the threshold values of c_{ex} as the shortest distances of these points to the straight line MN. As a result it is possible to plot the graph of threshold values of the amplitude of the external periodic force c_{ex} as a function of its frequency ω_{ex} (full curve in Fig. 315c).

In addition, in Fig. 315c the curve of distances from the points ω_{ex} in Fig. 315b to point L is given in broken line. Then the region I (Fig. 315c) will correspond to values of c_{ex} for which there is a single periodic solution, as in Fig. 312d (forced oscillations at frequency ω_{ex}). Region II has two periodic solutions (as for example in Fig. 312e), one of which—the stable one—defines the forced oscillations at frequency ω_{ex}. In region III (Fig. 315c) are values of the amplitude of external periodic force c_{ex} not capable of suppressing self-oscillation in the given system.

To estimate the amplitude of forced oscillations from the fundamental component (69.19) we use, as before, the curve W_1 (Fig. 315a).

To study the stability of self-oscillations and forced oscillations, by the above method (Fig. 313) we plot the curve $W^*(i\omega)$, which in the present case takes the form of Fig. 315*d*. Since it does not intersect the real axis anywhere, except at the point $\omega = 0$, then, as follows from the above theory, in the region *II* (Fig. 315*c*), of the two possible periodic solutions that one will be stable for which $|\varphi| < 90°$; it defines the forced oscillations which will be established in the system.

From the material presented in Part IV it is evident that the quality of a non-linear automatic system is either estimated very roughly or, in many cases, is not subject to a theoretical evaluation. Therefore to calculate and design non-linear automatic systems particularly great importance is ascribed to plotting the curve of the regulation process for various external forces. For this we may employ the numerical-graphical method (described below in Section 72), which permits plotting the regulation process for various elements with various values of their parameters. This permits a better basis for selecting one or another alternative of the projected system.

PART V

METHODS OF PLOTTING THE REGULATION-PROCESS CURVE

CHAPTER XVIII

NUMERICAL-GRAPHICAL METHOD

70. Basis of the Bashkirov numerical-graphical method. First and second-order linear equations

In the preceding parts of this book we have considered various methods of investigating stability, estimating the quality of transient responses, determining self-oscillations and forced oscillations. All this has served for the best choice of structure and parameters of various types of closed automatic systems.

However we cannot consider the investigation of the quality of the system completed with this. After the structure and parameters of the system have been chosen it is still necessary to verify that the entire regulation (or tracking) process in the given system proceeds in the necessary manner and satisfies the requirements placed on the system. This is achieved by plotting the curves of the regulation (or tracking) process by a theoretical method for various external perturbations and input commands, typical for the operation of the given system and then testing the system in a model and in the form of an experimental prototype.

In the present section of the book we shall consider methods of plotting the curves of the regulation process (in particular, the transient process) as the concluding stage of the theoretical study in the design of automatic systems. Questions of modelling and testing automatic systems are outside the scope of this book. They require very serious attention and particularly detailed discussion. We are also not presenting here methods of studying the influence of random forces on the system, given in terms of probability characteristics (statistical methods).

In view of the approximate character of many of the criteria of the quality of automatic systems described in the previous sections of the book, it is useful to construct the curves of the regulation process for several alternative possible structures and numerical values of the system parameters, and to select the best of them.

We present first a numerical-graphical method developed in 1948 by D. A. Bashkirov, which in application to automatic systems is the most universal in the sense that it is applicable both to the plotting of transient curves and the curves of regulation (and tracking) processes with arbitrary external forces variable in time; it is equally applicable both to ordinary linear systems and to systems with delay, to systems with time-variable parameters, to non-linear systems with arbitrary non-linearity (including relay systems).

The external perturbation $f(t)$ or the command $y(t)$ may be given arbitrarily as a function of time, either graphically or in tabular form.

Initial assumptions of the method. Let us consider the exponential (Fig. 316) of the form

$$x = C - C_1 e^{-\frac{t}{T}}, \tag{70.1}$$

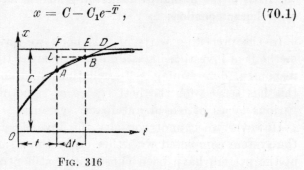

FIG. 316

where T is the time constant of the exponential, C_1 is an arbitrary constant, and, following Bashkirov, we shall prove that the projections of the secants, plotted through any two points of the exponential equidistant in time, are of constant length.

Let us take two arbitrary points of the exponential A and B (Fig. 316), separated in time by a certain quantity Δt, where A corresponds to an arbitrary time t. Let us plot through them the secant ABD and find the length of its projection FD. From the similarity of triangles BED and AFD we have:

$$\frac{ED}{FD} = \frac{BE}{AF}, \qquad \frac{AL}{BL} = \frac{AF}{DF}. \tag{70.2}$$

From equation (70.1) we find:

$$AF = C - x(t) = C_1 e^{-\frac{t}{T}},$$
$$BE = C - x(t + \Delta t) = C_1 e^{-\frac{t+\Delta t}{T}},$$

which gives:

$$\frac{BE}{AF} = \frac{C - x(t + \Delta t)}{C - x(t)} = e^{-\frac{\Delta t}{T}}. \tag{70.3}$$

Let us denote the length of the projection of the secant AD by T_s, i.e. $FD = T_s$. Then from the first of formulae (70.2), taking into account (70.3), we obtain

$$T_s = \frac{\Delta t}{1 - e^{-\frac{\Delta t}{T}}}, \tag{70.4}$$

which proves that the length T_s of the projection of the secant is constant, since T_s does not depend on t. Simultaneously this formula expresses a relation between the quantity T_s and the time constant T for any given exponential.

It is convenient, expanding the denominator of expression (70.4) in a series

$$1 - e^{-\frac{\Delta t}{T}} = \frac{\Delta t}{T} - \frac{1}{2!}\left(\frac{\Delta t}{T}\right)^2 + \frac{1}{3!}\left(\frac{\Delta t}{T}\right)^3 - \ldots$$

and dividing, to represent formula (70.4) in the form

$$T_s = T + \frac{\Delta t}{2}\left[1 + \frac{1}{6}\frac{\Delta t}{T} - \frac{1}{360}\left(\frac{\Delta t}{T}\right)^3 + \ldots\right] \approx T + \frac{\Delta t}{2} \tag{70.5}$$

(if $\Delta t < T$). It is of course possible not to carry out this substitution, but to use the exact formula (70.4), from which the method described below does not differ in principle. However for other considerations we shall always take $\Delta t \ll T$. Therefore the substitution (70.5) has practically no influence on the exactness of solution.

From the second of formulae (70.2) and from the drawing (Fig. 316) we have further

$$\frac{\Delta x}{\Delta t} = \frac{C - x}{T_s} \approx \frac{C - x}{T + \frac{\Delta t}{2}}. \tag{70.6}$$

The exponential (70.1) is, as is well known, the solution of the equation

$$T\dot{x} + x = C \tag{70.7}$$

with the initial condition

$$x(0) = C - C_1.$$

Graphical solution of a first-order nonhomogeneous equation. Let it be required to solve the differential equation

$$T\dot{x} + x = f(t) \tag{70.8}$$

with initial condition $x(0) = x_0$, where $f(t)$ is an arbitrary given function of time If equation (70.8) has the form

$$T\dot{x} + x = b_0 \dot{f}_1(t) + b_1 f_1(t) \quad \text{or} \quad T\dot{x} + x = b \dot{f}_1(t),$$

where $f_1(t)$ is given, then we first carry out the corresponding calculations in the right-hand side and obtain it in the form of a single prescribed function $f(t)$ as in (70.8)

We replace the prescribed curve $f(t)$ (Fig 317a) by a stepwise curve such that within each segment Δt it has a constant value, equal to $f(t+\Delta t/2)$ Then within each segment Δt equation (70.8) will have the form

$$T\dot{x} + x = C,$$

where

$$C = f\left(t + \frac{\Delta t}{2}\right).$$

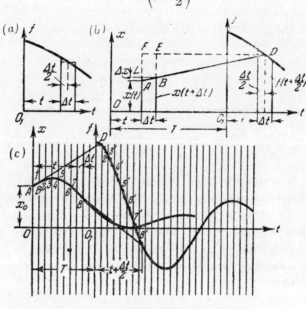

FIG. 317

Since this agrees with equation (70.7), it is possible to employ formula (70.6), for each segment, Δt, which in the present case gives:

$$\frac{\Delta x}{\Delta t} = \frac{f\left(t + \dfrac{\Delta t}{2}\right) - x(t)}{T + \dfrac{\Delta t}{2}}. \tag{70.9}$$

From this formula there follows the validity of the following graphical construction shown in Fig. 317b. The given curve $f(t)$ is shifted along the axis of abscissae by the quantity T, figuring in the equation to be solved (70.8). If a single point $A(t,x)$ of the required curve $x(t)$ is known, then, joining it to the point D, taken at the center of the segment Δt on the curve $f(t)$, we obtain the point B, constituting a new point $x(t+\Delta t)$ of the required solution, since here the triangle AFD has exactly the same form as in Fig. 316.

As a result the entire process of graphical solution of equation (70.8) appears as shown in Fig. 317c and consists only of simple plotting of straight lines of the type *ABD* (Fig. 317*b*). In this the point *D* is always given by the right-hand side of equation $f(t)$ while the point *A* in the first step by the condition $x(0) = x_0$. The quantity Δt is taken at will (it is convenient to take it so that it fits a whole number of times into the segment *T*). The point *B* (Fig. 317*c*) is found by plotting the straight line *AD* through the given points *A* and *D*; the following point 2 of the solution is found by plotting the straight line from the point *B* to the point 2′; then the point 3 by plotting the straight line from the point 2 to the point 3′, etc. In Fig. 317*c* we show as an example the straight line plotted from the point 7 to the point 8′ to obtain the point 8 of the required solution $x(t)$.

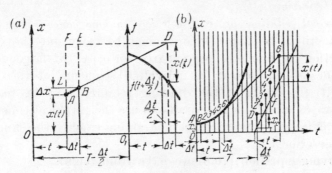

FIG. 318

All the points found in this manner belong (approximately) to the required solution. From the construction it is evident that with decrease of Δt the solution obtained tends to the exact solution.

We shall also indicate the graphical solution of the equation

$$T\dot{x} = f(t) .\qquad(70.10)$$

It is possible to write approximately

$$T\Delta x \approx f\left(t + \frac{\Delta t}{2}\right)\Delta t$$

or

$$\frac{\Delta x}{\Delta t} = \frac{f\left(t + \dfrac{\Delta t}{2}\right)}{T} .\qquad(70.11)$$

The construction based on this formula is shown in Fig. 318*a*. The technique of plotting differs from that of Fig. 317 only in shifting the point *D* above the curve *f* in each step by a certain quantity *x* (obtained from the preceding step of the integration). The given curve $f(t)$ is here shifted along the axis of abscissae not by *T* as before, but by $T - \Delta t/2$.

As a result the entire process of graphical solution of equation (70.10) thus reduces to plotting straight lines (Fig. 318*b*) of the type ABD (Fig. 318a). In this the point A is given at the start (Fig. 318b) by the condition $x(0) = x_0$, the point D is obtained by adding the segment x_0 to the ordinate of the prescribed function $f(t)$ at $t = \Delta t/2$ (i.e. at the distance T from the origin of coordinates). Plotting the straight line through the given points A and D, we obtain the point B (Fig. 318a), constituting the new point of the required solution $x(t)$. Laying out the new value x thus found from the following ordinate of the prescribed curve f, we obtain the point $2'$, which joined to the point B by a straight line, gives us the new point 2 of the required solution $x(t)$, etc. In Fig. 318b the line 5—6' is shown as an example, plotted to determine the point 6 of the required solution $x(t)$.

Numerical solution of a first-order nonhomogeneous equation. It may sometimes be found inconvenient to carry out the graphical construction in practice, particularly for cases of large angles of inclination of the secant in individual segments of the required curve $x(t)$ (the scale of the drawing required may be too large).

In all cases when it is undesirable to use the graphical construction, we may employ a numerical method giving exactly the same result. Let us describe it.

In solving equation (70.8) we have from (70.9):

$$\Delta x = \frac{\Delta t}{T + \dfrac{\Delta t}{2}}\left[f\left(t + \frac{\Delta t}{2}\right) - x(t)\right]$$

and, in addition,

$$x(t + \Delta t) = x(t) + \Delta x .$$

Consequently, the process of numerical solution of the problem will consist in the following. Taking the integration step Δt and having the prescribed function $f(t)$ and the value $x(0) = x_0$, we calculate:

$$
\left.
\begin{aligned}
x(\Delta t) &= \beta_1 x_0 + \beta_2 f\left(\frac{\Delta t}{2}\right), \\
x(2\Delta t) &= \beta_1 x(\Delta t) + \beta_2 f\left(\Delta t + \frac{\Delta t}{2}\right), \\
&\cdots\cdots\cdots\cdots\cdots\cdots\cdots\cdots\cdots \\
x(t + \Delta t) &= \beta_1 x(t) + \beta_2 f\left(t + \frac{\Delta t}{2}\right), \\
&\cdots\cdots\cdots\cdots\cdots\cdots\cdots\cdots\cdots
\end{aligned}
\right\}
\qquad (70.12)
$$

where

$$\beta_1 = 1 - \frac{\Delta t}{T + \dfrac{\Delta t}{2}}, \qquad \beta_2 = \frac{\Delta t}{T + \dfrac{\Delta t}{2}}. \qquad (70.13)$$

Here integration reduces to the simple operation of addition (subtraction) with multiplication by fixed numbers β_1 and β_2.

In Fig. 319a and 319b it is shown how the values of the given function $f(t)$ are taken and in which form the result of the solution $x(t)$ is obtained.

The process of multiplication by the constant numbers β_1 and β_2 may be speeded up using the inclined lines with the slopes $\tan \alpha_1 = \beta_1$ and $\tan \alpha_2 = \beta_2$ (taking into account the scale). Laying off the number

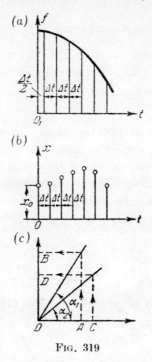

FIG. 319

to be multiplied in the form of segments OA and OC (Fig. 319c), we obtain the results of multiplication in the form of segments OB and OD.

To solve equation (70.10) we have from (70.11)

$$\Delta x = \frac{\Delta t}{T} f\left(t + \frac{\Delta t}{2}\right).$$

Therefore the process of solution appears as follows:

$$
\left.
\begin{aligned}
x(\Delta t) &= x_0 + \beta f\left(\frac{\Delta t}{2}\right), \\
x(2\Delta t) &= x(\Delta t) + \beta f\left(\Delta t + \frac{\Delta t}{2}\right), \\
&\cdots\cdots\cdots\cdots\cdots\cdots\cdots\cdots \\
x(t + \Delta t) &= x(t) + \beta f\left(t + \frac{\Delta t}{2}\right), \\
&\cdots\cdots\cdots\cdots\cdots\cdots\cdots
\end{aligned}
\right\}
\qquad (70.14)
$$

where

$$\beta = \frac{\Delta t}{T} . \tag{70.15}$$

These calculations are analogous to the preceding.

Graphical solution of a second-order nonhomogeneous equation. Let it be required to solve the differential equation

$$a_0\ddot{x} + a_1\dot{x} + a_2 x = f_1(t) \tag{70.16}$$

with initial conditions $x(0) = x_0$, $\dot{x}(0) = \dot{x}_0$, where $f_1(t)$ is an arbitrary prescribed function of time. If the equation of the system has the form

$$a_0\ddot{x} + a_1\dot{x} + a_2 x = b_0\ddot{f}_2(t) + b_1\dot{f}_2(t) + b_2 f_2(t) ,$$

where $f_2(t)$ is given, it is first necessary to calculate the complete right-hand side and to write the equation in the form (70.16). If $f_2(t)$ is a step or impulse, it is possible to solve the homogeneous equation, recalculating the initial conditions according to Section 6.

Equation (70.16) may be reduced to the form

$$T_1 T_2 \ddot{x} + T_2 \dot{x} + x = f(t) , \tag{70.17}$$

where

$$T_1 = \frac{a_0}{a_1}, \qquad T_2 = \frac{a_1}{a_2}, \qquad f(t) = \frac{f_1(t)}{a_2} .$$

Denoting $x_1 = T_2\dot{x}$, we separate equation (70.17) into a system of two equations

$$T_1\dot{x}_1 + x_1 = f(t) - x , \tag{70.18}$$
$$T_2\dot{x} = x_1 . \tag{70.19}$$

These equations are analogous to the above equations (70.8) and (70.10). Therefore, on the basis of (70.9) we have for the first equation:

$$\frac{\Delta x_1}{\Delta t} = \frac{f\left(t + \dfrac{\Delta t}{2}\right) - x\left(t + \dfrac{\Delta t}{2}\right) - x_1(t)}{T_1 + \dfrac{\Delta t}{2}} . \tag{70.20}$$

Formula (70.11) in application to (70.19) is written in the form

$$\frac{x(t + \Delta t) - x(t)}{\Delta t} = \frac{x_1\left(t + \dfrac{\Delta t}{2}\right)}{T_2} .$$

Shifting in this all values by the half-step of integration $\Delta t/2$, we obtain

$$\frac{\Delta x}{\Delta t} = \frac{x_1(t + \Delta t)}{T_2} . \tag{70.21}$$

where by Δx we denote

$$\Delta x = x\left(t + 3\,\frac{\Delta t}{2}\right) - x\left(t + \frac{\Delta t}{2}\right).$$

The graphical construction based on formulae (70.20) and (70.21) is shown in Fig. 320a. It combines two constructions, one of which (at the right) is analogous to Fig. 317, while the second (at the left) is analogous to Fig. 318. These constructions reduce to the following.

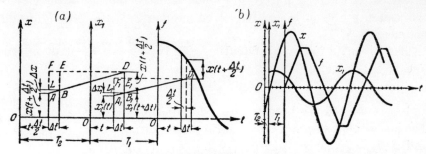

FIG. 320

An arbitrary intermediate integration step is represented in Fig. 320a. Here we know the curve $f(t)$ and have as well the points $A_1[x_1(t)]$ and $A[x(t + \Delta t/2)]$ from the preceding integration step. At the ordinate $f(t + \Delta t/2)$ we lay off the segment $x(t + \Delta t/2)$ downwards, if it is positive. Joining the point D_1 with the point A_1 by a straight line, we obtain the new point B_1 of the curve x_1. We add to this new ordinate $x_1(t + \Delta t)$ the segment $x(t + \Delta t/2)$ upwards, if it is positive. This gives us the point D. Joining the latter with the point A, we obtain the new point B of the required curve x.

Thus, the entire process of solution again reduces only to plotting straight lines. But if in solving a first-order equation each step of integration required plotting of only a single line, here it consists of plotting two lines A_1D_1 and AD.

The process of construction, as is evident from formulae (70.20) and (70.21) should begin from the values $f(\Delta t/2)$, $x(\Delta t/2)$ and $x_1(0)$. The first of these is known, since $f(t)$ is prescribed. The values $x(\Delta/2)$ and $x_1(0)$ should be found before proceeding with the solution. We express them in terms of the prescribed initial conditions $x(0) = x_0$ and $\dot{x}(0) = \dot{x}_0$.

From (70.19) we have

$$x_1(0) = T_2\dot{x}_0 . \qquad (70.22)$$

Further, since Δt is a fairly small interval, it is completely permissible to assume that in the segment $\Delta t/2$ the function x varies along its tangent, i.e.

$$x\left(\frac{\Delta t}{2}\right) = x_0 + \frac{\Delta t}{2}\,\dot{x}_0 . \qquad (70.23)$$

Thus, we have obtained the initial data for plotting the transient curve by the above method.

As an example, in Fig. 320b the graphical solution of equation (70.17) is shown for $T_1 = 2$ and $T_2 = 0.5$, for a sawtooth perturbation $f(t)$ given graphically, and with initial conditions $x(0) = -0.62$; $\dot{x}(0) = 0.8$. We take the integration step $\Delta t = 0.2$.

Numerical solution of a nonhomogeneous second-order equation. In all cases where a purely graphical construction is inconvenient, the same problem is easily solved numerically in the following manner.

The given differential equation (70.16) is represented in the form (70.17), i.e.

$$T_1 T_2 \ddot{x} + T_2 \dot{x} + x = f(t),$$

and is separated, as before, into two equations (70.18) and (70.19). The integration step Δt is chosen. From the initial conditions $x(0) = x_0$ and $\dot{x}(0) = \dot{x}_0$, according to (70.22) and (70.23) we calculate the quantities

$$x_1(0) = T_2 \dot{x}_0, \qquad x\left(\frac{\Delta t}{2}\right) = x_0 + \frac{\Delta t}{2}\dot{x}_0.$$

On the basis of formulae (70.20) and (70.21) the order of numerical calculations will be as follows: the first step

$$x_1(\Delta t) = \beta_1 x_1(0) + \beta_2\left[f\left(\frac{\Delta t}{2}\right) - x\left(\frac{\Delta t}{2}\right)\right],$$

$$x\left(3\,\frac{\Delta t}{2}\right) = x\left(\frac{\Delta t}{2}\right) + \beta_3 x_1(\Delta t),$$

where

$$\beta_1 = 1 - \frac{\Delta t}{T_1 + \frac{\Delta t}{2}}, \qquad \beta_2 = \frac{\Delta t}{T_1 + \frac{\Delta t}{2}}, \qquad \beta_3 = \frac{\Delta t}{T_2}; \qquad (70.24)$$

the following steps

$$x_1(2\Delta t) = \beta_1 x_1(\Delta t) + \beta_2\left[f\left(3\,\frac{\Delta t}{2}\right) - x\left(3\,\frac{\Delta t}{2}\right)\right],$$

$$x(5\Delta t) = x\left(3\,\frac{\Delta t}{2}\right) + \beta_3 x_1(2\Delta t),$$

$$\cdots\cdots\cdots\cdots\cdots\cdots\cdots\cdots\cdots$$

$$x_1(t + \Delta t) = \beta_1 x_1(t) + \beta_2\left[f\left(t + \frac{\Delta t}{2}\right) - x\left(t + \frac{\Delta t}{2}\right)\right],$$

$$x\left(t + 3\,\frac{\Delta t}{2}\right) = x\left(t + \frac{\Delta t}{2}\right) + \beta_3 x_1(t + \Delta t), \qquad (70.25)$$

$$\cdots\cdots\cdots\cdots\cdots\cdots\cdots\cdots\cdots$$

Plotting the regulation curve in a linear system with delay. Since the method is analogous to the preceding, we shall consider it immediately in a simple example. Let the equations of the regulated object and the regulator have the forms

$$T_1 \frac{dx_1}{dt} + x_1 = -x_2 + f(t) , \qquad (70.26)$$

$$x_2(t) = kx_1(t-\tau) , \qquad (70.27)$$

respectively, where $f(t)$ is an arbitrarily given perturbation, x_1 is the deviation of the regulated quantity, x_2 is the displacement of the regulating organ, τ is a constant time delay in the regulator.

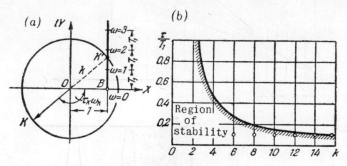

FIG. 321

Let us first find the stability region in the parameter plane $(k, \tau/T_1)$. The characteristic equation of the system, from (70.26) and (70.27), will be

$$T_1 z + 1 + k e^{-z\tau} = 0 .$$

The auxiliary Mikhailov curve (Section 49)

$$Q_1(i\omega) = T_1 i\omega + 1$$

has the form of a straight line (Fig. 321a). The circle of radius k intersects it under the condition $k > 1$. Therefore, if $k < 1$, the system is stable for arbitrary τ. If $k > 1$, there is a critical time delay. From the triangle $OK'B$ (Fig. 321a), we have

$$\cos(\pi - \tau_k \omega_k) = \frac{1}{k} ,$$

where

$$T_1 \omega_k = \sqrt{k^2 - 1} .$$

From this

$$\frac{\tau_k}{T_1} = \frac{\pi - \cos^{-1}\dfrac{1}{k}}{\sqrt{k^2 - 1}} , \qquad (70.28)$$

which is the boundary of stability represented in Fig. 321b.

Let the regulator time delay in our example be $\tau = 0.1 T_1$. By plotting the regulation curve for eight points of the stability region, denoted in Fig. 321b, following D. A. Bashkirov we verify the variation in shape of this process with increase of regulator transfer factor k. As the perturbation $f(t)$ let us take for simplicity and clarity the unit step $f(t) = 1(t)$. Here let $x_1 = 0$ with $t \leqslant 0$.

Comparing equations (70.26) and (70.8), we conclude on the basis of Fig. 317b that in the present case it is necessary, taking the

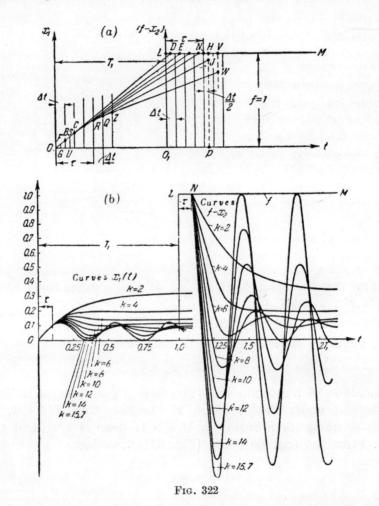

Fig. 322

distance along the axis of abscissae from the origin of coordinates T_1, to plot the graph of the function $(f-x_2)$ with respect to time. But we still do not know the quantity x_2. Therefore we as yet plot only $f(t)$, the straight line LM (Fig. 322a).

From (70.27) and the initial condition ($x_1 = 0$ with $t \leqslant 0$) we see that $x_2 = 0$ not only for $t \leqslant 0$, but also with $0 \leqslant t \leqslant \tau$. Therefore, laying off from the point L the segment τ (Fig. 322a), it may be stated that the segment LN of the function $f(t)$ represents simultaneously what is required to plot the function $(f-x_2)$ with $0 \leqslant t \leqslant \tau$.

Further we select the integration step Δt. Let us plot the corresponding grid in Fig. 322a. According to Fig. 317b we plot from the center point of the first integration step D (Fig. 322a) the straight line to the point 0 (since $x_1 = 0$ at $t = 0$). This gives us the first segment OB of the required curve of the regulation process $x_1(t)$. We then take the center of the next integration step E, joining it by a straight line to the point B, as a result of which we obtain the second segment BC of the curve $x_1(t)$. Continuing this construction, we arrive at the last step on the segment LN and, correspondingly, to a certain point R on the curve $x_1(t)$, lying at a distance τ from the origin of coordinates. Further, with $t > \tau$ we have now $x_2 \neq 0$. Therefore on the basis of (70.27) to determine the value of $f - x_2$ (at the center of the first step after the point N) we should take the value $x_1 = FG$ (at the center of the first step of the curve x_1, Fig. 322a), multiply it by the regulator transfer factor k and lay it off in the form of the segment HJ. Then the segment JP will have the required value $(f - x_2)$. The point J is now joined to the point R which gives the new segment RQ of the required regulation process curve $x_1(t)$.

All further construction proceeds analogously, namely, we take the segment SU (at the center of the second step of the curve x_1) and lay off $VW = k \cdot SU$ (at the center of the second step after the point N). We join the point W to the point Q, as a result of which we obtain the succeeding segment QZ of the required regulation curve $x_1(t)$, etc.

In this manner the eight regulation curves represented in Fig. 322b were plotted, corresponding to the eight points marked in the stability region in Fig. 321b.

The corresponding curves $(f - x_2)$ obtained during this construction are also shown (Fig. 322b). Since $f = 1$, these curves may be considered as graphs fo the displacement of the regulating organ x_2 with reversed sing, if we take the straight line LM as the axis of abscissae.

The regulation curves plotted clearly show that with constant delay τ and constant regulated object, with increase of regulator transfer factor k the regulation process progressively passes from aperiodic to oscillatory. The frequency and amplitude of these oscillations increase as the boundary of stability is approached.

At $k = 15 \cdot 7$ (at the boundary of stability) undamped oscillations with constant amplitude are obtained, as is evident from the graph of Fig. 322b. There is no doubt if we had taken $k > 15 \cdot 7$ (in the region of instability), the regulation process curve of the given system carried out by the above method would lead to a graph of divergent oscillations.

We note that the given system would be stable with arbitrary positive values of its parameters (k and T_1) in the absence of delay, as a first-order system (according to (70.26) and (70.27) with $\tau = 0$), where the regulation process with $f = $ constant would always be expressed by a simple exponential (oscillations would be completely impossible). Introduction of the constant time delay τ radically changes the properties of the system; oscillations and the possibility of instability of the system appear.

71. Numerical-graphical method for linear systems of arbitrary order

On the basis of the principles considered in Section 70 we shall now describe the Bashkirov numerical-graphical method for plotting the regulation curves in linear systems of arbitrary order. Here, as above, we assume arbitrary initial conditions and arbitrary external force on the system, given as functions of time (analytically, numerically or graphically).

If we have the differential equation of a system

$$(a_0 p^n + a_1 p^{n-1} + \ldots + a_{n-1} p + a_n)x = (b_0 p^\nu + b_1 p^{\nu-1} + \ldots$$
$$\ldots + b^{\nu-1} p + b_\nu) f_2(t) ,$$

where $f_2(t)$ and all coefficients are given in numerical form, it is first necessary to carry out all calculations in the right-hand side of the equation and to obtain the right-hand side in the form of a given function of time $f_1(t)$. It is then necessary to solve the differential equation of the system in the form

$$(a_0 p^n + a_1 p^{n-1} + \ldots + a_{n-1} p + a_n)x = f_1(t) , \qquad (71.1)$$

where $f_1(t)$ is an arbitrarily given function of time with arbitrarily given initial conditions: $x_0, \dot{x}_0, \ldots, x_0^{(n-1)}$ (on the initial conditions for transient processes see Section 6). We consider separately three different general cases.

The case where the roots of the characteristic equations of the system are known. Let it be required to plot the regulation process in the system, described by the differential equation (71.1), where the roots $z_1, z_2, \ldots, z_n$ of the characteristic equation of the system

$$a_0 z^n + a_1 z^{n-1} + \ldots + a_{n-1} z + a_n = 0$$

are known. They may be found, for example, by the simple numerical method (Section 39).

Since we consider only stable systems, all roots of the characteristic equation have negative real parts. Let us assume that of n roots m are real, and may be written in the form

$$z_1 = -\frac{1}{T_1}, \quad z_2 = -\frac{1}{T_2}, \quad \ldots, \quad z_m = \frac{-1}{T_m}, \qquad (71.2)$$

while the remaining $(n-m)$ roots are complex. For each pair of complex roots, for example,

$$z_{m+1,2} = -\alpha \pm i\omega \quad (\alpha > 0) ,$$

it is necessary to calculate the constants T_{m+1}, T_{m+2} in the following manner:

$$T_{m+1} = \frac{1}{2\alpha}, \quad T_{m+2} = \frac{2\alpha}{\omega^2 + \alpha^2} . \qquad (71.3)$$

Then the operational polynomial in the right-hand side of equation (71.1) may be decomposed into factors in the form

$$(T_1 p + 1)(T_2 p + 1) \dots (T_m p + 1)(T_{m+1} T_{m+2} p^2 + T_{m+2} p + 1) \dots$$
$$\dots (T_{n-1} T_n p^2 + T_n p + 1) x = f(t) , \qquad (71.4)$$

where

$$f(t) = \frac{f_1(t)}{a_n} .$$

Equation (71.4) may be further represented in the form of a system of first and second-order equations:

$$
\left.
\begin{aligned}
(T_1 p + 1) x_1 &= f(t) , \\
(T_2 p + 1) x_2 &= x_1 , \\
&\cdots\cdots\cdots\cdots\cdots\cdots\cdots\cdots \\
(T_m p + 1) x_m &= x_{m-1} , \\
(T_{m+1} T_{m+2} p^2 + T_{m+2} p + 1) x_{m+2} &= x_m , \\
(T_{m+3} T_{m+4} p^2 + T_{m+4} p + 1) x_{m+4} &= x_{m+2} , \\
&\cdots\cdots\cdots\cdots\cdots\cdots\cdots\cdots \\
(T_{n-1} T_n p^2 + T_n p + 1) x &= x_{n-2} .
\end{aligned}
\right\} \qquad (71.5)
$$

From the given initial conditions

$$x(0) = x_0 , \quad px(0) = \dot{x}_0 , \quad \dots, \quad p^{n-1} x(0) = x_0^{(n-1)} ,$$

employing (71.5) we easily find the initial values of all variables in succession, beginning from the last

$$x_{n-2}(0) = T_{n-1} T_n \ddot{x}_0 + T_n \dot{x}_0 + x_0 ,$$
$$\dot{x}_{n-2}(0) = T_{n-1} T_n \dddot{x}_0 + T_n \ddot{x}_0 + \dot{x}_0 .$$

etc. until we arrive at

$$x_1(0) = T_2 \dot{x}_2(0) + x_2(0) .$$

We then solve in succession graphically or numerically each of equations (71.5) individually in order, beginning with the first, and exactly following the methods described in Section 70.

The case where the roots of the characteristic equation are unknown. Let it be required to solve the differential equation (71.1) without calculating the roots of the characteristic equation of the system.

Let us transform the given equation. We first divide through the equation by a_n and substitute

$$T = \sqrt[n]{\frac{a_0}{a_n}}, \quad f(t) = \frac{f_1(t)}{a_n}, \qquad (71.6)$$

Then equation (71.1) takes the form

$$\left(T^m p^n + \frac{a_1}{a_n} p^{n-1} + \frac{a_2}{a_n} p^{n-2} + \ldots + \frac{a_{n-1}}{a_n} p + 1\right) x = f(t). \qquad (71.7)$$

The operational polynomial in the left-hand side of this equation is then divided by $(Tp+1)$. As a result of division, according to (39.10) we obtain the polynomial

$$T^{n-1} p^{n-1} + b_1 p^{n-2} + \ldots + b_{n-2} p + b_{n-1},$$

where

$$\left.\begin{array}{l} b_1 = \dfrac{a_1}{a_n T} - T^{n-2}, \\[2mm] b_i = \dfrac{a_i}{a_n T} - \dfrac{b_{i-1}}{T} \quad (i = 2, 3, \ldots, n-1) \end{array}\right\} \qquad (71.8)$$

and the remainder

$$k_1 = \frac{1 - b_{n-1}}{T}. \qquad (71.9)$$

Consequently, it is now possible to write equation (71.7) in the form of two equations

$$\left.\begin{array}{l} (Tp+1)x_1 = f(t) - k_1 x, \\[1mm] (T^{n-1} p^{n-1} + b_1 p^{n-2} + \ldots + b_{n-2} p + b_{n-1}) x = x_1. \end{array}\right\} \qquad (71.10)$$

We divide the last polynomial again by $(Tp+1)$. The result of division will be

$$T^{n-2} p^{n-2} + c_1 p^{n-3} + \ldots + c_{n-3} p + c_{n-2},$$

where

$$c_1 = \frac{b_1}{T} - T^{n-3},$$

$$c_i = \frac{b_i - c_{i-1}}{T} \quad (i = 2, 3, \ldots, n-2),$$

and the remainder

$$k_2 = \frac{b_{n-1} - c_{n-2}}{T}. \qquad (71.11)$$

Continuing these operations, we reduce the initial differential equation to the following system of n first-order equations:

$$
\left.
\begin{aligned}
T\dot{x}_1 + x_1 &= f(t) - k_1 x, \\
T\dot{x}_2 + x_2 &= x_1 - k_2 x, \\
T\dot{x}_3 + x_3 &= x_2 - k_3 x, \\
&\cdots\cdots\cdots\cdots \\
T\dot{x} + x &= x_{n-1} - k_n x.
\end{aligned}
\right\}
\tag{71.12}
$$

Each of these equations is analogous to equation (70.18). Therefore, according to (70.20) it is possible to write for them the relationships

$$
\left.
\begin{aligned}
\frac{\Delta x_1}{\Delta t} &= \frac{f\left(t + \dfrac{\Delta t}{2}\right) - k_1 x\left(t + \dfrac{\Delta t}{2}\right) - x_1(t)}{T + \dfrac{\Delta t}{2}}, \\[3ex]
\frac{\Delta x_2}{\Delta t} &= \frac{x_1\left(t + \dfrac{\Delta t}{2}\right) - k_2 x\left(t + \dfrac{\Delta t}{2}\right) - x_2(t)}{T + \dfrac{\Delta t}{2}}, \\[3ex]
&\cdots\cdots\cdots\cdots\cdots\cdots\cdots\cdots \\[1ex]
\frac{\Delta x}{\Delta t} &= \frac{x_{n-1}\left(t + \dfrac{\Delta t}{2}\right) - k_n x\left(t + \dfrac{\Delta t}{2}\right) - x\left(t + \dfrac{\Delta t}{2}\right)}{T + \dfrac{\Delta t}{2}}
\end{aligned}
\right\}
\tag{71.13}
$$

(for convenience of plotting in the last equation a deviation from the general rule has been made in the argument of the last term,

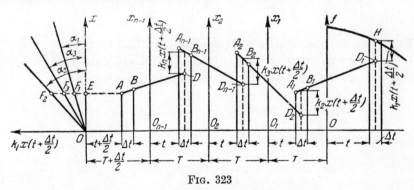

FIG. 323

which has no significance). D. A. Bashkirov gives a better method of interlaced secants, which will not be described here.

The system of relations (71.13) corresponds to the graphical construction shown in Fig. 323, where an arbitrary intermediate step of the solution is represented. First on the ordinate $f(t + \Delta t/2)$ the quantity $k_1 x(t + \Delta t/2)$ is laid out downwards, if it is positive.

The point obtained D_1 is joined to the point A_1, corresponding to the value of $x_1(t)$. The result is a new point B_1 of the curve x_1.

Then, from the center of the interval A_1B_1 the segment $k_2x(t+\Delta t/2)$ is laid out downwards, which gives the point D_2. Joining the latter with the point A_2, corresponding to the value of $x_2(t)$, we find the new point B_2 of the curve x_2. From the center of A_2B_2 we again lay off downwards the segment $k_3x(t+\Delta t/2)$ etc. These constructions are continued to the left until the entire system of equations (71.12) (or, which is the same, (71.13)) is exhausted. The last straight line DA in this construction gives the new point B of the required curve $x(t)$.

Each step of integration of the nth-order differential equation thus reduces to plotting n straight lines D_1A_1, D_2A_2, ..., DA.

From this construction it is clear that the quantities $x(t+\Delta t/2)$, $x_1(t)$, $x_2(t)$, ..., $x_{n-1}(t)$ should be known from the previous step. Therefore construction of the curve $x(t)$ is shifted by $\Delta t/2$ in comparison with the others. In order to avoid calculating the values of the products

$$k_1 x\left(t+\frac{\Delta t}{2}\right), \quad k_2 x\left(t+\frac{\Delta t}{2}\right), ..., k_n x\left(t+\frac{\Delta t}{2}\right),$$

to the left of the origin of coordinates 0 inclined rays are plotted at angles α_1, α_2, ... respectively, where

$$\operatorname{tg}\alpha_1 = k_1, \ \operatorname{tg}\alpha_2 = k_2, \ ..., \ \operatorname{tg}\alpha_n = k_n.$$

Then, obviously

$$k_1 x\left(t+\frac{\Delta t}{2}\right) = EF_1, \quad k_2 x\left(t+\frac{\Delta t}{2}\right) = EF_2, ...$$

From this it follows that to begin the very first step of integration it is necessary to know the quantities $x(\Delta t/2)$, $x_1(0)$, $x_2(0)$, ..., $x_{n-1}(0)$. These are all defined by the prescribed initial conditions

$$x(0) = x_0, \ px(0) = \dot{x}_0, \ ..., \ p^{n-1}x(0) = x_0^{(n-1)},$$

where according to formula (70.23)

$$x\left(\frac{\Delta t}{2}\right) \approx x_0 + \frac{\Delta t}{2}\dot{x}_0, \tag{71.14}$$

and all remaining quantities are calculated during the above-described division of the polynomial, namely (71.10):

$$\left.\begin{aligned} x_1(0) &= b_{n-1}x_0 + b_{n-2}\dot{x}_0 + ... + b_1 x_0^{(n-2)} + T^{n-1}x_0^{(n-1)}, \\ x_2(0) &= c_{n-2}x_0 + c_{n-3}\dot{x}_0 + ... + T^{n-2}x_0^{(n-2)}, \\ &\cdots\cdots\cdots\cdots\cdots\cdots\cdots\cdots\cdots\cdots\cdots\cdots \end{aligned}\right\} \tag{71.15}$$

Graphical integration may be substituted by numerical which according to (71.13), is carried out in the following order. The values of all functions at $t = 0$ and $t = \Delta t/2$ are calculated from formulae (71.15) and (71.14). The auxiliary quantities

$$\beta_1 = 1 - \frac{\Delta t}{T + \dfrac{\Delta t}{2}}, \qquad \beta_2 = \frac{\Delta t}{T + \dfrac{\Delta t}{2}}. \tag{71.16}$$

are introduced. Then numerical solution is carried out according to the formulae

$$\left.\begin{aligned}
x_1(t + \Delta t) &= \beta_1 x_1(t) + \beta_2 \left[f\left(t + \frac{\Delta t}{2}\right) - k_1 x\left(t + \frac{\Delta t}{2}\right)\right], \\
x_2(t + \Delta t) &= \beta_1 x_2(t) + \beta_2 \left[x_1\left(t + \frac{\Delta t}{2}\right) - k_2 x\left(t + \frac{\Delta t}{2}\right)\right], \\
&\cdots\cdots\cdots\cdots\cdots\cdots\cdots\cdots\cdots\cdots\cdots\cdots\cdots \\
x\left(t + \frac{3}{2}\Delta t\right) &= \beta_1 x\left(t + \frac{\Delta t}{2}\right) + \\
&\quad + \beta_2\left[x_{n-1}\left(t + \frac{\Delta t}{2}\right) - k_n x\left(t + \frac{\Delta t}{2}\right)\right].
\end{aligned}\right\} \tag{71.17}$$

It is also possible here to employ the graphical multiplication described above using inclined straight lines for $k_1, k_2, \ldots, k_n, \beta_1, \beta_2$.

We present an example of the graphical solution of a sixth-order differential equation carried out by D. A. Bashkirov (without calculating the roots of the characteristic equation). Let the equation

$$\begin{aligned}
(0{\cdot}03125 p^6 + 0{\cdot}28125 p^5 + 1{\cdot}1875 p^4 + 2{\cdot}8125 p^3 + \\
+ 3{\cdot}875 p^2 + 3 p + 1) x = 1(t)
\end{aligned} \tag{71.18}$$

be given, with zero initial conditions. We calculate

$$T = \sqrt[6]{0{\cdot}03125} = 0{\cdot}5612 .$$

Let us divide the operational polynomial by $(Tp + 1)$. We obtain the quotient

$$0{\cdot}0557 p^5 + 0{\cdot}402 p^4 + 1{\cdot}4 p^3 + 2{\cdot}518 p^2 + 2{\cdot}418 p + 1{\cdot}037 \tag{71.19}$$

and the remainder

$$k_1 = -0{\cdot}037 .$$

We divide the last polynomial again by $(Tp + 1)$, which gives:

$$0{\cdot}0992 p^4 + 0{\cdot}539 p^3 + 1{\cdot}535 p^2 + 1{\cdot}750 p + 1{\cdot}19 \tag{71.20}$$

and the second remainder

$$k_2 = -0{\cdot}153 .$$

Similarly we find the other remainders:

$$k_3 = 0\cdot896; \quad k_4 = -1\cdot478;$$
$$k_5 = 1\cdot721; \quad k_6 = -0\cdot949\ .$$

As a result, according (71.12) we obtain for the solution the following system of equations:

$$
\left.
\begin{aligned}
0\cdot5612\dot{x}_1 + x_1 &= 1(t) + 0\cdot037x\ , \\
0\cdot5612\dot{x}_2 + x_2 &= x_1 \quad + 0\cdot153x\ , \\
0\cdot5612\dot{x}_3 + x_3 &= x_2 \quad - 0\cdot896x\ , \\
0\cdot5612\dot{x}_4 + x_4 &= x_3 \quad + 1\cdot478x\ , \\
0\cdot5612\dot{x}_5 + x_5 &= x_4 \quad - 1\cdot721x\ , \\
0\cdot5612\dot{x} \ \ + x &= x_5 \quad + 0\cdot949x\ ,
\end{aligned}
\right\}
\qquad (71.21)
$$

the initial conditions remaining zero. We take the integration step $\Delta t = 0\cdot5T$.

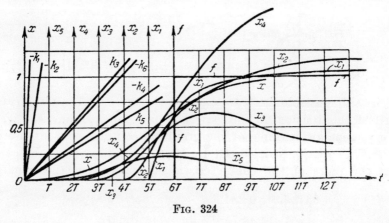

FIG. 324

In Fig. 324 the graphical solution of the system with all intermediate curves is shown. Comparison of the solution obtained with the exact analytic solution gives the following results:

t	0	$\pi/2$	π	$3\pi/2$
x exact	0	0·0795	0·5903	0·9281
x graphical	0	0·085	0·600	0·935

The exact solution has here the form

$$x = 2e^{-2t} - 6\cdot4e^{-t} + 0\cdot2e^{-2t}\cos\left(2t + \frac{\pi}{4}\right) +$$
$$+ 1\cdot6\sqrt{5}\,e^{-t}\cos(t - \tan^{-1}0\cdot5) + 1\ . \qquad (71.22)$$

This example clearly shows that the presence of complex roots in the characteristic equation does not necessarily signify an oscillatory transient, as has already been discussed in Section 36. In the present case, regardless of the presence of these roots, the process is monotonic for the regulated quantity $x(t)$.

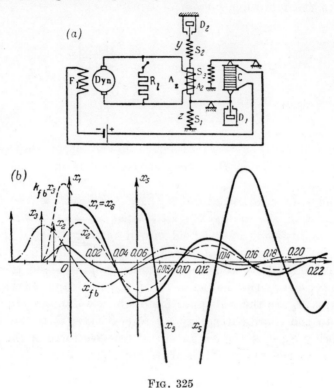

Fig. 325

In this example (Fig. 324) the perturbation is taken in the form of a unit step $1(t)$ only to make possible a comparison with the existing exact solution for this case. If we take $f(t)$ in arbitrary other form (even given graphically for numerically), the process of the graphical solution is in no way more complicated.

The case where the equation of the system is constructed according to elements (without further transformations). This case, following D. A Bashkirov, will be considered by an example of plotting the curve of an automatic voltage regulation system for a dynamo.

The schematic diagram of the system is shown in Fig. 325a. Its action is analogous to that of the system described in Section 24. Here W_2 and A_2 denote the winding and armature of the electro-magnet (sensitive element); C is the carbon column (regulating organ), connected in the field circuit F_1 of the dynamo (regulated object); S_1, S_2, S_3 are springs; the second of them with the damper T_2

comprise an isodromic device. The damper D_1 symbolises the resistance to the mechanical motion of the moving parts as well as the damping effect of eddy currents in the armature, etc. R_1 is the load into which the dynamo operates.

Similarly to the derivation of equations in Section 24, we may here write the following system of equations:

$$\left.\begin{aligned}
x_1 &= x_6 , \\
T_2\dot{x}_2 + x_2 &= x_1 , \\
T_3\dot{x}_3 + x_3 &= x_2 - x_{fb} , \\
T_{fb}\dot{x}_{fb} + x_{fb} &= k_{fb}x_3 , \\
T_5\dot{x}_5 &= -x_3 , \\
T_6\dot{x}_6 + x_6 &= x_5 ,
\end{aligned}\right\} \tag{71.23}$$

where $x_1 = (V - V^0)/V^0$ is the relative deviation of the regulated voltage V; $x_2 = (I_2 - I_2^0)/I_2^0$ is the relative deviation of the electromagnet current; $x_3 = T_4\dot{x}_4$, where $x_4 = (z - z^0)/z^0$ is the relative displacement of the armature A_2; $x_{43} = (z - y)/z^0$ is the relative displacement of the spring S_2; $x_{fb} = k_{43}x_{43}$; $x_5 = (r_c - r_c^0)/(R_1 + r_c^0)$ is the relative deviation of the field circuit resistance; $x_6 = (I_1 - I_1^0)/I_1^0$ is the relative deviation of the field current; R_1, R_2, r_c are the resistances of the field and electromagnet windings and the carbon column; L_1, L_2 are the inductances of the field and electromagnet windings; c_5, c_6 are the resistance factors of the dampers D_1 and D_2, reduce l to the coordinates z and y respectively; c_2 is the stiffness of the spring S_2; c_1 is the coefficient of tractive force of the electromagnet; m is the mass of the armature A_2;

$$T_2 = \frac{L_2}{R_2}, \qquad T_3 = \frac{m}{c_5}, \qquad T_4 = \frac{c_5 z^0}{c_1 I_2^0} ,$$

$$T_{fb} = \frac{c_6}{c_2}, \qquad T_5 = \frac{T_4}{k_5}, \qquad T_6 = \frac{L_1}{R_1 + r_c^0} ,$$

$$k_{43} = \frac{c_2 z^0}{c_1 I_2^0}, \qquad k_{fb} = \frac{T_{fb}}{T_4} ,$$

k_5 is a dimensionless coefficient, defined by $x_5 = -k_5x_4$. The following values of the parameters of the system are given:

$$T_2 = 0.015; \qquad T_3 = 0.01; \qquad T_{fb} = 0.03;$$
$$k_{fb} = 5; \qquad T_5 = 0.00165; \qquad T_6 = 0.06;$$

The initial conditions

$$x_1(0) = x_5(0) = x_6(0) = 0.07 \quad \text{and} \quad x_2(0) = x_3(0) = x_{fb}(0) = 0 ,$$

which correspond to a drop in the dynamo load from $I = 10A$ to zero.

We take the integration step $\Delta t = 0.005$ sec.

Since all equations (71.23) are first-order, we may employ them directly for plotting the transient curves by the above graphical or numerical methods.

Graphical plotting of the transient curves with a force in the shape of a unit step is carried out in Fig. 325b. None of the plotted curves are superfluous (auxiliary); each of these curves has a definite physical significance and practical value for calculating the system, namely: $x_1(t)$ is the variation of the deviation of regulated voltage, $x_2(t)$ is the current in the regulator electromagnet winding, $x_3(t)$ is the armature velocity, $x_5(t)$ is the variation in the field circuit, $x_{fb}(t)$ is the displacement of the spring S_2, comprising together with the damper D_2 in effect the transient feedback.

72. Numerical-graphical method for systems with time-variable parameters and for non-linear systems

The Bashkirov method described in Sections 70 and 71 was also developed by him for non-linear systems and systems with time-variable parameters. As before, it is possible to introduce here arbitrary variable perturbations or command functions and arbitrary initial conditions.

First-order nonhomogeneous equation with variable coefficients. Let it be required to plot a solution of the equation

$$a_0(t)\dot{x} + a_1(t)x = f_1(t)$$

with initial condition $x = x_0$ at $t = 0$. Dividing it by $a_1(t)$, we reduce the equation to the form

$$T(t)\dot{x} + x = f(t) , \qquad (72.1)$$

where

$$T(t) = \frac{a_0(t)}{a_1(t)}, \qquad f(t) = \frac{f_1(t)}{a_1(t)}.$$

Equation (72.1) may be solved graphically by the above method, as for equation (70.8), if we take T constant and equal to $T(t + \Delta t/2)$ within each interval of time $(t, t + \Delta t)$, but different in different intervals. Consequently, the formula for the solution, according to (70.9), will be

$$\frac{\Delta x}{\Delta t} = \frac{f\left(t + \dfrac{\Delta t}{2}\right) - x(t)}{T\left(t + \dfrac{\Delta t}{2}\right) + \dfrac{\Delta t}{2}},$$

while the process of plotting reduces to the following. We plot the given curves $f(t)$ and $T(t)$ (Fig. 326). From the point E on the curve $f(t)$, taken at the center of the first interval Δt, we lay out the horizontal segment $EM = T(\Delta t/2)$, with the length taken as the ordinate of the point H of the given curve $T(t)$, i.e. also at the center of the first interval Δt. The point obtained M, is joined by a straight line to the given initial point of the process A. As a result a new point B on the required curve $x(t)$ is obtained. We then take similarly the ordinate of the point I, laid off in the form of the segment FN and plot the straight line NB, giving the new point C of the solution $x(t)$, etc.

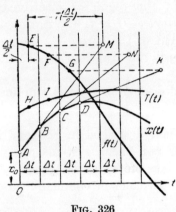

Fig. 326

Second-order nonhomogeneous equation with variable coefficients. Let it be required to plot a solution of the equation

$$a_0(t)\ddot{x} + a_1(t)\dot{x} + a_2(t)x = f_1(t),$$

which may also be written in the form

$$T_1(t)\,T_2(t)\,\ddot{x} + T_2(t)\,\dot{x} + x = f(t), \qquad (72.2)$$

where

$$T_1(t) = \frac{a_0(t)}{a_1(t)}, \qquad T_2(t) = \frac{a_1(t)}{a_2(t)}, \qquad f(t) = \frac{f_1(t)}{a_2(t)}$$

with initial conditions $x = x_0$, $\dot{x} = \dot{x}_0$ at $t = 0$. If there is an operational expression in the right-hand side of (72.2), we first calculate the right-hand side as in Section 70.

If we put $x_1 = T_2(t)\dot{x}$, equation (72.2) divides into two:

$$\left.\begin{array}{l} T_1(t)\,\dot{x}_1 + x_1 = f(t) - \varphi(t), \\[4pt] T_2(t)\,\dot{x} = x_1, \end{array}\right\} \qquad (72.3)$$

where

$$\varphi(t) = x - T_3(t)\dot{x}, \qquad T_3(t) = T_1(t)\frac{dT_2(t)}{dt}, \qquad (72.4)$$

and the initial conditions will be:

$$x = x_0, \qquad x_1 = x_{10} = T_2(0)\dot{x}_0 \qquad \text{at} \qquad t = 0.$$

Equations (72.3) are analogous to equations (70.18) and (70.19) substituting only in the first equation quantity x by the more complicated quantity $\varphi(t)$. Therefore the formulae for solving equations (72.3), according to (70.20) and (70.21), will be:

$$\left.\begin{aligned} \frac{\Delta x_1}{\Delta t} &= \frac{f\left(t+\dfrac{\Delta t}{2}\right)-\varphi\left(t+\dfrac{\Delta t}{2}\right)-x_1(t)}{T_1\left(t+\dfrac{\Delta t}{2}\right)+\dfrac{\Delta t}{2}}\,, \\[2mm] \frac{\Delta x}{\Delta t} &= \frac{x_1(t+\Delta t)}{T_2(t+\Delta t)}\,, \end{aligned}\right\} \qquad (72.5)$$

where

$$\varphi\left(t+\frac{\Delta t}{2}\right) = x\left(t+\frac{\Delta t}{2}\right)-T_3\left(t+\frac{\Delta t}{2}\right)\dot{x}(t)\,,$$

and in the second of formulae (72.5) the values of Δx are taken shifted by $\Delta t/2$ to the right in comparison with Δx_1.

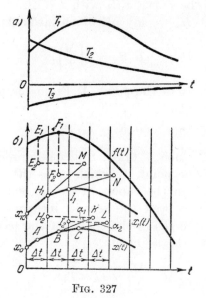

FIG. 327

From this there follows the following construction. We plot the prescribed curves $T_1(t)$ and $T_2(t)$ as well as the curve $T_3(t)$, defined by the second of formulae (72.4). They are shown in the graph of Fig. 327a.

On a second graph we plot the prescribed $f(t)$ (Fig. 327b). On the basis of the given initial conditions (see above) we plot in the last graph the points x_0, x_{10} and in the center of the first interval Δt (as in Section 70) the point A with the ordinate (70.23), i.e.

$$x\left(\frac{\Delta t}{2}\right) = x_0 + \frac{\Delta t}{2}\dot{x}_0\,.$$

From the point E_1 at the center of the first interval Δt we lay off on the curve $f(t)$ downwards the segment

$$E_1E_2 = \varphi\left(\frac{\Delta t}{2}\right) = x\left(\frac{\Delta t}{2}\right) - T_3\left(\frac{\Delta t}{2}\right)\dot{x}_0$$

(downwards when it is positive and upwards when it is negative). Here the quantity $x(\Delta t/2)$ is taken as the ordinate of the existing point A, the quantity $T_3(\Delta t/2)$ is taken from the graph $T_3(t)$, while the quantity $\dot{x}_0$ from the given initial conditions. From the point obtained E_2 we lay off the horizontal segment

$$E_2M = T_1\left(\frac{\Delta t}{2}\right),$$

the magnitude of which is taken from the graph of $T_1(t)$. We join the point M by a straight line to the point x_{10}, which gives us the new point H_1 of the curve $x_1(t)$ with $t = \Delta t$.

From the point H_1 we lay off downwards the segment

$$H_1H_2 = x\left(\frac{\Delta t}{2}\right),$$

equal to the ordinate of the point A. From the point H_2 we lay off a horizontal segment

$$H_2K = T_2(\Delta t),$$

the magnitude of which is taken from the graph of $T_2(t)$. We join the point K with the point A, which gives the new point B of the required curve $x(t)$ in the center of the second interval Δt.

Let us describe as well the second integration step. From the point F_1 of the curve $f(t)$ in the center of the second interval Δt we lay off downwards the segment

$$F_1F_2 = \varphi\left(\Delta t + \frac{\Delta t}{2}\right) = x_B - T_3\left(\Delta t + \frac{\Delta t}{2}\right)\cdot\tan\alpha_1,$$

where x_B is the ordinate of the point B obtained above; $\tan\alpha_1$ is the tangent of the angle of inclination α_1 of the straight line KA plotted previously (this gives the required value of $\dot{x}$). We lay off the segment

$$F_2N = T_1\left(\Delta t + \frac{\Delta t}{2}\right)$$

and plot the straight line NH_1, obtaining the new point I_1 of the curve $x_1(t)$.

From the point I_1 we lay off downwards

$$I_1I_2 = x_B,$$

and then to the right

$$I_2 L = T_2(2\Delta t) ,$$

after which we plot the straight line LB This gives the new point C of the required curve $x(t)$, etc.

Here, as in Section 70, the entire construction may be substituted by numerical calculations.

Second-order non-linear equation. Without considering the first-order non-linear equation, let us turn immediately to the second-order equation. We first rearrange it so that all non-linear terms are in the right-hand side of the equation together with the perturbation $f(t)$. We shall consider the coefficients of the left-hand side to be constant, but the solution may be extended on the basis of the preceding material to the case of variable coefficients.

Thus, we write the second-order non-linear equation in the form

$$T_1 T_2 \ddot{x} + T_2 \dot{x} + x = \Phi(t, x, \dot{x}) , \qquad (72.6)$$

where T_1 and T_2 are given constants, while all non-linear terms of the equation, dependent on x and its derivative, as well as the external perturbation, dependent on the time t, are included in the function $\Phi(t, x, \dot{x})$ (the non-linearity may have arbitrary form and may be expressed either analytically or graphically).

Similarly to Section 70 we divide equation (72.6) into two:

$$\left.\begin{aligned} T_1 \dot{x}_1 + x_1 &= \Phi\left(t, x, \frac{x_1}{T_2}\right) - x , \\ T_2 \dot{x} &= x_1 . \end{aligned}\right\} \qquad (72.7)$$

According to (70.20) and (70.21) we write:

$$\frac{\Delta x_1}{\Delta t} = \frac{\Phi\left[t + \dfrac{\Delta t}{2}, \ x\left(t + \dfrac{\Delta t}{2}\right), \ \dfrac{1}{T_2} x_1(t)\right] - x\left(t + \dfrac{\Delta t}{2}\right) - x_1(t)}{T_1 + \dfrac{\Delta t}{2}} , \qquad (72.8)$$

$$\frac{\Delta x}{\Delta t} = \frac{x_1(t + \Delta t)}{T_2} ; \qquad (72.9)$$

in formula (72.8) we have substituted $x_1(t + \Delta t/2)$ by $x_1(t)$ to simplify the construction and to make it agree with that in Section 70. This assumption does not have a substantial influence on the precision of the solution (a better method was proposed by D. A. Bashkirov).

The arbitrary integration step (Fig. 328) will have the same form as in Section 70 (Fig. 320), except that here in place of the preassigned graph $f(t)$ at the right there will be plotted points forming the graph of the function $\Phi(t, x, x_1/T_2)$ obtained during the process of solution. The procedure for the solution in an arbitrary step of the integration will be here as follows. Having obtained in the preceding step the points A and A_1, i.e. the values $x(t+\Delta t/2)$ and $x_1(t)$, we substitute them in the given expression $\Phi(t, x, x_1/T_2)$ and obtain the corresponding value of Φ, which we plot in the graph (the point D_1 Fig. 328). Then, joining the points A_1 and D_1 by

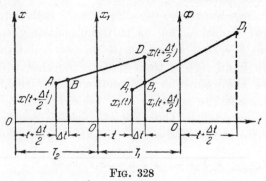

FIG. 328

a straight line, we obtain the point B_1, the new point of the solution for x_1. Laying off from the point obtained B_1 the magnitude $x(t+\Delta t/2)$, taken from the point A, we plot the point D. Joining the latter to the point A we obtain the new point B of the required solution x.

In the following integration step we shift by Δt to the right, employing as the initial points B and B_1.

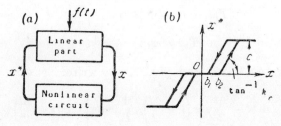

FIG. 329

From this it is evident that to start the solution it is necessary to know the values of $x(\Delta t/2)$ and $x_1(0)$. They are defined from the initial conditions $x(0) = x_0$ and $\dot{x}(0) = \dot{x}_0$, from formulae (70.22) and (70.23).

Non-linear system of arbitrary order. As before, we represent it as consisting of a linear part, having an arbitrary structure, and described by an nth-order differential equation (Fig. 329a):

$$Q(p)x = R(p)x^* + P(p)f(t), \qquad (72.10)$$

and of a non-linear component with the equation

$$x^* = F(x), \qquad (72.11)$$

where $F(x)$ is the non-linear characteristic of the element. We describe the method here by the example of a non-linear characteristic shown in Fig. 329b. This characteristic is of a fairly general form; various other characteristics considered previously, including the relay type, may be obtained as special cases of the given characteristic. The method may be applied to characteristics of any other arbitrary form.

Since the external perturbation $f(t)$ is given, we shall consider given as well the function

$$f_1(t) = P(p)f(t) .$$

Let us rewrite equations (72.10) and (72.11) in the form

$$Q(p)x = f_1(t) + R(p)F(x) , \tag{72.12}$$

where

$$\left.\begin{aligned}Q(p) &= a_0 p^n + a_1 p^{n-1} + \ldots + a_{n-1}p + a_n , \\ R(p) &= h_0 p^s + h_1 p^{s-1} + \ldots + h_{s-1}p + h_s .\end{aligned}\right\} \tag{72.13}$$

We denote that x here signifies the variable quantity at the input to the non-linear element. We shall seek the solution for it $x(t)$. The initial conditions $x(0) = x_0$, $px(0) = \dot{x}_0$, ..., $p^{n-1}x(0) = x_0^{(n-1)}$ are easily calculated from the given initial conditions for the regulated (or other) quantity from the equations of the corresponding elements of the linear part of the system.

We shall consider two cases: (1) the roots of the polynomial $Q(p)$ are known and (2) the roots of the polynomial $Q(p)$ are unknown.

1. When the roots of the polynomial $Q(p)$ are known we find according to (71.2) and (71.3) the quantities $T_1, T_2, \ldots, T_n$ and we write equation (72.12), according to (71.5), in the form of a system of equations

$$\left.\begin{aligned}(T_1 p + 1)x_1 &= \frac{1}{a_n}[f_1(t) + R(p)F(x)] , \\ (T_2 p + 1)x_2 &= x_1 , \\ &\cdots\cdots\cdots\cdots\cdots \\ (T_m p + 1)x_m &= x_{m-1} , \\ (T_{m+1}T_{m+2}p^2 + T_{m+2}p + 1)x_{m+2} &= x_m , \\ (T_{m+3}T_{m+4}p^2 + T_{m+4}p + 1)x_{m+4} &= x_{m+2} , \\ &\cdots\cdots\cdots\cdots\cdots \\ (T_{n-1}T_n p^2 + T_n p + 1)x &= x_{n-2} .\end{aligned}\right\} \tag{72.14}$$

These equations are solved individually in succession as first and second-order equations according to Section 70. Only the solution to the first of them requires some explanation. The formula for its solution (70.9) here takes the form

$$\frac{\Delta x_1}{\Delta t} = \frac{\frac{1}{a_n}\left\{f_1\left(t+\frac{\Delta t}{2}\right)+R(p)F\left[x\left(t+\frac{\Delta t}{2}\right)\right]\right\}-x_1(t)}{T+\frac{\Delta t}{2}}, \qquad (72.15)$$

where the value of $x(t+\Delta t/2)$ is known from the preceding step of the solution of the last of equations (72.14), as carried out according to the scheme of Fig. 320 (with $f = 0$).

Having the value of $x(t+\Delta t/2)$, from the given non-linear characteristic (Fig. 329b) we find the corresponding value of $F[x(t+\Delta t/2)]$. But for formula (72.15) we require $R(p)F[x(t+\Delta t/2)]$, where $R(p)$ is the operational polynomial (72.13). If the point $x(t+\Delta t/2)$ falls on the horizontal of the characteristic (Fig. 329b), the derivatives will be zero and we obtain:

$$R(p)F\left[x\left(t+\frac{\Delta t}{2}\right)\right]=h_sF\left[x\left(t+\frac{\Delta t}{2}\right)\right];$$

if the point $x(t+\Delta t/2)$ is incident on the inclined segment of the characteristic (Fig. 329b), then

$$R(p)F\left[x\left(t+\frac{\Delta t}{2}\right)\right]=\pm h_{s-1}k_c+h_sF\left[x\left(t+\frac{\Delta t}{2}\right)\right],$$

where the signs $+$ or $-$ apply according to whether the value of x is increasing or decreasing at the given step in the solution at the time t (this is determined according to which side of the hysteresis loop of the characteristic is being used at the given moment).

The process of solving the first of equations (72.14) will thus be the same as in Fig. 317b, but the point D at the right is determined not from the value of $f(t+\Delta t/2)$ as before, but by the value of

$$\frac{1}{a_n}\left\{f_1\left(t+\frac{\Delta t}{2}\right)+R(p)F\left[x\left(t+\frac{\Delta t}{2}\right)\right]\right\},$$

whose calculation is clear from the above. As a result, with this small addition the solution of the equations of a non-linear system reduces to the same simple graphical construction as the solution of linear equations.

2. When the roots of the polynomial $Q(p)$ are unknown, carrying out the division of the polynomial indicated in Section 71, according to (71.12) we reduce the initial equation (72.12) to a system of equations

$$T\dot{x}_1 + x_1 = \frac{1}{a_n}[f_1(t) + R(p)F(x)] - k_1 x \,,$$

$$T\dot{x}_2 + x_2 = x_1 - k_2 x \,,$$

$$T\dot{x}_3 + x_3 = x_2 - k_3 x \,,$$

$$\cdots\cdots\cdots\cdots\cdots\cdots\cdots\cdots\cdots\cdots$$

$$T\dot{x} + x = x_{n-1}k - {}_n x \,,$$

(72.16)

where

$$T = \sqrt[n]{\frac{a_0}{a_n}} \,,$$

and $k_1, k_2, ..., k_n$ are the corresponding remainders after division.

The formulae of the solution will have the form (71.13) if in the first in place of $f(t + \Delta t/2)$ we substitute the expression

$$\frac{1}{a_n}\left\{f_1\left(t + \frac{\Delta t}{2}\right) + R(p)F\left[x\left(t + \frac{\Delta t}{2}\right)\right]\right\}$$

(72.17)

and calculate it exactly as in the previous case. The process of the graphical solution of the entire system of equations (72.16) will have the form of Fig. 323, where the point H at the right is determined not from the value of $f(t + \Delta t/2)$ as before, but by the value of (72.17). By this method the process $x(t)$ is determined for the variable at the input to the non-linear part of the system. Knowing this process and the equations of individual linear elements of the system, it is possible by their use to pass to the regulated quantity or to any other variable characterising the process in any given element of the system.

More complex system. Let the equations of the automatic system be given in the form

$$(T_i p + 1)x_i = \Phi_i(t, x_1, x_2, ..., x_n) \,,$$

$$T_j p x_j = \Phi_j(t, x_1, x_2, ..., x_n) \,,$$

(72.18)

where

$$i = 1, 2, ..., k; \quad j = k+1, k+2, ..., n \,,$$

and the right-hand side of equations (72.18) may include any type of non-linearity and any prescribed functions of time. The initial conditions are prescribed:

$$x_i = x_{i_0} \quad \text{and} \quad x_j = x_{j_0} \quad \text{at} \quad t = 0 \,.$$

Let us calculate from (72.18) the values

$$\dot{x}_{i_0} = \frac{1}{T_i}[\Phi_i(0, x_{10}, x_{20}, ..., x_{n_0}) - x_{i_0}] \,,$$

$$\dot{x}_{j_0} = \frac{1}{T_j}\Phi_j(0, x_{10}, x_{20}, ..., x_{n_0}) \,,$$

after which, according to (70.23) we calculate

$$x_i\left(\frac{\Delta t}{2}\right) = x_{i_0} + \frac{\Delta t}{2}\,\dot{x}_{i_0}, \qquad x_j\left(\frac{\Delta t}{2}\right) = x_{j_0} + \frac{\Delta t}{2}\,\dot{x}_{j_0}.$$

Having these values, we may calculate also the values of the right-hand sides of equations (72.18) at $t = \Delta t/2$, which we denote for conciseness by $\Phi_i(\Delta t/2)$ and $\Phi_j(\Delta t/2)$.

As a result, for the solution of each of equations (72.18) we may employ formulae (70.9) and (70.11) in the form

$$\frac{\Delta x_i}{\Delta t} = \frac{\Phi_i\left(t + \dfrac{\Delta t}{2}\right) - x_i(t)}{T_i + \dfrac{\Delta t}{2}},$$

$$\frac{\Delta x_j}{\Delta t} = \frac{\Phi_j\left(t + \dfrac{\Delta t}{2}\right)}{T_j}.$$

This corresponds to constructions similar to those of Fig. 317 and 318 for the variables x_i and x_j respectively, where, in place of the prescribed curve $f(t)$, in this case we obtain the curves $\Phi_i(t, x_1, x_2, ..., x_n)$ and $\Phi_j(t, x_1, x_2, ..., x_n)$, calculated during the solution (the start of these calculations has been discussed above).

The graphical constructions may be substituted by a numerical solution according to the formulae

$$x_i(t + \Delta t) = x_i(t) + \frac{\Phi_i\left(t + \dfrac{\Delta t}{2}\right) - x_i(t)}{T_i + \dfrac{\Delta t}{2}},$$

$$x_j(t + \Delta t) = x_j(t) + \frac{\Phi_j\left(t + \dfrac{\Delta t}{2}\right)}{T_j},$$

where after each step of calculation it is necessary to shift only by $\Delta t/2$, in order that the succeeding step always have available the results of calculating the values of $\Phi_i(t + \Delta t/2)$ and $\Phi_j(t + \Delta t/2)$.

It is obvious that no difficulties will arise in the solution if equations (72.18) have time-variable coefficients $T_i(t)$ and $T_j(t)$.

Example. Using the graphical method D. A. Bashkirov constructed the transient curve for a non-linear system described by equations (66.45) and (66.46), already considered above in Section 66, for the following data

$$T_b^2 = T_a = 0{\cdot}2; \ \ \beta = k_1 = 1; \ \ k_2 = 0{\cdot}2; \ \ k_3 = k_4 = 0{\cdot}1; \ \ T_s = 5; \ \ T_q^2 = 1,$$

and the initial conditions

$$\varphi(0) = \dot{\varphi}(0) = 0; \quad \xi(0) = -0.2; \quad \dot{\xi}(0) = 0 .$$

For an ideal relay characteristic (Fig. 303c) as a result of the transient (F g. 330a) steady-state oscillations are established with

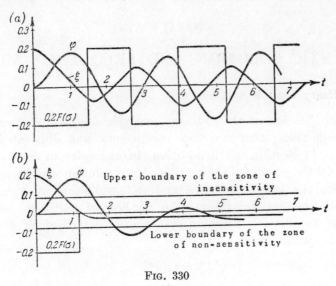

FIG. 330

period 2·6 and amplitude 0·174 for the deviation of the regulated quantity φ. In the presence of a zone of insensitivity $\sigma_0 = 0.08$ (Fig. 303d) a damped transient is obtained in the same system (Fig. 330b), which attenuates after the first operation of the regulating organ (duration of operation is equal to 1.12).

CHAPTER XIX

ANALYTIC SOLUTION AND FREQUENCY METHOD

73. Ordinary analytic solution

The application of the ordinary analytic solution of linear differential equations with constant coefficients was illustrated in the examples of Section 6. In addition, in examples of Section 9 and Section 59 the piecewise application of this solution was demonstrated to obtain the transient curve and self-oscillations in a non-linear automatic regulation system (the method of matching solutions).

Linear automatic regulation systems are described by differential equations of the type

$$(a_0 p^n + a_1 p^{n-1} + \ldots + a_{n-1} p + a_n) x^*$$
$$= (b_0 p^\nu + \ldots + b_{\nu-1} p + b_\nu) f(t) . \qquad (73.1)$$

Therefore, when it is necessary to find the transient curve caused by an input step or impulse: $f(t) = c \cdot 1(t)$ or $f(t) = c \cdot 1'(t)$, the problem reduces to solution of the homogeneous equation

$$(a_0 p^n + a_1 p^{n-1} + \ldots + a_{n-1} p + a_n) x = 0 , \qquad (73.2)$$

but with new initial conditions calculated by formulae (6.23) or (6.26).

Without repeating the ordinary method of the analytic solution, we describe here a useful procedure for calculating the arbitrary constants developed by A. I. Sud-Zlochevskii. In the usual solution two most cumbersome computations are encountered: (1) finding the roots of the characteristic equation and (2) determining the arbitrary constants for given initial conditions. The first of these operations may be carried out by the simple numerical method already described in Section 39. It is therefore now necessary to obtain a simpler method of determining the arbitrary constants of integration. Thus, let there exist a homogeneous differential equation (73.2) with arbitrary initial conditions and the roots of the characteristic equation found by the simple numerical method (Section 39).

Of the total number of roots n of the characteristic equation let there be m real $(z_1, z_2, \ldots, z_m)$, the remaining complex $(z_{m+1,2} = -\alpha_1 \pm i\omega_1$, etc.). As in the Bashkirov method we find the

732

constants $T_1, T_2, ..., T_n$ from formulae (71.2) and (71.3) and we write the given equation (73.2) in the form of a system of first and second-order equations (71.5), where in the present case $f(t) = 0$. As before, we find the initial conditions for the new variables $x_1, x_2, ...$

We shall now solve in succession each of equations (71.5), but analytically rather than graphically. The solution of the first of equations (71.5) with $f(t) = 0$ will be:

$$x_1 = A_{11}e^{-\frac{t}{T_1}},$$

where from the initial condition $x_1 = x_{10}$ at $t = 0$ we have:

$$A_{11} = x_{10}.$$

But, having now x_1, it is possible to write the second of equations (71.5) in the form

$$(T_2 p + 1)x_2 = A_{11}e^{-\frac{t}{T_1}}. \tag{73.3}$$

Its solution (particular plus general) will be

$$x_2 = A_{21}e^{-\frac{t}{T_1}} + A_{22}e^{-\frac{t}{T_2}}. \tag{73.4}$$

To determine the coefficient A_{21} of the particular solution (i.e. the first component of x_2) we substitute it in (73.3), from which we find

$$A_{21} = \frac{A_{11}}{1 - \dfrac{T_2}{T_1}},$$

after which from the initial condition $x_2 = x_{20}$ at $t = 0$, we have for equation (73.4)

$$A_{22} = x_{20} - A_{21}.$$

In turn x_2 is the right-hand side of the third of equations (71.5), etc. For the mth equation we obtain

$$x_m = A_{m1}e^{-\frac{t}{T_1}} + A_{m2}e^{-\frac{t}{T_2}} + ... + A_{m(m-1)}e^{-\frac{t}{T_{m-1}}} + A_{mm}e^{-\frac{t}{T_m}},$$

where the coefficients of the particular solutions will be here:

$$A_{m1} = \frac{A_{(m-1)1}}{1 - \dfrac{T_m}{T_1}}, \qquad A_{m2} = \frac{A_{(m-1)2}}{1 - \dfrac{T_m}{T_2}}, \qquad ..., \qquad A_{m(m-1)} = \frac{A_{(m-1)(m-1)}}{1 - \dfrac{T_m}{T_{m-1}}},$$

after which we find from the initial condition:

$$A_{mm} = x_{m0} - A_{m1} - A_{m2} - ... - A_{m(m-1)}.$$

The next equation in the system (71.5) is a second-order equation. Its solution will be

$$x_{m+2} = A_{(m+2)1} e^{-\frac{t}{T_1}} + A_{(m+2)2} e^{-\frac{t}{T_2}} + \ldots + A_{(m+2)m} e^{-\frac{t}{T_m}} +$$
$$+ B_{(m+2)1} e^{a_1 t} \cos \omega_1 t + C_{(m+2)1} e^{a_1 t} \sin \omega_1 t \,.$$

The coefficient $A_{(m+2)1}$ of the first particular solution is found by substituting it in the corresponding equation of system (71.5), which gives

$$A_{(m+2)1} = \frac{A_{m1}}{1 - \dfrac{T_{m+2}}{T_1} + \dfrac{T_{m+1} T_{m+2}}{T_1^2}} \,.$$

The coefficients of the remaining particular solutions

$$A_{(m+2)2} = \frac{A_{m2}}{1 - \dfrac{T_{m+2}}{T_2} + \dfrac{T_{m+1} T_{m+2}}{T_2^2}} , \; \ldots$$

$$\ldots , \; A_{(m+2)m} = \frac{A_{mm}}{1 - \dfrac{T_{m+2}}{T_m} + \dfrac{T_{m+1} T_{m+2}}{T_m^2}} ,$$

are found similarly, while from the initial conditions: $x_{m+2} = x_{(m+2)0}$ and $\dot{x}_{(m+2)} = \dot{x}_{(m+2)0}$ at $t = 0$, the arbitrary constants of integration

$$B_{(m+2)1} = x_{(m+2)0} - A_{(m+2)1} - A_{(m+2)2} - \ldots - A_{(m+2)m} ,$$

$$C_{(m+2)1} = \frac{1}{\omega_1} \left(\dot{x}_{(m+2)0} + \frac{A_{(m+2)1}}{T_1} + \frac{A_{(m+2)2}}{T_2} + \ldots + \frac{A_{(m+2)m}}{T_m} - B_{(m+2)1} \alpha_1 \right) .$$

are found.

We thus arrive at the solution of the last equation of the system (71.5), which gives the required curve of the transient process $x(t)$.

As a result we obtain the following general simple formulae for solving the entire problem of plotting the transient curve:

$$x_s = \sum_{j=1}^{s} A_{sj} e^{-\frac{t}{T_j}} \quad (s = 1, 2, \ldots, m) , \tag{73.5}$$

where for all $j < s$ we have:

$$A_{sj} = \frac{A_{(s-1)j}}{1 - \dfrac{T_s}{T_j}} , \tag{73.6}$$

while for $j = s$:

$$A_{sj} = x_{s0} - \sum_{q=1}^{s-1} A_{sq} ; \tag{73.7}$$

The further solution will be:

$$x_s = \sum_{j=1}^{m} A_{sj} e^{-\frac{t}{T_j}} + \sum_{j=1}^{\frac{s-m}{2}} (B_{sj} e^{\alpha_j t} \cos \omega_j t + C_{sj} e^{\alpha_j t} \sin \omega_j t)$$
$$(s = (m+2),\ (m+4),\ \dots,\ n),\qquad (73.8)$$

where

$$A_{sj} = \frac{A_{(s-2)j}}{1 - \dfrac{T_s}{T_j} + \dfrac{T_{s-1} T_s}{T_j^2}},\qquad (73.9)$$

and then for $j < (s-m)/2$ we calculate:

$$\left.\begin{aligned}
D_{(s-2)j} &= T_{s-1} T_s (\alpha_j^2 - \omega_j^2) + T_s \alpha_j + 1,\\
E_{(s-2)j} &= T_{s-1} T_s 2\alpha_j \omega_j + T_s \omega_j,\\
B_{sj} &= \frac{B_{(s-2)j} D_{(s-2)j} - C_{(s-2)j} E_{(s-2)j}}{D_{(s-2)j}^2 + E_{(s-2)j}^2},\\
C_{sj} &= \frac{C_{(s-2)j} D_{(s-2)j} + B_{(s-2)j} E_{(s-2)j}}{D_{(s-2)j}^2 + E_{(s-2)j}^2},
\end{aligned}\right\}\qquad (73.10)$$

while for $j = (s-m)/2$:

$$\left.\begin{aligned}
B_{sj} &= x_{s0} - \sum_{q=1}^{m} A_{sq} - \sum_{q=1}^{j-1} B_{sq},\\
C_{sj} &= \frac{1}{\omega_j}\left(\dot{x}_{s0} + \sum_{q=1}^{m} \frac{A_{sq}}{T_q} - \sum_{q=1}^{j} B_{sq} \alpha_q - \sum_{q=1}^{j-1} C_{sq} \omega_q\right).
\end{aligned}\right\}\qquad (73.11)$$

The last of these solutions, i.e. $x_n = x$ gives us the required transient curve.

Consequently, integration of the homogeneous nth-order differential equation with arbitrary initial conditions reduces to substitution in these formulae of the values of T_j, α_j, ω_j which correspond to the previously found roots of the characteristic equation.

Example Let it be required to plot the transient curve due to a unit step $f(t) = 1(t)$ when the regulation system equation has the form

$$(a_0 p^6 + a_1 p^5 + a_2 p^4 + a_3 p^3 + a_4 p^2 + a_5 p + a_6) x^*$$
$$= (b_0 p^3 + b_1 p^2 + b_2 p + b_3) 1(t),\qquad (73.12)$$

where

$$a_0 = 0.125; \qquad a_1 = 1.125; \qquad a_2 = 4.75;$$
$$a_3 = 11.25; \qquad a_4 = 15.5; \qquad a = 12; \qquad a_6 = 4;$$
$$b_0 = 2; \qquad b_1 = 5; \qquad b_2 = 10; \qquad b_3 = 4$$

with zero initial conditions. We substitute for this equation by the homogeneous differential equation

$$(a_0 p^6 + a_1 p^5 + a_2 p^4 + a_3 p^3 + a_4 p^2 + a_5 p + a_6) x = 0,\qquad (73.13)$$

but with initial conditions calculated by formulae (6.23), namely:

$$x_0 = -4 , \quad \dot{x}_0 = \ddot{x}_0 = 0 , \quad \dddot{x}_0 = 64 , \quad x_0^{(4)} = -416 , \quad x_0^{(5)} = 1632$$

The roots of the characteristic equation will be:

$$z_1 = -2 , \quad z_2 = -1 , \quad z_{3,4} = \alpha_1 \pm i\omega_1 = -2 \pm i2 ,$$
$$z_{5,6} = \alpha_2 \pm i\omega_2 = -1 \pm i1 .$$

From formulae (71.2) and (71.3) we find:

$$T_1 = 0{\cdot}5; \quad T_2 = 1; \quad T_3 = 0{\cdot}25; \quad T_4 = 0{\cdot}5;$$
$$T_5 = 0{\cdot}5; \quad T_6 = 1; \quad T_3 T_4 = 0{\cdot}125; \quad T_5 T_6 = 0{\cdot}5 ,$$

and then the initial values for the new variables of the system of equations (71.5), namely:

$$x_{40} = -4 , \quad \dot{x}_{40} = 32 , \quad \ddot{x}_{40} = -144 , \quad \dddot{x}_{40} = 464 ,$$
$$x_{20} = -6 , \quad \dot{x}_{20} = 18 , \quad x_{10} = 12 .$$

Putting in formulae (73.5) and (73.6) $s = 1$, we obtain

$$x_1 = A_{11} e^{-\frac{t}{T_1}} , \quad A_{11} = 12 ,$$

while with $s = 2$, from formulae (73.5) and (73.7) we have:

$$x_2 = A_{21} e^{-\frac{t}{T_1}} + A_{22} e^{-\frac{t}{T_2}} , \quad A_{21} = -12 , \quad A_{22} = 6 .$$

From formulae (73.8), (73.9) and (73.10) we find:

$$x_4 = A_{41} e^{-\frac{t}{T_1}} + A_{42} e^{-\frac{t}{T_2}} + B_{41} e^{\alpha_1 t} \cos \omega_1 t + C_{41} e^{\alpha_1 t} \sin \omega_1 t;$$
$$A_{41} = -24; \quad A_{42} = 9{\cdot}6; \quad B_{41} = 10{\cdot}4; \quad C_{41} = 7{\cdot}2 .$$

The last variable $x_6 = x$, from formulae (73.8), (73.9) and (73.11) will be:

$$x = A_{61} e^{-\frac{t}{T_1}} + A_{62} e^{-\frac{t}{T_2}} + B_{61} e^{\alpha_1 t} \cos \omega_1 t + C_{61} e^{\alpha_1 t} \sin \omega_1 t +$$
$$+ B_{62} e^{\alpha_2 t} \cos \omega_2 t + C_{62} e^{\alpha_2 t} \sin \omega_2 t;$$

$$A_{61} = -24; \quad A_{62} = 19{\cdot}2; \quad D_{41} = 3; \quad E_{41} = -2;$$
$$B_{61} = 3{\cdot}5; \quad C_{61} = 0{\cdot}0616; \quad B_{62} = -2{\cdot}7; \quad C_{62} = -24{\cdot}6 .$$

This is the solution of the homogeneous differential equation (73.13). Consequently, the transient curve for the initial equation (73.12) has the expression

$$x^* = \tfrac{1}{4}(4 + x) = 1 - 6e^{-2t} + 4{\cdot}8e^{-t} + 0{\cdot}875e^{-2t}\cos 2t +$$
$$+ 0{\cdot}0154e^{-2t}\sin 2t - 0{\cdot}675e^{-t}\cos t - 6{\cdot}15e^{-t}\sin t .$$

This example demonstrates the simplicity of calculation the solution of a linear system of arbitrary order, adequate for practical calculations (but only for the transient processes).

74. Operational method

Thus far we have been concerned with the symbolic operational notation of differential equations in which we denoted by p the operation of differentiation, where the differential equations of the system and its individual elements were written conventionally with factoring of the variables outside the parenthesis with introduction of the concept of operational polynomials (Section 5) and transfer functions (Section 8). It was shown that such a conventional notation is very convenient from the point of view of its conciseness, the simplicity of transforming the equations and the simplicity of determining forced oscillations in the system and its circuits (frequency characteristics).

In the present section we shall consider the operational calculus for the solution of linear differential equations.

The fundamentals of operational calculus are described in the books of: A. I. Lur'e (Reference 40), M. F. Gardner and J. L. Barnes (Reference 33), V. A. Ditkin and P. I. Kuznetsov (Reference 30), and others. Our problem consists only in describing certain practical applications of operational calculus to the solution of the differential equations of automatic regulation systems.

The method of operational calculus is used to solve not only the problem of finding the transient curve but also the regulation process for certain perturbations or input commands (for which it is possible to write an operational transform). In the operational method it is not necessary to determine the arbitrary constants of integration as a separate stage of the solution, since the prescribed initial conditions are "automatically" taken into account in the solution. It also has the possibility of a single notation for the entire process of solution in the presence of piecewise-continuous functions in the right-hand side (in place of the cumbersome matching of individual segments in the ordinary solution).

However in the operational method of solution the procedure of finding the roots of polynomials is retained. For high-degree equations this is possible only in the numerical form (Section 39). Therefore it is possible to find the regulation curve by the operational method, as by others, only with all the system parameters given in numerical form.

The operational transform. Let there be given the differential equation of a closed system in the ordinary notation (5.2). Each term of the equation, a certain function of time $\varphi(t)$, is transformed by use of the Laplace transformation (Reference 33)

$$\Phi(s) = \int_0^\infty e^{-st}\varphi(t)\,dt \qquad (t \geqslant 0) \qquad (74.1)$$

to a function $\Phi(s)$ of a different (complex) variable s, where the equation takes an algebraic form and may be subjected to algebraic manipulation. Here, in distinction to the symbolic operational method (Section 5) not the notation but the mathematical content of the expression changes.

The new function in s obtained in this manner is termed the transform of the given function of t, while the function itself is termed the original. We shall denote the transform by the same letter as the original, but capitalised. Thus, if the originals are the functions $\varphi(t)$, $x(t)$, $f(t)$, their transforms will be $\Phi(s)$, $X(s)$, $F(s)$.

In a number of books (Reference 40, 30) the transform of the function $\varphi(t)$ is defined by the Carson transformation

$$\Phi(s) = s \int_0^\infty e^{-st}\varphi(t)\,dt\,,$$

differing from the Laplace transformation by the factor s. Below we shall employ the Laplace transformation (74.1).

To write differential equation (5.2) in transforms, it is first necessary to know the transforms of derivatives of arbitrary order. Let us find the transform of the first derivative $d\varphi/dt = \dot{\varphi}(t)$ according to formula (74.1), i.e.

$$\int_0^\infty e^{-st}\dot{\varphi}(t)\,dt\,;$$

integration by parts gives

$$e^{-st}\varphi(t)\,\Big|_0^\infty + s \int_0^\infty e^{-st}\varphi(t)\,dt\,,$$

from which, taking into account (74.1), we obtain $-\varphi_0 + s\Phi(s)$, where φ_0 is the value of $\varphi(t)$ at $t = 0$.

The following transforms of derivatives and integrals are obtained analogously:

Original	Transform	
$\varphi(t)$	$\Phi(s)$	
$\dfrac{d\varphi}{dt}$	$s\Phi(s) - \varphi_0$	
$\dfrac{d^2\varphi}{dt^2}$	$s^2\Phi(s) - s\varphi_0 - \dot{\varphi}_0$	(74.2)
. . . .	. . . .	
$\dfrac{d^n\varphi}{dt^n}$	$s^n\Phi(s) - s^{n-1}\varphi_0 - s^{n-2}\dot{\varphi}_0 - \ldots - \varphi_0^{(n-1)}$	
$\int \varphi(t)\,dt$	$\dfrac{1}{s}[\Phi(s) + \varphi_0^{(-1)}]$	

where $\varphi_0, \dot{\varphi}_0, \ldots, \varphi_0^{(n-1)}$ are the values of the function φ and its derivatives with respect to time at the instant $t = 0$, while $\varphi_0^{(-1)}$ is the value of the integral at $t = 0$.

Let there be, for example, the second-order differential equation

$$a_0 \frac{d^2x}{dt^2} + a_1 \frac{dx}{dt} + a_2 x = b_0 \frac{df}{dt} + b_1 f(t) \qquad (74.3)$$

with the initial conditions: $x = x_0$, $\dot{x} = \dot{x}_0$ at $t = 0$, and with the initial value $f = f_0$ at $t = 0$ According to (74.2) this equation in transforms takes the form

$$a_0[s^2 X(s) - x_0 s - \dot{x}_0] + a_1[s X(s) - x_0] + a_2 X(s)$$
$$= b_0[s F(s) - f_0] + b_1 F(s)$$

or

$$(a_0 s^2 + a_1 s + a_2) X(s) = (b_0 s + b_1) F(s) +$$
$$+ a_0 x_0 s + a_0 \dot{x}_0 + a_1 x_0 - b_0 f_0 . \qquad (74.4)$$

This is no longer a differential but an algebraic equation in the single variable s (complex, as in general, in each algebraic equation). In contrast to this, equations (5.6) and (5.7), written in symbolic operational form, remain differential equations (but only with a different notation for the derivatives) and contain the functions of time $x(t)$, $y(t)$, $f(t)$ which are completely absent from equation (74 4).

If the function $f(t)$ in equation (74.3) is given, then from (74.1) its transform $F(s)$ is also known. It is therefore easily possible to find from the algebraic equation (74.4) the transform $X(s)$ of the required function $x(t)$, namely:

$$X(s) = \frac{(b_0 s + b_1) F(s) + a_0 x_0 s + a_0 \dot{x}_0 + a_1 x_0 - b_0 f_0}{a_0 s^2 + a_1 s + a_2} . \qquad (74.5)$$

Comparing this with the symbolic operational notation (Section 5), we note that in the general case, if the differential equation of the system has the form

$$L(p) x(t) = S(p) f(t) , \qquad (74.6)$$

the transform of the required solution $x(t)$ will be

$$X(s) = \frac{S(s) F(s) + L_0(s)}{L(s)} , \qquad (74.7)$$

where $F(s)$ is the transform of the given function $f(t)$ while $L_0(s)$ is a polynomial reflecting the initial conditions, which are found similarly to the above.

Regulation process for arbitrary perturbation. As a result, the entire problem of finding the solution of a differential equation is now reduced, firstly, to obtaining by a fairly simple method the transforms $F(s)$ for various types of functions $f(t)$ and, secondly, the method of finding the required function $x(t)$ from its transform $X(s)$.

For this purpose we employ the fundamental theorems of operational calculus. As a result tables of formulae are exampled which give final expressions for the transforms $F(s)$ for a large number of different functions of time $f(t)$ (Reference 33).

Naturally, it is possible in many cases from these same tables of formulae to solve the inverse problem of determining the required function $x(t)$ from its transform $X(s)$ (obtained on the basis of the given differential equation), for example (74.5) or (74.7). In this case the solution $x(t)$ of the differential equation may be written in the algebraic form in terms of ordinary or arbitrary special functions. But this concerns equations of low order or high-order equations of a very special type.

For an example we present the transforms of several frequently encountered functions (here everywhere we consider $f(t) = 0$ with $t < 0$, except in the third formula where $f(t-\tau) = 0$ with $t < \tau$):

$f(t)$	$F(s)$	$f(t)$	$F(s)$
$1(t)$	$\dfrac{1}{s}$	$e^{-\lambda t}\cos\omega t$	$\dfrac{s+\lambda}{(s+\lambda)^2+\omega^2}$
$1'(t)$	1	$e^{-\lambda t}\sin\omega t$	$\dfrac{\omega}{(s+\lambda)^2+\omega^2}$
$f(t-\tau)$	$e^{-\tau s}F(s)$		$\dfrac{1}{s}f_0\,\mathrm{th}\,\dfrac{Ts}{2}$
at	$\dfrac{a}{s^2}$		
at^n	$\dfrac{a(n-1)!}{s^{n-1}}$		$\dfrac{1}{s}f_0\,\dfrac{1-e^{-T_1 s}}{1-e^{-T_2 s}}$
$e^{-\lambda t}$	$\dfrac{1}{s+\lambda}$		
$\cos\omega t$	$\dfrac{s}{s^2+\omega^2}$		$\dfrac{1}{s}f_0(1-e^{-Ts})$
$\sin\omega t$	$\dfrac{\omega}{s^2+\omega^2}$		

There exists a formula convenient for solving numerical problems. Let the transform $X(s)$ of the required solution $x(t)$ be obtained in the form of the ratio of two polynomials

$$X(s) = \frac{X_1(s)}{X_2(s)}, \tag{74.8}$$

where the degree of polynomial $X_1(s)$ is lower or equal to the degree of $X_2(s)$. For example, if the transform of the given function $f(t)$ has the form

$$F(s) = \frac{F_1(s)}{F_2(s)},$$

from (74.7) we obtain

$$X(s) = \frac{S(s)F_1(s) + L_0(s)F_2(s)}{L(s)F_2(s)}.$$

Then, under the assumption that $X_2(s)$ does not have multiple or zero roots, the required solution is defined by the formula (expansion theorem)

$$x(t) = \sum_{k=1}^{n} \frac{X_1(s_k)}{X_2'(s_k)} e^{s_k t} \quad (t \geqslant 0), \qquad (74.9)$$

where n denotes the degree of the denominator $X_2(s)$ in the expression (74.8), $X_2'(s)$ is the derivative of $X_2(s)$ with respect to s; s_k are the roots of the polynomial $X_2(s)$. It is recommended to calculate the roots by the simple numerical method described in Section 39. The terms of the solution (74.9) corresponding to complex roots must be transformed as shown below in the example for the transient process.

If the denominator $X_2(s)$ in expression (74.8) has a zero root $s_1 = 0$, then, putting

$$X_2(s) = s\tilde{X}_2(s),$$

we find

$$x(t) = \frac{X_1(0)}{\tilde{X}_2(0)} + \sum_{k=2}^{n} \frac{X_1(s_k)}{s_k \cdot \tilde{X}_2'(s_k)} e^{s_k t}. \qquad (74.10)$$

Analogous formulae exist for multiple poles and for purely imaginary poles (Reference 33).

The convolution theorem is also important for the practical finding of the original of the solution. It states that if the transform is represented as the product:

$$X(s) = X_1(s) X_2(s),$$

the original is expressed by the formula

$$x(t) = \int_{0}^{t} x_1(\tau) x_2(t-\tau) d\tau, \qquad (74.11)$$

where x_1 and x_2 are the originals of the transforms $X_1(s)$ and $X_2(s)$.

In particular, if a unit impulse acts on the system described by the differential equation (74.6) $f(t) = 1'(t)$ with zero initial conditions, the transform cf the solution according to (74.7) will be

$$X_1(s) = \frac{S(s)}{L(s)}.$$

If on the same system an arbitrary perturbation $f(t)$ acts with zero initial conditions, then

$$X(s) = \frac{S(s)F(s)}{L(s)} = X_1(s)F(s).$$

Then according to formula (74.11) we find the regulation process in the system for a constantly present arbitrary external force $f(t)$:

$$x(t) = \int\limits_0^t x_1(\tau)f(t-\tau)\,d\tau,$$

if the transient process $x_1(t)$ in the given system caused by the unit impulse is known and if the initial conditions of the required process are zero.

Transient process. For the homogeneous differential equation with arbitrary initial conditions we have from (74.7)

$$X(s) = \frac{L_0(s)}{L(s)} \tag{74.12}$$

and from (74.9)

$$x(t) = \sum_{k=1}^n \frac{L_0(s_k)}{L'(s_k)} e^{s_k t}, \tag{74.13}$$

if $L(s)$ does not have zero or multiple roots.

Thus the solution of Example 1 Section 6 takes here the following form. The transform of the required variable $\Delta\omega$ is denoted by $\Omega(s)$. Then the transformed equation of the given system (6.38), according to (74.2), will be:

$$s^3\Omega(s) - s^2\Delta\omega_0 - s\Delta\dot\omega_0 - \Delta\ddot\omega_0 + a_1[s^2\Omega(s) - s\Delta\omega_0 - \Delta\dot\omega_0] +$$
$$+ a_2[s\Omega(s) - \Delta\omega_0] + a_3\Omega(s) = 0$$

or

$$L(s)\Omega(s) = L_0(s),$$

where

$$L(s) = s^3 + a_1 s^2 + a_2 s + a_3,$$
$$L_0(s) = \Delta\omega_0 s^2 + (\Delta\dot\omega_0 + a_1\Delta\omega_0)s + \Delta\ddot\omega_0 + a_1\Delta\dot\omega_0 + a_2\Delta\omega_0,$$

and all coefficients are given according to Example 1 of Section 6.

For formula (74.13) it is further necessary to have the expression

$$L'(s) = 3s^2 + 2a_1 s + a_2,$$

as well as to find the roots s_1, s_2, s_3 of the polynomial $L(s)$ by any means described in Section 39. After this formula (74.13) gives

$$\Delta\omega(t) = \frac{L_0(s_1)}{L'(s_1)}\, e^{s_1 t} + \frac{L_0(s_2)}{L'(s_2)}\, e^{s_2 t} + \frac{L_0(s_3)}{L'(s_3)}\, e^{s_3 t}. \tag{74.14}$$

The solution remains in this form if all roots s_1, s_2, s_3 are real. It is evident that this process of solution is somewhat simpler than in Example 1 of Section 6.

If the roots $s_{1,2} = \alpha \pm i\omega$ are complex, while s_3 is real, the first two terms of formula (74.14) will be complex conjugate. Employing the substitution $e^{\pm i\omega t} = \cos\omega t \pm i\sin\omega t$, we come to the solution in the form

$$x = e^{\alpha t}\left\{2\,\mathrm{Re}\left[\frac{L_0(s_1)}{L'(s_1)}\right]\cos\omega t - 2\,\mathrm{Im}\left[\frac{L_0(s_1)}{L'(s_1)}\right]\sin\omega t\right\} + \frac{L_0(s_3)}{L'(s_3)}\, e^{s_3 t},$$

where Re and Im denote the real and imaginary (without the coefficient i) parts respectively of the expressions in square brackets.

When the transient process is caused by a unit step of function $f(t)$, figuring in the equation of the given system (74.6), i.e. $f(t) = 1(t)$ and $F(s) = 1/s$, with zero initial conditions before the step (bearing in mind the presence of a steady-state of the system before the step), we obtain from (74.7)

$$X(s) = \frac{S(s)}{sL(s)}. \tag{74.15}$$

From a comparison of this expression with (74.12) we see that in the present case $S(s)$ plays the role of the polynomial $L_0(s)$, reflecting the initial conditions. It is just from such a comparison that the formulae are obtained for recalculating the initial conditions (6.23) for the given type of transient process.

Finally, for a transient process caused by a unit impulse of the function $f(t)$, i.e. when $f(t) = 1'(t)$ and $F(s) = 1$, with zero initial conditions before application of the impulse (also with a steady-state of the system before application of the impulse) from (74.7) we have

$$X(s) = \frac{S(s)}{L(s)}. \tag{74.16}$$

On the basis of the transforms (74.15) and (74.16) the transient curve is found in the same way as in the above example. In both cases in place of $S(s)$ we may have according to (5.7) a polynomial $N(s)$, if the transient process is not caused by the perturbation $f(t)$ but by the command $y(t)$.

These formulae for the solution of the differential equation are valid also for systems with delay, but the number of roots of the equation for $X_2(s)$ may here be infinite according to Section 49.

Transient process at application of an external force. Above we have considered the transient process about a certain constant value of the regulated quantity, arising for one of the following reasons: (1) as a result of the appearance of arbitrary initial conditions, (2) as a result of a discontinuous application of a constant load f or a constant adjustment y, (3) as the result of an instantaneous impulse in f or y.

The transient process with application of an arbitrary variable external force, as the deviation from the corresponding forced motion of the system will be something else; this process will depend on the form of the external forces (as noted in Section 6).

For example, with a unit step of the adjustment y (i.e. the command) according to (74.15), (5.7) and (74.10) the transient process will be

$$X(s) = \frac{N(s)}{sL(s)}, \qquad x(t) = \frac{N(0)}{L(0)} + \sum_{k=1}^{n} \frac{N(s_k)}{s_k L'(s_k)} e^{s_k t} \qquad (74.17)$$

(with the system in the steady-state before the step).

If an input command with constant velocity $y(t) = at$ and $Y(s) = a/s^2$ is applied, then from (5.7) and (74.7) we obtain

$$X(s) = \frac{aN(s) + L_0(s)}{s^2 L(s)},$$

where, if before the force is applied the system was in the steady-state with $x = 0$, then $L_0(s) = 0$. In this case we obtain

$$x(t) = \left[\frac{d}{ds}\frac{aN(s)}{L(s)}\right]_{s=0} + \frac{aN(0)}{L(0)}t + \sum_{k=1}^{n} \frac{aN(s_k)}{2s_k L(s_k) + s_k^2 L'(s_k)} e^{s_k t}, \qquad (74.18)$$

where s_k $(k = 1, 2, ..., n)$ are the roots of the polynomial $L(s)$, i.e. the characteristic equation of the system. The first component gives a constant stationary error, the second the steady-state process (forced motion) and the third, the transient process (Fig. 36).

From a comparison of (74.18) and (74.17) the essential difference between these two forms of transient process in the same system is evident.

From this there follows the practical conclusion that in those automatic systems for which the basic steady-state operation is not defined by a constant but by some time-variable value of the regulated quantity (in program-control systems and in servo-mechanisms), it is absolutely necessary to investigate the quality of the transient process with application of the most typical variable input command $y(t)$ for the given system. The general formula for the transform of the solution according to (74.7) and (5.7) will be

$$X(s) = \frac{N(s)\,Y(s) + L_0(s)}{L(s)}, \tag{74.19}$$

where $N(s)$ and $L(s)$ are the polynomials entering into the symbolic notation of the differential equation of the given system (5.7), $Y(s)$ is the transform of the typical variable input command $y(t)$, $L_0(s)$ reflects, as in (74.7), the initial conditions. If before application of the force $y(t)$ the system was in the steady-state with $x = 0$, then $L_0(s) = 0$.

Similarly to the above example it is also possible to study here the steady-state process, the stationary error of the system and the transient process.

We note that with oscillatory forces the steady-state process of forced oscillations and the stationary error are conveniently de-

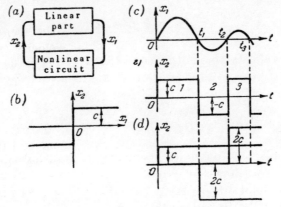

FIG. 331

termined from the frequency characteristics (Section 8). The general solution with respect to the transient process for certain forms of inputs may be found by the operational method described while for arbitrary forces, by the numerical-graphical method (see Chapter XVIII).

Application of the operational method to non-linear systems. Let there be for example, a non-linear system in which the linear part (Fig. 331a) may have an arbitrary structure and is described by a differential equation of arbitrary order (in symbolic operational notation):

$$Q(p)x_1(t) = R(p)x_2(t), \tag{74.20}$$

while the non-linear element has a simple relay characteristic in the form of Fig. 331b. Then each "period" of oscillation of the quantity x_1 (Fig. 331c) divides into two sections, in the first of which $x_2 = c$ and in the second $x_2 = -c$ (Fig. 331d).

The graph of Fig. 331d may be represented as the algebraic sum of step functions (Fig. 331e), namely:

$$x_2 = c \cdot 1(t) - 2c \cdot 1(t - t_1) + 2c \cdot 1(t - t_2) - 2c \cdot 1(t - t_3) + \ldots$$

Substituting this in equation (74.20), we obtain the equation of the overall closed non-linear system in the form

$$Q(p)x_1(t) = R(p)[c \cdot 1(t) - 2c \cdot 1(t - t_1) +$$
$$+ 2c \cdot 1(t - t_2) - 2c \cdot 1(t - t_3) + \ldots], \qquad (74.21)$$

where $x_1(t)$ is the required function and the quantities t_1, t_2, t_3 are unknown and are to be determined during the solution as the successive times at which $x_1(t)$ vanishes (Fig. 331c).

On the basis of the above table we write the transform of the solution to the differential equation (74.21) in the form

$$X_1(s) = \frac{cR(s)}{sQ(s)}(1 - 2e^{-st_1} + 2e^{-st_2} - 2e^{-st_3} + \ldots) + \frac{Q_0(s)}{Q(s)}, \quad (74.22)$$

where $Q_0(s)$ reflects the initial conditions.

We denote by $x_{11}(t)$ and $x_{10}(t)$ the originals corresponding to the transforms

$$X_{11}(s) = \frac{cR(s)}{sQ(s)} \quad \text{and} \quad X_{10}(s) = \frac{Q_0(s)}{Q(s)}. \qquad (74.23)$$

These originals are found on the basis of transforms (74.23) from the table of transforms or from formulae (74.8), (74.9) or (74.10).

Then the solution of the system equation (74.21), according to (74.22), will be in segments:

$$\left.\begin{array}{ll} x_1(t) = x_{10}(t) + x_{11}(t) & (0 \leqslant t \leqslant t_1), \\ x_1(t) = x_{10}(t) + x_{11}(t) - 2x_{11}(t - t_1) & (t_1 \leqslant t \leqslant t_2), \\ x_1(t) = x_{10}(t) + x_{11}(t) - 2x_{11}(t - t_1) + 2x_{11}(t - t_2) & (t_2 \leqslant t \leqslant t_3) \end{array}\right\} \quad (74.24)$$

etc. It remains to determine the quantities $t_1, t_2, t_3, \ldots$ The quantity t_1 is defined as the nearest value of t at which the first of formulae (74.24) gives the value $x_1(t) = 0$, as shown in Fig. 331c. Then the quantity t_2 is found as the first value of t after t_1 for which the second of formulae (74.24) gives $x_1(t) = 0$, etc.

Thus, the operational method defines the entire curve of the transient process in the given non-linear system. In the simplest cases, applying to (74.23) the tables of operational transforms (Reference 33), the solution obtained (74.24) may be expressed in algebraic form, while in more complicated cases in numerical form for given numerical parameters of the system, employing the numerical method for finding the roots of the polynomial (Section 39). In essence this is the same method of matching solutions as in the examples of Section 9 and Section 59, except for the use of operational calculus.

Analogous to this it is possible to apply the operational method of the solution of transient processes in closed automatic systems with certain other non-linear characteristics (with a corresponding complication of the procedure and the manner of separating it into sections).

To determine the possibility of self-oscillations arising in the system and to find their waveform it is necessary to take a single arbitrary period of oscillations in the transient process and apply the condition of periodicity similarly as was done in the simple examples of Section 9 and Section 59.

75. The Solodovnikov method of trapezoidal frequency characteristics

Let us describe a method for the approximate construction of the transient curve in an automatic system (with input in the form of a step or impulse) for a given real frequency characteristic of the closed system, as developed by V. V. Solodovnikov in 1948 (Reference 11). This method is useful when the calculation of the system is carried out from the very beginning by frequency methods. It is absolutely necessary if the equations of all elements of the system are not known, while a part of them are given by experimentally recorded frequency characteristics.

The method of obtaining the real frequency characteristic of a closed system $U_y(\omega)$ or $U_f(\omega)$ was described in Section 44. Now, knowing this, it is necessary to construct the curve of the transient process for a external perturbation in the form of a unit step or unit impulse. To solve the problem we employ formulae (44.18), (44.19) or (44.20). The approximateness of the solution consists in that the given continuous curve $U_y(\omega)$ is substituted by a polygonal curve. As a result the entire graph of $U_y(\omega)$ divides into a series of trapezoids.

We shall first consider plotting the transient curve for the characteristic $U_y(\omega)$ in a purely trapezoidal form, and then pass to the general case.

Trapezoidal frequency characteristic. A trapezoidal frequency characteristic is a real frequency characteristic $U_i(\omega)$ having the form of a trapezoid (Fig. 332a). The real frequency characteristics of actual systems do not have such shapes, but below we shall employ them for approximation to the real characteristics.

A trapezoidal frequency characteristic is defined by the following three quantities (Fig. 332a): the initial amplitude $U_i(0)$, the pass-band ω_{ip} and the inclination factor

$$\varkappa_i = \frac{\omega_{ia}}{\omega_{ip}}, \qquad (75.1)$$

where ω_{ia} is termed the interval of uniform transmission of frequencies, corresponding to a constant value of U_i in the segment

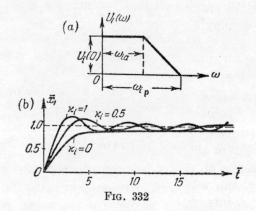

FIG. 332

$0 \leqslant \omega \leqslant \omega_{ia}$. These quantities may have the most varied values with the only restraint that $\omega_{ia} < \omega_{ip}$ and, consequently, $0 \leqslant \varkappa_i \leqslant 1$.

Let us introduce the dimensionless quantities

$$\bar{x}_i = \frac{x_i}{U_i(0)}, \qquad \bar{t} = t\omega_{ip} \qquad (75.2)$$

for the coordinates of the transient curve $x_i(t)$, corresponding to the trapezoidal frequency characteristic.

On the basis of formula (44.19) the transient function $\bar{x}_i(\bar{t})$ due to a unit input step is obtained (Reference 11) in the form

$$\bar{x}_i(\bar{t}) = \frac{2}{\pi}\left\{Si(\varkappa_i\bar{t}) + \frac{1}{1-\varkappa_i}\left[Si(\bar{t}) - Si(\varkappa_i\bar{t}) + \frac{\cos\bar{t} - \cos\varkappa_i\bar{t}}{\bar{t}}\right]\right\}, \qquad (75.3)$$

where we introduce the usual notation for the sine integral

$$Si(\varkappa_i\bar{t}) = \int\limits_0^{\varkappa_i} \frac{\sin(\bar{t}\varphi)}{\varphi}\,d\varphi\ .$$

The functions $\bar{x}_i(\bar{t})$ has been previously calculated from formula (75.3) for the values $\varkappa_i = 0;\ 0\!\cdot\!05;\ 0\!\cdot\!1;\ ...;\ 0\!\cdot\!95;\ 1\!\cdot\!00$. Their values for various values of the dimensionless time $\bar{t}$ in the interval $0 \leqslant \bar{t} \leqslant 26\!\cdot\!0$ are presented in the table on pp. 750–753 (according to V. V. Solodovnikov).

Plotting the curves $\bar{x}_i(\bar{t})$ from the table for the extreme and mean values of $\varkappa_i = 0$, $\varkappa_i = 0\cdot5$ and $\varkappa = 1$ is shown in Fig. 332b.

Let there now exist an arbitrary trapezoidal characteristic (Fig. 332a) with given values of $\varkappa_i$, $U_i(0)$ and ω_i. The transient curve $x_i(t)$ which corresponds to it is easily plotted using the above-mentioned table. We proceed as follows.

We find in the table the value of $\varkappa_i$ closest to that which occurs in the given trapezoidal characteristic. For this value of $\varkappa_i$ we take from the table the entire column of values of $\bar{x}_i$ and $\bar{t}$ and, according to (75.2), we employ the formulae

$$x_i = U_i(0)\bar{x}_i, \qquad t = \frac{\bar{t}}{\omega_{ip}}, \tag{75.4}$$

i.e. we multiply all values of $\bar{x}_i$ taken from the table by the amplitude $U_i(0)$ of the given trapezoidal frequency characteristic, and all values of $\bar{t}$ taken from the table we divide by the magnitude of the passband ω_{ip} of the given trapezoidal characteristic. As a result we obtain a series of values of x_i and a series of values of t corresponding to them, after which the required transient curve $x_i(t)$ is plotted by points.

Approximate plotting of the transient curve due to a unit input impulse. Let the real frequency characteristic of the closed system $U_y(\omega)$ be given in the form of the curve of Fig. 333a. We substitute this curve

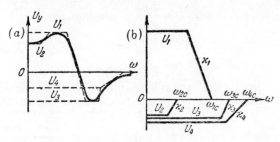

FIG. 333

by a polygon close to it, consisting of rectilinear segments (broken line in Fig. 333a) and then plot from each vertex straight lines parallel to the frequency axis ω.

As a result the given frequency characteristic $U_y(\omega)$ may be approximately substituted by the algebraic sum of several trapezoidal frequency characteristics $U_i(\omega)$ with initial heights $U_i(0)$, with passbands ω_{ip} and inclination factors $\varkappa_i$. In the present case (see Fig. 333b) we obtain four trapezoids $(i = 1, 2, 3, 4)$, where $U_1(0) > 0$, $U_2(0) < 0$, $U_3(0) < 0$, $U_4(0) < 0$.

Table of

t \ x_i	0·00	0·05	0·10	0·15	0·20	0·25	0·30	0·35	0·40	0·45
0·0	0·000	0·000	0·000	0·000	0·000	0·000	0·000	0·000	0·000	0·000
0·5	0·138	0·165	0·176	0·184	0·192	0·199	0·207	0·215	0·223	0·231
1·0	0·310	0·326	0·340	0·356	0·371	0·386	0·401	0·417	0·432	0·447
1·5	0·449	0·469	0·494	0·516	0·538	0·560	0·594	0·603	0·617	0·646
2·0	0·572	0·597	0·628	0·655	0·683	0·709	0·681	0·761	0·786	0·810
2·5	0·674	0·707	0·739	0·771	0·802	0·833	0·862	0·891	0·917	0·943
3·0	0·755	0·790	0·828	0·863	0·896	0·928	0·958	0·987	1·013	1·038
3·5	0·783	0·853	0·892	0·928	0·963	0·994	1·024	1·050	1·074	1·095
4·0	0·857	0·896	0·938	0·974	1·008	1·039	1·060	1·090	1·107	1·124
4·5	0·883	0·923	0·960	0·997	1·029	1·057	1·080	1·100	1·115	1·129
5·0	0·896	0·936	0·978	1·012	1·042	1·067	1·087	1·103	1·112	1·117
5·5	0·900	0·940	0·986	1·019	1·046	1·067	1·083	1·093	1·095	1·097
6·0	0·904	0·942	0·982	1·013	1·037	1·054	1·065	1·070	1·068	1·062
6·5	0·904	0·943	0·980	1·009	1·030	1·043	1·050	1·049	1·043	1·033
7·0	0·904	0·944	0·979	1·006	1·024	1·035	1·037	1·033	1·023	1·009
7·5	0·907	0·945	0·980	1·006	1·019	1·025	1·025	1·017	1·005	0·989
8·0	0·910	0·951	0·985	1·008	1·020	1·024	1·021	1·012	0·995	0·981
8·5	0·918	0·956	0·989	1·010	1·021	1·022	1·018	1·007	0·992	0·977
9·0	0·924	0·965	0·997	1·016	1·025	1·025	1·018	1·006	0·992	0·978
9·5	0·932	0·972	1·004	1·022	1·029	1·027	1·019	1·006	0·993	0·982
10·0	0·939	0·978	1·009	1·025	1·031	1·027	1·019	1·006	0·993	0·987
10·5	0·946	0·985	1·013	1·028	1·033	1·028	1·017	1·005	0·993	0·991
11·0	0·947	0·988	1·015	1·029	1·031	1·025	1·014	1·002	0·993	0·991
11·5	0·949	0·988	1·016	1·027	1·028	1·021	1·010	0·999	0·991	0·989
12·0	0·950	0·988	1·015	1·025	1·024	1·015	1·004	0·994	0·988	0·987
12·5	0·950	0·989	1·013	1·022	1·019	1·010	0·999	0·990	0·986	0·986
13·0	0·950	0·989	1·012	1·019	1·015	1·005	0·994	0·986	0·985	0·987

the function $\bar{x}_i(\bar{t})$

0·50	0·55	0·60	0·65	0·70	0·75	0·80	0·85	0·90	0·95	1·00
0·000	0·000	0·000	0·000	0·000	0·000	0·000	0·000	0·000	0·000	0·000
0·240	0·248	0·255	0·259	0·267	0·275	0·282	0·290	0·297	0·304	0·314
0·461	0·476	0·490	0·505	0·519	0·534	0·547	0·562	0·575	0·593	0·603
0·665	0·685	0·706	0·722	0·740	0·758	0·776	0·794	0·813	0·832	0·844
0·833	0·856	0·878	0·899	0·919	0·938	0·956	0·974	0·986	1·003	1·020
0·967	0·985	1·010	1·030	1·050	1·067	1·084	1·090	1·105	1·120	1·133
1·061	1·082	1·100	1·117	1·130	1·142	1·154	1·164	1·172	1·176	1·178
1·115	1·132	1·145	1·158	1·161	1·166	1·171	1·174	1·175	1·175	1·175
1·142	1·152	1·158	1·159	1·160	1·161	1·156	1·149	1·141	1·131	1·118
1·134	1·138	1·138	1·134	1·132	1·127	1·111	1·099	1·085	1·071	1·053
1·118	1·115	1·107	1·098	1·084	1·069	1·053	1·037	1·019	1·001	0·986
1·092	1·083	1·070	1·050	1·032	1·016	0·994	0·979	0·962	0·951	0·932
1·051	1·037	1·021	1·003	0·984	0·956	0·949	0·934	0·922	0·920	0·906
1·018	1·001	0·982	0·946	0·948	0·936	0·920	0·910	0·903	0·903	0·905
0·993	0·975	0·957	0·941	0·927	0·917	0·911	0·908	0·909	0·915	0·925
0·974	0·958	0·944	0·926	0·922	0·911	0·920	0·927	0·934	0·946	0·958
0·966	0·951	0·941	0·935	0·932	0·936	0·944	0·955	0·970	0·986	1·004
0·966	0·949	0·944	0·948	0·951	0·958	0·974	0·990	1·006	1·023	1·041
0·970	0·960	0·961	0·966	0·976	0·990	1·006	1·023	1·039	1·053	1·061
0·975	0·972	0·980	0·987	1·000	1·015	1·033	1·048	1·059	1·066	1·066
0·982	0·985	0·993	1·006	1·020	1·036	1·049	1·059	1·063	1·062	1·056
0·987	0·996	1·007	1·017	1·033	1·046	1·054	1·058	1·055	1·048	1·033
0·993	1·002	1·014	1·027	1·039	1·047	1·048	1·044	1·034	1·021	1·005
0·997	1·006	1·017	1·029	1·037	1·043	1·034	1·024	1·010	0·994	0·977
0·997	1·006	1·019	1·026	1·027	1·025	1·015	1·000	0·984	0·969	0·958
0·997	1·006	1·018	1·019	1·017	1·010	0·995	0·979	0·965	0·954	0·949
0·997	1·006	1·014	1·012	1·005	0·993	0·980	0·964	0·955	0·950	0·955

x_i / t	0·00	0·05	0·10	0·15	0·20	0·25	0·30	0·35	0·40	0·45
13·5	0·950	0·990	1·011	1·017	1·011	1·000	0·990	0·983	0·984	0·988
14·0	0·952	0·989	1·011	1·016	1·009	0·997	0·988	0·983	0·985	0·991
14·5	0·954	0·990	1·012	1·015	1·008	0·996	0·987	0·985	0·988	0·996
15·0	0·956	0·993	1·012	1·014	1·007	0·995	0·988	0·987	0·991	1·000
15·5	0·959	0·995	1·014	1·014	1·006	0·995	0·989	0·988	0·996	1·004
16·0	0·961	0·997	1·015	1·014	1·006	0·995	0·991	0·992	0·998	1·007
16·5	0·964	0·999	1·016	1·014	1·005	0·995	0·993	0·995	1·002	1·009
17·0	0·965	1·001	1·016	1·013	1·005	0·995	0·994	0·997	1·005	1·010
17·5	0·966	1·002	1·015	1·012	1·003	0·995	0·994	0·998	1·006	1·010
18·0	0·966	1·002	1·015	1·011	1·002	0·995	0·995	1·001	1·008	1·010
18·5	0·966	1·001	1·015	1·009	1·001	0·994	0·995	1·001	1·007	1·009
19·0	0·967	1·000	1·015	1·008	0·998	0·992	0·995	1·001	1·006	1·006
19·5	0·967	1·000	1·014	1·006	0·996	0·991	0·995	1·001	1·005	1·004
20·0	0·967	1·000	1·013	1·005	0·995	0·991	0·995	1·001	1·005	1·002
20·5	0·968	1·002	1·012	1·004	0·994	0·991	0·996	1·002	1·004	1·001
21·0	0·968	1·002	1·011	1·003	0·994	0·992	0·997	1·003	1·004	1·001
21·5	0·969	1·002	1·011	1·003	0·995	0·992	0·999	1·004	1·004	1·000
22·0	0·971	1·002	1·011	1·002	0·995	0·993	1·000	1·005	1·004	0·999
22·5	0·973	1·002	1·011	1·002	0·996	0·995	1·002	1·006	1·004	0·999
23·0	0·974	1·005	1·011	1·002	0·996	0·996	1·004	1·007	1·003	0·998
23·5	0·975	1·005	1·010	1·002	0·996	0·998	1·004	1·008	1·003	0·998
24·0	0·975	1·005	1·010	1·001	0·996	0·999	1·005	1·007	1·002	0·997
24·5	0·975	1·005	1·009	1·000	0·996	0·999	1·005	1·006	1·001	0·997
25·0	0·975	1·005	1·008	1·000	0·995	0·999	1·005	1·004	1·000	0·996
25·5	0·975	1·005	1·008	0·999	0·995	0·999	1·004	1·003	0·998	0·996
26·0	0·975	1·005	1·007	0·999	0·995	0·999	1·004	1·002	0·997	0·996

the function $\bar{x}_i(\bar{t})$ *(continued)*

0·50	0·55	0·60	0·65	0·70	0·75	0·80	0·85	0·90	0·95	1·00
0·998	1·006	1·010	1·005	0·995	0·982	0·968	0·958	0·954	0·958	0·970
1·000	1·006	1·008	0·999	0·987	0·974	0·965	0·961	0·965	0·976	0·990
1·002	1·006	1·005	0·994	0·983	0·970	0·969	0·971	0·981	0·997	1·010
1·005	1·007	1·002	0·993	0·983	0·976	0·978	0·987	1·001	1·017	1·030
1·008	1·007	1·001	0·993	0·985	0·984	0·991	1·003	1·019	1·032	1·040
1·011	1·008	1·000	0·994	0·990	0·993	1·003	1·018	1·031	1·039	1·039
1·011	1·008	1·001	0·996	0·995	1·001	1·014	1·027	1·036	1·038	1·028
1·012	1·007	0·999	0·997	0·999	1·008	1·020	1·030	1·032	1·027	1·012
1·009	1·005	0·997	0·998	1·002	1·012	1·023	1·027	1·023	1·013	0·988
1·008	1·002	0·997	0·998	1·004	1·014	1·020	1·018	1·008	0·993	0·979
1·006	0·999	0·995	0·998	1·003	1·012	1·014	1·007	0·933	0·978	0·969
1·001	0·995	0·993	0·997	1·004	1·009	1·006	1·007	0·981	0·969	0·956
0·998	0·992	0·992	0·996	1·003	1·005	0·998	0·985	0·973	0·967	0·973
0·996	0·991	0·992	0·995	1·003	1·001	0·991	0·979	0·972	0·974	0·985
0·995	0·991	0·994	0·996	1·001	0·996	0·986	0·976	0·974	0·990	1·001
0·995	0·993	0·997	0·996	0·999	0·993	0·983	0·975	0·981	1·002	1·016
0·996	0·995	1·000	0·995	0·998	0·992	0·986	0·988	0·997	1·013	1·024
0·996	0·996	1·000	0·997	0·997	0·991	0·991	0·997	1·012	1·024	1·029
0·997	1·000	1·004	1·000	0·996	0·992	0·998	1·008	1·022	1·028	1·026
0·998	1·001	1·006	1·001	0·997	0·994	1·002	1·015	1·025	1·027	1·016
0·999	1·002	1·007	1·002	0·998	0·997	1·007	1·017	1·023	1·023	1·002
1·000	1·002	1·008	1·003	0·999	1·000	1·008	1·017	1·015	1·012	0·988
1·000	1·002	1·006	1·003	1·000	1·002	1·008	1·014	1·005	0·995	0·979
1·000	1·002	1·004	1·003	1·001	1·003	1·005	1·008	0·991	0·985	0·975
1·000	1·002	1·002	1·002	1·002	1·004	1·004	1·001	0·986	0·978	0·977
1·000	1·002	1·000	1·001	1·002	1·004	1·002	0·987	0·984	0·977	0·983

Thus,

$$U_y(\omega) \approx \sum_{i=1}^{n} U_i(\omega) , \qquad (75.5)$$

where n is the number of trapezoids. We proceed in the same manner when $U_f(\omega)$ is prescribed.

Then, according to (44.19) and (75.5) we obtain

$$x(t) \approx \frac{2}{\pi} \sum_{i=1}^{n} \int_0^\infty \frac{U_i(\omega)}{\omega} \sin \omega t \, d\omega$$

or

$$x(t) \approx \sum_{i=1}^{n} x_i(t) , \qquad (75.6)$$

where the functions $x_i(t)$ define the transient curves for each of the trapezoidal characteristics individually. We already know how to determine these latter individually.

Consequently, we now easily obtain the required transient curve $x(t)$ in approximate form by the addition of these curves.

Following V. V. Solodovnikov, let us consider the example of an automatic system described in closed form by the equation

$$(p^4 + a_1 p^3 + a_2 p^2 + a_3 p + a_4) x = (b_0 p^2 + b_1 p + b_2) y(t) ,$$

where

$$a_1 = 103 , \quad a_2 = 3065 , \quad a_3 = 149{,}250 , \quad a_4 = 1{,}081{,}500 ,$$
$$b_0 = 0{\cdot}0035 , \quad b_1 = 0{\cdot}37 , \quad b_2 = 9{\cdot}5 .$$

The expression for the amplitude-phase characteristic of the closed system will be

$$W_y(i\omega) = \frac{-b_0 \omega^2 + b_1 i\omega + b_2}{\omega^4 - a_1 i\omega^3 - a_2 \omega^2 + a_3 i\omega + a_4} .$$

The real part of this expression has the form

$$U_y(\omega) = \frac{(b_2 - b_0\omega^2)(\omega^4 - a_2\omega^2 + a_4) + b_1\omega(a_3\omega - a_1\omega^3)}{(\omega^4 - a_2\omega^2 + a_4)^2 + (a_3\omega - a_1\omega^3)^2} .$$

This real frequency characteristic of the closed system for the above numerical values of the coefficients has the form of the continuous curve in Fig. 334a. In broken line we show there the polygon replacing it. As a result we obtain three trapezoidal characteristics $U_1(\omega)$, $U_2(\omega)$, $U_3(\omega)$ as shown in Fig. 334b, into which the real frequency characteristic of the given system $U_y(\omega)$ is approximately divided.

The parameters of the trapezoidal characteristics are as follows:

$$U_1(0) = 1\cdot4; \qquad \varkappa_1 = 0\cdot9; \qquad \omega_{1p} = 40;$$
$$U_2(0) = 0\cdot6; \qquad \varkappa_2 = 0\cdot1; \qquad \omega_{2p} = 12;$$
$$U_3(0) = -1; \qquad \varkappa_3 = 0\cdot8; \qquad \omega_{3p} = 54 \ .$$

From the numerical tables of pp. 750–753 we take the values $\bar{x}_i(\bar{t})$, corresponding to the individual trapezoidal characteristics for $\varkappa_i = 0\cdot9, \varkappa_i = 0\cdot1$ and $\varkappa_i = 0\cdot8$. Each of the values taken from the table for $\bar{x}_i$ and $\bar{t}$ are recalculated according to formulae (75.4), in which we substitute the given values $U_1(0), \omega_{1p}, U_2(0), \omega_{2p}, U_3(0), \omega_{3p}$.

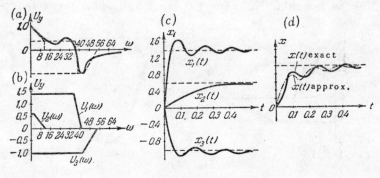

Fig. 334

From the points obtained (t, x_i) we plot the curves $x_1(t), x_2(t), x_3(t)$, shown in Fig. 334c corresponding to the three trapezoidal characteristics $U_1(\omega), U_2(\omega), U_3(\omega)$ (Fig. 334b).

By algebraic addition of the ordinates x_i of all three curves we obtain the required transient curve $x(t)$ in the system (Fig. 334d). For comparison we indicate there the exact transient curve, obtained by analytic solution of the equation. Their comparison illustrates the degree of precision of the given method (in the analysis of the quality of an automatic system such precision may be satisfactory).

Approximate plotting of the transient curve due to a unit input impulse. Here, as in the preceding case, the given real frequency characteristic is substituted by the approximate algebraic sum of trapezoidal frequency characteristics (75.5) (Fig. 333).

Then formula (44.20) may be represented in the form

$$x_1(t) \approx \frac{2}{\pi} \sum_{i=1}^{n} \int_0^\infty U_y(\omega) \cos \omega t \, d\omega \ ,$$

where n is the number of trapezoids into which the frequency characteristic $U_y(\omega)$ or $U_f(\omega)$ is decomposed.

49

It has been proved that this expression may be transformed to the form

$$x_1(t) \approx \frac{2}{\pi} \sum_{i=1}^{n} \left(A_i \frac{\sin \omega_i t}{\omega_i t} \cdot \frac{\sin \Omega_i t}{\Omega_i t} \right), \qquad (75.7)$$

where we put

$$\omega_i = \frac{1 - \varkappa_i}{2} \omega_{ip}, \qquad \Omega_i = \frac{1 + \varkappa_i}{2} \omega_{ip}, \qquad A_i = \Omega_i U_i(0). \qquad (75.8)$$

Consequently in the present case the curve of the transient process $x(t)$ is approximately defined by simple calculation of its ordinates according to formula (75.7) for various t and subsequent point-by-

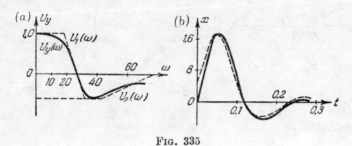

FIG. 335

point plotting. To facilitate the calculations it is possible to employ tables of $\sin\varphi/\varphi$, which are available, for example, in Jahnke and Emde (Reference 49) on p. 49.

For example, let there be known for the closed automatic system the amplitude-phase characteristic in the open state:

$$W(i\omega) = \frac{61}{i\omega(0{\cdot}0015i\omega + 1)(0{\cdot}027i\omega + 1)(0{\cdot}01i\omega + 1)},$$

while the amplitude-phase characteristic of the closed system is determined by formula (44.8) with $W_2(i\omega) = 1$, i.e.

$$W_y(i\omega) = \frac{W(i\omega)}{1 + W(i\omega)}.$$

The real part of this expression is the real frequency characteristic of the closed system $U_y(\omega)$ shown by the continuous curve in Fig. 335a. Broken line there indicates the polygon replacing it approximately.

The exact analytic solution of the equation of the given closed system with a unit impulse perturbation is

$$x_1(t) = -0{\cdot}244e^{-710t} + 10{\cdot}92e^{-112t} + 35{\cdot}86e^{-12{\cdot}1t}\cos[(27{\cdot}4t)^\circ - 107{\cdot}6^\circ],$$

which is shown in full line in Fig. 335b. We also give there in broken line the transient response plotted by calculation according to the approximate formula (75.7), i.e. with replacement of the true real characteristic $U_y(\omega)$ by the trapezoid. In the present case we have taken two trapezoids $U_1(\omega)$ and $U_2(\omega)$ (Fig. 335a).

Having the transient curve $x_1(t)$ for impulse input we may further employ the convolution formula (74.11) to determine the regulation curve for arbitrary external input to the system.

In conclusion we note that when plotting the transient curve from the trapezoidal frequency characteristics the greatest errors are obtained in the initial portion of the curve, since according to Section 44 the "tail" of the real frequency characteristic of the closed system which is dropped mainly influences the initial portion of the transient response.

In addition to the Solodovnikov frequency method described here there exists a similar method proposed by A. A. Voronov for plotting the transient curves from triangular frequency characteristics.

REFERENCES

1. Bol'shaia Sovetskaia Entsiklopediia. (Great Soviet Encyclopedia.) 2nd Ed., **1**, pp. 209–215 and 224–229 (1950).
2. J. C. Maxwell, I. A. Vyshnegradskii and A. Stodola, Teoria avtomaticheskogo regulirovaniia. (Theory of Automatic Regulation.) Edited with commentary by A. A. Andronov and I. N. Voznesenskii, U.S.S.R. Academy of Sciences (1949).
3. A. M. Liapunov, Obshchaia zadacha ob ustoichivosti dvizheniia. (The General Problem of Stability of Motion.) (1892, reprinted 1935 and 1950).
4. N. E. Zhukovskii, Teoriia regulirovaniia khoda mashin. (Theory of Machine Control.) (1909, reprinted 1933).
5. N. M. Krylov and N. N. Bogoliubov, Novye metody nelineinoi mekhaniki. (New Methods of Non-linear Mechanics.) (1934).
6. N. M. Krylov and N. N. Bogoliubov, Vvedenie v nelineinuiu mekhaniku. (Introduction to Non-linear Mechanics.) (1937).
7. A. A. Andronov and S. E. Khaikin, Teoriia kolebanii. (Theory of Oscillations.) United Scientific and Technical Press (1937).
8. A. V. Mikhailov, Metod garmonicheskogo analiza v teorii regulirovaniia. (Method of Harmonic Analysis in the Theory of Regulation.) Avtomatika i telemekhanika No. 3 (1938).
9. A. A. Sokolov, Kriterii ustoichivosti lineinykh sistem regulirovaniia s raspredelennymi parametrami i ego primeneniia. (The Stability Criterion in Linear Regulation Systems with distributed Parameters and its Application.) Inzhenernyi sbornik 2,2 (1946) (received 1940).
10. A. N. Krylov, Lektsii o priblizhennykh vychisleniiakh. (Lectures on Approximate Calculations.) Collected Works III, Pt. 1, U.S.S.R. Academy of Sciences (1949).
11. V. V. Solodovnikov, Chastotnyi metod analiza kachestva sistem avtomaticheskogo regulirovaniia. (Frequency Method of Analysing the Quality of Automatic Regulation Systems.) Mashgiz (1950).
12. V. V. Solodovnikov, Vvedenie v statisticheskuiu dinamiku sistem avtomaticheskogo upravleniia. (Introduction to Statistical Dynamics of Automatic Control Systems.) Gostekhizdat (1952).
13. Ya. Z. Tsypkin, Perekhodnye i ustanovivshiesia protsessy v impul'snykh tsepiakh. (Transient and Steady-state Processes in Pulse Systems.) Gostekhizdat (1951).
14. N. N. Bautin, Povedenie dinamicheskikh sistem vblizi granits oblasti ustoichivosti. (The Behaviour of Dynamic Systems near the Limits of Stability.) Gostekhizdat (1949).
15. B. V. Bulgakov, Nekotorye zadachi teorii regulirovaniia s nelineinymi kharakteristikami. (Some Problems of the Theory of Regulation with Non-linear Characteristics.) Prikl. mat. mekh. 3 (1946).
16. B. V. Bulgakov, Kolebaniia. (Oscillations.) Gostekhizdat (1949).
17. V. S. Vedrov, Dinamicheskaia ustoichivost' samoleta. (Dynamic Stability of Aircraft.) Oborongiz (1938).

18. **Yu. V. Vorob'ev,** Ustoichivost' lineinykh sistem s volnovymi protsessami. (Stability of Linear System with Wave Processes.) In collection: Issledovaniia v oblasti regulirovaniia parovykh turbin. (Studies in the Regulation of Steam Turbines.) (1950).

19. **G. N. Duboshin,** Osnovy teorii ustoichivosti dvizheniia. (Fundamental Theory of Stability of Motion.) Moscow State University (1952).

20. **A. I. Lur'e,** Nekotorye nelineinye zadachi teorii avtomaticheskogo regulirovaniia. (Some Non-linear Problems in the Theory of Automatic Regulation.) Gostekhizdat (1951).

21. **I. P. Kabakov,** O protsesse regulirovaniia davleniia para. (On the Regulation of Steam Pressure.) Inzhenernyi sbornik, 2,2 (1946) (Received 1940).

22. **T. N. Sokolov,** Elektromekhanicheskie sistemy avtomaticheskogo upravleniia. (Electro-mechanical Automatic-control Systems.) Gosenergoizdat (1952).

23. **S. P. Strelkov,** Vvedenie v teoriiu kolebanii. (Introduction to the Theory of Oscillations.) Gostekhizdat (1950).

24. **A. A. Fel'dbaum,** Vvedenie v teoriiu nelineihykh tsepei. (Introduction to the Theory of Non-linear Elements.) Gosenergoizdat (1948).

25. **N. G. Chetaev,** Ustoichivost' dvizheniia. (Stability of Motion.) Gostekhizdat (1946).

26. **M. A. Aizerman,** Teoriia avtomaticheskogo regulirovaniia dvigatelei. (Theory of Automatic Engine Regulation.) Gostekhizdat (1952).

27. **Z. Sh. Blokh,** Dinamika lineinykh sistem avtomaticheskogo regulirovaniia mashin. (Dynamics of Linear Automatic Machine Controls.) Gostekhizdat (1952).

28. **V. A. Bodner,** Avtomatika aviatsionnykh dvigatelei. (Automatic Control of Aircraft Engines.) Oborongiz (1952).

29. **A. A. Voronov,** Elementy teorii avtomaticheskogo regulirovaniia. (Elements of the Theory of Automatic Regulation.) Voenizdat (1954).

30. **V. A. Ditkin** and **P. I. Kuznetsov,** Spravochnik po operatsionnomu ischisleniiu. (Handbook of Operational Calculus.) Gostekhizdat (1951).

31. **K. P. Ivanov,** Tablitsy dlia vychisleniia mnogochlenov. (Tables for Calculating Polynomials.) Gostekhizdat (1949).

32. **Yu. G. Kornilov** and **V. D. Piven,** Osnovy teorii avtomaticheskogo regulirovaniia v prilozhenii k teplosilovym ustanovkam. (Basic Theory of Automatic Regulation Applied to Heat-engines.) Mashgiz (1947).

33. **K. A. Krug,** Perekhodnye protsessy v lineinykh elektricheskikh tsepiakh. (Transient Processes in Linear Electrical Circuits.) Gosenergoizdat (1948).

34. **V. S. Kulebakin,** O vybore optimal'nykh parametrov avtomaticheskikh regulatorov i slediashchikh sistem. (On the Optimal Choice of Automatic Regulation and Servomechanism Parameters.) Dokl. Akad. Nauk SSSR 77, 2 (1951).

35. **A. G. Kurosh,** Kurs vysshei algebry. (Course of Higher Algebra.) Gostekhizdat (1946).

36. **H. Lauer, R. Lesnick** and **L. E. Matson,** Servomechanism Fundamentals. McGraw-Hill (1947).

37. **L. G. Loitsianskii** and **A. I. Lur'e,** Kurs teoreticheskoi mekhaniki. (Course of Theoretical Mechanics.) Pt. 2, Gostekhizdat (1948).

38. **V. L. Lossievskii,** Avtomaticheskie regulatory. (Automatic Controls.) Oborongiz (1944).

39. **V. L. Lossievskii,** Osnovy avtomaticheskogo regulirovaniia tekhnologicheskikh Protsessov. (Fundamentals of Automatic Regulation of Technological Processes.) Oborongiz (1950).

40. **A. I. Lur'e,** Operatsionnoe ischislenie i ego prilozheniia k zadacham mekhaniki. (Operational Calculus and its Application to the Problems of Mechanics.) Gostekhizdat (1950).

41. **I. G. Malkin,** Teoriia ustoichivosti dvizheniia. (Theory of Stability of Motion.) Gostekhizdat (1952).

42. **M. V. Meerov,** Osnovy avtomaticheskogo regulirovaniia elektricheskikh mashin. (Fundamentals of Automatic Regulation of Electrical Machines.) Gosenergoizdat (1952).

43. **E. V. Ol'man, Ya. N. Solov'ev** and **V. P. Tokarev,** Avtopiloty. (Autopilots.) Oborongiz (1946).

44. Teoria slediashchikh sistem. (Servomechanism Theory.) Foreign Literature Publishing House (1951).

45. **I. I. Solov'ev,** Avtomatizatsiia energeticheskikh sistem. (Automation of Electric-power Systems.) Gosenergoizdat (1952).

46. **K. F. Teodorchik,** Avtokolebatel'nye sistemy. (Self-oscillatory Systems.) Gostekhizdat (1952).

47. **V. I. Feodos'ev,** Uprugie elementy tochnogo priborostroeniia. (Elastic Elements in Precision Mechanics.) (1949).

48. **A. F. Timofeev,** Integrirovanie funktsii. (Integration of Functions.) 53, Gostekhizdat (1948).

49. **E. Jahnke** and **F. Emde,** Tablitsy funktsii s formulami i krivymi. (Tables of Functions with Formulae and Curves.) Gostekhizdat (1948).

50. **N. N. Bogoliubov,** O nekotorykh statisticheskikh metodakh v matematicheskoi fizike. (On Certain Statistical Methods in Mathematical Physics.) (1945); Odnochastotnye kolebaniia v nelineinykh sistemakh so mnogimi stepeniami svobody. (Single-frequency Oscillations in Non-linear Systems with Many Degrees of Freedom.) Sbornik trudov Instituta stroitel'noi mekhaniki Akad. Nauk SSSR 10 (1949).

51. **V. A. Bodner,** O vybore optimal'nykh parametrov reguliruemykh sistem. (On the Optimal Choice of Parameters in Regulated Systems.) Oborongiz (1953).